INSTRUCTOR'S SOLUTIONS MANUAL

to accompany

CALCULUS

SINGLE VARIABLE   **FOURTH EDITION**

Deborah Hughes-Hallett
University of Arizona
Andrew M. Gleason
Harvard University
William G. McCallum
University of Arizona

et al.

Prepared by:

Rick Cangelosi
Scott Clark
Cristi Guevara
Elliot Marks
Igor Padure
Seung-Hye Song
Aaron Wootton

D1379236

WILEY

John Wiley & Sons, Inc.

©Pete Turner/The Image Bank/Getty Images

To order books or for customer service call 1-800-CALL-WILEY (225-5945).

ISBN 978-0-471-66003-3

Printed in the United States of America

10 9 8 7 6 5 4 3

Printed and bound by Malloy Lithographing, Inc.

CONTENTS

CHAPTER ONE

Solutions for Section 1.1

Exercises

1. $f(35)$ means the value of P corresponding to $t = 35$. Since t represents the number of years since 1950, we see that $f(35)$ means the population of the city in 1985. So, in 1985, the city's population was 12 million.

2. Since $T = f(P)$, we see that $f(200)$ is the value of T when $P = 200$; that is, the thickness of pelican eggs when the concentration of PCBs is 200 ppm.

3. (a) When the car is 5 years old, it is worth $6000.
   (b) Since the value of the car decreases as the car gets older, this is a decreasing function. A possible graph is in Figure 1.1:

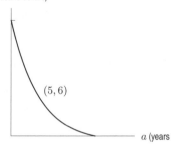

Figure 1.1

   (c) The vertical intercept is the value of V when $a = 0$, or the value of the car when it is new. The horizontal intercept is the value of a when $V = 0$, or the age of the car when it is worth nothing.

4. The slope is $(1 - 0)/(1 - 0) = 1$. So the equation of the line is $y = x$.

5. The slope is $(3 - 2)/(2 - 0) = 1/2$. So the equation of the line is $y = (1/2)x + 2$.

6. Using the points $(-2, 1)$ and $(2, 3)$, we have

$$\text{Slope} = \frac{3 - 1}{2 - (-2)} = \frac{2}{4} = \frac{1}{2}.$$

   Now we know that $y = (1/2)x + b$. Using the point $(-2, 1)$, we have $1 = -2/2 + b$, which yields $b = 2$. Thus, the equation of the line is $y = (1/2)x + 2$.

7. Rewriting the equation as

$$y = -\frac{12}{7}x + \frac{2}{7}$$

   shows that the line has slope $-12/7$ and vertical intercept $2/7$.

8. Rewriting the equation of the line as

$$-y = \frac{-2}{4}x - 2$$
$$y = \frac{1}{2}x + 2,$$

   we see the line has slope $1/2$ and vertical intercept 2.

9. Rewriting the equation of the line as

$$y = \frac{12}{6}x - \frac{4}{6}$$
$$y = 2x - \frac{2}{3},$$

   we see that the line has slope 2 and vertical intercept $-2/3$.

10. (a) is (V), because slope is positive, vertical intercept is negative
    (b) is (IV), because slope is negative, vertical intercept is positive
    (c) is (I), because slope is 0, vertical intercept is positive
    (d) is (VI), because slope and vertical intercept are both negative
    (e) is (II), because slope and vertical intercept are both positive
    (f) is (III), because slope is positive, vertical intercept is 0

11. (a) is (V), because slope is negative, vertical intercept is 0
    (b) is (VI), because slope and vertical intercept are both positive
    (c) is (I), because slope is negative, vertical intercept is positive
    (d) is (IV), because slope is positive, vertical intercept is negative
    (e) is (III), because slope and vertical intercept are both negative
    (f) is (II), because slope is positive, vertical intercept is 0

12. $y = 5x - 3$. Since the slope of this line is 5, we want a line with slope $-\frac{1}{5}$ passing through the point $(2, 1)$. The equation is $(y - 1) = -\frac{1}{5}(x - 2)$, or $y = -\frac{1}{5}x + \frac{7}{5}$.

13. The line $y + 4x = 7$ has slope -4. Therefore the parallel line has slope -4 and equation $y - 5 = -4(x - 1)$ or $y = -4x + 9$. The perpendicular line has slope $\frac{-1}{(-4)} = \frac{1}{4}$ and equation $y - 5 = \frac{1}{4}(x - 1)$ or $y = 0.25x + 4.75$.

14. The line parallel to $y = mx + c$ also has slope m, so its equation is

$$y = m(x - a) + b.$$

The line perpendicular to $y = mx + c$ has slope $-1/m$, so its equation will be

$$y = -\frac{1}{m}(x - a) + b.$$

15. Since the function goes from $x = 0$ to $x = 5$ and between $y = 0$ and $y = 4$, the domain is $0 \le x \le 5$ and the range is $0 \le y \le 4$.

16. Since the function goes from $x = -2$ to $x = 2$ and from $y = -2$ to $y = 2$, the domain is $-2 \le x \le 2$ and the range is $-2 \le y \le 2$.

17. Since x goes from 1 to 5 and y goes from 1 to 6, the domain is $1 \le x \le 5$ and the range is $1 \le y \le 6$.

18. The domain is all numbers. The range is all numbers ≥ 2, since $x^2 \ge 0$ for all x.

19. The domain is all x-values, as the denominator is never zero. The range is $0 < y \le \dfrac{1}{2}$.

20. The value of $f(t)$ is real provided $t^2 - 16 \ge 0$ or $t^2 \ge 16$. This occurs when either $t \ge 4$, or $t \le -4$. Solving $f(t) = 3$, we have

$$\sqrt{t^2 - 16} = 3$$
$$t^2 - 16 = 9$$
$$t^2 = 25$$

so

$$t = \pm 5.$$

21. Factoring gives

$$g(x) = \frac{(2 - x)(2 + x)}{x(x + 1)}.$$

The values of x which make $g(x)$ undefined are $x = 0$ and $x = -1$, when the denominator is 0. So the domain is all $x \ne 0, -1$. Solving $g(x) = 0$ means one of the numerator's factors is 0, so $x = \pm 2$.

22. For some constant k, we have $S = kh^2$.

23. We know that E is proportional to v^3, so $E = kv^3$, for some constant k.

24. We know that N is proportional to $1/l^2$, so

$$N = \frac{k}{l^2}, \quad \text{for some constant } k.$$

Problems

25. (a) The flat tire corresponds to a part of the graph where the velocity is zero. This could be (II) or (III). Since the velocity in (II) is higher for the later part of the interval, corresponding to speeding up, the answer is (II).

(b) This is (I), as the graph shows a positive velocity followed by a zero velocity.

(c) In (IV), the velocity is positive, zero (while the package is being dropped off) and then negative (the drive home).

(d) Graph (III) could represent a drive to the country, stopping to have lunch (velocity zero), and continuing on at a slower speed to look at the scenery. Other stories are possible.

26. See Figure 1.2.

27. See Figure 1.3.

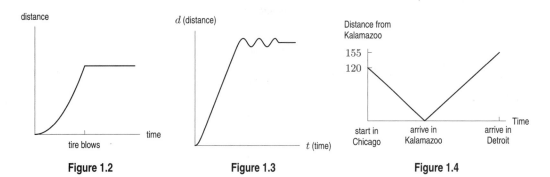

Figure 1.2   **Figure 1.3**   **Figure 1.4**

28. See Figure 1.4.

29. (a) We find the slope m and intercept b in the linear equation $C = b + mw$. To find the slope m, we use

$$m = \frac{\Delta C}{\Delta w} = \frac{48 - 32}{180 - 100} = 0.2.$$

We substitute to find b:

$$C = b + mw$$
$$32 = b + (0.2)(100)$$
$$b = 12.$$

The linear formula is $C = 12 + 0.2w$.

(b) The slope is 0.2 dollars per kilogram. Each additional kilogram of waste costs 20 cents.

(c) The intercept is 12 dollars. The flat monthly fee to subscribe to the waste collection service is $12. This is the amount charged even if there is no waste.

30. (a) Charge per cubic foot $= \dfrac{\Delta\$}{\Delta \text{ cu. ft.}} = \dfrac{105 - 90}{1600 - 1000} = \$0.025/\text{cu. ft.}$

Alternatively, if we let c = cost, w = cubic feet of water, b = fixed charge, and m = cost/cubic feet, we obtain $c = b + mw$. Substituting the information given in the problem, we have

$$90 = b + 1000m$$
$$105 = b + 1600m.$$

Subtracting the first equation from the second yields $15 = 600m$, so $m = 0.025$.

(b) $c = b + 0.025w$, so $90 = b + 0.025(1000)$, which yields $b = 65$. Thus the equation is $c = 65 + 0.025w$.

(c) We need to solve the equation $130 = 65 + 0.025w$, which yields $w = 2600$.

31. (a) Given the two points $(0, 32)$ and $(100, 212)$, and assuming the graph in Figure 1.5 is a line,

$$\text{Slope} = \frac{212 - 32}{100} = \frac{180}{100} = 1.8.$$

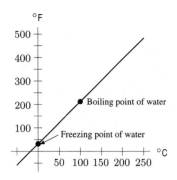

Figure 1.5

(b) The °F-intercept is $(0, 32)$, so
$$°F = 1.8(°C) + 32.$$

(c) If the temperature is $20°$Celsius, then
$$°F = 1.8(20) + 32 = 68°F.$$

(d) If $°F = °C$, then
$$°C = 1.8°C + 32$$
$$-32 = 0.8°C$$
$$°C = -40° = °F.$$

32. (a) $f(30) = 10$ means that the value of f at $t = 30$ was 10. In other words, the temperature at time $t = 30$ minutes was $10°$C. So, 30 minutes after the object was placed outside, it had cooled to 10 °C.

(b) The intercept a measures the value of $f(t)$ when $t = 0$. In other words, when the object was initially put outside, it had a temperature of $a°$C. The intercept b measures the value of t when $f(t) = 0$. In other words, at time b the object's temperature is 0 °C.

33. We are looking for a linear function $y = f(x)$ that, given a time x in years, gives a value y in dollars for the value of the refrigerator. We know that when $x = 0$, that is, when the refrigerator is new, $y = 950$, and when $x = 7$, the refrigerator is worthless, so $y = 0$. Thus $(0, 950)$ and $(7, 0)$ are on the line that we are looking for. The slope is then given by
$$m = \frac{950}{-7}$$
It is negative, indicating that the value decreases as time passes. Having found the slope, we can take the point $(7, 0)$ and use the point-slope formula:
$$y - y_1 = m(x - x_1).$$
So,
$$y - 0 = -\frac{950}{7}(x - 7)$$
$$y = -\frac{950}{7}x + 950.$$

34. (a) This could be a linear function because w increases by 5 as h increases by 1.

(b) We find the slope m and the intercept b in the linear equation $w = b + mh$. We first find the slope m using the first two points in the table. Since we want w to be a function of h, we take
$$m = \frac{\Delta w}{\Delta h} = \frac{171 - 166}{69 - 68} = 5.$$
Substituting the first point and the slope $m = 5$ into the linear equation $w = b + mh$, we have $166 = b + (5)(68)$, so $b = -174$. The linear function is
$$w = 5h - 174.$$
The slope, $m = 5$, is in units of pounds per inch.

(c) We find the slope and intercept in the linear function $h = b + mw$ using $m = \Delta h / \Delta w$ to obtain the linear function
$$h = 0.2w + 34.8.$$
Alternatively, we could solve the linear equation found in part (b) for h. The slope, $m = 0.2$, has units inches per pound.

35. (a) We have the following functions.

(i) Since a change in p of \$5 results in a decrease in q of 2, the slope of $q = D(p)$ is $-2/5$ items per dollar. So

$$q = b - \frac{2}{5}p.$$

Now we know that when $p = 550$ we have $q = 100$, so

$$100 = b - \frac{2}{5} \cdot 550$$
$$100 = b - 220$$
$$b = 320.$$

Thus a formula is

$$q = 320 - \frac{2}{5}p.$$

(ii) We can solve $q = 320 - \frac{2}{5}p$ for p in terms of q:

$$5q = 1600 - 2p$$
$$2p = 1600 - 5q$$
$$p = 800 - \frac{5}{2}q.$$

The slope of this function is $-5/2$ dollars per item, as we would expect.

(b) A graph of $p = 800 - \frac{5}{2}q$ is given in Figure 1.6.

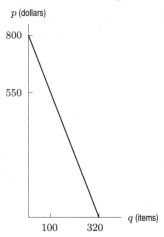

p (dollars)

800

550

100   320 q (items)

Figure 1.6

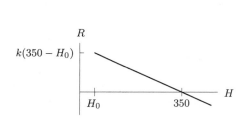

R

$k(350 - H_0)$

H_0 350 H

Figure 1.7

36. (a) $R = k(350 - H)$, where k is a positive constant.

If H is greater than $350°$, the rate is negative, indicating that a very hot yam will cool down toward the temperature of the oven.

(b) Letting H_0 equal the initial temperature of the yam, the graph of R against H looks like figure 1.7.

Note that by the temperature of the yam, we mean the average temperature of the yam, since the yam's surface will be hotter than its center.

37. Given $l - l_0 = al_0(t - t_0)$ with l_0, t_0 and a all constant,

(a) We have $l = al_0(t - t_0) + l_0 = al_0t - al_0t_0 + l_0$, which is a linear function of t with slope al_0 and y-intercept at $(0, -al_0t_0 + l_0)$.

(b) If $l_0 = 100$, $t_0 = 60°$F and $a = 10^{-5}$, then

$$l = 10^{-5}(100)t - 10^{-5}(100)(60) + 100 = 10^{-3}t + 99.94$$
$$= 0.001t + 99.94$$

(c) If the slope is positive, (as in (b)), then as the temperature rises, the length of the metal increases: it expands. If the slope were negative, then the metal would contract as the temperature rises.

38. (a) Assembling the given information, we have

$$F = ma = F_g - F_r = mg - kv,$$

where k is the constant that relates velocity to air resistance (which depends on the shape of the object).

(b) Solving the above equation for a, we have

$$a = g - \frac{k}{m}v$$

(c)

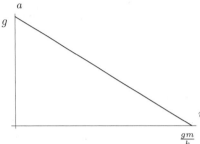

39. Looking at the given data, it seems that Galileo's hypothesis was incorrect. The first table suggests that velocity is not a linear function of distance, since the increases in velocity for each foot of distance are themselves getting smaller. Moreover, the second table suggests that velocity is instead proportional to *time*, since for each second of time, the velocity increases by 32 ft/sec.

Solutions for Section 1.2

Exercises

1. Initial quantity $= 5$; growth rate $= 0.07 = 7\%$.

2. Initial quantity $= 7.7$; growth rate $= -0.08 = -8\%$ (decay).

3. Initial quantity $= 3.2$; growth rate $= 0.03 = 3\%$ (continuous).

4. Initial quantity $= 15$; growth rate $= -0.06 = -6\%$ (continuous decay).

5. (a) The function is linear with initial population of 1000 and slope of 50, so $P = 1000 + 50t$.
(b) This function is exponential with initial population of 1000 and growth rate of 5%, so $P = 1000(1.05)^t$.

6. (a) This is a linear function with slope -2 grams per day and intercept 30 grams. The function is $Q = 30 - 2t$, and the graph is shown in Figure 1.8.

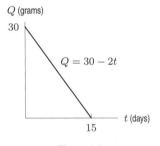

Figure 1.8

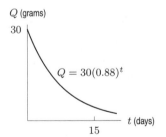

Figure 1.9

(b) Since the quantity is decreasing by a constant percent change, this is an exponential function with base $1 - 0.12 = 0.88$. The function is $Q = 30(0.88)^t$, and the graph is shown in Figure 1.9.

7. The graph shows a concave up function.

8. The graph shows a concave down function.

9. This graph is neither concave up or down.

10. The graph is concave up.

11. The function is increasing and concave up on the x-interval between D and E, and the x-interval between H and I. It is increasing and concave down on the x-interval between A and B, and the x-interval between E and F. It is decreasing and concave up on the x-interval between C and D, and the x-interval between G and H. Finally, it is decreasing and concave down on the x-interval between B and C, and the x-interval between F and G

Problems

12. (a) Let P represent the population of the world, and let t represent the number of years since 1999. Then we have $P = 6(1.013)^t$.
    (b) According to this formula, the population of the world in the year 2020 (at $t = 21$) will be $P = 6(1.013)^{21} = 7.87$ billion people.
    (c) The graph is shown in Figure 1.10. The population of the world has doubled when $P = 12$; we see on the graph that this occurs at approximately $t = 53.7$. Under these assumptions, the doubling time of the world's population is about 53.7 years.

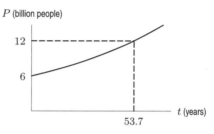

Figure 1.10

13. (a) We have
$$\text{Reduced size} = (0.80) \cdot \text{Original size}$$
or
$$\text{Original size} = \frac{1}{(0.80)} \text{Reduced size} = (1.25) \text{Reduced size},$$
so the copy must be enlarged by a factor of 1.25, which means it is enlarged to 125% of the reduced size.
    (b) If a page is copied n times, then
$$\text{New size} = (0.80)^n \cdot \text{Original}.$$
We want to solve for n so that
$$(0.80)^n = 0.15.$$
By trial and error, we find $(0.80)^8 = 0.168$ and $(0.80)^9 = 0.134$. So the page needs to be copied 9 times.

14. (a) Using $Q = Q_0(1 - r)^t$ for loss, we have
$$Q = 10{,}000(1 - 0.1)^{10} = 10{,}000(0.9)^{10} = 3486.78.$$
The investment was worth \$3486.78 after 10 years.
    (b) Measuring time from the moment at which the stock begins to gain value and letting $Q_0 = 3486.78$, the value after t years is
$$Q = 3486.78(1 + 0.1)^t = 3486.78(1.1)^t.$$
We can estimate the value of t when $Q = 10{,}000$ by tracing along a graph of Q, giving $t \approx 11$. It will take about 11 years to get the investment back to \$10,000.

15. (a)

    (b) "The rate at which new people try it" is the rate of change of the total number of people who have tried the product. Thus, the statement of the problem is telling you that the graph is concave down—the slope is positive but decreasing, as the graph shows.

16. (a) Advertising is generally cheaper in bulk; spending more money will give better and better marginal results initially, (Spending $5,000 could give you a big newspaper ad reaching 200,000 people; spending $100,000 could give you a series of TV spots reaching 50,000,000 people.) A graph is shown below, left.

(b) The temperature of a hot object decreases at a rate proportional to the difference between its temperature and the temperature of the air around it. Thus, the temperature of a very hot object decreases more quickly than a cooler object. The graph is decreasing and concave up. (We are assuming that the coffee is all at the same temperature.)

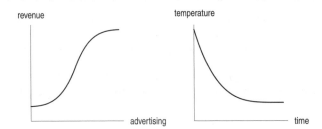

17. We look for an equation of the form $y = y_0 a^x$ since the graph looks exponential. The points $(0, 3)$ and $(2, 12)$ are on the graph, so

$$3 = y_0 a^0 = y_0$$

and

$$12 = y_0 \cdot a^2 = 3 \cdot a^2, \quad \text{giving} \quad a = \pm 2.$$

Since $a > 0$, our equation is $y = 3(2^x)$.

18. We look for an equation of the form $y = y_0 a^x$ since the graph looks exponential. The points $(-1, 8)$ and $(1, 2)$ are on the graph, so

$$8 = y_0 a^{-1} \quad \text{and} \quad 2 = y_0 a^1$$

Therefore $\dfrac{8}{2} = \dfrac{y_0 a^{-1}}{y_0 a} = \dfrac{1}{a^2}$, giving $a = \frac{1}{2}$, and so $2 = y_0 a^1 = y_0 \cdot \frac{1}{2}$, so $y_0 = 4$.
Hence $y = 4\left(\frac{1}{2}\right)^x = 4(2^{-x})$.

19. We look for an equation of the form $y = y_0 a^x$ since the graph looks exponential. The points $(1, 6)$ and $(2, 18)$ are on the graph, so

$$6 = y_0 a^1 \quad \text{and} \quad 18 = y_0 a^2$$

Therefore $a = \frac{y_0 a^2}{y_0 a} = \dfrac{18}{6} = 3$, and so $6 = y_0 a = y_0 \cdot 3$; thus, $y_0 = 2$. Hence $y = 2(3^x)$.

20. The difference, D, between the horizontal asymptote and the graph appears to decrease exponentially, so we look for an equation of the form

$$D = D_0 a^x$$

where $D_0 = 4 = $ difference when $x = 0$. Since $D = 4 - y$, we have

$$4 - y = 4a^x \quad \text{or} \quad y = 4 - 4a^x = 4(1 - a^x)$$

The point $(1, 2)$ is on the graph, so $2 = 4(1 - a^1)$, giving $a = \frac{1}{2}$.
Therefore $y = 4(1 - \left(\frac{1}{2}\right)^x) = 4(1 - 2^{-x})$.

21. (a) Let $Q = Q_0 a^t$. Then $Q_0 a^5 = 75.94$ and $Q_0 a^7 = 170.86$. So

$$\frac{Q_0 a^7}{Q_0 a^5} = \frac{170.86}{75.94} = 2.25 = a^2.$$

So $a = 1.5$.

(b) Since $a = 1.5$, the growth rate is $r = 0.5 = 50\%$.

22. (a) Let $Q = Q_0 a^t$. Then $Q_0 a^{0.02} = 25.02$ and $Q_0 a^{0.05} = 25.06$. So

$$\frac{Q_0 a^{0.05}}{Q_0 a^{0.02}} = \frac{25.06}{25.02} = 1.001 = a^{0.03}.$$

So

$$a = (1.001)^{\frac{100}{3}} = 1.05.$$

(b) Since $a = 1.05$, the growth rate is $r = 0.05 = 5\%$.

23. Since $e^{0.25t} = \left(e^{0.25}\right)^t \approx (1.2840)^t$, we have $P = 15(1.2840)^t$. This is exponential growth since 0.25 is positive. We can also see that this is growth because $1.2840 > 1$.

24. Since $e^{-0.5t} = (e^{-0.5})^t \approx (0.6065)^t$, we have $P = 2(0.6065)^t$. This is exponential decay since -0.5 is negative. We can also see that this is decay because $0.6065 < 1$.

25. $P = P_0(e^{0.2})^t = P_0(1.2214)^t$. Exponential growth because $0.2 > 0$ or $1.2214 > 1$.

26. $P = 7(e^{-\pi})^t = 7(0.0432)^t$. Exponential decay because $-\pi < 0$ or $0.0432 < 1$.

27. (a) We have $P_0 = 1$ million, and $k = 0.02$, so $P = (1{,}000{,}000)(e^{0.02t})$.

(b)

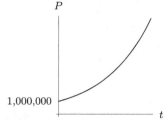

28. If the pressure at sea level is P_0, the pressure P at altitude h is given by

$$P = P_0 \left(1 - \frac{0.4}{100}\right)^{\frac{h}{100}},$$

since we want the pressure to be multiplied by a factor of $(1 - \frac{0.4}{100}) = 0.996$ for each 100 feet we go up to make it decrease by 0.4% over that interval. At Mexico City $h = 7340$, so the pressure is

$$P = P_0(0.996)^{\frac{7340}{100}} \approx 0.745P_0.$$

So the pressure is reduced from P_0 to approximately $0.745P_0$, a decrease of 25.5%.

29. (a) We compound the daily inflation rate 30 times to get the desired monthly rate r:

$$\left(1 + \frac{r}{100}\right)^1 = \left(1 + \frac{1.3}{100}\right)^{30}.$$

Solving for r, we get $r = 47.3$, so the inflation rate for June was 47.3%.

(b) We compound the daily inflation rate 366 times to get a yearly rate R for 1988, a leap year:

$$\left(1 + \frac{R}{100}\right)^1 = \left(1 + \frac{1.3}{100}\right)^{366}.$$

Solving for R, we get $R = 111.994$, so the yearly rate was 11,199.4% during 1988. We could have obtained approximately the same result by compounding the monthly rate 12 times. Computing the annual rate from the monthly gives a lower result, because 12 months of 30 days each is only 360 days.

30. (a) The formula is $Q = Q_0 \left(\frac{1}{2}\right)^{(t/1620)}$.

(b) The percentage left after 500 years is

$$\frac{Q_0\left(\frac{1}{2}\right)^{(500/1620)}}{Q_0}.$$

The Q_0s cancel giving

$$\left(\frac{1}{2}\right)^{(500/1620)} \approx 0.807,$$

so 80.7% is left.

31. Let Q_0 be the initial quantity absorbed in 1960. Then the quantity, Q of strontium-90 left after t years is

$$Q = Q_0 \left(\frac{1}{2}\right)^{(t/29)}.$$

Since $1990 - 1960 = 30$ years elapsed, the fraction of strontium-90 left in 1990 is

$$Q = \frac{Q_0 \left(\frac{1}{2}\right)^{(30/29)}}{Q_0} = \left(\frac{1}{2}\right)^{(30/29)} \approx .488 = 48.8\%.$$

32. The doubling time t depends only on the growth rate; it is the solution to

$$2 = (1.02)^t,$$

since 1.02^t represents the factor by which the population has grown after time t. Trial and error shows that $(1.02)^{35} \approx$ 1.9999 and $(1.02)^{36} \approx 2.0399$, so that the doubling time is about 35 years.

33. Because the population is growing exponentially, the time it takes to double is the same, regardless of the population levels we are considering. For example, the population is 20,000 at time 3.7, and 40,000 at time 6.0. This represents a doubling of the population in a span of $6.0 - 3.7 = 2.3$ years.

How long does it take the population to double a second time, from 40,000 to 80,000? Looking at the graph once again, we see that the population reaches 80,000 at time $t = 8.3$. This second doubling has taken $8.3 - 6.0 = 2.3$ years, the same amount of time as the first doubling.

Further comparison of any two populations on this graph that differ by a factor of two will show that the time that separates them is 2.3 years. Similarly, during any 2.3 year period, the population will double. Thus, the doubling time is 2.3 years.

Suppose $P = P_0 a^t$ doubles from time t to time $t + d$. We now have $P_0 a^{t+d} = 2P_0 a^t$, so $P_0 a^t a^d = 2P_0 a^t$. Thus, canceling P_0 and a^t, d must be the number such that $a^d = 2$, no matter what t is.

34. Direct calculation reveals that each 1000 foot increase in altitude results in a longer takeoff roll by a factor of about 1.096. Since the value of d when $h = 0$ (sea level) is $d = 670$, we are led to the formula

$$d = 670(1.096)^{h/1000},$$

where d is the takeoff roll, in feet, and h is the airport's elevation, in feet.

Alternatively, we can write

$$d = d_0 a^h,$$

where d_0 is the sea level value of d, $d_0 = 670$. In addition, when $h = 1000$, $d = 734$, so

$$734 = 670a^{1000}.$$

Solving for a gives

$$a = \left(\frac{734}{670}\right)^{1/1000} = 1.00009124,$$

so

$$d = 670(1.00009124)^h.$$

35. (a) This is the graph of a linear function, which increases at a constant rate, and thus corresponds to $k(t)$, which increases by 0.3 over each interval of 1.

(b) This graph is concave down, so it corresponds to a function whose increases are getting smaller, as is the case with $h(t)$, whose increases are 10, 9, 8, 7, and 6.

(c) This graph is concave up, so it corresponds to a function whose increases are getting bigger, as is the case with $g(t)$, whose increases are 1, 2, 3, 4, and 5.

36. (a) A linear function must change by exactly the same amount whenever x changes by some fixed quantity. While $h(x)$ decreases by 3 whenever x increases by 1, $f(x)$ and $g(x)$ fail this test, since both change by different amounts between $x = -2$ and $x = -1$ and between $x = -1$ and $x = 0$. So the only possible linear function is $h(x)$, so it will be given by a formula of the type: $h(x) = mx + b$. As noted, $m = -3$. Since the y-intercept of h is 31, the formula for $h(x)$ is $h(x) = 31 - 3x$.

(b) An exponential function must grow by exactly the same factor whenever x changes by some fixed quantity. Here, $g(x)$ increases by a factor of 1.5 whenever x increases by 1. Since the y-intercept of $g(x)$ is 36, $g(x)$ has the formula $g(x) = 36(1.5)^x$. The other two functions are not exponential; $h(x)$ is not because it is a linear function, and $f(x)$ is not because it both increases and decreases.

37. We see that $\frac{1.09}{1.06} \approx 1.03$, and therefore $h(s) = c(1.03)^s$; c must be 1. Similarly $\frac{2.42}{2.20} = 1.1$, and so $f(s) = a(1.1)^s$; $a = 2$. Lastly, $\frac{3.65}{3.47} \approx 1.05$, so $g(s) = b(1.05)^s$; $b \approx 3$.

38. Since f is linear, its slope is a constant

$$m = \frac{20 - 10}{2 - 0} = 5.$$

Thus f increases 5 units for unit increase in x, so

$$f(1) = 15, \quad f(3) = 25, \quad f(4) = 30.$$

Since g is exponential, its growth factor is constant. Writing $g(x) = ab^x$, we have $g(0) = a = 10$, so

$$g(x) = 10 \cdot b^x.$$

Since $g(2) = 10 \cdot b^2 = 20$, we have $b^2 = 2$ and since $b > 0$, we have

$$b = \sqrt{2}.$$

Thus g increases by a factor of $\sqrt{2}$ for unit increase in x, so

$$g(1) = 10\sqrt{2}, \quad g(3) = 10(\sqrt{2})^3 = 20\sqrt{2}, \quad g(4) = 10(\sqrt{2})^4 = 40.$$

Notice that the value of $g(x)$ doubles between $x = 0$ and $x = 2$ (from $g(0) = 10$ to $g(2) = 20$), so the doubling time of $g(x)$ is 2. Thus, $g(x)$ doubles again between $x = 2$ and $x = 4$, confirming that $g(4) = 40$.

39. (a) The slope is given by

$$m = \frac{P - P_1}{t - t_1} = \frac{100 - 50}{20 - 0} = \frac{50}{20} = 2.5.$$

We know $P = 50$ when $t = 0$, so

$$P = 2.5t + 50.$$

(b) Given $P = P_0 a^t$ and $P = 50$ when $t = 0$,

$$50 = P_0 a^0, \text{ so } P_0 = 50.$$

Then, using $P = 100$ when $t = 20$

$$100 = 50a^{20}$$
$$2 = a^{20}$$
$$a = 2^{1/20} = 1.035265.$$

And so we have

$$P = 50(1.035265)^t.$$

The completed table is found in Table 1.1.

Table 1.1 *The cost of a home*

t	(a) Linear Growth (price in $1000 units)	(b) Exponential Growth (price in $1000 units)
0	50	50
10	75	70.71
20	100	100
30	125	141.42
40	150	200

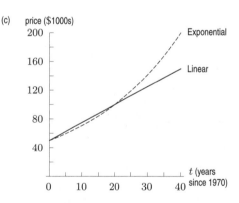

(d) Since economic growth (inflation, investments) are usually measured in percentage change per year, the exponential model is probably more realistic.

Solutions for Section 1.3

Exercises

1. (a) $f(g(1)) = f(1 + 1) = f(2) = 2^2 = 4$
(b) $g(f(1)) = g(1^2) = g(1) = 1 + 1 = 2$
(c) $f(g(x)) = f(x + 1) = (x + 1)^2$
(d) $g(f(x)) = g(x^2) = x^2 + 1$
(e) $f(t)g(t) = t^2(t + 1)$

2. (a) $f(g(1)) = f(1^2) = f(1) = \sqrt{1+4} = \sqrt{5}$
   (b) $g(f(1)) = g(\sqrt{1+4}) = g(\sqrt{5}) = (\sqrt{5})^2 = 5$
   (c) $f(g(x)) = f(x^2) = \sqrt{x^2 + 4}$
   (d) $g(f(x)) = g(\sqrt{x+4}) = (\sqrt{x+4})^2 = x + 4$
   (e) $f(t)g(t) = (\sqrt{t+4})t^2 = t^2\sqrt{t+4}$

3. (a) $f(g(1)) = f(1^2) = f(1) = e^1 = e$
   (b) $g(f(1)) = g(e^1) = g(e) = e^2$
   (c) $f(g(x)) = f(x^2) = e^{x^2}$
   (d) $g(f(x)) = g(e^x) = (e^x)^2 = e^{2x}$
   (e) $f(t)g(t) = e^t t^2$

4. (a) $f(g(1)) = f(3 \cdot 1 + 4) = f(7) = \dfrac{1}{7}$
   (b) $g(f(1)) = g(1/1) = g(1) = 7$
   (c) $f(g(x)) = f(3x + 4) = \dfrac{1}{3x + 4}$
   (d) $g(f(x)) = g\left(\dfrac{1}{x}\right) = 3\left(\dfrac{1}{x}\right) + 4 = \dfrac{3}{x} + 4$
   (e) $f(t)g(t) = \dfrac{1}{t}(3t + 4) = 3 + \dfrac{4}{t}$

5. This graph is the graph of $m(t)$ shifted upward by two units. See Figure 1.11.

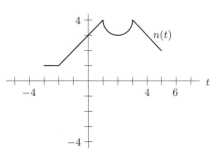

Figure 1.11

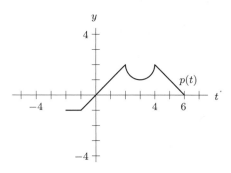

Figure 1.12

6. This graph is the graph of $m(t)$ shifted to the right by one unit. See Figure 1.12.

7. This graph is the graph of $m(t)$ shifted to the left by 1.5 units. See Figure 1.13.

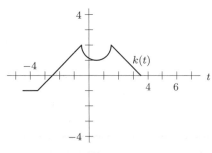

Figure 1.13

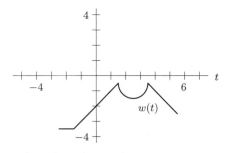

Figure 1.14

8. This graph is the graph of $m(t)$ shifted to the right by 0.5 units and downward by 2.5 units. See Figure 1.14.

9. For $f(-x)$, the graph is reflected in the y-axis. See Figure 1.15.

10. For $f(x) + 5$, the graph is shifted 5 upward. See Figure 1.16.

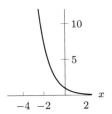

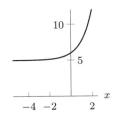

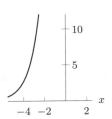

Figure 1.15

Figure 1.16

Figure 1.17

11. For $f(x + 5)$, the graph is shifted 5 units to the left. See Figure 1.17.

12. For $5f(x)$, the values are 5 times as large. See Figure 1.18.

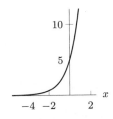

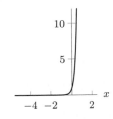

Figure 1.18

Figure 1.19

13. For $f(5x)$, the values increase 5 times as fast as we move right. See Figure 1.19.

14. (a) $g(2 + h) = (2 + h)^2 + 2(2 + h) + 3 = 4 + 4h + h^2 + 4 + 2h + 3 = h^2 + 6h + 11$.
 (b) $g(2) = 2^2 + 2(2) + 3 = 4 + 4 + 3 = 11$, which agrees with what we get by substituting $h = 0$ into (a).
 (c) $g(2 + h) - g(2) = (h^2 + 6h + 11) - (11) = h^2 + 6h$.

15. (a) $f(t + 1) = (t + 1)^2 + 1 = t^2 + 2t + 1 + 1 = t^2 + 2t + 2$.
 (b) $f(t^2 + 1) = (t^2 + 1)^2 + 1 = t^4 + 2t^2 + 1 + 1 = t^4 + 2t^2 + 2$.
 (c) $f(2) = 2^2 + 1 = 5$.
 (d) $2f(t) = 2(t^2 + 1) = 2t^2 + 2$.
 (e) $[f(t)]^2 + 1 = \left(t^2 + 1\right)^2 + 1 = t^4 + 2t^2 + 1 + 1 = t^4 + 2t^2 + 2$.

16. (a) $f(n) + g(n) = (3n^2 - 2) + (n + 1) = 3n^2 + n - 1$.
 (b) $f(n)g(n) = (3n^2 - 2)(n + 1) = 3n^3 + 3n^2 - 2n - 2$.
 (c) The domain of $f(n)/g(n)$ is defined everywhere where $g(n) \neq 0$, i.e. for all $n \neq -1$.
 (d) $f(g(n)) = 3(n + 1)^2 - 2 = 3n^2 + 6n + 1$.
 (e) $g(f(n)) = (3n^2 - 2) + 1 = 3n^2 - 1$.

17. $m(z + 1) - m(z) = (z + 1)^2 - z^2 = 2z + 1$.

18. $m(z + h) - m(z) = (z + h)^2 - z^2 = 2zh + h^2$.

19. $m(z) - m(z - h) = z^2 - (z - h)^2 = 2zh - h^2$.

20. $m(z + h) - m(z - h) = (z + h)^2 - (z - h)^2 = z^2 + 2hz + h^2 - (z^2 - 2hz + h^2) = 4hz$.

21. (a) $f(25)$ is q corresponding to $p = 25$, or, in other words, the number of items sold when the price is 25.
 (b) $f^{-1}(30)$ is p corresponding to $q = 30$, or the price at which 30 units will be sold.

22. (a) $f(10{,}000)$ represents the value of C corresponding to $A = 10{,}000$, or in other words the cost of building a 10,000 square-foot store.
 (b) $f^{-1}(20{,}000)$ represents the value of A corresponding to $C = 20{,}000$, or the area in square feet of a store which would cost $20,000 to build.

23. $f^{-1}(75)$ is the length of the column of mercury in the thermometer when the temperature is $75°\text{F}$.

24. (a) Since $m = f(A)$, we see that $f(100)$ represents the value of m when $A = 100$. Thus $f(100)$ is the minimum annual gross income needed (in thousands) to take out a 30-year mortgage loan of $100,000 at an interest rate of 9%.
 (b) Since $m = f(A)$, we have $A = f^{-1}(m)$. We see that $f^{-1}(75)$ represents the value of A when $m = 75$, or the size of a mortgage loan that could be obtained on an income of $75,000.

25. The function is not invertible since there are many horizontal lines which hit the function twice.

26. The function is not invertible since there are horizontal lines which hit the function more than once.

27. (a) We find $f^{-1}(2)$ by finding the x value corresponding to $f(x) = 2$. Looking at the graph, we see that $f^{-1}(2) = -1$.
(b) We construct the graph of $f^{-1}(x)$ by reflecting the graph of $f(x)$ over the line $y = x$. The graphs of $f^{-1}(x)$ and $f(x)$ are shown together in Figure 1.20.

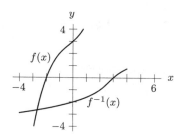

Figure 1.20

28. This looks like a shift of the graph $y = -x^2$. The graph is shifted to the left 1 unit and up 3 units, so a possible formula is $y = -(x + 1)^2 + 3$.

29. This looks like a shift of the graph $y = x^3$. The graph is shifted to the right 2 units and down 1 unit, so a possible formula is $y = (x - 2)^3 - 1$.

30.
$$f(-x) = (-x)^6 + (-x)^3 + 1 = x^6 - x^3 + 1.$$
Since $f(-x) \neq f(x)$ and $f(-x) \neq -f(x)$, this function is neither even nor odd.

31.
$$f(-x) = (-x)^3 + (-x)^2 + (-x) = -x^3 + x^2 - x.$$
Since $f(-x) \neq f(x)$ and $f(-x) \neq -f(x)$, this function is neither even nor odd.

32. Since
$$f(-x) = (-x)^4 - (-x)^2 + 3 = x^4 - x^2 + 3 = f(x),$$
we see f is even

33. Since
$$f(-x) = (-x)^3 + 1 = -x^3 + 1,$$
we see $f(-x) \neq f(x)$ and $f(-x) \neq -f(x)$, so f is neither even nor odd

34. Since
$$f(-x) = 2(-x) = -2x = -f(x),$$
we see f is odd.

35. Since
$$f(-x) = e^{(-x)^2 - 1} = e^{x^2 - 1} = f(x),$$
we see f is even.

36. Since
$$f(-x) = (-x)((-x)^2 - 1) = -x(x^2 - 1) = -f(x),$$
we see f is odd

37. Since
$$f(-x) = e^{-x} + x,$$
we see $f(-x) \neq f(x)$ and $f(-x) \neq -f(x)$, so f is neither even nor odd

Problems

38. (a) The equation is $y = 2x^2 + 1$. Note that its graph is narrower than the graph of $y = x^2$ which appears in gray. See Figure 1.21.

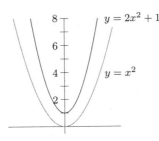

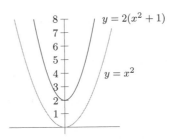

Figure 1.21   **Figure 1.22**

(b) $y = 2(x^2 + 1)$ moves the graph up one unit and *then* stretches it by a factor of two. See Figure 1.22.

(c) No, the graphs are not the same. Since $2(x^2 + 1) = (2x^2 + 1) + 1$, the second graph is always one unit higher than the first.

39. Not invertible. Given a certain number of customers, say $f(t) = 1500$, there could be many times, t, during the day at which that many people were in the store. So we don't know which time instant is the right one.

40. Probably not invertible. Since your calculus class probably has less than 363 students, there will be at least two days in the year, say a and b, with $f(a) = f(b) = 0$. Hence we don't know what to choose for $f^{-1}(0)$.

41. Invertible. Since at $4°C$, the mass of 1 liter of water is 1 kilogram, the mass of x liters is x kilograms. So $f(x) = x$ and therefore, $f^{-1}(x) = x$.

42. Not invertible, since it costs the same to mail a 50-gram letter as it does to mail a 51-gram letter.

43. $f(g(1)) = f(2) \approx 0.4$.

44. $g(f(2)) \approx g(0.4) \approx 1.1$.

45. $f(f(1)) \approx f(-0.4) \approx -0.9$.

46. Computing $f(g(x))$ as in Problem 43, we get the following table. From it we graph $f(g(x))$.

x	$g(x)$	$f(g(x))$
-3	0.6	-0.5
-2.5	-1.1	-1.3
-2	-1.9	-1.2
-1.5	-1.9	-1.2
-1	-1.4	-1.3
-0.5	-0.5	-1
0	0.5	-0.6
0.5	1.4	-0.2
1	2	0.4
1.5	2.2	0.5
2	1.6	0
2.5	0.1	-0.7
3	-2.5	0.1

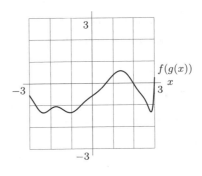

47. Using the same way to compute $g(f(x))$ as in Problem 44, we get the following table. Then we can plot the graph of $g(f(x))$.

x	$f(x)$	$g(f(x))$
-3	3	-2.6
-2.5	0.1	0.8
-2	-1	-1.4
-1.5	-1.3	-1.8
-1	-1.2	-1.7
-0.5	-1	-1.4
0	-0.8	-1
0.5	-0.6	-0.6
1	-0.4	-0.3
1.5	-0.1	0.3
2	0.3	1.1
2.5	0.9	2
3	1.6	2.2

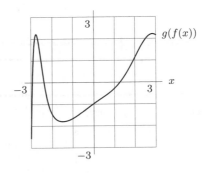

48. Using the same way to compute $f(f(x))$ as in Problem 45, we get the following table. Then we can plot the graph of $f(f(x))$.

x	$f(x)$	$f(f(x))$
-3	3	1.6
-2.5	0.1	-0.7
-2	-1	-1.2
-1.5	-1.3	-1.3
-1	-1.2	-1.3
-0.5	-1	-1.2
0	-0.8	-1.1
0.5	-0.6	-1
1	-0.4	-0.9
1.5	-0.1	-0.8
2	0.3	-0.6
2.5	0.9	-0.4
3	1.6	0

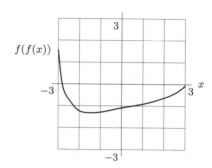

49. $f(x) = x^3$, $g(x) = x + 1$.

50. $f(x) = x + 1$, $g(x) = x^3$.

51. Since $B = y - 1$ and $n = 2B^2 - B$, substitution gives

$$\text{Average number of leaves} = Bn = (y-1)(2(y-1)^2 - (y-1)) = 2(y-1)^3 - (y-1)^2.$$

52. (a) The function f tells us C in terms of q. To get its inverse, we want q in terms of C, which we find by solving for q:

$$C = 100 + 2q,$$
$$C - 100 = 2q,$$
$$q = \frac{C - 100}{2} = f^{-1}(C).$$

(b) The inverse function tells us the number of articles that can be produced for a given cost.

53. (a) For each 2.2 pounds of weight the object has, it has 1 kilogram of mass, so the conversion formula is

$$k = f(p) = \frac{1}{2.2}p.$$

(b) The inverse function is

$$p = 2.2k,$$

and it gives the weight of an object in pounds as a function of its mass in kilograms.

54.

x	$f(x)$	$g(x)$	$h(x)$
-3	0	0	0
-2	2	2	-2
-1	2	2	-2
0	0	0	0
1	2	-2	-2
2	2	-2	-2
3	0	0	0

Solutions for Section 1.4

Exercises

1. Using the identity $e^{\ln x} = x$, we have $e^{\ln(1/2)} = \frac{1}{2}$.

2. Using the identity $10^{\log x} = x$, we have

$$10^{\log(AB)} = AB$$

3. Using the identity $e^{\ln x} = x$, we have $5A^2$.

4. Using the identity $\ln(e^x) = x$, we have 2AB.

5. Using the rules for ln, we have

$$\ln\left(\frac{1}{e}\right) + \ln AB = \ln 1 - \ln e + \ln A + \ln B$$
$$= 0 - 1 + \ln A + \ln B$$
$$= -1 + \ln A + \ln B.$$

6. Using the rules for ln, we have $2A + 3e \ln B$.

7. Taking logs of both sides

$$\log 3^x = x \log 3 = \log 11$$
$$x = \frac{\log 11}{\log 3} = 2.2.$$

8. Taking logs of both sides

$$\log 17^x = \log 2$$
$$x \log 17 = \log 2$$
$$x = \frac{\log 2}{\log 17} \approx 0.24.$$

9. Isolating the exponential term

$$20 = 50(1.04)^x$$
$$\frac{20}{50} = (1.04)^x.$$

Taking logs of both sides

$$\log \frac{2}{5} = \log(1.04)^x$$
$$\log \frac{2}{5} = x \log(1.04)$$
$$x = \frac{\log(2/5)}{\log(1.04)} = -23.4.$$

10.

$$\frac{4}{7} = \frac{5^x}{3^x}$$
$$\frac{4}{7} = \left(\frac{5}{3}\right)^x$$

Taking logs of both sides

$$\log\left(\frac{4}{7}\right) = x \log\left(\frac{5}{3}\right)$$
$$x = \frac{\log(4/7)}{\log(5/3)} \approx -1.1.$$

11. $\ln(2^x) = \ln(e^{x+1})$
$$x \ln 2 = (x+1) \ln e$$
$$x \ln 2 = x + 1$$
$$0.693x = x + 1$$
$$x = \frac{1}{0.693 - 1} \approx -3.26$$

12. To solve for x, we first divide both sides by 600 and then take the natural logarithm of both sides.

$$\frac{50}{600} = e^{-0.4x}$$
$$\ln(50/600) = -0.4x$$
$$x = \frac{\ln(50/600)}{-0.4} \approx 6.212.$$

13.
$$\ln(2e^{3x}) = \ln(4e^{5x})$$
$$\ln 2 + \ln(e^{3x}) = \ln 4 + \ln(e^{5x})$$
$$0.693 + 3x = 1.386 + 5x$$
$$x = -0.347$$

14. Using the rules for ln, we get

$$\ln 7^{x+2} = \ln e^{17x}$$
$$(x + 2)\ln 7 = 17x$$
$$x(\ln 7 - 17) = -2\ln 7$$
$$x = \frac{-2\ln 7}{\ln 7 - 17} \approx 0.26.$$

15.
$$\ln(10^{x+3}) = \ln(5e^{7-x})$$
$$(x + 3)\ln 10 = \ln 5 + (7 - x)\ln e$$
$$2.303(x + 3) = 1.609 + (7 - x)$$
$$3.303x = 1.609 + 7 - 2.303(3)$$
$$x = 0.515$$

16. Using the rules for ln, we have

$$2x - 1 = x^2$$
$$x^2 - 2x + 1 = 0$$
$$(x - 1)^2 = 0$$
$$x = 1.$$

17. Using the rules for ln, we get

$$\ln 9^x = \ln 2e^{x^2}$$
$$x \ln 9 = \ln 2 + x^2$$
$$x^2 - x \ln 9 + \ln 2 = 0.$$

We can use the quadratic formula to get $x = \dfrac{\ln 9 \pm \sqrt{(\ln 9)^2 - 4\ln 2}}{2}$, so $x \approx 0.382$, $x \approx 1.815$.

18. $t = \dfrac{\log a}{\log b}.$

19. $t = \dfrac{\log\left(\frac{P}{P_0}\right)}{\log a} = \dfrac{\log P - \log P_0}{\log a}.$

20. Taking logs of both sides yields

$$nt = \frac{\log\left(\frac{Q}{Q_0}\right)}{\log a}.$$

Hence

$$t = \frac{\log\left(\frac{Q}{Q_0}\right)}{n\log a} = \frac{\log Q - \log Q_0}{n\log a}.$$

21. Collecting similar terms yields

$$\left(\frac{a}{b}\right)^t = \frac{Q_0}{P_0}.$$

Hence

$$t = \frac{\log\left(\frac{Q_0}{P_0}\right)}{\log\left(\frac{a}{b}\right)}.$$

22. $t = \ln\dfrac{a}{b}.$

23. $\ln\dfrac{P}{P_0} = kt$, so $t = \dfrac{\ln\frac{P}{P_0}}{k}.$

24. Since we want $(1.5)^t = e^{kt} = (e^k)^t$, so $1.5 = e^k$, and $k = \ln 1.5 = 0.4055$. Thus, $P = 15e^{0.4055t}$. Since 0.4055 is positive, this is exponential growth.

25. We want $1.7^t = e^{kt}$ so $1.7 = e^k$ and $k = \ln 1.7 = 0.5306$. Thus $P = 10e^{0.5306t}$.

26. We want $0.9^t = e^{kt}$ so $0.9 = e^k$ and $k = \ln 0.9 = -0.1054$. Thus $P = 174e^{-0.1054t}$.

27. Since we want $(0.55)^t = e^{kt} = (e^k)^t$, so $0.55 = e^k$, and $k = \ln 0.55 = -0.5978$. Thus $P = 4e^{-0.5978t}$. Since -0.5978 is negative, this represents exponential decay.

28. If $p(t) = (1.04)^t$, then, for p^{-1} the inverse of p, we should have

$$(1.04)^{p^{-1}(t)} = t,$$
$$p^{-1}(t) \log(1.04) = \log t,$$
$$p^{-1}(t) = \frac{\log t}{\log(1.04)} \approx 58.708 \log t.$$

29. Since f is increasing, f has an inverse. To find the inverse of $f(t) = 50e^{0.1t}$, we replace t with $f^{-1}(t)$, and, since $f(f^{-1}(t)) = t$, we have

$$t = 50e^{0.1f^{-1}(t)}.$$

We then solve for $f^{-1}(t)$:

$$t = 50e^{0.1f^{-1}(t)}$$
$$\frac{t}{50} = e^{0.1f^{-1}(t)}$$
$$\ln\left(\frac{t}{50}\right) = 0.1f^{-1}(t)$$
$$f^{-1}(t) = \frac{1}{0.1}\ln\left(\frac{t}{50}\right) = 10\ln\left(\frac{t}{50}\right).$$

30. Using $f(f^{-1}(t)) = t$, we see

$$f(f^{-1}(t)) = 1 + \ln f^{-1}(t) = t.$$

So

$$\ln f^{-1}(t) = t - 1$$
$$f^{-1}(t) = e^{t-1}.$$

Problems

31. The function e^x has a vertical intercept of 1, so must be A. The function $\ln x$ has an x-intercept of 1, so must be D. The graphs of x^2 and $x^{1/2}$ go through the origin. The graph of $x^{1/2}$ is concave down so it corresponds to graph C and the graph of x^2 is concave up so it corresponds to graph B.

32. The population has increased by a factor of $56,000,000/40,000,000 = 1.4$ in 10 years. Thus we have the formula

$$P = 40,000,000(1.4)^{t/10},$$

and $t/10$ gives the number of 10-year periods that have passed since 1980.
In 1980, $t/10 = 0$, so we have $P = 40,000,000$.
In 1990, $t/10 = 1$, so $P = 40,000,000(1.4) = 56,000,000$.
In 2000, $t/10 = 2$, so $P = 40,000,000(1.4)^2 = 78,400,000$.
To find the doubling time, solve $80,000,000 = 40,000,000(1.4)^{t/10}$, to get $t \approx 20.6$ years.

33. Since the factor by which the prices have increased after time t is given by $(1.05)^t$, the time after which the prices have doubled solves

$$2 = (1.05)^t$$
$$\log 2 = \log(1.05^t) = t \log(1.05)$$
$$t = \frac{\log 2}{\log 1.05} \approx 14.21 \text{ years.}$$

34. Given the doubling time of 5 hours, we can solve for the bacteria's growth rate;

$$2P_0 = P_0 e^{k5}$$
$$k = \frac{\ln 2}{5}.$$

So the growth of the bacteria population is given by:

$$P = P_0 e^{\ln(2)t/5}.$$

We want to find t such that

$$3P_0 = P_0 e^{\ln(2)t/5}.$$

Therefore we cancel P_0 and apply ln. We get

$$t = \frac{5 \ln(3)}{\ln(2)} = 7.925 \text{ hours.}$$

35. In ten years, the substance has decayed to 40% of its original mass. In another ten years, it will decay by an additional factor of 40%, so the amount remaining after 20 years will be $100 \cdot 40\% \cdot 40\% = 16$ kg.

36. Using the exponential decay equation $P = P_0 e^{-kt}$, we can solve for the substance's decay constant k:

$$(P_0 - 0.3P_0) = P_0 e^{-20k}$$
$$k = \frac{\ln(0.7)}{-20}.$$

Knowing this decay constant, we can solve for the half-life t using the formula

$$0.5P_0 = P_0 e^{\ln(0.7)t/20}$$
$$t = \frac{20 \ln(0.5)}{\ln(0.7)} \approx 38.87 \text{ hours.}$$

37. Let B represent the sales (in millions of dollars) at Borders bookstores t years since 1991. Since $B = 78$ when $t = 0$ and we want the continuous growth rate, we write $B = 78e^{kt}$. We use the information from 1994, that $B = 412$ when $t = 3$, to find k:

$$412 = 78e^{k \cdot 3}$$
$$5.282 = e^{3k}$$
$$\ln(5.282) = 3k$$
$$k = 0.555.$$

We have $B = 78e^{0.555t}$, which represents a continuous growth rate of 55.5% per year.

38. Let n be the infant mortality of Senegal. As a function of time t, n is given by

$$n = n_0 (0.90)^t.$$

To find when $n = 0.50n_0$ (so the number of cases has been reduced by 50%), we solve

$$0.50 = (0.90)^t,$$
$$\log(0.50) = t \log(0.90),$$
$$t = \frac{\log(0.50)}{\log(0.90)} \approx 6.58 \text{ years.}$$

39. We know that the y-intercept of the line is at $(0,1)$, so we need one other point to determine the equation of the line. We observe that it intersects the graph of $f(x) = 10^x$ at the point $x = \log 2$. The y-coordinate of this point is then

$$y = 10^x = 10^{\log 2} = 2,$$

so $(\log 2, 2)$ is the point of intersection. We can now find the slope of the line:

$$m = \frac{2 - 1}{\log 2 - 0} = \frac{1}{\log 2}.$$

Plugging this into the point-slope formula for a line, we have

$$y - y_1 = m(x - x_1)$$
$$y - 1 = \frac{1}{\log 2}(x - 0)$$
$$y = \frac{1}{\log 2}x + 1 \approx 3.3219x + 1.$$

40. (a) The initial dose is 10 mg.

(b) Since $0.82 = 1 - 0.18$, the decay rate is 0.18, so 18% leaves the body each hour.

(c) When $t = 6$, we have $A = 10(0.82)^6 = 3.04$. The amount in the body after 6 hours is 3.04 mg.

(d) We want to find the value of t when $A = 1$. Using logarithms:

$$1 = 10(0.82)^t$$
$$0.1 = (0.82)^t$$
$$\ln(0.1) = t\ln(0.82)$$
$$t = 11.60 \text{ hours.}$$

After 11.60 hours, the amount is 1 mg.

41. (a) Since the initial amount of caffeine is 100 mg and the exponential decay rate is -0.17, we have $A = 100e^{-0.17t}$.

(b) See Figure 1.23. We estimate the half-life by estimating t when the caffeine is reduced by half (so $A = 50$); this occurs at approximately $t = 4$ hours.

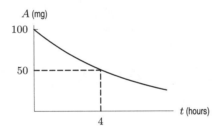

Figure 1.23

(c) We want to find the value of t when $A = 50$:

$$50 = 100e^{-0.17t}$$
$$0.5 = e^{-0.17t}$$
$$\ln 0.5 = -0.17t$$
$$t = 4.077.$$

The half-life of caffeine is about 4.077 hours. This agrees with what we saw in Figure 1.23.

42. Let $t = $ number of years since 1980. Then the number of vehicles, V, in millions, at time t is given by

$$V = 170(1.04)^t$$

and the number of people, P, in millions, at time t is given by

$$P = 227(1.01)^t.$$

There is an average of one vehicle per person when $\frac{V}{P} = 1$, or $V = P$. Thus, we must solve for t the equation:

$$170(1.04)^t = 227(1.01)^t,$$

which implies

$$\left(\frac{1.04}{1.01}\right)^t = \frac{(1.04)^t}{(1.01)^t} = \frac{227}{170}$$

Taking logs on both sides,

$$t \log \frac{1.04}{1.01} = \log \frac{227}{170}.$$

Therefore,

$$t = \frac{\log \left(\frac{227}{170} \right)}{\log \left(\frac{1.04}{1.01} \right)} \approx 9.9 \text{ years.}$$

So there was, according to this model, about one vehicle per person in 1990.

43. (a) We know the decay follows the equation

$$P = P_0 e^{-kt},$$

and that 10% of the pollution is removed after 5 hours (meaning that 90% is left). Therefore,

$$0.90 P_0 = P_0 e^{-5k}$$
$$k = -\frac{1}{5} \ln(0.90).$$

Thus, after 10 hours:

$$P = P_0 e^{-10((-0.2)\ln 0.90)}$$
$$P = P_0 (0.9)^2 = 0.81 P_0$$

so 81% of the original amount is left.

(b) We want to solve for the time when $P = 0.50 P_0$:

$$0.50 P_0 = P_0 e^{t((0.2)\ln 0.90)}$$
$$0.50 = e^{\ln(0.90^{0.2t})}$$
$$0.50 = 0.90^{0.2t}$$
$$t = \frac{5 \ln(0.50)}{\ln(0.90)} \approx 32.9 \text{ hours.}$$

(c)

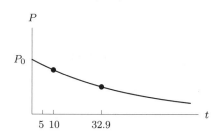

(d) When highly polluted air is filtered, there is more pollutant per liter of air to remove. If a fixed amount of air is cleaned every day, there is a higher amount of pollutant removed earlier in the process.

44. (a) The pressure P at 6198 meters is given in terms of the pressure P_0 at sea level to be

$$P = P_0 e^{-0.00012h}$$
$$= P_0 e^{(-0.00012)6198}$$
$$= P_0 e^{-0.74376}$$
$$\approx 0.4753 P_0 \quad \text{or about 47.5\% of sea level pressure.}$$

(b) At $h = 12{,}000$ meters, we have

$$P = P_0 e^{-0.00012h}$$
$$= P_0 e^{(-0.00012)12{,}000}$$
$$= P_0 e^{-1.44}$$
$$\approx 0.2369 P_0 \quad \text{or about 23.7\% of sea level pressure.}$$

45. Since the amount of strontium-90 remaining halves every 29 years, we can solve for the decay constant;

$$0.5P_0 = P_0 e^{-29k}$$
$$k = \frac{\ln(1/2)}{-29}.$$

Knowing this, we can look for the time t in which $P = 0.10P_0$, or

$$0.10P_0 = P_0 e^{\ln(0.5)t/29}$$
$$t = \frac{29\ln(0.10)}{\ln(0.5)} = 96.34 \text{ years.}$$

46. We assume exponential decay and solve for k using the half-life:

$$e^{-k(5730)} = 0.5 \quad \text{so} \quad k = 1.21 \cdot 10^{-4}.$$

Now find t, the age of the painting:

$$e^{-1.21\cdot 10^{-4}t} = 0.995, \quad \text{so} \quad t = \frac{\ln 0.995}{-1.21 \cdot 10^{-4}} = 41.43 \text{ years.}$$

Since Vermeer died in 1675, the painting is a fake.

Solutions for Section 1.5

Exercises

1. See Figure 1.24.

$$\sin\left(\frac{3\pi}{2}\right) = -1 \quad \text{is negative.}$$
$$\cos\left(\frac{3\pi}{2}\right) = 0$$
$$\tan\left(\frac{3\pi}{2}\right) \quad \text{is undefined.}$$

2. See Figure 1.25.

$$\sin(2\pi) = 0$$
$$\cos(2\pi) = 1 \text{ is positive.}$$
$$\tan(2\pi) = 0$$

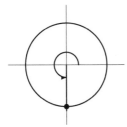

Figure 1.24

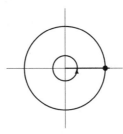

Figure 1.25

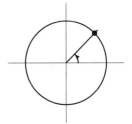

Figure 1.26

3. See Figure 1.26.

$$\sin\frac{\pi}{4} \quad \text{is positive}$$
$$\cos\frac{\pi}{4} \quad \text{is positive}$$
$$\tan\frac{\pi}{4} \quad \text{is positive}$$

4. See Figure 1.27.

$$\sin 3\pi = 0$$
$$\cos 3\pi = -1 \text{ is negative}$$
$$\tan 3\pi = 0$$

5. See Figure 1.28.

$$\sin\left(\frac{\pi}{6}\right) \text{ is positive.}$$
$$\cos\left(\frac{\pi}{6}\right) \text{ is positive.}$$
$$\tan\left(\frac{\pi}{6}\right) \text{ is positive.}$$

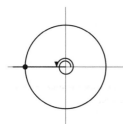

Figure 1.27

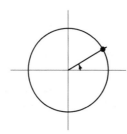

Figure 1.28

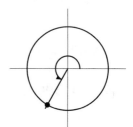

Figure 1.29

6. See Figure 1.29.

$$\sin\frac{4\pi}{3} \text{ is negative}$$
$$\cos\frac{4\pi}{3} \text{ is negative}$$
$$\tan\frac{4\pi}{3} \text{ is positive}$$

7. See Figure 1.30.

$$\sin\left(\frac{-4\pi}{3}\right) \text{ is positive.}$$
$$\cos\left(\frac{-4\pi}{3}\right) \text{ is negative.}$$
$$\tan\left(\frac{-4\pi}{3}\right) \text{ is negative.}$$

8. $4 \text{ radians} \cdot \dfrac{180°}{\pi \text{ radians}} = \left(\dfrac{720}{\pi}\right)° \approx 240°$. See Figure 1.31.

$$\sin 4 \text{ is negative}$$
$$\cos 4 \text{ is negative}$$
$$\tan 4 \text{ is positive.}$$

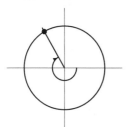

Figure 1.30

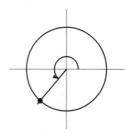

Figure 1.31

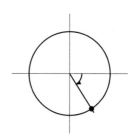

Figure 1.32

9. -1 radian $\cdot \frac{180°}{\pi \text{ radians}} = -\left(\frac{180°}{\pi}\right) \approx -60°$. See Figure 1.32.

$$\sin(-1) \quad \text{is negative}$$
$$\cos(-1) \quad \text{is positive}$$
$$\tan(-1) \quad \text{is negative.}$$

10.

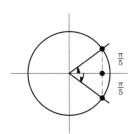

$$\cos\left(-\frac{\pi}{5}\right) = \cos\frac{\pi}{5} \quad \text{(by picture)}$$
$$= 0.809.$$

11.

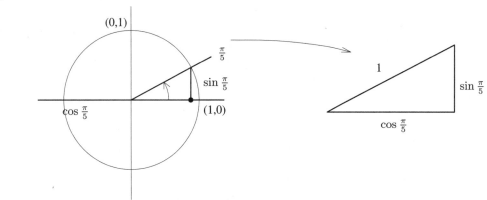

By the Pythagorean Theorem, $(\cos\frac{\pi}{5})^2 + (\sin\frac{\pi}{5})^2 = 1^2$;
so $(\sin\frac{\pi}{5})^2 = 1 - (\cos\frac{\pi}{5})^2$, and $\sin\frac{\pi}{5} = \sqrt{1 - (\cos\frac{\pi}{5})^2} = \sqrt{1 - (0.809)^2} \approx 0.588$.
We take the positive square root since by the picture we know that $\sin\frac{\pi}{5}$ is positive.

12.

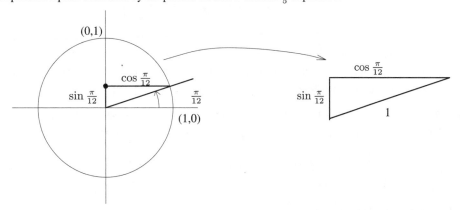

By the Pythagorean Theorem, $(\cos\frac{\pi}{12})^2 + (\sin\frac{\pi}{12})^2 = 1^2$; so $(\cos\frac{\pi}{12})^2 = 1 - (\sin\frac{\pi}{12})^2$ and $\cos\frac{\pi}{12} = \sqrt{1 - (\sin\frac{\pi}{12})^2} = \sqrt{1 - (0.259)^2} \approx 0.966$. We take the positive square root since by the picture we know that $\cos\frac{\pi}{12}$ is positive.

13. (a) We determine the amplitude of y by looking at the coefficient of the cosine term. Here, the coefficient is 1, so the amplitude of y is 1. Note that the constant term does not affect the amplitude.

(b) We know that the cosine function $\cos x$ repeats itself at $x = 2\pi$, so the function $\cos(3x)$ must repeat itself when $3x = 2\pi$, or at $x = 2\pi/3$. So the period of y is $2\pi/3$. Here as well the constant term has no effect.

(c) The graph of y is shown in the figure below.

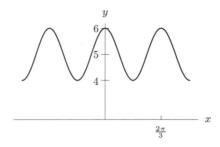

14. The period is $2\pi/3$, because when t varies from 0 to $2\pi/3$, the quantity $3t$ varies from 0 to 2π. The amplitude is 7, since the value of the function oscillates between -7 and 7.

15. The period is $2\pi/(1/4) = 8\pi$, because when u varies from 0 to 8π, the quantity $u/4$ varies from 0 to 2π. The amplitude is 3, since the function oscillates between 2 and 8.

16. The period is $2\pi/2 = \pi$, because as x varies from $-\pi/2$ to $\pi/2$, the quantity $2x + \pi$ varies from 0 to 2π. The amplitude is 4, since the function oscillates between 4 and 12.

17. The period is $2\pi/\pi = 2$, since when t increases from 0 to 2, the value of πt increases from 0 to 2π. The amplitude is 0.1, since the function oscillates between 1.9 and 2.1.

18. (a) $h(t) = 2\cos(t - \pi/2)$
   (b) $f(t) = 2\cos t$
   (c) $g(t) = 2\cos(t + \pi/2)$

19. This graph is a sine curve with period 8π and amplitude 2, so it is given by $f(x) = 2\sin\left(\dfrac{x}{4}\right)$.

20. This graph is a cosine curve with period 6π and amplitude 5, so it is given by $f(x) = 5\cos\left(\dfrac{x}{3}\right)$.

21. This graph is an inverted sine curve with amplitude 4 and period π, so it is given by $f(x) = -4\sin(2x)$.

22. This graph is an inverted cosine curve with amplitude 8 and period 20π, so it is given by $f(x) = -8\cos\left(\dfrac{x}{10}\right)$.

23. This graph has period 6, amplitude 5 and no vertical or horizontal shift, so it is given by

$$f(x) = 5\sin\left(\frac{2\pi}{6}x\right) = 5\sin\left(\frac{\pi}{3}x\right).$$

24. The graph is a cosine curve with period $2\pi/5$ and amplitude 2, so it is given by $f(x) = 2\cos(5x)$.

25. The graph is an inverted sine curve with amplitude 1 and period 2π, shifted up by 2, so it is given by $f(x) = 2 - \sin x$.

26. The graph is a sine curve which has been shifted up by 2, so $f(x) = (\sin x) + 2$.

27. This graph is the same as in Problem 19 but shifted up by 2, so it is given by $f(x) = 2\sin\left(\dfrac{x}{4}\right) + 2$.

28. This graph has period 8, amplitude 3, and a vertical shift of 3 with no horizontal shift. It is given by

$$f(x) = 3 + 3\sin\left(\frac{2\pi}{8}x\right) = 3 + 3\sin\left(\frac{\pi}{4}x\right).$$

29. We first divide by 5 and then use inverse sine:

$$\frac{2}{5} = \sin(3x)$$
$$\sin^{-1}(2/5) = 3x$$
$$x = \frac{\sin^{-1}(2/5)}{3} \approx 0.1372.$$

There are infinitely many other possible solutions since the sine is periodic.

30. We first isolate $\cos(2x + 1)$ and then use inverse cosine:

$$1 = 8\cos(2x + 1) - 3$$
$$4 = 8\cos(2x + 1)$$
$$0.5 = \cos(2x + 1)$$
$$\cos^{-1}(0.5) = 2x + 1$$
$$x = \frac{\cos^{-1}(0.5) - 1}{2} \approx 0.0236.$$

There are infinitely many other possible solutions since the cosine is periodic.

31. We first isolate $\tan(5x)$ and then use inverse tangent:

$$8 = 4\tan(5x)$$
$$2 = \tan(5x)$$
$$\tan^{-1} 2 = 5x$$
$$x = \frac{\tan^{-1} 2}{5} = 0.221.$$

There are infinitely many other possible solutions since the tangent is periodic.

32. We first isolate $(2x + 1)$ and then use inverse tangent:

$$1 = 8\tan(2x + 1) - 3$$
$$4 = 8\tan(2x + 1)$$
$$0.5 = \tan(2x + 1)$$
$$\arctan(0.5) = 2x + 1$$
$$x = \frac{\arctan(0.5) - 1}{2} = -0.268.$$

There are infinitely many other possible solutions since the tangent is periodic.

33. We first isolate $\sin(5x)$ and then use inverse sine:

$$8 = 4\sin(5x)$$
$$2 = \sin(5x).$$

But this equation has no solution since $-1 \le \sin(5x) \le 1$.

Problems

34. Using the fact that 1 revolution $= 2\pi$ radians and 1 minute $= 60$ seconds, we have

$$200\frac{\text{rev}}{\text{min}} = (200) \cdot 2\pi\frac{\text{rad}}{\text{min}} = 200 \cdot 2\pi\frac{1}{60}\frac{\text{rad}}{\text{sec}}$$
$$\approx \frac{(200)(6.283)}{60}$$
$$\approx 20.94 \text{ radians per second.}$$

Similarly, 500 rpm is equivalent to 52.36 radians per second.

35. 200 revolutions per minute is $\frac{1}{200}$ minutes per revolution, so the period is $\frac{1}{200}$ minutes, or 0.3 seconds.

36. $\sin x^2$ is by convention $\sin(x^2)$, which means you square the x first and then take the sine.
$\sin^2 x = (\sin x)^2$ means find $\sin x$ and then square it.
$\sin(\sin x)$ means find $\sin x$ and then take the sine of that.
Expressing each as a composition: If $f(x) = \sin x$ and $g(x) = x^2$, then
$\sin x^2 = f(g(x))$
$\sin^2 x = g(f(x))$
$\sin(\sin x) = f(f(x)).$

37. Suppose P is at the point $(3\pi/2, -1)$ and Q is at the point $(5\pi/2, 1)$. Then

$$\text{Slope} = \frac{1 - (-1)}{5\pi/2 - 3\pi/2} = \frac{2}{\pi}.$$

If P had been picked to the right of Q, the slope would have been $-2/\pi$.

38. (a) D = the average depth of the water.

(b) A = the amplitude = $15/2 = 7.5$.

(c) Period = 12.4 hours. Thus $(B)(12.4) = 2\pi$ so $B = 2\pi/12.4 \approx 0.507$.

(d) C is the time of a high tide.

39. (a) The amplitude, y_0, is the maximum value of y; that is, the maximum displacement from the equilibrium position.

(b) One complete cycle is executed when

$$2\pi\omega t = 2\pi, \quad \text{so} \quad t = \frac{1}{\omega}.$$

Therefore, the period is $1/\omega$ seconds, and the number of complete oscillations that take place in 1 second is ω.

40. (a) V_0 represents the maximum voltage.

(b) The period is $2\pi/(120\pi) = 1/60$ second.

(c) Since each oscillation takes $1/60$ second, in 1 second there are 60 complete oscillations.

41. The US voltage has a maximum value of 156 volts and has a period of $1/60$ of a second, so it executes 60 cycles a second. The European voltage has a higher maximum of 339 volts, and a slightly longer period of $1/50$ seconds, so it oscillates at 50 cycles per second.

42. The function R has period of π, so its graph is as shown in Figure 1.33. The maximum value of the range is v_0^2/g and occurs when $\theta = \pi/4$.

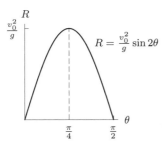

Figure 1.33

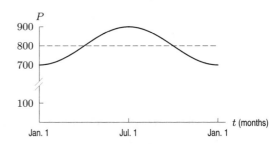

Figure 1.34

43. (a) See Figure 1.34.

(b) Average value of population = $\frac{700+900}{2} = 800$, amplitude = $\frac{900-700}{2} = 100$, and period = 12 months, so $B = 2\pi/12 = \pi/6$. Since the population is at its minimum when $t = 0$, we use a negative cosine:

$$P = 800 - 100\cos\left(\frac{\pi t}{6}\right).$$

44. We use a cosine of the form

$$H = A\cos(Bt) + C$$

and choose B so that the period is 24 hours, so $2\pi/B = 24$ giving $B = \pi/12$.

The temperature oscillates around an average value of $60°$ F, so $C = 60$. The amplitude of the oscillation is $20°$ F. To arrange that the temperature be at its lowest when $t = 0$, we take A negative, so $A = -20$. Thus

$$A = 60 - 20\cos\left(\frac{\pi}{12}t\right).$$

45. (a) Reading the graph of θ against t shows that $\theta \approx 5.2$ when $t = 1.5$. Since the coordinates of P are $x = 5\cos\theta$, $y = 5\sin\theta$, when $t = 1.5$ the coordinates are

$$(x, y) \approx (5\cos 5.2, 5\sin 5.2) = (2.3, -4.4).$$

(b) As t increases from 0 to 5, the angle θ increases from 0 to about 6.3 and then decreases to 0 again. Since $6.3 \approx 2\pi$, this means that P starts on the x-axis at the point $(5, 0)$, moves counterclockwise the whole way around the circle (at which time $\theta \approx 2\pi$), and then moves back clockwise to its starting point.

46.

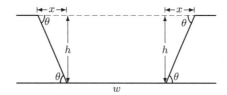

Figure 1.35

Figure 1.35 shows that the cross-sectional area is one rectangle of area hw and two triangles. Each triangle has height h and base x, where

$$\frac{h}{x} = \tan \theta \quad \text{so} \quad x = \frac{h}{\tan \theta}.$$

$$\text{Area of triangle} = \frac{1}{2}xh = \frac{h^2}{2\tan\theta}$$

$$\text{Total area} = \text{Area of rectangle} + 2(\text{Area of triangle})$$

$$= hw + 2 \cdot \frac{h^2}{2\tan\theta} = hw + \frac{h^2}{\tan\theta}.$$

47. (a) A table of values for $g(x)$ is given below.

x	-1	-0.8	-0.6	-0.4	-0.2	0	0.2	0.4	0.6	0.8	1
$\arccos x$	3.14	2.50	2.21	1.98	1.77	1.57	1.37	1.16	0.93	0.64	0

(b)

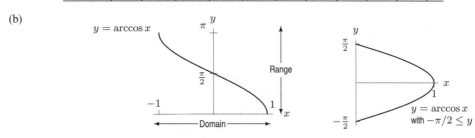

Figure 1.36

Figure 1.37

(c) The domain of arccos and arcsin are the same, $-1 \le x \le 1$, since their inverses (sine and cosine) only take on values in this range.

(d) The domain of the original sine function was restricted to the the interval $\left[-\frac{\pi}{2}, \frac{\pi}{2}\right]$ to construct the arcsine function. Hence, the range of arcsine is also $\left[-\frac{\pi}{2}, \frac{\pi}{2}\right]$. Now, if we restrict the domain of cosine in the same way, we obtain an arccosine curve which is not a function. (See Figure 1.37.) For example, for $x = 0$, $y = \arccos x$ will have two values, $-\frac{\pi}{2}$, and $\frac{\pi}{2}$. Also, it gives no values for $x < 0$, so it is not very useful. The domain of cosine should instead be restricted to $[0, \pi]$, so that $y = \arccos x$ gives a unique y for each value of x.

Solutions for Section 1.6

Exercises

1. Exponential growth dominates power growth as $x \to \infty$, so $10 \cdot 2^x$ is larger.

2. As $x \to \infty$, $0.25x^{1/2}$ is larger than $25{,}000x^{-3}$.

3. As $x \to \infty$, $y \to \infty$.
As $x \to -\infty$, $y \to -\infty$.

4. As $x \to \infty$, $y \to \infty$.
As $x \to -\infty$, $y \to 0$.

5. (I) (a) Minimum degree is 3 because graph turns around twice.
  (b) Leading coefficient is negative because $y \to -\infty$ as $x \to \infty$.
(II) (a) Minimum degree is 4 because graph turns around three times.
  (b) Leading coefficient is positive because $y \to \infty$ as $x \to \infty$.

(III) **(a)** Minimum degree is 4 because graph turns around three times.

(b) Leading coefficient is negative because $y \to -\infty$ as $x \to \infty$.

(IV) **(a)** Minimum degree is 5 because graph turns around four times.

(b) Leading coefficient is negative because $y \to -\infty$ as $x \to \infty$.

(V) **(a)** Minimum degree is 5 because graph turns around four times.

(b) Leading coefficient is positive because $y \to \infty$ as $x \to \infty$.

6. (a) A polynomial has the same end behavior as its leading term, so this polynomial behaves as $-5x^4$ globally. Thus we have:
$$f(x) \to -\infty \text{ as } x \to -\infty, \quad \text{and} \quad f(x) \to -\infty \text{ as } x \to +\infty.$$

(b) Polynomials behave globally as their leading term, so this rational function behaves globally as $(3x^2)/(2x^2)$, or $3/2$. Thus we have:
$$f(x) \to 3/2 \text{ as } x \to -\infty, \quad \text{and} \quad f(x) \to 3/2 \text{ as } x \to +\infty.$$

(c) We see from a graph of $y = e^x$ that
$$f(x) \to 0 \text{ as } x \to -\infty, \quad \text{and} \quad f(x) \to +\infty \text{ as } x \to +\infty.$$

7. $f(x) = k(x+3)(x-1)(x-4) = k(x^3 - 2x^2 - 11x + 12)$, where $k < 0$. ($k \approx -\frac{1}{6}$ if the horizontal and vertical scales are equal; otherwise one can't tell how large k is.)

8. $f(x) = kx(x+3)(x-4) = k(x^3 - x^2 - 12x)$, where $k < 0$. ($k \approx -\frac{2}{9}$ if the horizontal and vertical scales are equal; otherwise one can't tell how large k is.)

9. $f(x) = k(x+2)(x-1)(x-3)(x-5) = k(x^4 - 7x^3 + 5x^2 + 31x - 30)$, where $k > 0$. ($k \approx \frac{1}{15}$ if the horizontal and vertical scales are equal; otherwise one can't tell how large k is.)

10. $f(x) = k(x+2)(x-2)^2(x-5) = k(x^4 - 7x^3 + 6x^2 + 28x - 40)$, where $k < 0$. ($k \approx -\frac{1}{15}$ if the scales are equal; otherwise one can't tell how large k is.)

11. Figure 1.38 shows the appropriate graphs. Note that asymptotes are shown as dashed lines and x- or y-intercepts are shown as filled circles.

(a)
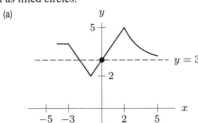

(b)
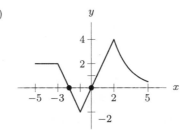

(c)
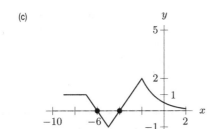

(d)
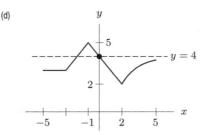

Figure 1.38

Problems

12. (a) From the x-intercepts, we know the equation has the form
$$y = k(x+2)(x-1)(x-5).$$

Since $y = 2$ when $x = 0$,
$$2 = k(2)(-1)(-5) = k \cdot 10$$
$$k = \frac{1}{5}.$$

Thus we have
$$y = \frac{1}{5}(x+2)(x-1)(x-5).$$

13. (a) Because our cubic has a root at 2 and a double root at -2, it has the form

$$y = k(x+2)(x+2)(x-2).$$

Since $y = 4$ when $x = 0$,

$$4 = k(2)(2)(-2) = -8k,$$
$$k = -\frac{1}{2}.$$

Thus our equation is

$$y = -\frac{1}{2}(x+2)^2(x-2).$$

14. (a) II and III because in both cases, the numerator and denominator each have x^2 as the highest power, with coefficient $= 1$. Therefore,

$$y \to \frac{x^2}{x^2} = 1 \quad \text{as } x \to \pm\infty.$$

(b) I, since

$$y \to \frac{x}{x^2} = 0 \quad \text{as } x \to \pm\infty.$$

(c) II and III, since replacing x by $-x$ leaves the graph of the function unchanged.
(d) None
(e) III, since the denominator is zero and $f(x)$ tends to $\pm\infty$ when $x = \pm 1$.

15. Substituting $w = 65$ and $h = 160$, we have

(a)
$$s = 0.01(65^{0.25})(160^{0.75}) = 1.3 \text{ m}^2.$$

(b) We substitute $s = 1.5$ and $h = 180$ and solve for w:

$$1.5 = 0.01 w^{0.25}(180^{0.75}).$$

We have

$$w^{0.25} = \frac{1.5}{0.01(180^{0.75})} = 3.05.$$

Since $w^{0.25} = w^{1/4}$, we take the fourth power of both sides, giving

$$w = 86.8 \text{ kg}.$$

(c) We substitute $w = 70$ and solve for h in terms of s:

$$s = 0.01(70^{0.25})h^{0.75},$$

so

$$h^{0.75} = \frac{s}{0.01(70^{0.25})}.$$

Since $h^{0.75} = h^{3/4}$, we take the $4/3$ power of each side, giving

$$h = \left(\frac{s}{0.01(70^{0.25})}\right)^{4/3} = \frac{s^{4/3}}{(0.01^{4/3})(70^{1/3})}$$

so

$$h = 112.6s^{4/3}.$$

16. Let us represent the height by h. Since the volume is V, we have

$$x^2 h = V.$$

Solving for h gives

$$h = \frac{V}{x^2}.$$

The graph is in Figure 1.39. We are assuming V is a positive constant.

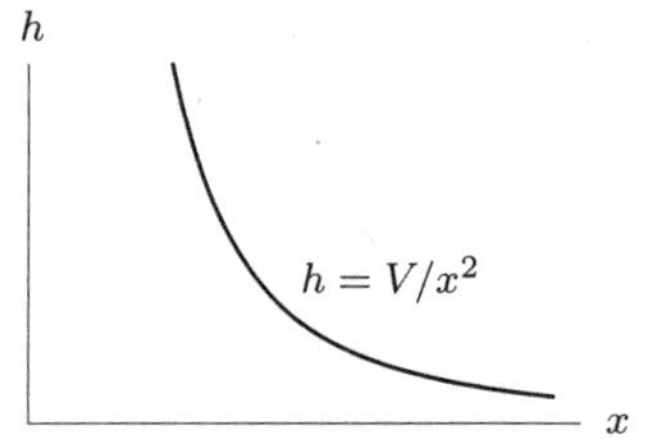

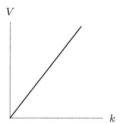

Figure 1.39

17. Let $D(v)$ be the stopping distance required by an Alpha Romeo as a function of its velocity. The assumption that stopping distance is proportional to the square of velocity is equivalent to the equation

$$D(v) = kv^2$$

where k is a constant of proportionality. To determine the value of k, we use the fact that $D(70) = 177$.

$$D(70) = k(70)^2 = 177.$$

Thus,

$$k = \frac{177}{70^2} \approx 0.0361.$$

It follows that

$$D(35) = \left(\frac{177}{70^2}\right)(35)^2 = \frac{177}{4} = 44.25 \text{ ft}$$

and

$$D(140) = \left(\frac{177}{70^2}\right)(140)^2 = 708 \text{ ft.}$$

Thus, at half the speed it requires one fourth the distance, whereas at twice the speed it requires four times the distance, as we would expect from the equation. (We could in fact have figured it out that way, without solving for k explicitly.)

18. (a) (i) The water that has flowed out of the pipe in 1 second is a cylinder of radius r and length 3 cm. Its volume is

$$V = \pi r^2(3) = 3\pi r^2.$$

(ii) If the rate of flow is k cm/sec instead of 3 cm/sec, the volume is given by

$$V = \pi r^2(k) = \pi r^2 k.$$

(b) (i) The graph of V as a function of r is a quadratic. See Figure 1.40.

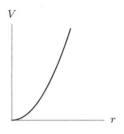

Figure 1.40

Figure 1.41

(ii) The graph of V as a function of k is a line. See Figure 1.41.

19. (a) Since the rate R varies directly with the fourth power of the radius r, we have the formula

$$R = kr^4$$

where k is a constant.

(b) Given $R = 400$ for $r = 3$, we can determine the constant k.

$$400 = k(3)^4$$
$$400 = k(81)$$
$$k = \frac{400}{81} \approx 4.938.$$

So the formula is

$$R = 4.938r^4$$

(c) Evaluating the formula above at $r = 5$ yields

$$R = 4.928(5)^4 = 3086.42 \frac{cm^3}{sec}.$$

20. (a) The object starts at $t = 0$, when $s = v_0(0) - g(0)^2/2 = 0$. Thus it starts on the ground, with zero height.

(b) The object hits the ground when $s = 0$. This is satisfied at $t = 0$, before it has left the ground, and at some later time t that we must solve for.

$$0 = v_0 t - gt^2/2 = t(v_0 - gt/2)$$

Thus $s = 0$ when $t = 0$ and when $v_0 - gt/2 = 0$, i.e., when $t = 2v_0/g$. The starting time is $t = 0$, so it must hit the ground at time $t = 2v_0/g$.

(c) The object reaches its maximum height halfway between when it is released and when it hits the ground, or at

$$t = (2v_0/g)/2 = v_0/g.$$

(d) Since we know the time at which the object reaches its maximum height, to find the height it actually reaches we just use the given formula, which tells us s at any given t. Substituting $t = v_0/g$,

$$s = v_0\left(\frac{v_0}{g}\right) - \frac{1}{2}g\left(\frac{v_0^2}{g^2}\right) = \frac{v_0^2}{g} - \frac{v_0^2}{2g}$$
$$= \frac{2v_0^2 - v_0^2}{2g} = \frac{v_0^2}{2g}.$$

21. The pomegranate is at ground level when $f(t) = -16t^2 + 64t = -16t(t-4) = 0$, so when $t = 0$ or $t = 4$. At time $t = 0$ it is thrown, so it must hit the ground at $t = 4$ seconds. The symmetry of its path with respect to time may convince you that it reaches its maximum height after 2 seconds. Alternatively, we can think of the graph of $f(t) = -16t^2 + 64t = -16(t-2)^2 + 64$, which is a downward parabola with vertex (i.e., highest point) at $(2, 64)$. The maximum height is $f(2) = 64$ feet.

22. (a) (i) If $(1, 1)$ is on the graph, we know that

$$1 = a(1)^2 + b(1) + c = a + b + c.$$

(ii) If $(1, 1)$ is the vertex, then the axis of symmetry is $x = 1$, so

$$-\frac{b}{2a} = 1,$$

and thus

$$a = -\frac{b}{2}, \text{ so } b = -2a.$$

But to be the vertex, $(1, 1)$ must also be on the graph, so we know that $a + b + c = 1$. Substituting $b = -2a$, we get $-a + c = 1$, which we can rewrite as $a = c - 1$, or $c = 1 + a$.

(iii) For $(0, 6)$ to be on the graph, we must have $f(0) = 6$. But $f(0) = a(0^2) + b(0) + c = c$, so $c = 6$.

(b) To satisfy all the conditions, we must first, from (a)(iii), have $c = 6$. From (a)(ii), $a = c - 1$ so $a = 5$. Also from (a)(ii), $b = -2a$, so $b = -10$. Thus the completed equation is

$$y = f(x) = 5x^2 - 10x + 6,$$

which satisfies all the given conditions.

23. $h(t)$ cannot be of the form ct^2 or kt^3 since $h(0.0) = 2.04$. Therefore $h(t)$ must be the exponential, and we see that the ratio of successive values of h is approximately 1.5. Therefore $h(t) = 2.04(1.5)^t$. If $g(t) = ct^2$, then $c = 3$ since $g(1.0) = 3.00$. However, $g(2.0) = 24.00 \neq 3 \cdot 2^2$. Therefore $g(t) = kt^3$, and using $g(1.0) = 3.00$, we obtain $g(t) = 3t^3$. Thus $f(t) = ct^2$, and since $f(2.0) = 4.40$, we have $f(t) = 1.1t^2$.

24. Looking at g, we see that the ratio of the values is:

$$\frac{3.12}{3.74} \approx \frac{3.74}{4.49} \approx \frac{4.49}{5.39} \approx \frac{5.39}{6.47} \approx \frac{6.47}{7.76} \approx 0.83.$$

Thus g is an exponential function, and so f and k are the power functions. Each is of the form ax^2 or ax^3, and since $k(1.0) = 9.01$ we see that for k, the constant coefficient is 9.01. Trial and error gives

$$k(x) = 9.01x^2,$$

since $k(2.2) = 43.61 \approx 9.01(4.84) = 9.01(2.2)^2$. Thus $f(x) = ax^3$ and we find a by noting that $f(9) = 7.29 = a(9^3)$ so

$$a = \frac{7.29}{9^3} = 0.01$$

and $f(x) = 0.01x^3$.

25. The function is a cubic polynomial with positive leading coefficient. Since the figure given in the text shows that the function turns around once, we know that the function has the shape shown in Figure 1.42. The function is below the x-axis for $x = 5$ in the given graph, and we know that it goes to $+\infty$ as $x \to +\infty$ because the leading coefficient is positive. Therefore, there are exactly three zeros. Two zeros are shown, and occur at approximately $x = -1$ and $x = 3$. The third zero must be to the right of $x = 10$ and so occurs for some $x > 10$.

Figure 1.42

26. Consider the end behavior of the graph; that is, as $x \to +\infty$ and $x \to -\infty$. The ends of a degree 5 polynomial are in Quadrants I and III if the leading coefficient is positive or in Quadrants II and IV if the leading coefficient is negative. Thus, there must be at least one root. Since the degree is 5, there can be no more than 5 roots. Thus, there may be 1, 2, 3, 4, or 5 roots. Graphs showing these five possibilities are shown in Figure 1.43.

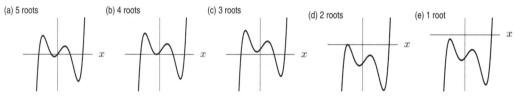

Figure 1.43

27. (a) Since $a_1 = -2a_2 = 2c$, we have $a_1 = 2c$ and $a_2 = -c$. So, $f(x) = (x + 2c)^2$ and $g(x) = (x - c)^2$. Then we have

$$f(x) = g(x)$$
$$(x + 2c)^2 = (x - c)^2$$
$$x^2 + 4cx + 4c^2 = x^2 - 2cx + c^2$$
$$4cx + 4c^2 = -2cx + c^2$$
$$6cx = -3c^2$$
$$x = \frac{-3c^2}{6c}$$
$$x = \frac{-c}{2}.$$

(b) Since $c > 0$, the graph of $f(x)$ is the parabola $y = x^2$ shifted left $2c$; the graph of $g(x)$ is the parabola $y = x^2$ shifted right c. We have

$$y\text{-intercept of } g(x) = g(0) = c^2,$$
$$y\text{-intercept of } f(x) = f(0) = 4c^2.$$

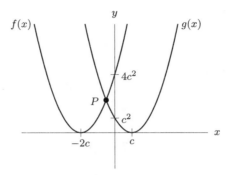

Figure 1.44

(c) The coordinates of the point of intersection P are given by $x = -c/2$ and $y = f(-c/2) = 9c^2/4$. As c increases, the x-coordinate of P, $x = -c/2$, moves left and the y-coordinate, $y = 9c^2/4$, moves up.

28. $g(x) = 2x^2$, $h(x) = x^2 + k$ for any $k > 0$. Notice that the graph is symmetric about the y-axis and $\lim_{x \to \infty} f(x) = 2$.

29. (a) III
  (b) IV
  (c) I
  (d) II

30. The graphs of both these functions will resemble that of x^3 on a large enough window. One way to tackle the problem is to graph them both (along with x^3 if you like) in successively larger windows until the graphs come together. In Figure 1.45, f, g and x^3 are graphed in four windows. In the largest of the four windows the graphs are indistinguishable, as required. Answers may vary.

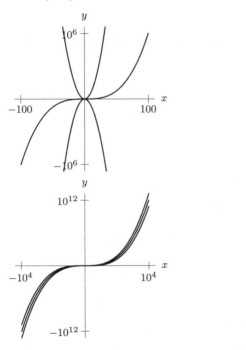
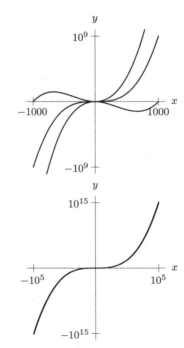

Figure 1.45

31. The graphs are shown in Figure 1.46.

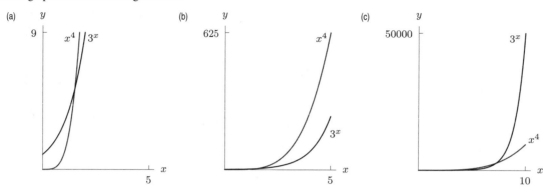

Figure 1.46

32. (a) $a(v) = \frac{1}{m}(\text{ENGINE} - \text{WIND}) = \frac{1}{m}(F_E - kv^2)$, where k is a positive constant.

(b) A possible graph is in Figure 1.47.

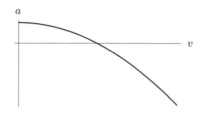

Figure 1.47

Solutions for Section 1.7

Exercises

1. Yes, because $2x + x^{2/3}$ is defined for all x.

2. No, because $2x + x^{-1}$ is undefined at $x = 0$.

3. Yes, because $x - 2$ is not zero on this interval.

4. No, because $x - 2 = 0$ at $x = 2$.

5. Yes, because $2x - 5$ is positive for $3 \leq x \leq 4$.

6. Yes, because the denominator is never zero.

7. No, because $\cos(\pi/2) = 0$.

8. No, because $\sin 0 = 0$.

9. No, because $e^x - 1 = 0$ at $x = 0$.

10. Yes, because $\cos\theta$ is not zero on this interval.

11. We have that $f(0) = -1 < 0$ and $f(1) = 1 > 0$ and that f is continuous. Thus, by the Intermediate Value Theorem applied to $k = 0$, there is a number c in $[0, 1]$ such that $f(c) = k = 0$.

12. We have that $f(0) = 1 > 0$ and $f(1) = e - 3 < 0$ and that f is continuous. Thus, by the Intermediate Value Theorem applied to $k = 0$, there is a number c in $[0, 1]$ such that $f(c) = k = 0$.

13. We have that $f(0) = -1 < 0$ and $f(1) = 1 - \cos 1 > 0$ and that f is continuous. Thus, by the Intermediate Value Theorem applied to $k = 0$, there is a number c in $[0, 1]$ such that $f(c) = k = 0$.

14. Since f is not continuous at $x = 0$, we consider instead the smaller interval $[0.01, 1]$. We have that $f(0.01) = 2^{0.01} - 100 < 0$ and $f(1) = 2 - 1/1 = 1 > 0$ and that f is continuous. Thus, by the Intermediate Value Theorem applied to $k = 0$, there is a number c in $[0.01, 1]$, and hence in $[0, 1]$, such that $f(c) = k = 0$.

Problems

15. The voltage $f(t)$ is graphed in Figure 1.48.

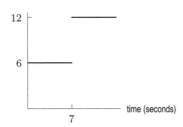

Figure 1.48: Voltage change from 6V to 12V

Using formulas, the voltage, $f(t)$, is represented by

$$f(t) = \begin{cases} 6, & 0 < t \le 7 \\ 12, & 7 < t \end{cases}$$

Although a real physical voltage is continuous, the voltage in this circuit is well-approximated by the function $f(t)$, which is not continuous on any interval around 7 seconds.

16. Two possible graphs are shown in Figures 1.49 and 1.50.

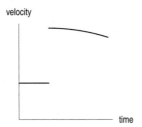

Figure 1.49: Velocity of the car

Figure 1.50: Distance

The distance moved by the car is continuous. (Figure 1.50 has no breaks in it.) In actual fact, the velocity of the car is also continuous; however, in this case, it is well-approximated by the function in Figure 1.49, which is not continuous on any interval containing the moment of impact.

17. For any value of k, the function is continuous at every point except $x = 2$. We choose k to make the function continuous at $x = 2$.

Since $3x^2$ takes the value $3(2^2) = 12$ at $x = 2$, we choose k so that kx goes through the point $(2, 12)$. Thus $k = 6$.

18. For $x > 0$, we have $|x| = x$, so $f(x) = 1$. For $x < 0$, we have $|x| = -x$, so $f(x) = -1$. Thus, the function is given by

$$f(x) = \begin{cases} 1 & x > 0 \\ 0 & x = 0 \\ -1 & x < 1 \end{cases},$$

so f is not continuous on any interval containing $x = 0$.

19. For any values of k, the function is continuous on any interval that does not contain $x = 2$.

Since $5x^3 - 10x^2 = 5x^2(x - 2)$, we can cancel $(x - 2)$ provided $x \ne 2$, giving

$$f(x) = \frac{5x^3 - 10x^2}{x - 2} = 5x^2 \qquad x \ne 2.$$

Thus, if we pick $k = 5(2)^2 = 20$, the function is continuous.

20. The graph of g suggests that g is not continuous on any interval containing $\theta = 0$, since $g(0) = 1/2$.

21.

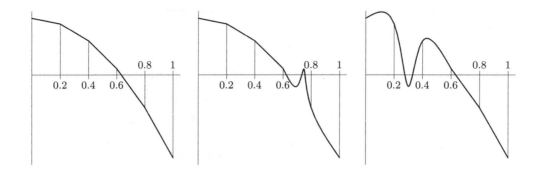

22. (a) Figure 1.51 shows a possible graph of $f(x)$, yours may be different.

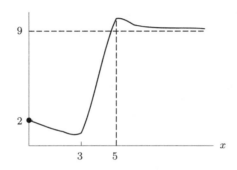

Figure 1.51

(b) In order for f to approach the horizontal asymptote at 9 from above it is necessary that f eventually become concave up. It is therefore not possible for f to be concave down for all $x > 6$.

23. The drug first increases linearly for half a second, at the end of which time there is 0.6 ml in the body. Thus, for $0 \le t \le 0.5$, the function is linear with slope $0.6/0.5 = 1.2$:

$$Q = 1.2t \quad \text{for} \quad 0 \le t \le 0.5.$$

At $t = 0.5$, we have $Q = 0.6$. For $t > 0.5$, the quantity decays exponentially at a continuous rate of 0.002, so Q has the form

$$Q = Ae^{-0.002t} \qquad 0.5 < t.$$

We choose A so that $Q = 0.6$ when $t = 0.5$:

$$0.6 = Ae^{-0.002(0.5)} = Ae^{-0.001}$$
$$A = 0.6e^{0.001}.$$

Thus

$$Q = \begin{cases} 1.2t & 0 \le t \le 0.5 \\ 0.6e^{0.001}e^{-.002t} & 0.5 < t. \end{cases}$$

24. The functions $y(x) = \sin x$ and $z_k(x) = ke^{-x}$ for $k = 1, 2, 4, 6, 8, 10$ are shown in Figure 1.52. The values of $f(k)$ for $k = 1, 2, 4, 6, 8, 10$ are given in Table 1.2. These values can be obtained using either tracing or a numerical root finder on a calculator or computer.

From Figure 1.52 it is clear that the smallest solution of $\sin x = ke^{-x}$ for $k = 1, 2, 4, 6$ occurs on the first period of the sine curve. For small changes in k, there are correspondingly small changes in the intersection point. For $k = 8$ and $k = 10$, the solution jumps to the second period because $\sin x < 0$ between π and 2π, but ke^{-x} is uniformly positive. Somewhere in the interval $6 \le k \le 8$, $f(k)$ has a discontinuity.

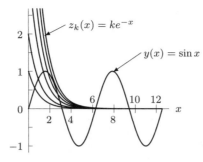

Figure 1.52

Table 1.2

k	$f(k)$
1	0.588
2	0.921
4	1.401
6	1.824
8	6.298
10	6.302

Solutions for Section 1.8

Exercises

1. (a) As x approaches -2 from either side, the values of $f(x)$ get closer and closer to 3, so the limit appears to be about 3.

   (b) As x approaches 0 from either side, the values of $f(x)$ get closer and closer to 7. (Recall that to find a limit, we are interested in what happens to the function near x but not at x.) The limit appears to be about 7.

   (c) As x approaches 2 from either side, the values of $f(x)$ get closer and closer to 3 on one side of $x = 2$ and get closer and closer to 2 on the other side of $x = 2$. Thus the limit does not exist.

   (d) As x approaches 4 from either side, the values of $f(x)$ get closer and closer to 8. (Again, recall that we don't care what happens right at $x = 4$.) The limit appears to be about 8.

2. From the graphs of f and g, we estimate $\lim\limits_{x \to 1^-} f(x) = 3$, $\lim\limits_{x \to 1^-} g(x) = 5$,

   $\lim\limits_{x \to 1^+} f(x) = 4$, $\lim\limits_{x \to 1^+} g(x) = 1$.

   (a) $\lim\limits_{x \to 1^-} (f(x) + g(x)) = 3 + 5 = 8$

   (b) $\lim\limits_{x \to 1^+} (f(x) + 2g(x)) = \lim\limits_{x \to 1^+} f(x) + 2 \lim\limits_{x \to 1^+} g(x) = 4 + 2(1) = 6$

   (c) $\lim\limits_{x \to 1^-} (f(x)g(x)) = (\lim\limits_{x \to 1^-} f(x))(\lim\limits_{x \to 1^-} g(x)) = (3)(5) = 15$

   (d) $\lim\limits_{x \to 1^+} (f(x)/g(x)) = \left(\lim\limits_{x \to 1^+} f(x)\right) / \left(\lim\limits_{x \to 1^+} g(x)\right) = 4/1 = 4$

3. For $-0.5 \le \theta \le 0.5$, $0 \le y \le 3$, the graph of $y = \dfrac{\sin(2\theta)}{\theta}$ is shown in Figure 1.53. Therefore, $\lim\limits_{\theta \to 0} \dfrac{\sin(2\theta)}{\theta} = 2$.

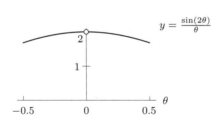

Figure 1.53

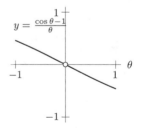

Figure 1.54

4. For $-1 \le \theta \le 1$, $-1 \le y \le 1$, the graph of $y = \dfrac{\cos\theta - 1}{\theta}$ is shown in Figure 1.54. Therefore, $\lim\limits_{\theta \to 0} \dfrac{\cos\theta - 1}{\theta} = 0$.

5. For $-90° \le \theta \le 90°$, $0 \le y \le 0.02$, the graph of $y = \dfrac{\sin\theta}{\theta}$ is shown in Figure 1.55. Therefore, by tracing along the curve, we see that in degrees, $\lim\limits_{\theta \to 0} \dfrac{\sin\theta}{\theta} = 0.01745\ldots$.

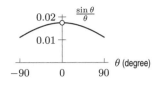

Figure 1.55

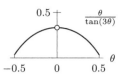

Figure 1.56

6. For $-0.5 \leq \theta \leq 0.5, 0 \leq y \leq 0.5$, the graph of $y = \dfrac{\theta}{\tan(3\theta)}$ is shown in Figure 1.56. Therefore, by tracing along the curve, we see that $\displaystyle\lim_{\theta \to 0} \frac{\theta}{\tan(3\theta)} = 0.3333\ldots$.

7. From Table 1.3, it appears the limit is 1. This is confirmed by Figure 1.57. An appropriate window is $-0.0033 < x < 0.0033, 0.99 < y < 1.01$.

Table 1.3

x	$f(x)$		x	$f(x)$
0.1	1.3		-0.0001	0.9997
0.01	1.03		-0.001	0.997
0.001	1.003		-0.01	0.97
0.0001	1.0003		-0.1	0.7

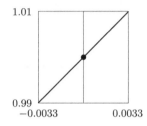

Figure 1.57

8. From Table 1.4, it appears the limit is -1. This is confirmed by Figure 1.58. An appropriate window is $-0.099 < x < 0.099, -1.01 < y < -0.99$.

Table 1.4

x	$f(x)$		x	$f(x)$
0.1	-0.99		-0.0001	-0.99999999
0.01	-0.9999		-0.001	-0.999999
0.001	-0.999999		-0.01	-0.9999
0.0001	-0.99999999		-0.1	-0.99

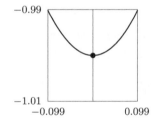

Figure 1.58

9. From Table 1.5, it appears the limit is 0. This is confirmed by Figure 1.59. An appropriate window is $-0.005 < x < 0.005, -0.01 < y < 0.01$.

Table 1.5

x	$f(x)$		x	$f(x)$
0.1	0.1987		-0.0001	-0.0002
0.01	0.0200		-0.001	-0.0020
0.001	0.0020		-0.01	-0.0200
0.0001	0.0002		-0.1	-0.1987

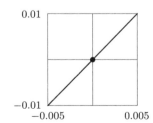

Figure 1.59

10. From Table 1.6, it appears the limit is 0. This is confirmed by Figure 1.60. An appropriate window is $-0.0033 < x < 0.0033$, $-0.01 < y < 0.01$.

Table 1.6

x	$f(x)$
0.1	0.2955
0.01	0.0300
0.001	0.0030
0.0001	0.0003

x	$f(x)$
-0.0001	-0.0003
-0.001	-0.0030
-0.01	-0.0300
-0.1	-0.2955

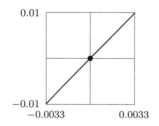

Figure 1.60

11. From Table 1.7, it appears the limit is 2. This is confirmed by Figure 1.61. An appropriate window is $-0.0865 < x < 0.0865$, $1.99 < y < 2.01$.

Table 1.7

x	$f(x)$
0.1	1.9867
0.01	1.9999
0.001	2.0000
0.0001	2.0000

x	$f(x)$
-0.0001	2.0000
-0.001	2.0000
-0.01	1.9999
-0.1	1.9867

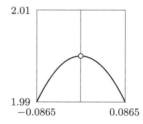

Figure 1.61

12. From Table 1.8, it appears the limit is 3. This is confirmed by Figure 1.62. An appropriate window is $-0.047 < x < 0.047$, $2.99 < y < 3.01$.

Table 1.8

x	$f(x)$
0.1	2.9552
0.01	2.9996
0.001	3.0000
0.0001	3.0000

x	$f(x)$
-0.0001	3.0000
-0.001	3.0000
-0.01	2.9996
-0.1	2.9552

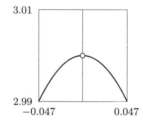

Figure 1.62

13. From Table 1.9, it appears the limit is 1. This is confirmed by Figure 1.63. An appropriate window is $-0.0198 < x < 0.0198$, $0.99 < y < 1.01$.

Table 1.9

x	$f(x)$
0.1	1.0517
0.01	1.0050
0.001	1.0005
0.0001	1.0001

x	$f(x)$
-0.0001	1.0000
-0.001	0.9995
-0.01	0.9950
-0.1	0.9516

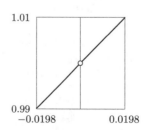

Figure 1.63

14. From Table 1.10, it appears the limit is 2. This is confirmed by Figure 1.64. An appropriate window is $-0.0049 < x < 0.0049$, $1.99 < y < 2.01$.

Table 1.10

x	$f(x)$
0.1	2.2140
0.01	2.0201
0.001	2.0020
0.0001	2.0002

x	$f(x)$
-0.0001	1.9998
-0.001	1.9980
-0.01	1.9801
-0.1	1.8127

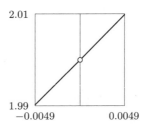

Figure 1.64

15. From Table 1.11, it appears the limit is 4. Figure 1.65 confirms this. An appropriate window is $1.99 < x < 2.01$, $3.99 < y < 4.01$.

Table 1.11

x	$f(x)$
2.1	4.1
2.01	4.01
2.001	4.001
2.0001	4.0001
1.9999	3.9999
1.999	3.999
1.99	3.99
1.9	3.9

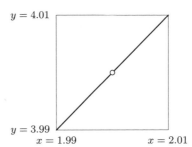

Figure 1.65

16. From Table 1.12, it appears the limit is 6. Figure 1.66 confirms this. An appropriate window is $2.99 < x < 3.01$, $5.99 < y < 6.01$.

Table 1.12

x	$f(x)$
3.1	6.1
3.01	6.01
3.001	6.001
3.0001	6.0001
2.9999	5.9999
2.999	5.999
2.99	5.99
2.9	5.9

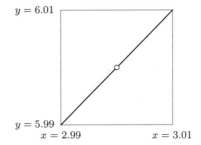

Figure 1.66

17. From Table 1.13, it appears the limit is 0. Figure 1.67 confirms this. An appropriate window is $1.55 < x < 1.59$, $-0.01 < y < 0.01$.

Table 1.13

x	$f(x)$
1.6708	-0.0500
1.5808	-0.0050
1.5718	-0.0005
1.5709	-0.0001
1.5707	0.0001
1.5698	0.0005
1.5608	0.0050
1.4708	0.0500

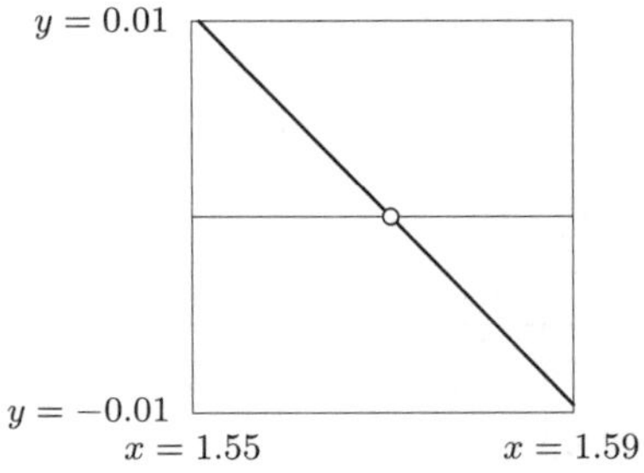

Figure 1.67

18. From Table 1.14, it appears the limit is 2. Figure 1.68 confirms this. An appropriate window is $0.995 < x < 1.004$, $1.99 < y < 2.01$.

Table 1.14

x	$f(x)$
1.1	2.2140
1.01	2.0201
1.001	2.0020
1.0001	2.0002
0.9999	1.9998
0.999	1.9980
0.99	1.9801
0.9	1.8127

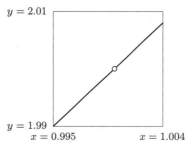

Figure 1.68

19. $f(x) = \dfrac{|x-4|}{x-4} = \begin{cases} \dfrac{x-4}{x-4} & x > 4 \\ -\dfrac{x-4}{x-4} & x < 4 \end{cases} = \begin{cases} 1 & x > 4 \\ -1 & x < 4 \end{cases}$

Figure 1.69 confirms that $\lim\limits_{x \to 4^+} f(x) = 1$, $\lim\limits_{x \to 4^-} f(x) = -1$ so $\lim\limits_{x \to 4} f(x)$ does not exist.

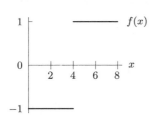

Figure 1.69

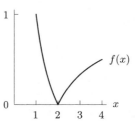

Figure 1.70

20. $f(x) = \dfrac{|x-2|}{x} = \begin{cases} \dfrac{x-2}{x}, & x > 2 \\ \\ -\dfrac{x-2}{x}, & x < 2 \end{cases}$

Figure 1.70 confirms that $\lim\limits_{x \to 2^+} f(x) = \lim\limits_{x \to 2^-} f(x) = \lim\limits_{x \to 2} f(x) = 0$.

21. $f(x) = \begin{cases} x^2 - 2 & 0 < x < 3 \\ 2 & x = 3 \\ 2x + 1 & 3 < x \end{cases}$

Figure 1.71 confirms that $\lim\limits_{x \to 3^-} f(x) = \lim\limits_{x \to 3^-} (x^2 - 2) = 7$ and that $\lim\limits_{x \to 3^+} f(x) = \lim\limits_{x \to 3^+} (2x + 1) = 7$, so $\lim\limits_{x \to 3} f(x) = 7$. Note, however, that $f(x)$ is not continuous at $x = 3$ since $f(3) = 2$.

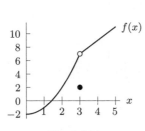

Figure 1.71

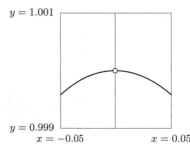

Figure 1.72: Graph of $(\sin \theta)/\theta$ with $-0.05 < \theta < 0.05$

22. The graph in Figure 1.72 suggests that

$$\text{if } -0.05 < \theta < 0.05, \quad \text{then} \quad 0.999 < (\sin \theta)/\theta < 1.001.$$

Thus, if θ is within 0.05 of 0, we see that $(\sin \theta)/\theta$ is within 0.001 of 1.

23. The statement
$$\lim_{h \to a} g(h) = K$$
means that we can make the value of $g(h)$ as close to K as we want by choosing h sufficiently close to, but not equal to, a.

In symbols, for any $\epsilon > 0$, there is a $\delta > 0$ such that
$$|g(h) - K| < \epsilon \quad \text{for all } 0 < |h - a| < \delta.$$

Problems

24. The only change is that, instead of considering all x near c, we only consider x near to and greater than c. Thus the phrase "$|x - c| < \delta$" must be replaced by "$c < x < c + \delta$." Thus, we define
$$\lim_{x \to c^+} f(x) = L$$
to mean that for any $\epsilon > 0$ (as small as we want), there is a $\delta > 0$ (sufficiently small) such that if $c < x < c + \delta$, then $|f(x) - L| < \epsilon$.

25. The only change is that, instead of considering all x near c, we only consider x near to and less than c. Thus the phrase "$|x - c| < \delta$" must be replaced by "$c - \delta < x < c$." Thus, we define
$$\lim_{x \to c^-} f(x) = L$$
to mean that for any $\epsilon > 0$ (as small as we want), there is a $\delta > 0$ (sufficiently small) such that if $c - \delta < x < c$, then $|f(x) - L| < \epsilon$.

26. Instead of being "sufficiently close to c," we want x to be "sufficiently large." Using N to measure how large x must be, we define
$$\lim_{x \to \infty} f(x) = L$$
to mean that for any $\epsilon > 0$ (as small as we want), there is a $N > 0$ (sufficiently large) such that if $x > N$, then $|f(x) - L| < \epsilon$.

27. If $x > 1$ and x approaches 1, then $p(x) = 55$. If $x < 1$ and x approaches 1, then $p(x) = 34$. There is not a single number that $p(x)$ approaches as x approaches 1, so we say that $\lim_{x \to 1} p(x)$ does not exist.

28. We use values of h approaching, but not equal to, zero. If we let $h = 0.01, 0.001, 0.0001, 0.00001$, we calculate the values 2.7048, 2.7169, 2.7181, and 2.7183. If we let $h = -0.01\ -0.001, -0.0001, -0.00001$, we get values 2.7320, 2.7196, 2.7184, and 2.7183. These numbers suggest that the limit is the number $e = 2.71828\ldots$. However, these calculations cannot tell us that the limit is exactly e; for that a proof is needed.

29. The limit appears to be 1; a graph and table of values is shown below.

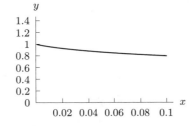

x	x^x
0.1	0.7943
0.01	0.9550
0.001	0.9931
0.0001	0.9990
0.00001	0.9999

30. Divide numerator and denominator by x:
$$f(x) = \frac{x + 3}{2 - x} = \frac{1 + 3/x}{2/x - 1},$$
so
$$\lim_{x \to \infty} f(x) = \lim_{x \to \infty} \frac{1 + 3/x}{2/x - 1} = \frac{\lim_{x \to \infty}(1 + 3/x)}{\lim_{x \to \infty}(2/x - 1)} = \frac{1}{-1} = -1.$$

31. Divide numerator and denominator by x^2, giving

$$f(x) = \frac{x^2 + 2x - 1}{3 + 3x^2} = \frac{1 + 2/x - 1/x^2}{3/x^2 + 3},$$

so

$$\lim_{x \to \infty} f(x) = \lim_{x \to \infty} \frac{1 + 2/x - 1/x^2}{3/x^2 + 3} = \frac{\lim_{x \to \infty}(1 + 2/x - 1/x^2)}{\lim_{x \to \infty}(3/x^2 + 3)} = \frac{1}{3}.$$

32. Divide numerator and denominator by x, giving

$$f(x) = \frac{x^2 + 4}{x + 3} = \frac{x + 4/x}{1 + 3/x},$$

so

$$\lim_{x \to \infty} f(x) = +\infty.$$

33. Divide numerator and denominator by x^3, giving

$$f(x) = \frac{2x^3 - 16x^2}{4x^2 + 3x^3} = \frac{2 - 16/x}{4/x + 3},$$

so

$$\lim_{x \to \infty} f(x) = \lim_{x \to \infty} \frac{2 - 16/x}{4/x + 3} = \frac{\lim_{x \to \infty}(2 - 16/x)}{\lim_{x \to \infty}(4/x + 3)} = \frac{2}{3}.$$

34. Divide numerator and denominator by x^5, giving

$$f(x) = \frac{x^4 + 3x}{x^4 + 2x^5} = \frac{1/x + 3/x^4}{1/x + 2},$$

so

$$\lim_{x \to \infty} f(x) = \frac{\lim_{x \to \infty}(1/x + 3/x^4)}{\lim_{x \to \infty}(1/x + 2)} = \frac{0}{2} = 0.$$

35. Divide numerator and denominator by e^x, giving

$$f(x) = \frac{3e^x + 2}{2e^x + 3} = \frac{3 + 2e^{-x}}{2 + 3e^{-x}},$$

so

$$\lim_{x \to \infty} f(x) = \frac{\lim_{x \to \infty}(3 + 2e^{-x})}{\lim_{x \to \infty}(2 + 3e^{-x})} = \frac{3}{2}.$$

36. $f(x) = \dfrac{2e^{-x} + 3}{3e^{-x} + 2}$, so $\lim_{x \to \infty} f(x) = \dfrac{\lim_{x \to \infty}(2e^{-x} + 3)}{\lim_{x \to \infty}(3e^{-x} + 2)} = \dfrac{3}{2}$.

37. Because the denominator equals 0 when $x = 4$, so must the numerator. This means $k^2 = 16$ and the choices for k are 4 or -4.

38. Because the denominator equals 0 when $x = 1$, so must the numerator. So $1 - k + 4 = 0$. The only possible value of k is 5.

39. Because the denominator equals 0 when $x = -2$, so must the numerator. So $4 - 8 + k = 0$ and the only possible value of k is 4.

40. Division of numerator and denominator by x^2 yields

$$\frac{x^2 + 3x + 5}{4x + 1 + x^k} = \frac{1 + 3/x + 5/x^2}{4/x + 1/x^2 + x^{k-2}}.$$

As $x \to \infty$, the limit of the numerator is 1. The limit of the denominator depends upon k. If $k > 2$, the denominator approaches ∞ as $x \to \infty$, so the limit of the quotient is 0. If $k = 2$, the denominator approaches 1 as $x \to \infty$, so the limit of the quotient is 1. If $k < 2$ the denominator approaches 0^+ as $x \to \infty$, so the limit of the quotient is ∞. Therefore the values of k we are looking for are $k \geq 2$.

41. For the numerator, $\lim_{x \to -\infty} \left(e^{2x} - 5\right) = -5$. If $k > 0$, $\lim_{x \to -\infty} \left(e^{kx} + 3\right) = 3$, so the quotient has a limit of $-5/3$. If $k = 0$, $\lim_{x \to -\infty} \left(e^{kx} + 3\right) = 4$, so the quotient has limit of $-5/4$. If $k < 0$, the limit of the quotient is given by $\lim_{x \to -\infty} \left(e^{2x} - 5\right)/\left(e^{kx} + 3\right) = 0$.

42. Division of numerator and denominator by x^3 yields

$$\frac{x^3 - 6}{x^k + 3} = \frac{1 - 6/x^3}{x^{k-3} + 3/x^3}.$$

As $x \to \infty$, the limit of the numerator is 1. The limit of the denominator depends upon k. If $k > 3$, the denominator approaches ∞ as $x \to \infty$, so the limit of the quotient is 0. If $k = 3$, the denominator approaches 1 as $x \to \infty$, so the limit of the quotient is 1. If $k < 3$ the denominator approaches 0^+ as $x \to \infty$, so the limit of the quotient is ∞. Therefore the values of k we are looking for are $k \geq 3$.

43. We divide both the numerator and denominator by 3^{2x}, giving

$$\lim_{x \to \infty} \frac{3^{kx} + 6}{3^{2x} + 4} = \frac{3^{(k-2)x} + 6/3^{2x}}{1 + 4/3^{2x}}.$$

In the denominator, $\lim_{x \to \infty} 1 + 4/3^{2x} = 1$. In the numerator, if $k < 2$, we have $\lim_{x \to \infty} 3^{(k-2)x} + 6/3^{2x} = 0$, so the quotient has a limit of 0. If $k = 2$, we have $\lim_{x \to \infty} 3^{(k-2)x} + 6/3^{2x} = 1$, so the quotient has a limit of 1. If $k > 2$, we have $\lim_{x \to \infty} 3^{(k-2)x} + 6/3^{2x} = \infty$, so the quotient has a limit of ∞.

44. In the denominator, we have $\lim_{x \to -\infty} 3^{2x} + 4 = 4$. In the numerator, if $k < 0$, we have $\lim_{x \to -\infty} 3^{kx} + 6 = \infty$, so the quotient has a limit of ∞. If $k = 0$, we have $\lim_{x \to -\infty} 3^{kx} + 6 = 7$, so the quotient has a limit of $7/4$. If $k > 0$, we have $\lim_{x \to -\infty} 3^{kx} + 6 = 6$, so the quotient has a limit of $6/4$.

45. By tracing on a calculator or solving equations, we find the following values of δ:
For $\epsilon = 0.2$, $\delta \leq 0.1$.
For $\epsilon = 0.1$, $\delta \leq 0.05$.
For $\epsilon = 0.02$, $\delta \leq 0.01$.
For $\epsilon = 0.01$, $\delta \leq 0.005$.
For $\epsilon = 0.002$, $\delta \leq 0.001$.
For $\epsilon = 0.001$, $\delta \leq 0.0005$.

46. By tracing on a calculator or solving equations, we find the following values of δ:
For $\epsilon = 0.1$, $\delta \leq 0.46$.
For $\epsilon = 0.01$, $\delta \leq 0.21$.
For $\epsilon = 0.001$, $\delta < 0.1$. Thus, we can take $\delta \leq 0.09$.

47. The results of Problem 45 suggest that we can choose $\delta = \epsilon/2$. For any $\epsilon > 0$, we want to find the δ such that

$$|f(x) - 3| = |-2x + 3 - 3| = |2x| < \epsilon.$$

Then if $|x| < \delta = \epsilon/2$, it follows that $|f(x) - 3| = |2x| < \epsilon$. So $\lim_{x \to 0}(-2x + 3) = 3$.

48. (a) Since $\sin(n\pi) = 0$ for $n = 1, 2, 3, \ldots$ the sequence of x-values

$$\frac{1}{\pi}, \frac{1}{2\pi}, \frac{1}{3\pi}, \ldots$$

works. These x-values $\to 0$ and are zeroes of $f(x)$.

(b) Since $\sin(n\pi/2) = 1$ for $n = 1, 5, 9 \ldots$ the sequence of x-values

$$\frac{2}{\pi}, \frac{2}{5\pi}, \frac{2}{9\pi}, \ldots$$

works.

(c) Since $\sin(n\pi)/2 = -1$ for $n = 3, 7, 11, \ldots$ the sequence of x-values

$$\frac{2}{3\pi}, \frac{2}{7\pi}, \frac{2}{11\pi} \ldots$$

works.

(d) Any two of these sequences of x-values show that if the limit were to exist, then it would have to have two (different) values: 0 and 1, or 0 and -1, or 1 and -1. Hence, the limit can not exist.

49. (a) If $b = 0$, then the property says $\lim_{x \to c} 0 = 0$, which is easy to see is true.

(b) If $|f(x) - L| < \frac{\epsilon}{|b|}$, then multiplying by $|b|$ gives

$$|b||f(x) - L| < \epsilon.$$

Since

$$|b||f(x) - L| = |b(f(x) - L)| = |bf(x) - bL|,$$

we have

$$|bf(x) - bL| < \epsilon.$$

(c) Suppose that $\lim_{x \to c} f(x) = L$. We want to show that $\lim_{x \to c} bf(x) = bL$. If we are to have

$$|bf(x) - bL| < \epsilon,$$

then we will need

$$|f(x) - L| < \frac{\epsilon}{|b|}.$$

We choose δ small enough that

$$|x - c| < \delta \quad \text{implies} \quad |f(x) - L| < \frac{\epsilon}{|b|}.$$

By part (b), this ensures that

$$|bf(x) - bL| < \epsilon,$$

as we wanted.

50. Suppose $\lim_{x \to c} f(x) = L_1$ and $\lim_{x \to c} g(x) = L_2$. Then we need to show that

$$\lim_{x \to c} (f(x) + g(x)) = L_1 + L_2.$$

Let $\epsilon > 0$ be given. We need to show that we can choose $\delta > 0$ so that whenever $|x - c| < \delta$, we will have $|(f(x) + g(x)) - (L_1 + L_2)| < \epsilon$. First choose $\delta_1 > 0$ so that $|x - c| < \delta_1$ implies $|f(x) - L_1| < \frac{\epsilon}{2}$; we can do this since $\lim_{x \to c} f(x) = L_1$. Similarly, choose $\delta_2 > 0$ so that $|x - c| < \delta_2$ implies $|g(x) - L_2| < \frac{\epsilon}{2}$. Now, set δ equal to the smaller of δ_1 and δ_2. Thus $|x - c| < \delta$ will make both $|x - c| < \delta_1$ and $|x - c| < \delta_2$. Then, for $|x - c| < \delta$, we have

$$\begin{aligned} |f(x) + g(x) - (L_1 + L_2)| &= |(f(x) - L_1) + (g(x) - L_2)| \\ &\leq |(f(x) - L_1)| + |(g(x) - L_2)| \\ &\leq \frac{\epsilon}{2} + \frac{\epsilon}{2} = \epsilon. \end{aligned}$$

This proves $\lim_{x \to c}(f(x) + g(x)) = \lim_{x \to c} f(x) + \lim_{x \to c} g(x)$, which is the result we wanted to prove.

51. (a) We need to show that for any given $\epsilon > 0$, there is a $\delta > 0$ so that $|x - c| < \delta$ implies $|f(x)g(x)| < \epsilon$. If $\epsilon > 0$ is given, choose δ_1 so that when $|x - c| < \delta_1$, we have $|f(x)| < \sqrt{\epsilon}$. This can be done since $\lim_{x \to 0} f(x) = 0$. Similarly, choose δ_2 so that when $|x - c| < \delta_2$, we have $|g(x)| < \sqrt{\epsilon}$. Then, if we take δ to be the smaller of δ_1 and δ_2, we'll have that $|x - c| < \delta$ implies both $|f(x)| < \sqrt{\epsilon}$ and $|g(x)| < \sqrt{\epsilon}$. So when $|x - c| < \delta$, we have $|f(x)g(x)| = |f(x)||g(x)| < \sqrt{\epsilon} \cdot \sqrt{\epsilon} = \epsilon$. Thus $\lim_{x \to c} f(x)g(x) = 0$.

(b) $(f(x) - L_1)(g(x) - L_2) + L_1 g(x) + L_2 f(x) - L_1 L_2$
$= f(x)g(x) - L_1 g(x) - L_2 f(x) + L_1 L_2 + L_1 g(x) + L_2 f(x) - L_1 L_2 = f(x)g(x).$

(c) $\lim_{x \to c} (f(x) - L_1) = \lim_{x \to c} f(x) - \lim_{x \to c} L_1 = L_1 - L_1 = 0$, using the second limit property. Similarly, $\lim_{x \to c} (g(x) - L_2) = 0$.

(d) Since $\lim_{x \to c} (f(x) - L_1) = \lim_{x \to c} (g(x) - L_2) = 0$, we have that $\lim_{x \to c} (f(x) - L_1)(g(x) - L_2) = 0$ by part (a).

(e) From part (b), we have

$$\begin{aligned} \lim_{x \to c} f(x)g(x) &= \lim_{x \to c} ((f(x) - L_1)(g(x) - L_2) + L_1 g(x) + L_2 f(x) - L_1 L_2) \\ &= \lim_{x \to c} (f(x) - L_1)(g(x) - L_2) + \lim_{x \to c} L_1 g(x) + \lim_{x \to c} L_2 f(x) + \lim_{x \to c} (-L_1 L_2) \\ &\quad \text{(using limit property 2)} \\ &= 0 + L_1 \lim_{x \to c} g(x) + L_2 \lim_{x \to c} f(x) - L_1 L_2 \\ &\quad \text{(using limit property 1 and part (d))} \\ &= L_1 L_2 + L_2 L_1 - L_1 L_2 = L_1 L_2. \end{aligned}$$

52. We will show $f(x) = x$ is continuous at $x = c$. Since $f(c) = c$, we need to show that

$$\lim_{x \to c} f(x) = c$$

that is, since $f(x) = x$, we need to show

$$\lim_{x \to c} x = c.$$

Pick any $\epsilon > 0$, then take $\delta = \epsilon$. Thus,

$$|f(x) - c| = |x - c| < \epsilon \quad \text{for all} \quad |x - c| < \delta = \epsilon.$$

53. Since $f(x) = x$ is continuous, Theorem 1.3 on page 54 shows that products of the form $f(x) \cdot f(x) = x^2$ and $f(x) \cdot x^2 = x^3$, etc., are continuous. By a similar argument, x^n is continuous for any $n > 0$.

54. If c is in the interval, we know $\lim_{x \to c} f(x) = f(c)$ and $\lim_{x \to c} g(x) = g(c)$. Then,

$$\lim_{x \to c} (f(x) + g(x)) = \lim_{x \to c} f(x) + \lim_{x \to c} g(x) \quad \text{by limit property 2}$$

$$= f(c) + g(c), \quad \text{so } f + g \text{ is continuous at } x = c.$$

Also,

$$\lim_{x \to c} (f(x)g(x)) = \lim_{x \to c} f(x) \lim_{x \to c} g(x) \quad \text{by limit property 3}$$

$$= f(c)g(c) \quad \text{so } fg \text{ is continuous at } x = c.$$

Finally,

$$\lim_{x \to c} \frac{f(x)}{g(x)} = \frac{\lim_{x \to c} f(x)}{\lim_{x \to c} g(x)} \quad \text{by limit property 4}$$

$$= \frac{f(c)}{g(c)}, \quad \text{so } \frac{f}{g} \text{ is continuous at } x = c.$$

Solutions for Chapter 1 Review

Exercises

1. (a) The domain of f is the set of values of x for which the function is defined. Since the function is defined by the graph and the graph goes from $x = 0$ to $x = 7$, the domain of f is $[0, 7]$.
   (b) The range of f is the set of values of y attainable over the domain. Looking at the graph, we can see that y gets as high as 5 and as low as -2, so the range is $[-2, 5]$.
   (c) Only at $x = 5$ does $f(x) = 0$. So 5 is the only zero of $f(x)$.
   (d) Looking at the graph, we can see that $f(x)$ is decreasing on $(1, 7)$.
   (e) The graph indicates that $f(x)$ is concave up at $x = 6$.
   (f) The value $f(4)$ is the y-value that corresponds to $x = 4$. From the graph, we can see that $f(4)$ is approximately 1.
   (g) This function is not invertible, since it fails the horizontal-line test. A horizontal line at $y = 3$ would cut the graph of $f(x)$ in two places, instead of the required one.

2. Taking logs of both sides

$$\log 10 = \log 4^x = x \log 4$$

$$x = \frac{\log 10}{\log 4} = \frac{1}{\log 4} \approx 1.66.$$

3. Taking logs of both sides

$$\log \frac{25}{2} = \log 5^x = x \log 5$$

$$x = \frac{\log\left(\frac{25}{2}\right)}{\log 5} \approx 1.57.$$

4.

$$\frac{2}{11} = \frac{7^x}{5^x}$$

$$\frac{2}{11} = \left(\frac{7}{5}\right)^x$$

Taking logs of both sides

$$\log \frac{2}{11} = \log \left(\frac{7}{5}\right)^x$$

$$\log \frac{2}{11} = x \log \left(\frac{7}{5}\right)$$

$$x = \frac{\log(2/11)}{\log(7/5)} \approx -5.07.$$

5. To solve for x, we first divide both sides by 5 and then take the natural logarithm of both sides.

$$\frac{7}{5} = e^{0.2x}$$

$$\ln(7/5) = 0.2x$$

$$x = \frac{\ln(7/5)}{0.2} \approx 1.68.$$

6. The amplitude is 5. The period is 6π. See Figure 1.73.

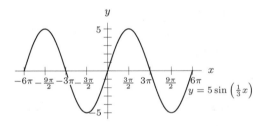

Figure 1.73

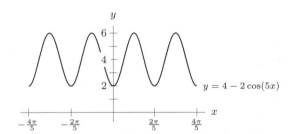

Figure 1.74

7. The amplitude is 2. The period is $2\pi/5$. See Figure 1.74.

8. This is a line with slope $-3/7$ and y-intercept 3, so a possible formula is

$$y = -\frac{3}{7}x + 3.$$

9. Starting with the general exponential equation $y = Ae^{kx}$, we first find that for $(0, 1)$ to be on the graph, we must have $A = 1$. Then to make $(3, 4)$ lie on the graph, we require

$$4 = e^{3k}$$

$$\ln 4 = 3k$$

$$k = \frac{\ln 4}{3} \approx 0.4621.$$

Thus the equation is

$$y = e^{0.4621x}.$$

Alternatively, we can use the form $y = a^x$, in which case we find $y = (1.5874)^x$.

10. This looks like an exponential function. The y-intercept is 3 and we use the form $y = 3e^{kt}$. We substitute the point $(5, 9)$ to solve for k:

$$9 = 3e^{k5}$$
$$3 = e^{5k}$$
$$\ln 3 = 5k$$
$$k = 0.2197.$$

A possible formula is

$$y = 3e^{0.2197t}.$$

Alternatively, we can use the form $y = 3a^t$, in which case we find $y = 3(1.2457)^t$.

11. $y = -kx(x + 5) = -k(x^2 + 5x)$, where $k > 0$ is any constant.

12. Since this function has a y-intercept at $(0, 2)$, we expect it to have the form $y = 2e^{kx}$. Again, we find k by forcing the other point to lie on the graph:

$$1 = 2e^{2k}$$
$$\frac{1}{2} = e^{2k}$$
$$\ln\left(\frac{1}{2}\right) = 2k$$
$$k = \frac{\ln(\frac{1}{2})}{2} \approx -0.34657.$$

This value is negative, which makes sense since the graph shows exponential decay. The final equation, then, is

$$y = 2e^{-0.34657x}.$$

Alternatively, we can use the form $y = 2a^x$, in which case we find $y = 2(0.707)^x$.

13. $z = 1 - \cos\theta$

14. $y = k(x + 2)(x + 1)(x - 1) = k(x^3 + 2x^2 - x - 2)$, where $k > 0$ is any constant.

15. $x = ky(y - 4) = k(y^2 - 4y)$, where $k > 0$ is any constant.

16. $y = 5\sin\left(\frac{\pi t}{20}\right)$

17. This looks like a fourth degree polynomial with roots at -5 and -1 and a double root at 3. The leading coefficient is negative, and so a possible formula is

$$y = -(x + 5)(x + 1)(x - 3)^2.$$

18. This looks like a rational function. There are vertical asymptotes at $x = -2$ and $x = 2$ and so one possibility for the denominator is $x^2 - 4$. There is a horizontal asymptote at $y = 3$ and so the numerator might be $3x^2$. In addition, $y(0) = 0$ which is the case with the numerator of $3x^2$. A possible formula is

$$y = \frac{3x^2}{x^2 - 4}.$$

19. There are many solutions for a graph like this one. The simplest is $y = 1 - e^{-x}$, which gives the graph of $y = e^x$, flipped over the x-axis and moved up by 1. The resulting graph passes through the origin and approaches $y = 1$ as an upper bound, the two features of the given graph.

20. This can be represented by a sine function of amplitude 3 and period 18. Thus,

$$f(x) = 3\sin\left(\frac{\pi}{9}x\right).$$

21. This graph has period 5, amplitude 1 and no vertical shift or horizontal shift from $\sin x$, so it is given by

$$f(x) = \sin\left(\frac{2\pi}{5}x\right).$$

22. $f(x) = \ln x, \quad g(x) = x^3$. (Another possibility: $f(x) = 3x, \quad g(x) = \ln x$.)

23. $f(x) = x^3, \quad g(x) = \ln x$.

24. There is no break in the graph of $f(x)$ although it does have a 'corner' at $x = 0$, so $f(x)$ is continuous.

25. The graph of $g(x)$ is shown in Figure 1.75. It has a break at $x = 0$, so $g(x)$ is not continuous on $[-1, 1]$.

26. The graph has no breaks and is therefore continuous. See Figure 1.76.

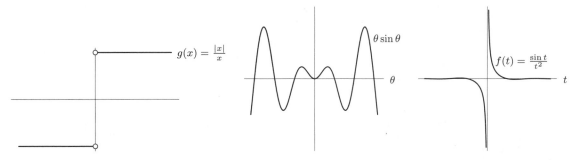

Figure 1.75   Figure 1.76   Figure 1.77

27. The graph appears to have a vertical asymptote at $t = 0$, so $f(t)$ is not continuous on $[-1, 1]$. See Figure 1.77.

28. From Table 1.15, it appears the limit is 0. This is confirmed by Figure 1.78. An appropriate window is $-0.015 < x < 0.015, -0.01 < y < 0.01$.

Table 1.15

x	$f(x)$
0.1	0.0666
0.01	0.0067
0.001	0.0007
0.0001	0

x	$f(x)$
-0.0001	-0.0001
-0.001	-0.0007
-0.01	-0.0067
-0.1	-0.0666

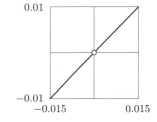

Figure 1.78

29. From Table 1.16, it appears the limit is 0. This is confirmed by Figure 1.79. An appropriate window is $-0.0029 < x < 0.0029, -0.01 < y < 0.01$.

Table 1.16

x	$f(x)$
0.1	0.3365
0.01	0.0337
0.001	0.0034
0.0001	0.0004

x	$f(x)$
-0.0001	-0.0004
-0.001	-0.0034
-0.01	-0.0337
-0.1	-0.3365

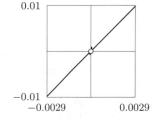

Figure 1.79

30. From Table 1.17, it appears the limit is 0. Figure 1.80 confirms this. An appropriate window is $1.570 < x < 1.5715$, $-0.01 < y < 0.01$.

Table 1.17

x	$f(x)$
1.6708	-1.2242
1.5808	-0.1250
1.5718	-0.0125
1.5709	-0.0013
1.5707	0.0012
1.5698	0.0125
1.5608	0.1249
1.4708	1.2241

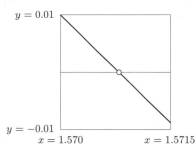

Figure 1.80

31. From Table 1.18, it appears the limit is $1/2$. Figure 1.81 confirms this. An appropriate window is $1.92 < x < 2.07$, $0.49 < y < 0.51$.

Table 1.18

x	$f(x)$
2.1	0.5127
2.01	0.5013
2.001	0.5001
2.0001	0.5000
1.9999	0.5000
1.999	0.4999
1.99	0.4988
1.9	0.4877

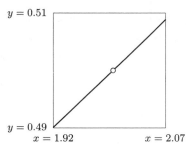

Figure 1.81

32. $f(x) = \dfrac{x^3|2x-6|}{x-3} = \begin{cases} \dfrac{x^3(2x-6)}{x-3} = 2x^3, & x > 3 \\ \dfrac{x^3(-2x+6)}{x-3} = -2x^3, & x < 3 \end{cases}$

Figure 1.82 confirms that $\lim\limits_{x \to 3^+} f(x) = 54$ while $\lim\limits_{x \to 3^-} f(x) = -54$; thus $\lim\limits_{x \to 3} f(x)$ does not exist.

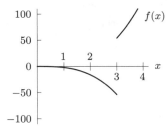

Figure 1.82

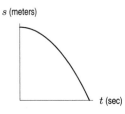

Figure 1.83

33. $f(x) = \begin{cases} e^x & -1 < x < 0 \\ 1 & x = 0 \\ \cos x & 0 < x < 1 \end{cases}$

Figure 1.83 confirms that $\lim\limits_{x \to 0^-} f(x) = \lim\limits_{x \to 0^-} e^x = e^0 = 1$, and that $\lim\limits_{x \to 0^+} f(x) = \lim\limits_{x \to 0^+} \cos x = \cos 0 = 1$, so $\lim\limits_{x \to 0} f(x) = 1$.

Problems

34. (a) More fertilizer increases the yield until about 40 lbs.; then it is too much and ruins crops, lowering yield.

(b) The vertical intercept is at $Y = 200$. If there is no fertilizer, then the yield is 200 bushels.

(c) The horizontal intercept is at $a = 80$. If you use 80 lbs. of fertilizer, then you will grow no apples at all.

(d) The range is the set of values of Y attainable over the domain $0 \leq a \leq 80$. Looking at the graph, we can see that Y goes as high as 550 and as low as 0. So the range is $0 \leq Y \leq 550$.

(e) Looking at the graph, we can see that Y is decreasing at $a = 60$.

(f) Looking at the graph, we can see that Y is concave down everywhere, so it is certainly concave down at $a = 40$.

35. (a) The height of the rock decreases as time passes, so the graph falls as you move from left to right. One possibility is shown in Figure 1.84.

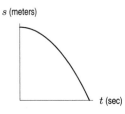

Figure 1.84

(b) The statement $f(7) = 12$ tells us that 7 seconds after the rock is dropped, it is 12 meters above the ground.

(c) The vertical intercept is the value of s when $t = 0$; that is, the height from which the rock is dropped. The horizontal intercept is the value of t when $s = 0$; that is, the time it takes for the rock to hit the ground.

36. Given the doubling time of 2 hours, $200 = 100e^{k(2)}$, we can solve for the growth rate k using the equation:

$$2P_0 = P_0 e^{2k}$$
$$\ln 2 = 2k$$
$$k = \frac{\ln 2}{2}.$$

Using the growth rate, we wish to solve for the time t in the formula

$$P = 100e^{\frac{\ln 2}{2}t}$$

where $P = 3{,}200$, so

$$3{,}200 = 100e^{\frac{\ln 2}{2}t}$$
$$t = 10 \text{ hours.}$$

37. (a) We find the slope m and intercept b in the linear equation $S = b + mt$. To find the slope m, we use

$$m = \frac{\Delta S}{\Delta t} = \frac{66 - 113}{50 - 0} = -0.94.$$

When $t = 0$, we have $S = 113$, so the intercept b is 113. The linear formula is

$$S = 113 - 0.94t.$$

(b) We use the formula $S = 113 - 0.94t$. When $S = 20$, we have $20 = 113 - 0.94t$ and so $t = 98.9$. If this linear model were correct, the average male sperm count would drop below the fertility level during the year 2038.

38. To find a half-life, we want to find at what t value $Q = \frac{1}{2}Q_0$. Plugging this into the equation of the decay of plutonium-240, we have

$$\frac{1}{2} = e^{-0.00011t}$$
$$t = \frac{\ln(1/2)}{-0.00011} \approx 6{,}301 \text{ years.}$$

The only difference in the case of plutonium-242 is that the constant -0.00011 in the exponent is now -0.0000018. Thus, following the same procedure, the solution for t is

$$t = \frac{\ln(1/2)}{-0.0000018} \approx 385{,}081 \text{ years.}$$

39. We can solve for the growth rate k of the bacteria using the formula $P = P_0 e^{kt}$:

$$1500 = 500e^{k(2)}$$
$$k = \frac{\ln(1500/500)}{2}.$$

Knowing the growth rate, we can find the population P at time $t = 6$:

$$P = 500e^{(\frac{\ln 3}{2})6}$$
$$\approx 13{,}500 \text{ bacteria.}$$

40. Assuming the US population grows exponentially, we have

$$248.7 = 226.5e^{10k}$$
$$k = \frac{\ln(1.098)}{10} = 0.00935.$$

We want to find the time t in which

$$300 = 226.5e^{0.00935t}$$
$$t = \frac{\ln(1.324)}{0.00935} = 30 \text{ years.}$$

Thus, the population will go over 300 million around the year 2010.

41. Since we are told that the rate of decay is *continuous*, we use the function $Q(t) = Q_0 e^{rt}$ to model the decay, where $Q(t)$ is the amount of strontium-90 which remains at time t, and Q_0 is the original amount. Then

$$Q(t) = Q_0 e^{-0.0247t}.$$

So after 100 years,

$$Q(100) = Q_0 e^{-0.0247 \cdot 100}$$

and

$$\frac{Q(100)}{Q_0} = e^{-2.47} \approx 0.0846$$

so about 8.46% of the strontium-90 remains.

42. If r was the average yearly inflation rate, in decimals, then $\frac{1}{4}(1+r)^3 = 2{,}400{,}000$, so $r = 211.53$, i.e. $r = 21{,}153\%$.

43. We will let

$$
\begin{aligned}
T &= \text{ amount of fuel for take-off,} \\
L &= \text{ amount of fuel for landing,} \\
P &= \text{ amount of fuel per mile in the air,} \\
m &= \text{ the length of the trip in miles.}
\end{aligned}
$$

Then Q, the total amount of fuel needed, is given by

$$Q(m) = T + L + Pm.$$

44. The period T_E of the earth is (by definition!) one year or about 365.24 days. Since the semimajor axis of the earth is 150 million km, we can use Kepler's Law to derive the constant of proportionality, k.

$$T_E = k(S_E)^{\frac{3}{2}}$$

where S_E is the earth's semimajor axis, or 150 million km.

$$365.24 = k(150)^{\frac{3}{2}}$$

$$k = \frac{365.24}{(150)^{\frac{3}{2}}} \approx 0.198.$$

Now that we know the constant of proportionality, we can use it to derive the periods of Mercury and Pluto. For Mercury,

$$T_M = (0.198)(58)^{\frac{3}{2}} \approx 87.818 \text{ days.}$$

For Pluto,

$$T_P = (0.198)(6000)^{\frac{3}{2}} \approx 92{,}400 \text{ days,}$$

or (converting Pluto's period to years),

$$\frac{(0.198)(6000)^{\frac{3}{2}}}{365.24} \approx 253 \text{ years.}$$

45. (a) Let the height of the can be h. Then

$$V = \pi r^2 h.$$

The surface area consists of the area of the ends (each is πr^2) and the curved sides (area $2\pi rh$), so

$$S = 2\pi r^2 + 2\pi rh.$$

Solving for h from the formula for V, we have

$$h = \frac{V}{\pi r^2}.$$

Substituting into the formula for S, we get

$$S = 2\pi r^2 + 2\pi r \cdot \frac{V}{\pi r^2} = 2\pi r^2 + \frac{2V}{r}.$$

(b) For large r, the $2V/r$ term becomes negligible, meaning $S \approx 2\pi r^2$, and thus $S \to \infty$ as $r \to \infty$.

(c) The graph is in Figure 1.85.

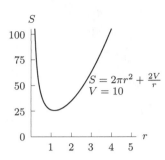

$$S = 2\pi r^2 + \frac{2V}{r}$$
$$V = 10$$

Figure 1.85

46. (a) The line given by $(0,2)$ and $(1,1)$ has slope $m = \frac{2-1}{-1} = -1$ and y-intercept 2, so its equation is

$$y = -x + 2.$$

The points of intersection of this line with the parabola $y = x^2$ are given by

$$x^2 = -x + 2$$
$$x^2 + x - 2 = 0$$
$$(x + 2)(x - 1) = 0.$$

The solution $x = 1$ corresponds to the point we are already given, so the other solution, $x = -2$, gives the x-coordinate of C. When we substitute back into either equation to get y, we get the coordinates for C, $(-2, 4)$.

(b) The line given by $(0, b)$ and $(1, 1)$ has slope $m = \frac{b-1}{-1} = 1 - b$, and y-intercept at $(0, b)$, so we can write the equation for the line as we did in part (a):

$$y = (1 - b)x + b.$$

We then solve for the points of intersection with $y = x^2$ the same way:

$$x^2 = (1 - b)x + b$$
$$x^2 - (1 - b)x - b = 0$$
$$x^2 + (b - 1)x - b = 0$$
$$(x + b)(x - 1) = 0$$

Again, we have the solution at the given point $(1, 1)$, and a new solution at $x = -b$, corresponding to the other point of intersection C. Substituting back into either equation, we can find the y-coordinate for C is b^2, and thus C is given by $(-b, b^2)$. This result agrees with the particular case of part (a) where $b = 2$.

47. Depth $= 7 + 1.5 \sin\left(\frac{\pi}{3}t\right)$

48. Over the one-year period, the average value is about $75°$ and the amplitude of the variation is about $\frac{90-60}{2} = 15°$. The function assumes its minimum value right at the beginning of the year, so we want a negative cosine function. Thus, for t in years, we have the function

$$f(t) = 75 - 15 \cos\left(\frac{2\pi}{12}t\right).$$

(Many other answers are possible, depending on how you read the chart.)

49. (a) Yes, f is invertible, since f is increasing everywhere.

(b) $f^{-1}(400)$ is the year in which 400 million motor vehicles were registered in the world. From the picture, we see that $f^{-1}(400)$ is around 1979.

(c) Since the graph of f^{-1} is the reflection of the graph of f over the line $y = x$, we get Figure 1.86.

(year)

'88

'82

'76

'70

'64

'58

'52

'46

0   100 200 300 400 500   (millions)

Figure 1.86: Graph of f^{-1}

50. (a) is $g(x)$ since it is linear. (b) is $f(x)$ since it has decreasing slope; the slope starts out about 1 and then decreases to about $\frac{1}{10}$. (c) is $h(x)$ since it has increasing slope; the slope starts out about $\frac{1}{10}$ and then increases to about 1.

51. (a) The period is 2π.
    (b) After π, the values of $\cos 2\theta$ repeat, but the values of $2\sin\theta$ do not (in fact, they repeat but flipped over the x-axis). After another π, that is after a total of 2π, the values of $\cos 2\theta$ repeat *again*, and now the values of $2\sin\theta$ repeat also, so the function $2\sin\theta + 3\cos 2\theta$ repeats at that point.

52. (a) The rate R is the difference of the rate at which the glucose is being injected, which is given to be constant, and the rate at which the glucose is being broken down, which is given to be proportional to the amount of glucose present. Thus we have the formula
$$R = k - aG$$
where k is the rate that the glucose is being injected, a is the constant relating the rate that it is broken down to the amount present, and G is the amount present.
    (b)

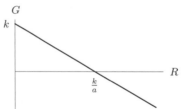

53. (a) $r(p) = kp(A - p)$, where $k > 0$ is a constant.
    (b) $p = A/2$.

54. (a) The domain is $(0, 4000)$, the range is $(0, 10^8)$.
    (b) The domain is $(0, 3000)$, the range is $(0, 10^7)$.
    (c) The domain is $(0, 0.2)$, the range is $(0, 0.04)$.

55. By tracing on a calculator or solving equations, we find the following values of δ:
    For $\epsilon = 0.1$, $\delta \leq 0.1$
    For $\epsilon = 0.05$, $\delta \leq 0.05$.
    For $\epsilon = 0.0007$, $\delta \leq 0.00007$.

56. By tracing on a calculator or solving equations, we find the following values of δ:
    For $\epsilon = 0.1$, $\delta \leq 0.45$.
    For $\epsilon = 0.001$, $\delta \leq 0.0447$.
    For $\epsilon = 0.00001$, $\delta \leq 0.00447$.

CAS Challenge Problems

57. (a) A CAS gives $f(x) = (x - a)(x + a)(x + b)(x - c)$.
    (b) The graph of $f(x)$ crosses the x-axis at $x = a$, $x = -a$, $x = -b$, $x = c$; it crosses the y-axis at a^2bc. Since the coefficient of x^4 (namely 1) is positive, the graph of f looks like that shown in Figure 1.87.

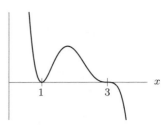

Figure 1.87: Graph of $f(x) = (x-a)(x+a)(x+b)(x-c)$

Figure 1.88: Graph of $f(x) = -(x-1)^2(x-3)^3$

58. (a) A CAS gives $f(x) = -(x-1)^2(x-3)^3$.

(b) For large $|x|$, the graph of $f(x)$ looks like the graph of $y = -x^5$, so $f(x) \to \infty$ as $x \to -\infty$ and $f(x) \to -\infty$ as $x \to \infty$. The answer to part (a) shows that f has a double root at $x = 1$, so near $x = 1$, the graph of f looks like a parabola touching the x-axis at $x = 1$. Similarly, f has a triple root at $x = 3$. Near $x = 3$, the graph of f looks like the graph of $y = x^3$, flipped over the x-axis and shifted to the right by 3, so that the "seat" is at $x = 3$. See Figure 1.88.

59. (a) As $x \to \infty$, the term e^{6x} dominates and tends to ∞. Thus, $f(x) \to \infty$ as $x \to \infty$.

As $x \to -\infty$, the terms of the form e^{kx}, where $k = 6, 5, 4, 3, 2, 1$, all tend to zero. Thus, $f(x) \to 16$ as $x \to -\infty$.

(b) A CAS gives

$$f(x) = (e^x + 1)(e^{2x} - 2)(e^x - 2)(e^{2x} + 2e^x + 4).$$

Since e^x is always positive, the factors $(e^x + 1)$ and $(e^{2x} + 2e^x + 4)$ are never zero. The other factors each lead to a zero, so there are two zeros.

(c) The zeros are given by

$$e^{2x} = 2 \quad \text{so} \quad x = \frac{\ln 2}{2}$$

$$e^x = 2 \quad \text{so} \quad x = \ln 2.$$

Thus, one zero is twice the size of the other.

60. (a) Since $f(x) = x^2 - x$,

$$f(f(x)) = (f(x))^2 - f(x) = (x^2 - x)^2 - (x^2 - x) = x - 2x^3 + x^4.$$

Using the CAS to define the function $f(x)$, and then asking it to expand $f(f(f(x)))$, we get

$$f(f(f(x))) = -x + x^2 + 2x^3 - 5x^4 + 2x^5 + 4x^6 - 4x^7 + x^8.$$

(b) The degree of $f(f(x))$ (that is, f composed with itself 2 times) is $4 = 2^2$. The degree of $f(f(f(x)))$ (that is, f composed with itself 3 times), is $8 = 2^3$. Each time you substitute f into itself, the degree is multiplied by 2, because you are substituting in a degree 2 polynomial. So we expect the degree of $f(f(f(f(f(f(x))))))$ (that is, f composed with itself 6 times) to be $64 = 2^6$.

61. (a) A CAS or division gives

$$f(x) = \frac{x^3 - 30}{x - 3} = x^2 + 3x + 9 - \frac{3}{x - 3},$$

so $p(x) = x^2 + 3x + 9$, and $r(x) = -3$, and $q(x) = x - 3$.

(b) The vertical asymptote is $x = 3$. Near $x = 3$, the values of $p(x)$ are much smaller than the values of $r(x)/q(x)$. Thus

$$f(x) \approx \frac{-3}{x - 3} \qquad \text{for } x \text{ near } 3.$$

(c) For large x, the values of $p(x)$ are much larger than the value of $r(x)/q(x)$. Thus

$$f(x) \approx x^2 + 3x + 9 \qquad \text{as } x \to \infty, x \to -\infty.$$

(d) Figure 1.89 shows $f(x)$ and $y = -3/(x - 3)$ for x near 3. Figure 1.90 shows $f(x)$ and $y = x^2 + 3x + 9$ for $-20 \le x \le 20$. Note that in each case the graphs of f and the approximating function are close.

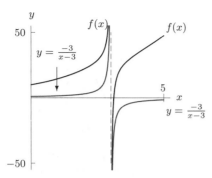

Figure 1.89: Close-up view of $f(x)$ and
$y = -3/(x-3)$

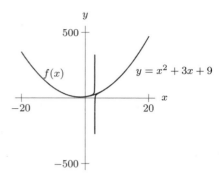

Figure 1.90: Far-away view of $f(x)$ and
$y = x^2 + 3x + 9$

62. Using the trigonometric expansion capabilities of your CAS, you get something like

$$\sin(5x) = 5\cos^4(x)\sin(x) - 10\cos^2(x)\sin^3(x) + \sin^5(x).$$

Answers may vary. To get rid of the powers of cosine, use the identity $\cos^2(x) = 1 - \sin^2(x)$. This gives

$$\sin(5x) = 5\sin(x)\left(1 - \sin^2(x)\right)^2 - 10\sin^3(x)\left(1 - \sin^2(x)\right) + \sin^5(x).$$

Finally, using the CAS to simplify,

$$\sin(5x) = 5\sin(x) - 20\sin^3(x) + 16\sin^5(x).$$

63. Using the trigonometric expansion capabilities of your computer algebra system, you get something like

$$\cos(4x) = \cos^4(x) - 6\cos^2(x)\sin^2(x) + \sin^4(x).$$

Answers may vary.

(a) To get rid of the powers of cosine, use the identity $\cos^2(x) = 1 - \sin^2(x)$. This gives

$$\cos(4x) = \cos^4(x) - 6\cos^2(x)\left(1 - \cos^2(x)\right) + \left(1 - \cos^2(x)\right)^2.$$

Finally, using the CAS to simplify,

$$\cos(4x) = 1 - 8\cos^2(x) + 8\cos^4(x).$$

(b) This time we use $\sin^2(x) = 1 - \cos^2(x)$ to get rid of powers of sine. We get

$$\cos(4x) = \left(1 - \sin^2(x)\right)^2 - 6\sin^2(x)\left(1 - \sin^2(x)\right) + \sin^4(x) = 1 - 8\sin^2(x) + 8\sin^4(x).$$

CHECK YOUR UNDERSTANDING

1. False. A line can be put through any two points in the plane. However, if the line is vertical, it is not the graph of a function.

2. True. The graph of $y = 10^x$ is moved horizontally by h units if we replace x by $x - h$ for some number h. Writing $100 = 10^2$, we have $f(x) = 100(10^x) = 10^2 \cdot 10^x = 10^{x+2}$. The graph of $f(x) = 10^{x+2}$ is the graph of $g(x) = 10^x$ shifted two units to the left.

3. True, as seen from the graph.

4. False, since $\log(x - 1) = 0$ if $x - 1 = 10$, so $x = 11$.

5. True. The highest degree term in a polynomial determines how the polynomial behaves when x is very large in the positive or negative direction. When n is odd, x^n is positive when x is large and positive but negative when x is large and negative. Thus if a polynomial $p(x)$ has odd degree, it will be positive for some values of x and negative for other values of x. Since every polynomial is continuous, the Intermediate Value Theorem then guarantees that $p(x) = 0$ for some value of x.

6. False. The y-intercept is $y = 2 + 3e^{-0} = 5$.

7. True, since, as $t \to \infty$, we know $e^{-4t} \to 0$, so $y = 5 - 3e^{-4t} \to 5$.

8. True. Suppose we start at $x = x_1$ and increase x by 1 unit to $x_1 + 1$. If $y = b + mx$, the corresponding values of y are $b + mx_1$ and $b + m(x_1 + 1)$. Thus y increases by

$$\Delta y = b + m(x_1 + 1) - (b + mx_1) = m.$$

9. False. Suppose $y = 5^x$. Then increasing x by 1 increases y by a factor of 5. However increasing x by 2 increases y by a factor of 25, not 10, since

$$y = 5^{x+2} = 5^x \cdot 5^2 = 25 \cdot 5^x.$$

(Other examples are possible.)

10. True. Suppose $y = Ab^x$ and we start at the point (x_1, y_1), so $y_1 = Ab^{x_1}$. Then increasing x_1 by 1 gives $x_1 + 1$, so the new y-value, y_2, is given by

$$y_2 = Ab^{x_1+1} = Ab^{x_1}b = (Ab^{x_1})b,$$

so

$$y_2 = by_1.$$

Thus, y has increased by a factor of b, so $b = 3$, and the function is $y = A3^x$.

However, if x_1 is increased by 2, giving $x_1 + 2$, then the new y-value, y_3, is given by

$$y_3 = A3^{x_1+2} = A3^{x_1}3^2 = 9A3^{x_1} = 9y_1.$$

Thus, y has increased by a factor of 9.

11. False, since $\cos \theta$ is decreasing and $\sin \theta$ is increasing.

12. False. The period is $2\pi/(0.05\pi) = 40$

13. True. The period is $2\pi/(200\pi) = 1/100$ seconds. Thus, the function executes 100 cycles in 1 second.

14. False. If $\theta = \pi/2, 3\pi/2, 5\pi/2 \ldots$, then $\theta - \pi/2 = 0, \pi, 2\pi \ldots$, and the tangent is defined (it is zero) at these values.

15. False. For example, $\sin(0) \neq \sin((2\pi)^2)$, since $\sin(0) = 0$ but $\sin((2\pi)^2) = 0.98$.

16. True. Since $\sin(\theta + 2\pi) = \sin \theta$ for all θ, we have $g(\theta + 2\pi) = e^{\sin(\theta+2\pi)} = e^{\sin \theta} = g(\theta)$ for all θ.

17. False. A counterexample is given by $f(x) = \sin x$, which has period 2π, and $g(x) = x^2$. The graph of $f(g(x)) = \sin(x^2)$ in Figure 1.91 is not periodic with period 2π.

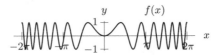

Figure 1.91

18. True. If $g(x)$ has period k, then $g(x + k) = g(x)$. Thus we have

$$f(g(x + k)) = f(g(x))$$

which shows that $f(g(x))$ is periodic with period k.

19. False. For $x < 0$, as x increases, x^2 decreases, so e^{-x^2} increases.

20. False. The inverse function is $y = 10^x$.

21. True. If f is increasing then its reflection about the line $y = x$ is also increasing. An example is shown in Figure 1.92. The statement is true.

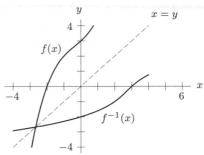

Figure 1.92

22. True, since $|\sin(-x)| = |-\sin x| = \sin x$.

23. True. If $f(x)$ is even, we have $f(x) = f(-x)$ for all x. For example, $f(-2) = f(2)$. This means that the graph of $f(x)$ intersects the horizontal line $y = f(2)$ at two points, $x = 2$ and $x = -2$. Thus, f has no inverse function.

24. False. For example, $f(x) = x$ and $g(x) = x^3$ are both odd. Their inverses are $f^{-1}(x) = x$ and $g^{-1}(x) = x^{1/3}$.

25. True. If $b > 1$, then $ab^x \to 0$ as $x \to -\infty$. If $0 < b < 1$, then $ab^x \to 0$ as $x \to \infty$. In either case, the function $y = a + ab^x$ has $y = a$ as the horizontal asymptote.

26. False, since $ax + b = 0$ if $x = -b/a$. Thus $y = \ln(ax + b)$ has a vertical asymptote at $x = -b/a$.

27. True, since $e^{-kt} \to 0$ as $t \to \infty$, so $y \to 20$ as $t \to \infty$.

28. True. We have $g(-x) = g(x)$ since g is even, and therefore $f(g(-x)) = f(g(x))$.

29. False. A counterexample is given by $f(x) = x^2$ and $g(x) = x + 1$. The function $f(g(x)) = (x+1)^2$ is not even because $f(g(1)) = 4$ and $f(g(-1)) = 0 \neq 4$.

30. False. All we know is that if h is close enough to zero then $f(h)$ will be as close as we please to L. We do not know how close would be close enough to zero for $f(h)$ to be closer to L than is $f(0.01)$. It might be that we have to get a lot closer than 0.0001. It is even possible that $f(0.01) = L$ but $f(0.0001) \neq L$ so $f(h)$ could never get closer to L than $f(0.01)$.

31. Let $f(x) = \begin{cases} 1 & x \le 2 \\ x & x > 2 \end{cases}$. Then $f(x)$ is continuous at every point in $[0, 3]$ except at $x = 2$. Other answers are possible.

32. Let $f(x) = \begin{cases} x & x \le 3 \\ 2x & x > 3 \end{cases}$. Then $f(x)$ is increasing for all x but $f(x)$ is not continuous at $x = 3$. Other answers are possible.

33. Let $f(x) = \dfrac{1}{x + 7\pi}$. Other answers are possible.

34. Let $f(x) = \dfrac{1}{(x-1)(x-2)(x-3)\cdots(x-16)(x-17)}$. This function has an asymptote corresponding to every factor in the denominator. Other answers are possible.

35. The function $f(x) = \dfrac{x-1}{x-2}$ has $y = 1$ as the horizontal asymptote and $x = 2$ as the vertical asymptote. These lines cross at the point $(2, 1)$. Other answers are possible.

36. We have
$$g(x) = f(x + 2)$$
because the graph of g is obtained by moving the graph of f to the left by 2 units. We also have
$$g(x) = f(x) + 3$$
because the graph of g is obtained by moving the graph of f up by 3 units. Thus, we have $f(x+2) = f(x)+3$. The graph of f climbs 3 units whenever x increases by 2. The simplest choice for f is a linear function of slope $3/2$, for example $f(x) = 1.5x$, so $g(x) = 1.5x + 3$.

37. Let $f(x) = x$ and $g(x) = -2x$. Then $f(x) + g(x) = -x$, which is decreasing. Note f is increasing since it has positive slope, and g is decreasing since it has negative slope.

38. This is impossible. If $a < b$, then $f(a) < f(b)$, since f is increasing, and $g(a) > g(b)$, since g is decreasing, so $-g(a) < -g(b)$. Therefore, if $a < b$, then $f(a) - g(a) < f(b) - g(b)$, which means that $f(x) + g(x)$ is increasing.

39. Let $f(x) = e^x$ and let $g(x) = e^{-2x}$. Note f is increasing since it is an exponential growth function, and g is decreasing since it is an exponential decay function. Then $f(x)g(x) = e^{-x}$, which is decreasing.

40. This is impossible. As x increases, $g(x)$ decreases. As $g(x)$ decreases, so does $f(g(x))$ because f is increasing (an increasing function increases as its variable increases, so it decreases as its variable decreases).

41. False. For example, $f(x) = x/(x^2 + 1)$ has no vertical asymptote since the denominator is never 0.

42. False. For example, let $f(x) = \log x$. Then $f(x)$ is increasing on $[1, 2]$, but $f(x)$ is concave down. (Other examples are possible.)

43. False. For example, let $y = x + 1$. Then the points $(1, 2)$ and $(2, 3)$ are on the line. However the ratios
$$\frac{2}{1} = 2 \qquad \text{and} \qquad \frac{3}{2} = 1.5$$
are different. The ratio y/x is constant for linear functions of the form $y = mx$, but not in general. (Other examples are possible.)

44. True. For example, $f(x) = (0.5)^x$ is an exponential function which decreases. (Other examples are possible.)

45. False. For example, if $y = 4x + 1$ (so $m = 4$) and $x = 1$, then $y = 5$. Increasing x by 2 units gives 3, so $y = 4(3) + 1 = 13$. Thus, y has increased by 8 units, not $4 + 2 = 6$. (Other examples are possible.)

46. False. For example, let $f(x) = \begin{cases} 1 & x \le 3 \\ 2 & x > 3 \end{cases}$, then $f(x)$ is defined at $x = 3$ but it is not continuous at $x = 3$. (Other examples are possible.)

47. False. A counterexample is graphed in Figure 1.93, in which $f(5) < 0$.

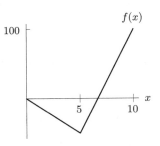

Figure 1.93

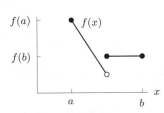

Figure 1.94

48. False. A counterexample is graphed in Figure 1.94.

49. True. The constant function $f(x) = 0$ is the only function that is both even and odd. This follows, since if f is both even and odd, then, for all x, $f(-x) = f(x)$ (if f is even) and $f(-x) = -f(x)$ (if f is odd). Thus, for all x, $f(x) = -f(x)$ i.e. $f(x) = 0$, for all x. So $f(x) = 0$ is both even and odd and is the only such function.

50. True, by Property 3 of limits in Theorem 1.2, since $\lim_{x \to 3} x = 3$.

51. False. If $\lim_{x \to 3} g(x)$ does not exist, then $\lim_{x \to 3} f(x)g(x)$ may not even exist. For example, let $f(x) = 2x + 1$ and define g by:
$$g(x) = \begin{cases} 1/(x-3) & \text{if } x \ne 3 \\ 4 & \text{if } x = 3 \end{cases}$$
Then $\lim_{x \to 3} f(x) = 7$ and $g(3) = 4$, but $\lim_{x \to 3} f(x)g(x) \ne 28$, since $\lim_{x \to 3} (2x+1)/(x-3)$ does not exist.

52. True, by Property 2 of limits in Theorem 1.2.

53. True, by Properties 2 and 3 of limits in Theorem 1.2.
$$\lim_{x \to 3} g(x) = \lim_{x \to 3} (f(x) + g(x) + (-1)f(x)) = \lim_{x \to 3} (f(x) + g(x)) + (-1)\lim_{x \to 3} f(x) = 12 + (-1)7 = 5.$$

54. False. For example, define f as follows:
$$f(x) = \begin{cases} 2x + 1 & \text{if } x \ne 2.99 \\ 1000 & \text{if } x = 2.99. \end{cases}$$
Then $f(2.9) = 2(2.9) + 1 = 6.8$, whereas $f(2.99) = 1000$.

55. False. For example, define f as follows:
$$f(x) = \begin{cases} 2x + 1 & \text{if } x \ne 3.01 \\ -1000 & \text{if } x = 3.01. \end{cases}$$
Then $f(3.1) = 2(3.1) + 1 = 7.2$, whereas $f(3.01) = -1000$.

56. True. Suppose instead that $\lim_{x \to 3} g(x)$ does not exist but $\lim_{x \to 3}(f(x)g(x))$ did exist. Since $\lim_{x \to 3} f(x)$ exists and is not zero, then $\lim_{x \to 3}((f(x)g(x))/f(x))$ exists, by Property 4 of limits in Theorem 1.2. Furthermore, $f(x) \ne 0$ for all x in some interval about 3, so $(f(x)g(x))/f(x) = g(x)$ for all x in that interval. Thus $\lim_{x \to 3} g(x)$ exists. This contradicts our assumption that $\lim_{x \to 3} g(x)$ does not exist.

57. False. For some functions we need to pick smaller values of δ. For example, if $f(x) = x^{1/3} + 2$ and $c = 0$ and $L = 2$, then $f(x)$ is within 10^{-3} of 2 if $|x^{1/3}| < 10^{-3}$. This only happens if x is within $(10^{-3})^3 = 10^{-9}$ of 0. If $x = 10^{-3}$ then $x^{1/3} = (10^{-3})^{1/3} = 10^{-1}$, which is too large.

58. False. The definition of a limit guarantees that, for any positive ϵ, there is a δ. This statement, which guarantees an ϵ for a specific $\delta = 10^{-3}$, is not equivalent to $\lim_{x \to c} f(x) = L$. For example, consider a function with a vertical asymptote within 10^{-3} of 0, such as $c = 0$, $L = 0$, $f(x) = x/(x - 10^{-4})$.

59. True. This is equivalent to the definition of a limit.

60. False. Although x may be far from c, the value of $f(x)$ could be close to L. For example, suppose $f(x) = L$, the constant function.

61. False. The definition of the limit says that if x is within δ of c, then $f(x)$ is within ϵ of L, not the other way round.

62. (a) This statement follows: if we interchange the roles of f and g in the original statement, we get this statement.
   (b) This statement is true, but it does not follow directly from the original statement, which says nothing about the case $g(a) = 0$.
   (c) This follows, since if $g(a) \neq 0$ the original statement would imply f/g is continuous at $x = a$, but we are told it is not.
   (d) This does not follow. Given that f is continuous at $x = a$ and $g(a) \neq 0$, then the original statement says g continuous implies f/g continuous, not the other way around. In fact, statement (d) is not true: if $f(x) = 0$ for all x, then g could be any discontinuous, non-zero function, and f/g would be zero, and therefore continuous. Thus the conditions of the statement would be satisfied, but not the conclusion.

PROJECTS FOR CHAPTER ONE

1. Notice that whenever x increases by 0.5, $f(x)$ increases by 1, indicating that $f(x)$ is linear. By inspection, we see that $f(x) = 2x$.

Similarly, $g(x)$ decreases by 1 each time x increases by 0.5. We know, therefore, that $g(x)$ is a linear function with slope $\frac{-1}{0.5} = -2$. The y-intercept is 10, so $g(x) = 10 - 2x$.

$h(x)$ is an even function which is always positive. Comparing the values of x and $h(x)$, it appears that $h(x) = x^2$.

$F(x)$ is an odd function that seems to vary between -1 and 1. We guess that $F(x) = \sin x$ and check with a calculator.

$G(x)$ is also an odd function that varies between -1 and 1. Notice that $G(x) = F(2x)$, and thus $G(x) = \sin 2x$.

Notice also that $H(x)$ is exactly 2 more than $F(x)$ for all x, so $H(x) = 2 + \sin x$.

2. (a) Compounding daily (continuously),

$$P = P_0 e^{rt}$$
$$= \$450,000 e^{(0.06)(213)}$$
$$\approx \$1.5977 \cdot 10^{11}.$$

This amounts to approximately $160 billion.

   (b) Compounding yearly,

$$A = \$450,000 \left(1 + 0.06\right)^{213}$$
$$= \$450,000(1.06)^{213} \approx \$450,000(245,555.29)$$
$$\approx \$1.10499882 \cdot 10^{11}.$$

This is only about $110.5 billion.

   (c) We first wish to find the interest that will accrue during 1990. For 1990, the principal is $\$1.105 \cdot 10^{11}$. At 6% annual interest, during 1990 the money will earn

$$0.06 \cdot \$1.105 \cdot 10^{11} = \$6.63 \cdot 10^9.$$

The number of seconds in a year is

$$\left(365 \frac{\text{days}}{\text{year}}\right) \left(24 \frac{\text{hours}}{\text{day}}\right) \left(60 \frac{\text{mins}}{\text{hour}}\right) \left(60 \frac{\text{secs}}{\text{min}}\right) = 31,536,000 \text{ sec}.$$

Thus, over 1990, interest is accumulating at the rate of

$$\frac{\$6.63 \cdot 10^9}{31,536,000 \text{ sec}} \approx \$210.24 \text{ /sec}.$$

CHAPTER TWO

Solutions for Section 2.1

Exercises

1. For t between 2 and 5, we have

$$\text{Average velocity} = \frac{\Delta s}{\Delta t} = \frac{400 - 135}{5 - 2} = \frac{265}{3} \text{ km/hr.}$$

The average velocity on this part of the trip was $265/3$ km/hr.

2. (a) Let $s = f(t)$.
   (i) We wish to find the average velocity between $t = 1$ and $t = 1.1$. We have

$$\text{Average velocity} = \frac{f(1.1) - f(1)}{1.1 - 1} = \frac{3.63 - 3}{0.1} = 6.3 \text{ m/sec.}$$

   (ii) We have

$$\text{Average velocity} = \frac{f(1.01) - f(1)}{1.01 - 1} = \frac{3.0603 - 3}{0.01} = 6.03 \text{ m/sec.}$$

   (iii) We have

$$\text{Average velocity} = \frac{f(1.001) - f(1)}{1.001 - 1} = \frac{3.006003 - 3}{0.001} = 6.003 \text{ m/sec.}$$

   (b) We see in part (a) that as we choose a smaller and smaller interval around $t = 1$ the average velocity appears to be getting closer and closer to 6, so we estimate the instantaneous velocity at $t = 1$ to be 6 m/sec.

3. (a) Let $s = f(t)$.
   (i) We wish to find the average velocity between $t = 1$ and $t = 1.1$. We have

$$\text{Average velocity} = \frac{f(1.1) - f(1)}{1.1 - 1} = \frac{7.84 - 7}{0.1} = 8.4 \text{ m/sec.}$$

   (ii) We have

$$\text{Average velocity} = \frac{f(1.01) - f(1)}{1.01 - 1} = \frac{7.0804 - 7}{0.01} = 8.04 \text{ m/sec.}$$

   (iii) We have

$$\text{Average velocity} = \frac{f(1.001) - f(1)}{1.001 - 1} = \frac{7.008004 - 7}{0.001} = 8.004 \text{ m/sec.}$$

   (b) We see in part (a) that as we choose a smaller and smaller interval around $t = 1$ the average velocity appears to be getting closer and closer to 8, so we estimate the instantaneous velocity at $t = 1$ to be 8 m/sec.

4. (a) Let $s = f(t)$.
   (i) We wish to find the average velocity between $t = 1$ and $t = 1.1$. We have

$$\text{Average velocity} = \frac{f(1.1) - f(1)}{1.1 - 1} = \frac{0.808496 - 0.909297}{0.1} = -1.00801 \text{ m/sec.}$$

   (ii) We have

$$\text{Average velocity} = \frac{f(1.01) - f(1)}{1.01 - 1} = \frac{0.900793 - 0.909297}{0.01} = -0.8504 \text{ m/sec.}$$

   (iii) We have

$$\text{Average velocity} = \frac{f(1.001) - f(1)}{1.001 - 1} = \frac{0.908463 - 0.909297}{0.001} = -0.834 \text{ m/sec.}$$

   (b) We see in part (a) that as we choose a smaller and smaller interval around $t = 1$ the average velocity appears to be getting closer and closer to -0.83, so we estimate the instantaneous velocity at $t = 1$ to be -0.83 m/sec. In this case, more estimates with smaller values of h would be very helpful in making a better estimate.

5.

Slope	-3	-1	0	1/2	1	2
Point	F	C	E	A	B	D

6. The slope is positive at A and D; negative at C and F. The slope is most positive at A; most negative at F.

7. Using $h = 0.1, 0.01, 0.001$, we see

$$\frac{(3 + 0.1)^3 - 27}{0.1} = 27.91$$

$$\frac{(3 + 0.01)^3 - 27}{0.01} = 27.09$$

$$\frac{(3 + 0.001)^3 - 27}{0.001} = 27.009.$$

These calculations suggest that $\lim_{h \to 0} \dfrac{(3 + h)^3 - 27}{h} = 27$.

8. Using radians,

h	$(\cos h - 1)/h$
0.01	-0.005
0.001	-0.0005
0.0001	-0.00005

These values suggest that $\lim_{h \to 0} \dfrac{\cos h - 1}{h} = 0$.

9. Using $h = 0.1, 0.01, 0.001$, we see

$$\frac{7^{0.1} - 1}{0.1} = 2.148$$

$$\frac{7^{0.01} - 1}{0.01} = 1.965$$

$$\frac{7^{0.001} - 1}{0.001} = 1.948$$

$$\frac{7^{0.0001} - 1}{0.0001} = 1.946.$$

This suggests that $\lim_{h \to 0} \dfrac{7^h - 1}{h} \approx 1.9$.

10. Using $h = 0.1, 0.01, 0.001$, we see

h	$(e^{1+h} - e)/h$
0.01	2.7319
0.001	2.7196
0.0001	2.7184

These values suggest that $\lim_{h \to 0} \dfrac{e^{1+h} - e}{h} = 2.7$. In fact, this limit is e.

Problems

11. See Figure 2.1.

12. See Figure 2.2.

13. See Figure 2.3.

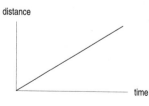

Figure 2.1

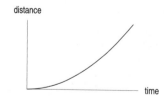

Figure 2.2

Figure 2.3

14. $0 <$ slope at $C <$ slope at $B <$ slope of $AB < 1 <$ slope at A. (Note that the line $y = x$, has slope 1.)

15. Since $f(t)$ is concave down between $t = 1$ and $t = 3$, the average velocity between the two times should be less than the instantaneous velocity at $t = 1$ but greater than the instantaneous velocity at time $t = 3$, so $D < A < C$. For analogous reasons, $F < B < E$. Finally, note that f is decreasing at $t = 5$ so $E < 0$, but increasing at $t = 0$, so $D > 0$. Therefore, the ordering from smallest to greatest of the given quantities is

$$F < B < E < 0 < D < A < C.$$

16. One possibility is shown in Figure 2.4.

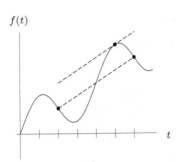

Figure 2.4

17.

$$\left(\begin{array}{c} \text{Average velocity} \\ 0 < t < 0.2 \end{array} \right) = \frac{s(0.2) - s(0)}{0.2 - 0} = \frac{0.5}{0.2} = 2.5 \text{ ft/sec.}$$

$$\left(\begin{array}{c} \text{Average velocity} \\ 0.2 < t < 0.4 \end{array} \right) = \frac{s(0.4) - s(0.2)}{0.4 - 0.2} = \frac{1.3}{0.2} = 6.5 \text{ ft/sec.}$$

A reasonable estimate of the velocity at $t = 0.2$ is the average: $\frac{1}{2}(6.5 + 2.5) = 4.5$ ft/sec.

18. $\lim\limits_{h \to 0} \dfrac{(2 + h)^2 - 4}{h} = \lim\limits_{h \to 0} \dfrac{4 + 4h + h^2 - 4}{h} = \lim\limits_{h \to 0}(4 + h) = 4$

19. $\lim\limits_{h \to 0} \dfrac{(1 + h)^3 - 1}{h} = \lim\limits_{h \to 0} \dfrac{1 + 3h + 3h^2 + h^3 - 1}{h} = \lim\limits_{h \to 0} \dfrac{h(3 + 3h + h^2)}{h} = \lim\limits_{h \to 0} 3 + 3h + h^2 = 3.$

20. $\lim\limits_{h \to 0} \dfrac{3(2 + h)^2 - 12}{h} = \lim\limits_{h \to 0} \dfrac{12 + 12h + 3h^2 - 12}{h} = \lim\limits_{h \to 0} \dfrac{h(12 + 3h)}{h} = \lim\limits_{h \to 0} 12 + 3h = 12.$

21. $\lim\limits_{h \to 0} \dfrac{(3 + h)^2 - (3 - h)^2}{2h} = \lim\limits_{h \to 0} \dfrac{9 + 6h + h^2 - 9 + 6h - h^2}{2h} = \lim\limits_{h \to 0} \dfrac{12h}{2h} = \lim\limits_{h \to 0} 6 = 6.$

Solutions for Section 2.2

Exercises

1. The derivative, $f'(2)$, is the rate of change of x^3 at $x = 2$. Notice that each time x changes by 0.001 in the table, the value of x^3 changes by 0.012. Therefore, we estimate

$$f'(2) = \begin{array}{c} \text{Rate of change} \\ \text{of } f \text{ at } x = 2 \end{array} \approx \frac{0.012}{0.001} = 12.$$

The function values in the table look exactly linear because they have been rounded. For example, the exact value of x^3 when $x = 2.001$ is 8.012006001, not 8.012. Thus, the table can tell us only that the derivative is approximately 12. Example 5 on page 85 shows how to compute the derivative of $f(x)$ exactly.

2. (a) Using a calculator we obtain the values found in the table below:

x	1	1.5	2	2.5	3
e^x	2.72	4.48	7.39	12.18	20.09

(b) The average rate of change of $f(x) = e^x$ between $x = 1$ and $x = 3$ is

$$\text{Average rate of change} = \frac{f(3) - f(1)}{3 - 1} = \frac{e^3 - e}{3 - 1} \approx \frac{20.09 - 2.72}{2} = 8.69.$$

(c) First we find the average rates of change of $f(x) = e^x$ between $x = 1.5$ and $x = 2$, and between $x = 2$ and $x = 2.5$:

$$\text{Average rate of change} = \frac{f(2) - f(1.5)}{2 - 1.5} = \frac{e^2 - e^{1.5}}{2 - 1.5} \approx \frac{7.39 - 4.48}{0.5} = 5.82$$

$$\text{Average rate of change} = \frac{f(2.5) - f(2)}{2.5 - 2} = \frac{e^{2.5} - e^2}{2.5 - 2} \approx \frac{12.18 - 7.39}{0.5} = 9.58.$$

Now we approximate the instantaneous rate of change at $x = 2$ by averaging these two rates:

$$\text{Instantaneous rate of change} \approx \frac{5.82 + 9.58}{2} = 7.7.$$

3. (a)

Table 2.1

x	1	1.5	2	2.5	3
$\log x$	0	0.18	0.30	0.40	0.48

(b) The average rate of change of $f(x) = \log x$ between $x = 1$ and $x = 3$ is

$$\frac{f(3) - f(1)}{3 - 1} = \frac{\log 3 - \log 1}{3 - 1} \approx \frac{0.48 - 0}{2} = 0.24$$

(c) First we find the average rates of change of $f(x) = \log x$ between $x = 1.5$ and $x = 2$, and between $x = 2$ and $x = 2.5$.

$$\frac{\log 2 - \log 1.5}{2 - 1.5} = \frac{0.30 - 0.18}{0.5} \approx 0.24$$

$$\frac{\log 2.5 - \log 2}{2.5 - 2} = \frac{0.40 - 0.30}{0.5} \approx 0.20$$

Now we approximate the instantaneous rate of change at $x = 2$ by finding the average of the above rates, i.e.

$$\left(\begin{array}{c} \text{the instantaneous rate of change} \\ \text{of } f(x) = \log x \text{ at } x = 2 \end{array} \right) \approx \frac{0.24 + 0.20}{2} = 0.22.$$

4. (a) Table 2.2 shows that near $x = 1$, every time the value of x increases by 0.001, the value of x^2 increases by approximately 0.002. This suggests that

$$f'(1) \approx \frac{0.002}{0.001} = 2.$$

Table 2.2   *Values of $f(x) = x^2$ near $x = 1$*

x	x^2	Difference in successive x^2 values
0.998	0.996004	
		0.001997
0.999	0.998001	
		0.001999
1.000	1.000000	
		0.002001
1.001	1.002001	
		0.002003
1.002	1.004004	
↑		↑
x increments of 0.001		All approximately 0.002

(b) The derivative is the limit of the difference quotient, so we look at

$$f'(1) = \lim_{h \to 0} \frac{f(1 + h) - f(1)}{h}.$$

Using the formula for f, we have

$$f'(1) = \lim_{h \to 0} \frac{(1 + h)^2 - 1^2}{h} = \lim_{h \to 0} \frac{(1 + 2h + h^2) - 1}{h} = \lim_{h \to 0} \frac{2h + h^2}{h}.$$

Since the limit only examines values of h close to, but not equal to zero, we can cancel h in the expression $(2h + h^2)/h$. We get

$$f'(1) = \lim_{h \to 0} \frac{h(2 + h)}{h} = \lim_{h \to 0} (2 + h).$$

This limit is 2, so $f'(1) = 2$. At $x = 1$ the rate of change of x^2 is 2.

(c) Since the derivative is the rate of change, $f'(1) = 2$ means that for small changes in x near $x = 1$, the change in $f(x) = x^2$ is about twice as big as the change in x. As an example, if x changes from 1 to 1.1, a net change of 0.1, then $f(x)$ changes by about 0.2. Figure 2.5 shows this geometrically. Near $x = 1$ the function is approximately linear with slope of 2.

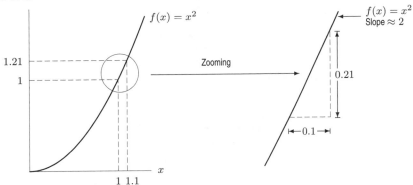

Figure 2.5: Graph of $f(x) = x^2$ near $x = 1$ has slope ≈ 2

5.

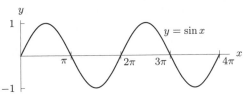

Since $\sin x$ is decreasing for values near $x = 3\pi$, its derivative at $x = 3\pi$ is negative.

6. $f'(1) = \lim_{h \to 0} \dfrac{\log(1 + h) - \log 1}{h} = \lim_{h \to 0} \dfrac{\log(1 + h)}{h}$

Evaluating $\frac{\log(1+h)}{h}$ for $h = 0.01, 0.001$, and 0.0001, we get $0.43214, 0.43408, 0.43427$, so $f'(1) \approx 0.43427$. The corresponding secant lines are getting steeper, because the graph of $\log x$ is concave down. We thus expect the limit to be more than 0.43427. If we consider negative values of h, the estimates are too large. We can also see this from the graph below:

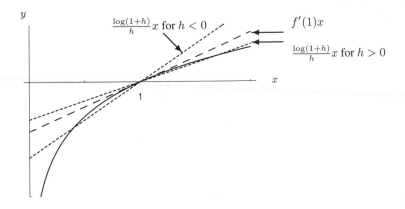

7. We estimate $f'(2)$ using the average rate of change formula on a small interval around 2. We use the interval $x = 2$ to $x = 2.001$. (Any small interval around 2 gives a reasonable answer.) We have

$$f'(2) \approx \frac{f(2.001) - f(2)}{2.001 - 2} = \frac{3^{2.001} - 3^2}{2.001 - 2} = \frac{9.00989 - 9}{0.001} = 9.89.$$

8. Since $f'(x) = 0$ where the graph is horizontal, $f'(x) = 0$ at $x = d$. The derivative is positive at points b and c, but the graph is steeper at $x = c$. Thus $f'(x) = 0.5$ at $x = b$ and $f'(x) = 2$ at $x = c$. Finally, the derivative is negative at points a and e but the graph is steeper at $x = e$. Thus, $f'(x) = -0.5$ at $x = a$ and $f'(x) = -2$ at $x = e$. See Table 2.3.

Thus, we have $f'(d) = 0, f'(b) = 0.5, f'(c) = 2, f'(a) = -0.5, f'(e) = -2$.

Table 2.3

x	$f'(x)$
d	0
b	0.5
c	2
a	-0.5
e	-2

9. One possible choice of points is shown below.

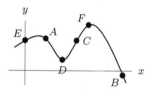

10. (a) The average rate of change from $x = a$ to $x = b$ is the slope of the line between the points on the curve with $x = a$ and $x = b$. Since the curve is concave down, the line from $x = 1$ to $x = 3$ has a greater slope than the line from $x = 3$ to $x = 5$, and so the average rate of change between $x = 1$ and $x = 3$ is greater than that between $x = 3$ and $x = 5$.

(b) Since f is increasing, $f(5)$ is the greater.

(c) As in part (a), f is concave down and f' is decreasing throughout so $f'(1)$ is the greater.

Problems

11. The statements $f(100) = 35$ and $f'(100) = 3$ tell us that at $x = 100$, the value of the function is 35 and the function is increasing at a rate of 3 units for a unit increase in x. Since we increase x by 2 units in going from 100 to 102, the value of the function goes up by approximately $2 \cdot 3 = 6$ units, so

$$f(102) \approx 35 + 2 \cdot 3 = 35 + 6 = 41.$$

12. The coordinates of A are $(4, 25)$. See Figure 2.6. The coordinates of B and C are obtained using the slope of the tangent line. Since $f'(4) = 1.5$, the slope is 1.5

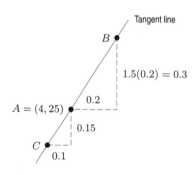

Figure 2.6

From A to B, $\Delta x = 0.2$, so $\Delta y = 1.5(0.2) = 0.3$. Thus, at C we have $y = 25 + 0.3 = 25.3$. The coordinates of B are $(4.2, 25.3)$.

From A to C, $\Delta x = -0.1$, so $\Delta y = 1.5(-0.1) = -0.15$. Thus, at C we have $y = 25 - 0.15 = 24.85$. The coordinates of C are $(3.9, 24.85)$.

13. (a) Since the point $B = (2, 5)$ is on the graph of g, we have $g(2) = 5$.

(b) The slope of the tangent line touching the graph at $x = 2$ is given by

$$\text{Slope} = \frac{\text{Rise}}{\text{Run}} = \frac{5 - 5.02}{2 - 1.95} = \frac{-0.02}{0.05} = -0.4.$$

Thus, $g'(2) = -0.4$.

14. The answers to parts (a)–(d) are shown in Figure 2.7.

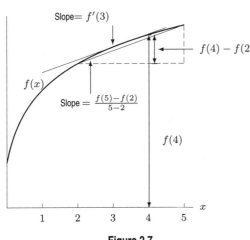

Figure 2.7

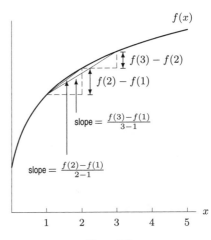

Figure 2.8

15. (a) Since f is increasing, $f(4) > f(3)$.

(b) From Figure 2.8, it appears that $f(2) - f(1) > f(3) - f(2)$.

(c) The quantity $\dfrac{f(2) - f(1)}{2 - 1}$ represents the slope of the secant line connecting the points on the graph at $x = 1$ and $x = 2$. This is greater than the slope of the secant line connecting the points at $x = 1$ and $x = 3$ which is $\dfrac{f(3) - f(1)}{3 - 1}$.

(d) The function is steeper at $x = 1$ than at $x = 4$ so $f'(1) > f'(4)$.

16. Figure 2.9 shows the quantities in which we are interested.

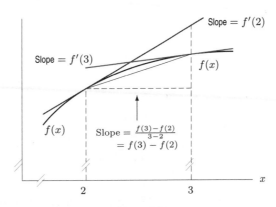

Figure 2.9

The quantities $f'(2), f'(3)$ and $f(3) - f(2)$ have the following interpretations:

- $f'(2) = $ slope of the tangent line at $x = 2$
- $f'(3) = $ slope of the tangent line at $x = 3$

- $f(3) - f(2) = \frac{f(3)-f(2)}{3-2} =$ slope of the secant line from $f(2)$ to $f(3)$.

From Figure 2.9, it is clear that $0 < f(3) - f(2) < f'(2)$. By extending the secant line past the point $(3, f(3))$, we can see that it lies above the tangent line at $x = 3$.

Thus

$$0 < f'(3) < f(3) - f(2) < f'(2).$$

17. (a) $f(4)/4$ is the slope of the line connecting $(0,0)$ to $(4, f(4))$. (See Figure 2.10.)

(b) It is clear from Figure 2.10 that $f(3)/3 > f(4)/4$.

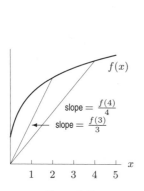

Figure 2.10

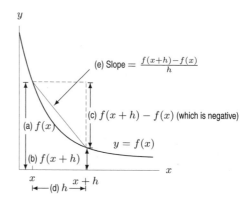

Figure 2.11

18. See Figure 2.11.

19. (a) For the line from A to B,

$$\text{Slope} = \frac{f(b) - f(a)}{b - a}.$$

(b) The tangent line at point C appears to be parallel to the line from A to B. Assuming this to be the case, the lines have the same slope.

(c) There is only one other point, labeled D in Figure 2.12, at which the tangent line is parallel to the line joining A and B.

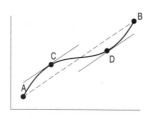

Figure 2.12

20. (a)

$$f'(0) = \lim_{h \to 0} \overbrace{\frac{\sin h - \sin 0}{h}}^{h \text{ in degrees } 0} = \frac{\sin h}{h}.$$

To four decimal places,

$$\frac{\sin 0.2}{0.2} \approx \frac{\sin 0.1}{0.1} \approx \frac{\sin 0.01}{0.01} \approx \frac{\sin 0.001}{0.001} \approx 0.01745$$

so $f'(0) \approx 0.01745$.

(b) Consider the ratio $\frac{\sin h}{h}$. As we approach 0, the numerator, $\sin h$, will be much smaller in magnitude if h is in degrees than it would be if h were in radians. For example, if $h = 1°$ radian, $\sin h = 0.8415$, but if $h = 1$ degree, $\sin h = 0.01745$. Thus, since the numerator is smaller for h measured in degrees while the denominator is the same, we expect the ratio $\frac{\sin h}{h}$ to be smaller.

21. We want $f'(2)$. The exact answer is

$$f'(2) = \lim_{h \to 0} \frac{f(2+h) - f(2)}{h} = \lim_{h \to 0} \frac{(2+h)^{2+h} - 4}{h},$$

but we can approximate this. If $h = 0.001$, then

$$\frac{(2.001)^{2.001} - 4}{0.001} \approx 6.779$$

and if $h = 0.0001$ then

$$\frac{(2.0001)^{2.0001} - 4}{0.0001} \approx 6.773,$$

so $f'(2) \approx 6.77$.

22. Notice that we can't get all the information we want just from the graph of f for $0 \leq x \leq 2$, shown on the left in Figure 2.13. Looking at this graph, it looks as if the slope at $x = 0$ is 0. But if we zoom in on the graph near $x = 0$, we get the graph of f for $0 \leq x \leq 0.05$, shown on the right in Figure 2.13. We see that f does dip down quite a bit between $x = 0$ and $x \approx 0.11$. In fact, it now looks like $f'(0)$ is around -1. Note that since $f(x)$ is undefined for $x < 0$, this derivative only makes sense as we approach zero from the right.

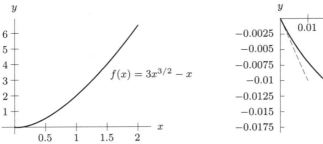

Figure 2.13

We zoom in on the graph of f near $x = 1$ to get a more accurate picture from which to estimate $f'(1)$. A graph of f for $0.7 \leq x \leq 1.3$ is shown in Figure 2.14. [Keep in mind that the axes shown in this graph don't cross at the origin!] Here we see that $f'(1) \approx 3.5$.

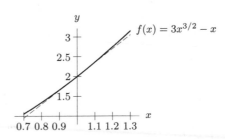

Figure 2.14

23.

$$f'(1) = \lim_{h \to 0} \frac{f(1+h) - f(1)}{h} = \lim_{h \to 0} \frac{\ln(\cos(1+h)) - \ln(\cos 1)}{h}$$

For $h = 0.001$, the difference quotient $= -1.55912$; for $h = 0.0001$, the difference quotient $= -1.55758$. The instantaneous rate of change of f therefore appears to be about -1.558 at $x = 1$.
At $x = \frac{\pi}{4}$, if we try $h = 0.0001$, then

$$\text{difference quotient} = \frac{\ln[\cos(\frac{\pi}{4} + 0.0001)] - \ln(\cos \frac{\pi}{4})}{0.0001} \approx -1.0001.$$

The instantaneous rate of change of f appears to be about -1 at $x = \frac{\pi}{4}$.

24. We want to approximate $P'(0)$ and $P'(2)$. Since for small h

$$P'(0) \approx \frac{P(h) - P(0)}{h},$$

if we take $h = 0.01$, we get

$$P'(0) \approx \frac{1.15(1.014)^{0.01} - 1.15}{0.01} = 0.01599 \text{ billion/year}$$

$$= 16.0 \text{ million people/year}$$

$$P'(2) \approx \frac{1.15(1.014)^{2.01} - 1.15(1.014)^2}{0.01} = 0.0164 \text{ billion/year}$$

$$= 16.4 \text{ million people/year}$$

25. (a) From Figure 2.15, it appears that the slopes of the tangent lines to the two graphs are the same at each x. For $x = 0$, the slopes of the tangents to the graphs of $f(x)$ and $g(x)$ at 0 are

$$f'(0) = \lim_{h \to 0} \frac{f(0 + h) - f(0)}{h}$$

$$= \lim_{h \to 0} \frac{f(h) - 0}{h}$$

$$= \lim_{h \to 0} \frac{\frac{1}{2}h^2}{h}$$

$$= \lim_{h \to 0} \frac{1}{2}h$$

$$= 0,$$

$$g'(0) = \lim_{h \to 0} \frac{g(0 + h) - g(0)}{h}$$

$$= \lim_{h \to 0} \frac{g(h) - g(0)}{h}$$

$$= \lim_{h \to 0} \frac{\frac{1}{2}h^2 + 3 - 3}{h}$$

$$= \lim_{h \to 0} \frac{\frac{1}{2}h^2}{h}$$

$$= \lim_{h \to 0} \frac{1}{2}h$$

$$= 0.$$

For $x = 2$, the slopes of the tangents to the graphs of $f(x)$ and $g(x)$ are

$$f'(2) = \lim_{h \to 0} \frac{f(2 + h) - f(2)}{h}$$

$$= \lim_{h \to 0} \frac{\frac{1}{2}(2 + h)^2 - \frac{1}{2}(2)^2}{h}$$

$$= \lim_{h \to 0} \frac{\frac{1}{2}(4 + 4h + h^2) - 2}{h}$$

$$= \lim_{h \to 0} \frac{2 + 2h + \frac{1}{2}h^2 - 2}{h}$$

$$= \lim_{h \to 0} \frac{2h + \frac{1}{2}h^2}{h}$$

$$= \lim_{h \to 0} \left(2 + \frac{1}{2}h\right)$$

$$= 2,$$

$$g'(2) = \lim_{h \to 0} \frac{g(2 + h) - g(2)}{h}$$

$$= \lim_{h \to 0} \frac{\frac{1}{2}(2 + h)^2 + 3 - (\frac{1}{2}(2)^2 + 3)}{h}$$

$$= \lim_{h \to 0} \frac{\frac{1}{2}(2 + h)^2 - \frac{1}{2}(2)^2}{h}$$

$$= \lim_{h \to 0} \frac{\frac{1}{2}(4 + 4h + h^2) - 2}{h}$$

$$= \lim_{h \to 0} \frac{2 + 2h + \frac{1}{2}(h^2) - 2}{h}$$

$$= \lim_{h \to 0} \frac{2h + \frac{1}{2}(h^2)}{h}$$

$$= \lim_{h \to 0} \left(2 + \frac{1}{2}h\right)$$

$$= 2.$$

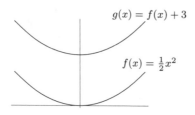

$$g(x) = f(x) + 3$$

$$f(x) = \tfrac{1}{2}x^2$$

Figure 2.15

For $x = x_0$, the slopes of the tangents to the graphs of $f(x)$ and $g(x)$ are

$$f'(x_0) = \lim_{h \to 0} \frac{f(x_0 + h) - f(x_0)}{h}$$

$$= \lim_{h \to 0} \frac{\frac{1}{2}(x_0 + h)^2 - \frac{1}{2}x_0^2}{h}$$

$$= \lim_{h \to 0} \frac{\frac{1}{2}(x_0^2 + 2x_0 h + h^2) - \frac{1}{2}x_0^2}{h}$$

$$= \lim_{h \to 0} \frac{x_0 h + \frac{1}{2}h^2}{h}$$

$$= \lim_{h \to 0} \left(x_0 + \frac{1}{2}h\right)$$

$$= x_0,$$

$$g'(x_0) = \lim_{h \to 0} \frac{g(x_0 + h) - g(x_0)}{h}$$

$$= \lim_{h \to 0} \frac{\frac{1}{2}(x_0 + h)^2 + 3 - (\frac{1}{2}(x_0)^2 + 3)}{h}$$

$$= \lim_{h \to 0} \frac{\frac{1}{2}(x_0 + h)^2 - \frac{1}{2}(x_0)^2}{h}$$

$$= \lim_{h \to 0} \frac{\frac{1}{2}(x_0^2 + 2x_0 h + h^2) - \frac{1}{2}x_0^2}{h}$$

$$= \lim_{h \to 0} \frac{x_0 h + \frac{1}{2}h^2}{h}$$

$$= \lim_{h \to 0} \left(x_0 + \frac{1}{2}h\right)$$

$$= x_0.$$

(b)

$$g'(x) = \lim_{h \to 0} \frac{g(x + h) - g(x)}{h}$$

$$= \lim_{h \to 0} \frac{f(x + h) + C - (f(x) + C)}{h}$$

$$= \lim_{h \to 0} \frac{f(x + h) - f(x)}{h}$$

$$= f'(x).$$

26. As h gets smaller, round-off error becomes important. When $h = 10^{-12}$, the quantity $2^h - 1$ is so close to 0 that the calculator rounds off the difference to 0, making the difference quotient 0. The same thing will happen when $h = 10^{-20}$.

27. $\displaystyle \lim_{h \to 0} \frac{(-3 + h)^2 - 9}{h} = \lim_{h \to 0} \frac{9 - 6h + h^2 - 9}{h} = \lim_{h \to 0} \frac{h(-6 + h)}{h} = \lim_{h \to 0} -6 + h = -6.$

28. $\displaystyle \lim_{h \to 0} \frac{(2 - h)^3 - 8}{h} = \lim_{h \to 0} \frac{8 - 12h + 6h^2 - h^3 - 8}{h} = \lim_{h \to 0} \frac{h(-12 + 6h - h^2)}{h} = \lim_{h \to 0} -12 + 6h - h^2 = -12.$

29. $\displaystyle \lim_{h \to 0} \frac{1}{h}\left(\frac{1}{1 + h} - 1\right) = \lim_{h \to 0} \frac{1 - (1 + h)}{(1 + h)h} = \lim_{h \to 0} \frac{-1}{1 + h} = -1$

30. $\displaystyle \lim_{h \to 0} \frac{1}{h}\left(\frac{1}{(1 + h)^2} - 1\right) = \lim_{h \to 0} \frac{1 - (1 + 2h + h^2)}{h(1 + h)^2} = \lim_{h \to 0} \frac{-2 - h}{(1 + h)^2} = -2$

31. $\displaystyle \sqrt{4 + h} - 2 = \frac{(\sqrt{4 + h} - 2)(\sqrt{4 + h} + 2)}{\sqrt{4 + h} + 2} = \frac{4 + h - 4}{\sqrt{4 + h} + 2} = \frac{h}{\sqrt{4 + h} + 2}.$

Therefore $\displaystyle \lim_{h \to 0} \frac{\sqrt{4 + h} - 2}{h} = \lim_{h \to 0} \frac{1}{\sqrt{4 + h} + 2} = \frac{1}{4}$

32. $\displaystyle \frac{1}{\sqrt{4 + h}} - \frac{1}{2} = \frac{2 - \sqrt{4 + h}}{2\sqrt{4 + h}} = \frac{(2 - \sqrt{4 + h})(2 + \sqrt{4 + h})}{2\sqrt{4 + h}(2 + \sqrt{4 + h})} = \frac{4 - (4 + h)}{2\sqrt{4 + h}(2 + \sqrt{4 + h})}.$

Therefore $\displaystyle \lim_{h \to 0} \frac{1}{h}\left(\frac{1}{\sqrt{4 + h}} - \frac{1}{2}\right) = \lim_{h \to 0} \frac{-1}{2\sqrt{4 + h}(2 + \sqrt{4 + h})} = -\frac{1}{16}$

33. Using the definition of the derivative, we have

$$f'(10) = \lim_{h \to 0} \frac{f(10 + h) - f(10)}{h}$$

$$= \lim_{h \to 0} \frac{5(10 + h)^2 - 5(10)^2}{h}$$

$$= \lim_{h \to 0} \frac{500 + 100h + 5h^2 - 500}{h}$$

$$= \lim_{h \to 0} \frac{100h + 5h^2}{h}$$

$$= \lim_{h \to 0} \frac{h(100 + 5h)}{h}$$

$$= \lim_{h \to 0} 100 + 5h$$

$$= 100.$$

34. Using the definition of the derivative, we have

$$f'(-2) = \lim_{h \to 0} \frac{f(-2 + h) - f(-2)}{h}$$

$$= \lim_{h \to 0} \frac{(-2 + h)^3 - (-2)^3}{h}$$

$$= \lim_{h \to 0} \frac{(-8 + 12h - 6h^2 + h^3) - (-8)}{h}$$

$$= \lim_{h \to 0} \frac{12h - 6h^2 + h^3}{h}$$

$$= \lim_{h \to 0} \frac{h(12 - 6h + h^2)}{h}$$

$$= \lim_{h \to 0} (12 - 6h + h^2),$$

which goes to 12 as $h \to 0$. So $f'(-2) = 12$.

35. Using the definition of the derivative

$$g'(-1) = \lim_{h \to 0} \frac{g(-1 + h) - g(-1)}{h}$$

$$= \lim_{h \to 0} \frac{((-1 + h)^2 + (-1 + h)) - ((-1)^2 + (-1))}{h}$$

$$= \lim_{h \to 0} \frac{(1 - 2h + h^2 - 1 + h) - (0)}{h}$$

$$= \lim_{h \to 0} \frac{-h + h^2}{h} = \lim_{h \to 0} (-1 + h) = -1.$$

36.

$$f'(1) = \lim_{h \to 0} \frac{f(1 + h) - f(1)}{h} = \lim_{h \to 0} \frac{((1 + h)^3 + 5) - (1^3 + 5)}{h}$$

$$= \lim_{h \to 0} \frac{1 + 3h + 3h^2 + h^3 + 5 - 1 - 5}{h} = \lim_{h \to 0} \frac{3h + 3h^2 + h^3}{h}$$

$$= \lim_{h \to 0} (3 + 3h + h^2) = 3.$$

37.

$$g'(2) = \lim_{h \to 0} \frac{g(2 + h) - g(2)}{h} = \lim_{h \to 0} \frac{\frac{1}{2+h} - \frac{1}{2}}{h}$$

$$= \lim_{h \to 0} \frac{2 - (2 + h)}{h(2 + h)2} = \lim_{h \to 0} \frac{-h}{h(2 + h)2}$$

$$= \lim_{h \to 0} \frac{-1}{(2 + h)2} = -\frac{1}{4}$$

38.

$$g'(2) = \lim_{h \to 0} \frac{g(2+h) - g(2)}{h} = \lim_{h \to 0} \frac{\frac{1}{(2+h)^2} - \frac{1}{2^2}}{h}$$

$$= \lim_{h \to 0} \frac{2^2 - (2+h)^2}{2^2(2+h)^2 h} = \lim_{h \to 0} \frac{4 - 4 - 4h - h^2}{4h(2+h)^2}$$

$$= \lim_{h \to 0} \frac{-4h - h^2}{4h(2+h)^2} = \lim_{h \to 0} \frac{-4 - h}{4(2+h)^2}$$

$$= \frac{-4}{4(2)^2} = -\frac{1}{4}.$$

39. As we saw in the answer to Problem 33, the slope of the tangent line to $f(x) = 5x^2$ at $x = 10$ is 100. When $x = 10$, $f(x) = 500$ so $(10, 500)$ is a point on the tangent line. Thus $y = 100(x - 10) + 500 = 100x - 500$.

40. As we saw in the answer to Problem 34, the slope of the tangent line to $f(x) = x^3$ at $x = -2$ is 12. When $x = -2$, $f(x) = -8$ so we know the point $(-2, -8)$ is on the tangent line. Thus the equation of the tangent line is $y = 12(x + 2) - 8 = 12x + 16$.

41. We know that the slope of the tangent line to $f(x) = x$ when $x = 20$ is 1. When $x = 20$, $f(x) = 20$ so $(20, 20)$ is on the tangent line. Thus the equation of the tangent line is $y = 1(x - 20) + 20 = x$.

42. First find the derivative of $f(x) = 1/x^2$ at $x = 1$.

$$f'(1) = \lim_{h \to 0} \frac{f(1+h) - f(1)}{h} = \lim_{h \to 0} \frac{\frac{1}{(1+h)^2} - \frac{1}{1^2}}{h}$$

$$= \lim_{h \to 0} \frac{1^2 - (1+h)^2}{h(1+h)^2} = \lim_{h \to 0} \frac{1 - (1 + 2h + h^2)}{h(1+h)^2}$$

$$= \lim_{h \to 0} \frac{-2h - h^2}{h(1+h)^2} = \lim_{h \to 0} \frac{-2 - h}{(1+h)^2} = -2$$

Thus the tangent line has a slope of -2 and goes through the point $(1, 1)$, and so its equation is

$$y - 1 = -2(x - 1) \quad \text{or} \quad y = -2x + 3.$$

Solutions for Section 2.3

Exercises

1. The graph is that of the line $y = -2x + 2$. The slope, and hence the derivative, is -2. See Figure 2.16.

2. See Figure 2.17.

3. See Figure 2.18.

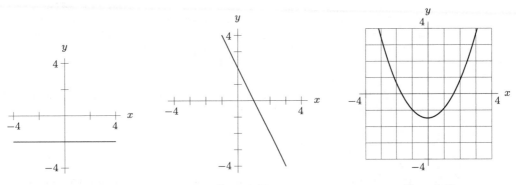

Figure 2.16   Figure 2.17   Figure 2.18

4. The slope of this curve is approximately -1 at $x = -4$ and at $x = 4$, approximately 0 at $x = -2.5$ and $x = 1.5$, and approximately 1 at $x = 0$. See Figure 2.19.

5. See Figure 2.20.

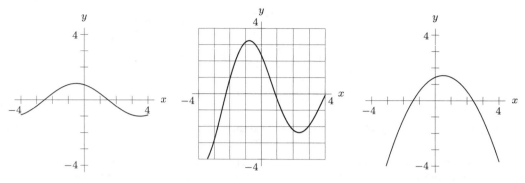

Figure 2.19	Figure 2.20	Figure 2.21

6. See Figure 2.21.

7. See Figure 2.22.

8. See Figure 2.23.

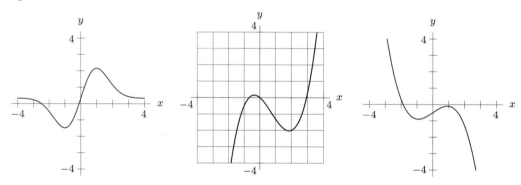

Figure 2.22	Figure 2.23	Figure 2.24

9. See Figure 2.24.

10.

x	$\ln x$		x	$\ln x$		x	$\ln x$		x	$\ln x$
0.998	-0.0020		1.998	0.6921		4.998	1.6090		9.998	2.3024
0.999	-0.0010		1.999	0.6926		4.999	1.6092		9.999	2.3025
1.000	0.0000		2.000	0.6931		5.000	1.6094		10.000	2.3026
1.001	0.0010		2.001	0.6936		5.001	1.6096		10.001	2.3027
1.002	0.0020		2.002	0.6941		5.002	1.6098		10.002	2.3028

At $x = 1$, the values of $\ln x$ are increasing by 0.001 for each increase in x of 0.001, so the derivative appears to be 1. At $x = 2$, the increase is 0.0005 for each increase of 0.001, so the derivative appears to be 0.5. At $x = 5$, $\ln x$ increases by 0.0002 for each increase of 0.001 in x, so the derivative appears to be 0.2. And at $x = 10$, the increase is 0.0001 over intervals of 0.001, so the derivative appears to be 0.1. These values suggest an inverse relationship between x and $f'(x)$, namely $f'(x) = \frac{1}{x}$.

11. (a) We use the interval to the right of $x = 2$ to estimate the derivative. (Alternately, we could use the interval to the left of 2, or we could use both and average the results.) We have

$$f'(2) \approx \frac{f(4) - f(2)}{4 - 2} = \frac{24 - 18}{4 - 2} = \frac{6}{2} = 3.$$

We estimate $f'(2) \approx 3$.

(b) We know that $f'(x)$ is positive when $f(x)$ is increasing and negative when $f(x)$ is decreasing, so it appears that $f'(x)$ is positive for $0 < x < 4$ and is negative for $4 < x < 12$.

12. For $x = 0, 5, 10$, and 15, we use the interval to the right to estimate the derivative. For $x = 20$, we use the interval to the left. For $x = 0$, we have

$$f'(0) \approx \frac{f(5) - f(0)}{5 - 0} = \frac{70 - 100}{5 - 0} = \frac{-30}{5} = -6.$$

Similarly, we find the other estimates in Table 2.4.

Table 2.4

x	0	5	10	15	20
$f'(x)$	-6	-3	-1.8	-1.2	-1.2

13. Since $1/x = x^{-1}$, using the power rule gives

$$k'(x) = (-1)x^{-2} = -\frac{1}{x^2}.$$

Using the definition of the derivative, we have

$$k'(x) = \lim_{h \to 0} \frac{k(x + h) - k(x)}{h} = \lim_{h \to 0} \frac{\frac{1}{x+h} - \frac{1}{x}}{h} = \lim_{h \to 0} \frac{x - (x + h)}{h(x + h)x}$$

$$= \lim_{h \to 0} \frac{-h}{h(x + h)x} = \lim_{h \to 0} \frac{-1}{(x + h)x} = -\frac{1}{x^2}.$$

14. Since $1/x^2 = x^{-2}$, using the power rule gives

$$l'(x) = -2x^{-3} = -\frac{2}{x^3}.$$

Using the definition of the derivative, we have

$$l'(x) = \lim_{h \to 0} \frac{\frac{1}{(x+h)^2} - \frac{1}{x^2}}{h} = \lim_{h \to 0} \frac{x^2 - (x + h)^2}{h(x + h)^2 x^2}$$

$$= \lim_{h \to 0} \frac{x^2 - (x^2 + 2xh + h^2)}{h(x + h)^2 x^2} = \lim_{h \to 0} \frac{-2xh - h^2}{h(x + h)^2 x^2}$$

$$= \lim_{h \to 0} \frac{-2x - h}{(x + h)^2 x^2} = \frac{-2x}{x^2 x^2} = -\frac{2}{x^3}.$$

15. Using the definition of the derivative,

$$g'(x) = \lim_{h \to 0} \frac{g(x + h) - g(x)}{h} = \lim_{h \to 0} \frac{2(x + h)^2 - 3 - (2x^2 - 3)}{h}$$

$$= \lim_{h \to 0} \frac{2(x^2 + 2xh + h^2) - 3 - 2x^2 + 3}{h} = \lim_{h \to 0} \frac{4xh + 2h^2}{h}$$

$$= \lim_{h \to 0} (4x + 2h) = 4x.$$

16. Using the definition of the derivative, we have

$$m'(x) = \lim_{h \to 0} \frac{m(x + h) - m(x)}{h} = \lim_{h \to 0} \frac{1}{h} \left(\frac{1}{x + h + 1} - \frac{1}{x + 1} \right)$$

$$= \lim_{h \to 0} \frac{1}{h} \left(\frac{x + 1 - x - h - 1}{(x + 1)(x + h + 1)} \right) = \lim_{h \to 0} \frac{-h}{h(x + 1)(x + h + 1)}$$

$$= \lim_{h \to 0} \frac{-1}{(x + 1)(x + h + 1)}$$

$$= \frac{-1}{(x + 1)^2}.$$

17.

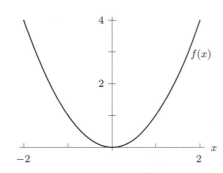 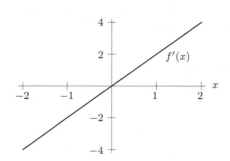

18.

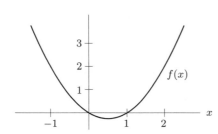 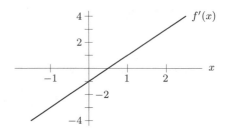

19.

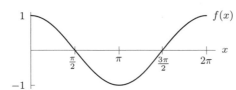 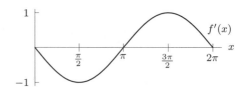

20.

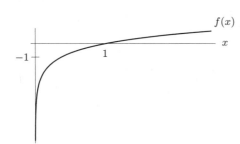 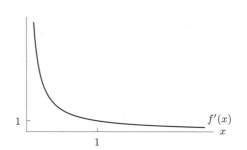

Problems

21. We know that $f'(x) \approx \dfrac{f(x+h) - f(x)}{h}$. For this problem, we'll take the average of the values obtained for $h = 1$ and $h = -1$; that's the average of $f(x+1) - f(x)$ and $f(x) - f(x-1)$ which equals $\dfrac{f(x+1) - f(x-1)}{2}$. Thus,

$f'(0) \approx f(1) - f(0) = 13 - 18 = -5.$
$f'(1) \approx [f(2) - f(0)]/2 = [10 - 18]/2 = -4.$
$f'(2) \approx [f(3) - f(1)]/2 = [9 - 13]/2 = -2.$
$f'(3) \approx [f(4) - f(2)]/2 = [9 - 10]/2 = -0.5.$
$f'(4) \approx [f(5) - f(3)]/2 = [11 - 9]/2 = 1.$
$f'(5) \approx [f(6) - f(4)]/2 = [15 - 9]/2 = 3.$
$f'(6) \approx [f(7) - f(5)]/2 = [21 - 11]/2 = 5.$
$f'(7) \approx [f(8) - f(6)]/2 = [30 - 15]/2 = 7.5.$
$f'(8) \approx f(8) - f(7) = 30 - 21 = 9.$

The rate of change of $f(x)$ is positive for $4 \leq x \leq 8$, negative for $0 \leq x \leq 3$. The rate of change is greatest at about $x = 8$.

22. The value of $g(x)$ is increasing at a decreasing rate for $2.7 < x < 4.2$ and increasing at an increasing rate for $x > 4.2$.

$$\frac{\Delta y}{\Delta x} = \frac{7.4 - 6.0}{5.2 - 4.7} = 2.8 \qquad \text{between } x = 4.7 \text{ and } x = 5.2$$

$$\frac{\Delta y}{\Delta x} = \frac{9.0 - 7.4}{5.7 - 5.2} = 3.2 \qquad \text{between } x = 5.2 \text{ and } x = 5.7$$

Thus $g'(x)$ should be close to 3 near $x = 5.2$.

23. This is a line with slope 1, so the derivative is the constant function $f'(x) = 1$. The graph is the horizontal line $y = 1$. See Figure 2.25.

24. This is a line with slope -2, so the derivative is the constant function $f'(x) = -2$. The graph is a horizontal line at $y = -2$. See Figure 2.26.

25. See Figure 2.27.

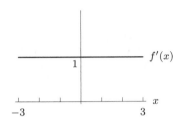

Figure 2.25

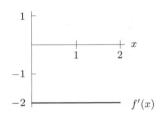

Figure 2.26

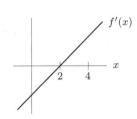

Figure 2.27

26. See Figure 2.28.

27. See Figure 2.29.

28. See Figure 2.30.

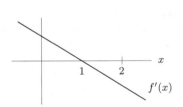

Figure 2.28

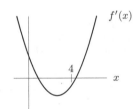

Figure 2.29

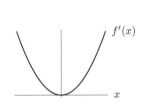

Figure 2.30

29. See Figure 2.31.

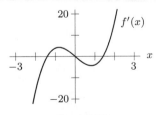

Figure 2.31

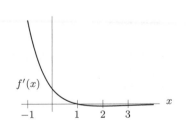

Figure 2.32

30. One possible graph is shown in Figure 2.32. Notice that as x gets large, the graph of $f(x)$ gets more and more horizontal. Thus, as x gets large, $f'(x)$ gets closer and closer to 0.

31. See Figure 2.33.

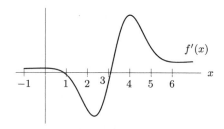

Figure 2.33

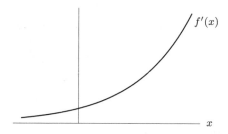

Figure 2.34

32. See Figure 2.34.

33. (a) x_3 (b) x_4 (c) x_5 (d) x_3

34. The derivative is zero whenever the graph of the original function is horizontal. Since the current is proportional to the derivative of the voltage, segments where the current is zero alternate with positive segments where the voltage is increasing and negative segments where the voltage is decreasing. See Figure 2.35. Note that the derivative does not exist where the graph has a corner.

Figure 2.35

35. (a) Graph II
   (b) Graph I
   (c) Graph III

36. On intervals where $f' = 0$, f is not changing at all, and is therefore constant. On the small interval where $f' > 0$, f is increasing; at the point where f' hits the top of its spike, f is increasing quite sharply. So f should be constant for a while, have a sudden increase, and then be constant again. A possible graph for f is shown in Figure 2.36.

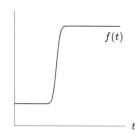

Figure 2.36: Step function

37. (a) $t = 3$
   (b) $t = 9$
   (c) $t = 14$
   (d)

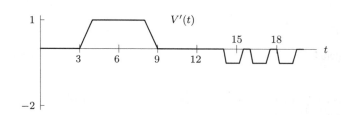

38. (a) The population varies periodically with a period of 1 year. See below.

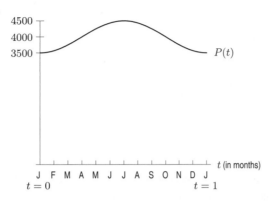

(b) The population is at a maximum on July 1st. At this time $\sin(2\pi t - \frac{\pi}{2}) = 1$, so the actual maximum population is $4000 + 500(1) = 4500$. Similarly, the population is at a minimum on January 1st. At this time, $\sin(2\pi t - \frac{\pi}{2}) = -1$, so the minimum population is $4000 + 500(-1) = 3500$.

(c) The rate of change is most positive about April 1st and most negative around October 1st.

(d) Since the population is at its maximum around July 1st, its rate of change is about 0 then.

39. The derivative of the accumulated federal debt with respect to time is shown in Figure 2.37. The derivative represents the rate of change of the federal debt with respect to time and is measured in trillions of dollars per year.

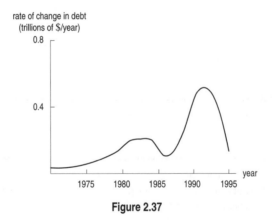

Figure 2.37

40. From the given information we know that f is increasing for values of x less than -2, is decreasing between $x = -2$ and $x = 2$, and is constant for $x > 2$. Figure 2.38 shows a possible graph—yours may be different.

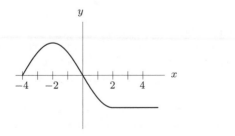

Figure 2.38

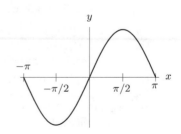

Figure 2.39

41. Figure 2.39 shows a possible graph – yours may be different.

42. (a) The function f is increasing where f' is positive, so for $x_1 < x < x_3$.

(b) The function f is decreasing where f' is negative, so for $0 < x < x_1$ or $x_3 < x < x_5$.

43. If $f(x)$ is even, its graph is symmetric about the y-axis. So the tangent line to f at $x = x_0$ is the same as that at $x = -x_0$ reflected about the y-axis.

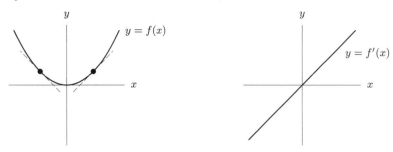

So the slopes of these two tangent lines are opposite in sign, so $f'(x_0) = -f'(-x_0)$, and f' is odd.

44. If $g(x)$ is odd, its graph remains the same if you rotate it $180°$ about the origin. So the tangent line to g at $x = x_0$ is the tangent line to g at $x = -x_0$, rotated $180°$.

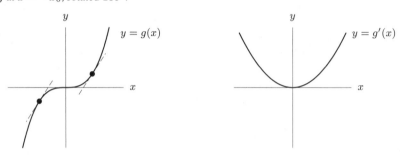

But the slope of a line stays constant if you rotate it $180°$. So $g'(x_0) = g'(-x_0)$; g' is even.

Solutions for Section 2.4

Exercises

1. (a) As the cup of coffee cools, the temperature decreases, so $f'(t)$ is negative.
   (b) Since $f'(t) = dH/dt$, the units are degrees Celsius per minute. The quantity $f'(20)$ represents the rate at which the coffee is cooling, in degrees per minute, 20 minutes after the cup is put on the counter.

2. (Note that we are considering the average temperature of the yam, since its temperature is different at different points inside it.)
   (a) It is positive, because the temperature of the yam increases the longer it sits in the oven.
   (b) The units of $f'(20)$ are $°$F/min. $f'(20) = 2$ means that at time $t = 20$ minutes, the temperature T increases by approximately $2°$F for each additional minute in the oven.

3. (a) The statement $f(200) = 350$ means that it costs $350 to produce 200 gallons of ice cream.
   (b) The statement $f'(200) = 1.4$ means that when the number of gallons produced is 200, costs are increasing by about $1.40 per gallon. In other words, it costs about $1.40 to produce the next (the 201st) gallon of ice cream.

4. (a) The statement $f(5) = 18$ means that when 5 milliliters of catalyst are present, the reaction will take 18 minutes. Thus, the units for 5 are ml while the units for 18 are minutes.
   (b) As in part (a), 5 is measured in ml. Since f' tells how fast T changes per unit a, we have f' measured in minutes/ml. If the amount of catalyst increases by 1 ml (from 5 to 6 ml), the reaction time decreases by about 3 minutes.

5. Since B is measured in dollars and t is measured in years, dB/dt is measured in dollars per year. We can interpret dB as the extra money added to your balance in dt years. Therefore dB/dt represents how fast your balance is growing, in units of dollars/year.

6. Units of $C'(r)$ are dollars/percent. Approximately, $C'(r)$ means the additional amount needed to pay off the loan when the interest rate is increased by 1%. The sign of $C'(r)$ is positive, because increasing the interest rate will increase the amount it costs to pay off a loan.

7. Units of $P'(t)$ are dollars/year. The practical meaning of $P'(t)$ is the rate at which the monthly payments change as the duration of the mortgage increases. Approximately, $P'(t)$ represents the change in the monthly payment if the duration is increased by one year. $P'(t)$ is negative because increasing the duration of a mortgage decreases the monthly payments.

8. (a) This means that investing the $1000 at 5% would yield $1649 after 10 years.

    (b) Writing $g'(r)$ as dB/dr, we see that the units of dB/dr are dollars per percent (interest). We can interpret dB as the extra money earned if interest rate is increased by dr percent. Therefore $g'(5) = \frac{dB}{dr}\big|_{r=5} \approx 165$ means that the balance, at 5% interest, would increase by about $165 if the interest rate were increased by 1%. In other words, $g(6) \approx g(5) + 165 = 1649 + 165 = 1814$.

9. The units of $f'(x)$ are feet/mile. The derivative, $f'(x)$, represents the rate of change of elevation with distance from the source, so if the river is flowing downhill everywhere, the elevation is always decreasing and $f'(x)$ is always negative. (In fact, there may be some stretches where the elevation is more or less constant, so $f'(x) = 0$.)

10. (a) If the price is $150, then 2000 items will be sold.

    (b) If the price goes up from $150 by $1 per item, about 25 fewer items will be sold. Equivalently, if the price is decreased from $150 by $1 per item, about 25 more items will be sold.

Problems

11. (a) Since $W = f(c)$ where W is weight in pounds and c is the number of Calories consumed per day:

$f(1800) = 155$	means that	consuming 1800 Calories per day results in a weight of 155 pounds.
$f'(2000) = 0$	means that	consuming 2000 Calories per day causes neither weight gain nor loss.
$f^{-1}(162) = 2200$	means that	a weight of 162 pounds is caused by a consumption of 2200 Calories per day.

    (b) The units of dW/dc are pounds/(Calories/day).

12. The graph is increasing for $0 < t < 10$ and is decreasing for $10 < t < 20$. One possible graph is shown in Figure 2.40. The units on the horizontal axis are years and the units on the vertical axis are people.

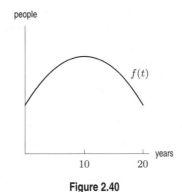

Figure 2.40

The derivative is positive for $0 < t < 10$ and negative for $10 < t < 20$. Two possible graphs are shown in Figure 2.41. The units on the horizontal axes are years and the units on the vertical axes are people per year.

Figure 2.41

13. Since $f(t) = 1.15(1.014)^t$, we have

$$f(6) = 1.15(1.014)^6 = 1.25.$$

To estimate $f'(6)$, we use a small interval around 6:

$$f'(6) \approx \frac{f(6.001) - f(6)}{6.001 - 6} = \frac{1.15(1.014)^{6.001} - 1.15(1.014)^6}{0.001} = 0.0174.$$

We see that $f(6) = 1.25$ billion people and $f'(6) = 0.0174$ billion people per year. This model tells us that the population of China was about 1,250,000,000 people in 1999 and was growing at a rate of about 17,400,000 people per year at that time.

14. (a) The statement $f(140) = 120$ means that a patient weighing 140 pounds should receive a dose of 120 mg of the painkiller. The statement $f'(140) = 3$ tells us that if the weight of a patient increases by about one pound (from 140 pounds), the dose should be increased by about 3 mg.

(b) Since the dose for a weight of 140 lbs is 120 mg and at this weight the dose goes up by 3 mg for each pound, a 145 lb patient should get an additional $3(5) = 15$ mg. Thus, for a 145 lb patient, the correct dose is approximately

$$f(145) \approx 120 + 3(5) = 135 \text{ mg}.$$

15. (a) When $t = 10$, that is, at 10 am, 3.1 cm of rain has fallen.

(b) We are told that when 5 cm of rain has fallen, 16 hours have passed ($t = 16$); that is, 5 cm of rain has fallen by 4 pm.

(c) The rate at which rain is falling is 0.4 cm/hr at $t = 10$, that is, at 10 am.

(d) The units of $(f^{-1})'(5)$ are hours/cm. Thus, we are being told that when 5 cm of rain has fallen, rain is falling at a rate such that it will take 2 additional hours for another centimeter to fall.

16. (a) The pressure in dynes/cm^2 at a depth of 100 meters.

(b) The depth of water in meters giving a pressure of $1.2 \cdot 10^6$ dynes/cm^2.

(c) The pressure at a depth of h meters plus a pressure of 20 dynes/cm^2.

(d) The pressure at a depth of 20 meters below the diver.

(e) The rate of increase of pressure with respect to depth, at 100 meters, in units of dynes/cm^2 per meter. Approximately, $p'(100)$ represents the increase in pressure in going from 100 meters to 101 meters.

(f) The depth, in meters, at which the rate of change of pressure with respect to depth is 20 dynes/cm^2 per meter.

17. Units of $g'(55)$ are mpg/mph. The statement $g'(55) = -0.54$ means that at 55 miles per hour the fuel efficiency (in miles per gallon, or mpg) of the car decreases at a rate of approximately one half mpg as the velocity increases by one mph.

18. (a)

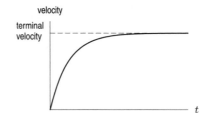

(b) The graph should be concave down because air resistance decreases your acceleration as you speed up, and so the slope of the graph of velocity is decreasing.

(c) The slope represents the acceleration due to gravity.

19. (a) The company hopes that increased advertising always brings in more customers instead of turning them away. Therefore, it hopes $f'(a)$ is always positive.

(b) If $f'(100) = 2$, it means that if the advertising budget is \$100,000, each extra dollar spent on advertising will bring in \$2 worth of sales. If $f'(100) = 0.5$, each dollar above \$100 thousand spent on advertising will bring in \$0.50 worth of sales.

(c) If $f'(100) = 2$, then as we saw in part (b), spending slightly more than \$100,000 will increase revenue by an amount greater than the additional expense, and thus more should be spent on advertising. If $f'(100) = 0.5$, then the increase in revenue is less than the additional expense, hence too much is being spent on advertising. The optimum amount to spend is an amount that makes $f'(a) = 1$. At this point, the increases in advertising expenditures just pay for themselves. If $f'(a) < 1$, too much is being spent; if $f'(a) > 1$, more should be spent.

20. Since $\frac{P(67) - P(66)}{67 - 66}$ is an estimate of $P'(66)$, we may think of $P'(66)$ as an estimate of $P(67) - P(66)$, and the latter is the number of people between 66 and 67 inches tall. Alternatively, since $\frac{P(66.5) - P(65.5)}{66.5 - 65.5}$ is a better estimate of $P'(66)$, we may regard $P'(66)$ as an estimate of the number of people of height between 65.5 and 66.5 inches. The units for $P'(x)$ are people per inch. Since there were 250 million people at the 1990 census, we might guess that there are about 200 million full-grown persons in the US whose heights are distributed between $60''(5')$ and $75''(6'3'')$. There are probably quite a few people of height $66''$–perhaps $1\frac{1}{2}$ what you'd expect from an even, or uniform, distribution–because it's nearly average. An even distribution would yield $P'(66) = \frac{200 \text{ million}}{15''} \approx 13$ million per inch–so we can expect $P'(66)$ to be perhaps $13(1.5) \approx 20$.

$P'(x)$ is never negative because $P(x)$ is never decreasing. To see this, let's look at an example involving a particular value of x, say $x = 70$. The value $P(70)$ represents the number of people whose height is less than or equal to 70 inches, and $P(71)$ represents the number of people whose height is less than or equal to 71 inches. Since everyone shorter than 70 inches is also shorter than 71 inches, $P(70) \leq P(71)$. In general, $P(x)$ is 0 for small x, and increases as x increases, and is eventually constant (for large enough x).

21. (a) The units of compliance are units of volume per units of pressure, or liters per centimeter of water.

(b) The increase in volume for a 5 cm reduction in pressure is largest between 10 and 15 cm. Thus, the compliance appears maximum between 10 and 15 cm of pressure reduction. The derivative is given by the slope, so

$$\text{Compliance} \approx \frac{0.70 - 0.49}{15 - 10} = 0.042 \text{ liters per centimeter.}$$

(c) When the lung is nearly full, it cannot expand much more to accommodate more air.

22. Solving for $dp/d\delta$, we get

$$\frac{dp}{d\delta} = \left(\frac{p}{\delta + (p/c^2)} \right) \gamma.$$

(a) For $\delta \approx 10$ g/cm^3, we have $\log \delta \approx 1$, so, from Figure 2.37 in the text, we have $\gamma \approx 2.6$ and $\log p \approx 13$.
    Thus $p \approx 10^{13}$, so $p/c^2 \approx 10^{13}/(9 \cdot 10^{20}) \approx 10^{-8}$, and

$$\frac{dp}{d\delta} \approx \frac{10^{13}}{10 + 10^{-8}} 2.6 \approx 2.6 \cdot 10^{12}.$$

The derivative can be interpreted as the ratio between a change in pressure and the corresponding change in density. The fact that it is so large says that a very large change in pressure brings about a very small change in density. This says that cold iron is not a very compressible material.

(b) For $\delta \approx 10^6$, we have $\log \delta \approx 6$, so, from Figure 2.37 in the text, $\gamma \approx 1.5$ and $\log p \approx 23$.
    Thus $p \approx 10^{23}$, so $p/c^2 \approx 10^{23}/(9 \cdot 10^{20}) \approx 10^2$, and

$$\frac{dp}{d\delta} \approx \frac{10^{23}}{10^6 + 10^2} 1.5 \approx 1.5 \cdot 10^{17}.$$

This tells us that the matter in a white dwarf is even less compressible than cold iron.

Solutions for Section 2.5

Exercises

1. (a) Since the graph is below the x-axis at $x = 2$, the value of $f(2)$ is negative.
(b) Since $f(x)$ is decreasing at $x = 2$, the value of $f'(2)$ is negative.
(c) Since $f(x)$ is concave up at $x = 2$, the value of $f''(2)$ is positive.

2. At B both dy/dx and d^2y/dx^2 could be positive because y is increasing and the graph is concave up there. At all the other points one or both of the derivatives could not be positive.

3. The two points at which $f' = 0$ are A and B. Since f' is nonzero at C and D and f'' is nonzero at all four points, we get the completed Table 2.5:

Table 2.5

Point	f	f'	f''
A	$-$	0	$+$
B	$+$	0	$-$
C	$+$	$-$	$-$
D	$-$	$+$	$+$

4. The function is everywhere increasing and concave up. One possible graph is shown in Figure 2.42.

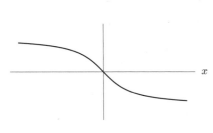

Figure 2.42

5. The graph must be everywhere decreasing and concave up on some intervals and concave down on other intervals. One possibility is shown in Figure 2.43.

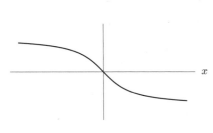

Figure 2.43

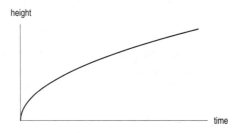

Figure 2.44

6. Since velocity is positive and acceleration is negative, we have $f' > 0$ and $f'' < 0$, and so the graph is increasing and concave down. See Figure 2.44.

7. $f'(x) > 0$
   $f''(x) > 0$

8. $f'(x) = 0$
   $f''(x) = 0$

9. $f'(x) < 0$
   $f''(x) = 0$

10. $f'(x) < 0$
   $f''(x) > 0$

11. $f'(x) > 0$
   $f''(x) < 0$

12. $f'(x) < 0$
   $f''(x) < 0$

13. The velocity is the derivative of the distance, that is, $v(t) = s'(t)$. Therefore, we have

$$v(t) = \lim_{h \to 0} \frac{s(t+h) - s(t)}{h}$$

$$= \lim_{h \to 0} \frac{(5(t+h)^2 + 3) - (5t^2 + 3)}{h}$$

$$= \lim_{h \to 0} \frac{10th + 5h^2}{h}$$

$$= \lim_{h \to 0} \frac{h(10t + 5h)}{h} = \lim_{h \to 0} (10t + 5h) = 10t$$

The acceleration is the derivative of velocity, so $a(t) = v'(t)$:

$$a(t) = \lim_{h \to 0} \frac{10(t+h) - 10t}{h}$$

$$= \lim_{h \to 0} \frac{10h}{h} = 10.$$

Problems

14. (a) The derivative, $f'(t)$, appears to be positive since the number of cars is increasing. The second derivative, $f''(t)$, appears to be positive because the rate of change is increasing. For example, between 1940 and 1950, the rate of change is $(40.3 - 27.5)/10 = 1.28$ million cars per year, while between 1950 and 1960, the rate of change is 2.14 million cars per year.

(b) We use the average rate of change formula on the interval 1970 to 1980 to estimate $f'(1975)$:

$$f'(1975) \approx \frac{121.6 - 89.3}{1980 - 1970} = \frac{32.3}{10} = 3.23.$$

We see that $f'(1975) \approx 3.23$ million cars per year. The number of passenger cars in the US was increasing at a rate of about 3.23 million cars per year in 1975.

15. To measure the average acceleration over an interval, we calculate the average rate of change of velocity over the interval. The units of acceleration are ft/sec per second, or (ft/sec)/sec, written ft/sec^2.

$$\begin{array}{l}\text{Average acceleration} \\ \text{for } 0 \le t \le 1\end{array} = \frac{\text{Change in velocity}}{\text{Time}} = \frac{v(1) - v(0)}{1} = \frac{30 - 0}{1} = 30 \text{ ft/sec}^2$$

$$\begin{array}{l}\text{Average acceleration} \\ \text{for } 1 \le t \le 2\end{array} = \frac{52 - 30}{2 - 1} = 22 \text{ ft/sec}^2$$

16. (a) $dP/dt > 0$ and $d^2P/dt^2 > 0$.

(b) $dP/dt < 0$ and $d^2P/dt^2 > 0$ (but dP/dt is close to zero).

17. (a)

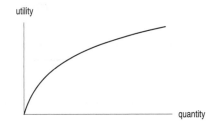

(b) As a function of quantity, utility is increasing but at a decreasing rate; the graph is increasing but concave down. So the derivative of utility is positive, but the second derivative of utility is negative.

18. (a) The EPA will say that the rate of discharge is still rising. The industry will say that the rate of discharge is increasing less quickly, and may soon level off or even start to fall.

(b) The EPA will say that the rate at which pollutants are being discharged is leveling off, but not to zero—so pollutants will continue to be dumped in the lake. The industry will say that the rate of discharge has decreased significantly.

19. (a) At x_4 and x_5, because the graph is below the x-axis there.

(b) At x_3 and x_4, because the graph is sloping down there.

(c) At x_3 and x_4, because the graph is sloping down there. This is the same condition as part (b).

(d) At x_2 and x_3, because the graph is bending downward there.

(e) At x_1, x_2, and x_5, because the graph is sloping upward there.

(f) At x_1, x_4, and x_5, because the graph is bending upward there.

20. (a) At t_3, t_4, and t_5, because the graph is above the t-axis there.

(b) At t_2 and t_3, because the graph is sloping up there.

(c) At t_1, t_2, and t_5, because the graph is concave up there.

(d) At t_1, t_4, and t_5, because the graph is sloping down there.

(e) At t_3 and t_4, because the graph is concave down there.

21. Since f' is everywhere positive, f is everywhere increasing. Hence the greatest value of f is at x_6 and the least value of f is at x_1. Directly from the graph, we see that f' is greatest at x_3 and least at x_2. Since f'' gives the slope of the graph of f', f'' is greatest where f' is rising most rapidly, namely at x_6, and f'' is least where f' is falling most rapidly, namely at x_1.

22. To the right of $x = 5$, the function starts by increasing, since $f'(5) = 2 > 0$ (though f may subsequently decrease) and is concave down, so its graph looks like the graph shown in Figure 2.45. Also, the tangent line to the curve at $x = 5$ has slope 2 and lies above the curve for $x > 5$. If we follow the tangent line until $x = 7$, we reach a height of 24. Therefore, $f(7)$ must be smaller than 24, meaning 22 is the only possible value for $f(7)$ from among the choices given.

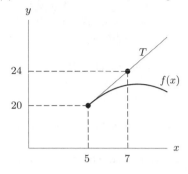

Figure 2.45

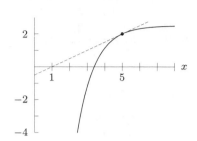

Figure 2.46

23. (a) See Figure 2.46.
   (b) Exactly one. There can't be more than one zero because f is increasing everywhere. There does have to be one zero because f stays below its tangent line (dotted line in above graph), and therefore f must cross the x-axis.
   (c) The equation of the (dotted) tangent line is $y = \frac{1}{2}x - \frac{1}{2}$, and so it crosses the x-axis at $x = 1$. Therefore the zero of f must be between $x = 1$ and $x = 5$.
   (d) $\lim\limits_{x \to -\infty} f(x) = -\infty$, because f is increasing and concave down. Thus, as $x \to -\infty$, $f(x)$ decreases, at a faster and faster rate.
   (e) Yes.
   (f) No. The slope is decreasing since f is concave down, so $f'(1) > f'(5)$, i.e. $f'(1) > \frac{1}{2}$.

Solutions for Section 2.6

Exercises

1. (a) Function f is not continuous at $x = 1$.
   (b) Function f appears not differentiable at $x = 1, 2, 3$.

2. (a) Function g appears continuous at all x-values shown.
   (b) Function g appears not differentiable at $x = 2, 4$. At $x = 2$, the curve is vertical, so the derivative does not exist. At $x = 4$, the graph has a corner, so the derivative does not exist.

3. (a) The function is continuous everywhere. See Figure 2.47.
   (b) The function appears not to be differentiable at $x = -1$ because the graph has a corner at $x = -1$. (See Figure 2.47.) This is confirmed by the fact that the limit of the difference quotient

$$\lim_{h \to 0} \frac{f(x+h) - f(x)}{h}$$

does not exist for $x = -1$, since the following limit does not exist:

$$\lim_{h \to 0} \frac{|-1 + h + 1| - |-1 + 1|}{h} = \lim_{h \to 0} \frac{|h|}{h}.$$

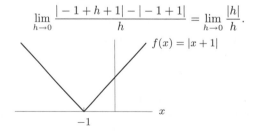

Figure 2.47

4. No, there are sharp turning points.

5. Yes.

Problems

6. We want to look at

$$\lim_{h \to 0} \frac{(h^2 + 0.0001)^{1/2} - (0.0001)^{1/2}}{h}.$$

As $h \to 0$ from positive or negative numbers, the difference quotient approaches 0. (Try evaluating it for $h = 0.001$, 0.0001, etc.) So it appears there is a derivative at $x = 0$ and that this derivative is zero. How can this be if f has a corner at $x = 0$?

The answer lies in the fact that what appears to be a corner is in fact smooth—when you zoom in, the graph of f looks like a straight line with slope 0! See Figure 2.48.

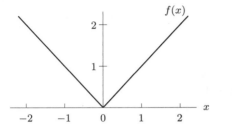
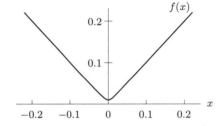

Figure 2.48: Close-ups of $f(x) = (x^2 + 0.0001)^{1/2}$ showing differentiability at $x = 0$

7. Yes, f is differentiable at $x = 0$, since its graph does not have a "corner" at $x = 0$. See below.

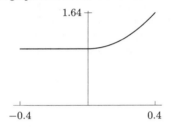

Another way to see this is by computing:

$$\lim_{h \to 0} \frac{f(h) - f(0)}{h} = \lim_{h \to 0} \frac{(h + |h|)^2}{h} = \lim_{h \to 0} \frac{h^2 + 2h|h| + |h|^2}{h}.$$

Since $|h|^2 = h^2$, we have:

$$\lim_{h \to 0} \frac{f(h) - f(0)}{h} = \lim_{h \to 0} \frac{2h^2 + 2h|h|}{h} = \lim_{h \to 0} 2(h + |h|) = 0.$$

So f is differentiable at 0 and $f'(0) = 0$.

8. As we can see in Figure 2.49, f oscillates infinitely often between the x-axis and the line $y = 2x$ near the origin. This means a line from $(0, 0)$ to a point $(h, f(h))$ on the graph of f alternates between slope 0 (when $f(h) = 0$) and slope 2 (when $f(h) = 2h$) infinitely often as h tends to zero. Therefore, there is no limit of the slope of this line as h tends to zero, and thus there is no derivative at the origin. Another way to see this is by noting that

$$\lim_{h \to 0} \frac{f(h) - f(0)}{h} = \lim_{h \to 0} \frac{h \sin(\frac{1}{h}) + h}{h} = \lim_{h \to 0} \left(\sin\left(\frac{1}{h}\right) + 1 \right)$$

does not exist, since $\sin(\frac{1}{h})$ does not have a limit as h tends to zero. Thus, f is not differentiable at $x = 0$.

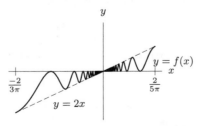

Figure 2.49

9. We can see from Figure 2.50 that the graph of f oscillates infinitely often between the curves $y = x^2$ and $y = -x^2$ near the origin. Thus the slope of the line from $(0,0)$ to $(h, f(h))$ oscillates between h (when $f(h) = h^2$ and $\frac{f(h)-0}{h-0} = h$) and $-h$ (when $f(h) = -h^2$ and $\frac{f(h)-0}{h-0} = -h$) as h tends to zero. So, the limit of the slope as h tends to zero is 0, which is the derivative of f at the origin. Another way to see this is to observe that

$$\lim_{h \to 0} \frac{f(h) - f(0)}{h} = \lim_{h \to 0} \left(\frac{h^2 \sin(\frac{1}{h})}{h} \right)$$
$$= \lim_{h \to 0} h \sin(\frac{1}{h})$$
$$= 0,$$

since $\lim_{h \to 0} h = 0$ and $-1 \le \sin(\frac{1}{h}) \le 1$ for any h. Thus f is differentiable at $x = 0$, and $f'(0) = 0$.

Figure 2.50

10. (a) The graph is concave up everywhere, except at $x = 2$ where the derivative is undefined. This is the case if the graph has a corner at $x = 2$. One possible graph is shown in Figure 2.51.

(b) The graph is concave up for $x < 2$ and concave down for $x > 2$, and the derivative is undefined at $x = 2$. This is the case if the graph is vertical at $x = 2$. One possible graph is shown in Figure 2.52.

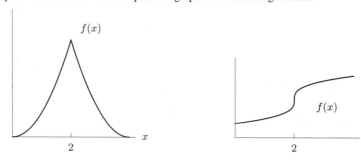

Figure 2.51   **Figure 2.52**

11. (a)

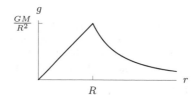

Figure 2.53

(b) The graph certainly looks continuous. The only point in question is $r = R$. Using the second formula with $r = R$ gives

$$g = \frac{GM}{R^2}.$$

Then, using the first formula with r approaching R from below, we see that as we get close to the surface of the earth

$$g \approx \frac{GMR}{R^3} = \frac{GM}{R^2}.$$

Since we get the same value for g from both formulas, g is continuous.

(c) For $r < R$, the graph of g is a line with a positive slope of $= \frac{GM}{R^3}$. For $r > R$, the graph of g looks like $1/x^2$, and so has a negative slope. Therefore the graph has a "corner" at $r = R$ and so is not differentiable there.

12. (a) The graph of Q against t does not have a break at $t = 0$, so Q appears to be continuous at $t = 0$. See Figure 2.54.

    (b) The slope dQ/dt is zero for $t < 0$, and negative for all $t > 0$. At $t = 0$, there appears to be a corner, which does not disappear as you zoom in, suggesting that I is defined for all times t except $t = 0$.

13. (a) Notice that B is a linear function of r for $r \leq r_0$ and a reciprocal for $r > r_0$. The constant B_0 is the value of B at $r = r_0$ and the maximum value of B. See Figure 2.55.

    (b) B is continuous at $r = r_0$ because there is no break in the graph there. Using the formula for B, we have

$$\lim_{r \to r_0^-} B = \frac{r_0}{r_0} B_0 = B_0 \quad \text{and} \quad \lim_{r \to r_0^+} B = \frac{r_0}{r_0} B_0 = B_0.$$

    (c) The function B is not differentiable at $r = r_0$ because the graph has a corner there. The slope is positive for $r < r_0$ and the slope is negative for $r > r_0$.

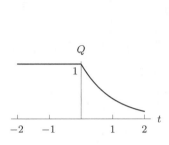

Figure 2.54

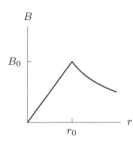

Figure 2.55

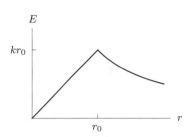

Figure 2.56

14. (a) Since

$$\lim_{r \to r_0^-} E = kr_0$$

and

$$\lim_{r \to r_0^+} E = \frac{kr_0^2}{r_0} = kr_0$$

and

$$E(r_0) = kr_0,$$

we see that E is continuous at r_0.

    (b) The function E is not differentiable at $r = r_0$ because the graph has a corner there. The slope is positive for $r < r_0$ and the slope is negative for $r > r_0$.

    (c) See Figure 2.56.

15. (a) The graph of $g(r)$ does not have a break or jump at $r = 2$, and so $g(r)$ is continuous there. See Figure 2.57. This is confirmed by the fact that

$$g(2) = 1 + \cos(\pi 2/2) = 1 + (-1) = 0$$

so the value of $g(r)$ as you approach $r = 2$ from the left is the same as the value when you approach $r = 2$ from the right.

    (b) The graph of $g(r)$ does not have a corner at $r = 2$, even after zooming in, so $g(r)$ appears to be differentiable at $r = 0$. This is confirmed by the fact that $\cos(\pi r/2)$ is at the bottom of a trough at $r = 2$, and so its slope is 0 there. Thus the slope to the left of $r = 2$ is the same as the slope to the right of $r = 2$.

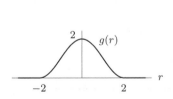

Figure 2.57

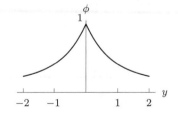

Figure 2.58

16. (a) The graph of ϕ does not have a break at $y = 0$, and so ϕ appears to be continuous there. See figure Figure 2.58.

    (b) The graph of ϕ has a corner at $y = 0$ which does not disappear as you zoom in. Therefore ϕ appears not be differentiable at $y = 0$.

17. (a) The graph of

$$f(x) = \begin{cases} 0 & \text{if } x < 0. \\ x^2 & \text{if } x \geq 0. \end{cases}$$

is shown to the right. The graph is continuous and has no vertical segments or corners, so $f(x)$ is differentiable everywhere.

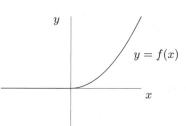

By Example 4 on page 84,

$$f'(x) = \begin{cases} 0 & \text{if } x < 0 \\ 2x & \text{if } x \geq 0 \end{cases}$$

So its graph is shown to the right.

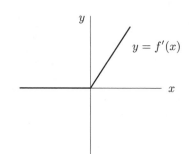

(b) The graph of the derivative has a corner at $x = 0$ so $f'(x)$ is not differentiable at $x = 0$. The graph of

$$f''(x) = \begin{cases} 0 & \text{if } x < 0 \\ 2 & \text{if } x > 0 \end{cases}$$

looks like:

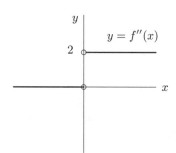

The second derivative is not defined at $x = 0$. So it is certainly neither differentiable nor continuous at $x = 0$.

Solutions for Chapter 2 Review

Exercises

1. See Figure 2.59.

Figure 2.59

Figure 2.60

2. See Figure 2.60.

3. See Figure 2.61.

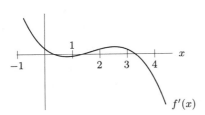

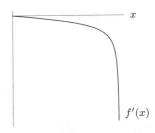

Figure 2.61

Figure 2.62

4. See Figure 2.62.

5. See Figure 2.63.

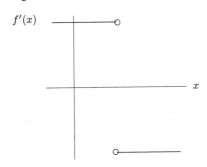

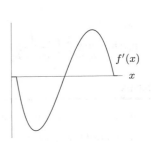

Figure 2.63

Figure 2.64

6. See Figure 2.64.

7. Using the definition of the derivative

$$
\begin{aligned}
f'(x) &= \lim_{h \to 0} \frac{f(x+h) - f(x)}{h} \\
&= \lim_{h \to 0} \frac{5(x+h)^2 + x + h - (5x^2 + x)}{h} \\
&= \lim_{h \to 0} \frac{5(x^2 + 2xh + h^2) + x + h - 5x^2 - x}{h} \\
&= \lim_{h \to 0} \frac{10xh + 5h^2 + h}{h} \\
&= \lim_{h \to 0} (10x + 5h + 1) = 10x + 1
\end{aligned}
$$

8. Using the definition of the derivative, we have

$$
\begin{aligned}
n'(x) &= \lim_{h \to 0} \frac{n(x+h) - n(x)}{h} \\
&= \lim_{h \to 0} \frac{1}{h} \left[\left(\frac{1}{x+h} + 1 \right) - \left(\frac{1}{x} + 1 \right) \right] \\
&= \lim_{h \to 0} \frac{1}{h} \left(\frac{1}{x+h} - \frac{1}{x} \right) \\
&= \lim_{h \to 0} \frac{x - (x+h)}{hx(x+h)} \\
&= \lim_{h \to 0} \frac{-h}{hx(x+h)} \\
&= \lim_{h \to 0} \frac{-1}{x(x+h)} = \frac{-1}{x^2}.
\end{aligned}
$$

9. $\lim_{h \to 0} \dfrac{(a+h)^2 - a^2}{h} = \lim_{h \to 0} \dfrac{a^2 + 2ah + h^2 - a^2}{h} = \lim_{h \to 0}(2a + h) = 2a$

10. $\lim_{h \to 0} \dfrac{1}{h}\left(\dfrac{1}{a+h} - \dfrac{1}{a}\right) = \lim_{h \to 0} \dfrac{a - (a+h)}{(a+h)ah} = \lim_{h \to 0} \dfrac{-1}{(a+h)a} = \dfrac{-1}{a^2}$

11. $\lim_{h \to 0} \dfrac{1}{h}\left(\dfrac{1}{(a+h)^2} - \dfrac{1}{a^2}\right) = \lim_{h \to 0} \dfrac{a^2 - (a^2 + 2ah + h^2)}{(a+h)^2 a^2 h} = \lim_{h \to 0} \dfrac{(-2a - h)}{(a+h)^2 a^2} = \dfrac{-2}{a^3}$

12. $\sqrt{a+h} - \sqrt{a} = \dfrac{(\sqrt{a+h} - \sqrt{a})(\sqrt{a+h} + \sqrt{a})}{\sqrt{a+h} + \sqrt{a}} = \dfrac{a+h-a}{\sqrt{a+h} + \sqrt{a}} = \dfrac{h}{\sqrt{a+h} + \sqrt{a}}$.

Therefore $\lim_{h \to 0} \dfrac{\sqrt{a+h} - \sqrt{a}}{h} = \lim_{h \to 0} \dfrac{1}{\sqrt{a+h} + \sqrt{a}} = \dfrac{1}{2\sqrt{a}}$

13. We combine terms in the numerator and multiply top and bottom by $\sqrt{a} + \sqrt{a+h}$.

$$\dfrac{1}{\sqrt{a+h}} - \dfrac{1}{\sqrt{a}} = \dfrac{\sqrt{a} - \sqrt{a+h}}{\sqrt{a+h}\sqrt{a}} = \dfrac{(\sqrt{a} - \sqrt{a+h})(\sqrt{a} + \sqrt{a+h})}{\sqrt{a+h}\sqrt{a}(\sqrt{a} + \sqrt{a+h})}$$

$$= \dfrac{a - (a+h)}{\sqrt{a+h}\sqrt{a}(\sqrt{a} + \sqrt{a+h})}$$

Therefore $\lim_{h \to 0} \dfrac{1}{h}\left(\dfrac{1}{\sqrt{a+h}} - \dfrac{1}{\sqrt{a}}\right) = \lim_{h \to 0} \dfrac{-1}{\sqrt{a+h}\sqrt{a}(\sqrt{a} + \sqrt{a+h})} = \dfrac{-1}{2(\sqrt{a})^3}$

Problems

14. (a) A possible example is $f(x) = 1/|x - 2|$ as $\lim_{x \to 2} 1/|x - 2| = \infty$.

(b) A possible example is $f(x) = -1/(x - 2)^2$ as $\lim_{x \to 2} -1/(x - 2)^2 = -\infty$.

15. Since $f(2) = 3$ and $f'(2) = 1$, near $x = 2$ the graph looks like the segment shown in Figure 2.65.

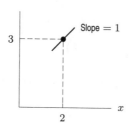

Figure 2.65

(a) If $f(x)$ is even, then the graph of $f(x)$ near $x = 2$ and $x = -2$ looks like Figure 2.66. Thus $f(-2) = 3$ and $f'(-2) = -1$.

(b) If $f(x)$ is odd, then the graph of $f(x)$ near $x = 2$ and $x = -2$ looks like Figure 2.67. Thus $f(-2) = -3$ and $f'(-2) = 1$.

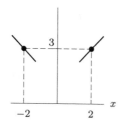

Figure 2.66: For f even

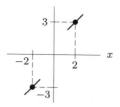

Figure 2.67: For f odd

16. The slopes of the lines drawn through successive pairs of points are negative but increasing, suggesting that $f''(x) > 0$ for $1 \le x \le 3.3$ and that the graph of $f(x)$ is concave up.

17. Using the approximation $\Delta y \approx f'(x)\Delta x$ with $\Delta x = 2$, we have $\Delta y \approx f'(20) \cdot 2 = 6 \cdot 2$, so

$$f(22) \approx f(20) + f'(20) \cdot 2 = 345 + 6 \cdot 2 = 357.$$

18. (a)

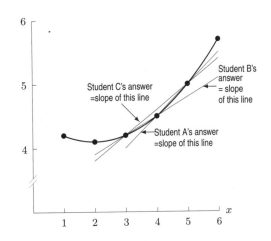

(b) The slope of f appears to be somewhere between student A's answer and student B's, so student C's answer, halfway in between, is probably the most accurate.

(c) Student A's estimate is $f'(x) \approx \frac{f(x+h)-f(x)}{h}$, while student B's estimate is $f'(x) \approx \frac{f(x)-f(x-h)}{h}$. Student C's estimate is the average of these two, or

$$f'(x) \approx \frac{1}{2}\left[\frac{f(x+h)-f(x)}{h} + \frac{f(x)-f(x-h)}{h}\right] = \frac{f(x+h)-f(x-h)}{2h}.$$

This estimate is the slope of the chord connecting $(x-h, f(x-h))$ to $(x+h, f(x+h))$. Thus, we estimate that the tangent to a curve is nearly parallel to a chord connecting points h units to the right and left, as shown below.

19. (a) Since the point $A = (7, 3)$ is on the graph of f, we have $f(7) = 3$.

(b) The slope of the tangent line touching the curve at $x = 7$ is given by

$$\text{Slope} = \frac{\text{Rise}}{\text{Run}} = \frac{3.8 - 3}{7.2 - 7} = \frac{0.8}{0.2} = 4.$$

Thus, $f'(7) = 4$.

20. At point A, we are told that $x = 1$ and $f(1) = 3$. Since $A = (x_2, y_2)$, we have $x_2 = 1$ and $y_2 = 3$. Since $h = 0.1$, we know $x_1 = 1 - 0.1 = 0.9$ and $x_3 = 1 + 0.1 = 1.1$.

Now consider Figure 2.68. Since $f'(1) = 2$, the slope of the tangent line AD is 2. Since $AB = 0.1$,

$$\frac{\text{Rise}}{\text{Run}} = \frac{BD}{0.1} = 2,$$

so $BD = 2(0.1) = 0.2$. Therefore $y_1 = 3 - 0.2 = 2.8$ and $y_3 = 3 + 0.2 = 3.2$.

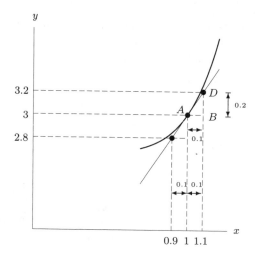

Figure 2.68

21. A possible graph of $y = f(x)$ is shown in Figure 2.69.

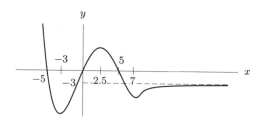

Figure 2.69

22. (a) The yam is cooling off so T is decreasing and $f'(t)$ is negative.
(b) Since $f(t)$ is measured in degrees Fahrenheit and t is measured in minutes, df/dt must be measured in units of °F/min.

23. $f(10) = 240,000$ means that if the commodity costs \$10, then 240,000 units of it will be sold. $f'(10) = -29,000$ means that if the commodity costs \$10 now, each \$1 increase in price will cause a decline in sales of 29,000 units.

24. The rate of change of the US population is $P'(t)$, so

$$P'(t) = 0.8\% \cdot \text{Current population} = 0.008P(t).$$

25. (a) $f'(0.6) \approx \dfrac{f(0.8) - f(0.6)}{0.8 - 0.6} = \dfrac{4.0 - 3.9}{0.2} = 0.5.$ $f'(0.5) \approx \dfrac{f(0.6) - f(0.4)}{0.6 - 0.4} = \dfrac{0.4}{0.2} = 2.$

(b) Using the values of f' from part (a), we get $f''(0.6) \approx \dfrac{f'(0.6) - f'(0.5)}{0.6 - 0.5} = \dfrac{0.5 - 2}{0.1} = \dfrac{-1.5}{0.1} = -15.$

(c) The maximum value of f is probably near $x = 0.8$. The minimum value of f is probably near $x = 0.3$.

26. (a) Slope of tangent line $= \lim_{h \to 0} \dfrac{\sqrt{4+h} - \sqrt{4}}{h}$. Using $h = 0.001$, $\dfrac{\sqrt{4.001} - \sqrt{4}}{0.001} = 0.249984$. Hence the slope of the tangent line is about 0.25.

(b)

$$y - y_1 = m(x - x_1)$$
$$y - 2 = 0.25(x - 4)$$
$$y - 2 = 0.25x - 1$$
$$y = 0.25x + 1$$

(c) $f(x) = kx^2$
If $(4, 2)$ is on the graph of f, then $f(4) = 2$, so $k \cdot 4^2 = 2$. Thus $k = \frac{1}{8}$, and $f(x) = \frac{1}{8}x^2$.

(d) To find where the graph of f crosses then line $y = 0.25x + 1$, we solve:

$$\frac{1}{8}x^2 = 0.25x + 1$$
$$x^2 = 2x + 8$$
$$x^2 - 2x - 8 = 0$$
$$(x - 4)(x + 2) = 0$$
$$x = 4 \text{ or } x = -2$$
$$f(-2) = \frac{1}{8}(4) = 0.5$$

Therefore, $(-2, 0.5)$ is the other point of intersection. (Of course, $(4, 2)$ is a point of intersection; we know that from the start.)

27. (a) The slope of the tangent line at $(0, \sqrt{19})$ is zero: it is horizontal.
The slope of the tangent line at $(\sqrt{19}, 0)$ is undefined: it is vertical.

(b) The slope appears to be about $\frac{1}{2}$. (Note that when x is 2, y is about -4, but when x is 4, y is approximately -3.)

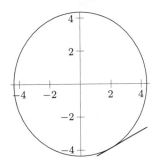

(c) Using symmetry we can determine: Slope at $(-2, \sqrt{15})$: about $\frac{1}{2}$. Slope at $(-2, -\sqrt{15})$: about $-\frac{1}{2}$. Slope at $(2, \sqrt{15})$: about $-\frac{1}{2}$.

28. (a) IV, (b) III, (c) II, (d) I, (e) IV, (f) II

29. (a) The population varies periodically with a period of 12 months (i.e. one year).

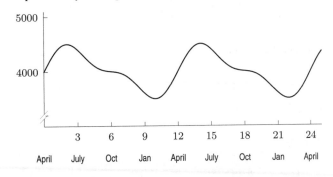

(b) The herd is largest about June 1st when there are about 4500 deer.

(c) The herd is smallest about February 1st when there are about 3500 deer.

(d) The herd grows the fastest about April 1st. The herd shrinks the fastest about July 15 and again about December 15.

(e) It grows the fastest about April 1st when the rate of growth is about 400 deer/month, i.e about 13 new fawns per day.

30. (a) The graph looks straight because the graph shows only a small part of the curve magnified greatly.

(b) The month is March: We see that about the 21st of the month there are twelve hours of daylight and hence twelve hours of night. This phenomenon (the length of the day equaling the length of the night) occurs at the equinox, midway between winter and summer. Since the length of the days is increasing, and Madrid is in the northern hemisphere, we are looking at March, not September.

(c) The slope of the curve is found from the graph to be about 0.04 (the rise is about 0.8 hours in 20 days or 0.04 hours/day). This means that the amount of daylight is increasing by about 0.04 hours (about $2\frac{1}{2}$ minutes) per calendar day, or that each day is $2\frac{1}{2}$ minutes longer than its predecessor.

31. (a) A possible graph is shown in Figure 2.70. At first, the yam heats up very quickly, since the difference in temperature between it and its surroundings is so large. As time goes by, the yam gets hotter and hotter, its rate of temperature increase slows down, and its temperature approaches the temperature of the oven as an asymptote. The graph is thus concave down. (We are considering the average temperature of the yam, since the temperature in its center and on its surface will vary in different ways.)

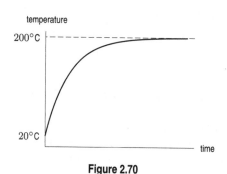

Figure 2.70

(b) If the rate of temperature increase were to remain $2°$/min, in ten minutes the yam's temperature would increase $20°$, from $120°$ to $140°$. Since we know the graph is not linear, but concave down, the actual temperature is between $120°$ and $140°$.

(c) In 30 minutes, we know the yam increases in temperature by $45°$ at an average rate of $45/30 = 1.5°$/min. Since the graph is concave down, the temperature at $t = 40$ is therefore between $120 + 1.5(10) = 135°$ and $140°$.

(d) If the temperature increases at $2°$/minute, it reaches $150°$ after 15 minutes, at $t = 45$. If the temperature increases at $1.5°$/minute, it reaches $150°$ after 20 minutes, at $t = 50$. So t is between 45 and 50 mins.

32. (a) We construct the difference quotient using $\text{erf}(0)$ and each of the other given values:

$$\text{erf}'(0) \approx \frac{\text{erf}(1) - \text{erf}(0)}{1 - 0} = 0.84270079$$

$$\text{erf}'(0) \approx \frac{\text{erf}(0.1) - \text{erf}(0)}{0.1 - 0} = 1.1246292$$

$$\text{erf}'(0) \approx \frac{\text{erf}(0.01) - \text{erf}(0)}{0.01 - 0} = 1.128342.$$

Based on these estimates, the best estimate is $\text{erf}'(0) \approx 1.12$; the subsequent digits have not yet stabilized.

(b) Using $\text{erf}(0.001)$, we have

$$\text{erf}'(0) \approx \frac{\text{erf}(0.001) - \text{erf}(0)}{0.001 - 0} = 1.12838$$

and so the best estimate is now 1.1283.

33. (a)

Table 2.6

x	$\frac{\sinh(x+0.001)-\sinh(x)}{0.001}$	$\frac{\sinh(x+0.0001)-\sinh(x)}{0.0001}$	so $f'(0) \approx$	$\cosh(x)$
0	1.00000	1.00000	1.00000	1.00000
0.3	1.04549	1.04535	1.04535	1.04534
0.7	1.25555	1.25521	1.25521	1.25517
1	1.54367	1.54314	1.54314	1.54308

(b) It seems that they are approximately the same, i.e. the derivative of $\sinh(x) = \cosh(x)$ for $x = 0, 0.3, 0.7$, and 1.

CAS Challenge Problems

34. The CAS says the derivative is zero. This can be explained by the fact that $f(x) = \sin^2 x + \cos^2 x = 1$, so $f'(x)$ is the derivative of the constant function 1. The derivative of a constant function is zero.

35. (a) The CAS gives $f'(x) = 2\cos^2 x - 2\sin^2 x$. Form of answers may vary.

(b) Using the double angle formulas for sine and cosine, we have

$$f(x) = 2\sin x \cos x = \sin(2x)$$
$$f'(x) = 2\cos^2 x - 2\sin^2 x = 2(\cos^2 x - \sin^2 x) = 2\cos(2x).$$

Thus we get

$$\frac{d}{dx}\sin(2x) = 2\cos(2x).$$

36. (a) The first derivative is $g'(x) = -2axe^{-ax^2}$, so the second derivative is

$$g''(x) = \frac{d^2}{dx^2}e^{-ax^2} = \frac{-2a}{e^{ax^2}} + \frac{4a^2x^2}{e^{ax^2}}.$$

Form of answers may vary.

(b) Both graphs get narrow as a gets larger; the graph of g'' is below the x-axis along the interval where g is concave down, and is above the x-axis where g is concave up. See Figure 2.71.

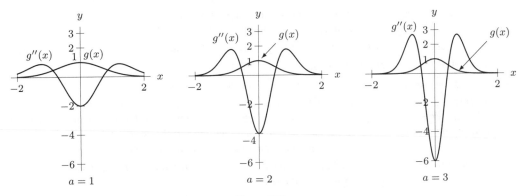

Figure 2.71

(c) The second derivative of a function is positive when the graph of the function is concave up and negative when it is concave down.

37. (a) The CAS gives the same derivative, $1/x$, in all three cases.

(b) From the properties of logarithms, $g(x) = \ln(2x) = \ln 2 + \ln x = f(x) + \ln 2$. So the graph of g is the same shape as the graph of f, only shifted up by $\ln 2$. So the graphs have the same slope everywhere, and therefore the two functions have the same derivative. By the same reasoning, $h(x) = f(x) + \ln 3$, so h and f have the same derivative as well.

38. (a) The computer algebra system gives

$$\frac{d}{dx}(x^2 + 1)^2 = 4x(x^2 + 1)$$
$$\frac{d}{dx}(x^2 + 1)^3 = 6x(x^2 + 1)^2$$
$$\frac{d}{dx}(x^2 + 1)^4 = 8x(x^2 + 1)^3$$

(b) The pattern suggests that

$$\frac{d}{dx}(x^2 + 1)^n = 2nx(x^2 + 1)^{n-1}.$$

Taking the derivative of $(x^2 + 1)^n$ with a CAS confirms this.

39. (a) Using a CAS, we find

$$\frac{d}{dx} \sin x = \cos x$$

$$\frac{d}{dx} \cos x = -\sin x$$

$$\frac{d}{dx}(\sin x \cos x) = \cos^2 x - \sin^2 x = 2\cos^2 x - 1.$$

(b) The product of the derivatives of $\sin x$ and $\cos x$ is $\cos x(-\sin x) = -\cos x \sin x$. On the other hand, the derivative of the product is $\cos^2 x - \sin^2 x$, which is not the same. So no, the derivative of a product is not always equal to the product of the derivatives.

CHECK YOUR UNDERSTANDING

1. False. For example, the car could slow down or even stop at one minute after 2 pm, and then speed back up to 60 mph at one minute before 3 pm. In this case the car would travel only a few miles during the hour, much less than 50 miles.

2. False. Its average velocity for the time between 2 pm and 4 pm is 40 mph, but the car could change its speed a lot during that time period. For example, the car might be motionless for an hour then go 80 mph for the second hour. In that case the velocity at 2 pm would be 0 mph.

3. True. During a short enough time interval the car can not change its velocity very much, and so it velocity will be nearly constant. It will be nearly equal to the average velocity over the interval.

4. True. The instantaneous velocity is a limit of the average velocities. The limit of a constant equals that constant.

5. True. By definition, Average velocity = Distance traveled/Time.

6. False. Instantaneous velocity equals a *limit* of difference quotients.

7. True. This is seen graphically. The derivative $f'(a)$ is the slope of the line tangent to the graph of f at the point P where $x = a$. The difference quotient $(f(b) - f(a))/(b - a)$ is the slope of the secant line with endpoints on the graph of f at the points where $x = a$ and $x = b$. The tangent and secant lines cross at the point P. The secant line goes above the tangent line for $x > a$ because f is concave up, and so the secant line has higher slope.

8. True. The derivative of a function is the limit of difference quotients. A few difference quotients can be computed from the table, but the limit can not be computed from the table.

9. False. If $f'(x)$ is increasing then $f(x)$ is concave up. However, $f(x)$ may be either increasing or decreasing. For example, the exponential decay function $f(x) = e^{-x}$ is decreasing but $f'(x)$ is increasing because the graph of f is concave up.

10. False. A counterexample is given by $f(x) = 5$ and $g(x) = 10$, two different functions with the same derivatives: $f'(x) = g'(x) = 0$.

11. True. The graph of a linear function $f(x) = mx + b$ is a straight line with the same slope m at every point. Thus $f'(x) = m$ for all x.

12. True. Shifting a graph vertically does not change the shape of the graph and so it does not change the slopes of the tangent lines to the graph.

13. False. The function $f(x)$ may be discontinuous at $x = 0$, for instance $f(x) = \begin{cases} 0 \text{ if } x \le 0 \\ 1 \text{ if } x > 0 \end{cases}$. The graph of f may have a vertical tangent line at $x = 0$, for instance $f(x) = x^{1/3}$.

14. True. The two sides of the equation are different frequently used notations for the very same quantity, the derivative of f at the point a.

15. True. The derivative $f'(10)$ is the slope of the tangent line to the graph of $y = f(x)$ at the point where $x = 10$. When you zoom in on $y = f(x)$ close enough it is not possible to see the difference between the tangent line and the graph of f on the calculator screen. The line you see on the calculator is a little piece of the tangent line, so its slope is the derivative $f'(10)$.

16. True. The second derivative $f''(x)$ is the derivative of $f'(x)$. Thus the derivative of $f'(x)$ is positive, and so $f'(x)$ is increasing.

17. True. Instantaneous acceleration is a derivative, and all derivatives are limits of difference quotients. More precisely, instantaneous acceleration $a(t)$ is the derivative of the velocity $v(t)$, so

$$a(t) = \lim_{h \to 0} \frac{v(t+h) - v(t)}{h}.$$

18. True. The derivatives $f'(t)$ and $g'(t)$ measure the same thing, the rate of chemical production at the same time t, but they measure it in different units. The units of $f'(t)$ are grams per minute, and the units of $g'(t)$ are kilograms per minute. To convert from kg/min to g/min, multiply by 1000.

19. False. The derivatives $f'(t)$ and $g'(t)$ measure different things because they measure the rate of chemical production at different times. There is no conversion possible from one to the other.

20. True. Let $f(x) = |x - 3|$. Then $f(x)$ is continuous for all x but not differentiable at $x = 3$ because its graph has a corner there. Other answers are possible.

21. True. If a function is differentiable at a point, then it is continuous at that point. For example, $f(x) = x^2$ is both differentiable and continuous on any interval. However, *one* example does not establish the truth of this statement; it merely illustrates the statement.

22. False. Being continuous does not imply differentiability. For example, $f(x) = |x|$ is continuous but not differentiable at $x = 0$.

23. True. If a function were differentiable, then it would be continuous. For example,
$$f(x) = \begin{cases} 1 & x \geq 0 \\ -1 & x < 0 \end{cases}$$
is neither differentiable nor continuous at $x = 0$. However, *one* example does not establish the truth of this statement; it merely illustrates the statement.

24. False. For example, $f(x) = |x|$ is not differentiable at $x = 0$, but it is continuous at $x = 0$.

25. (a) This is not a counterexample, since it does not satisfy the conditions of the statement, and therefore does not have the potential to contradict the statement.
    (b) This contradicts the statement, because it satisfies its conditions but not its conclusion. Hence it is a counterexample. Notice that this counterexample could not actually exist, since the statement is true.
    (c) This is an example illustrating the statement; it is not a counterexample.
    (d) This is not a counterexample, for the same reason as in part (a).

PROJECTS FOR CHAPTER TWO

1. (a) $S(0) = 12$ since the days are always 12 hours long at the equator.
   (b) Since $S(0) = 12$ from part (a) and the formula gives $S(0) = a$, we have $a = 12$. Since $S(x)$ must be continuous at $x = x_0$, and the formula gives $S(x_0) = a + b \arcsin(1) = 12 + b \left(\frac{\pi}{2} \right)$ and also $S(x_0) = 24$, we must have $12 + b \left(\frac{\pi}{2} \right) = 24$ so $b \left(\frac{\pi}{2} \right) = 12$ and $b = \frac{24}{\pi} \approx 7.64$.
   (c) $S(32°13') \approx 14.12$ and $S(46°4') \approx 15.58$.
   (d)

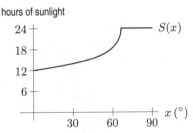

hours of sunlight

Figure 2.72

   (e) The graph in Figure 2.72 appears to have a corner at $x_0 = 66°30'$. We compare the slope to the right of x_0 and to the left of x_0. To the right of S_0, the function is constant, so $S'(x) = 0$ for $x > 66°30'$.
   We estimate the slope immediately to the left of x_0. We want to calculate the following:
$$\lim_{h \to 0^-} \frac{S(x_0 + h) - S(x_0)}{h}.$$
We approximate it by taking $x_0 = 66.5$ and $h = -0.1, -0.01, -0.001$:
$$\frac{S(66.49) - S(66.5)}{-0.1} \approx \frac{22.3633 - 24}{-0.1} = 16.38,$$

$$\frac{S(66.499) - S(66.5)}{-0.01} \approx \frac{23.4826 - 24}{-0.01} = 51.83,$$

$$\frac{S(66.4999) - S(66.5)}{-0.001} \approx \frac{23.8370 - 24}{-0.001} = 163.9.$$

These approximations suggest that, for $x_0 = 66.5$,

$$\lim_{h \to 0^-} \frac{S(x_0 + h) - S(x_0)}{h} \quad \text{does not exist.}$$

This evidence suggests that $S(x)$ is not differentiable at x_0. A proof requires the techniques found in Chapter 3.

2. (a) (i) Estimating derivatives using difference quotients (but other answers are possible):

$$P'(1900) \approx \frac{P(1910) - P(1900)}{10} = \frac{92.0 - 76.0}{10} = 1.6 \text{ million people per year}$$

$$P'(1945) \approx \frac{P(1950) - P(1940)}{10} = \frac{150.7 - 131.7}{10} = 1.9 \text{ million people per year}$$

$$P'(1990) \approx \frac{P(1990) - P(1980)}{10} = \frac{248.7 - 226.5}{10} = 2.22 \text{ million people per year}$$

(ii) The population growth was maximal somewhere between 1950 and 1960.

(iii) $P'(1950) \approx \frac{P(1960) - P(1950)}{10} = \frac{179.0 - 150.7}{10} = 2.83$ million people per year, so $P(1956) \approx P(1950) + P'(1950)(1956 - 1950) = 150.7 + 2.83(6) \approx 167.7$ million people.

(iv) If the growth rate between 1990 and 2000 was the same as the growth rate from 1980 to 1990, then the total population should be about 271 million people in 2000.

(b) (i) $f^{-1}(100)$ is the point in time when the population of the US was 100 million people (somewhere between 1910 and 1920).

(ii) The derivative of $f^{-1}(P)$ at $P = 100$ represents the ratio of change in time to change in population, and its units are years per million people. In other words, this derivative represents about how long it took for the population to increase by 1 million, when the population was 100 million.

(iii) Since the population increased by $105.7 - 92.0 = 13.7$ million people in 10 years, the average rate of increase is 1.37 million people per year. If the rate is fairly constant in that period, the amount of time it would take for an increase of 8 million people (100 million $-$ 92.0 million) would be

$$\frac{8 \text{ million people}}{1.37 \text{ million people/year}} \approx 5.8 \text{ years} \approx 6 \text{ years}$$

Adding this to our starting point of 1910, we estimate that the population of the US reached 100 million around 1916, i.e. $f^{-1}(100) \approx 1916$.

(iv) Since it took 10 years between 1910 and 1920 for the population to increase by $105.7 - 92.0 = 13.7$ million people, the derivative of $f^{-1}(P)$ at $P = 100$ is approximately

$$\frac{10 \text{ years}}{13.7 \text{ million people}} = 0.73 \text{ years/million people}$$

(c) (i) Clearly the population of the US at any instant is an integer that varies up and down every few seconds as a child is born, a person dies, or a new immigrant arrives. So $f(t)$ has "jumps;" it is not a smooth function. But these jumps are small relative to the values of f, so f appears smooth unless we zoom in very closely on its graph (to within a few seconds).

Major land acquisitions such as the Louisiana Purchase caused larger jumps in the population, but since the census is taken only every ten years and the territories acquired were rather sparsely populated, we cannot see these jumps in the census data.

(ii) We can regard rate of change of the population for a particular time t as representing an estimate of how much the population will increase during the year after time t.

(iii) Many economic indicators are treated as smooth, such as the Gross National Product, the Dow Jones Industrial Average, volumes of trading, and the price of commodities like gold. But these figures only change in increments, not continuously.

CHAPTER THREE

Solutions for Section 3.1

Exercises

1. The derivative, $f'(x)$, is defined as

$$f'(x) = \lim_{h \to 0} \frac{f(x+h) - f(x)}{h}.$$

If $f(x) = 7$, then

$$f'(x) = \lim_{h \to 0} \frac{7 - 7}{h} = \lim_{h \to 0} \frac{0}{h} = 0.$$

2. The definition of the derivative says that

$$f'(x) = \lim_{h \to 0} \frac{f(x+h) - f(x)}{h}.$$

Therefore,

$$f'(x) = \lim_{h \to 0} \frac{[17(x+h) + 11] - [17x + 11]}{h} = \lim_{h \to 0} \frac{17h}{h} = 17.$$

3. $y' = 11x^{10}$.

4. $y' = 12x^{11}$.

5. $y' = -12x^{-13}$.

6. $y' = 11x^{-12}$.

7. $y' = 3.2x^{2.2}$.

8. $y' = \frac{4}{3}x^{1/3}$.

9. $y' = \frac{3}{4}x^{-1/4}$.

10. $y' = -\frac{3}{4}x^{-7/4}$.

11. $f'(x) = -4x^{-5}$.

12. Since $g(t) = \dfrac{1}{t^5} = t^{-5}$, we have $g'(t) = -5t^{-6}$.

13. Since $f(z) = -\dfrac{1}{z^{6.1}} = -z^{-6.1}$, we have $f'(z) = -(-6.1)z^{-7.1} = 6.1z^{-7.1}$.

14. Since $y = \dfrac{1}{r^{7/2}} = r^{-7/2}$, we have $\dfrac{dy}{dx} = -\dfrac{7}{2}r^{-9/2}$.

15. Since $y = \sqrt{x} = x^{1/2}$, we have $\dfrac{dy}{dx} = \dfrac{1}{2}x^{-1/2}$.

16. $f'(x) = \frac{1}{4}x^{-3/4}$.

17. Since $h(\theta) = \dfrac{1}{\sqrt[3]{\theta}} = \theta^{-1/3}$, we have $h'(\theta) = -\dfrac{1}{3}\theta^{-4/3}$.

18. Since $f(x) = \sqrt{\dfrac{1}{x^3}} = \dfrac{1}{x^{3/2}} = x^{-3/2}$, we have $f'(x) = -\dfrac{3}{2}x^{-5/2}$.

19. $f'(x) = ex^{e-1}$.

20. $y' = 6x^{1/2} - \frac{5}{2}x^{-1/2}$.

21. $f'(t) = 6t - 4$.

22. $y' = 17 + 12x^{-1/2}$.

23. $y' = 2z - \frac{1}{2z^2}$.

24. The power rule gives $f'(x) = 20x^3 - \dfrac{2}{x^3}$.

25. $h'(w) = 6w^{-4} + \dfrac{3}{2}w^{-1/2}$

26. $y' = 18x^2 + 8x - 2$.

27. $y' = 15t^4 - \frac{5}{2}t^{-1/2} - \frac{7}{t^2}$.

28. $y' = 6t - \frac{6}{t^{3/2}} + \frac{2}{t^3}$.

29. Since $y = \sqrt{x}(x+1) = x^{1/2}x + x^{1/2} \cdot 1 = x^{3/2} + x^{1/2}$, we have $\frac{dy}{dx} = \frac{3}{2}x^{1/2} + \frac{1}{2}x^{-1/2}$.

30. Since $y = t^{3/2}(2 + \sqrt{t}) = 2t^{3/2} + t^{3/2}t^{1/2} = 2t^{3/2} + t^2$, we have $\frac{dy}{dx} = 3t^{1/2} + 2t$.

31. Since $h(t) = \frac{3}{t} + \frac{4}{t^2} = 3t^{-1} + 4t^{-2}$, we have $h'(t) = -3t^{-2} - 8t^{-3}$.

32. Since $y = \sqrt{\theta}\left(\sqrt{\theta} + \frac{1}{\sqrt{\theta}}\right) = \theta^{1/2}\theta^{1/2} + \frac{\sqrt{\theta}}{\sqrt{\theta}} = \theta + 1$, we have $\frac{dy}{dx} = 1$.

33. $y = x + \frac{1}{x}$, so $y' = 1 - \frac{1}{x^2}$.

34. $f(z) = \frac{z}{3} + \frac{1}{3}z^{-1} = \frac{1}{3}\left(z + z^{-1}\right)$, so $f'(z) = \frac{1}{3}\left(1 - z^{-2}\right) = \frac{1}{3}\left(\frac{z^2 - 1}{z^2}\right)$.

35. $f(t) = \frac{1}{t^2} + \frac{1}{t} - \frac{1}{t^4} = t^{-2} + t^{-1} - t^{-4}$
$f'(t) = -2t^{-3} - t^{-2} + 4t^{-5}$.

36. $y = \frac{\theta}{\sqrt{\theta}} - \frac{1}{\sqrt{\theta}} = \sqrt{\theta} - \frac{1}{\sqrt{\theta}}$
$y' = \frac{1}{2\sqrt{\theta}} + \frac{1}{2\theta^{3/2}}$.

37. $j'(x) = \frac{3x^2}{a} + \frac{2ax}{b} - c$

38. Since $f(x) = \frac{ax+b}{x} = \frac{ax}{x} + \frac{b}{x} = a + bx^{-1}$, we have $f'(x) = -bx^{-2}$.

39. Since $h(x) = \frac{ax+b}{c} = \frac{a}{c}x + \frac{b}{c}$, we have $h'(x) = \frac{a}{c}$.

40. Since $g(t) = \frac{\sqrt{t}(1+t)}{t^2} = \frac{t^{1/2} \cdot 1 + t^{1/2}t}{t^2} = \frac{t^{1/2}}{t^2} + \frac{t^{3/2}}{t^2} = t^{-3/2} + t^{-1/2}$, we have $g'(t) = -\frac{3}{2}t^{-5/2} - \frac{1}{2}t^{-3/2}$.

41. Since $4/3$, π, and b are all constants, we have

$$\frac{dV}{dr} = \frac{4}{3}\pi(2r)b = \frac{8}{3}\pi r b.$$

42. Since w is a constant times q, we have $dw/dq = 3ab^2$.

43. Since a, b, and c are all constants, we have

$$\frac{dy}{dx} = a(2x) + b(1) + 0 = 2ax + b.$$

44. Since a and b are constants, we have

$$\frac{dP}{dt} = 0 + b\frac{1}{2}t^{-1/2} = \frac{b}{2\sqrt{t}}.$$

Problems

45. So far, we can only take the derivative of powers of x and the sums of constant multiples of powers of x. Since we cannot write $\sqrt{x+3}$ in this form, we cannot yet take its derivative.

46. The x is in the exponent and we haven't learned how to handle that yet.

47. $g'(x) = \pi x^{(\pi-1)} + \pi x^{-(\pi+1)}$, by the power and sum rules.

48. $y' = 6x$.   (power rule and sum rule)

49. We cannot write $\frac{1}{3x^2+4}$ as the sum of powers of x multiplied by constants.

50. $y' = -2/3z^3$.   (power rule and sum rule)

51. $f'(t) = 6t^2 - 8t + 3$ and $f''(t) = 12t - 8$.

52.

$$f'(x) = -8 + 2\sqrt{2}x$$
$$f'(r) = -8 + 2\sqrt{2}r = 4$$
$$r = \frac{12}{2\sqrt{2}} = 3\sqrt{2}.$$

53. Differentiating gives
$$f'(x) = 6x^2 - 4x \quad \text{so} \quad f'(1) = 6 - 4 = 2.$$
Thus the equation of the tangent line is $(y - 1) = 2(x - 1)$ or $y = 2x - 1$.

54. (a) We have $f(2) = 8$, so a point on the tangent line is $(2, 8)$. Since $f'(x) = 3x^2$, the slope of the tangent is given by
$$m = f'(2) = 3(2)^2 = 12.$$
Thus, the equation is
$$y - 8 = 12(x - 2) \quad \text{or} \quad y = 12x - 16.$$

(b) See Figure 3.1. The tangent line lies below the function $f(x) = x^3$, so estimates made using the tangent line are underestimates.

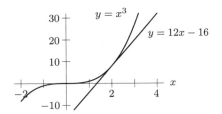

Figure 3.1

55.

$$f'(x) = 12x^2 + 12x - 23 \geq 1$$
$$12x^2 + 12x - 24 \geq 0$$
$$12(x^2 + x - 2) \geq 0$$
$$12(x + 2)(x - 1) \geq 0.$$

Hence $x \geq 1 \quad \text{or} \quad x \leq -2$.

56. The slopes of the tangent lines to $y = x^2 - 2x + 4$ are given by $y' = 2x - 2$. A line through the origin has equation $y = mx$. So, at the tangent point, $x^2 - 2x + 4 = mx$ where $m = y' = 2x - 2$.

$$x^2 - 2x + 4 = (2x - 2)x$$
$$x^2 - 2x + 4 = 2x^2 - 2x$$
$$-x^2 + 4 = 0$$
$$-(x + 2)(x - 2) = 0$$
$$x = 2, -2.$$

Thus, the points of tangency are $(2, 4)$ and $(-2, 12)$. The lines through these points and the origin are $y = 2x$ and $y = -6x$, respectively. Graphically, this can be seen in Figure 3.2:

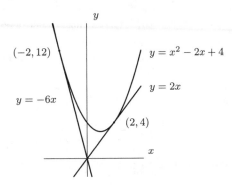

Figure 3.2

57. Decreasing means $f'(x) < 0$:

$$f'(x) = 4x^3 - 12x^2 = 4x^2(x - 3),$$

so $f'(x) < 0$ when $x < 3$ and $x \neq 0$. Concave up means $f''(x) > 0$:

$$f''(x) = 12x^2 - 24x = 12x(x - 2)$$

so $f''(x) > 0$ when

$$12x(x - 2) > 0$$
$$x < 0 \quad \text{or} \quad x > 2.$$

So, both conditions hold for $x < 0$ or $2 < x < 3$.

58. The graph increases when $dy/dx > 0$:

$$\frac{dy}{dx} = 5x^4 - 5 > 0$$
$$5(x^4 - 1) > 0 \quad \text{so} \quad x^4 > 1 \quad \text{so} \quad x > 1 \text{ or } x < -1.$$

The graph is concave up when $d^2y/dx^2 > 0$:

$$\frac{d^2y}{dx^2} = 20x^3 > 0 \quad \text{so} \quad x > 0.$$

We need values of x where $\{x > 1 \text{ or } x < -1\}$ AND $\{x > 0\}$, which implies $x > 1$. Thus, both conditions hold for all values of x larger than 1.

59. Since $f(x) = x^3 - 6x^2 - 15x + 20$, we have $f'(x) = 3x^2 - 12x - 15$. To find the points at which $f'(x) = 0$, we solve

$$3x^2 - 12x - 15 = 0$$
$$3(x^2 - 4x - 5) = 0$$
$$3(x + 1)(x - 5) = 0.$$

We see that $f'(x) = 0$ at $x = -1$ and at $x = 5$. The graph of $f(x)$ in Figure 3.3 appears to be horizontal at $x = -1$ and at $x = 5$, confirming what we found analytically.

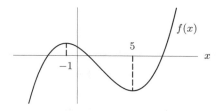

Figure 3.3

60. (a) Since the power of x will go down by one every time you take a derivative (until the exponent is zero after which the derivative will be zero), we can see immediately that $f^{(8)}(x) = 0$.

(b) $f^{(7)}(x) = 7 \cdot 6 \cdot 5 \cdot 4 \cdot 3 \cdot 2 \cdot 1 \cdot x^0 = 5040$.

61. Since $f(t) = 700 - 3t^2$, we have $f(5) = 700 - 3(25) = 625$ cm. Since $f'(t) = -6t$, we have $f'(5) = -30$ cm/year. In the year 2000, the sand dune was 625 cm high and it was eroding at a rate of 30 centimeters per year.

62. (a) Velocity $v(t) = \frac{dy}{dt} = \frac{d}{dt}(1250 - 16t^2) = -32t$.

Since $t \geq 0$, the ball's velocity is negative. This is reasonable, since its height y is decreasing.

(b) Acceleration $a(t) = \frac{dv}{dt} = \frac{d}{dt}(-32t) = -32$.

So its acceleration is the negative constant -32.

(c) The ball hits the ground when its height $y = 0$. This gives

$$1250 - 16t^2 = 0$$
$$t = \pm 8.84 \text{ seconds}$$

We discard $t = -8.84$ because time t is nonnegative. So the ball hits the ground 8.84 seconds after its release, at which time its velocity is

$$v(8.84) = -32(8.84) = -282.88 \text{ feet/sec} = -192.84 \text{ mph}.$$

63. (a) The average velocity between $t = 0$ and $t = 2$ is given by

$$\text{Average velocity} = \frac{f(2) - f(0)}{2 - 0} = \frac{-4.9(2^2) + 25(2) + 3 - 3}{2 - 0} = \frac{33.4 - 3}{2} = 15.2 \text{ m/sec.}$$

(b) Since $f'(t) = -9.8t + 25$, we have

$$\text{Instantaneous velocity} = f'(2) = -9.8(2) + 25 = 5.4 \text{ m/sec.}$$

(c) Acceleration is given $f''(t) = -9.8$. The acceleration at $t = 2$ (and all other times) is the acceleration due to gravity, which is -9.8 m/sec^2.

(d) We can use a graph of height against time to estimate the maximum height of the tomato. See Figure 3.4. Alternately, we can find the answer analytically. The maximum height occurs when the velocity is zero and $v(t) = -9.8t + 25 = 0$ when $t = 2.6$ sec. At this time the tomato is at a height of $f(2.6) = 34.9$. The maximum height is 34.9 meters.

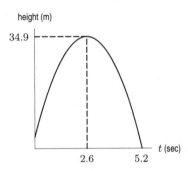

Figure 3.4

(e) We see in Figure 3.4 that the tomato hits ground at about $t = 5.2$ seconds. Alternately, we can find the answer analytically. The tomato hits the ground when

$$f(t) = -4.9t^2 + 25t + 3 = 0.$$

We solve for t using the quadratic formula:

$$t = \frac{-25 \pm \sqrt{(25)^2 - 4(-4.9)(3)}}{2(-4.9)}$$

$$t = \frac{-25 \pm \sqrt{683.8}}{-9.8}$$

$$t = -0.12 \quad \text{and} \quad t = 5.2.$$

We use the positive values, so the tomato hits the ground at $t = 5.2$ seconds.

64. $\dfrac{dF}{dr} = -\dfrac{2GMm}{r^3}$.

65. (a) $T = 2\pi\sqrt{\dfrac{l}{g}} = \dfrac{2\pi}{\sqrt{g}}\left(l^{\frac{1}{2}}\right)$, so $\dfrac{dT}{dl} = \dfrac{2\pi}{\sqrt{g}}\left(\dfrac{1}{2}l^{-\frac{1}{2}}\right) = \dfrac{\pi}{\sqrt{gl}}$.

(b) Since $\dfrac{dT}{dl}$ is positive, the period T increases as the length l increases.

66. (a) $A = \pi r^2$
$\dfrac{dA}{dr} = 2\pi r$.

(b) This is the formula for the circumference of a circle.

(c) $A'(r) \approx \dfrac{A(r+h) - A(r)}{h}$ for small h. When $h > 0$, the numerator of the difference quotient denotes the area of the region contained between the inner circle (radius r) and the outer circle (radius $r + h$). See figure below. As h approaches 0, this area can be approximated by the product of the circumference of the inner circle and the "width" of the region, i.e., h. Dividing this by the denominator, h, we get $A' = $ the circumference of the circle with radius r.

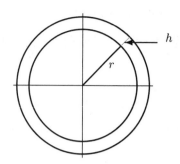

We can also think about the derivative of A as the rate of change of area for a small change in radius. If the radius increases by a tiny amount, the area will increase by a thin ring whose area is simply the circumference at that radius times the small amount. To get the rate of change, we divide by the small amount and obtain the circumference.

67. $V = \frac{4}{3}\pi r^3$. Differentiating gives $\frac{dV}{dr} = 4\pi r^2 = $ surface area of a sphere.

The difference quotient $\frac{V(r+h)-V(r)}{h}$ is the volume between two spheres divided by the change in radius. Furthermore, when h is very small, the difference between volumes, $V(r+h) - V(r)$, is like a coating of paint of depth h applied to the surface of the sphere. The volume of the paint is about $h \cdot$ (Surface Area) for small h: dividing by h gives back the surface area.

Thinking about the derivative as the rate of change of the function for a small change in the variable gives another way of seeing the result. If you increase the radius of a sphere a small amount, the volume increases by a very thin layer whose volume is the surface area at that radius multiplied by that small amount.

68. If $f(x) = x^n$, then $f'(x) = nx^{n-1}$. This means $f'(1) = n \cdot 1^{n-1} = n \cdot 1 = n$, because any power of 1 equals 1.

69. Since $f(x) = ax^n$, $f'(x) = anx^{n-1}$. We know that $f'(2) = (an)2^{n-1} = 3$, and $f'(4) = (an)4^{n-1} = 24$. Therefore,

$$\frac{f'(4)}{f'(2)} = \frac{24}{3}$$

$$\frac{(an)4^{n-1}}{(an)2^{n-1}} = \left(\frac{4}{2}\right)^{n-1} = 8$$

$$2^{n-1} = 8, \text{ and thus } n = 4.$$

Substituting $n = 4$ into the expression for $f'(2)$, we get $3 = a(4)(8)$, or $a = 3/32$.

70. Yes. To see why, we substitute $y = x^n$ into the equation $13x\frac{dy}{dx} = y$. We first calculate $\frac{dy}{dx} = \frac{d}{dx}(x^n) = nx^{n-1}$. The differential equation becomes

$$13x(nx^{n-1}) = x^n$$

But $13x(nx^{n-1}) = 13n(x \cdot x^{n-1}) = 13nx^n$, so we have

$$13n(x^n) = x^n$$

This equality must hold for all x, so we get $13n = 1$, so $n = 1/13$. Thus, $y = x^{1/13}$ is a solution.

71. (a)

$$\frac{d(x^{-1})}{dx} = \lim_{h \to 0} \frac{(x+h)^{-1} - x^{-1}}{h} = \lim_{h \to 0} \frac{1}{h}\left[\frac{1}{x+h} - \frac{1}{x}\right]$$

$$= \lim_{h \to 0} \frac{1}{h}\left[\frac{x - (x+h)}{x(x+h)}\right] = \lim_{h \to 0} \frac{1}{h}\left[\frac{-h}{x(x+h)}\right]$$

$$= \lim_{h \to 0} \frac{-1}{x(x+h)} = \frac{-1}{x^2} = -1x^{-2}.$$

$$\frac{d(x^{-3})}{dx} = \lim_{h \to 0} \frac{(x+h)^{-3} - x^{-3}}{h}$$

$$= \lim_{h \to 0} \frac{1}{h}\left[\frac{1}{(x+h)^3} - \frac{1}{x^3}\right]$$

$$= \lim_{h \to 0} \frac{1}{h} \left[\frac{x^3 - (x+h)^3}{x^3(x+h)^3} \right]$$

$$= \lim_{h \to 0} \frac{1}{h} \left[\frac{x^3 - (x^3 + 3hx^2 + 3h^2x + h^3)}{x^3(x+h)^3} \right]$$

$$= \lim_{h \to 0} \frac{1}{h} \left[\frac{-3hx^2 - 3xh^2 - h^3}{x^3(x+h)^3} \right]$$

$$= \lim_{h \to 0} \frac{-3x^2 - 3xh - h^2}{x^3(x+h)^3}$$

$$= \frac{-3x^2}{x^6} = -3x^{-4}.$$

(b) For clarity, let $n = -k$, where k is a positive integer. So $x^n = x^{-k}$.

$$\frac{d(x^{-k})}{dx} = \lim_{h \to 0} \frac{(x+h)^{-k} - x^{-k}}{h}$$

$$= \lim_{h \to 0} \frac{1}{h} \left[\frac{1}{(x+h)^k} - \frac{1}{x^k} \right]$$

$$= \lim_{h \to 0} \frac{1}{h} \left[\frac{x^k - (x+h)^k}{x^k(x+h)^k} \right]$$

terms involving h^2 and higher powers of h

$$= \lim_{h \to 0} \frac{1}{h} \left[\frac{x^k - x^k - khx^{k-1} - \overbrace{\ldots - h^k}}{x^k(x+h)^k} \right]$$

$$= \frac{-kx^{k-1}}{x^k(x)^k} = \frac{-k}{x^{k+1}} = -kx^{-(k+1)} = -kx^{-k-1}.$$

Solutions for Section 3.2

Exercises

1. $f'(x) = 2e^x + 2x.$

2. $y' = 10t + 4e^t.$

3. $y' = (\ln 5)5^x.$

4. $f'(x) = 12e^x + (\ln 11)11^x.$

5. $y' = 10x + (\ln 2)2^x.$

6. $f'(x) = (\ln 2)2^x + 2(\ln 3)3^x.$

7. $\dfrac{dy}{dx} = 4(\ln 10)10^x - 3x^2.$

8. $\dfrac{dy}{dx} = 3 - 2(\ln 4)4^x.$

9. Since $y = 2^x + \dfrac{2}{x^3} = 2^x + 2x^{-3}$, we have $\dfrac{dy}{dx} = (\ln 2)2^x - 6x^{-4}.$

10. $\dfrac{dy}{dx} = \dfrac{1}{3}(\ln 3)3^x - \dfrac{33}{2}(x^{-\frac{3}{2}}).$

11. $z' = (\ln 4)e^x.$

12. $z' = (\ln 4)^2 4^x.$

13. $f'(t) = (\ln(\ln 3))(\ln 3)^t.$

14. $\dfrac{dy}{dx} = 5 \cdot 5^t \ln 5 + 6 \cdot 6^t \ln 6$

15. $h'(z) = (\ln(\ln 2))(\ln 2)^z.$

16. $f'(x) = ex^{e-1}.$

17. $f'(x) = 3x^2 + 3^x \ln 3$

18. $\dfrac{dy}{dx} = \pi^x \ln \pi$

19. $f'(x) = (\ln \pi)\pi^x$.

20. This is the sum of an exponential function and a power function, so $f'(x) = \ln(\pi)\pi^x + \pi x^{\pi-1}$.

21. Since e and k are constants, e^k is constant, so we have $f'(x) = (\ln k)k^x$.

22. $f(x) = e^{1+x} = e^1 \cdot e^x$. Then, since e^1 is just a constant,
$f'(x) = e \cdot e^x = e^{1+x}$.

23. $f(t) = e^t \cdot e^2$. Then, since e^2 is just a constant, $f'(t) = \frac{d}{dt}(e^t e^2) = e^2 \frac{d}{dt} e^t = e^2 e^t = e^{t+2}$.

24. $y = e^\theta e^{-1}$ $y' = \dfrac{d}{d\theta}(e^\theta e^{-1}) = e^{-1}\dfrac{d}{d\theta}e^\theta = e^\theta e^{-1} = e^{\theta-1}$.

25. $y'(x) = a^x \ln a + ax^{a-1}$.

26. $f'(x) = \pi^2 x^{(\pi^2-1)} + (\pi^2)^x \ln(\pi^2)$

27. $y' = 2x + (\ln 2)2^x$.

28. $y' = \frac{1}{2}x^{-\frac{1}{2}} - \ln\frac{1}{2}(\frac{1}{2})^x = \frac{1}{2\sqrt{x}} + \ln 2(\frac{1}{2})^x$.

29. We can take the derivative of the sum $x^2 + 2^x$, but not the product.

30. Once again, this is a product of two functions, 2^x and $\frac{1}{x}$, each of which we can take the derivative of; but we don't know how to take the derivative of the product.

31. Since $y = e^5 e^x$, $y' = e^5 e^x = e^{x+5}$.

32. $y = e^{5x} = (e^5)^x$, so $y' = \ln(e^5) \cdot (e^5)^x = 5e^{5x}$.

33. The exponent is x^2, and we haven't learned what to do about that yet.

34. $f'(z) = (\ln \sqrt{4})(\sqrt{4})^z = (\ln 2)2^z$.

35. We can't use our rules if the exponent is $\sqrt{\theta}$.

Problems

36. Since $P = 1 \cdot (1.05)^t$, $\frac{dP}{dt} = \ln(1.05)1.05^t$. When $t = 10$,

$$\frac{dP}{dt} = (\ln 1.05)(1.05)^{10} \approx \$0.07947/\text{year} \approx 7.95\cent/\text{year}.$$

37.
$$\frac{dP}{dt} = 35{,}000 \cdot (\ln 0.98)(0.98^t).$$

At $t = 23$, this is $35{,}000(\ln 0.98)(0.98^{23}) \approx -444.3$ people/year. (Note: the negative sign indicates that the population is decreasing.)

38. We have $f(t) = 5.3(1.018)^t$ so $f'(t) = 5.3(\ln 1.018)(1.018)^t = 0.095(1.018)^t$. Therefore

$$f(0) = 5.3 \text{ billion people}$$

and

$$f'(0) = 0.095 \text{ billion people per year}.$$

In 1990, the population of the world was 5.3 billion people and was increasing at a rate of 0.095 billion people per year.
We also have
$$f(30) = 5.3(1.018)^{30} = 9.1 \text{ billion people},$$

and
$$f'(30) = 0.095(1.018)^{30} = 0.16 \text{ billion people per year.}$$

In the year 2020, this model predicts that the population of the world will be 9.1 billion people and will be increasing at a rate of 0.16 billion people per year.

39. $\dfrac{dV}{dt} = 75(1.35)^t \ln 1.35 \approx 22.5(1.35)^t$.

40. (a) $V(4) = 25(0.85)^4 = 25(0.522) = 13{,}050$. Thus the value of the car after 4 years is \$13,050.

(b) We have a function of the form $f(t) = Ca^t$. We know that such functions have a derivative of the form $(C \ln a) \cdot a^t$. Thus, $V'(t) = 25(0.85)^t \cdot \ln 0.85 = -4.063(0.85)^t$. The units would be the change in value (in thousands of dollars) with respect to time (in years), or thousands of dollars/year.

(c) $V'(4) = -4.063(0.85)^4 = -4.063(0.522) = -2.121$. This means that at the end of the fourth year, the value of the car is decreasing by \$2121 per year.

(d) $V(t)$ is a positive decreasing function, so that the value of the automobile is positive and decreasing. $V'(t)$ is a negative function whose magnitude is decreasing, meaning the value of the automobile is always dropping, but the yearly loss of value is less as time goes on. The graphs of $V(t)$ and $V'(t)$ confirm that the value of the car decreases with time. What they do not take into account are the *costs* associated with owning the vehicle. At some time, t, it is likely that the yearly costs of owning the vehicle will outweigh its value. At that time, it may no longer be worthwhile to keep the car.

41. (a) $f(x) = 1 - e^x$ crosses the x-axis where $0 = 1 - e^x$, which happens when $e^x = 1$, so $x = 0$. Since $f'(x) = -e^x$, $f'(0) = -e^0 = -1$.

(b) $y = -x$

(c) The negative of the reciprocal of -1 is 1, so the equation of the normal line is $y = x$.

42. Since $y = 2^x$, $y' = (\ln 2)2^x$. At $(0, 1)$, the tangent line has slope $\ln 2$ so its equation is $y = (\ln 2)x + 1$. At c, $y = 0$, so $0 = (\ln 2)c + 1$, thus $c = -\frac{1}{\ln 2}$.

43.

$$g(x) = ax^2 + bx + c \qquad\qquad f(x) = e^x$$
$$g'(x) = 2ax + b \qquad\qquad\quad f'(x) = e^x$$
$$g''(x) = 2a \qquad\qquad\qquad\quad f''(x) = e^x$$

So, using $g''(0) = f''(0)$, etc., we have $2a = 1$, $b = 1$, and $c = 1$, and thus $g(x) = \frac{1}{2}x^2 + x + 1$, as shown in Figure 3.5.

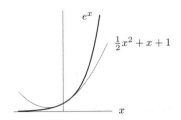

Figure 3.5

The two functions do look very much alike near $x = 0$. They both increase for large values of x, but e^x increases much more quickly. For very negative values of x, the quadratic goes to ∞ whereas the exponential goes to 0. By choosing a function whose first few derivatives agreed with the exponential when $x = 0$, we got a function which looks like the exponential for x-values near 0.

44. The first and second derivatives of e^x are e^x. Thus, the graph of $y = e^x$ is concave up. The tangent line at $x = 0$ has slope $e^0 = 1$ and equation $y = x + 1$. A graph that is always concave up is always above any of its tangent lines. Thus $e^x \geq x + 1$ for all x, as shown in the following figure.

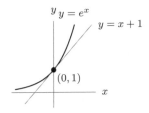

45. The equation $2^x = 2x$ has solutions $x = 1$ and $x = 2$. (Check this by substituting these values into the equation). The graph below suggests that these are the only solutions, but how can we be sure?

Let's look at the slope of the curve $f(x) = 2^x$, which is $f'(x) = (\ln 2)2^x \approx (0.693)2^x$, and the slope of the line $g(x) = 2x$ which is 2. At $x = 1$, the slope of $f(x)$ is less than 2; at $x = 2$, the slope of $f(x)$ is more than 2. Since the slope of $f(x)$ is always increasing, there can be no other point of intersection. (If there were another point of intersection, the graph f would have to "turn around".)

Here's another way of seeing this. Suppose $g(x)$ represents the position of a car going a steady 2 mph, while $f(x)$ represents a car which starts ahead of g (because the graph of f is above g) and is initially going slower than g. The car f is first overtaken by g. All the while, however, f is speeding up until eventually it overtakes g again. Notice that the two cars will only meet twice (corresponding to the two intersections of the curve): once when g overtakes f and once when f overtakes g.

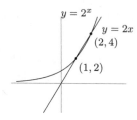

46. For $x = 0$, we have $y = a^0 = 1$ and $y = 1 + 0 = 1$, so both curves go through the point $(0, 1)$ for all values of a. Differentiating gives

$$\left.\frac{d(a^x)}{dx}\right|_{x=0} = a^x \ln a\big|_{x=0} = a^0 \ln a = \ln a$$

$$\left.\frac{d(1 + x)}{dx}\right|_{x=0} = 1.$$

The graphs are tangent at $x = 0$ if

$$\ln a = 1 \qquad \text{so} \qquad a = e.$$

Solutions for Section 3.3

Exercises

1. By the product rule, $f'(x) = 2x(x^3 + 5) + x^2(3x^2) = 2x^4 + 3x^4 + 10x = 5x^4 + 10x$. Alternatively, $f'(x) = (x^5 + 5x^2)' = 5x^4 + 10x$. The two answers should, and do, match.

2. Using the product rule,

$$f'(x) = (\ln 2)2^x 3^x + (\ln 3)2^x 3^x = (\ln 2 + \ln 3)(2^x \cdot 3^x) = \ln(2 \cdot 3)(2 \cdot 3)^x = (\ln 6)6^x$$

or, since $2^x \cdot 3^x = (2 \cdot 3)^x = 6^x$,

$$f'(x) = (6^x)' = (\ln 6)(6^x).$$

The two answers should, and do, match.

3. $f'(x) = x \cdot e^x + e^x \cdot 1 = e^x(x + 1)$.

4. $y' = 2^x + x(\ln 2)2^x = 2^x(1 + x \ln 2)$.

5. $y' = \frac{1}{2\sqrt{x}}2^x + \sqrt{x}(\ln 2)2^x$.

6. $\frac{dy}{dt} = 2te^t + (t^2 + 3)e^t = e^t(t^2 + 2t + 3)$.

7. $f'(x) = (x^2 - x^{\frac{1}{2}}) \cdot 3^x(\ln 3) + 3^x\left(2x - \frac{1}{2}x^{-\frac{1}{2}}\right) = 3^x\left[(\ln 3)(x^2 - x^{\frac{1}{2}}) + \left(2x - \frac{1}{2\sqrt{x}}\right)\right].$

8. It is easier to do this by multiplying it out first, rather than using the product rule first: $z = s^4 - s$, $\quad z' = 4s^3 - 1$.

9. $f'(y) = (\ln 4)4^y(2 - y^2) + 4^y(-2y) = 4^y((\ln 4)(2 - y^2) - 2y)$.

10. $y' = (3t^2 - 14t)e^t + (t^3 - 7t^2 + 1)e^t = (t^3 - 4t^2 - 14t + 1)e^t$.

11. $f'(x) = \dfrac{e^x \cdot 1 - x \cdot e^x}{(e^x)^2} = \dfrac{e^x(1 - x)}{(e^x)^2} = \dfrac{1 - x}{e^x}$.

12. $g'(x) = \dfrac{50xe^x - 25x^2e^x}{e^{2x}} = \dfrac{50x - 25x^2}{e^x}$.

13. $\dfrac{dy}{dx} = \dfrac{1 \cdot 2^t - (t + 1)(\ln 2)2^t}{(2^t)^2} = \dfrac{2^t(1 - (t + 1)\ln 2)}{(2^t)^2} = \dfrac{1 - (t + 1)\ln 2}{2^t}$.

14. $g'(w) = \dfrac{3.2w^{2.2}(5^w) - (\ln 5)(w^{3.2})5^w}{5^{2w}} = \dfrac{3.2w^{2.2} - w^{3.2}(\ln 5)}{5^w}$.

15. $q'(r) = \dfrac{3(5r + 2) - 3r(5)}{(5r + 2)^2} = \dfrac{15r + 6 - 15r}{(5r + 2)^2} = \dfrac{6}{(5r + 2)^2}$.

16. $g'(t) = \dfrac{(t + 4) - (t - 4)}{(t + 4)^2} = \dfrac{8}{(t + 4)^2}$.

17. $\dfrac{dz}{dt} = \dfrac{3(5t + 2) - (3t + 1)5}{(5t + 2)^2} = \dfrac{15t + 6 - 15t - 5}{(5t + 2)^2} = \dfrac{1}{(5t + 2)^2}$.

18. $z' = \dfrac{(2t + 5)(t + 3) - (t^2 + 5t + 2)}{(t + 3)^2} = \dfrac{t^2 + 6t + 13}{(t + 3)^2}$.

19. Using the quotient rule gives $\dfrac{dz}{dt} = \dfrac{(2t + 3)(t + 1) - (t^2 + 3t + 1)}{(t + 1)^2}$ $\quad$ or $\quad$ $\dfrac{dz}{dt} = \dfrac{t^2 + 2t + 2}{(t + 1)^2}$.

20. Divide and then differentiate

$$f(x) = x + \frac{3}{x}$$

$$f'(x) = 1 - \frac{3}{x^2}.$$

21. $w = y^2 - 6y + 7$. $\quad w' = 2y - 6, y \neq 0$.

22. $y' = \dfrac{\frac{1}{2\sqrt{t}}(t^2 + 1) - \sqrt{t}(2t)}{(t^2 + 1)^2}$.

23. $\dfrac{d}{dz}\left(\dfrac{z^2 + 1}{\sqrt{z}}\right) = \dfrac{d}{dz}(z^{\frac{3}{2}} + z^{-\frac{1}{2}}) = \dfrac{3}{2}z^{\frac{1}{2}} - \dfrac{1}{2}z^{-\frac{3}{2}} = \dfrac{\sqrt{z}}{2}(3 - z^{-2})$.

24. $g'(t) = -4(3 + \sqrt{t})^{-2}\left(\dfrac{1}{2}t^{-1/2}\right) = \dfrac{-2}{\sqrt{t}(3 + \sqrt{t})^2}$

25. $h'(r) = \dfrac{d}{dr}\left(\dfrac{r^2}{2r + 1}\right) = \dfrac{(2r)(2r + 1) - 2r^2}{(2r + 1)^2} = \dfrac{2r(r + 1)}{(2r + 1)^2}$.

26. Notice that you can cancel a z out of the numerator and denominator to get

$$f(z) = \frac{3z}{5z + 7}, \qquad z \neq 0$$

Then

$$f'(z) = \frac{(5z + 7)3 - 3z(5)}{(5z + 7)^2}$$

$$= \frac{15z + 21 - 15z}{(5z + 7)^2}$$

$$= \frac{21}{(5z + 7)^2}, z \neq 0.$$

[If you used the quotient rule correctly without canceling the z out first, your answer should simplify to this one, but it is usually a good idea to simplify as much as possible before differentiating.]

27. $w'(x) = \dfrac{17e^x(2^x) - (\ln 2)(17e^x)2^x}{2^{2x}} = \dfrac{17e^x(2^x)(1 - \ln 2)}{2^{2x}} = \dfrac{17e^x(1 - \ln 2)}{2^x}$.

28. $h'(p) = \dfrac{2p(3 + 2p^2) - 4p(1 + p^2)}{(3 + 2p^2)^2} = \dfrac{6p + 4p^3 - 4p - 4p^3}{(3 + 2p^2)^2} = \dfrac{2p}{(3 + 2p^2)^2}.$

29.

$$
\begin{aligned}
f'(x) &= \frac{(2 + 3x + 4x^2)(1) - (1 + x)(3 + 8x)}{(2 + 3x + 4x^2)^2} \\
&= \frac{2 + 3x + 4x^2 - 3 - 11x - 8x^2}{(2 + 3x + 4x^2)^2} \\
&= \frac{-4x^2 - 8x - 1}{(2 + 3x + 4x^2)^2}.
\end{aligned}
$$

30. We use the quotient rule. We have

$$
f'(x) = \frac{(cx + k)(a) - (ax + b)(c)}{(cx + k)^2} = \frac{acx + ak - acx - bc}{(cx + k)^2} = \frac{ak - bc}{(cx + k)^2}.
$$

Problems

31. Using the product rule, we know that $h'(x) = f'(x) \cdot g(x) + f(x) \cdot g'(x)$. We use slope to compute the derivatives. Since $f(x)$ is linear on the interval $0 < x < 2$, we compute the slope of the line to see that $f'(x) = 2$ on this interval. Similarly, we compute the slope on the interval $2 < x < 4$ to see that $f'(x) = -2$ on the interval $2 < x < 4$. Since $f(x)$ has a corner at $x = 2$, we know that $f'(2)$ does not exist.

Similarly, $g(x)$ is linear on the interval shown, and we see that the slope of $g(x)$ on this interval is -1 so we have $g'(x) = -1$ on this interval.

(a) We have $h'(1) = f'(1) \cdot g(1) + f(1) \cdot g'(1) = 2 \cdot 3 + 2(-1) = 6 - 2 = 4$.

(b) We have $h'(2) = f'(2) \cdot g(2) + f(2) \cdot g'(2)$. Since $f(x)$ has a corner at $x = 2$, we know that $f'(2)$ does not exist. Therefore, $h'(2)$ does not exist.

(c) We have $h'(3) = f'(3) \cdot g(3) + f(3) \cdot g'(3) = (-2)1 + 2(-1) = -2 - 2 = -4$.

32. Using the quotient rule, we know that $k'(x) = (f'(x) \cdot g(x) - f(x) \cdot g'(x))/(g(x))^2$. We use slope to compute the derivatives. Since $f(x)$ is linear on the interval $0 < x < 2$, we compute the slope of the line to see that $f'(x) = 2$ on this interval. Similarly, we compute the slope on the interval $2 < x < 4$ to see that $f'(x) = -2$ on the interval $2 < x < 4$. Since $f(x)$ has a corner at $x = 2$, we know that $f'(2)$ does not exist.

Similarly, $g(x)$ is linear on the interval shown, and we see that the slope of $g(x)$ on this interval is -1 so we have $g'(x) = -1$ on this interval.

(a) We have

$$
k'(1) = \frac{f'(1) \cdot g(1) - f(1) \cdot g'(1)}{(g(1))^2} = \frac{2 \cdot 3 - 2(-1)}{3^2} = \frac{6 + 2}{9} = \frac{8}{9}.
$$

(b) We have $k'(2) = (f'(2) \cdot g(2) - f(2) \cdot g'(2))/(g(2)^2)$. Since $f(x)$ has a corner at $x = 2$, we know that $f'(2)$ does not exist. Therefore, $k'(2)$ does not exist.

(c) We have

$$
k'(3) = \frac{f'(3) \cdot g(3) - f(3) \cdot g'(3)}{(g(3))^2} = \frac{(-2)1 - 2(-1)}{1^2} = \frac{-2 + 2}{1} = 0.
$$

33. Using the quotient rule, we know that $j'(x) = (g'(x) \cdot f(x) - g(x) \cdot f'(x))/(f(x))^2$. We use slope to compute the derivatives. Since $f(x)$ is linear on the interval $0 < x < 2$, we compute the slope of the line to see that $f'(x) = 2$ on this interval. Similarly, we compute the slope on the interval $2 < x < 4$ to see that $f'(x) = -2$ on the interval $2 < x < 4$. Since $f(x)$ has a corner at $x = 2$, we know that $f'(2)$ does not exist.

Similarly, $g(x)$ is linear on the interval shown, and we see that the slope of $g(x)$ on this interval is -1 so we have $g'(x) = -1$ on this interval.

(a) We have

$$
j'(1) = \frac{g'(1) \cdot f(1) - g(1) \cdot f'(1)}{(f(1))^2} = \frac{(-1)2 - 3 \cdot 2}{2^2} = \frac{-2 - 6}{4} = \frac{-8}{4} = -2.
$$

(b) We have $j'(2) = (g'(2) \cdot f(2) - g(2) \cdot f'(2))/(f(2)^2)$. Since $f(x)$ has a corner at $x = 2$, we know that $f'(2)$ does not exist. Therefore, $j'(2)$ does not exist.

(c) We have

$$
j'(3) = \frac{g'(3) \cdot f(3) - g(3) \cdot f'(3)}{(f(3))^2} = \frac{(-1)2 - 1(-2)}{2^2} = \frac{-2 + 2}{4} = 0.
$$

34. From the graphs, we estimate $f(1) \approx -0.4$, $f'(1) \approx 0.5$, $g(1) \approx 2$, and $g'(1) \approx 1$. By the product rule,

$$h'(1) = f'(1) \cdot g(1) + f(1) \cdot g'(1) \approx (0.5)2 + (-0.4)1 = 0.6.$$

35. From the graphs, we estimate $f(1) \approx -0.4$, $f'(1) \approx 0.5$, $g(1) \approx 2$, and $g'(1) \approx 1$. By the quotient rule,

$$k'(1) = \frac{f'(1) \cdot g(1) - f(1) \cdot g'(1)}{(g(1))^2} \approx \frac{(0.5)2 - (-0.4)1}{2^2} = 0.35.$$

36. From the graphs, we estimate $f(2) \approx 0.3$, $f'(2) \approx 1.1$, $g(2) \approx 1.6$, and $g'(2) \approx -0.5$. By the product rule,

$$h'(2) = f'(2) \cdot g(2) + f(2) \cdot g'(2) \approx 1.1(1.6) + 0.3(-0.5) = 1.61.$$

37. From the graphs, we estimate $f(2) \approx 0.3$, $f'(2) \approx 1.1$, $g(2) \approx 1.6$, and $g'(2) \approx -0.5$. By the quotient rule,

$$k'(2) = \frac{f'(2) \cdot g(2) - f(2) \cdot g'(2)}{(g(2))^2} \approx \frac{1.1(1.6) - 0.3(-0.5)}{(1.6)^2} = 0.75.$$

38. From the graphs, we estimate $f(1) \approx -0.4$, $f'(1) \approx 0.5$, $g(1) \approx 2$, and $g'(1) \approx 1$. By the quotient rule,

$$l'(1) = \frac{g'(1) \cdot f(1) - g(1) \cdot f'(1)}{(f(1))^2} \approx \frac{1(-0.4) - 2(0.5)}{(-0.4)^2} = -8.75.$$

39. From the graphs, we estimate $f(2) \approx 0.3$, $f'(2) \approx 1.1$, $g(2) \approx 1.6$, and $g'(2) \approx -0.5$. By the quotient rule,

$$l'(2) = \frac{g'(2) \cdot f(2) - g(2) \cdot f'(2)}{(f(2))^2} \approx \frac{(-0.5)0.3 - 1.6(1.1)}{(0.3)^2} = -21.22.$$

40.

$$f'(x) = 3(2x - 5) + 2(3x + 8) = 12x + 1$$
$$f''(x) = 12.$$

41.

$$f(t) = \frac{1}{e^t}$$
$$f'(t) = \frac{e^t \cdot 0 - e^t \cdot 1}{(e^t)^2}$$
$$= \frac{-1}{e^t} = -e^{-t}.$$

42. $f(x) = e^x \cdot e^x$
$f'(x) = e^x \cdot e^x + e^x \cdot e^x = 2e^{2x}.$

43.

$$f(x) = e^x e^{2x}$$
$$f'(x) = e^x (e^{2x})' + (e^x)' e^{2x}$$
$$= 2e^x e^{2x} + e^x e^{2x} \text{ (from Problem 42)}$$
$$= 3e^{3x}.$$

44. We have

$$f'(x) = e^x + xe^x$$
$$f''(x) = e^x + e^x + xe^x = (2 + x)e^x.$$

Since $f(x)$ is concave up when $f''(x) > 0$, we see that $f(x)$ is concave up when $x > -2$.

45. Using the quotient rule, we have

$$g'(x) = \frac{0 - 1(2x)}{(x^2 + 1)^2} = \frac{-2x}{(x^2 + 1)^2}$$

$$g''(x) = \frac{-2(x^2 + 1)^2 + 2x(4x^3 + 4x)}{(x^2 + 1)^4}$$

$$= \frac{-2(x^2 + 1)^2 + 8x^2(x^2 + 1)}{(x^2 + 1)^4}$$

$$= \frac{-2(x^2 + 1) + 8x^2}{(x^2 + 1)^3}$$

$$= \frac{2(3x^2 - 1)}{(x^2 + 1)^3}.$$

Since $(x^2 + 1)^3 > 0$ for all x, we have $g''(x) < 0$ if $(3x^2 - 1) < 0$, or when

$$3x^2 < 1$$

$$-\frac{1}{\sqrt{3}} < x < \frac{1}{\sqrt{3}}.$$

46. Since $f(0) = -5/1 = -5$, the tangent line passes through the point $(0, -5)$, so its vertical intercept is -5. To find the slope of the tangent line, we find the derivative of $f(x)$ using the quotient rule:

$$f'(x) = \frac{(x + 1) \cdot 2 - (2x - 5) \cdot 1}{(x + 1)^2} = \frac{7}{(x + 1)^2}.$$

At $x = 0$, the slope of the tangent line is $m = f'(0) = 7$. The equation of the tangent line is $y = 7x - 5$.

47. (a) Although the answer you would get by using the quotient rule is equivalent, the answer looks simpler in this case if you just use the product rule:

$$\frac{d}{dx}\left(\frac{e^x}{x}\right) = \frac{d}{dx}\left(e^x \cdot \frac{1}{x}\right) = \frac{e^x}{x} - \frac{e^x}{x^2}$$

$$\frac{d}{dx}\left(\frac{e^x}{x^2}\right) = \frac{d}{dx}\left(e^x \cdot \frac{1}{x^2}\right) = \frac{e^x}{x^2} - \frac{2e^x}{x^3}$$

$$\frac{d}{dx}\left(\frac{e^x}{x^3}\right) = \frac{d}{dx}\left(e^x \cdot \frac{1}{x^3}\right) = \frac{e^x}{x^3} - \frac{3e^x}{x^4}.$$

(b) $\dfrac{d}{dx}\dfrac{e^x}{x^n} = \dfrac{e^x}{x^n} - \dfrac{ne^x}{x^{n+1}}.$

48.

$$\frac{d(x^2)}{dx} = \frac{d}{dx}(x \cdot x) \qquad\qquad \frac{d(x^3)}{dx} = \frac{d}{dx}(x^2 \cdot x)$$

$$= x\frac{d(x)}{dx} + x\frac{d(x)}{dx} \qquad\qquad = x^2\frac{d(x)}{dx} + x\frac{d(x^2)}{dx}$$

$$= 2x. \qquad\qquad\qquad = x^2\frac{d(x)}{dx} + x\left[x\frac{d(x)}{dx} + x\frac{d(x)}{dx}\right]$$

$$\qquad\qquad\qquad = x^2\frac{d(x)}{dx} + x^2\frac{d(x)}{dx} + x^2\frac{d(x)}{dx}$$

$$\qquad\qquad\qquad = 3x^2.$$

49. Since

$$x^{1/2} \cdot x^{1/2} = x,$$

we differentiate to obtain

$$\frac{d}{dx}(x^{1/2}) \cdot x^{1/2} + x^{1/2} \cdot \frac{d}{dx}(x^{1/2}) = 1.$$

Now solve for $d(x^{1/2})/dx$:

$$2x^{1/2}\frac{d}{dx}(x^{1/2}) = 1$$

$$\frac{d}{dx}(x^{1/2}) = \frac{1}{2x^{1/2}}.$$

50. (a) We have $h'(2) = f'(2) + g'(2) = 5 - 2 = 3$.
   (b) We have $h'(2) = f'(2)g(2) + f(2)g'(2) = 5(4) + 3(-2) = 14$.
   (c) We have $h'(2) = \dfrac{f'(2)g(2) - f(2)g'(2)}{(g(2))^2} = \dfrac{5(4) - 3(-2)}{4^2} = \dfrac{26}{16} = \dfrac{13}{8}$.

51. (a) $G'(z) = F'(z)H(z) + H'(z)F(z)$, so
   $G'(3) = F'(3)H(3) + H'(3)F(3) = 4 \cdot 1 + 3 \cdot 5 = 19$.
   (b) $G'(w) = \dfrac{F'(w)H(w) - H'(w)F(w)}{[H(w)]^2}$, so $G'(3) = \dfrac{4(1) - 3(5)}{1^2} = -11$.

52. $f'(x) = 10x^9 e^x + x^{10}e^x$ is of the form $g'h + h'g$, where

$$g(x) = x^{10},\ g'(x) = 10x^9$$

and

$$h(x) = e^x,\ h'(x) = e^x.$$

Therefore, using the product rule, let $f = g \cdot h$, with $g(x) = x^{10}$ and $h(x) = e^x$. Thus

$$f(x) = x^{10}e^x.$$

53. (a) $f(140) = 15{,}000$ says that 15,000 skateboards are sold when the cost is \$140 per board.
   $f'(140) = -100$ means that if the price is increased from \$140, roughly speaking, every dollar of increase will decrease the total sales by 100 boards.
   (b) $\dfrac{dR}{dp} = \dfrac{d}{dp}(p \cdot q) = \dfrac{d}{dp}(p \cdot f(p)) = f(p) + pf'(p)$.
   So,

$$\left.\frac{dR}{dp}\right|_{p=140} = f(140) + 140f'(140)$$

$$= 15{,}000 + 140(-100) = 1000.$$

   (c) From (b) we see that $\left.\dfrac{dR}{dp}\right|_{p=140} = 1000 > 0$. This means that the revenue will increase by about \$1000 if the price is raised by \$1.

54. We want dR/dr_1. Solving for R:

$$\frac{1}{R} = \frac{1}{r_1} + \frac{1}{r_2} = \frac{r_2 + r_1}{r_1 r_2},\ \text{which gives }R = \frac{r_1 r_2}{r_2 + r_1}.$$

So, thinking of r_2 as a constant and using the quotient rule,

$$\frac{dR}{dr_1} = \frac{r_2(r_2 + r_1) - r_1 r_2(1)}{(r_2 + r_1)^2} = \frac{r_2^2}{(r_1 + r_2)^2}.$$

55. (a) If the museum sells the painting and invests the proceeds $P(t)$ at time t, then t years have elapsed since 2000, and the time span up to 2020 is $20 - t$. This is how long the proceeds $P(t)$ are earning interest in the bank. Each year the money is in the bank it earns 5% interest, which means the amount in the bank is multiplied by a factor of 1.05. So, at the end of $(20 - t)$ years, the balance is given by

$$B(t) = P(t)(1 + 0.05)^{20-t} = P(t)(1.05)^{20-t}.$$

(b)

$$B(t) = P(t)(1.05)^{20}(1.05)^{-t} = (1.05)^{20}\frac{P(t)}{(1.05)^t}.$$

(c) By the quotient rule,

$$B'(t) = (1.05)^{20}\left[\frac{P'(t)(1.05)^t - P(t)(1.05)^t \ln 1.05}{(1.05)^{2t}}\right].$$

So,

$$B'(10) = (1.05)^{20}\left[\frac{5000(1.05)^{10} - 150{,}000(1.05)^{10}\ln 1.05}{(1.05)^{20}}\right]$$

$$= (1.05)^{10}(5000 - 150{,}000\ln 1.05)$$

$$\approx -3776.63.$$

56. Note first that $f(v)$ is in $\frac{\text{liters}}{\text{km}}$, and v is in $\frac{\text{km}}{\text{hour}}$.

(a) $g(v) = \frac{1}{f(v)}$. (This is in $\frac{\text{km}}{\text{liter}}$.) Differentiating gives

$$g'(v) = \frac{-f'(v)}{(f(v))^2}.$$

So,

$$g(80) = \frac{1}{0.05} = 20\frac{\text{km}}{\text{liter}}.$$

$$g'(80) = \frac{-0.0005}{(0.05)^2} = -\frac{1}{5}\frac{\text{km}}{\text{liter}} \text{ for each } 1\frac{\text{km}}{\text{hr}} \text{ increase in speed.}$$

(b) $h(v) = v \cdot f(v)$. (This is in $\frac{\text{km}}{\text{hour}} \cdot \frac{\text{liters}}{\text{km}} = \frac{\text{liters}}{\text{hour}}$.) Differentiating gives

$$h'(v) = f(v) + v \cdot f'(v),$$

so

$$h(80) = 80(0.05) = 4\frac{\text{liters}}{\text{hr}}.$$

$$h'(80) = 0.05 + 80(0.0005) = 0.09\frac{\text{liters}}{\text{hr}} \text{ for each } 1\frac{\text{km}}{\text{hr}} \text{ increase in speed.}$$

(c) Part (a) tells us that at 80 km/hr, the car can go 20 km on 1 liter. Since the first derivative evaluated at this velocity is negative, this implies that as velocity increases, fuel efficiency decreases, i.e., at higher velocities the car will not go as far on 1 liter of gas. Part (b) tells us that at 80 km/hr, the car uses 4 liters in an hour. Since the first derivative evaluated at this velocity is positive, this means that at higher velocities, the car will use more gas per hour.

57. Assume for $g(x) \neq f(x)$, $g'(x) = g(x)$ and $g(0) = 1$. Then for

$$h(x) = \frac{g(x)}{e^x}$$

$$h'(x) = \frac{g'(x)e^x - g(x)e^x}{(e^x)^2} = \frac{e^x(g'(x) - g(x))}{(e^x)^2} = \frac{g'(x) - g(x)}{e^x}.$$

But, since $g(x) = g'(x)$, $h'(x) = 0$, so $h(x)$ is constant. Thus, the ratio of $g(x)$ to e^x is constant. Since $\frac{g(0)}{e^0} = \frac{1}{1} = 1$, $\frac{g(x)}{e^x}$ must equal 1 for all x. Thus $g(x) = e^x = f(x)$ for all x, so f and g are the same function.

58. (a) $f'(x) = (x - 2) + (x - 1)$.

(b) Think of f as the product of two factors, with the first as $(x - 1)(x - 2)$. (The reason for this is that we have already differentiated $(x - 1)(x - 2)$).

$$f(x) = [(x - 1)(x - 2)](x - 3).$$

Now $f'(x) = [(x - 1)(x - 2)]'(x - 3) + [(x - 1)(x - 2)](x - 3)'$
Using the result of a):

$$f'(x) = [(x - 2) + (x - 1)](x - 3) + [(x - 1)(x - 2)] \cdot 1$$

$$= (x - 2)(x - 3) + (x - 1)(x - 3) + (x - 1)(x - 2).$$

(c) Because we have already differentiated $(x-1)(x-2)(x-3)$, rewrite f as the product of two factors, the first being $(x-1)(x-2)(x-3)$:

$$f(x) = [(x-1)(x-2)(x-3)](x-4)$$

Now $f'(x) = [(x-1)(x-2)(x-3)]'(x-4) + [(x-1)(x-2)(x-3)](x-4)'$.

$$f'(x) = [(x-2)(x-3) + (x-1)(x-3) + (x-1)(x-2)](x-4)$$
$$+ [(x-1)(x-2)(x-3)] \cdot 1$$
$$= (x-2)(x-3)(x-4) + (x-1)(x-3)(x-4)$$
$$+ (x-1)(x-2)(x-4) + (x-1)(x-2)(x-3).$$

From the solutions above, we can observe that when f is a product, its derivative is obtained by differentiating each factor in turn (leaving the other factors alone), and adding the results.

59. From the answer to Problem 58, we find that

$$f'(x) = (x-r_1)(x-r_2)\cdots(x-r_{n-1}) \cdot 1$$
$$+ (x-r_1)(x-r_2)\cdots(x-r_{n-2}) \cdot 1 \cdot (x-r_n)$$
$$+ (x-r_1)(x-r_2)\cdots(x-r_{n-3}) \cdot 1 \cdot (x-r_{n-1})(x-r_n)$$
$$+ \cdots + 1 \cdot (x-r_2)(x-r_3)\cdots(x-r_n)$$
$$= f(x)\left(\frac{1}{x-r_1} + \frac{1}{x-r_2} + \cdots + \frac{1}{x-r_n}\right).$$

60. (a) We can approximate $\frac{d}{dx}[F(x)G(x)H(x)]$ using the large rectangular solids by which our original cube is increased:

$$\text{Volume of whole } - \text{ volume of original solid } = \text{ change in volume.}$$

$$F(x+h)G(x+h)H(x+h) - F(x)G(x)H(x) = \text{change in volume.}$$

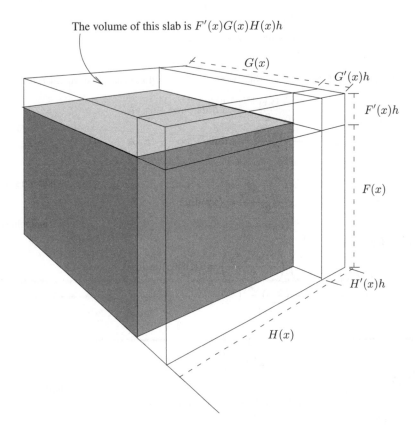

The volume of this slab is $F'(x)G(x)H(x)h$

As in the book, we will ignore the <u>smaller</u> regions which are added (the long, thin rectangular boxes and the small cube in the corner.) This can be justified by recognizing that as $h \to 0$, these volumes will shrink much faster than the volumes of the big slabs and will therefore be insignificant. (Note that these smaller regions have an h^2 or h^3 in the formulas of their volumes.) Then we can approximate the change in volume above by:

$$F(x+h)G(x+h)H(x+h) - F(x)G(x)H(x) \approx F'(x)G(x)H(x)h \quad \text{(top slab)}$$
$$+ F(x)G'(x)H(x)h \quad \text{(front slab)}$$
$$+ F(x)G(x)H'(x)h \quad \text{(other slab)}.$$

Dividing by h gives

$$\frac{F(x+h)G(x+h)H(x+h) - F(x)G(x)H(x)}{h}$$
$$\approx F'(x)G(x)H(x) + F(x)G'(x)H(x) + F(x)G(x)H'(x).$$

Letting $h \to 0$

$$(FGH)' = F'GH + FG'H + FGH'.$$

(b) Verifying,

$$\frac{d}{dx}[(F(x) \cdot G(x)) \cdot H(x)] = (F \cdot G)'(H) + (F \cdot G)(H)'$$
$$= [F'G + FG']H + FGH'$$
$$= F'GH + FG'H + FGH'$$

as before.

(c) From the answer to (b), we observe that the derivative of a product is obtained by differentiating each factor in turn (leaving the other factors alone), and adding the results. So, in general,

$$(f_1 \cdot f_2 \cdot f_3 \cdot \ldots \cdot f_n)' = f_1'f_2f_3 \cdots f_n + f_1f_2'f_3 \cdots f_n + \cdots + f_1 \cdots f_{n-1}f_n'.$$

61. (a) Since $x = a$ is a double zero of a polynomial $P(x)$, we can write $P(x) = (x-a)^2Q(x)$, so $P(a) = 0$. Using the product rule, we have

$$P'(x) = 2(x-a)Q(x) + (x-a)^2Q'(x).$$

Substituting in $x = a$, we see $P'(a) = 0$ also.

(b) Since $P(a) = 0$, we know $x = a$ is a zero of P, so that $x - a$ is a factor of P and we can write

$$P(x) = (x-a)Q(x),$$

where Q is some polynomial. Differentiating this expression for P using the product rule, we get

$$P'(x) = Q(x) + (x-a)Q'(x).$$

Since we are told that $P'(a) = 0$, we have

$$P'(a) = Q(a) + (a-a)Q'(a) = 0$$

and so $Q(a) = 0$. Therefore $x = a$ is a zero of Q, so again we can write

$$Q(x) = (x-a)R(x),$$

where R is some other polynomial. As a result,

$$P(x) = (x-a)Q(x) = (x-a)^2R(x),$$

so that $x = a$ is a double zero of P.

Solutions for Section 3.4

Exercises

1. $f'(x) = 99(x+1)^{98} \cdot 1 = 99(x+1)^{98}$.

2. $w' = 100(t^2+1)^{99}(2t) = 200t(t^2+1)^{99}$.

3. $w' = 100(t^3+1)^{99}(3t^2) = 300t^2(t^3+1)^{99}$.

4. $\frac{d}{dx}\left((4x^2+1)^7\right) = 7(4x^2+1)^6\frac{d}{dx}(4x^2+1) = 7(4x^2+1)^6 \cdot 8x = 56x(4x^2+1)^6$.

5. $f'(x) = \frac{1}{2}(1-x^2)^{-\frac{1}{2}}(-2x) = \dfrac{-x}{\sqrt{1-x^2}}.$

6. $\dfrac{d}{dx}(\sqrt{e^x+1}) = \dfrac{d}{dx}(e^x+1)^{1/2} = \dfrac{1}{2}(e^x+1)^{-1/2}\dfrac{d}{dx}(e^x+1) = \dfrac{e^x}{2\sqrt{e^x+1}}.$

7. $w' = 100(\sqrt{t}+1)^{99}\left(\frac{1}{2\sqrt{t}}\right) = \frac{50}{\sqrt{t}}(\sqrt{t}+1)^{99}.$

8. $h'(w) = 5(w^4-2w)^4(4w^3-2)$

9. We can write $w(r) = (r^4+1)^{1/2}$, so
$$w'(r) = \frac{1}{2}(r^4+1)^{-1/2}(4r^3) = \frac{2r^3}{\sqrt{r^4+1}}.$$

10. $k'(x) = 4(x^3+e^x)^3(3x^2+e^x).$

11. $f'(x) = 2e^{2x}[x^2+5^x] + e^{2x}[2x + (\ln 5)5^x] = e^{2x}[2x^2 + 2x + (\ln 5 + 2)5^x].$

12. $f'(t) = e^{3t}\cdot 3 = 3e^{3t}.$

13. $g(x) = \pi e^{\pi x}.$

14. $f(\theta) = (2^{-1})^\theta = (\frac{1}{2})^\theta$ so $f'(\theta) = (\ln \frac{1}{2})2^{-\theta}.$

15. $y' = (\ln \pi)\pi^{(x+2)}.$

16. $g'(x) = 2(\ln 3)3^{(2x+7)}.$

17. $f'(t) = 1\cdot e^{5-2t} + te^{5-2t}(-2) = e^{5-2t}(1-2t).$

18. $p'(t) = 4e^{4t+2}.$

19. Using the product rule gives $v'(t) = 2te^{-ct} - ce^{-ct}t^2 = (2t-ct^2)e^{-ct}.$

20. $\dfrac{d}{dt}e^{(1+3t)^2} = e^{(1+3t)^2}\dfrac{d}{dt}(1+3t)^2 = e^{(1+3t)^2}\cdot 2(1+3t)\cdot 3 = 6(1+3t)e^{(1+3t)^2}.$

21. $y' = \frac{3}{2}e^{\frac{3}{2}w}.$

22. $y' = -4e^{-4t}.$

23. $y' = \dfrac{3s^2}{2\sqrt{s^3+1}}.$

24. $w' = \dfrac{1}{2\sqrt{s}}e^{\sqrt{s}}.$

25. $y' = 1\cdot e^{-t^2} + te^{-t^2}(-2t)$

26. $f'(z) = \dfrac{1}{2\sqrt{z}}e^{-z} - \sqrt{z}e^{-z}.$

27. $z'(x) = \dfrac{(\ln 2)2^x}{3\sqrt[3]{(2^x+5)^2}}.$

28. $z' = 5\cdot \ln 2\cdot 2^{5t-3}.$

29. $w' = \dfrac{3}{2}\sqrt{x^2\cdot 5^x}[2x(5^x) + (\ln 5)(x^2)(5^x)] = \dfrac{3}{2}x^2\sqrt{5^{3x}}(2 + x\ln 5).$

30. $f(y) = \left[10^{(5-y)}\right]^{\frac{1}{2}} = 10^{\frac{5}{2}-\frac{1}{2}y}$
$$f'(y) = (\ln 10)\left(10^{\frac{5}{2}-\frac{1}{2}y}\right)\left(-\frac{1}{2}\right) = -\frac{1}{2}(\ln 10)(10^{\frac{5}{2}-\frac{1}{2}y}).$$

31. We can write this as $f(z) = \sqrt{z}e^{-z}$, in which case it is the same as problem 26. So $f'(z) = \dfrac{1}{2\sqrt{z}}e^{-z} - \sqrt{z}e^{-z}.$

32. $y' = \dfrac{\frac{2^z}{2\sqrt{z}} - (\sqrt{z})(\ln 2)(2^z)}{2^{2z}} = \dfrac{1-2z\ln 2}{2^{z+1}\sqrt{z}}.$

33. $y' = 2\left(\dfrac{x^2+2}{3}\right)\left(\dfrac{2x}{3}\right) = \dfrac{4}{9}x\left(x^2+2\right).$

34. We can write $h(x) = \left(\dfrac{x^2+9}{x+3}\right)^{1/2}$, so
$$h'(x) = \frac{1}{2}\left(\frac{x^2+9}{x+3}\right)^{-1/2}\left[\frac{2x(x+3)-(x^2+9)}{(x+3)^2}\right] = \frac{1}{2}\sqrt{\frac{x+3}{x^2+9}}\left[\frac{x^2+6x-9}{(x+3)^2}\right].$$

35. $\dfrac{dy}{dx} = \dfrac{2e^{2x}(x^2+1) - e^{2x}(2x)}{(x^2+1)^2} = \dfrac{2e^{2x}(x^2+1-x)}{(x^2+1)^2}$

36. $y' = \dfrac{-(3e^{3x}+2x)}{(e^{3x}+x^2)^2}.$

37. $h'(z) = \dfrac{-8b^4 z}{(a+z^2)^5}$

38. $f'(z) = -2(e^z+1)^{-3} \cdot e^z = \dfrac{-2e^z}{(e^z+1)^3}.$

39. $w' = (2t+3)(1-e^{-2t}) + (t^2+3t)(2e^{-2t}).$

40. $h'(x) = (\ln 2)(3e^{3x})2^{e^{3x}} = 3e^{3x}2^{e^{3x}} \ln 2.$

41. $f'(x) = 6(e^{5x})(5) + (e^{-x^2})(-2x) = 30e^{5x} - 2xe^{-x^2}.$

42. $f'(x) = e^{-(x-1)^2} \cdot (-2)(x-1).$

43.

$$\begin{aligned} f'(w) &= (e^{w^2})(10w) + (5w^2+3)(e^{w^2})(2w) \\ &= 2we^{w^2}(5+5w^2+3) \\ &= 2we^{w^2}(5w^2+8). \end{aligned}$$

44. The power and chain rules give

$$f'(\theta) = -1(e^\theta+e^{-\theta})^{-2} \cdot \frac{d}{d\theta}(e^\theta+e^{-\theta}) = -(e^\theta+e^{-\theta})^{-2}(e^\theta+e^{-\theta}(-1)) = -\left(\frac{e^\theta-e^{-\theta}}{e^\theta+e^{-\theta}}\right).$$

45. We write $y = (e^{-3t^2}+5)^{1/2}$, so

$$\begin{aligned} \frac{dy}{dt} &= \frac{1}{2}(e^{-3t^2}+5)^{-1/2} \cdot \frac{d}{dt}(e^{-3t^2}+5) = \frac{1}{2}(e^{-3t^2}+5)^{-1/2} \cdot e^{-3t^2} \cdot \frac{d}{dt}(-3t^2) \\ &= \frac{1}{2}(e^{-3t^2}+5)^{-1/2} \cdot e^{-3t^2} \cdot (-6t) = -\frac{3te^{-3t^2}}{\sqrt{e^{-3t^2}+5}}. \end{aligned}$$

46. Using the product and chain rules, we have

$$\begin{aligned} \frac{dz}{dt} &= 9(te^{3t}+e^{5t})^8 \cdot \frac{d}{dt}(te^{3t}+e^{5t}) = 9(te^{3t}+e^{5t})^8(1 \cdot e^{3t} + t \cdot e^{3t} \cdot 3 + e^{5t} \cdot 5) \\ &= 9(te^{3t}+e^{5t})^8(e^{3t}+3te^{3t}+5e^{5t}). \end{aligned}$$

47. $f'(y) = e^{e^{(y^2)}}\left[(e^{y^2})(2y)\right] = 2ye^{[e^{(y^2)}+y^2]}.$

48. $f'(t) = 2(e^{-2e^{2t}})(-2e^{2t})2 = -8(e^{-2e^{2t}+2t}).$

49. Since a and b are constants, we have $f'(x) = 3(ax^2+b)^2(2ax) = 6ax(ax^2+b)^2.$

50. Since a and b are constants, we have $f'(t) = ae^{bt}(b) = abe^{bt}.$

51. We use the product rule. We have

$$f'(x) = (ax)(e^{-bx}(-b)) + (a)(e^{-bx}) = -abxe^{-bx} + ae^{-bx}.$$

52. Using the product and chain rules, we have

$$\begin{aligned} g'(\alpha) &= e^{\alpha e^{-2\alpha}} \cdot \frac{d}{dx}(\alpha e^{-2\alpha}) = e^{\alpha e^{-2\alpha}}(1 \cdot e^{-2\alpha} + \alpha e^{-2\alpha}(-2)) \\ &= e^{\alpha e^{-2\alpha}}(e^{-2\alpha} - 2\alpha e^{-2\alpha}) \\ &= (1-2\alpha)e^{-2\alpha}e^{\alpha e^{-2\alpha}}. \end{aligned}$$

Problems

53. Using the chain rule, we know that $h'(x) = f'(g(x)) \cdot g'(x)$. We use slope to compute the derivatives. Since $f(x)$ is linear on the interval $0 < x < 2$, we compute the slope of the line to see that $f'(x) = 2$ on this interval. Similarly, we compute the slope on the interval $2 < x < 4$ to see that $f'(x) = -2$ on the interval $2 < x < 4$. Since $f(x)$ has a corner at $x = 2$, we know that $f'(2)$ does not exist.

Similarly, $g(x)$ is linear on the interval shown, and we see that the slope of $g(x)$ on this interval is -1 so we have $g'(x) = -1$ on this interval.

(a) We have $h'(1) = f'(g(1)) \cdot g'(1) = (f'(3))(-1) = (-2)(-1) = 2$.

(b) We have $h'(2) = f'(g(2)) \cdot g'(2) = (f'(2))(-1)$. Since $f(x)$ has a corner at $x = 2$, we know that $f'(2)$ does not exist. Therefore, $h'(2)$ does not exist.

(c) We have $h'(3) = f'(g(3)) \cdot g'(3) = (f'(1))(-1) = 2(-1) = -2$.

54. Using the chain rule, we know that $u'(x) = g'(f(x)) \cdot f'(x)$. We use slope to compute the derivatives. Since $f(x)$ is linear on the interval $0 < x < 2$, we compute the slope of the line to see that $f'(x) = 2$ on this interval. Similarly, we compute the slope on the interval $2 < x < 4$ to see that $f'(x) = -2$ on the interval $2 < x < 4$. Since $f(x)$ has a corner at $x = 2$, we know that $f'(2)$ does not exist.

Similarly, $g(x)$ is linear on the interval shown, and we see that the slope of $g(x)$ on this interval is -1 so we have $g'(x) = -1$ on this interval.

(a) We have $u'(1) = g'(f(1)) \cdot f'(1) = (g'(2))2 = (-1)2 = -2$.

(b) We have $u'(2) = g'(f(2)) \cdot f'(2)$. Since $f(x)$ has a corner at $x = 2$, we know that $f'(2)$ does not exist. Therefore, $u'(2)$ does not exist.

(c) We have $u'(3) = g'(f(3)) \cdot f'(3) = (g'(2))(-2) = (-1)(-2) = 2$.

55. Using the chain rule, we know that $v'(x) = f'(f(x)) \cdot f'(x)$. We use slope to compute the derivatives. Since $f(x)$ is linear on the interval $0 < x < 2$, we compute the slope of the line to see that $f'(x) = 2$ on this interval. Similarly, we compute the slope on the interval $2 < x < 4$ to see that $f'(x) = -2$ on the interval $2 < x < 4$. Since $f(x)$ has a corner at $x = 2$, we know that $f'(2)$ does not exist.

(a) We have $v'(1) = f'(f(1)) \cdot f'(1) = f'(2) \cdot 2$. Since $f(x)$ has a corner at $x = 2$, we know that $f'(2)$ does not exist. Therefore, $v'(1)$ does not exist.

(b) We have $v'(2) = f'(f(2)) \cdot f'(2)$. Since $f(x)$ has a corner at $x = 2$, we know that $f'(2)$ does not exist. Therefore, $v'(2)$ does not exist.

(c) We have $v'(3) = f'(f(3)) \cdot f'(3) = (f'(2))(-2)$. Since $f(x)$ has a corner at $x = 2$, we know that $f'(2)$ does not exist. Therefore, $v'(3)$ does not exist.

56. Using the chain rule, we know that $w'(x) = g'(g(x)) \cdot g'(x)$. We use slope to compute the derivatives. Since $g(x)$ is linear on the interval shown, with slope equal to -1, we have $g'(x) = -1$ on this interval.

(a) We have $w'(1) = g'(g(1)) \cdot g'(1) = (g'(3))(-1) = (-1)(-1) = 1$.

(b) We have $w'(2) = g'(g(2)) \cdot g'(2) = (g'(2))(-1) = (-1)(-1) = 1$.

(c) We have $w'(3) = g'(g(3)) \cdot g'(3) = (g'(1))(-1) = (-1)(-1) = 1$.

57. The chain rule gives

$$\frac{d}{dx} f(g(x)) \Big|_{x=30} = f'(g(30))g'(30) = f'(55)g'(30) = (1)(\tfrac{1}{2}) = \frac{1}{2}.$$

58. The chain rule gives

$$\frac{d}{dx} f(g(x)) \Big|_{x=70} = f'(g(70))g'(70) = f'(60)g'(70) = (1)(0) = 0.$$

59. The chain rule gives

$$\frac{d}{dx} g(f(x)) \Big|_{x=30} = g'(f(30))f'(30) = g'(20)f'(30) = (1/2)(-2) = -1.$$

60. The chain rule gives

$$\frac{d}{dx} g(f(x)) \Big|_{x=70} = g'(f(70))f'(70) = g'(30)f'(70) = (1)(\tfrac{1}{2}) = \frac{1}{2}.$$

61. We have $f(2) = (2-1)^3 = 1$, so $(2, 1)$ is a point on the tangent line. Since $f'(x) = 3(x-1)^2$, the slope of the tangent line is
$$m = f'(2) = 3(2-1)^2 = 3.$$
The equation of the line is
$$y - 1 = 3(x - 2) \quad \text{or} \quad y = 3x - 5.$$

62.

$$f(x) = 6e^{5x} + e^{-x^2} \qquad\qquad f'(x) = 30e^{5x} - 2xe^{-x^2}$$
$$f(1) = 6e^5 + e^{-1} \qquad\qquad f'(1) = 30e^5 - 2(1)e^{-1}$$

$$y - y_1 = m(x - x_1)$$
$$y - (6e^5 + e^{-1}) = (30e^5 - 2e^{-1})(x - 1)$$
$$y - (6e^5 + e^{-1}) = (30e^5 - 2e^{-1})x - (30e^5 - 2e^{-1})$$
$$y = (30e^5 - 2e^{-1})x - 30e^5 + 2e^{-1} + 6e^5 + e^{-1}$$
$$\approx 4451.66x - 3560.81.$$

63. The graph is concave down when $f''(x) < 0$.

$$f'(x) = e^{-x^2}(-2x)$$
$$f''(x) = \left[e^{-x^2}(-2x)\right](-2x) + e^{-x^2}(-2)$$
$$= \frac{4x^2}{e^{x^2}} - \frac{2}{e^{x^2}}$$
$$= \frac{4x^2 - 2}{e^{x^2}} < 0$$

The graph is concave down when $4x^2 < 2$. This occurs when $x^2 < \frac{1}{2}$, or $-\frac{1}{\sqrt{2}} < x < \frac{1}{\sqrt{2}}$.

64. We rewrite $e^{-x} = 1/e^x$ so that we can use the quotient rule, then

$$f(x) = \frac{x}{e^x},$$
$$f'(x) = \frac{1 \cdot e^x - x \cdot e^x}{(e^x)^2} = \frac{(1-x)e^x}{(e^x)^2} = \frac{1-x}{e^x},$$
$$f''(x) = \frac{-1 \cdot e^x - (1-x)e^x}{(e^x)^2} = \frac{-e^x - e^x + xe^x}{(e^x)^2} = \frac{(-2+x)e^x}{(e^x)^2} = \frac{x-2}{e^x}.$$

Since $e^{-x} > 0$, for all x, we have $f''(x) < 0$ if $x - 2 < 0$, that is, $x < 2$.

65.

$$f'(x) = [10(2x+1)^9(2)][(3x-1)^7] + [(2x+1)^{10}][7(3x-1)^6(3)]$$
$$= (2x+1)^9(3x-1)^6[20(3x-1) + 21(2x+1)]$$
$$= [(2x+1)^9(3x-1)^6](102x+1)$$
$$f''(x) = [9(2x+1)^8(2)(3x-1)^6 + (2x+1)^9(6)(3x-1)^5(3)](102x+1)$$
$$+ (2x+1)^9(3x-1)^6(102).$$

66. (a) The rate of change of the population is $P'(t)$. If $P'(t)$ is proportional to $P(t)$, we have
$$P'(t) = kP(t).$$

(b) If $P(t) = Ae^{kt}$, then $P'(t) = kAe^{kt} = kP(t)$.

67. (a) With μ and σ constant, differentiating $m(t) = e^{\mu t + \sigma^2 t^2/2}$ with respect to t gives

$$m'(t) = e^{ut+\sigma^2 t^2/2} \cdot \left(\mu + \frac{2\sigma^2 t}{2}\right) = e^{\mu t + \sigma^2 t^2/2}(\mu + \sigma^2 t).$$

Thus,

$$\text{Mean} = m'(0) = e^0(\mu + 0) = \mu.$$

(b) Differentiating $m'(t) = e^{\mu t + \sigma^2 t^2/2}(\mu + \sigma^2 t)$, we have

$$m''(t) = e^{\mu t + \sigma^2 t^2/2}(\mu + \sigma^2 t)^2 + e^{\mu t + \sigma^2 t^2/2}\sigma^2.$$

Thus

$$\text{Variance} = m''(0) - (m'(0))^2 = e^0\mu^2 + e^0\sigma^2 - \mu^2 = \sigma^2.$$

68. (a) If

$$p(x) = k(2x),$$

then

$$p'(x) = k'(2x) \cdot 2.$$

When $x = \frac{1}{2}$,

$$p'\left(\frac{1}{2}\right) = k'\left(2 \cdot \frac{1}{2}\right)(2) = 2 \cdot 2 = 4.$$

(b) If

$$q(x) = k(x + 1),$$

then

$$q'(x) = k'(x + 1) \cdot 1.$$

When $x = 0$,

$$q'(0) = k'(0 + 1)(1) = 2 \cdot 1 = 2.$$

(c) If

$$r(x) = k\left(\frac{1}{4}x\right),$$

then

$$r'(x) = k'\left(\frac{1}{4}x\right) \cdot \frac{1}{4}.$$

When $x = 4$,

$$r'(4) = k'\left(\frac{1}{4}4\right)\frac{1}{4} = 2 \cdot \frac{1}{4} = \frac{1}{2}.$$

69. Yes. To see why, simply plug $x = \sqrt[3]{2t + 5}$ into the expression $3x^2\dfrac{dx}{dt}$ and evaluate it. To do this, first we calculate $\dfrac{dx}{dt}$. By the chain rule,

$$\frac{dx}{dt} = \frac{d}{dt}(2t + 5)^{\frac{1}{3}} = \frac{2}{3}(2t + 5)^{-\frac{2}{3}} = \frac{2}{3}[(2t + 5)^{\frac{1}{3}}]^{-2}.$$

But since $x = (2t + 5)^{\frac{1}{3}}$, we have (by substitution)

$$\frac{dx}{dt} = \frac{2}{3}x^{-2}.$$

It follows that $3x^2\dfrac{dx}{dt} = 3x^2\left(\dfrac{2}{3}x^{-2}\right) = 2.$

70. We see that $m'(x)$ is nearly of the form $f'(g(x)) \cdot g'(x)$ where

$$f(g) = e^g \quad \text{and} \quad g(x) = x^6,$$

but $g'(x)$ is off by a multiple of 6. Therefore, using the chain rule, let

$$m(x) = \frac{f(g(x))}{6} = \frac{e^{(x^6)}}{6}.$$

71. (a) $H(x) = F(G(x))$
$H(4) = F(G(4)) = F(2) = 1$
(b) $H(x) = F(G(x))$
$H'(x) = F'(G(x)) \cdot G'(x)$
$H'(4) = F'(G(4)) \cdot G'(4) = F'(2) \cdot 6 = 5 \cdot 6 = 30$
(c) $H(x) = G(F(x))$
$H(4) = G(F(4)) = G(3) = 4$
(d) $H(x) = G(F(x))$
$H'(x) = G'(F(x)) \cdot F'(x)$
$H'(4) = G'(F(4)) \cdot F'(4) = G'(3) \cdot 7 = 8 \cdot 7 = 56$
(e) $H(x) = \frac{F(x)}{G(x)}$
$H'(x) = \frac{G(x) \cdot F'(x) - F(x) \cdot G'(x)}{[G(x)]^2}$
$H'(4) = \frac{G(4) \cdot F'(4) - F(4) \cdot G'(4)}{[G(4)]^2} = \frac{2 \cdot 7 - 3 \cdot 6}{2^2} = \frac{14 - 18}{4} = \frac{-4}{4} = -1$

72. (a) Differentiating $g(x) = \sqrt{f(x)} = (f(x))^{1/2}$, we have

$$g'(x) = \frac{1}{2}(f(x))^{-1/2} \cdot f'(x) = \frac{f'(x)}{2\sqrt{f(x)}}$$

$$g'(1) = \frac{f'(1)}{2\sqrt{f(1)}} = \frac{3}{2\sqrt{4}} = \frac{3}{4}.$$

(b) Differentiating $h(x) = f(\sqrt{x})$, we have

$$h'(x) = f'(\sqrt{x}) \cdot \frac{1}{2\sqrt{x}}$$

$$h'(1) = f'(\sqrt{1}) \cdot \frac{1}{2\sqrt{1}} = \frac{f'(1)}{2} = \frac{3}{2}.$$

73. We have $h(0) = f(g(0)) = f(d) = d$. From the chain rule, $h'(0) = f'(g(0))g'(0)$. From the graph of g, we see that $g'(0) = 0$, so $h'(0) = f'(g(0)) \cdot 0 = 0$.

74. We have $h(-c) = f(g(-c)) = f(-b) = 0$. From the chain rule,

$$h'(-c) = f'(g(-c))g'(-c).$$

Since g is increasing at $x = -c$, we know that $g'(-c) > 0$. We have

$$f'(g(-c)) = f'(-b),$$

and since f is decreasing at $x = -b$, we have $f'(g(-c)) < 0$. Thus,

$$h'(-c) = \underbrace{f'(g(-c))}_{-} \cdot \underbrace{g'(-c)}_{+} < 0,$$

so h is decreasing at $x = -c$.

75. We have

$$h'(a) = f'(g(a))g'(a).$$

From the graph of g, we see that g is decreasing at $x = a$, so $g'(a) < 0$. We have

$$f'(g(a)) = f'(b),$$

and from the graph of f, we see that f is increasing at $x = b$, so $f'(b) > 0$. Thus,

$$h'(a) = \underbrace{f'(g(a))}_{+} \cdot \underbrace{g'(a)}_{-} < 0,$$

so h is decreasing at $x = a$.

76. We have $h(d) = f(g(d)) = f(-d) = d$ so $h(d)$ is positive. From the chain rule,

$$h'(d) = f'(g(d))g'(d).$$

We have

$$f'(g(d)) = f'(-d).$$

From the graph of f, we see that $f'(-d) < 0$, and from the graph of g, we see that $g'(d) < 0$. This means the sign of $h'(d)$ is the product of two negative numbers, so $h'(d) > 0$.

77. On the interval $-d < x < -b$, we see that the value of $g(x)$ increases from $-d$ to 0. On the interval $-d < x < 0$, the value of $f(x)$ decreases from d to $-d$. Thus, the value of $h(x) = f(g(x))$ decreases on the interval $-d < x < -b$ from

$$h(-d) = f(g(-d)) = f(-d) = d \quad \text{to} \quad h(-b) = f(g(-b)) = f(0) - d.$$

Confirming this using derivatives and the chain rule, we see

$$h'(x) = f'(g(x)) \cdot g'(x),$$

and since $g'(x)$ is negative on $-d < x < -b$ and $f'(g(x))$ is positive on this interval, the value of $h(x)$ is decreasing.

78. We have $f(0) = 6$ and $f(10) = 6e^{0.013(10)} = 6.833$. The derivative of $f(t)$ is

$$f'(t) = 6e^{0.013t} \cdot 0.013 = 0.078e^{0.013t},$$

and so $f'(0) = 0.078$ and $f'(10) = 0.089$.

These values tell us that in 1999 (at $t = 0$), the population of the world was 6 billion people and the population was growing at a rate of 0.078 billion people per year. In the year 2009 (at $t = 10$), this model predicts that the population of the world will be 6.833 billion people and growing at a rate of 0.089 billion people per year.

79. (a) $\dfrac{dB}{dt} = P\left(1 + \dfrac{r}{100}\right)^t \ln\left(1 + \dfrac{r}{100}\right)$. The expression $\dfrac{dB}{dt}$ tells us how fast the amount of money in the bank is changing with respect to time for fixed initial investment P and interest rate r.

(b) $\dfrac{dB}{dr} = Pt\left(1 + \dfrac{r}{100}\right)^{t-1} \dfrac{1}{100}$. The expression $\dfrac{dB}{dr}$ indicates how fast the amount of money changes with respect to the interest rate r, assuming fixed initial investment P and time t.

80. (a)

$$\frac{dm}{dv} = \frac{d}{dv}\left[m_0\left(1 - \frac{v^2}{c^2}\right)^{-1/2}\right]$$

$$= m_0\left(-\frac{1}{2}\right)\left(1 - \frac{v^2}{c^2}\right)^{-3/2}\left(-\frac{2v}{c^2}\right)$$

$$= \frac{m_0 v}{c^2}\frac{1}{\sqrt{\left(1 - \frac{v^2}{c^2}\right)^3}}.$$

(b) $\dfrac{dm}{dv}$ represents the rate of change of mass with respect to the speed v.

81. (a) For $t < 0$, $I = \dfrac{dQ}{dt} = 0$.

For $t > 0$, $I = \dfrac{dQ}{dt} = -\dfrac{Q_0}{RC}e^{-t/RC}$.

(b) For $t > 0$, $t \to 0$ (that is, as $t \to 0^+$),

$$I = -\frac{Q_0}{RC}e^{-t/RC} \to -\frac{Q_0}{RC}.$$

Since $I = 0$ just to the left of $t = 0$ and $I = -Q_0/RC$ just to the right of $t = 0$, it is not possible to define I at $t = 0$.

(c) Q is not differentiable at $t = 0$ because there is no tangent line at $t = 0$.

82. Recall that $v = dx/dt$. We want to find the acceleration, dv/dt, when $x = 2$. Differentiating the expression for v with respect to t using the chain rule and substituting for v gives

$$\frac{dv}{dt} = \frac{d}{dx}(x^2 + 3x - 2) \cdot \frac{dx}{dt} = (2x + 3)v = (2x + 3)(x^2 + 3x - 2).$$

Substituting $x = 2$ gives

$$\text{Acceleration} = \frac{dv}{dt}\bigg|_{x=2} = (2(2) + 3)(2^2 + 3 \cdot 2 - 2) = 56 \text{ cm/sec}^2.$$

83. Let f have a zero of multiplicity m at $x = a$ so that

$$f(x) = (x - a)^m h(x), \quad h(a) \neq 0.$$

Differentiating this expression gives

$$f'(x) = (x - a)^m h'(x) + m(x - a)^{(m-1)} h(x)$$

and both terms in the sum are zero when $x = a$ so $f'(a) = 0$. Taking another derivative gives

$$f''(x) = (x - a)^m h''(x) + 2m(x - a)^{(m-1)} h'(x) + m(m - 1)(x - a)^{(m-2)} h(x).$$

Again, each term in the sum contains a factor of $(x - a)$ to some positive power, so at $x = a$ this will evaluate to 0. Differentiating repeatedly, all derivatives will have positive integer powers of $(x - a)$ until the mth and will therefore vanish. However,

$$f^{(m)}(a) = m!h(a) \neq 0.$$

84. Since $2x$ is the derivative of $x^2 + 1$, the chain rule tells us that

$$\frac{d}{dx}f(x^2 + 1) = 2xf'(x^2 + 1).$$

Thus using the information given in the problem, we have

$$2xf'(x^2 + 1) = \frac{2x}{x^2 + 1},$$

so

$$f'(x^2 + 1) = \frac{1}{x^2 + 1}.$$

Thus, replacing $x^2 + 1$ by x, we have

$$f'(x) = \frac{1}{x}.$$

85. The problem tells us that

$$\frac{d}{dt}G(a - bt) = H(a - bt).$$

Since $\frac{d}{dt}(a - bt) = -b$, the chain rule tells us that

$$-bG'(a - bt) = H(a - bt),$$

so

$$G'(a - bt) = \left(-\frac{1}{b}\right)H(a - bt).$$

Replacing $a - bt$ by t, we have

$$G'(t) = \left(-\frac{1}{b}\right)H(t)$$

86. By the product rule, $\frac{d}{dt}tf(t) = f(t) + tf'(t)$. Thus, using the information given in the problem, we have

$$f(t) + tf'(t) = 1 + f(t).$$

Subtracting $f(t)$ from both sides gives $tf'(t) = 1$, so $f'(t) = 1/t$.

87. By the chain rule,

$$\frac{d}{dx}f(e^x) = f'(e^x)\frac{d}{dx}(e^x) = f'(e^x)e^x,$$

so, using the information given in the problem, we have

$$f'(e^x)e^x = 2e^{2x}.$$

Dividing by e^x we get

$$f'(e^x) = \frac{2e^{2x}}{e^x},$$

so

$$f'(e^x) = 2e^x.$$

Thus, replacing e^x by x, we have

$$f'(x) = 2x,$$

so

$$f(x) = x^2.$$

Solutions for Section 3.5

Exercises

1.

Table 3.1

x	$\cos x$	Difference Quotient	$-\sin x$
0	1.0	-0.0005	0.0
0.1	0.995	-0.10033	-0.099833
0.2	0.98007	-0.19916	-0.19867
0.3	0.95534	-0.296	-0.29552
0.4	0.92106	-0.38988	-0.38942
0.5	0.87758	-0.47986	-0.47943
0.6	0.82534	-0.56506	-0.56464

2. $r'(\theta) = \cos\theta - \sin\theta$.

3. $s'(\theta) = -\sin\theta\sin\theta + \cos\theta\cos\theta = \cos^2\theta - \sin^2\theta = \cos 2\theta$.

4. $z' = -4\sin(4\theta)$.

5. $f'(x) = \cos(3x) \cdot 3 = 3\cos(3x)$.

6. $\dfrac{d}{dx}\sin(2-3x) = \cos(2-3x)\dfrac{d}{dx}(2-3x) = -3\cos(2-3x)$.

7. Using the chain rule gives $R'(x) = 3\pi\sin(\pi x)$.

8. $g'(\theta) = 2\sin(2\theta)\cos(2\theta)\cdot 2 - \pi = 4\sin(2\theta)\cos(2\theta) - \pi$

9. $f'(x) = (2x)(\cos x) + x^2(-\sin x) = 2x\cos x - x^2\sin x$.

10. $w' = e^t\cos(e^t)$.

11. $f'(x) = (e^{\cos x})(-\sin x) = -\sin x e^{\cos x}$.

12. $f'(y) = (\cos y)e^{\sin y}$.

13. $z' = e^{\cos\theta} - \theta(\sin\theta)e^{\cos\theta}$.

14. Using the chain rule gives $R'(\theta) = 3\cos(3\theta)e^{\sin(3\theta)}$.

15. $g'(\theta) = \dfrac{\cos(\tan\theta)}{\cos^2\theta}$

16. $w'(x) = \dfrac{2x}{\cos^2(x^2)}$

17.

$$f(x) = (1 - \cos x)^{\frac{1}{2}}$$

$$f'(x) = \frac{1}{2}(1 - \cos x)^{-\frac{1}{2}}(-(-\sin x))$$

$$= \frac{\sin x}{2\sqrt{1 - \cos x}}.$$

18. $f'(x) = [-\sin(\sin x)](\cos x)$.

19. $f'(x) = \dfrac{\cos x}{\cos^2(\sin x)}$.

20. $k'(x) = \frac{3}{2}\sqrt{\sin(2x)}(2\cos(2x)) = 3\cos(2x)\sqrt{\sin(2x)}$.

21. $f'(x) = 2 \cdot [\sin(3x)] + 2x[\cos(3x)] \cdot 3 = 2\sin(3x) + 6x\cos(3x)$

22. $y' = e^\theta \sin(2\theta) + 2e^\theta \cos(2\theta)$.

23. $f'(x) = (e^{-2x})(-2)(\sin x) + (e^{-2x})(\cos x) = -2\sin x(e^{-2x}) + (e^{-2x})(\cos x) = e^{-2x}[\cos x - 2\sin x]$.

24. $z' = \dfrac{\cos t}{2\sqrt{\sin t}}$.

25. $y' = 5\sin^4\theta\cos\theta$.

26. $g'(z) = \dfrac{e^z}{\cos^2(e^z)}$.

27. $z' = \dfrac{-3e^{-3\theta}}{\cos^2(e^{-3\theta})}$.

28. $w' = (-\cos\theta)e^{-\sin\theta}$.

29. $h'(t) = 1 \cdot (\cos t) + t(-\sin t) + \frac{1}{\cos^2 t} = \cos t - t\sin t + \frac{1}{\cos^2 t}$.

30. $f'(\alpha) = -\sin\alpha + 3\cos\alpha$

31. $k'(\alpha) = (5\sin^4\alpha\cos\alpha)\cos^3\alpha + \sin^5\alpha(3\cos^2\alpha(-\sin\alpha)) = 5\sin^4\alpha\cos^4\alpha - 3\sin^6\alpha\cos^2\alpha$

32. $f'(\theta) = 3\theta^2\cos\theta - \theta^3\sin\theta$.

33. $y' = -2\cos w\sin w - \sin(w^2)(2w) = -2(\cos w\sin w + w\sin(w^2))$

34. $y' = \cos(\cos x + \sin x)(\cos x - \sin x)$

35. $y' = 2\cos(2x)\sin(3x) + 3\sin(2x)\cos(3x)$.

36. $t'(\theta) = \dfrac{-\sin\theta\sin\theta - \cos\theta\cos\theta}{\sin^2\theta} = -\dfrac{(\sin^2\theta + \cos^2\theta)}{\sin^2\theta} = -\dfrac{1}{\sin^2\theta}$.

37. Using the power and quotient rules gives

$$f'(x) = \frac{1}{2}\left(\frac{1 - \sin x}{1 - \cos x}\right)^{-1/2}\left[\frac{-\cos x(1 - \cos x) - (1 - \sin x)\sin x}{(1 - \cos x)^2}\right]$$

$$= \frac{1}{2}\sqrt{\frac{1 - \cos x}{1 - \sin x}}\left[\frac{-\cos x(1 - \cos x) - (1 - \sin x)\sin x}{(1 - \cos x)^2}\right]$$

$$= \frac{1}{2}\sqrt{\frac{1 - \cos x}{1 - \sin x}}\left[\frac{1 - \cos x - \sin x}{(1 - \cos x)^2}\right].$$

38. $\dfrac{d}{dy}\left(\dfrac{y}{\cos y + a}\right) = \dfrac{\cos y + a - y(-\sin y)}{(\cos y + a)^2} = \dfrac{\cos y + a + y\sin y}{(\cos y + a)^2}$.

39. The quotient rule gives $G'(x) = \dfrac{2\sin x\cos x(\cos^2 x + 1) + 2\sin x\cos x(\sin^2 x + 1)}{(\cos^2 x + 1)^2}$

or, using $\sin^2 x + \cos^2 x = 1$,

$$G'(x) = \frac{6\sin x\cos x}{(\cos^2 x + 1)^2}.$$

Problems

40. We begin by taking the derivative of $y = \sin(x^4)$ and evaluating at $x = 10$:

$$\frac{dy}{dx} = \cos(x^4) \cdot 4x^3.$$

Evaluating $\cos(10,000)$ on a calculator (in radians) we see $\cos(10,000) < 0$, so we know that $dy/dx < 0$, and therefore the function is decreasing.

Next, we take the second derivative and evaluate it at $x = 10$, giving $\sin(10,000) < 0$:

$$\frac{d^2y}{dx^2} = \underbrace{\cos(x^4) \cdot (12x^2)}_{\text{negative}} + \underbrace{4x^3 \cdot (-\sin(x^4))(4x^3)}_{\substack{\text{positive, but much} \\ \text{larger in magnitude}}}.$$

From this we can see that $d^2y/dx^2 > 0$, thus the graph is concave up.

41. The pattern in the table below allows us to generalize and say that the $(4n)^{\text{th}}$ derivative of $\cos x$ is $\cos x$, i.e.,

$$\frac{d^4y}{dx^4} = \frac{d^8y}{dx^8} = \cdots = \frac{d^{4n}y}{dx^{4n}} = \cos x.$$

Thus we can say that $d^{48}y/dx^{48} = \cos x$. From there we differentiate twice more to obtain $d^{50}y/dx^{50} = -\cos x$.

n	1	2	3	4	$\cdots$	48	49	50
n^{th} derivative	$-\sin x$	$-\cos x$	$\sin x$	$\cos x$		$\cos x$	$-\sin x$	$-\cos x$

42. We see that $q'(x)$ is of the form

$$\frac{g(x) \cdot f'(x) - f(x) \cdot g'(x)}{(g(x))^2},$$

with $f(x) = e^x$ and $g(x) = \sin x$. Therefore, using the quotient rule, let

$$q(x) = \frac{f(x)}{g(x)} = \frac{e^x}{\sin x}.$$

43. Since $F'(x)$ is of the form $\sin u$, we can make an initial guess that

$$F(x) = \cos(4x),$$

then

$$F'(x) = -4\sin(4x)$$

so we're off by a factor of -4. To fix this problem, we modify our guess by a factor of -4, so the next try is

$$F(x) = -(1/4)\cos(4x),$$

which has

$$F'(x) = \sin(4x).$$

44. (a) Differentiating gives

$$\frac{dy}{dt} = -\frac{4.9\pi}{6}\sin\left(\frac{\pi}{6}t\right).$$

The derivative represents the rate of change of the depth of the water in feet/hour.

(b) The derivative, dy/dt, is zero where the tangent line to the curve y is horizontal. This occurs when $dy/dt = \sin(\frac{\pi}{6}t) = 0$, or at $t = 6$, 12, 18 and 24 (6 am, noon, 6 pm, and midnight). When $dy/dt = 0$, the depth of the water is no longer changing. Therefore, it has either just finished rising or just finished falling, and we know that the harbor's level is at a maximum or a minimum.

45. (a) $v(t) = \dfrac{dy}{dt} = \dfrac{d}{dt}(15 + \sin(2\pi t)) = 2\pi \cos(2\pi t).$

(b)

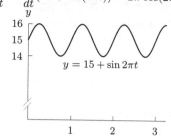

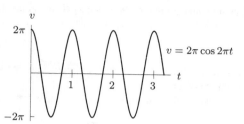

46. (a) Differentiating, we find

$$\begin{array}{l}\text{Rate of change of voltage} \\ \text{with time}\end{array} = \dfrac{dV}{dt} = -120\pi \cdot 156 \sin(120\pi t)$$

$$= -18720\pi \sin(120\pi t) \text{ volts per second.}$$

(b) The rate of change of voltage with time is zero when $\sin(120\pi t) = 0$. This occurs when $120\pi t$ equals any multiple of π. For example, $\sin(120\pi t) = 0$ when $120\pi t = \pi$, or at $t = 1/120$ seconds. Since there are an infinite number of multiples of π, there are many times when the rate of change dV/dt is zero.

(c) The maximum value of the rate of change is $18720\pi = 58810.6$ volts/sec.

47. (a) When $\sqrt{\frac{k}{m}}\, t = \frac{\pi}{2}$ the spring is farthest from the equilibrium position. This occurs at time $t = \frac{\pi}{2}\sqrt{\frac{m}{k}}$

$v = A\sqrt{\frac{k}{m}} \cos\left(\sqrt{\frac{k}{m}}\, t\right)$, so the maximum velocity occurs when $t = 0$

$a = -A\frac{k}{m} \sin\left(\sqrt{\frac{k}{m}}\, t\right)$, so the maximum acceleration occurs when $\sqrt{\frac{k}{m}}\, t = \frac{3\pi}{2}$, which is at time $t = \frac{3\pi}{2}\sqrt{\frac{m}{k}}$

(b) $T = \dfrac{2\pi}{\sqrt{k/m}} = 2\pi\sqrt{\frac{m}{k}}$

(c) $\dfrac{dT}{dm} = \dfrac{2\pi}{\sqrt{k}} \cdot \dfrac{1}{2} m^{-\frac{1}{2}} = \dfrac{\pi}{\sqrt{km}}$

Since $\dfrac{dT}{dm} > 0$, an increase in the mass causes the period to increase.

48. The tangent lines to $f(x) = \sin x$ have slope $\dfrac{d}{dx}(\sin x) = \cos x$. The tangent line at $x = 0$ has slope $f'(0) = \cos 0 = 1$ and goes through the point $(0, 0)$. Consequently, its equation is $y = g(x) = x$. The approximate value of $\sin(\pi/6)$ given by this equation is $g(\pi/6) = \pi/6 \approx 0.524$.

Similarly, the tangent line at $x = \frac{\pi}{3}$ has slope

$$f'\left(\frac{\pi}{3}\right) = \cos\frac{\pi}{3} = \frac{1}{2}$$

and goes through the point $(\pi/3, \sqrt{3}/2)$. Consequently, its equation is

$$y = h(x) = \frac{1}{2}x + \frac{3\sqrt{3} - \pi}{6}.$$

The approximate value of $\sin(\pi/6)$ given by this equation is then

$$h\left(\frac{\pi}{6}\right) = \frac{6\sqrt{3} - \pi}{12} \approx 0.604.$$

The actual value of $\sin(\pi/6)$ is $\frac{1}{2}$, so the approximation from 0 is better than that from $\pi/3$. This is because the slope of the function changes less between $x = 0$ and $x = \pi/6$ than it does between $x = \pi/6$ and $x = \pi/3$. This is illustrated by the following figure.

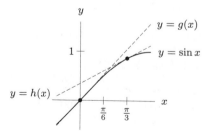

49. If the graphs of $y = \sin x$ and $y = ke^{-x}$ are tangent, then the y-values and the derivatives, $\dfrac{dy}{dx} = \cos x$ and $\dfrac{dy}{dx} = -ke^{-x}$, are equal at that point, so

$$\sin x = ke^{-x} \qquad \text{and} \qquad \cos x = -ke^{-x}.$$

Thus $\sin x = -\cos x$ so $\tan x = -1$. The smallest x-value is $x = 3\pi/4$, which leads to the smallest k value

$$k = \frac{\sin(3\pi/4)}{e^{-3\pi/4}} = 7.46.$$

When $x = \dfrac{3\pi}{4}$, we have $y = \sin\left(\dfrac{3\pi}{4}\right) = \dfrac{1}{\sqrt{2}}$ so the point is $\left(\dfrac{3\pi}{4}, \dfrac{1}{\sqrt{2}}\right)$.

50. Differentiating with respect to t using the chain rule and substituting for dx/dt gives

$$\frac{d^2x}{dt^2} = \frac{d}{dt}\left(\frac{dx}{dt}\right) = \frac{d}{dx}(x\sin x)\cdot\frac{dx}{dt} = (\sin x + x\cos x)x\sin x.$$

51. (a) If $f(x) = \sin x$, then

$$\begin{aligned}
f'(x) &= \lim_{h\to 0}\frac{\sin(x+h) - \sin x}{h}\\
&= \lim_{h\to 0}\frac{(\sin x\cos h + \sin h\cos x) - \sin x}{h}\\
&= \lim_{h\to 0}\frac{\sin x(\cos h - 1) + \sin h\cos x}{h}\\
&= \sin x\lim_{h\to 0}\frac{\cos h - 1}{h} + \cos x\lim_{h\to 0}\frac{\sin h}{h}.
\end{aligned}$$

(b) $\dfrac{\cos h - 1}{h} \to 0$ and $\dfrac{\sin h}{h} \to 1$, as $h \to 0$. Thus, $f'(x) = \sin x\cdot 0 + \cos x\cdot 1 = \cos x$.

(c) Similarly,

$$\begin{aligned}
g'(x) &= \lim_{h\to 0}\frac{\cos(x+h) - \cos x}{h}\\
&= \lim_{h\to 0}\frac{(\cos x\cos h - \sin x\sin h) - \cos x}{h}\\
&= \lim_{h\to 0}\frac{\cos x(\cos h - 1) - \sin x\sin h}{h}\\
&= \cos x\lim_{h\to 0}\frac{\cos h - 1}{h} - \sin x\lim_{h\to 0}\frac{\sin h}{h}\\
&= -\sin x.
\end{aligned}$$

52. (a) Sector OAQ is a sector of a circle with radius $\dfrac{1}{\cos\theta}$ and angle $\Delta\theta$. Thus its area is the left side of the inequality. Similarly, the area of Sector OBR is the right side of the equality. The area of the triangle OQR is $\frac{1}{2}\Delta\tan\theta$ since it is a triangle with base $\Delta\tan\theta$ (the segment QR) and height 1 (if you turn it sideways, it is easier to see this). Thus, using the given fact about areas (which is also clear from looking at the picture), we have

$$\frac{\Delta\theta}{2\pi}\cdot\pi\left(\frac{1}{\cos\theta}\right)^2 \le \frac{1}{2}\cdot\Delta(\tan\theta) \le \frac{\Delta\theta}{2\pi}\cdot\pi\left(\frac{1}{\cos(\theta+\Delta\theta)}\right)^2.$$

(b) Dividing the inequality through by $\frac{\Delta\theta}{2}$ and canceling the π's gives:

$$\left(\frac{1}{\cos\theta}\right)^2 \le \frac{\Delta\tan\theta}{\Delta\theta} \le \left(\frac{1}{\cos(\theta+\Delta\theta)}\right)^2$$

Then as $\Delta\theta \to 0$, the right and left sides both tend toward $\left(\frac{1}{\cos\theta}\right)^2$ while the middle (which is the difference quotient for tangent) tends to $(\tan\theta)'$. Thus, the derivative of tangent is "squeezed" between two values heading toward the same thing and must, itself, also tend to that value. Therefore, $(\tan\theta)' = \left(\frac{1}{\cos\theta}\right)^2$.

(c) Take the identity $\sin^2 \theta + \cos^2 \theta = 1$ and divide through by $\cos^2 \theta$ to get $(\tan \theta)^2 + 1 = \left(\frac{1}{\cos \theta}\right)^2$. Differentiating with respect to θ yields:

$$2(\tan \theta) \cdot (\tan \theta)' = 2\left(\frac{1}{\cos \theta}\right) \cdot \left(\frac{1}{\cos \theta}\right)'$$

$$2\left(\frac{\sin \theta}{\cos \theta}\right) \cdot \left(\frac{1}{\cos \theta}\right)^2 = 2\left(\frac{1}{\cos \theta}\right) \cdot (-1)\left(\frac{1}{\cos \theta}\right)^2 (\cos \theta)'$$

$$2\frac{\sin \theta}{\cos^3 \theta} = (-1)2\frac{1}{\cos^3 \theta}(\cos \theta)'$$

$$-\sin \theta = (\cos \theta)'.$$

(d)

$$\frac{d}{d\theta}\left(\sin^2 \theta + \cos^2 \theta\right) = \frac{d}{d\theta}(1)$$

$$2\sin \theta \cdot (\sin \theta)' + 2\cos \theta \cdot (\cos \theta)' = 0$$

$$2\sin \theta \cdot (\sin \theta)' + 2\cos \theta \cdot (-\sin \theta) = 0$$

$$(\sin \theta)' - \cos \theta = 0$$

$$(\sin \theta)' = \cos \theta.$$

Solutions for Section 3.6

Exercises

1. $f'(t) = \dfrac{2t}{t^2 + 1}$.

2. $f'(x) = \dfrac{-1}{1 - x} = \dfrac{1}{x - 1}$.

3. Since $\ln(e^{2x}) = 2x$, the derivative $f'(x) = 2$.

4. Since $e^{\ln(e^{2x^2+3})} = e^{2x^2+3}$, the derivative $f'(x) = 4xe^{2x^2+3}$.

5. $f'(x) = \dfrac{1}{1 - e^{-x}} \cdot (-e^{-x})(-1) = \dfrac{e^{-x}}{1 - e^{-x}}$.

6. $f'(\alpha) = \dfrac{1}{\sin \alpha} \cdot \cos \alpha = \dfrac{\cos \alpha}{\sin \alpha}$.

7. $f'(x) = \dfrac{1}{e^x + 1} \cdot e^x$.

8. $\dfrac{dy}{dx} = \ln x + x\left(\dfrac{1}{x}\right) - 1 = \ln x$

9. $j'(x) = \dfrac{ae^{ax}}{(e^{ax} + b)}$

10. Using the product and chain rules gives $h'(w) = 3w^2 \ln(10w) + w^3 \dfrac{10}{10w} = 3w^2 \ln(10w) + w^2$.

11. $f'(x) = \dfrac{1}{e^{7x}} \cdot (e^{7x})7 = 7$.

    (Note also that $\ln(e^{7x}) = 7x$ implies $f'(x) = 7$.)

12. Note that $f(x) = e^{\ln x} \cdot e^1 = x \cdot e = ex$. So $f'(x) = e$. (Remember, e is just a constant.) You might also use the chain rule to get:

    $f'(x) = e^{(\ln x)+1} \cdot \frac{1}{x}$.

    [Are the two answers the same? Of course they are, since

    $$e^{(\ln x)+1}\left(\frac{1}{x}\right) = e^{\ln x} \cdot e\left(\frac{1}{x}\right) = xe\left(\frac{1}{x}\right) = e.]$$

13. $f'(w) = \dfrac{1}{\cos(w-1)}[-\sin(w-1)] = -\tan(w-1)$.

   [This could be done easily using the answer from Problem 6 and the chain rule.]

14. $f(t) = \ln t$ (because $\ln e^x = x$ *or* because $e^{\ln t} = t$), so $f'(t) = \frac{1}{t}$.

15. $f'(y) = \dfrac{2y}{\sqrt{1-y^4}}$.

16. $g'(t) = \dfrac{3}{(3t-4)^2+1}$.

17. $g(\alpha) = \alpha$, so $g'(\alpha) = 1$.

18. $g'(t) = e^{\arctan(3t^2)}\left(\dfrac{1}{1+(3t^2)^2}\right)(6t) = e^{\arctan(3t^2)}\left(\dfrac{6t}{1+9t^4}\right)$.

19. $g'(t) = \dfrac{-\sin(\ln t)}{t}$.

20. $h'(z) = (\ln 2)z^{(\ln 2 - 1)}$.

21. $h'(w) = \arcsin w + \dfrac{w}{\sqrt{1-w^2}}$.

22. Note that $f(x) = kx$ so, $f'(x) = k$.

23. Using the chain rule gives $r'(t) = \dfrac{2}{\sqrt{1-4t^2}}$.

24. $j'(x) = -\sin\left(\sin^{-1}x\right)\cdot\left[\dfrac{1}{\sqrt{1-x^2}}\right] = -\dfrac{x}{\sqrt{1-x^2}}$

25. $f'(x) = -\sin(\arctan 3x)\left(\dfrac{1}{1+(3x)^2}\right)(3) = \dfrac{-3\sin(\arctan 3x)}{1+9x^2}$.

26. Note that $g(x) = \arcsin(\sin \pi x) = \pi x$.
    Thus, $g'(x) = \pi$.

27. $f'(z) = -1(\ln z)^{-2}\cdot\dfrac{1}{z} = \dfrac{-1}{z(\ln z)^2}$.

28. Using the quotient rule gives

$$f'(x) = \dfrac{1 + \ln x - x(\frac{1}{x})}{(1+\ln x)^2}$$
$$= \dfrac{\ln x}{(1+\ln x)^2}.$$

29. $\dfrac{dy}{dx} = 2(\ln x + \ln 2) + 2x\left(\dfrac{1}{x}\right) - 2 = 2(\ln x + \ln 2) = 2\ln(2x)$

30. Using the chain rule gives $f'(x) = \dfrac{\cos x - \sin x}{\sin x + \cos x}$.

31. $f'(t) = \dfrac{1}{\ln t}\cdot\dfrac{1}{t} = \dfrac{1}{t\ln t}$

32. Using the chain rule gives

$$T'(u) = \left[\dfrac{1}{1+\left(\frac{u}{1+u}\right)^2}\right]\left[\dfrac{(1+u)-u}{(1+u)^2}\right]$$
$$= \dfrac{(1+u)^2}{(1+u)^2+u^2}\left[\dfrac{1}{(1+u)^2}\right]$$
$$= \dfrac{1}{1+2u+2u^2}.$$

33. Since $\ln\left[\left(\dfrac{1-\cos t}{1+\cos t}\right)^4\right] = 4\ln\left[\left(\dfrac{1-\cos t}{1+\cos t}\right)\right]$ we have

$$
\begin{aligned}
a'(t) &= 4\left(\frac{1+\cos t}{1-\cos t}\right)\left[\frac{\sin t(1+\cos t) + \sin t(1-\cos t)}{(1+\cos t)^2}\right] \\
&= \left[\frac{1+\cos t}{1-\cos t}\right]\left[\frac{8\sin t}{(1+\cos t)^2}\right] \\
&= \frac{8\sin t}{1-\cos^2 t} \\
&= \frac{8}{\sin t}.
\end{aligned}
$$

34. $f'(x) = -\sin(\arcsin(x+1))\left(\dfrac{1}{\sqrt{1-(x+1)^2}}\right) = \dfrac{-(x+1)}{\sqrt{1-(x+1)^2}}.$

Problems

35. From the graphs, we estimate $g(1) \approx 2$, $g'(1) \approx 1$, and $f'(2) \approx 0.8$. Thus, by the chain rule,

$$h'(1) = f'(g(1)) \cdot g'(1) \approx f'(2) \cdot g'(1) \approx 0.8 \cdot 1 = 0.8.$$

36. From the graphs, we estimate $f(1) \approx -0.4$, $f'(1) \approx 0.5$, and $g'(-0.4) \approx 2$. Thus, by the chain rule,

$$k'(1) = g'(f(1)) \cdot f'(1) \approx g'(-0.4) \cdot 0.5 \approx 2 \cdot 0.5 = 1.$$

37. From the graphs, we estimate $g(2) \approx 1.6$, $g'(2) \approx -0.5$, and $f'(1.6) \approx 0.8$. Thus, by the chain rule,

$$h'(2) = f'(g(2)) \cdot g'(2) \approx f'(1.6) \cdot g'(2) \approx 0.8(-0.5) = -0.4.$$

38. From the graphs, we estimate $f(2) \approx 0.3$, $f'(2) \approx 1.1$, and $g'(0.3) \approx 1.7$. Thus, by the chain rule,

$$k'(2) = g'(f(2)) \cdot f'(2) \approx g'(0.3) \cdot f'(2) \approx 1.7 \cdot 1.1 \approx 1.9.$$

39. Differentiating

$$
\begin{aligned}
f'(x) &= \frac{1}{x^2+1} \cdot 2x = 2x(x^2+1)^{-1} \\
f''(x) &= 2(x^2+1)^{-1} - 2x(x^2+1)^{-2} \cdot 2x \\
&= \frac{2}{(x^2+1)} - \frac{4x^2}{(x^2+1)^2} = \frac{2x^2+2}{(x^2+1)^2} - \frac{4x^2}{(x^2+1)^2} \\
&= \frac{2(1-x^2)}{(x^2+1)^2}.
\end{aligned}
$$

Since $(x^2+1)^2 > 0$ for all x, we see that $f''(0) > 0$ for $1-x^2 > 0$ or $x^2 < 1$. That is, $\ln(x^2+1)$ is concave up on the interval $-1 < x < 1$.

40. Let

$$g(x) = \arcsin x$$

so

$$\sin[g(x)] = x.$$

Differentiating,

$$
\begin{aligned}
\cos[g(x)] \cdot g'(x) &= 1 \\
g'(x) &= \frac{1}{\cos[g(x)]}
\end{aligned}
$$

Using the fact that $\sin^2\theta + \cos^2\theta = 1$, and $\cos[g(x)] \geq 0$, since $-\frac{\pi}{2} \leq g(x) \leq \frac{\pi}{2}$, we get

$$\cos[g(x)] = \sqrt{1 - (\sin[g(x)])^2}.$$

Therefore,

$$g'(x) = \frac{1}{\sqrt{1 - (\sin[g(x)])^2}}$$

Since $\sin[g(x)] = x$, we have

$$g'(x) = \frac{1}{\sqrt{1 - x^2}}, -1 < x < 1.$$

41. Let

$$g(x) = \log x.$$

Then

$$10^{g(x)} = x.$$

Differentiating,

$$(\ln 10)[10^{g(x)}]g'(x) = 1$$
$$g'(x) = \frac{1}{(\ln 10)[10^{g(x)}]}$$
$$g'(x) = \frac{1}{(\ln 10)x}.$$

42. pH $= 2 = -\log x$ means $\log x = -2$ so $x = 10^{-2}$. Rate of change of pH with hydrogen ion concentration is

$$\frac{d}{dx}\text{pH} = -\frac{d}{dx}(\log x) = \frac{-1}{x(\ln 10)} = -\frac{1}{(10^{-2})\ln 10} = -43.4$$

43. (a) For $y = \ln x$, we have $y' = 1/x$, so the slope of the tangent line is $f'(1) = 1/1 = 1$. The equation of the tangent line is $y - 0 = 1(x - 1)$, so, on the tangent line, $y = g(x) = x - 1$.

(b) Using a value on the tangent line to approximate $\ln(1, 1)$, we have

$$\ln(1.1) \approx g(1.1) = 1.1 - 1 = 0.1.$$

Similarly, $\ln(2)$ is approximated by

$$\ln(2) \approx g(2) = 2 - 1 = 1.$$

(c) From Figure 3.6, we see that $f(1.1)$ and $f(2)$ are below $g(x) = x - 1$. Similarly, $f(0.9)$ and $f(0.5)$ are also below $g(x)$. This is true for any approximation of this function by a tangent line since f is concave down ($f''(x) = -\frac{1}{x^2} < 0$ for all $x > 0$). Thus, for a given x-value, the y-value given by the function is always below the value given by the tangent line.

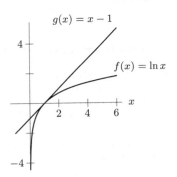

Figure 3.6

44. (a) Let $g(x) = ax^2 + bx + c$ be our quadratic and $f(x) = \ln x$. For the best approximation, we want to find a quadratic with the same value as $\ln x$ at $x = 1$ and the same first and second derivatives as $\ln x$ at $x = 1$. $g'(x) = 2ax + b, g''(x) = 2a, f'(x) = \frac{1}{x}, f''(x) = -\frac{1}{x^2}$.

$$g(1) = a(1)^2 + b(1) + c \quad f(1) = 0$$
$$g'(1) = 2a(1) + b \quad f'(1) = 1$$
$$g''(1) = 2a \quad f''(1) = -1$$

Thus, we obtain the equations

$$a + b + c = 0$$
$$2a + b = 1$$
$$2a = -1$$

We find $a = -\frac{1}{2}, b = 2$ and $c = -\frac{3}{2}$. Thus our approximation is:

$$g(x) = -\frac{1}{2}x^2 + 2x - \frac{3}{2}$$

(b) From the graph below, we notice that around $x = 1$, the value of $f(x) = \ln x$ and the value of $g(x) = -\frac{1}{2}x^2 + 2x - \frac{3}{2}$ are very close.

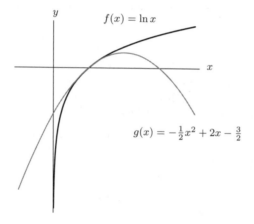

(c) $g(1.1) = 0.095 \quad g(2) = 0.5$
Compare with $f(1.1) = 0.0953, f(2) = 0.693$.

45. (a)

$$f'(x) = \frac{1}{1 + x^2} + \frac{1}{1 + \frac{1}{x^2}} \cdot \left(-\frac{1}{x^2}\right)$$
$$= \frac{1}{1 + x^2} + \left(-\frac{1}{x^2 + 1}\right)$$
$$= \frac{1}{1 + x^2} - \frac{1}{1 + x^2}$$
$$= 0$$

(b) f is a constant function. Checking at a few values of x,

Table 3.2

x	$\arctan x$	$\arctan x^{-1}$	$f(x) = \arctan x + \arctan x^{-1}$
1	0.785392	0.7853982	1.5707963
2	1.1071487	0.4636476	1.5707963
3	1.2490458	0.3217506	1.5707963

46. The closer you look at the function, the more it begins to look like a line with slope equal to the derivative of the function at $x = 0$. Hence, functions whose derivatives at $x = 0$ are equal will look the same there.

The following functions look like the line $y = x$ since, in all cases, $y' = 1$ at $x = 0$.

$y = x$	$y' = 1$
$y = \sin x$	$y' = \cos x$
$y = \tan x$	$y' = \frac{1}{\cos^2 x}$
$y = \ln(x + 1)$	$y' = \frac{1}{x+1}$

The following functions look like the line $y = 0$ since, in all cases, $y' = 0$ at $x = 0$.

$y = x^2$	$y' = 2x$
$y = x \sin x$	$y' = x \cos x + \sin x$
$y = x^3$	$y' = 3x^2$
$y = \frac{1}{2} \ln (x^2 + 1)$	$y' = 2x \cdot \frac{1}{2} \cdot \frac{1}{x^2+1} = \frac{x}{x^2+1}$
$y = 1 - \cos x$	$y' = \sin x$

The following functions look like the line $x = 0$ since, in all cases, as $x \to 0^+$, the slope $y' \to \infty$.

$y = \sqrt{x}$	$y' = \frac{1}{2\sqrt{x}}$
$y = \sqrt{\frac{x}{x+1}}$	$y' = \frac{(x+1)-x}{(x+1)^2} \cdot \frac{1}{2} \cdot \frac{1}{\sqrt{\frac{x}{x+1}}} = \frac{1}{2(x+1)^2} \cdot \sqrt{\frac{x+1}{x}}$
$y = \sqrt{2x - x^2}$	$y' = (2 - 2x)\frac{1}{2} \cdot \frac{1}{\sqrt{2x-x^2}} = \frac{1-x}{\sqrt{2x-x^2}}$

47. Since the chain rule gives $h'(x) = n'(m(x))m'(x) = -2$ we must find values a and x such that $a = m(x)$ and $n'(a)m'(x) = -2$.

Calculating slopes from the graph of n gives

$$n'(a) = \begin{cases} 1 & \text{if} \quad 0 < a < 50 \\ 1/2 & \text{if} \quad 50 < a < 100. \end{cases}$$

Calculating slopes from the graph of m gives

$$m'(x) = \begin{cases} -2 & \text{if} \quad 0 < x < 50 \\ 2 & \text{if} \quad 50 < x < 100. \end{cases}$$

The only values of the derivative n' are 1 and $1/2$ and the only values of the derivative m' are 2 and -2. In order to have $n'(a)m'(x) = -2$ we must therefore have $n'(a) = 1$ and $m'(x) = -2$. Thus $0 < a < 50$ and $0 < x < 50$.

Now $a = m(x)$ and from the graph of m we see that $0 < m(x) < 50$ for $25 < x < 75$.

The two conditions on x we have found are both satisfied when $25 < x < 50$. Thus $h'(x) = -2$ for all x in the interval $25 < x < 50$. The question asks for just one of these x values, for example $x = 40$.

48. Since the chain rule gives $h'(x) = n'(m(x))m'(x) = 2$ we must find values a and x such that $a = m(x)$ and $n'(a)m'(x) = 2$.

Calculating slopes from the graph of n gives

$$n'(a) = \begin{cases} 1 & \text{if} \quad 0 < a < 50 \\ 1/2 & \text{if} \quad 50 < a < 100. \end{cases}$$

Calculating slopes from the graph of m gives

$$m'(x) = \begin{cases} -2 & \text{if} \quad 0 < x < 50 \\ 2 & \text{if} \quad 50 < x < 100. \end{cases}$$

The only values of the derivative n' are 1 and $1/2$ and the only values of the derivative m' are 2 and -2. In order to have $n'(a)m'(x) = 2$ we must therefore have $n'(a) = 1$ and $m'(x) = 2$. Thus $0 < a < 50$ and $50 < x < 100$.

Now $a = m(x)$ and from the graph of m we see that $0 < m(x) < 50$ for $25 < x < 75$.

The two conditions on x we have found are both satisfied when $50 < x < 75$. Thus $h'(x) = 2$ for all x in the interval $50 < x < 75$. The question asks for just one of these x values, for example $x = 60$.

49. Since the chain rule gives $h'(x) = n'(m(x))m'(x) = 1$ we must find values a and x such that $a = m(x)$ and $n'(a)m'(x) = 1$.

Calculating slopes from the graph of n gives

$$n'(a) = \begin{cases} 1 & \text{if } 0 < a < 50 \\ 1/2 & \text{if } 50 < a < 100. \end{cases}$$

Calculating slopes from the graph of m gives

$$m'(x) = \begin{cases} -2 & \text{if } 0 < x < 50 \\ 2 & \text{if } 50 < x < 100. \end{cases}$$

The only values of the derivative n' are 1 and $1/2$ and the only values of the derivative m' are 2 and -2. In order to have $n'(a)m'(x) = 1$ we must therefore have $n'(a) = 1/2$ and $m'(x) = 2$. Thus $50 < a < 100$ and $50 < x < 100$.

Now $a = m(x)$ and from the graph of m we see that $50 < m(x) < 100$ for $0 < x < 25$ or $75 < x < 100$.

The two conditions on x we have found are both satisfied when $75 < x < 100$. Thus $h'(x) = 1$ for all x in the interval $75 < x < 100$. The question asks for just one of these x values, for example $x = 80$.

50. Since the chain rule gives $h'(x) = n'(m(x))m'(x) = -1$ we must find values a and x such that $a = m(x)$ and $n'(a)m'(x) = -1$.

Calculating slopes from the graph of n gives

$$n'(a) = \begin{cases} 1 & \text{if } 0 < a < 50 \\ 1/2 & \text{if } 50 < a < 100. \end{cases}$$

Calculating slopes from the graph of m gives

$$m'(x) = \begin{cases} -2 & \text{if } 0 < x < 50 \\ 2 & \text{if } 50 < x < 100. \end{cases}$$

The only values of the derivative n' are 1 and $1/2$ and the only values of the derivative m' are 2 and -2. In order to have $n'(a)m'(x) = -1$ we must therefore have $n'(a) = 1/2$ and $m'(x) = -2$. Thus $50 < a < 100$ and $0 < x < 50$.

Now $a = m(x)$ and from the graph of m we see that $50 < m(x) < 100$ for $0 < x < 25$ or $75 < x < 100$.

The two conditions on x we have found are both satisfied when $0 < x < 25$. Thus $h'(x) = -1$ for all x in the interval $0 < x < 25$. The question asks for just one of these x values, for example $x = 10$.

51. Since the point $(2, 5)$ is on the curve, we know $f(2) = 5$. The point $(2.1, 5.3)$ is on the tangent line, so

$$\text{Slope tangent} = \frac{5.3 - 5}{2.1 - 2} = \frac{0.3}{0.1} = 3.$$

Thus, $f'(2) = 3$.

By the chain rule

$$h'(2) = 3(f(2))^2 \cdot f'(2) = 3 \cdot 5^2 \cdot 3 = 225.$$

52. Since the point $(2, 5)$ is on the curve, we know $f(2) = 5$. The point $(2.1, 5.3)$ is on the tangent line, so

$$\text{Slope tangent} = \frac{5.3 - 5}{2.1 - 2} = \frac{0.3}{0.1} = 3.$$

Thus, $f'(2) = 3$.

By the chain rule

$$k'(2) = -(f(2))^{-2} \cdot f'(2) = -5^{-2} \cdot 3 = -0.12.$$

53. Since the point $(2, 5)$ is on the curve, we know $f(2) = 5$. The point $(2.1, 5.3)$ is on the tangent line, so

$$\text{Slope tangent} = \frac{5.3 - 5}{2.1 - 2} = \frac{0.3}{0.1} = 3.$$

Thus, $f'(2) = 3$. Since g is the inverse function of f and $f(2) = 5$, we know $f^{-1}(5) = 2$, so $g(5) = 2$.

Differentiating, we have

$$g'(2) = \frac{1}{f'(g(5))} = \frac{1}{f'(2)} = \frac{1}{3}.$$

54. (a) Since $f(x) = x^3$, we have $f'(x) = 3x^2$. Thus, $f'(2) = 3(2)^2 = 12$.

    (b) To find $f^{-1}(x)$, we switch xs and ys and solve for y.

        Since $y = x^3$, we get $x = y^3$.

        Solving for y gives $y = \sqrt[3]{x}$.

        Thus, $f^{-1}(x) = \sqrt[3]{x}$.

    (c) To find $(f^{-1})'(x)$, we differentiate. Since $f^{-1}(x) = \sqrt[3]{x} = x^{1/3}$, we get

$$(f^{-1})'(x) = \frac{1}{3}x^{-2/3}.$$

Thus,

$$(f^{-1})'(8) = \frac{1}{3}(8)^{-2/3} = \frac{1}{3 \cdot 8^{2/3}} = \frac{1}{3 \cdot 4} = \frac{1}{12}.$$

    (d) The point $(2, 8)$ is on the graph of f. Thus the point $(8, 2)$ is on the graph of f^{-1}, so $f^{-1}(8) = 2$. Therefore,

$$(f^{-1})'(8) = \frac{1}{f'(f^{-1}(8))} = \frac{1}{f'(2)} = \frac{1}{12}.$$

55. (a) Since $f(x) = 2x^5 + 3x^3 + x$, we differentiate to get $f'(x) = 10x^4 + 9x^2 + 1$.

    (b) Because $f'(x)$ is always positive, we know that $f(x)$ is increasing everywhere. Thus, $f(x)$ is a one-to-one function and is invertible.

    (c) To find $f(1)$, substitute 1 for x into $f(x)$. We get $f(1) = 2(1)^5 + 3(1)^3 + 1 = 2 + 3 + 1 = 6$.

    (d) To find $f'(1)$, substitute 1 for x into $f'(x)$. We get $f'(1) = 10(1)^4 + 9(1)^2 + 1 = 20$.

    (e) Since $f(1) = 6$, we have $f^{-1}(6) = 1$, so

$$(f^{-1})'(6) = \frac{1}{f'(f^{-1}(6))} = \frac{1}{f'(1)} = \frac{1}{20}.$$

56. Since g is the inverse of f, we know that $g(4) = f^{-1}(4) = 3$, so

$$g'(4) = \frac{1}{f'(g(4))} = \frac{1}{f'(3)} = \frac{1}{6}.$$

57. To find $(f^{-1})'(3)$, we first look in the table to find that $3 = f(9)$, so $f^{-1}(3) = 9$. Thus,

$$(f^{-1})'(3) = \frac{1}{f'(f^{-1}(3))} = \frac{1}{f'(9)} = \frac{1}{5}.$$

58. (a) Knowing $f(2000) = 281$ tells us that the US population was 281 million in the year 2000.

    (b) Since $f(2000) = 281$, we have $f^{-1}(281) = 2000$. This tells us that the year in which the US population was 281 million was 2000.

    (c) Knowing $f'(2000) = 3.476$ tells us that in the year 2000, the US population was growing at a rate of 3.476 million people per year.

    (d) Using parts (b) and (c), we have

$$(f^{-1})'(281) = \frac{1}{f'(f^{-1}(281))} = \frac{1}{f'(2000)} = \frac{1}{3.476} = 0.288.$$

The units of the derivative of f^{-1} are years per million people (the reciprocal of the units of f'). The statement $(f^{-1})'(281) = 0.288$ tells us that when the US population was 281 million, it took 0.288 of a year (between 3 and 4 months) for the population to increase by another million.

59. Each grid mark on the horizontal axis represents 3 years and each grid mark on the vertical axis represents 50 million vehicles.

    (a) Reading from the graph

$$f(21) \approx 200 \text{ million vehicles}.$$

This tells us that 21 years after 1946, in 1967, there were 200 million registered vehicles.

    (b) Drawing a tangent line to the curve at $t = 21$, we have

$$\text{Slope} = f'(21) \approx \frac{90}{6} = 15 \text{ million vehicles/year}.$$

Thus, 21 years after 1946, in 1967, the number of registered vehicles was increasing at 15 million vehicles per year.

(c) From the graph or part (a)

$$f^{-1}(200) = 21 \text{ years.}$$

Thus, there were 200 million cars registered when $t = 21$, that is, in 1967.

(d) We have

$$(f^{-1})'(200) = \frac{1}{f'(f^{-1}(200))} = \frac{1}{f'(21)} = \frac{1}{15} = 0.0667 \text{ years/million.}$$

Thus, when 200 million vehicles were already registered, it took 0.0667 year, or about 24 days, for another million to be registered.

60. We have $(f^{-1})'(8) = 1/f'(f^{-1}(8))$. From the graph we see $f^{-1}(8) = 4$. Thus $(f^{-1})'(8) = \dfrac{1}{f'(4)} = \dfrac{1}{3.0}$.

61. We must have

$$(f^{-1})'(5) = \frac{1}{f'(f^{-1}(5))} = \frac{1}{f'(10)} = \frac{1}{8}.$$

62. All three values equal 1.

(a) We have $f^{-1}(A) = a$, so $(f^{-1})'(A) = \frac{1}{f'(f^{-1}(A))} = \frac{1}{f'(a)}$. Thus $f'(a)(f^{-1})'(A) = 1$.

(b) We have $f^{-1}(B) = b$, so $(f^{-1})'(B) = \frac{1}{f'(f^{-1}(B))} = \frac{1}{f'(b)}$. Thus $f'(b)(f^{-1})'(B) = 1$.

(c) We have $f^{-1}(C) = c$, so $(f^{-1})'(C) = \frac{1}{f'(f^{-1}(C))} = \frac{1}{f'(c)}$. Thus $f'(c)(f^{-1})'(C) = 1$.

63. A continuous invertible function $f(x)$ cannot be increasing on one interval and decreasing on another because it would fail the horizontal line test. The same is true of the inverse function $f^{-1}(x)$. Either $f^{-1}(x)$ is increasing and $(f^{-1})'(x) \geq 0$ for all x, or $f^{-1}(x)$ is decreasing and $(f^{-1})'(x) \leq 0$ for all x. We can not have both $(f^{-1})'(10) = 8$ and $(f^{-1})'(20) = -6$.

64. (a) The definition of the derivative of $\ln(1 + x)$ at $x = 0$ is

$$\lim_{h \to 0} \frac{\ln(1 + h) - \ln 1}{h} = \lim_{h \to 0} \frac{\ln(1 + h)}{h} = \left. \frac{1}{1 + x} \right|_{x=0} = 1.$$

(b) The rules of logarithms give

$$\lim_{h \to 0} \frac{\ln(1 + h)}{h} = \lim_{h \to 0} \frac{1}{h} \ln(1 + h) = \lim_{h \to 0} \ln(1 + h)^{1/h} = 1.$$

Thus, taking e to both sides and using the fact that $e^{\ln A} = A$, we have

$$e^{\lim_{h \to 0} \ln(1+h)^{1/h}} = \lim_{h \to 0} e^{\ln(1+h)^{1/h}} = e^1$$

$$\lim_{h \to 0} (1 + h)^{1/h} = e.$$

This limit is sometimes used as the definition of e.

(c) Let $n = 1/h$. Then as $h \to 0^+$, we have $n \to \infty$. Since

$$\lim_{h \to 0^+} (1 + h)^{1/h} = \lim_{h \to 0} (1 + h)^{1/h} = e,$$

we have

$$\lim_{n \to \infty} \left(1 + \frac{1}{n} \right)^n = e.$$

This limit is also sometimes used as the definition of e.

Solutions for Section 3.7

Exercises

1. We differentiate implicitly both sides of the equation with respect to x.

$$2x + 2y \frac{dy}{dx} = 0,$$

$$\frac{dy}{dx} = -\frac{2x}{2y} = -\frac{x}{y}.$$

2. We differentiate implicitly both sides of the equation with respect to x.

$$2x + \left(y + x\frac{dy}{dx}\right) - 3y^2\frac{dy}{dx} = y^2 + x(2y)\frac{dy}{dx} \, ,$$

$$x\frac{dy}{dx} - 3y^2\frac{dy}{dx} - 2xy\frac{dy}{dx} = y^2 - y - 2x \, ,$$

$$\frac{dy}{dx} = \frac{y^2 - y - 2x}{x - 3y^2 - 2xy}.$$

3. Implicit differentiation gives

$$1 \cdot y + x \cdot \frac{dy}{dx} + 1 + \frac{dy}{dx} = 0.$$

Solving for dy/dx, we have

$$\frac{dy}{dx} = -\frac{1+y}{1+x}.$$

4.

$$2xy + x^2\frac{dy}{dx} - 2\frac{dy}{dx} = 0$$

$$(x^2 - 2)\frac{dy}{dx} = -2xy$$

$$\frac{dy}{dx} = \frac{-2xy}{(x^2 - 2)}$$

5. We differentiate implicitly both sides of the equation with respect to x.

$$x^{1/2} = 5y^{1/2}$$

$$\frac{1}{2}x^{-1/2} = \frac{5}{2}y^{-1/2}\frac{dy}{dx}$$

$$\frac{dy}{dx} = \frac{\frac{1}{2}x^{-1/2}}{\frac{5}{2}y^{-1/2}} = \frac{1}{5}\sqrt{\frac{y}{x}} = \frac{1}{25}.$$

We can also obtain this answer by realizing that the original equation represents part of the line $x = 25y$ which has slope $1/25$.

6. We differentiate implicitly both sides of the equation with respect to x.

$$x^{\frac{1}{2}} + y^{\frac{1}{2}} = 25 \, ,$$

$$\frac{1}{2}x^{-\frac{1}{2}} + \frac{1}{2}y^{-\frac{1}{2}}\frac{dy}{dx} = 0 \, ,$$

$$\frac{dy}{dx} = -\frac{\frac{1}{2}x^{-\frac{1}{2}}}{\frac{1}{2}y^{-\frac{1}{2}}} = -\frac{x^{-\frac{1}{2}}}{y^{-\frac{1}{2}}} = -\frac{\sqrt{y}}{\sqrt{x}} = -\sqrt{\frac{y}{x}}.$$

7. We differentiate implicitly with respect to x.

$$y + x\frac{dy}{dx} - 1 - \frac{3dy}{dx} = 0$$

$$(x - 3)\frac{dy}{dx} = 1 - y$$

$$\frac{dy}{dx} = \frac{1 - y}{x - 3}$$

8.

$$12x + 8y\frac{dy}{dx} = 0$$

$$\frac{dy}{dx} = \frac{-12x}{8y} = \frac{-3x}{2y}$$

9.

$$2ax - 2by\frac{dy}{dx} = 0$$

$$\frac{dy}{dx} = \frac{-2ax}{-2by} = \frac{ax}{by}$$

10. We differentiate implicitly both sides of the equation with respect to x.

$$\ln x + \ln(y^2) = 3$$

$$\frac{1}{x} + \frac{1}{y^2}(2y)\frac{dy}{dx} = 0$$

$$\frac{dy}{dx} = \frac{-1/x}{2y/y^2} = -\frac{y}{2x}.$$

11. We differentiate implicitly both sides of the equation with respect to x.

$$\ln y + x\frac{1}{y}\frac{dy}{dx} + 3y^2\frac{dy}{dx} = \frac{1}{x}$$

$$\frac{x}{y}\frac{dy}{dx} + 3y^2\frac{dy}{dx} = \frac{1}{x} - \ln y$$

$$\frac{dy}{dx}\left(\frac{x}{y} + 3y^2\right) = \frac{1 - x\ln y}{x}$$

$$\frac{dy}{dx}\left(\frac{x + 3y^3}{y}\right) = \frac{1 - x\ln y}{x}$$

$$\frac{dy}{dx} = \frac{(1 - x\ln y)}{x} \cdot \frac{y}{(x + 3y^3)}$$

12. We differentiate implicitly both sides of the equation with respect to x.

$$\cos(xy)\left(y + x\frac{dy}{dx}\right) = 2$$

$$y\cos(xy) + x\cos(xy)\frac{dy}{dx} = 2$$

$$\frac{dy}{dx} = \frac{2 - y\cos(xy)}{x\cos(xy)}.$$

13. Using the relation $\cos^2 y + \sin^2 y = 1$, the equation becomes:

$1 = y + 2$ or $y = -1$. Hence, $\frac{dy}{dx} = 0$.

14. We differentiate implicitly both sides of the equation with respect to x.

$$e^{\cos y}(-\sin y)\frac{dy}{dx} = 3x^2\arctan y + x^3\frac{1}{1 + y^2}\frac{dy}{dx}$$

$$\frac{dy}{dx}\left(-e^{\cos y}\sin y - \frac{x^3}{1 + y^2}\right) = 3x^2\arctan y$$

$$\frac{dy}{dx} = \frac{3x^2\arctan y}{-e^{\cos y}\sin y - x^3(1 + y^2)^{-1}}.$$

15. We differentiate implicitly both sides of the equation with respect to x.

$$\arctan(x^2 y) = xy^2$$

$$\frac{1}{1 + x^4 y^2}\left(2xy + x^2\frac{dy}{dx}\right) = y^2 + 2xy\frac{dy}{dx}$$

$$2xy + x^2\frac{dy}{dx} = [1 + x^4 y^2][y^2 + 2xy\frac{dy}{dx}]$$

$$\frac{dy}{dx}[x^2 - (1 + x^4 y^2)(2xy)] = (1 + x^4 y^2)y^2 - 2xy$$

$$\frac{dy}{dx} = \frac{y^2 + x^4 y^4 - 2xy}{x^2 - 2xy - 2x^5 y^3}.$$

16. We differentiate implicitly both sides of the equation with respect to x.

$$e^{x^2} + \ln y = 0$$

$$2xe^{x^2} + \frac{1}{y}\frac{dy}{dx} = 0$$

$$\frac{dy}{dx} = -2xye^{x^2}.$$

17. We differentiate implicitly both sides of the equation with respect to x.

$$(x-a)^2 + y^2 = a^2$$

$$2(x-a) + 2y\frac{dy}{dx} = 0$$

$$2y\frac{dy}{dx} = 2a - 2x$$

$$\frac{dy}{dx} = \frac{2a-2x}{2y} = \frac{a-x}{y}.$$

18. $\dfrac{2}{3}x^{-1/3} + \dfrac{2}{3}y^{-1/3} \cdot \dfrac{dy}{dx} = 0, \dfrac{dy}{dx} = -\dfrac{x^{-1/3}}{y^{-1/3}} = -\dfrac{y^{1/3}}{x^{1/3}}.$

19. Differentiating $x^2 + y^2 = 1$ with respect to x gives

$$2x + 2yy' = 0$$

so that

$$y' = -\frac{x}{y}$$

At the point $(0,1)$ the slope is 0.

20. Differentiating $\sin(xy) = x$ with respect to x gives

$$(y + xy')\cos(xy) = 1$$

or

$$xy'\cos(xy) = 1 - y\cos(xy)$$

so that

$$y' = \frac{1 - y\cos(xy)}{x\cos(xy)}.$$

As we move along the curve to the point $(1, \frac{\pi}{2})$, the value of $dy/dx \to \infty$, which tells us the tangent to the curve at $(1, \frac{\pi}{2})$ has infinite slope; the tangent is the vertical line $x = 1$.

21. Differentiating with respect to x gives

$$3x^2 + 2xy' + 2y + 2yy' = 0$$

so that

$$y' = -\frac{3x^2 + 2y}{2x + 2y}$$

At the point $(1,1)$ the slope is $-\frac{5}{4}$.

22. The slope is given by dy/dx, which we find using implicit differentiation. Notice that the product rule is needed for the second term. We differentiate to obtain:

$$3x^2 + 5x^2\frac{dy}{dx} + 10xy + 4y\frac{dy}{dx} = 4\frac{dy}{dx}$$

$$(5x^2 + 4y - 4)\frac{dy}{dx} = -3x^2 - 10xy$$

$$\frac{dy}{dx} = \frac{-3x^2 - 10xy}{5x^2 + 4y - 4}.$$

At the point $(1,2)$, we have $dy/dx = (-3 - 20)/(5 + 8 - 4) = -23/9$. The slope of this curve at the point $(1,2)$ is $-23/9$.

23. First, we must find the slope of the tangent, i.e. $\dfrac{dy}{dx}\bigg|_{(1,-1)}$. Differentiating implicitly, we have:

$$y^2 + x(2y)\frac{dy}{dx} = 0,$$

$$\frac{dy}{dx} = -\frac{y^2}{2xy} = -\frac{y}{2x}.$$

Substitution yields $\dfrac{dy}{dx}\bigg|_{(1,-1)} = -\dfrac{-1}{2} = \dfrac{1}{2}$. Using the point-slope formula for a line, we have that the equation for the tangent line is $y + 1 = \frac{1}{2}(x - 1)$ or $y = \frac{1}{2}x - \frac{3}{2}$.

24. First we must find the slope of the tangent, $\dfrac{dy}{dx}$, at $(1, e^2)$. Differentiating implicitly, we have:

$$\frac{1}{xy}\left(x\frac{dy}{dx} + y\right) = 2$$

$$\frac{dy}{dx} = \frac{2xy - y}{x}.$$

Evaluating dy/dx at $(1, e^2)$ yields $(2(1)e^2 - e^2)/1 = e^2$. Using the point-slope formula for the equation of the line, we have:

$$y - e^2 = e^2(x - 1),$$

or

$$y = e^2 x.$$

25. First, we must find the slope of the tangent, $\dfrac{dy}{dx}\bigg|_{(4,2)}$. Implicit differentiation yields:

$$2y\frac{dy}{dx} = \frac{2x(xy - 4) - x^2\left(x\frac{dy}{dx} + y\right)}{(xy - 4)^2}.$$

Given the complexity of the above equation, we first want to substitute 4 for x and 2 for y (the coordinates of the point where we are constructing our tangent line), then solve for $\dfrac{dy}{dx}$. Substitution yields:

$$2 \cdot 2\frac{dy}{dx} = \frac{(2 \cdot 4)(4 \cdot 2 - 4) - 4^2\left(4\frac{dy}{dx} + 2\right)}{(4 \cdot 2 - 4)^2} = \frac{8(4) - 16(4\frac{dy}{dx} + 2)}{16} = -4\frac{dy}{dx}.$$

$$4\frac{dy}{dx} = -4\frac{dy}{dx},$$

Solving for $\dfrac{dy}{dx}$, we have:

$$\frac{dy}{dx} = 0.$$

The tangent is a horizontal line through $(4, 2)$, hence its equation is $y = 2$.

26. First, we must find the slope of the tangent at the origin, that is $\dfrac{dy}{dx}\bigg|_{(0,0)}$. Rewriting $y = \dfrac{x}{y + a}$ as $y(y + a) = x$ so that we have

$$y^2 + ay = x$$

and differentiating implicitly gives

$$2y\frac{dy}{dx} + a\frac{dy}{dx} = 1$$

$$\frac{dy}{dx}(2y + a) = 1$$

$$\frac{dy}{dx} = \frac{1}{2y + a}.$$

Substituting $x = 0$, $y = 0$ yields $\dfrac{dy}{dx}\bigg|_{(0,0)} = \dfrac{1}{a}$. Using the point-slope formula for a line, we have that the equation for the tangent line is

$$y - 0 = \frac{1}{a}(x - 0) \quad \text{or} \quad y = \frac{x}{a}.$$

27. First, we must find the slope of the tangent, $\dfrac{dy}{dx}\Big|_{(a,0)}$. We differentiate implicitly, obtaining:

$$\frac{2}{3}x^{-\frac{1}{3}} + \frac{2}{3}y^{-\frac{1}{3}}\frac{dy}{dx} = 0,$$

$$\frac{dy}{dx} = -\frac{\frac{2}{3}x^{-\frac{1}{3}}}{\frac{2}{3}y^{-\frac{1}{3}}} = -\frac{\sqrt[3]{y}}{\sqrt[3]{x}}.$$

Substitution yields, $\dfrac{dy}{dx}\Big|_{(a,0)} = \dfrac{\sqrt[3]{0}}{\sqrt[3]{a}} = 0$. The tangent is a horizontal line through $(a, 0)$, hence its equation is $y = 0$.

Problems

28. (a) By implicit differentiation, we have:

$$2x + 2y\frac{dy}{dx} - 4 + 7\frac{dy}{dx} = 0$$

$$(2y + 7)\frac{dy}{dx} = 4 - 2x$$

$$\frac{dy}{dx} = \frac{4 - 2x}{2y + 7}.$$

(b) The curve has a horizontal tangent line when $dy/dx = 0$, which occurs when $4 - 2x = 0$ or $x = 2$. The curve has a horizontal tangent line at all points where $x = 2$.

The curve has a vertical tangent line when dy/dx is undefined, which occurs when $2y + 7 = 0$ or when $y = -7/2$. The curve has a vertical tangent line at all points where $y = -7/2$.

29. (a) Taking derivatives implicitly, we get

$$\frac{2}{25}x + \frac{2}{9}y\frac{dy}{dx} = 0$$

$$\frac{dy}{dx} = \frac{-9x}{25y}.$$

(b) The slope is not defined anywhere along the line $y = 0$. This ellipse intersects that line in two places, $(-5, 0)$ and $(5, 0)$. (These are the "ends" of the ellipse where the tangent is vertical.)

30. (a) If $x = 4$ then $16 + y^2 = 25$, so $y = \pm 3$. We find $\dfrac{dy}{dx}$ implicitly:

$$2x + 2y\frac{dy}{dx} = 0$$

$$\frac{dy}{dx} = -\frac{x}{y}.$$

So the slope at $(4, 3)$ is $-\frac{4}{3}$ and at $(4, -3)$ is $\frac{4}{3}$. The tangent lines are:

$$(y - 3) = -\frac{4}{3}(x - 4) \quad \text{and} \quad (y + 3) = \frac{4}{3}(x - 4)$$

(b) The normal lines have slopes that are the negative of the reciprocal of the slopes of the tangent lines. Thus,

$$(y - 3) = \frac{3}{4}(x - 4) \quad \text{so} \quad y = \frac{3}{4}x$$

and

$$(y + 3) = -\frac{3}{4}(x - 4) \quad \text{so} \quad y = -\frac{3}{4}x$$

are the normal lines.

(c) These lines meet at the origin, which is the center of the circle.

31. (a) Solving for $\frac{dy}{dx}$ by implicit differentiation yields

$$3x^2 + 3y^2\frac{dy}{dx} - y^2 - 2xy\frac{dy}{dx} = 0$$

$$\frac{dy}{dx} = \frac{y^2 - 3x^2}{3y^2 - 2xy}.$$

(b) We can approximate the curve near $x = 1$, $y = 2$ by its tangent line. The tangent line will have slope $\frac{(2)^2 - 3(1)^2}{3(2)^2 - 2(1)(2)} = \frac{1}{8} = 0.125$. Thus its equation is

$$y = 0.125x + 1.875$$

Using the y-values of the tangent line to approximate the y-values of the curve, we get:

x	0.96	0.98	1	1.02	1.04
approximate y	1.995	1.9975	2.000	2.0025	2.005

(c) When $x = 0.96$, we get the equation $0.96^3 + y^3 - 0.96y^2 = 5$, whose solution by numerical methods is 1.9945, which is close to the one above.

(d) The tangent line is horizontal when $\frac{dy}{dx}$ is zero and vertical when $\frac{dy}{dx}$ is undefined. These will occur when the numerator is zero and when the denominator is zero, respectively.

Thus, we know that the tangent is horizontal when $y^2 - 3x^2 = 0 \Rightarrow y = \pm\sqrt{3}x$. To find the points that satisfy this condition, we substitute back into the original equation for the curve:

$$x^3 + y^3 - xy^2 = 5$$
$$x^3 \pm 3\sqrt{3}x^3 - 3x^3 = 5$$
$$x^3 = \frac{5}{\pm 3\sqrt{3} - 2}$$

So $x \approx 1.1609$ or $x \approx -0.8857$.

Substituting,

$$y = \pm\sqrt{3}x \quad \text{so} \quad y \approx 2.0107 \quad \text{or} \quad y \approx 1.5341.$$

Thus, the tangent line is horizontal at $(1.1609, 2.0107)$ and $(-0.8857, 1.5341)$.

Also, we know that the tangent is vertical whenever $3y^2 - 2xy = 0$, that is, when $y = \frac{2}{3}x$ or $y = 0$. Substituting into the original equation for the curve gives us $x^3 + (\frac{2}{3}x)^3 - (\frac{2}{3})^2x^3 = 5$. This means $x^3 \approx 5.8696$, so $x \approx 1.8039$, $y \approx 1.2026$. The other vertical tangent is at $y = 0$, $x = \sqrt[3]{5}$.

32. The slope of the tangent to the curve $y = x^2$ at $x = 1$ is 2 so the equation of such a tangent will be of the form $y = 2x + c$. As the tangent must pass through $(1, 1)$, $c = -1$ and so the required tangent is $y = 2x - 1$.

Any circle centered at $(8, 0)$ will be of the form

$$(x - 8)^2 + y^2 = R^2.$$

The slope of this curve at (x, y) is given by implicit differentiation:

$$2(x - 8) + 2yy' = 0$$

or

$$y' = \frac{8 - x}{y}$$

For the tangent to the parabola to be tangential to the circle we need

$$\frac{8 - x}{y} = 2$$

so that at the point of contact of the circle and the line the coordinates are given by (x, y) when $y = 4 - x/2$. Substituting into the equation of the tangent line gives $x = 2$ and $y = 3$. From this we conclude that $R^2 = 45$ so that the equation of the circle is

$$(x - 8)^2 + y^2 = 45.$$

33. (a) Differentiating both sides of the equation with respect to P gives

$$\frac{d}{dP}\left(\frac{4f^2P}{1 - f^2}\right) = \frac{dK}{dP} = 0.$$

By the product rule

$$\frac{d}{dP}\left(\frac{4f^2P}{1-f^2}\right) = \frac{d}{dP}\left(\frac{4f^2}{1-f^2}\right)P + \left(\frac{4f^2}{1-f^2}\right)\cdot 1$$

$$= \left(\frac{(1-f^2)(8f) - 4f^2(-2f)}{(1-f^2)^2}\right)\frac{df}{dP}P + \left(\frac{4f^2}{1-f^2}\right)$$

$$= \left(\frac{8f}{(1-f^2)^2}\right)\frac{df}{dP}P + \left(\frac{4f^2}{1-f^2}\right) = 0.$$

So

$$\frac{df}{dP} = \frac{-4f^2/(1-f^2)}{8fP/(1-f^2)^2} = \frac{-1}{2P}f(1-f^2).$$

(b) Since f is a fraction of a gas, $0 \le f \le 1$. Also, in the equation relating f and P we can't have $f = 0$, since that would imply $K = 0$, and we can't have $f = 1$, since the left side is undefined there. So $0 < f < 1$. Thus $1 - f^2 > 0$. Also, pressure can't be negative, and from the equation relating f and P, we see that P can't be zero either, so $P > 0$. Therefore $df/dP = -(1/2P)f(1-f^2) < 0$ always. This means that at larger pressures less of the gas decomposes.

34. Let the point of intersection of the tangent line with the smaller circle be (x_1, y_1) and the point of intersection with the larger be (x_2, y_2). Let the tangent line be $y = mx + c$. Then at (x_1, y_1) and (x_2, y_2) the slopes of $x^2 + y^2 = 1$ and $y^2 + (x-3)^2 = 4$ are also m. The slope of $x^2 + y^2 = 1$ is found by implicit differentiation: $2x + 2yy' = 0$ so $y' = -x/y$. Similarly, the slope of $y^2 + (x-3)^2 = 4$ is $y' = -(x-3)/y$. Thus,

$$m = \frac{y_2 - y_1}{x_2 - x_1} = -\frac{x_1}{y_1} = -\frac{(x_2 - 3)}{y_2},$$

where $y_1 = \sqrt{1 - x_1^2}$ and $y_2 = \sqrt{4 - (x_2 - 3)^2}$. The positive values for y_1 and y_2 follow from Figure 3.7 and from our choice of $m > 0$. We obtain

$$\frac{x_1}{\sqrt{1 - x_1^2}} = \frac{x_2 - 3}{\sqrt{4 - (x_2 - 3)^2}}$$

$$\frac{x_1^2}{1 - x_1^2} = \frac{(x_2 - 3)^2}{4 - (x_2 - 3)^2}$$

$$x_1^2[4 - (x_2 - 3)^2] = (1 - x_1^2)(x_2 - 3)^2$$

$$4x_1^2 - (x_1^2)(x_2 - 3)^2 = (x_2 - 3)^2 - x_1^2(x_2 - 3)^2$$

$$4x_1^2 = (x_2 - 3)^2$$

$$2|x_1| = |x_2 - 3|.$$

From the picture $x_1 < 0$ and $x_2 < 3$. This gives $x_2 = 2x_1 + 3$ and $y_2 = 2y_1$. From

$$\frac{y_2 - y_1}{x_2 - x_1} = -\frac{x_1}{y_1},$$

substituting $y_1 = \sqrt{1 - x_1^2}$, $y_2 = 2y_1$ and $x_2 = 2x_1 + 3$ gives

$$x_1 = -\frac{1}{3}.$$

From $x_2 = 2x_1 + 3$ we get $x_2 = 7/3$. In addition, $y_1 = \sqrt{1 - x_1^2}$ gives $y_1 = 2\sqrt{2}/3$, and finally $y_2 = 2y_1$ gives $y_2 = 4\sqrt{2}/3$.

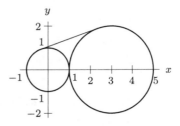

Figure 3.7

35. $y = x^{\frac{m}{n}}$. Taking n^{th} powers of both sides of this expression yields $(y)^n = (x^{\frac{m}{n}})^n$, or $y^n = x^m$.

$$\frac{d}{dx}(y^n) = \frac{d}{dx}(x^m)$$

$$ny^{n-1}\frac{dy}{dx} = mx^{m-1}$$

$$\frac{dy}{dx} = \frac{m}{n}\frac{x^{m-1}}{y^{n-1}}$$

$$= \frac{m}{n}\frac{x^{m-1}}{(x^{m/n})^{n-1}}$$

$$= \frac{m}{n}\frac{x^{m-1}}{x^{m-\frac{m}{n}}}$$

$$= \frac{m}{n}x^{(m-1)-(m-\frac{m}{n})} = \frac{m}{n}x^{\frac{m}{n}-1}.$$

Solutions for Section 3.8

Exercises

1. Using the chain rule, $\dfrac{d}{dx}(\cosh(2x)) = (\sinh(2x)) \cdot 2 = 2\sinh(2x)$.

2. Using the chain rule, $\dfrac{d}{dz}(\sinh(3z+5)) = \cosh(3z+5) \cdot 3 = 3\cosh(3z+5)$.

3. Using the chain rule,

$$\frac{d}{dt}(\cosh(\sinh t)) = \sinh(\sinh t) \cdot \cosh t$$

4. Using the product rule,

$$\frac{d}{dt}\left(t^3 \sinh t\right) = 3t^2 \sinh t + t^3 \cosh t.$$

5. Using the chain rule,

$$\frac{d}{dt}\left(\cosh^2 t\right) = 2\cosh t \cdot \sinh t.$$

6. Using the product and chain rules, $\dfrac{d}{dt}(\cosh(3t)\sinh(4t)) = 3\sinh(3t)\sinh(4t) + 4\cosh(3t)\cosh(4t)$.

7. Using the chain rule twice, $\dfrac{d}{dt}\left(\cosh(e^{t^2})\right) = \sinh(e^{t^2}) \cdot e^{t^2} \cdot 2t = 2te^{t^2}\sinh(e^{t^2})$.

8. Using the chain rule, $\dfrac{d}{dx}(\tanh(3+\sinh x)) = \dfrac{1}{\cosh^2(3+\sinh x)} \cdot \cosh x$.

9. Using the chain rule twice,

$$\frac{d}{dy}(\sinh(\sinh(3y))) = \cosh(\sinh(3y)) \cdot \cosh(3y) \cdot 3$$

$$= 3\cosh(3y) \cdot \cosh(\sinh(3y)).$$

10. Using the chain rule,

$$\frac{d}{d\theta}(\ln(\cosh(1+\theta))) = \frac{1}{\cosh(1+\theta)} \cdot \sinh(1+\theta) = \frac{\sinh(1+\theta)}{\cosh(1+\theta)} = \tanh(1+\theta).$$

11. Using the chain rule, $f'(t) = 2\cosh t \sinh t - 2\sinh t \cosh t = 0$. This is to be expected since $\cosh^2 t - \sinh^2 t = 1$.

12. Substitute $x = 0$ into the formula for $\sinh x$. This yields

$$\sinh 0 = \frac{e^0 - e^{-0}}{2} = \frac{1-1}{2} = 0.$$

13. Substituting $-x$ for x in the formula for $\sinh x$ gives

$$\sinh(-x) = \frac{e^{-x} - e^{-(-x)}}{2} = \frac{e^{-x} - e^x}{2} = -\frac{e^x - e^{-x}}{2} = -\sinh x.$$

14. Using the formula for $\sinh x$ and the fact that $d(e^{-x})/dx = -e^{-x}$, we see that

$$\frac{d}{dx}\left(\frac{e^x - e^{-x}}{2}\right) = \frac{e^x + e^{-x}}{2} = \cosh x.$$

15. By definition $\sinh x = (e^x - e^{-x})/2$ so, since $e^{\ln t} = t$ and $e^{-\ln t} = 1/e^{\ln t} = 1/t$, we have

$$\sinh(\ln t) = \frac{e^{\ln t} - e^{-\ln t}}{2} = \frac{t - 1/t}{2} = \frac{t^2 - 1}{2t}.$$

16. By definition $\cosh x = (e^x + e^{-x})/2$ so, since $e^{\ln t} = t$ and $e^{-\ln t} = 1/e^{\ln t} = 1/t$, we have

$$\cosh(\ln t) = \frac{e^{\ln t} + e^{-\ln t}}{2} = \frac{t + 1/t}{2} = \frac{t^2 + 1}{2t}.$$

Problems

17. The graph of $\sinh x$ in the text suggests that

$$\text{As } x \to \infty, \quad \sinh x \to \frac{1}{2}e^x.$$
$$\text{As } x \to -\infty, \quad \sinh x \to -\frac{1}{2}e^{-x}.$$

Using the facts that

$$\text{As } x \to \infty, \quad e^{-x} \to 0,$$
$$\text{As } x \to -\infty, \quad e^x \to 0,$$

we can obtain the same results analytically:

$$\text{As } x \to \infty, \quad \sinh x = \frac{e^x - e^{-x}}{2} \to \frac{1}{2}e^x.$$
$$\text{As } x \to -\infty, \quad \sinh x = \frac{e^x - e^{-x}}{2} \to -\frac{1}{2}e^{-x}.$$

18. First we observe that

$$\sinh(2x) = \frac{e^{2x} - e^{-2x}}{2}.$$

Now let's calculate

$$\begin{aligned}
(\sinh x)(\cosh x) &= \left(\frac{e^x - e^{-x}}{2}\right)\left(\frac{e^x + e^{-x}}{2}\right) \\
&= \frac{(e^x)^2 - (e^{-x})^2}{4} \\
&= \frac{e^{2x} - e^{-2x}}{4} \\
&= \frac{1}{2}\sinh(2x).
\end{aligned}$$

Thus, we see that

$$\sinh(2x) = 2\sinh x \cosh x.$$

19. First, we observe that

$$\cosh(2x) = \frac{e^{2x} + e^{-2x}}{2}.$$

Now let's use the fact that $e^x \cdot e^{-x} = 1$ to calculate

$$\cosh^2 x = \left(\frac{e^x + e^{-x}}{2} \right)^2$$

$$= \frac{(e^x)^2 + 2e^x \cdot e^{-x} + (e^{-x})^2}{4}$$

$$= \frac{e^{2x} + 2 + e^{-2x}}{4}.$$

Similarly, we have

$$\sinh^2 x = \left(\frac{e^x - e^{-x}}{2} \right)^2$$

$$= \frac{(e^x)^2 - 2e^x \cdot e^{-x} + (e^{-x})^2}{4}$$

$$= \frac{e^{2x} - 2 + e^{-2x}}{4}.$$

Thus, to obtain $\cosh(2x)$, we need to add (rather than subtract) $\cosh^2 x$ and $\sinh^2 x$, giving

$$\cosh^2 x + \sinh^2 x = \frac{e^{2x} + 2 + e^{-2x} + e^{2x} - 2 + e^{-2x}}{4}$$

$$= \frac{2e^{2x} + 2e^{-2x}}{4}$$

$$= \frac{e^{2x} + e^{-2x}}{2}$$

$$= \cosh(2x).$$

Thus, we see that the identity relating $\cosh(2x)$ to $\cosh x$ and $\sinh x$ is

$$\cosh(2x) = \cosh^2 x + \sinh^2 x.$$

20. Recall that

$$\sinh A = \frac{1}{2}(e^A - e^{-A}) \quad \text{and} \quad \cosh A = \frac{1}{2}(e^A + e^{-A}).$$

Now substitute, expand and collect terms:

$$\sinh A \cosh B + \sinh B \cosh A = \frac{1}{2}(e^A - e^{-A}) \cdot \frac{1}{2}(e^B + e^{-B}) + \frac{1}{2}(e^B - e^{-B}) \cdot \frac{1}{2}(e^A + e^{-A})$$

$$= \frac{1}{4} \left(e^{A+B} + e^{A-B} - e^{-A+B} - e^{-(A+B)} \right.$$

$$\left. + e^{B+A} + e^{B-A} - e^{-B+A} - e^{-A-B} \right)$$

$$= \frac{1}{2} \left(e^{A+B} - e^{-(A+B)} \right)$$

$$= \sinh(A + B).$$

21. Recall that

$$\sinh A = \frac{1}{2}(e^A - e^{-A}) \quad \text{and} \quad \cosh A = \frac{1}{2}(e^A + e^{-A}).$$

Now substitute, expand and collect terms:

$$\cosh A \cosh B + \sinh B \sinh A = \frac{1}{2}(e^A + e^{-A}) \cdot \frac{1}{2}(e^B + e^{-B}) + \frac{1}{2}(e^B - e^{-B}) \cdot \frac{1}{2}(e^A - e^{-A})$$

$$= \frac{1}{4}\left(e^{A+B} + e^{A-B} + e^{-A+B} + e^{-(A+B)}\right.$$

$$\left. + e^{B+A} - e^{B-A} - e^{-B+A} + e^{-A-B}\right)$$

$$= \frac{1}{2}\left(e^{A+B} + e^{-(A+B)}\right)$$

$$= \cosh(A+B).$$

22. Using the definition of $\cosh x$ and $\sinh x$, we have $\cosh 2x = \dfrac{e^{2x} + e^{-2x}}{2}$ and $\sinh 3x = \dfrac{e^{3x} - e^{-3x}}{2}$. Therefore

$$\lim_{x \to \infty} \frac{\cosh(2x)}{\sinh(3x)} = \lim_{x \to \infty} \frac{e^{2x} + e^{-2x}}{e^{3x} - e^{-3x}}$$

$$= \lim_{x \to \infty} \frac{e^{2x}(1 + e^{-4x})}{e^{2x}(e^x - e^{-5x})}$$

$$= \lim_{x \to \infty} \frac{1 + e^{-4x}}{e^x - e^{-5x}}$$

$$= 0.$$

23. Using the definition of $\sinh x$, we have $\sinh 2x = \dfrac{e^{2x} - e^{-2x}}{2}$. Therefore

$$\lim_{x \to \infty} \frac{e^{2x}}{\sinh(2x)} = \lim_{x \to \infty} \frac{2e^{2x}}{e^{2x} - e^{-2x}}$$

$$= \lim_{x \to \infty} \frac{2}{1 - e^{-4x}}$$

$$= 2.$$

24. Using the definition of $\cosh x$ and $\sinh x$, we have $\cosh x^2 = \dfrac{e^{x^2} + e^{-x^2}}{2}$ and $\sinh x^2 = \dfrac{e^{x^2} - e^{-x^2}}{2}$. Therefore

$$\lim_{x \to \infty} \frac{\sinh(x^2)}{\cosh(x^2)} = \lim_{x \to \infty} \frac{e^{x^2} - e^{-x^2}}{e^{x^2} + e^{-x^2}}$$

$$= \lim_{x \to \infty} \frac{e^{x^2}(1 - e^{-2x^2})}{e^{x^2}(1 + e^{-2x^2})}$$

$$= \lim_{x \to \infty} \frac{1 - e^{-2x^2}}{1 + e^{-2x^2}}$$

$$= 1.$$

25. Note that

$$\frac{\sinh kx}{\cosh 2x} = \frac{e^{kx} - e^{-kx}}{e^{2x} + e^{-2x}}$$

$$= \frac{e^{2x}(e^{(k-2)x} - e^{-(k+2)x})}{e^{2x}(1 + e^{-4x})}$$

$$= \frac{e^{(k-2)x} - e^{-(k+2)x}}{1 + e^{-4x}}.$$

If $k = 2$, then the limit as $x \to \infty$ is 1.

If $|k| > 2$, then the limit as $x \to \infty$ does not exist.

If $|k| < 2$, then the limit as $x \to \infty$ is 0.

26. Note that

$$e^{-3x}\cosh kx = e^{-3x}\frac{e^{kx}+e^{-kx}}{2}$$

$$= \frac{e^{(k-3)x}+e^{-(k+3)x}}{2}.$$

If $|k| = 3$, then the limit as $x \to \infty$ is 1/2.
If $|k| > 3$, then the limit as $x \to \infty$ does not exist.
If $|k| < 3$, then the limit as $x \to \infty$ is 0.

27. (a) The graph in Figure 3.8 looks like the graph of $y = \cosh x$, with the minimum at about $(0.5, 6.3)$.

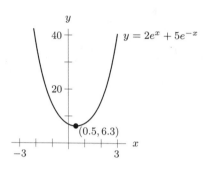

Figure 3.8

(b) We want to write

$$y = 2e^x + 5e^{-x} = A\cosh(x - c) = \frac{A}{2}e^{x-c} + \frac{A}{2}e^{-(x-c)}$$

$$= \frac{A}{2}e^x e^{-c} + \frac{A}{2}e^{-x}e^c$$

$$= \left(\frac{Ae^{-c}}{2}\right)e^x + \left(\frac{Ae^c}{2}\right)e^{-x}.$$

Thus, we need to choose A and c so that

$$\frac{Ae^{-c}}{2} = 2 \quad \text{and} \quad \frac{Ae^c}{2} = 5.$$

Dividing gives

$$\frac{Ae^c}{Ae^{-c}} = \frac{5}{2}$$

$$e^{2c} = 2.5$$

$$c = \frac{1}{2}\ln 2.5 \approx 0.458.$$

Solving for A gives

$$A = \frac{4}{e^{-c}} = 4e^c \approx 6.325.$$

Thus,

$$y = 6.325\cosh(x - 0.458).$$

Rewriting the function in this way shows that the graph in part (a) is the graph of $\cosh x$ shifted to the right by 0.458 and stretched vertically by a factor of 6.325.

28. We want to show that for any A, B with $A > 0$, $B > 0$, we can find K and c such that

$$y = Ae^x + Be^{-x} = \frac{Ke^{(x-c)} + Ke^{-(x-c)}}{2}$$

$$= \frac{K}{2}e^x e^{-c} + \frac{K}{2}e^{-x}e^c$$

$$= \left(\frac{Ke^{-c}}{2}\right)e^x + \left(\frac{Ke^c}{2}\right)e^{-x}.$$

Thus, we want to find K and c such that

$$\frac{Ke^{-c}}{2} = A \quad \text{and} \quad \frac{Ke^c}{2} = B.$$

Dividing, we have

$$\frac{Ke^c}{Ke^{-c}} = \frac{B}{A}$$

$$e^{2c} = \frac{B}{A}$$

$$c = \frac{1}{2}\ln\left(\frac{B}{A}\right).$$

If $A > 0$, $B > 0$, then there is a solution for c. Substituting to find K, we have

$$\frac{Ke^{-c}}{2} = A$$

$$K = 2Ae^c = 2Ae^{(\ln(B/A))/2}$$

$$= 2Ae^{\ln\sqrt{B/A}} = 2A\sqrt{\frac{B}{A}} = 2\sqrt{AB}.$$

Thus, if $A > 0$, $B > 0$, there is a solution for K also.

The fact that $y = Ae^x + Be^{-x}$ can be rewritten in this way shows that the graph of $y = Ae^x + Be^{-x}$ is the graph of $\cosh x$, shifted over by c and stretched (or shrunk) vertically by a factor of K.

29. (a) Since the cosh function is even, the height, y, is the same at $x = -T/w$ and $x = T/w$. The height at these endpoints is

$$y = \frac{T}{w}\cosh\left(\frac{w}{T}\cdot\frac{T}{w}\right) = \frac{T}{w}\cosh 1 = \frac{T}{w}\left(\frac{e^1 + e^{-1}}{2}\right).$$

At the lowest point, $x = 0$, and the height is

$$y = \frac{T}{w}\cosh 0 = \frac{T}{w}.$$

Thus the "sag" in the cable is given by

$$\text{Sag} = \frac{T}{w}\left(\frac{e + e^{-1}}{2}\right) - \frac{T}{w} = \frac{T}{w}\left(\frac{e + e^{-1}}{2} - 1\right) \approx 0.54\frac{T}{w}.$$

(b) To show that the differential equation is satisfied, take derivatives

$$\frac{dy}{dx} = \frac{T}{w}\cdot\frac{w}{T}\sinh\left(\frac{wx}{T}\right) = \sinh\left(\frac{wx}{T}\right)$$

$$\frac{d^2y}{dx^2} = \frac{w}{T}\cosh\left(\frac{wx}{T}\right).$$

Therefore, using the fact that $1 + \sinh^2 a = \cosh^2 a$ and that cosh is always positive, we have:

$$\frac{w}{T}\sqrt{1 + \left(\frac{dy}{dx}\right)^2} = \frac{w}{T}\sqrt{1 + \sinh^2\left(\frac{wx}{T}\right)} = \frac{w}{T}\sqrt{\cosh^2\left(\frac{wx}{T}\right)}$$

$$= \frac{w}{T}\cosh\left(\frac{wx}{T}\right).$$

So

$$\frac{w}{T}\sqrt{1 + \left(\frac{dy}{dx}\right)^2} = \frac{d^2y}{dx^2}.$$

30.

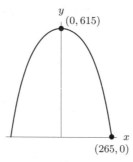

We know $x = 0$ and $y = 615$ at the top of the arch, so

$$615 = b - a\cosh(0/a) = b - a.$$

This means $b = a + 615$. We also know that $x = 265$ and $y = 0$ where the arch hits the ground, so

$$0 = b - a\cosh(265/a) = a + 615 - a\cosh(265/a).$$

We can solve this equation numerically on a calculator and get $a \approx 100$, which means $b \approx 715$. This results in the equation

$$y \approx 715 - 100\cosh\left(\frac{x}{100}\right).$$

31. (a) Substituting $x = 0$ gives

$$\tanh 0 = \frac{e^0 - e^{-0}}{e^0 + e^{-0}} = \frac{1 - 1}{2} = 0.$$

(b) Since $\tanh x = \dfrac{e^x - e^{-x}}{e^x + e^{-x}}$ and $e^x + e^{-x}$ is always positive, $\tanh x$ has the same sign as $e^x - e^{-x}$. For $x > 0$, we have $e^x > 1$ and $e^{-x} < 1$, so $e^x - e^{-x} > 0$. For $x < 0$, we have $e^x < 1$ and $e^{-x} > 1$, so $e^x - e^{-x} < 0$. For $x = 0$, we have $e^x = 1$ and $e^{-x} = 1$, so $e^x - e^{-x} = 0$. Thus, $\tanh x$ is positive for $x > 0$, negative for $x < 0$, and zero for $x = 0$.

(c) Taking the derivative, we have

$$\frac{d}{dx}(\tanh x) = \frac{1}{\cosh^2 x}.$$

Thus, for all x,

$$\frac{d}{dx}(\tanh x) > 0.$$

Thus, $\tanh x$ is increasing everywhere.

(d) As $x \to \infty$ we have $e^{-x} \to 0$; as $x \to -\infty$, we have $e^x \to 0$. Thus

$$\lim_{x \to \infty} \tanh x = \lim_{x \to \infty}\left(\frac{e^x - e^{-x}}{e^x + e^{-x}}\right) = 1,$$

$$\lim_{x \to -\infty} \tanh x = \lim_{x \to -\infty}\left(\frac{e^x - e^{-x}}{e^x + e^{-x}}\right) = -1.$$

Thus, $y = 1$ and $y = -1$ are horizontal asymptotes to the graph of $\tanh x$. See Figure 3.9.

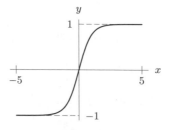

Figure 3.9: Graph of $y = \tanh x$

(e) The graph of $\tanh x$ suggests that $\tanh x$ is increasing everywhere; the fact that the derivative of $\tanh x$ is positive for all x confirms this. Since $\tanh x$ is increasing for all x, different values of x lead to different values of y, and therefore $\tanh x$ does have an inverse.

Solutions for Section 3.9

Exercises

1. With $f(x) = \sqrt{1+x}$, the chain rule gives $f'(x) = 1/(2\sqrt{1+x})$, so $f(0) = 1$ and $f'(0) = 1/2$. Therefore the tangent line approximation of f near $x = 0$,

$$f(x) \approx f(0) + f'(0)(x - 0),$$

becomes

$$\sqrt{1+x} \approx 1 + \frac{x}{2}.$$

This means that, near $x = 0$, the function $\sqrt{1+x}$ can be approximated by its tangent line $y = 1 + x/2$. (See Figure 3.10.)

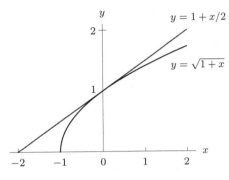

Figure 3.10

2. With $f(x) = e^x$, the tangent line approximation to f near $x = 0$ is $f(x) \approx f(0) + f'(0)(x - 0)$ which becomes $e^x \approx e^0 + e^0 x = 1 + 1x = 1 + x$. Thus, our local linearization of e^x near $x = 0$ is $e^x \approx 1 + x$.

3. With $f(x) = 1/x$, we see that the tangent line approximation to f near $x = 1$ is

$$f(x) \approx f(1) + f'(1)(x - 1),$$

which becomes

$$\frac{1}{x} \approx 1 + f'(1)(x - 1).$$

Since $f'(x) = -1/x^2$, $f'(1) = -1$. Thus our formula reduces to

$$\frac{1}{x} \approx 1 - (x - 1) = 2 - x.$$

This is the local linearization of $1/x$ near $x = 1$.

4. With $f(x) = 1/(\sqrt{1+x})$, we see that the tangent line approximation to f near $x = 0$ is

$$f(x) \approx f(0) + f'(0)(x - 0),$$

which becomes

$$\frac{1}{\sqrt{1+x}} \approx 1 + f'(0)x.$$

Since $f'(x) = (-1/2)(1+x)^{-3/2}$, $f'(0) = -1/2$. Thus our formula reduces to

$$\frac{1}{\sqrt{1+x}} \approx 1 - x/2.$$

This is the local linearization of $\dfrac{1}{\sqrt{1+x}}$ near $x = 0$.

5. Let $f(x) = e^{-x}$. Then $f'(x) = -e^{-x}$. So $f(0) = 1$, $f'(0) = -e^0 = -1$. Therefore, $e^{-x} \approx f(0) + f'(0)x = 1 - x$.

6. With $f(x) = e^{x^2}$, we get a tangent line approximation of $f(x) \approx f(1) + f'(1)(x - 1)$ which becomes $e^{x^2} \approx e + \left(2xe^{x^2}\right)\Big|_{x=1} (x - 1) = e + 2e(x - 1) = 2ex - e$. Thus, our local linearization of e^{x^2} near $x = 1$ is $e^{x^2} \approx 2ex - e$.

7. From Figure 3.11, we see that the error has its maximum magnitude at the end points of the interval, $x = \pm 1$. The magnitude of the error can be read off the graph as less than 0.2 or estimated as

$$|\text{Error}| \leq |1 - \sin 1| = 0.159 < 0.2.$$

The approximation is an overestimate for $x > 0$ and an underestimate for $x < 0$.

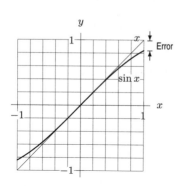

Figure 3.11

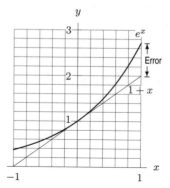

Figure 3.12

8. Figure 3.12 shows that $1 + x$ is an underestimate of e^x for $-1 \leq x \leq 1$. On this interval, the error has the largest magnitude at $x = 1$. Its magnitude can be estimated from the graph as less than 0.8, or estimated as

$$|\text{Error}| = e - 1 - 1 = 0.718 < 0.8.$$

Problems

9. (a) Since

$$\frac{d}{dx}(\cos x) = -\sin x,$$

the slope of the tangent line is $-\sin(\pi/4) = -1/\sqrt{2}$. Since the tangent line passes through the point $(\pi/4, \cos(\pi/4)) = (\pi/4, 1/\sqrt{2})$, its equation is

$$y - \frac{1}{\sqrt{2}} = -\frac{1}{\sqrt{2}}\left(x - \frac{\pi}{4}\right)$$

$$y = -\frac{1}{\sqrt{2}}x + \frac{1}{\sqrt{2}}\left(\frac{\pi}{4} + 1\right).$$

Thus, the tangent line approximation to $\cos x$ is

$$\cos x \approx -\frac{1}{\sqrt{2}}x + \frac{1}{\sqrt{2}}\left(\frac{\pi}{4} + 1\right).$$

(b) From Figure 3.13, we see that the tangent line approximation is an overestimate.
(c) From Figure 3.13, we see that the maximum error for $0 \leq x \leq \pi/2$ is either at $x = 0$ or at $x = \pi/2$. The error can either be estimated from the graph, or as follows. At $x = 0$,

$$|\text{Error}| = \left|\cos 0 - \frac{1}{\sqrt{2}}\left(\frac{\pi}{4} + 1\right)\right| = 0.262 < 0.3.$$

At $x = \pi/2$,

$$|\text{Error}| = \left|\cos\frac{\pi}{2} + \frac{1}{\sqrt{2}}\frac{\pi}{2} - \frac{1}{\sqrt{2}}\left(\frac{\pi}{4} + 1\right)\right| = 0.152 < 0.2.$$

Thus, for $0 \leq x \leq \pi/2$, we have

$$|\text{Error}| < 0.3.$$

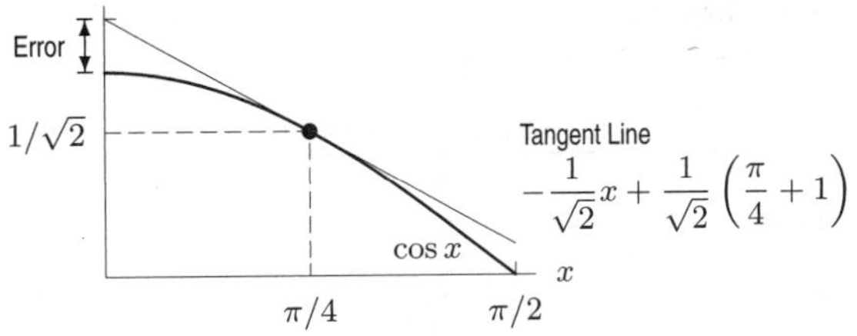

Figure 3.13

10. (a) Let $f(x) = (1 + x)^k$. Then $f'(x) = k(1 + x)^{k-1}$. Since

$$f(x) \approx f(0) + f'(0)(x - 0)$$

is the tangent line approximation, and $f(0) = 1$, $f'(0) = k$, for small x we get

$$f(x) \approx 1 + kx.$$

(b) Since $\sqrt{1.1} = (1 + 0.1)^{1/2} \approx 1 + (1/2)0.1 = 1.05$ by the above method, this estimate is about right.

(c) The real answer is less than 1.05. Since $(1.05)^2 = (1 + 0.05)^2 = 1 + 2(1)(0.05) + (0.05)^2 = 1.1 + (0.05)^2 > 1.1$, we have $(1.05)^2 > 1.1$ Therefore

$$\sqrt{1.1} < 1.05.$$

Graphically, this because the graph of $\sqrt{1 + x}$ is concave down, so it bends below its tangent line. Therefore the true value ($\sqrt{1.1}$) which is on the curve is below the approximate value (1.05) which is on the tangent line.

11. Since the line meets the curve at $x = 1$, we have $a = 1$. Since the point with $x = 1$ lies on both the line and the curve, we have

$$f(a) = f(1) = 2 \cdot 1 - 1 = 1.$$

The approximation is an underestimate because the line lies under the curve. Since the linear function approximates $f(x)$, we have

$$f(1.2) \approx 2(1.2) - 1 = 1.4.$$

12. (a) From the figure, we see $a = 2$. The point with $x = 2$ lies on both the line and the curve. Since

$$y = -3 \cdot 2 + 7 = 1,$$

we have

$$f(a) = 1.$$

Since the slope of the line is -3, we have

$$f'(a) = -3.$$

(b) We use the line to approximate the function, so

$$f(2.1) \approx -3(2.1) + 7 = 0.7.$$

This is an underestimate, because the line is beneath the curve for $x > 2$. Similarly,

$$f(1.98) \approx -3(1.98) + 7 = 1.06.$$

This is an overestimate because the line is above the curve for $x < 2$.

The approximation $f(1.98) \approx 1.06$ is likely to be more accurate because 1.98 is closer to 2 than 2.1 is. Since the graph of $f(x)$ appears to bend away from the line at approximately the same rate on either side of $x = 2$, in this example, the error is larger for points farther from $x = 2$.

13. We have $f(1) = 1$ and $f'(1) = 4$. Thus

$$E(x) = x^4 - (1 + 4(x - 1)).$$

Values of $E(x)/(x - 1)$ near $x = 1$ are in Table 3.3.

Table 3.3

x	1.1	1.01	1.001
$E(x)/(x-1)$	0.641	0.060401	0.006004

From the table, we can see that

$$\frac{E(x)}{(x-1)} \approx 6(x-1),$$

so $k = 6$ and

$$E(x) \approx 6(x-1)^2.$$

In addition, $f''(1) = 12$, so

$$E(x) \approx 6(x-1)^2 = \frac{f''(1)}{2}(x-1)^2.$$

The same result can be obtained by rewriting the function x^4 using $x = 1 + (x-1)$ and expanding:

$$x^4 = (1 + (x-1))^4 = 1 + 4(x-1) + 6(x-1)^2 + 4(x-1)^3 + (x-1)^4.$$

Thus,

$$E(x) = x^4 - (1 + 4(x-1)) = 6(x-1)^2 + 4(x-1)^3 + (x-1)^4.$$

For x near 1, the value of $x-1$ is small, so we ignore powers of $x-1$ higher than the first, giving

$$E(x) \approx 6(x-1)^2.$$

14. We have $f(0) = 1$ and $f'(0) = 0$. Thus

$$E(x) = \cos x - 1.$$

Values for $E(x)/(x-0)$ near $x = 0$ are in Table 3.4.

Table 3.4

x	0.1	0.01	0.001
$E(x)/(x-0)$	-0.050	-0.0050	-0.00050

From the table, we can see that

$$\frac{E(x)}{(x-0)} \approx -0.5(x-0),$$

so $k = -1/2$ and

$$E(x) \approx -\frac{1}{2}(x-0)^2 = -\frac{1}{2}x^2.$$

In addition, $f''(0) = -1$, so

$$E(x) \approx -\frac{1}{2}x^2 = \frac{f''(0)}{2}x^2.$$

15. We have $f(0) = 1$ and $f'(0) = 1$. Thus

$$E(x) = e^x - (1 + x).$$

Values of $E(x)/(x-0)$ near $x = 0$ are in Table 3.5.

Table 3.5

x	0.1	0.01	0.001
$E(x)/(x-0)$	0.052	0.0050	0.00050

From the table, we can see that

$$\frac{E(x)}{(x-0)} \approx 0.5(x-0)$$

so $k = 1/2$ and

$$E(x) \approx \frac{1}{2}(x-0)^2 = \frac{1}{2}x^2.$$

In addition, $f''(0) = 1$, so

$$E(x) \approx \frac{1}{2}x^2 = \frac{f''(0)}{2}x^2$$

16. We have $f(1) = 1$ and $f'(1) = 1/2$. Thus

$$E(x) = \sqrt{x} - \left(1 + \frac{1}{2}(x-1)\right).$$

Values of $E(x)/(x-1)$ near $x = 1$ are in Table 3.6.

Table 3.6

x	1.1	1.01	1.001
$E(x)/(x-1)$	-0.0119	-0.00124	-0.000125

From the table, we can see that

$$\frac{E(x)}{(x-1)} \approx -0.125(x-1)$$

so $k = -1/8$ and

$$E(x) \approx -\frac{1}{8}(x-1)^2.$$

In addition, $f''(1) = -1/4$, so

$$E(x) \approx -\frac{1}{8}(x-1)^2 = \frac{f''(1)}{2}(x-1)^2.$$

17. We have $f(1) = 0$ and $f'(1) = 1$. Thus

$$E(x) = \ln x - (x-1).$$

Values of $E(x)/(x-1)$ near $x = 1$ are in Table 3.7.

Table 3.7

x	1.1	1.01	1.001
$E(x)/(x-1)$	-0.047	-0.0050	-0.00050

From the table, we see that

$$\frac{E(x)}{(x-1)} \approx -0.5(x-1),$$

so $k = -1/2$ and

$$E(x) \approx -\frac{1}{2}(x-1)^2.$$

In addition, $f''(1) = -1$, so

$$E(x) \approx -\frac{1}{2}(x-1)^2 = \frac{f''(1)}{2}(x-1)^2.$$

18. The local linearization of e^x near $x = 0$ is $1 + 1x$ so

$$e^x \approx 1 + x.$$

Squaring this yields, for small x,

$$e^{2x} = (e^x)^2 \approx (1+x)^2 = 1 + 2x + x^2.$$

Local linearization of e^{2x} directly yields

$$e^{2x} \approx 1 + 2x$$

for small x. The two approximations are consistent because they agree: the tangent line approximation to $1 + 2x + x^2$ is just $1 + 2x$.

The first approximation is more accurate. One can see this numerically or by noting that the approximation for e^{2x} given by $1 + 2x$ is really the same as approximating e^y at $y = 2x$. Since the other approximation approximates e^y at $y = x$, which is twice as close to 0 and therefore a better general estimate, it's more likely to be correct.

19. (a) Let $f(x) = 1/(1+x)$. Then $f'(x) = -1/(1+x)^2$ by the chain rule. So $f(0) = 1$, and $f'(0) = -1$. Therefore, for x near 0, $1/(1+x) \approx f(0) + f'(0)x = 1 - x$.

(b) We know that for small y, $1/(1+y) \approx 1 - y$. Let $y = x^2$; when x is small, so is $y = x^2$. Hence, for small x, $1/(1+x^2) \approx 1 - x^2$.

(c) Since the linearization of $1/(1+x^2)$ is the line $y = 1$, and this line has a slope of 0, the derivative of $1/(1+x^2)$ is zero at $x = 0$.

20. The local linearizations of $f(x) = e^x$ and $g(x) = \sin x$ near $x = 0$ are

$$f(x) = e^x \approx 1 + x$$

and

$$g(x) = \sin x \approx x.$$

Thus, the local linearization of $e^x \sin x$ is the local linearization of the product:

$$e^x \sin x \approx (1 + x)x = x + x^2 \approx x.$$

We therefore know that the derivative of $e^x \sin x$ at $x = 0$ must be 1. Similarly, using the local linearization of $1/(1 + x)$ near $x = 0$, $1/(1 + x) \approx 1 - x$, we have

$$\frac{e^x \sin x}{1 + x} = (e^x)(\sin x)\left(\frac{1}{1+x}\right) \approx (1 + x)(x)(1 - x) = x - x^3$$

so the local linearization of the triple product $\dfrac{e^x \sin x}{1 + x}$ at $x = 0$ is simply x. And therefore the derivative of $\dfrac{e^x \sin x}{1 + x}$ at $x = 0$ is 1.

21. (a) Suppose

$$g = f(r) = \frac{GM}{r^2}.$$

Then

$$f'(r) = \frac{-2GM}{r^3}.$$

So

$$f(r + \Delta r) \approx f(r) - \frac{2GM}{r^3}(\Delta r).$$

Since $f(r + \Delta r) - f(r) = \Delta g$, and $g = GM/r^2$, we have

$$\Delta g \approx -2\frac{GM}{r^3}(\Delta r) = -2g\frac{\Delta r}{r}.$$

(b) The negative sign tells us that the acceleration due to gravity decreases as the distance from the center of the earth increases.

(c) The fractional change in g is given by

$$\frac{\Delta g}{g} \approx -2\frac{\Delta r}{r}.$$

So, since $\Delta r = 4.315$ km and $r = 6400$ km, we have

$$\frac{\Delta g}{g} \approx -2\left(\frac{4.315}{6400}\right) = -0.00135 = -0.135\%.$$

22. (a) Suppose g is a constant and

$$T = f(l) = 2\pi\sqrt{\frac{l}{g}}.$$

Then

$$f'(l) = \frac{2\pi}{\sqrt{g}}\frac{1}{2}l^{-1/2} = \frac{\pi}{\sqrt{gl}}.$$

Thus, local linearity tells us that

$$f(l + \Delta l) \approx f(l) + \frac{\pi}{\sqrt{gl}}\Delta l.$$

Now $T = f(l)$ and $\Delta T = f(l + \Delta l) - f(l)$, so

$$\Delta T \approx \frac{\pi}{\sqrt{gl}}\Delta l = 2\pi\sqrt{\frac{l}{g}} \cdot \frac{1}{2}\frac{\Delta l}{l} = \frac{T}{2}\frac{\Delta l}{l}.$$

(b) Knowing that the length of the pendulum increases by 2% tells us that

$$\frac{\Delta l}{l} = 0.02.$$

Thus,

$$\Delta T \approx \frac{T}{2}(0.02) = 0.01T.$$

So

$$\frac{\Delta T}{T} \approx 0.01.$$

Thus, T increases by 1%.

23. (a) Considering l as a constant, we have

$$T = f(g) = 2\pi\sqrt{\frac{l}{g}}.$$

Then,

$$f'(g) = 2\pi\sqrt{l}\left(-\frac{1}{2}g^{-3/2}\right) = -\pi\sqrt{\frac{l}{g^3}}.$$

Thus, local linearity gives

$$f(g + \Delta g) \approx f(g) - \pi\sqrt{\frac{l}{g^3}}(\Delta g).$$

Since $T = f(g)$ and $\Delta T = f(g + \Delta g) - f(g)$, we have

$$\Delta T \approx -\pi\sqrt{\frac{l}{g^3}}\Delta g = -2\pi\sqrt{\frac{l}{g}}\frac{\Delta g}{2g} = \frac{-T}{2}\frac{\Delta g}{g}.$$
$$\Delta T \approx \frac{-T}{2}\frac{\Delta g}{g}.$$

(b) If g increases by 1%, we know

$$\frac{\Delta g}{g} = 0.01.$$

Thus,

$$\frac{\Delta T}{T} \approx -\frac{1}{2}\frac{\Delta g}{g} = -\frac{1}{2}(0.01) = -0.005,$$

So, T decreases by 0.5%.

24. Since f has a positive second derivative, its graph is concave up, as in Figure 3.14 or 3.15. This means that the graph of $f(x)$ is above its tangent line. We see that in both cases

$$f(1 + \Delta x) \geq f(1) + f'(1)\Delta x.$$

(The diagrams show Δx positive, but the result is also true if Δx is negative.)

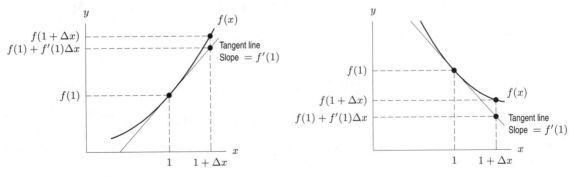

Figure 3.14   Figure 3.15

25. (a) Since f' is decreasing, $f'(5)$ is larger.
(b) Since f' is decreasing, its derivative, f'', is negative. Thus, $f''(5)$ is negative, so 0 is larger.
(c) Since $f''(x)$ is negative for all x, the graph of f is concave down. Thus the graph of $f(x)$ is below its tangent line. From Figure 3.16, we see that $f(5 + \Delta x)$ is below $f(5) + f'(5)\Delta x$. Thus, $f(5) + f'(5)\Delta x$ is larger.

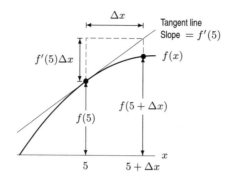

Figure 3.16

26. Note that

$$[f(x)g(x)]' = \lim_{h \to 0} \frac{f(x+h)g(x+h) - f(x)g(x)}{h}.$$

We use the hint: For small h, $f(x + h) \approx f(x) + f'(x)h$, and $g(x + h) \approx g(x) + g'(x)h$. Therefore

$$\begin{aligned} f(x+h)g(x+h) - f(x)g(x) &\approx [f(x) + hf'(x)][g(x) + hg'(x)] - f(x)g(x) \\ &= f(x)g(x) + hf'(x)g(x) + hf(x)g'(x) \\ &\quad + h^2 f'(x)g'(x) - f(x)g(x) \\ &= hf'(x)g(x) + hf(x)g'(x) + h^2 f'(x)g'(x). \end{aligned}$$

Therefore

$$\begin{aligned} \lim_{h \to 0} \frac{f(x+h)g(x+h) - f(x)g(x)}{h} &= \lim_{h \to 0} \frac{hf'(x)g(x) + hf(x)g'(x) + h^2 f'(x)g'(x)}{h} \\ &= \lim_{h \to 0} \frac{h\left(f'(x)g(x) + f(x)g'(x) + hf'(x)g'(x)\right)}{h} \\ &= \lim_{h \to 0} \left(f'(x)g(x) + f(x)g'(x) + hf'(x)g'(x)\right) \\ &= f'(x)g(x) + f(x)g'(x). \end{aligned}$$

A more complete derivation can be given using the error term discussed in the section on Differentiability and Linear Approximation in Chapter 2. Adapting the notation of that section to this problem, we write

$$f(x + h) = f(x) + f'(x)h + E_f(h) \quad \text{and} \quad g(x + h) = g(x) + g'(x)h + E_g(h),$$

where $\lim\limits_{h \to 0} \dfrac{E_f(h)}{h} = \lim\limits_{h \to 0} \dfrac{E_g(h)}{h} = 0$. (This implies that $\lim\limits_{h \to 0} E_f(h) = \lim\limits_{h \to 0} E_g(h) = 0$.)

We have

$$\begin{aligned} \frac{f(x+h)g(x+h) - f(x)g(x)}{h} &= \frac{f(x)g(x)}{h} + f(x)g'(x) + f'(x)g(x) + f(x)\frac{E_g(h)}{h} + g(x)\frac{E_f(h)}{h} \\ &\quad + f'(x)g'(x)h + f'(x)E_g(h) + g'(x)E_f(h) + \frac{E_f(h)E_g(h)}{h} - \frac{f(x)g(x)}{h}. \end{aligned}$$

The terms $f(x)g(x)/h$ and $-f(x)g(x)/h$ cancel out. All the remaining terms on the right, with the exception of the second and third terms, go to zero as $h \to 0$. Thus, we have

$$[f(x)g(x)]' = \lim_{h \to 0} \frac{f(x+h)g(x+h) - f(x)g(x)}{h} = f(x)g'(x) + f'(x)g(x).$$

27. Note that

$$[f(g(x))]' = \lim_{h \to 0} \frac{f(g(x+h)) - f(g(x))}{h}.$$

Using the local linearizations of f and g, we get that

$$f(g(x+h)) - f(g(x)) \approx f\left(g(x) + g'(x)h\right) - f(g(x))$$
$$\approx f\left(g(x)\right) + f'(g(x))g'(x)h - f(g(x))$$
$$= f'(g(x))g'(x)h.$$

Therefore,

$$[f(g(x))]' = \lim_{h \to 0} \frac{f(g(x+h)) - f(g(x))}{h}$$
$$= \lim_{h \to 0} \frac{f'(g(x))g'(x)h}{h}$$
$$= \lim_{h \to 0} f'(g(x))g'(x) = f'(g(x))g'(x).$$

A more complete derivation can be given using the error term discussed in the section on Differentiability and Linear Approximation in Chapter 2. Adapting the notation of that section to this problem, we write

$$f(z+k) = f(z) + f'(z)k + E_f(k) \quad \text{and} \quad g(x+h) = g(x) + g'(x)h + E_g(h),$$

where $\displaystyle \lim_{h \to 0} \frac{E_g(h)}{h} = \lim_{k \to 0} \frac{E_f(k)}{k} = 0.$

Now we let $z = g(x)$ and $k = g(x+h) - g(x)$. Then we have $k = g'(x)h + E_g(h)$. Thus,

$$\frac{f(g(x+h)) - f(g(x))}{h} = \frac{f(z+k) - f(z)}{h}$$
$$= \frac{f(z) + f'(z)k + E_f(k) - f(z)}{h} = \frac{f'(z)k + E_f(k)}{h}$$
$$= \frac{f'(z)g'(x)h + f'(z)E_g(h)}{h} + \frac{E_f(k)}{k} \cdot \left(\frac{k}{h}\right)$$
$$= f'(z)g'(x) + \frac{f'(z)E_g(h)}{h} + \frac{E_f(k)}{k}\left[\frac{g'(x)h + E_g(h)}{h}\right]$$
$$= f'(z)g'(x) + \frac{f'(z)E_g(h)}{h} + \frac{g'(x)E_f(k)}{k} + \frac{E_g(h) \cdot E_f(k)}{h \cdot k}$$

Now, if $h \to 0$ then $k \to 0$ as well, and all the terms on the right except the first go to zero, leaving us with the term $f'(z)g'(x)$. Substituting $g(x)$ for z, we obtain

$$[f(g(x))]' = \lim_{h \to 0} \frac{f(g(x+h)) - f(g(x))}{h} = f'(g(x))g'(x).$$

28. We want to show that

$$\lim_{x \to a} \frac{f(x) - f(a)}{x - a} = L.$$

Substituting for $f(x)$ we have

$$\lim_{x \to a} \frac{f(x) - f(a)}{x - a} = \lim_{x \to a} \frac{f(a) + L(x - a) + E_L(x) - f(a)}{x - a}$$
$$= \lim_{x \to a} \left(L + \frac{E_L(x)}{x - a}\right) = L + \lim_{x \to 0} \frac{E_L(x)}{x - a} = L.$$

Thus, we have shown that f is differentiable at $x = a$ and that its derivative is L, that is, $f'(a) = L$.

Solutions for Section 3.10

Exercises

1. False. The derivative, $f'(x)$, is not equal to zero everywhere, because the function is not continuous at integral values of x, so $f'(x)$ does not exist there. Thus, the Constant Function Theorem does not apply.

2. False. The horse that wins the race may have been moving faster for some, but not all, of the race. The Racetrack Principle guarantees the converse—that if the horses start at the same time and one moves faster throughout the race, then that horse wins.

3. True. If $g(x)$ is the position of the slower horse at time x and $h(x)$ is the position of the faster, then $g'(x) \leq h'(x)$ for $a < x < b$. Since the horses start at the same time, $g(a) = h(a)$, so, by the Racetrack Principle, $g(x) \leq h(x)$ for $a \leq x \leq b$. Therefore, $g(b) \leq h(b)$, so the slower horse loses the race.

4. True. If f' is positive on $[a, b]$, then f is continuous and the Increasing Function Theorem applies. Thus, f is increasing on $[a, b]$, so $f(a) < f(b)$.

5. False. Let $f(x) = x^3$ on $[-1, 1]$. Then $f(x)$ is increasing but $f'(x) = 0$ for $x = 0$.

6. No, it does not satisfy the hypotheses. The function does not appear to be differentiable. There appears to be no tangent line, and hence no derivative, at the "corner."

No, it does not satisfy the conclusion as there is no horizontal tangent.

7. Yes, it satisfies the hypotheses and the conclusion. This function has two points, c, at which the tangent to the curve is parallel to the secant joining $(a, f(a))$ to $(b, f(b))$, but this does not contradict the Mean Value Theorem. The function is continuous and differentiable on the interval $[a, b]$.

8. No, it does not satisfy the hypotheses. This function does not appear to be continuous.

No, it does not satisfy the conclusion as there is no horizontal tangent.

9. No. This function does not satisfy the hypotheses of the Mean Value Theorem, as it is not continuous.

However, the function has a point c such that

$$f'(c) = \frac{f(b) - f(a)}{b - a}.$$

Thus, this satisfies the conclusion of the theorem.

Problems

10. Let $f(x) = \sin x$ and $g(x) = x$. Then $f(0) = 0$ and $g(0) = 0$. Also $f'(x) = \cos x$ and $g'(x) = 1$, so for all $x \geq 0$ we have $f'(x) \leq g'(x)$. So the graphs of f and g both go through the origin and the graph of f climbs slower than the graph of g. Thus the graph of f is below the graph of g for $x \geq 0$ by the Racetrack Principle. In other words, $\sin x \leq x$ for $x \geq 0$.

11. Let $g(x) = \ln x$ and $h(x) = x - 1$. For $x \geq 1$, we have $g'(x) = 1/x \leq 1 = h'(x)$. Since $g(1) = h(1)$, the Racetrack Principle with $a = 1$ says that $g(x) \leq h(x)$ for $x \geq 1$, that is, $\ln x \leq x - 1$ for $x \geq 1$. For $0 < x \leq 1$, we have $h'(x) = 1 \leq 1/x = g'(x)$. Since $g(1) = h(1)$, the Racetrack Principle with $b = 1$ says that $g(x) \leq h(x)$ for $0 < x \leq 1$, that is, $\ln x \leq x - 1$ for $0 < x \leq 1$.

12.

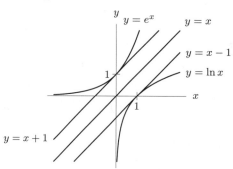

Graphical solution: If f and g are inverse functions then the graph of g is just the graph of f reflected through the line $y = x$. But e^x and $\ln x$ are inverse functions, and so are the functions $x + 1$ and $x - 1$. Thus the equivalence is clear from the figure.

Algebraic solution: If $x > 0$ and

$$x + 1 \leq e^x,$$

then, replacing x by $x - 1$, we have

$$x \leq e^{x-1}.$$

Taking logarithms, and using the fact that $\ln$ is an increasing function, gives

$$\ln x \leq x - 1.$$

We can also go in the opposite direction, which establishes the equivalence.

13. The Decreasing Function Theorem is: Suppose that f is continuous on $[a, b]$ and differentiable on (a, b). If $f'(x) < 0$ on (a, b), then f is decreasing on $[a, b]$. If $f'(x) \leq 0$ on (a, b), then f is nonincreasing on $[a, b]$.

To prove the theorem, we note that if f is decreasing then $-f$ is increasing and vice-versa. Similarly, if f is non-increasing, then $-f$ is nondecreasing. Thus if $f'(x) < 0$, then $-f'(x) > 0$, so $-f$ is increasing, which means f is decreasing. And if $f'(x) \leq 0$, then $-f'(x) \geq 0$, so $-f$ is nondecreasing, which means f is nonincreasing.

14. Use the Racetrack Principle, Theorem 3.10, with $g(x) = x$. Since $f'(x) \leq g'(x)$ for all x and $f(0) = g(0)$, then $f(x) \leq g(x) = x$ for all $x \geq 0$.

15. First apply the Racetrack Principle, Theorem 3.10, to $f'(t)$ and $g(t) = 3t$. Since $f''(t) \leq g'(t)$ for all t and $f'(0) = 0 = g(0)$, then $f'(t) \leq 3t$ for all $t \geq 0$. Next apply the Racetrack Principle again to $f(t)$ and $h(t) = \frac{3}{2}t^2$. Since $f'(t) \leq h'(t)$ for all $t \geq 0$ and $f(0) = 0 = h(0)$, then $f(t) \leq h(t) = \frac{3}{2}t^2$ for all $t \geq 0$.

16. Apply the Constant Function Theorem, Theorem 3.9, to $h(x) = f(x) - g(x)$. Then $h'(x) = 0$ for all x, so $h(x)$ is constant for all x. Since $h(5) = f(5) - g(5) = 0$, we have $h(x) = 0$ for all x. Therefore $f(x) - g(x) = 0$ for all x, so $f(x) = g(x)$ for all x.

17. By the Mean Value Theorem, Theorem 3.7, there is a number c, with $0 < c < 1$, such that

$$f'(c) = \frac{f(1) - f(0)}{1 - 0}.$$

Since $f(1) - f(0) > 0$, we have $f'(c) > 0$.

Alternatively if $f'(c) \leq 0$ for all c in $(0, 1)$, then by the Increasing Function Theorem, $f(0) \geq f(1)$.

18. Since $f''(t) \leq 7$ for $0 \leq t \leq 2$, if we apply the Racetrack Principle with $a = 0$ to the functions $f'(t) - f'(0)$ and $7t$, both of which go through the origin, we get

$$f'(t) - f'(0) \leq 7t \quad \text{for } 0 \leq t \leq 2.$$

The left side of this inequality is the derivative of $f(t) - f'(0)t$, so if we apply the Racetrack Principle with $a = 0$ again, this time to the functions $f(t) - f'(0)t$ and $(7/2)t^2 + 3$, both of which have the value 3 at $t = 0$, we get

$$f(t) - f'(0)t \leq \frac{7}{2}t^2 + 3 \quad \text{for } 0 \leq t \leq 2.$$

That is,

$$f(t) \leq 3 + 4t + \frac{7}{2}t^2 \quad \text{for } 0 \leq t \leq 2.$$

In the same way, we can show that the lower bound on the acceleration, $5 \leq f''(t)$ leads to:

$$f(t) \geq 3 + 4t + \frac{5}{2}t^2 \quad \text{for } 0 \leq t \leq 2.$$

If we substitute $t = 2$ into these two inequalities, we get bounds on the position at time 2:

$$21 \leq f(2) \leq 25.$$

19. Consider the function $f(x) = h(x) - g(x)$. Since $f'(x) = h'(x) - g'(x) \geq 0$, we know that f is nondecreasing by the Increasing Function Theorem. This means $f(x) \leq f(b)$ for $a \leq x \leq b$. However, $f(b) = h(b) - g(b) = 0$, so $f(x) \leq 0$, which means $h(x) \leq g(x)$.

20. If $f'(x) = 0$, then both $f'(x) \geq 0$ and $f'(x) \leq 0$. By the Increasing and Decreasing Function Theorems, f is both nondecreasing and nonincreasing, so f is constant.

21. Let $h(x) = f(x) - g(x)$. Then $h'(x) = f'(x) - g'(x) = 0$ for all x in (a, b). Hence, by the Constant Function Theorem, there is a constant C such that $h(x) = C$ on (a, b). Thus $f(x) = g(x) + C$.

22. We will show $f(x) = Ce^x$ by deducing that $f(x)/e^x$ is a constant. By the Constant Function Theorem, we need only show the derivative of $g(x) = f(x)/e^x$ is zero. By the quotient rule (since $e^x \neq 0$), we have

$$g'(x) = \frac{f'(x)e^x - e^x f(x)}{(e^x)^2}.$$

Since $f'(x) = f(x)$, we simplify and obtain

$$g'(x) = \frac{f(x)e^x - e^x f(x)}{(e^x)^2} = \frac{0}{e^{2x}} = 0,$$

which is what we needed to show.

23. Apply the Racetrack Principle to the functions $f(x) - f(a)$ and $M(x - a)$; we can do this since $f(a) - f(a) = M(a - a)$ and $f'(x) \leq M$. We conclude that $f(x) - f(a) \leq M(x - a)$. Similarly, apply the Racetrack Principle to the functions $m(x - a)$ and $f(x) - f(a)$ to obtain $m(x - a) \leq f(x) - f(a)$. If we substitute $x = b$ into these inequalities we get

$$m(b - a) \leq f(b) - f(a) \leq M(b - a).$$

Now, divide by $b - a$.

24. (a) Since $f''(x) \geq 0$, $f'(x)$ is nondecreasing on (a, b). Thus $f'(c) \leq f'(x)$ for $c \leq x < b$ and $f'(x) \leq f'(c)$ for $a < x \leq c$.

(b) Let $g(x) = f(c) + f'(c)(x - c)$ and $h(x) = f(x)$. Then $g(c) = f(c) = h(c)$, and $g'(x) = f'(c)$ and $h'(x) = f'(x)$. If $c \leq x < b$, then $g'(x) \leq h'(x)$, and if $a < x \leq c$, then $g'(x) \geq h'(x)$, by (a). By the Racetrack Principle, $g(x) \leq h'(x)$ for $c \leq x < b$ and for $a < x \leq c$, as we wanted.

Solutions for Chapter 3 Review

Exercises

1. $f'(t) = \dfrac{d}{dt}\left(2te^t - \dfrac{1}{\sqrt{t}}\right) = 2e^t + 2te^t + \dfrac{1}{2t^{3/2}}.$

2.

$$\begin{aligned}
\frac{dw}{dz} &= \frac{(-3)(5 + 3z) - (5 - 3z)(3)}{(5 + 3z)^2} \\
&= \frac{-15 - 9z - 15 + 9z}{(5 + 3z)^2} = \frac{-30}{(5 + 3z)^2}
\end{aligned}$$

3. $f'(x) = \dfrac{3x^2}{9}(3\ln x - 1) + \dfrac{x^3}{9}\left(\dfrac{3}{x}\right) = x^2 \ln x - \dfrac{x^2}{3} + \dfrac{x^2}{3} = x^2 \ln x$

4. $f'(\theta) = -1(1 + e^{-\theta})^{-2}(e^{-\theta})(-1) = \dfrac{e^{-\theta}}{(1 + e^{-\theta})^2}.$

5. Since $h(\theta) = \theta(\theta^{-1/2} - \theta^{-2}) = \theta\theta^{-1/2} - \theta\theta^{-2} = \theta^{1/2} - \theta^{-1}$, we have $h'(\theta) = \dfrac{1}{2}\theta^{-1/2} + \theta^{-2}.$

6. $f'(\theta) = \dfrac{-\sin\theta}{\cos\theta} = -\tan\theta.$

7. $\dfrac{d}{dy} \ln\ln(2y^3) = \dfrac{1}{\ln(2y^3)}\dfrac{1}{2y^3}6y^2 = \dfrac{3}{y\ln(2y^3)}.$

8. $g'(x) = \dfrac{d}{dx}\left(x^k + k^x\right) = kx^{k-1} + k^x \ln k.$

9. $y' = 0$

10. $\dfrac{dz}{d\theta} = 3\sin^2\theta\cos\theta$

11.

$$f'(t) = 2\cos(3t+5) \cdot (-\sin(3t+5))3$$
$$= -6\cos(3t+5) \cdot \sin(3t+5)$$

12.

$$M'(\alpha) = 2\tan(2+3\alpha) \cdot \frac{1}{\cos^2(2+3\alpha)} \cdot 3$$
$$= 6 \cdot \frac{\tan(2+3\alpha)}{\cos^2(2+3\alpha)}$$

13. $s'(\theta) = \dfrac{d}{d\theta}\sin^2(3\theta-\pi) = 6\cos(3\theta-\pi)\sin(3\theta-\pi).$

14. $h'(t) = \dfrac{1}{e^{-t}-t}\left(-e^{-t}-1\right).$

15.

$$\frac{d}{d\theta}\left(\frac{\sin(5-\theta)}{\theta^2}\right) = \frac{\cos(5-\theta)(-1)\theta^2 - \sin(5-\theta)(2\theta)}{\theta^4}$$
$$= -\frac{\theta\cos(5-\theta) + 2\sin(5-\theta)}{\theta^3}.$$

16. $w'(\theta) = \dfrac{1}{\sin^2\theta} - \dfrac{2\theta\cos\theta}{\sin^3\theta}$

17. $g'(x) = \dfrac{d}{dx}\left(x^{\frac{1}{2}} + x^{-1} + x^{-\frac{3}{2}}\right) = \dfrac{1}{2}x^{-\frac{1}{2}} - x^{-2} - \dfrac{3}{2}x^{-\frac{5}{2}}.$

18. $g'(w) = \dfrac{d}{dw}\left(\dfrac{1}{2^w + e^w}\right) = -\dfrac{2^w\ln 2 + e^w}{(2^w + e^w)^2}.$

19. $s'(x) = \dfrac{d}{dx}\left(\arctan(2-x)\right) = \dfrac{-1}{1+(2-x)^2}.$

20. $r'(\theta) = \dfrac{d}{d\theta}\left(e^{\left(e^\theta + e^{-\theta}\right)}\right) = e^{\left(e^\theta + e^{-\theta}\right)}\left(e^\theta - e^{-\theta}\right).$

21. Using the chain rule, we get:

$$m'(n) = \cos(e^n) \cdot (e^n)$$

22. Using the chain rule we get:

$$k'(\alpha) = e^{\tan(\sin\alpha)}(\tan(\sin\alpha))' = e^{\tan(\sin\alpha)} \cdot \frac{1}{\cos^2(\sin\alpha)} \cdot \cos\alpha.$$

23. Here we use the product rule, and then the chain rule, and then the product rule.

$$g'(t) = \cos(\sqrt{t}e^t) + t(\cos\sqrt{t}e^t)' = \cos(\sqrt{t}e^t) + t(-\sin(\sqrt{t}e^t) \cdot (\sqrt{t}e^t)')$$
$$= \cos(\sqrt{t}e^t) - t\sin(\sqrt{t}e^t) \cdot \left(\sqrt{t}e^t + \frac{1}{2\sqrt{t}}e^t\right)$$

24. $f'(r) = e(\tan 2 + \tan r)^{e-1}(\tan 2 + \tan r)' = e(\tan 2 + \tan r)^{e-1}\left(\dfrac{1}{\cos^2 r}\right)$

25. $\dfrac{d}{dx}xe^{\tan x} = e^{\tan x} + xe^{\tan x}\dfrac{1}{\cos^2 x}.$

26. $\dfrac{dy}{dx} = 2e^{2x}\sin^2(3x) + e^{2x}(2\sin(3x)\cos(3x)3) = 2e^{2x}\sin(3x)(\sin(3x) + 3\cos(3x))$

27. $g'(x) = \dfrac{6x}{1+(3x^2+1)^2} = \dfrac{6x}{9x^4 + 6x^2 + 2}$

28. $\dfrac{dy}{dx} = (\ln 2)2^{\sin x}\cos x \cdot \cos x + 2^{\sin x}(-\sin x) = 2^{\sin x}\left((\ln 2)\cos^2 x - \sin x\right)$

29. $h(x) = ax \cdot \ln e = ax$, so $h'(x) = a$.

30. $k'(x) = a$

31. $f'(\theta) = ke^{k\theta}$

32. Using the product rule and factoring gives $f'(t) = e^{-4kt}(\cos t - 4k \sin t)$.

33. Using the product rule gives

$$
\begin{aligned}
H'(t) &= 2ate^{-ct} - c(at^2 + b)e^{-ct} \\
&= (-cat^2 + 2at - bc)e^{-ct}.
\end{aligned}
$$

34. $\dfrac{d}{d\theta} \sqrt{a^2 - \sin^2 \theta} = \dfrac{1}{2\sqrt{a^2 - \sin^2 \theta}}(-2\sin\theta\cos\theta) = -\dfrac{\sin\theta\cos\theta}{\sqrt{a^2 - \sin^2\theta}}$.

35. Using the chain rule gives $f'(x) = 5\ln(a)a^{5x}$.

36. Using the quotient rule gives

$$
f'(x) = \frac{(-2x)(a^2 + x^2) - (2x)(a^2 - x^2)}{(a^2 + x^2)^2} = \frac{-4a^2 x}{(a^2 + x^2)^2}.
$$

37. Using the quotient rule gives

$$
\begin{aligned}
w'(r) &= \frac{2ar(b + r^3) - 3r^2(ar^2)}{(b + r^3)^2} \\
&= \frac{2abr - ar^4}{(b + r^3)^2}.
\end{aligned}
$$

38. Using the quotient rule gives

$$
\begin{aligned}
f'(s) &= \frac{-2s\sqrt{a^2 + s^2} - \frac{s}{\sqrt{a^2+s^2}}(a^2 - s^2)}{(a^2 + s^2)} \\
&= \frac{-2s(a^2 + s^2) - s(a^2 - s^2)}{(a^2 + s^2)^{3/2}} \\
&= \frac{-2a^2 s - 2s^3 - a^2 s + s^3}{(a^2 + s^2)^{3/2}} \\
&= \frac{-3a^2 s - s^3}{(a^2 + s^2)^{3/2}}.
\end{aligned}
$$

39. $\dfrac{dy}{dx} = \dfrac{1}{1 + \left(\frac{2}{x}\right)^2}\left(\dfrac{-2}{x^2}\right) = \dfrac{-2}{x^2 + 4}$

40. Using the chain rule gives $r'(t) = \dfrac{\cos(\frac{t}{k})}{\sin(\frac{t}{k})}\left(\dfrac{1}{k}\right)$.

41. Since $g(w) = 5(a^2 - w^2)^{-2}$, $g'(w) = -10(a^2 - w^2)^{-3}(-2w) = \dfrac{20w}{(a^2 - w^2)^3}$

42.

$$
\begin{aligned}
\frac{dy}{dx} &= \frac{(e^x + e^{-x})(e^x + e^{-x}) - (e^x - e^{-x})(e^x - e^{-x})}{(e^x + e^{-x})^2} \\
&= \frac{(e^x + e^{-x})^2 - (e^x - e^{-x})^2}{(e^x + e^{-x})^2} = \frac{(e^{2x} + 2 + e^{-2x}) - (e^{2x} - 2 + e^{-2x})}{(e^x + e^{-x})^2} \\
&= \frac{4}{(e^x + e^{-x})^2}
\end{aligned}
$$

43. $g'(u) = \dfrac{ae^{au}}{a^2 + b^2}$

44. Using the quotient and chain rules, we have

$$
\begin{aligned}
\frac{dy}{dx} &= \frac{(ae^{ax} + ae^{-ax})(e^{ax} + e^{-ax}) - (e^{ax} - e^{-ax})(ae^{ax} - ae^{-ax})}{(e^{ax} + e^{-ax})^2} \\
&= \frac{a(e^{ax} + e^{-ax})^2 - a(e^{ax} - e^{-ax})^2}{(e^{ax} + e^{-ax})^2} \\
&= \frac{a[(e^{2ax} + 2 + e^{-2ax}) - (e^{2ax} - 2 + e^{-2ax})]}{(e^{ax} + e^{-ax})^2} \\
&= \frac{4a}{(e^{ax} + e^{-ax})^2}
\end{aligned}
$$

45. Using the quotient rule gives

$$
\begin{aligned}
g'(t) &= \frac{\left(\frac{k}{kt} + 1\right)(\ln(kt) - t) - (\ln(kt) + t)\left(\frac{k}{kt} - 1\right)}{(\ln(kt) - t)^2} \\
g'(t) &= \frac{\left(\frac{1}{t} + 1\right)(\ln(kt) - t) - (\ln(kt) + t)\left(\frac{1}{t} - 1\right)}{(\ln(kt) - t)^2} \\
g'(t) &= \frac{\ln(kt)/t - 1 + \ln(kt) - t - \ln(kt)/t - 1 + \ln(kt) + t}{(\ln(kt) - t)^2} \\
g'(t) &= \frac{2\ln(kt) - 2}{(\ln(kt) - t)^2}.
\end{aligned}
$$

46. Using the quotient and chain rules

$$
\begin{aligned}
\frac{dz}{dt} &= \frac{\frac{d}{dt}(e^{t^2} + t) \cdot \sin(2t) - (e^{t^2} + t)\frac{d}{dt}(\sin(2t))}{(\sin(2t))^2} \\
&= \frac{\left(e^{t^2} \cdot \frac{d}{dt}(t^2) + 1\right)\sin(2t) - (e^{t^2} + t)\cos(2t)\frac{d}{dt}(2t)}{\sin^2(2t)} \\
&= \frac{(2te^{t^2} + 1)\sin(2t) - (e^{t^2} + t)2\cos(2t)}{\sin^2(2t)}.
\end{aligned}
$$

47. Using the chain rule twice:

$$
f'(t) = \cos\sqrt{e^t + 1}\,\frac{d}{dt}\sqrt{e^t + 1} = \cos\sqrt{e^t + 1}\,\frac{1}{2\sqrt{e^t + 1}} \cdot \frac{d}{dt}(e^t + 1) = \cos\sqrt{e^t + 1}\,\frac{1}{2\sqrt{e^t + 1}}e^t = e^t\frac{\cos\sqrt{e^t + 1}}{2\sqrt{e^t + 1}}.
$$

48. Using the chain rule twice:

$$
g'(y) = e^{2e^{(y^3)}}\frac{d}{dy}\left(2e^{(y^3)}\right) = 2e^{2e^{(y^3)}}e^{(y^3)}\frac{d}{dy}(y^3) = 6y^2 e^{(y^3)}e^{2e^{(y^3)}}.
$$

49. $g'(x) = -\dfrac{1}{2}(5x^4 + 2).$

50. $y' = -12x^3 - 12x^2 - 6.$

51. $g(z) = z^5 + 5z^4 - z$
$g'(z) = 5z^4 + 20z^3 - 1.$

52. $f'(z) = (2\ln 3)z + (\ln 4)e^z.$

53. $g'(x) = \dfrac{d}{dx}(2x - x^{-1/3} + 3^x - e) = 2 + \dfrac{1}{3x^{\frac{4}{3}}} + 3^x\ln 3.$

54. $f'(x) = 6x(e^x - 4) + (3x^2 + \pi)e^x = 6xe^x - 24x + 3x^2e^x + \pi e^x.$

55. $f'(\theta) = 2\theta \sin\theta + \theta^2 \cos\theta + 2\cos\theta - 2\theta \sin\theta - 2\cos\theta = \theta^2 \cos\theta.$

56.

$$\begin{aligned}
\frac{dy}{d\theta} &= \frac{1}{2}(\cos(5\theta))^{-\frac{1}{2}}(-\sin(5\theta) \cdot 5) + 2\sin(6\theta)\cos(6\theta) \cdot 6 \\
&= -\frac{5}{2}\frac{\sin(5\theta)}{\sqrt{\cos(5\theta)}} + 12\sin(6\theta)\cos(6\theta)
\end{aligned}$$

57. $r'(\theta) = \dfrac{d}{d\theta}\sin[(3\theta - \pi)^2] = \cos[(3\theta - \pi)^2] \cdot 2(3\theta - \pi) \cdot 3 = 6(3\theta - \pi)\cos[(3\theta - \pi)^2].$

58. Using the product and chain rules, we have

$$\begin{aligned}
\frac{dy}{dx} &= 3(x^2 + 5)^2(2x)(3x^3 - 2)^2 + (x^2 + 5)^3[2(3x^3 - 2)(9x^2)] \\
&= 3(2x)(x^2 + 5)^2(3x^3 - 2)[(3x^3 - 2) + (x^2 + 5)(3x)] \\
&= 6x(x^2 + 5)^2(3x^3 - 2)[6x^3 + 15x - 2].
\end{aligned}$$

59. Since $\tan(\arctan(k\theta)) = k\theta$, because tangent and arctangent are inverse functions, we have $N'(\theta) = k$.

60. Using the product rule gives $h'(t) = ke^{kt}(\sin at + \cos bt) + e^{kt}(a\cos at - b\sin bt).$

61. $f'(x) = \dfrac{d}{dx}(2 - 4x - 3x^2)(6x^e - 3\pi) = (-4 - 6x)(6x^e - 3\pi) + (2 - 4x - 3x^2)(6ex^{e-1}).$

62. $f'(t) = 4(\sin(2t) - \cos(3t))^3[2\cos(2t) + 3\sin(3t)]$

63. Since $\cos^2 y + \sin^2 y = 1$, we have $s(y) = \sqrt[3]{1 + 3} = \sqrt[3]{4}.$ Thus $s'(y) = 0.$

64.

$$\begin{aligned}
f'(x) &= (-2x + 6x^2)(6 - 4x + x^7) + (4 - x^2 + 2x^3)(-4 + 7x^6) \\
&= (-12x + 44x^2 - 24x^3 - 2x^8 + 6x^9) + (-16 + 4x^2 - 8x^3 + 28x^6 - 7x^8 + 14x^9) \\
&= -16 - 12x + 48x^2 - 32x^3 + 28x^6 - 9x^8 + 20x^9
\end{aligned}$$

65.

$$\begin{aligned}
h'(x) &= \left(-\frac{1}{x^2} + \frac{2}{x^3}\right)(2x^3 + 4) + \left(\frac{1}{x} - \frac{1}{x^2}\right)(6x^2) \\
&= -2x + 4 - \frac{4}{x^2} + \frac{8}{x^3} + 6x - 6 \\
&= 4x - 2 - 4x^{-2} + 8x^{-3}
\end{aligned}$$

66. Note: $f(z) = (5z)^{1/2} + 5z^{1/2} + 5z^{-1/2} - \sqrt{5}z^{-1/2} + \sqrt{5}$, so $f'(z) = \dfrac{5}{2}(5z)^{-1/2} + \dfrac{5}{2}z^{-1/2} - \dfrac{5}{2}z^{-3/2} + \dfrac{\sqrt{5}}{2}z^{-3/2}.$

67.

$$\begin{aligned}
3x^2 + 3y^2\frac{dy}{dx} - 8xy - 4x^2\frac{dy}{dx} &= 0 \\
(3y^2 - 4x^2)\frac{dy}{dx} &= 8xy - 3x^2 \\
\frac{dy}{dx} &= \frac{8xy - 3x^2}{3y^2 - 4x^2}
\end{aligned}$$

68. Differentiating implicitly on both sides with respect to x,

$$\begin{aligned}
a\cos(ay)\frac{dy}{dx} - b\sin(bx) &= y + x\frac{dy}{dx} \\
(a\cos(ay) - x)\frac{dy}{dx} &= y + b\sin(bx) \\
\frac{dy}{dx} &= \frac{y + b\sin(bx)}{a\cos(ay) - x}.
\end{aligned}$$

69. We wish to find the slope $m = dy/dx$. To do this, we can implicitly differentiate the given formula in terms of x:

$$x^2 + 3y^2 = 7$$
$$2x + 6y\frac{dy}{dx} = \frac{d}{dx}(7) = 0$$
$$\frac{dy}{dx} = \frac{-2x}{6y} = \frac{-x}{3y}.$$

Thus, at $(2, -1)$, $m = -(2)/3(-1) = 2/3$.

70. Taking derivatives implicitly, we find

$$\frac{dy}{dx} + \cos y\frac{dy}{dx} + 2x = 0$$
$$\frac{dy}{dx} = \frac{-2x}{1 + \cos y}$$

So, at the point $x = 3, y = 0$,

$$\frac{dy}{dx} = \frac{(-2)(3)}{1 + \cos 0} = \frac{-6}{2} = -3.$$

71. First, we differentiate with respect to x:

$$x \cdot \frac{dy}{dx} + y \cdot 1 + 2y\frac{dy}{dx} = 0$$
$$\frac{dy}{dx}(x + 2y) = -y$$
$$\frac{dy}{dx} = \frac{-y}{x + 2y}.$$

At $x = 3$, we have

$$3y + y^2 = 4$$
$$y^2 + 3y - 4 = 0$$
$$(y - 1)(y + 4) = 0.$$

Our two points, then, are $(3, 1)$ and $(3, -4)$.

$$\text{At } (3, 1), \quad \frac{dy}{dx} = \frac{-1}{3 + 2(1)} = -\frac{1}{5}; \quad \text{Tangent line: } (y - 1) = -\frac{1}{5}(x - 3).$$

$$\text{At } (3, -4), \quad \frac{dy}{dx} = \frac{-(-4)}{3 + 2(-4)} = -\frac{4}{5}; \quad \text{Tangent line: } (y + 4) = -\frac{4}{5}(x - 3).$$

Problems

72. (a) Applying the product rule to $h(x)$ we get $h'(1) = t'(1)s(1) + t(1)s'(1) \approx (-2) \cdot 3 + 0 \cdot 0 = -6$.

(b) Applying the product rule to $h(x)$ we get $h'(0) = t'(0)s(0) + t(0)s'(0) \approx (-2) \cdot 2 + 2 \cdot 2 = 0$.

(c) Applying the quotient rule to $p(x)$ we get $p'(0) = \dfrac{t'(0)s(0) - t(0)s'(0)}{(s(0))^2} \approx \dfrac{(-2) \cdot 2 - 2 \cdot 2}{2^2} = -2.$

Note that since $t(x)$ is a linear function whose slope looks like -2 from the graph, $t'(x) \approx -2$ everywhere. To find $s'(1)$, draw a line tangent to the curve at the point $(1, s(1))$, and estimate the slope.

73. Since $r(x) = s(t(x))$, the chain rule gives $r'(x) = s'(t(x)) \cdot t'(x)$. Thus,

$$r'(0) = s'(t(0)) \cdot t'(0) \approx s'(2) \cdot (-2) \approx (-2)(-2) = 4.$$

Note that since $t(x)$ is a linear function whose slope looks like -2 from the graph, $t'(x) \approx -2$ everywhere. To find $s'(2)$, draw a line tangent to the curve at the point $(2, s(2))$, and estimate the slope.

74. (a) Applying the chain rule we get $h'(1) = s'(s(1)) \cdot s'(1) \approx s'(3) \cdot 0 = 0$.
   (b) Applying the chain rule we get $h'(2) = s'(s(2)) \cdot s'(2) \approx s'(2) \cdot s'(2) = (-2)^2 = 4$.
   To find $s'(2)$, draw a line tangent to the curve at the point $(2, s(2))$, and estimate the slope.

75. We need to find all values for x such that
$$\frac{dy}{dx} = s'(s(x)) \cdot s'(x) = 0.$$

This is the case when either $s'(s(x)) = 0$ or $s'(x) = 0$. From the graph we see that $s'(x) = 0$ when $x \approx 1$. Also, $s'(s(x)) = 0$ when $s(x) \approx 1$, which happens when $x \approx -0.4$ or $x \approx 2.4$.
   To find $s'(a)$, for any a, draw a line tangent to the curve at the point $(a, s(a))$, and estimate the slope.

76. (a) Applying the product rule we get $h'(-1) = 2 \cdot (-1) \cdot t(-1) + (-1)^2 \cdot t'(-1) \approx (-2) \cdot 4 + 1 \cdot (-2) = -10$.
   (b) Applying the chain rule we get $p'(-1) = t'((-1)^2) \cdot 2 \cdot (-1) = -2 \cdot t'(1) \approx (-2) \cdot (-2) = 4$.
   Note that since $t(x)$ is a linear function whose slope looks like -2 from the graph, $t'(x) \approx -2$ everywhere.

77. We have $r(1) = s(t(1)) \approx s(0) \approx 2$. By the chain rule, $r'(x) = s'(t(x)) \cdot t'(x)$, so
$$r'(1) = s'(t(1)) \cdot t'(1) \approx s'(0) \cdot (-2) \approx 2(-2) = -4.$$

Thus the equation of the tangent line is
$$y - 2 = -4(x - 1)$$
$$y = -4x + 6.$$

Note that since $t(x)$ is a linear function whose slope looks like -2 from the graph, $t'(x) \approx -2$ everywhere. To find $s'(0)$, draw a line tangent to the curve at the point $(0, s(0))$, and estimate the slope.

78. We have
$$(f^{-1})'(5) = \frac{1}{f'(f^{-1}(5))}.$$

From the graph of $f(x)$ we see that $f^{-1}(5) = 13$. From the graph of $f'(x)$ we see that $f'(13) = 0.36$. Thus $(f^{-1})'(5) = 1/0.36 = 2.8$.

79. We have
$$(f^{-1})'(10) = \frac{1}{f'(f^{-1}(10))}.$$

From the graph of $f(x)$ we see that $f^{-1}(10) = 23$. From the graph of $f'(x)$ we see that $f'(23) = 0.62$. Thus $(f^{-1})'(10) = 1/0.62 = 1.6$.

80. We have
$$(f^{-1})'(15) = \frac{1}{f'(f^{-1}(15))}.$$

From the graph of $f(x)$ we see that $f^{-1}(15) = 30$. From the graph of $f'(x)$ we see that $f'(30) = 0.73$. Thus $(f^{-1})'(15) = 1/0.73 = 1.4$.

81. Since W is proportional to r^3, we have $W = kr^3$ for some constant k. Thus, $dW/dr = k(3r^2) = 3kr^2$. Thus, dW/dr is proportional to r^2.

82. Taking the values of f, f', g, and g' from the table we get:
   (a) $h(4) = f(g(4)) = f(3) = 1$.
   (b) $h'(4) = f'(g(4))g'(4) = f'(3) \cdot 1 = 2$.
   (c) $h(4) = g(f(4)) = g(4) = 3$.
   (d) $h'(4) = g'(f(4))f'(4) = g'(4) \cdot 3 = 3$.
   (e) $h'(4) = (f(4)g'(4) - g(4)f'(4))/f^2(4) = -5/16$.
   (f) $h'(4) = f(4)g'(4) + g(4)f'(4) = 13$.

83. (a) $H'(2) = r'(2)s(2) + r(2)s'(2) = -1 \cdot 1 + 4 \cdot 3 = 11$.
   (b) $H'(2) = \dfrac{r'(2)}{2\sqrt{r(2)}} = \dfrac{-1}{2\sqrt{4}} = -\dfrac{1}{4}$.
   (c) $H'(2) = r'(s(2))s'(2) = r'(1) \cdot 3$, but we don't know $r'(1)$.
   (d) $H'(2) = s'(r(2))r'(2) = s'(4)r'(2) = -3$.

84. (a) $f(x) = x^2 - 4g(x)$
   $f'(x) = 2x - 4g'(x)$
   $f'(2) = 2(2) - 4(-4) = 4 + 16 = 20$

(b) $f(x) = \frac{x}{g(x)}$

$f'(x) = \frac{g(x) - xg'(x)}{(g(x))^2}$

$f'(2) = \frac{g(2) - 2g'(2)}{(g(2))^2} = \frac{3 - 2(-4)}{(3)^2} = \frac{11}{9}$

(c) $f(x) = x^2 g(x)$

$f'(x) = 2xg(x) + x^2 g'(x)$

$f'(2) = 2(2)(3) + (2)^2(-4) = 12 - 16 = -4$

(d) $f(x) = (g(x))^2$

$f'(x) = 2g(x) \cdot g'(x)$

$f'(2) = 2(3)(-4) = -24$

(e) $f(x) = x\sin(g(x))$

$f'(x) = \sin(g(x)) + x\cos(g(x)) \cdot g'(x)$

$f'(2) = \sin(g(2)) + 2\cos(g(2)) \cdot g'(2)$

$\qquad = \sin 3 + 2\cos(3) \cdot (-4)$

$\qquad = \sin 3 - 8\cos 3$

(f) $f(x) = x^2 \ln(g(x))$

$f'(x) = 2x\ln(g(x)) + x^2\left(\frac{g'(x)}{g(x)}\right)$

$f'(2) = 2(2)\ln 3 + (2)^2\left(\frac{-4}{3}\right)$

$\qquad = 4\ln 3 - \frac{16}{3}$

85. (a) $f(x) = x^2 - 4g(x)$

$f(2) = 4 - 4(3) = -8$

$f'(2) = 20$

Thus, we have a point $(2, -8)$ and slope $m = 20$. This gives

$$-8 = 2(20) + b$$
$$b = -48, \quad \text{so}$$
$$y = 20x - 48.$$

(b) $f(x) = \dfrac{x}{g(x)}$

$f(2) = \dfrac{2}{3}$

$f'(2) = \dfrac{11}{9}$

Thus, we have point $(2, \frac{2}{3})$ and slope $m = \frac{11}{9}$. This gives

$$\frac{2}{3} = \left(\frac{11}{9}\right)(2) + b$$
$$b = \frac{2}{3} - \frac{22}{9} = \frac{-16}{9}, \quad \text{so}$$
$$y = \frac{11}{9}x - \frac{16}{9}.$$

(c) $f(x) = x^2 g(x)$

$f(2) = 4 \cdot g(2) = 4(3) = 12$

$f'(2) = -4$

Thus, we have point $(2, 12)$ and slope $m = -4$. This gives

$$12 = 2(-4) + b$$
$$b = 20, \quad \text{so}$$
$$y = -4x + 20.$$

(d) $f(x) = (g(x))^2$

$f(2) = (g(2))^2 = (3)^2 = 9$

$f'(2) = -24$

Thus, we have point $(2, 9)$ and slope $m = -24$. This gives

$$9 = 2(-24) + b$$
$$b = 57, \quad \text{so}$$
$$y = -24x + 57.$$

(e) $f(x) = x \sin(g(x))$
$f(2) = 2\sin(g(2)) = 2\sin 3$
$f'(2) = \sin 3 - 8\cos 3$
We will use a decimal approximation for $f(2)$ and $f'(2)$, so the point $(2, 2\sin 3) \approx (2, 0.28)$ and $m \approx 8.06$. Thus,

$$0.28 = 2(8.06) + b$$
$$b = -15.84, \quad \text{so}$$
$$y = 8.06x - 15.84.$$

(f) $f(x) = x^2 \ln g(x)$
$f(2) = 4\ln g(2) = 4\ln 3 \approx 4.39$
$f'(2) = 4\ln 3 - \dfrac{16}{3} \approx -0.94.$
Thus, we have point $(2, 4.39)$ and slope $m = -0.94$. This gives

$$4.39 = 2(-0.94) + b$$
$$b = 6.27, \quad \text{so}$$
$$y = -0.94x + 6.27.$$

86. When we zoom in on the origin, we find that two functions are not defined there. The other functions all look like straight lines through the origin. The only way we can tell them apart is their slope.

The following functions all have slope 0 and are therefore indistinguishable:
$\sin x - \tan x$, $\dfrac{x^2}{x^2+1}$, $x - \sin x$, and $\dfrac{1-\cos x}{\cos x}$.

These functions all have slope 1 at the origin, and are thus indistinguishable:
$\arcsin x$, $\dfrac{\sin x}{1+\sin x}$, $\arctan x$, $e^x - 1$, $\dfrac{x}{x+1}$, and $\dfrac{x}{x^2+1}$.

Now, $\dfrac{\sin x}{x} - 1$ and $-x\ln x$ both are undefined at the origin, so they are distinguishable from the other functions. In addition, while $\dfrac{\sin x}{x} - 1$ has a slope that approaches zero near the origin, $-x\ln x$ becomes vertical near the origin, so they are distinguishable from each other.

Finally, $x^{10} + \sqrt[10]{x}$ is the only function defined at the origin and with a vertical tangent there, so it is distinguishable from the others.

87. It makes sense to define the angle between two curves to be the angle between their tangent lines. (The tangent lines are the best linear approximations to the curves). See Figure 3.17. The functions $\sin x$ and $\cos x$ are equal at $x = \dfrac{\pi}{4}$.

$$\text{For } f_1(x) = \sin x, \quad f_1'\left(\frac{\pi}{4}\right) = \cos\left(\frac{\pi}{4}\right) = \frac{\sqrt{2}}{2}$$
$$\text{For } f_2(x) = \cos x, \quad f_2'\left(\frac{\pi}{4}\right) = -\sin\left(\frac{\pi}{4}\right) = -\frac{\sqrt{2}}{2}.$$

Using the point $\left(\frac{\pi}{4}, \frac{\sqrt{2}}{2}\right)$ for each tangent line we get $y = \frac{\sqrt{2}}{2}x + \frac{\sqrt{2}}{2}\left(1 - \frac{\pi}{4}\right)$ and $y = -\frac{\sqrt{2}}{2}x + \frac{\sqrt{2}}{2}\left(1 + \frac{\pi}{4}\right)$, respectively.

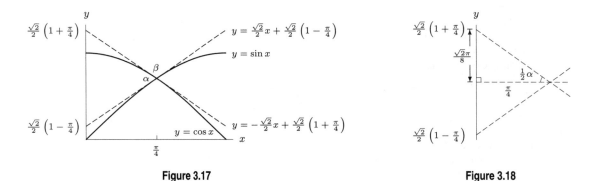

Figure 3.17   **Figure 3.18**

There are two possibilities of how to define the angle between the tangent lines, indicated by α and β above. The choice is arbitrary, so we will solve for both. To find the angle, α, we consider the triangle formed by these two lines and the y-axis. See Figure 3.18.

$$\tan\left(\frac{1}{2}\alpha\right) = \frac{\sqrt{2}\pi/8}{\pi/4} = \frac{\sqrt{2}}{2}$$

$$\frac{1}{2}\alpha = 0.61548 \text{ radians}$$

$$\alpha = 1.231 \text{ radians, or } 70.5°.$$

Now let us solve for β, the other possible measure of the angle between the two tangent lines. Since α and β are supplementary, $\beta = \pi - 1.231 = 1.909$ radians, or $109.4°$.

88. The curves meet when $1 + x - x^2 = 1 - x + x^2$, that is when $2x(1 - x) = 0$ so that $x = 1$ or $x = 0$. Let

$$y_1(x) = 1 + x - x^2 \quad \text{and} \quad y_2(x) = 1 - x + x^2.$$

Then

$$y_1' = 1 - 2x \quad \text{and} \quad y_2' = -1 + 2x.$$

At $x = 0$, $y_1' = 1$, $y_2' = -1$ so that $y_1' \cdot y_2' = -1$ and the curves are perpendicular. At $x = 1$, $y_1' = -1$, $y_2' = 1$ so that $y_1' \cdot y_2' = -1$ and the curves are perpendicular.

89. The curves meet when $1 - x^3/3 = x - 1$, that is when $x^3 + 3x - 6 = 0$. So the roots of this equation give us the x-coordinates of the intersection point. By numerical methods, we see there is one solution near $x = 1.3$. See Figure 3.19. Let

$$y_1(x) = 1 - \frac{x^3}{3} \quad \text{and} \quad y_2(x) = x - 1.$$

So we have

$$y_1' = -x^2 \quad \text{and} \quad y_2' = 1.$$

However, $y_2'(x) = +1$, so if the curves are to be perpendicular when they cross, then y_1' must be -1. Since $y_1' = -x^2$, $y_1' = -1$ only at $x = \pm 1$ which is not the point of intersection. The curves are therefore not perpendicular when they cross.

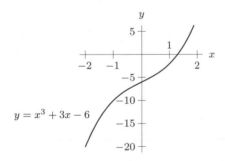

Figure 3.19

90. Differentiating gives $\dfrac{dy}{dx} = \ln x + 1 - b$.

To find the point at which the graph crosses the x-axis, set $y = 0$ and solve for x:

$$0 = x \ln x - bx$$
$$0 = x(\ln x - b).$$

Since $x > 0$, we have

$$\ln x - b = 0$$
$$x = e^b.$$

At the point $(e^b, 0)$, the slope is

$$\frac{dy}{dx} = \ln\left(e^b\right) + 1 - b = b + 1 - b = 1.$$

Thus the equation of the tangent line is

$$y - 0 = 1(x - e^b)$$
$$y = x - e^b.$$

91. Using the definition of $\cosh x$ and $\sinh x$, we have $\cosh 2x = \dfrac{e^{2x} + e^{-2x}}{2}$ and $\sinh 3x = \dfrac{e^{3x} - e^{-3x}}{2}$. Therefore

$$
\begin{aligned}
\lim_{x \to -\infty} \frac{\cosh(2x)}{\sinh(2x)} &= \lim_{x \to -\infty} \frac{e^{2x} + e^{-2x}}{e^{3x} - e^{-3x}} \\
&= \lim_{x \to -\infty} \frac{e^{-2x}(e^{4x} + 1)}{e^{-2x}(e^{5x} - e^{-x})} \\
&= \lim_{x \to -\infty} \frac{e^{4x} + 1}{e^{5x} - e^{-x}} \\
&= 0.
\end{aligned}
$$

92. Using the definition of $\sinh x$ we have $\sinh 2x = \dfrac{e^{2x} - e^{-2x}}{2}$. Therefore

$$
\begin{aligned}
\lim_{x \to -\infty} \frac{e^{-2x}}{\sinh(2x)} &= \lim_{x \to -\infty} \frac{2e^{-2x}}{e^{2x} - e^{-2x}} \\
&= \lim_{x \to -\infty} \frac{2}{e^{4x} - 1} \\
&= -2.
\end{aligned}
$$

93. Using the definition of $\cosh x$ and $\sinh x$, we have $\cosh x^2 = \dfrac{e^{x^2} + e^{-x^2}}{2}$ and $\sinh x^2 = \dfrac{e^{x^2} - e^{-x^2}}{2}$. Therefore

$$
\begin{aligned}
\lim_{x \to -\infty} \frac{\sinh(x^2)}{\cosh(x^2)} &= \lim_{x \to -\infty} \frac{e^{x^2} - e^{-x^2}}{e^{x^2} + e^{-x^2}} \\
&= \lim_{x \to -\infty} \frac{e^{x^2}(1 - e^{-2x^2})}{e^{x^2}(1 + e^{-2x^2})} \\
&= \lim_{x \to -\infty} \frac{1 - e^{-2x^2}}{1 + e^{-2x^2}} \\
&= 1.
\end{aligned}
$$

94. (a) $\dfrac{dg}{dr} = GM \dfrac{d}{dr}\left(\dfrac{1}{r^2}\right) = GM \dfrac{d}{dr}\left(r^{-2}\right) = GM(-2)r^{-3} = -\dfrac{2GM}{r^3}$.

   (b) $\dfrac{dg}{dr}$ is the rate of change of acceleration due to the pull of gravity. The further away from the center of the earth, the weaker the pull of gravity is. So g is decreasing and therefore its derivative, $\dfrac{dg}{dr}$, is negative.

   (c) By part (a),

$$
\left.\frac{dg}{dr}\right|_{r=6400} = \left.-\frac{2GM}{r^3}\right|_{r=6400} = -\frac{2(6.67 \times 10^{-20})(6 \times 10^{24})}{(6400)^3} \approx -3.05 \times 10^{-6}.
$$

   (d) It is reasonable to assume that g is a constant near the surface of the earth.

95. The population of Mexico is given by the formula

$$
M = 84(1 + 0.026)^t = 84(1.026)^t \text{ million}
$$

and that of the US by

$$
U = 250(1 + 0.007)^t = 250(1.007)^t \text{ million},
$$

where t is measured in years ($t = 0$ corresponds to the year 1990). So,

$$
\left.\frac{dM}{dt}\right|_{t=0} = 84\frac{d}{dt}(1.026)^t\bigg|_{t=0} = 84(1.026)^t \ln(1.026)\bigg|_{t=0} \approx 2.156
$$

and

$$
\left.\frac{dU}{dt}\right|_{t=0} = 250\frac{d}{dt}(1.007)^t\bigg|_{t=0} = 250(1.007)^t \ln(1.007)\bigg|_{t=0} \approx 1.744
$$

Since $\left.\dfrac{dM}{dt}\right|_{t=0} > \left.\dfrac{dU}{dt}\right|_{t=0}$, the population of Mexico was growing faster in 1990.

96. (a) If the distance $s(t) = 20e^{\frac{t}{2}}$, then the velocity, $v(t)$, is given by

$$v(t) = s'(t) = \left(20e^{\frac{t}{2}}\right)' = \left(\frac{1}{2}\right)\left(20e^{\frac{t}{2}}\right) = 10e^{\frac{t}{2}}.$$

(b) Observing the differentiation in (a), we note that

$$s'(t) = v(t) = \frac{1}{2}\left(20e^{\frac{t}{2}}\right) = \frac{1}{2}s(t).$$

Substituting $s(t)$ for $20e^{\frac{t}{2}}$, we obtain $s'(t) = \frac{1}{2}s(t)$.

97. (a)

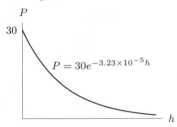

(b)

$$\frac{dP}{dh} = 30e^{-3.23\times10^{-5}h}(-3.23 \times 10^{-5})$$

so

$$\left.\frac{dP}{dh}\right|_{h=0} = -30(3.23 \times 10^{-5}) = -9.69 \times 10^{-4}$$

Hence, at $h = 0$, the slope of the tangent line is -9.69×10^{-4}, so the equation of the tangent line is

$$y - 30 = (-9.69 \times 10^{-4})(h - 0)$$
$$y = (-9.69 \times 10^{-4})h + 30.$$

(c) The rule of thumb says

$$\frac{\text{Drop in pressure from}}{\text{sea level to height } h} = \frac{h}{1000}$$

But since the pressure at sea level is 30 inches of mercury, this drop in pressure is also $(30 - P)$, so

$$30 - P = \frac{h}{1000}$$

giving

$$P = 30 - 0.001h.$$

(d) The equations in (b) and (c) are almost the same: both have P intercepts of 30, and the slopes are almost the same $(9.69 \times 10^{-4} \approx 0.001)$. The rule of thumb calculates values of P which are very close to the tangent lines, and therefore yields values very close to the curve.

(e) The tangent line is slightly below the curve, and the rule of thumb line, having a slightly more negative slope, is slightly below the tangent line (for $h > 0$). Thus, the rule of thumb values are slightly smaller.

98.

$$\frac{dy}{dt} = -7.5(0.507)\sin(0.507t) = -3.80\sin(0.507t)$$

(a) When $t = 6$, we have $\dfrac{dy}{dt} = -3.80\sin(0.507 \cdot 6) = -0.38$ meters/hour. So the tide is falling at 0.38 meters/hour.

(b) When $t = 9$, we have $\dfrac{dy}{dt} = -3.80\sin(0.507 \cdot 9) = 3.76$ meters/hour. So the tide is rising at 3.76 meters/hour.

(c) When $t = 12$, we have $\dfrac{dy}{dt} = -3.80\sin(0.507 \cdot 12) = 0.75$ meters/hour. So the tide is rising at 0.75 meters/hour.

(d) When $t = 18$, we have $\dfrac{dy}{dt} = -3.80\sin(0.507 \cdot 18) = -1.12$ meters/hour. So the tide is falling at 1.12 meters/hour.

99. Since we're given that the instantaneous rate of change of T at $t = 30$ is 2, we want to choose a and b so that the derivative of T agrees with this value. Differentiating, $T'(t) = ab \cdot e^{-bt}$. Then we have

$$2 = T'(30) = abe^{-30b} \quad \text{or} \quad e^{-30b} = \frac{2}{ab}$$

We also know that at $t = 30$, $T = 120$, so

$$120 = T(30) = 200 - ae^{-30b} \quad \text{or} \quad e^{-30b} = \frac{80}{a}$$

Thus $\dfrac{80}{a} = e^{-30b} = \dfrac{2}{ab}$, so $b = \frac{1}{40} = 0.025$ and $a = 169.36$.

100. (a) Differentiating, we see

$$v = \frac{dy}{dt} = -2\pi\omega y_0 \sin(2\pi\omega t)$$

$$a = \frac{dv}{dt} = -4\pi^2\omega^2 y_0 \cos(2\pi\omega t).$$

(b) We have

$$y = y_0 \cos(2\pi\omega t)$$
$$v = -2\pi\omega y_0 \sin(2\pi\omega t)$$
$$a = -4\pi^2\omega^2 y_0 \cos(2\pi\omega t).$$

So

$$\text{Amplitude of } y \text{ is } |y_0|,$$
$$\text{Amplitude of } v \text{ is } |2\pi\omega y_0| = 2\pi\omega|y_0|,$$
$$\text{Amplitude of } a \text{ is } |4\pi^2\omega^2 y_0| = 4\pi^2\omega^2|y_0|.$$

The amplitudes are different (provided $2\pi\omega \neq 1$). The periods of the three functions are all the same, namely $1/\omega$.

(c) Looking at the answer to part (a), we see

$$\frac{d^2 y}{dt^2} = a = -4\pi^2\omega^2 \left(y_0 \cos(2\pi\omega t) \right)$$
$$= -4\pi^2\omega^2 y.$$

So we see that

$$\frac{d^2 y}{dt^2} + 4\pi^2\omega^2 y = 0.$$

101. (a) Since $\lim\limits_{t \to \infty} e^{-0.1t} = 0$, we see that $\lim\limits_{t \to \infty} \dfrac{1000000}{1 + 5000e^{-0.1t}} = 1000000$. Thus, in the long run, close to 1,000,000 people will have had the disease. This can be seen in the figure below.

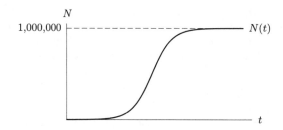

(b) The rate at which people fall sick is given by the first derivative $N'(t)$.
$N'(t) \approx \dfrac{\Delta N}{\Delta t}$, where $\Delta t = 1$ day.

$$N'(t) = \frac{500,000,000}{e^{0.1t}(1 + 5000e^{-0.1t})^2} = \frac{500,000,000}{e^{0.1t} + 25,000,000e^{-0.1t} + 10^4}$$

In Figure 3.20, we see that the maximum value of $N'(t)$ is approximately 25,000. Therefore the maximum number of people to fall sick on any given day is 25,000. Thus there are no days on which a quarter million or more get sick.

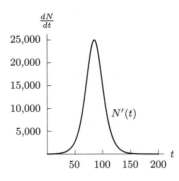

Figure 3.20

102. (a) The statement $f(2) = 4023$ tells us that when the price is $2 per gallon, 4023 gallons of gas are sold.
(b) Since $f(2) = 4023$, we have $f^{-1}(4023) = 2$. Thus, 4023 gallons are sold when the price is $2 per gallon.
(c) The statement $f'(2) = -1250$ tells us that if the price increases from $2 per gallon, the sales decrease at a rate of 1250 gallons per $1 increase in price.
(d) The units of $(f^{-1})'(4023)$ are dollars per gallon. We have

$$(f^{-1})'(4023) = \frac{1}{f'(f^{-1}(4023))} = \frac{1}{f'(2)} = -\frac{1}{1250} = -0.0008.$$

Thus, when 4023 gallons are already sold, sales decrease at the rate of one gallon per price increase of 0.0008 dollars. In others words, an additional gallon is sold if the price drops by 0.0008 dollars.

103. Since $f(20) = 10$, we have $f^{-1}(10) = 20$, so $(f^{-1})'(10) = \frac{1}{f'(f^{-1}(10))} = \frac{1}{f'(20)}$. Therefore $(f^{-1})'(10)f'(20) = 1$.

Option (b) is wrong.

104. Since $f(x)$ is decreasing, its inverse function $f^{-1}(x)$ is also decreasing. Thus $(f^{-1})'(x) \le 0$ for all x. Option (b) is incorrect.

105. (a) If $y = \ln x$, then

$$y' = \frac{1}{x}$$
$$y'' = -\frac{1}{x^2}$$
$$y''' = \frac{2}{x^3}$$
$$y'''' = -\frac{3 \cdot 2}{x^4}$$

and so

$$y^{(n)} = (-1)^{n+1}(n-1)!x^{-n}.$$

(b) If $y = xe^x$, then

$$y' = xe^x + e^x$$
$$y'' = xe^x + 2e^x$$
$$y''' = xe^x + 3e^x$$

so that

$$y^{(n)} = xe^x + ne^x.$$

(c) If $y = e^x \cos x$, then

$$y' = e^x(\cos x - \sin x)$$
$$y'' = -2e^x \sin x$$
$$y''' = e^x(-2\cos x - 2\sin x)$$
$$y^{(4)} = -4e^x \cos x$$
$$y^{(5)} = e^x(-4\cos x + 4\sin x)$$
$$y^{(6)} = 8e^x \sin x.$$

Combining these results we get

$$
\begin{aligned}
y^{(n)} &= (-4)^{(n-1)/4}e^x(\cos x - \sin x), &\quad n &= 4m+1, &\quad m &= 0, 1, 2, 3, \ldots \\
y^{(n)} &= -2(-4)^{(n-2)/4}e^x \sin x, &\quad n &= 4m+2, &\quad m &= 0, 1, 2, 3, \ldots \\
y^{(n)} &= -2(-4)^{(n-3)/4}e^x(\cos x + \sin x), &\quad n &= 4m+3, &\quad m &= 0, 1, 2, 3, \ldots \\
y^{(n)} &= (-4)^{(n/4)}e^x \cos x, &\quad n &= 4m, &\quad m &= 1, 2, 3, \ldots.
\end{aligned}
$$

106. (a) We multiply through by $h = f \cdot g$ and cancel as follows:

$$\frac{f'}{f} + \frac{g'}{g} = \frac{h'}{h}$$
$$\left(\frac{f'}{f} + \frac{g'}{g}\right) \cdot fg = \frac{h'}{h} \cdot fg$$
$$\frac{f'}{f} \cdot fg + \frac{g'}{g} \cdot fg = \frac{h'}{h} \cdot h$$
$$f' \cdot g + g' \cdot f = h',$$

which is the product rule.

(b) We start with the product rule, multiply through by $1/(fg)$ and cancel as follows:

$$f' \cdot g + g' \cdot f = h'$$
$$(f' \cdot g + g' \cdot f) \cdot \frac{1}{fg} = h' \cdot \frac{1}{fg}$$
$$(f' \cdot g) \cdot \frac{1}{fg} + (g' \cdot f) \cdot \frac{1}{fg} = h' \cdot \frac{1}{fg}$$
$$\frac{f'}{f} + \frac{g'}{g} = \frac{h'}{h},$$

which is the additive rule shown in part (a).

107. This problem can be solved by using either the quotient rule or the fact that

$$\frac{f'}{f} = \frac{d}{dx}(\ln f) \quad \text{and} \quad \frac{g'}{g} = \frac{d}{dx}(\ln g).$$

We use the second method. The relative rate of change of f/g is $(f/g)'/(f/g)$, so

$$\frac{(f/g)'}{f/g} = \frac{d}{dx}\ln\left(\frac{f}{g}\right) = \frac{d}{dx}(\ln f - \ln g) = \frac{d}{dx}(\ln f) - \frac{d}{dx}(\ln g) = \frac{f'}{f} - \frac{g'}{g}.$$

Thus, the relative rate of change of f/g is the difference between the relative rates of change of f and of g.

CAS Challenge Problems

108. (a) Answers from different computer algebra systems may be in different forms. One form is:

$$\frac{d}{dx}(x+1)^x = x(x+1)^{x-1} + (x+1)^x \ln(x+1)$$
$$\frac{d}{dx}(\sin x)^x = x \cos x(\sin x)^{x-1} + (\sin x)^x \ln(\sin x)$$

(b) Both the answers in part (a) follow the general rule:

$$\frac{d}{dx} f(x)^x = xf'(x)\,(f(x))^{x-1} + (f(x))^x \ln(f(x)).$$

(c) Applying this rule to $g(x)$, we get

$$\frac{d}{dx}(\ln x)^x = x(1/x)(\ln x)^{x-1} + (\ln x)^x \ln(\ln x) = (\ln x)^{x-1} + (\ln x)^x \ln(\ln x).$$

This agrees with the answer given by the computer algebra system.

(d) We can write $f(x) = e^{\ln(f(x))}$. So

$$(f(x))^x = (e^{\ln(f(x))})^x = e^{x\ln(f(x))}.$$

Therefore, using the chain rule and the product rule,

$$\frac{d}{dx}(f(x))^x = \frac{d}{dx}(x\ln(f(x))) \cdot e^{x\ln(f(x))} = \left(\ln(f(x)) + x\frac{d}{dx}\ln(f(x))\right) e^{x\ln(f(x))}$$

$$= \left(\ln(f(x)) + x\frac{f'(x)}{f(x)}\right)(f(x))^x = \ln(f(x))\,(f(x))^x + xf'(x)\,(f(x))^{x-1}$$

$$= xf'(x)\,(f(x))^{x-1} + (f(x))^x \ln(f(x)).$$

109. (a) A CAS gives $f'(x) = 1$.

(b) By the chain rule,

$$f'(x) = \cos(\arcsin x) \cdot \frac{1}{\sqrt{1-x^2}}.$$

Now $\cos t = \pm\sqrt{1 - \sin^2 t}$. Furthermore, if $-\pi/2 \le t \le \pi/2$ then $\cos t \ge 0$, so we take the positive square root and get $\cos t = \sqrt{1 - \sin^2 t}$. Since $-\pi/2 \le \arcsin x \le \pi/2$ for all x in the domain of arcsin, we have

$$\cos(\arcsin x) = \sqrt{1 - (\sin(\arcsin x))^2} = \sqrt{1-x^2},$$

so

$$\frac{d}{dx}\sin(\arcsin(x)) = \sqrt{1-x^2} \cdot \frac{1}{\sqrt{1-x^2}} = 1.$$

(c) Since $\sin(\arcsin(x)) = x$, its derivative is 1.

110. (a) A CAS gives $g'(r) = 0$.

(b) Using the product rule,

$$g'(r) = \frac{d}{dr}(2^{-2r}) \cdot 4^r + 2^{-2r}\frac{d}{dr}(4^r) = -2\ln 2 \cdot 2^{-2r}4^r + 2^{-2r}\ln 4 \cdot 4^r$$

$$= -\ln 4 \cdot 2^{-2r}4^r + \ln 4 \cdot 2^{-2r}4^r = (-\ln 4 + \ln 4)2^{-2r}4^r = 0 \cdot 2^{-2r}4^r = 0.$$

(c) By the laws of exponents, $4^r = (2^2)^r = 2^{2r}$, so $2^{-2r}4^r = 2^{-2r}2^{2r} = 2^0 = 1$. Therefore, its derivative is zero.

111. (a) A CAS gives $h'(t) = 0$

(b) By the chain rule

$$h'(t) = \frac{\frac{d}{dt}\left(1 - \frac{1}{t}\right)}{1 - \frac{1}{t}} + \frac{\frac{d}{dt}\left(\frac{t}{t-1}\right)}{\frac{t}{t-1}} = \frac{\frac{1}{t^2}}{\frac{t-1}{t}} + \frac{\frac{1}{t-1} - \frac{t}{(t-1)^2}}{\frac{t}{t-1}}$$

$$= \frac{1}{t^2 - t} + \frac{(t-1) - t}{t^2 - t} = \frac{1}{t^2 - t} + \frac{-1}{t^2 - t} = 0.$$

(c) The expression inside the first logarithm is $1 - (1/t) = (t-1)/t$. Using the property $\log A + \log B = \log(AB)$, we get

$$\ln\left(1 - \frac{1}{t}\right) + \ln\left(\frac{t}{t-1}\right) = \ln\left(\frac{t-1}{t}\right) + \ln\left(\frac{t}{t-1}\right)$$

$$= \ln\left(\frac{t-1}{t} \cdot \frac{t}{1-t}\right) = \ln 1 = 0.$$

Thus $h(t) = 0$, so $h'(t) = 0$ also.

CHECK YOUR UNDERSTANDING

1. True. Since $d(x^n)/dx = nx^{n-1}$, the derivative of a power function is a power function, so the derivative of a polynomial is a polynomial.

2. False, since

$$\frac{d}{dx}\left(\frac{\pi}{x^2}\right) = \frac{d}{dx}\left(\pi x^{-2}\right) = -2\pi x^{-3} = \frac{-2\pi}{x^3}.$$

3. True, since $\cos\theta$ and therefore $\cos^2\theta$ are periodic, and

$$\frac{d}{d\theta}(\tan\theta) = \frac{1}{\cos^2\theta}.$$

4. False. Since

$$\frac{d}{dx}\ln(x^2) = \frac{1}{x^2}\cdot 2x = \frac{2}{x} \quad \text{and} \quad \frac{d^2}{dx^2}\ln(x^2) = \frac{d}{dx}\left(\frac{2}{x}\right) = -\frac{2}{x^2},$$

we see that the second derivative of $\ln(x^2)$ is negative for $x > 0$. Thus, the graph is concave down.

5. True. Since $f'(x)$ is the limit

$$f'(x) = \lim_{h\to 0}\frac{f(x+h) - f(x)}{h},$$

the function f must be defined for all x.

6. True. The slope of $f(x) + g(x)$ at $x = 2$ is the sum of the derivatives, $f'(2) + g'(2) = 3.1 + 7.3 = 10.4$.

7. False. The product rule gives

$$(fg)' = fg' + f'g.$$

Differentiating this and using the product rule again, we get

$$(fg)'' = f'g' + fg'' + f'g' + f''g = fg'' + 2f'g' + f''g.$$

Thus, the right hand side is not equal to $fg'' + f''g$ in general.

8. True. If $f(x)$ is periodic with period c, then $f(x+c) = f(x)$ for all x. By the definition of the derivative, we have

$$f'(x) = \lim_{h\to 0}\frac{f(x+h) - f(x)}{h}$$

and

$$f'(x+c) = \lim_{h\to 0}\frac{f(x+c+h) - f(x+c)}{h}.$$

Since f is periodic, for any $h \neq 0$, we have

$$\frac{f(x+h) - f(x)}{h} = \frac{f(x+c+h) - f(x+c)}{h}.$$

Taking the limit as $h \to 0$, we get that $f'(x) = f'(x+c)$, so f' is periodic with the same period as $f(x)$.

9. True; differentiating the equation with respect to x, we get

$$2y\frac{dy}{dx} + y + x\frac{dy}{dx} = 0.$$

Solving for dy/dx, we get that

$$\frac{dy}{dx} = \frac{-y}{2y+x}.$$

Thus dy/dx exists where $2y + x \neq 0$. Now if $2y + x = 0$, then $x = -2y$. Substituting for x in the original equation, $y^2 + xy - 1 = 0$, we get

$$y^2 - 2y^2 - 1 = 0.$$

This simplifies to $y^2 + 1 = 0$, which has no solutions. Thus dy/dx exists everywhere.

10. True. We have $\tanh x = (\sinh x)/\cosh x = (e^x - e^{-x})/(e^x + e^{-x})$. Replacing x by $-x$ in this expression gives $(e^{-x} - e^x)/(e^{-x} + e^x) = -\tanh x$.

11. False. The second, fourth and all even derivatives of $\sinh x$ are all $\sinh x$.

12. True. The definitions of $\sinh x$ and $\cosh x$ give

$$\sinh x + \cosh x = \frac{e^x - e^{-x}}{2} + \frac{e^x + e^{-x}}{2} = \frac{2e^x}{2} = e^x.$$

13. False. Since $(\sinh x)' = \cosh x > 0$, the function $\sinh x$ is increasing everywhere so can never repeat any of its values.

14. False. Since $(\sinh^2 x)' = 2\sinh x \cosh x$ and $(2\sinh x \cosh x)' = 2\sinh^2 x + 2\cosh^2 x > 0$, the function $\sinh^2 x$ is concave up everywhere.

15. False. If $f(x) = |x|$, then $f(x)$ is not differentiable at $x = 0$ and $f'(x)$ does not exist at $x = 0$.

16. False. If $f(x) = \ln x$, then $f'(x) = 1/x$, which is decreasing for $x > 0$.

17. False; the fourth derivative of $\cos t + C$, where C is any constant, is indeed $\cos t$. But any function of the form $\cos t + p(t)$, where $p(t)$ is a polynomial of degree less than or equal to 3, also has its fourth derivative equal to $\cos t$. So $\cos t + t^2$ will work.

18. False; For example, the inverse function of $f(x) = x^3$ is $x^{1/3}$, and the derivative of $x^{1/3}$ is $(1/3)x^{-2/3}$, which is not $1/f'(x) = 1/(3x^2)$.

19. False; for example, if both $f(x)$ and $g(x)$ are constant functions, such as $f(x) = 6, g(x) = 10$, then $(fg)'(x) = 0$, and $f'(x) = 0$ and $g'(x) = 0$.

20. True; looking at the statement from the other direction, if both $f(x)$ and $g(x)$ are differentiable at $x = 1$, then so is their quotient, $f(x)/g(x)$, as long as it is defined there, which requires that $g(1) \neq 0$. So the only way in which $f(x)/g(x)$ can be defined but not differentiable at $x = 1$ is if either $f(x)$ or $g(x)$, or both, is not differentiable there.

21. False; for example, if both f and g are constant functions, then the derivative of $f(g(x))$ is zero, as is the derivative of $f(x)$. Another example is $f(x) = 5x + 7$ and $g(x) = x + 2$.

22. True. Since $f''(x) > 0$ and $g''(x) > 0$ for all x, we have $f''(x) + g''(x) > 0$ for all x, which means that $f(x) + g(x)$ is concave up.

23. False. Let $f(x) = x^2$ and $g(x) = x^2 - 1$. Let $h(x) = f(x)g(x)$. Then $h''(x) = 12x^2 - 2$. Since $h''(0) < 0$, clearly h is not concave up for all x.

24. False. Let $f(x) = 2x^2$ and $g(x) = x^2$. Then $f(x) - g(x) = x^2$, which is concave up for all x.

25. False. Let $f(x) = e^{-x}$ and $g(x) = x^2$. Let $h(x) = f(g(x)) = e^{-x^2}$. Then $h'(x) = -2xe^{-x^2}$ and $h''(x) = (-2 + 4x^2)e^{-x^2}$. Since $h''(0) < 0$, clearly h is not concave up for all x.

26. (a) False. Only if $k = f'(a)$ is L the local linearization of f.
   (b) False. Since $f(a) = L(a)$ for any k, we have $\lim_{x \to a}(f(x) - L(x)) = f(a) - L(a) = 0$, but only if $k = f'(a)$ is L the local linearization of f.

27. (a) This is not a counterexample. Although the product rule says that $(fg)' = f'g + fg'$, that does not rule out the possibility that also $(fg)' = f'g'$. In fact, if f and g are both constant functions, then both $f'g + fg'$ and $f'g'$ are zero, so they are equal to each other.
   (b) This is not a counterexample. In fact, it agrees with the product rule:

$$\frac{d}{dx}(xf(x)) = \left(\frac{d}{dx}(x)\right)f(x) + x\frac{d}{dx}f(x) = f(x) + xf'(x) = xf'(x) + f(x).$$

   (c) This is not a counterexample. Although the product rule says that

$$\frac{d}{dx}(f(x)^2) = \frac{d}{dx}f(x) \cdot f(x) = f'(x)f(x) + f(x)f'(x) = 2f(x)f'(x),$$

   it could be true that $f'(x) = 1$, so that the derivative is also just $2f(x)$. In fact, $f(x) = x$ is an example where this happens.
   (d) This would be a counterexample. If $f'(a) = g'(a) = 0$, then

$$\frac{d}{dx}(f(x)g(x))\Big|_{x=a} = f'(a)g(a) + f(a)g'(a) = 0.$$

   So fg cannot have positive slope at $x = a$. Of course such a counterexample could not exist, since the product rule is true.

28. True, by the Increasing Function Theorem, Theorem 3.8.

29. False. For example, let $f(x) = x + 5$, and $g(x) = 2x - 3$. Then $f'(x) \leq g'(x)$ for all x, but $f(0) > g(0)$.

30. False. For example, let $f(x) = 3x + 1$ and $g(x) = 3x + 7$.

31. False. For example, if $f(x) = -x$, then $f'(x) \leq 1$ for all x, but $f(-2) = 2$, so $f(-2) > -2$.

32. The function $f(x) = |x|$ is continuous on $[-1, 1]$, but there is no number c, with $-1 < c < 1$, such that

$$f'(c) = \frac{|1| - |-1|}{1 - (-1)} = 0;$$

that is, the slope of $f(x) = |x|$ is never 0.

33. Let f be defined by

$$f(x) = \begin{cases} x & \text{if } 0 \leq x < 2 \\ 19 & \text{if } x = 2 \end{cases}$$

Then f is differentiable on $(0, 2)$ and $f'(x) = 1$ for all x in $(0, 2)$. Thus there is no c in $(0, 2)$ such that

$$f'(c) = \frac{f(2) - f(0)}{2 - 0} = \frac{19}{2}.$$

The reason that this function does not satisfy the conclusion of the Mean Value Theorem is that it is not continuous at $x = 2$.

34. Let f be defined by

$$f(x) = \begin{cases} x^2 & \text{if } 0 \leq x < 1 \\ 1/2 & \text{if } x = 1. \end{cases}$$

Then f is not continuous at $x = 1$, but f is differentiable on $(0, 1)$ and $f'(x) = 2x$ for $0 < x < 1$. Thus, $c = 1/4$ satisfies

$$f'(c) = \frac{f(1) - f(0)}{1 - 0} = \frac{1}{2}, \quad \text{since} \quad f'\left(\frac{1}{4}\right) = 2 \cdot \frac{1}{4} = \frac{1}{2}.$$

PROJECTS FOR CHAPTER THREE

1. Let $r = i/100$. (For example if $i = 5\%$, $r = 0.05$.) Then the balance, $\$B$, after t years is given by

$$B = P(1 + r)^t,$$

where $\$P$ is the original deposit. If we are doubling our money, then $B = 2P$, so we wish to solve for t in the equation $2P = P(1 + r)^t$. This is equivalent to

$$2 = (1 + r)^t.$$

Taking natural logarithms of both sides and solving for t yields

$$\ln 2 = t \ln(1 + r),$$
$$t = \frac{\ln 2}{\ln(1 + r)}.$$

We now approximate $\ln(1 + r)$ near $r = 0$. Let $f(r) = \ln(1 + r)$. Then $f'(r) = 1/(1 + r)$. Thus, $f(0) = 0$ and $f'(0) = 1$, so

$$f(r) \approx f(0) + f'(0)r$$

becomes

$$\ln(1 + r) \approx r.$$

Therefore,

$$t = \frac{\ln 2}{\ln(1 + r)} \approx \frac{\ln 2}{r} = \frac{100 \ln 2}{i} \approx \frac{70}{i},$$

as claimed. We expect this approximation to hold for small values of i; it turns out that values of i up to 10 give good enough answers for most everyday purposes.

2. (a) (i) Set $f(x) = \sin x$, so $f'(x) = \cos x$. Guess $x_0 = 3$. Then

$$x_1 = 3 - \frac{\sin 3}{\cos 3} \approx 3.1425$$

$$x_2 = x_1 - \frac{\sin x_1}{\cos x_1} \approx 3.1415926533,$$

which is correct to one billionth!

(ii) Newton's method uses the tangent line at $x = 3$, i.e. $y - \sin 3 = \cos(3)(x - 3)$. Around $x = 3$, however, $\sin x$ is almost linear, since the second derivative $\sin''(\pi) = 0$. Thus using the tangent line to get an approximate value for the root gives us a very good approximation.

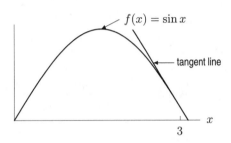

(iii) For $f(x) = \sin x$, we have

$$f(3) = 0.14112$$
$$f(4) = -0.7568,$$

so there is a root in $[3, 4]$. We now continue bisecting:

$$[3, 3.5] : f(3.5) = -0.35078 \text{ (bisection 1)}$$
$$[3, 3.25] : f(3.25) = -0.10819 \text{ (bisection 2)}$$
$$[3.125, 3.25] : f(3.125) = 0.01659 \text{ (bisection 3)}$$
$$[3.125, 3.1875] : f(3.1875) = -0.04584 \text{ (bisection 4)}$$

We continue this process; after 11 bisections, we know the root lies between 3.1411 and 3.1416, which still is not as good an approximation as what we get from Newton's method in just two steps.

(b) (i) We have $f(x) = \sin x - \frac{2}{3}x$ and $f'(x) = \cos x - \frac{2}{3}$.

Using $x_0 = 0.904$,

$$x_1 = 0.904 - \frac{\sin(0.904) - \frac{2}{3}(0.904)}{\cos(0.904) - \frac{2}{3}} \approx 4.704,$$

$$x_2 = 4.704 - \frac{\sin(4.704) - \frac{2}{3}(4.704)}{\cos(4.704) - \frac{2}{3}} \approx -1.423,$$

$$x_3 = -1.433 - \frac{\sin(-1.423) - \frac{2}{3}(-1.423)}{\cos(-1.423) - \frac{2}{3}} \approx -1.501,$$

$$x_4 = -1.499 - \frac{\sin(-1.501) - \frac{2}{3}(-1.501)}{\cos(-1.501) - \frac{2}{3}} \approx -1.496,$$

$$x_5 = -1.496 - \frac{\sin(-1.496) - \frac{2}{3}(-1.496)}{\cos(-1.496) - \frac{2}{3}} \approx -1.496.$$

Using $x_0 = 0.905$,

$$x_1 = 0.905 - \frac{\sin(0.905) - \frac{2}{3}(0.905)}{\cos(0.905) - \frac{2}{3}} \approx 4.643,$$

$$x_2 = 4.643 - \frac{\sin(4.643) - \frac{2}{3}(4.643)}{\cos(4.643) - \frac{2}{3}} \approx -0.918,$$

$$x_3 = -0.918 - \frac{\sin(-0.918) - \frac{2}{3}(-0.918)}{\cos(-0.918) - \frac{2}{3}} \approx -3.996,$$

$$x_4 = -3.996 - \frac{\sin(-3.996) - \frac{2}{3}(-3.996)}{\cos(-3.996) - \frac{2}{3}} \approx -1.413,$$

$$x_5 = -1.413 - \frac{\sin(-1.413) - \frac{2}{3}(-1.413)}{\cos(-1.413) - \frac{2}{3}} \approx -1.502,$$

$$x_6 = -1.502 - \frac{\sin(-1.502) - \frac{2}{3}(-1.502)}{\cos(-1.502) - \frac{2}{3}} \approx -1.496.$$

Now using $x_0 = 0.906$,

$$x_1 = 0.906 - \frac{\sin(0.906) - \frac{2}{3}(0.906)}{\cos(0.906) - \frac{2}{3}} \approx 4.584,$$

$$x_2 = 4.584 - \frac{\sin(4.584) - \frac{2}{3}(4.584)}{\cos(4.584) - \frac{2}{3}} \approx -0.509,$$

$$x_3 = -0.510 - \frac{\sin(-0.509) - \frac{2}{3}(-0.509)}{\cos(-0.509) - \frac{2}{3}} \approx .207,$$

$$x_4 = -1.300 - \frac{\sin(.207) - \frac{2}{3}(.207)}{\cos(.207) - \frac{2}{3}} \approx -0.009,$$

$$x_5 = -1.543 - \frac{\sin(-0.009) - \frac{2}{3}(-0.009)}{\cos(-0.009) - \frac{2}{3}} \approx 0,$$

(ii) Starting with 0.904 and 0.905 yields the same value, but the two paths to get to the root are very different. Starting with 0.906 leads to a different root. Our starting points were near the maximum value of f. Consequently, a small change in x_0 makes a large change in x_1.

CHAPTER FOUR

Solutions for Section 4.1

Exercises

1. There are many possible answers. One possible graph is shown in Figure 4.1.

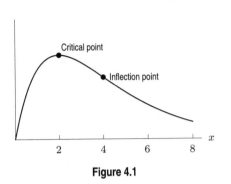

Figure 4.1

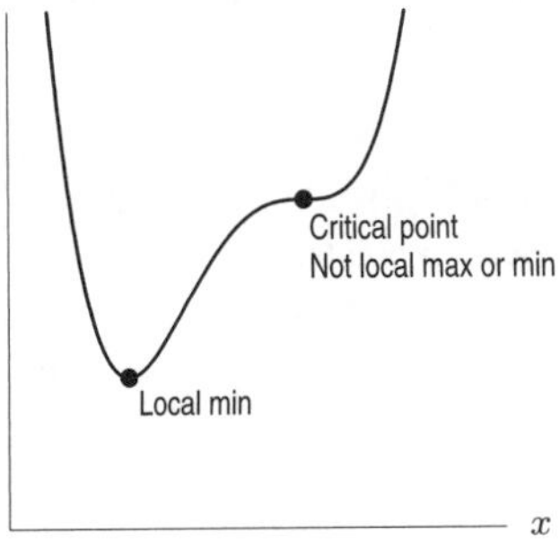

Figure 4.2

2. We sketch a graph which is horizontal at the two critical points. One possibility is shown in Figure 4.2.

3. (a) A graph of $f(x) = e^{-x^2}$ is shown in Figure 4.3. It appears to have one critical point, at $x = 0$, and two inflection points, one between 0 and 1 and the other between 0 and -1.

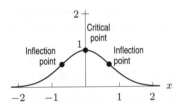

Figure 4.3

(b) To find the critical points, we set $f'(x) = 0$. Since $f'(x) = -2xe^{-x^2} = 0$, there is one solution, $x = 0$. The only critical point is at $x = 0$.

To find the inflection points, we first use the product rule to find $f''(x)$. We have

$$f''(x) = (-2x)(e^{-x^2}(-2x)) + (-2)(e^{-x^2}) = 4x^2 e^{-x^2} - 2e^{-x^2}.$$

We set $f''(x) = 0$ and solve for x by factoring:

$$4x^2 e^{-x^2} - 2e^{-x^2} = 0$$
$$(4x^2 - 2)e^{-x^2} = 0.$$

Since e^{-x^2} is never zero, we have

$$4x^2 - 2 = 0$$
$$x^2 = \frac{1}{2}$$
$$x = \pm 1/\sqrt{2}.$$

There are exactly two inflection points, at $x = 1/\sqrt{2} \approx 0.707$ and $x = -1/\sqrt{2} \approx -0.707$.

4. We use the product rule to find $f'(x)$:

$$f'(x) = (10.2x^2)(e^{-0.4x}(-0.4)) + (20.4x)(e^{-0.4x}) = -4.08x^2e^{-0.4x} + 20.4xe^{-0.4x}.$$

To find the critical points, we set $f'(x) = 0$ and solve for x by factoring:

$$-4.08x^2e^{-0.4x} + 20.4xe^{-0.4x} = 0$$
$$x(-4.08x + 20.4)e^{-0.4x} = 0.$$

Since $e^{-0.4x}$ is never zero, the only two solutions to this equation are $x = 0$ and $x = 20.4/4.08 = 5$. There are exactly two critical points, at $x = 0$ and at $x = 5$. You can sketch a graph of $f(x)$ to check your results.

5. From the graph of $f(x)$ in the figure below, we see that the function must have two inflection points. We calculate $f'(x) = 4x^3 + 3x^2 - 6x$, and $f''(x) = 12x^2 + 6x - 6$. Solving $f''(x) = 0$ we find that:

$$x_1 = -1 \quad \text{and} \quad x_2 = \frac{1}{2}.$$

Since $f''(x) > 0$ for $x < x_1$, $f''(x) < 0$ for $x_1 < x < x_2$, and $f''(x) > 0$ for $x_2 < x$, it follows that both points are inflection points.

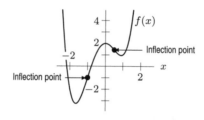

6. We have

$$g'(x) = e^{-x} - xe^{-x} = (1 - x)e^{-x}.$$

Hence $x = 1$ is the only critical point. We see that g' changes from positive to negative at $x = 1$ since e^{-x} is always positive, so by the first-derivative test g has a local maximum at $x = 1$. If we wish to use the second-derivative test, we compute

$$g''(x) = (x - 2)e^{-x}$$

and thus $g''(1) = (-1)e^{-1} < 0$, so again $x = 1$ gives a local maximum.

7. For $h(x) = x + \dfrac{1}{x}$, we calculate

$$h'(x) = 1 - \frac{1}{x^2}$$

and so the critical points of h are at $x = \pm 1$. Now

$$h''(x) = \frac{2}{x^3}$$

so $h''(1) = 2 > 0$ and $x = 1$ gives a local minimum. On the other hand, $h''(-1) = -2 < 0$ so $x = -1$ gives a local maximum.

8.

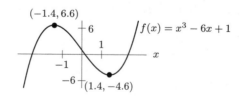

The graph of f above appears to be increasing for $x < -1.4$, decreasing for $-1.4 < x < 1.4$, and increasing for $x > 1.4$. There is a local maximum near $x = -1.4$ and local minimum near $x = 1.4$. The derivative of f is $f'(x) = 3x^2 - 6$. Thus $f'(x) = 0$ when $x^2 = 2$, that is $x = \pm\sqrt{2}$. This explains the critical points near $x = \pm 1.4$. Since $f'(x)$ changes from positive to negative at $x = -\sqrt{2}$, and from negative to positive at $x = \sqrt{2}$, there is a local maximum at $x = -\sqrt{2}$ and a local minimum at $x = \sqrt{2}$.

9. The graph of f in Figure 4.4 appears to be increasing for all x, with no critical points. Since $f'(x) = 3x^2 + 6$ and $x^2 \geq 0$ for all x, we have $f'(x) > 0$ for all x. That explains why f is increasing for all x.

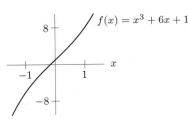

Figure 4.4

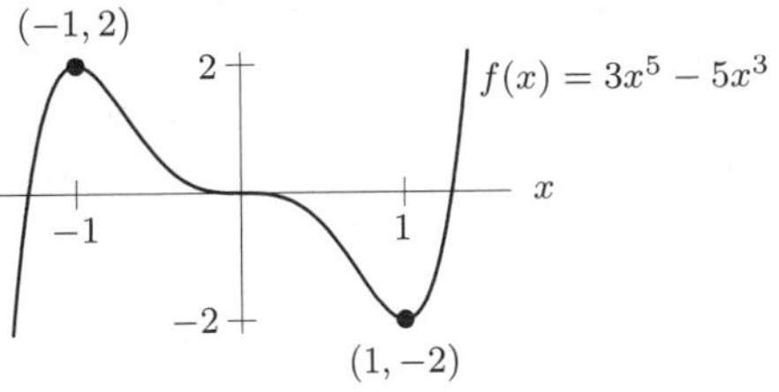

Figure 4.5

10. The graph of f in Figure 4.5 appears to be increasing for $x < -1$, decreasing for $-1 < x < 1$ although it is flat at $x = 0$, and increasing for $x > 1$. There are critical points at $x = -1$ and $x = 1$, and apparently also at $x = 0$.
Since $f'(x) = 15x^4 - 15x^2 = 15x^2(x^2 - 1)$, we have $f'(x) = 0$ at $x = 0, -1, 1$. Notice that although $f'(0) = 0$, making $x = 0$ a critical point, there is no change in sign of $f'(x)$ at $x = 0$; the only sign changes are at $x = \pm 1$. Thus the graph of f must alternate increasing/decreasing for $x < -1, -1 < x < 1, x > 1$, just as we described.

11. The graph of f in Figure 4.6 looks like a climbing sine curve, alternately increasing and decreasing, with more time spent increasing than decreasing. Here $f'(x) = 1 + 2\cos x$, so $f'(x) = 0$ when $\cos x = -1/2$; this occurs when

$$x = \pm\frac{2\pi}{3}, \pm\frac{4\pi}{3}, \pm\frac{8\pi}{3}, \pm\frac{10\pi}{3}, \pm\frac{14\pi}{3}, \pm\frac{16\pi}{3} \cdots$$

Since $f'(x)$ changes sign at each of these values, the graph of f must alternate increasing/decreasing. However, the distance between values of x for critical points alternates between $(2\pi)/3$ and $(4\pi)/3$, with $f'(x) > 0$ on the intervals of length $(4\pi)/3$. For example, $f'(x) > 0$ on the interval $(4\pi)/3 < x < (8\pi)/3$. As a result, f is increasing on the intervals of length $(4\pi/3)$ and decreasing on the intervals of length $(2\pi/3)$.

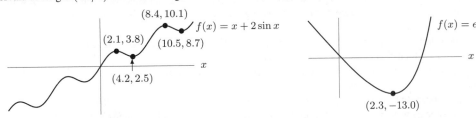

Figure 4.6

Figure 4.7

12. The graph of f in Figure 4.7 appears to be decreasing for $x < 2.3$ (almost like a straight line for $x < 0$), and increasing sharply for $x > 2.3$. Here $f'(x) = e^x - 10$, so $f'(x) = 0$ when $e^x = 10$, that is $x = \ln 10 = 2.302\ldots$ This is the only place where $f'(x)$ changes sign, and it is a minimum of f. Notice that e^x is small for $x < 0$ so $f'(x) \approx -10$ for $x < 0$, which means the graph looks like a straight line of slope -10 for $x < 0$. However, e^x gets large quickly for $x > 0$, so $f'(x)$ gets large quickly for $x > \ln 10$, meaning the graph increases sharply there.

13. The graph of f in Figure 4.8 looks like $\sin x$ for $x < 0$ and e^x for $x > 0$. In particular, there are no waves for $x > 0$. We have $f'(x) = \cos x + e^x$, and so the critical points of f occur at those values of x for which $\cos x = -e^x$. Since $e^x > 1$ for all $x > 0$, we know immediately that there are no critical points at positive values of x. The specific locations of the critical points at $x < 0$ must be determined numerically; the first few are $x \approx -1.7, -4.7, -7.9$. For $x < 0$, the quantity e^x is small so that the graph looks like the graph of $\sin x$. For $x > 0$, we have $f'(x) > 0$ since $-1 \leq \cos x$ and $e^x > 1$. Thus, the graph is increasing for all $x > 0$ and there are no such waves.

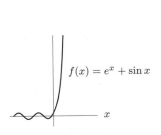

Figure 4.8

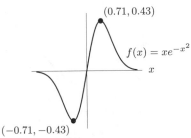

Figure 4.9

14. The graph of f in Figure 4.9 appears to be asymptotic to the x-axis from below for large negative x, decreasing to a local minimum at about $x = -0.71$, increasing to a local maximum at about $x = 0.71$ (passing through the origin along the way), and then decreasing asymptotically to the x-axis from above.

We have $f'(x) = e^{-x^2} + xe^{-x^2}(-2x) = e^{-x^2}(1 - 2x^2)$. Since $e^{-x^2} > 0$ for all x, the sign of $f'(x)$ is the same as the sign of $(1 - 2x^2)$. Thus $f'(x)$ changes sign at $x = \pm 1/\sqrt{2} \approx \pm 0.71$, going from negative to positive to negative, which explains the critical points and increasing/decreasing behavior described. Note that $xe^{-x^2} = x/e^{x^2}$ clearly approaches 0 as $x \to \pm\infty$, since e^{x^2} is much larger than x when $|x|$ is large. Thus the graph is asymptotic to the x-axis as $x \to \pm\infty$. Note also that the sign of $f(x) = xe^{-x^2}$ is the same as x, so $f(x) < 0$ for $x < 0$ and $f(x) > 0$ for $x > 0$. Since the graph increases from $x = 0$ to $x = 0.71$ and then decreases, $x = 1/\sqrt{2}$ is a local maximum. The local minimum at $x = -1/\sqrt{2}$ can be explained similarly.

15. The graph of f below appears to be decreasing for $0 < x < 0.37$, and then increasing for $x > 0.37$. We have $f'(x) = \ln x + x(1/x) = \ln x + 1$, so $f'(x) = 0$ when $\ln x = -1$, that is, $x = e^{-1} \approx 0.37$. This is the only place where f' changes sign and $f'(1) = 1 > 0$, so the graph must decrease for $0 < x < e^{-1}$ and increase for $x > e^{-1}$. Thus, there is a local minimum at $x = e^{-1}$.

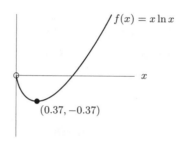

16. (8) The graph of $f(x) = x^3 - 6x + 1$ appears to be concave up for $x > 0$ and concave down for $x < 0$, with a point of inflection at $x = 0$. This is because $f''(x) = 6x$ is negative for $x < 0$ and positive for $x > 0$.
(9) Same answer as number 8.
(10) There appear to be three points of inflection at about $x = \pm 0.7$ and $x = 0$. This is because $f''(x) = 60x^3 - 30x = 30x(2x^2 - 1)$, which changes sign at $x = 0$ and $x = \pm 1/\sqrt{2}$.
(11) There appear to be points of inflection equally spaced about 3 units apart. This is because $f''(x) = -2\sin x$, which changes sign at $x = 0, \pm\pi, \pm 2\pi, \ldots$.
(12) The graph appears to be concave up for all x. This is because $f''(x) = e^x > 0$ for all x.
(13) The graph appears to be concave up for all $x > 0$, and has almost periodic changes in concavity for $x < 0$. This is because for $x > 0$, $f''(x) = e^x - \sin x > 0$, and for $x < 0$, since e^x is small, $f''(x)$ changes sign at approximately the same values of x as $\sin x$.
(14) There appears to be a point of inflection for some $x < -0.71$, for $x = 0$, and for some $x > 0.71$. This is because $f'(x) = e^{-x^2}(1 - 2x^2)$ so

$$f''(x) = e^{-x^2}(-4x) + (1 - 2x^2)e^{-x^2}(-2x)$$
$$= e^{-x^2}(4x^3 - 6x).$$

Since $e^{-x^2} > 0$, this means $f''(x)$ has the same sign as $(4x^3 - 6x) = 2x(2x^2 - 3)$. Thus $f''(x)$ changes sign at $x = 0$ and $x = \pm\sqrt{3/2} \approx \pm 1.22$.
(15) The graph appears to be concave up for all x. This is because $f'(x) = 1 + \ln x$, so $f''(x) = 1/x$, which is greater than 0 for all $x > 0$.

17. See Figure 4.10.

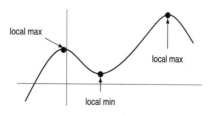

Figure 4.10

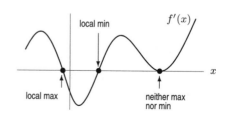

Figure 4.11

18. The critical points of f are zeros of f'. Just to the left of the first critical point $f' > 0$, so f is increasing. Immediately to the right of the first critical point $f' < 0$, so f is decreasing. Thus, the first point must be a maximum. To the left of the second critical point, $f' < 0$, and to its right, $f' > 0$; hence it is a minimum. On either side of the last critical point, $f' > 0$, so it is neither a maximum nor a minimum. See the figure below. See Figure 4.11.

19. To find inflection points of the function f we must find points where f'' changes sign. However, because f'' is the derivative of f', any point where f'' changes sign will be a local maximum or minimum on the graph of f'. See Figure 4.12.

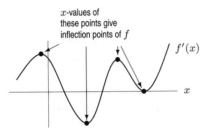

x-values of these points give inflection points of f

$f'(x)$

Figure 4.12

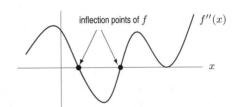

inflection points of f

$f''(x)$

Figure 4.13

20. The inflection points of f are the points where f'' changes sign. See Figure 4.13.

Problems

21. Differentiating using the product rule gives

$$f'(x) = 3x^2(1-x)^4 - 4x^3(1-x)^3 = x^2(1-x)^3(3(1-x) - 4x) = x^2(1-x)^3(3-7x).$$

The critical points are the solutions to

$$f'(x) = x^2(1-x)^3(3-7x) = 0$$
$$x = 0, 1, \frac{3}{7}.$$

For $x < 0$, since $1 - x > 0$ and $3 - 7x > 0$, we have $f'(x) > 0$.
For $0 < x < \frac{3}{7}$, since $1 - x > 0$ and $3 - 7x > 0$, we have $f'(x) > 0$.
For $\frac{3}{7} < x < 1$, since $1 - x > 0$ and $3 - 7x < 0$, we have $f'(x) < 0$.
For $1 < x$, since $1 - x < 0$ and $3 - 7x < 0$, we have $f'(x) > 0$.
Thus, $x = 0$ is neither a local maximum nor a local minimum; $x = 3/7$ is a local maximum; $x = 1$ is a local minimum.

22. By the product rule

$$f'(x) = \frac{dx^m(1-x)^n}{dt} = mx^{m-1}(1-x)^n - nx^m(1-x)^{n-1}$$
$$= x^{m-1}(1-x)^{n-1}(m(1-x) - nx)$$
$$= x^{m-1}(1-x)^{n-1}(m - (m+n)x).$$

We have $f'(x) = 0$ at $x = 0$, $x = 1$, and $x = m/(m+n)$, so these are the three critical points of f.

We can classify the critical points by determining the sign of $f'(x)$.
If $x < 0$, then $f'(x)$ has the same sign as $(-1)^{m-1}$: negative if m is even, positive if m is odd.
If $0 < x < m/(m+n)$, then $f'(x)$ is positive.
If $m/(m+n) < x < 1$, then $f'(x)$ is negative.
If $1 < x$, then $f'(x)$ has the same sign as $(-1)^n$: positive if n is even, negative if n is odd.
If m is even, then $f'(x)$ changes from negative to positive at $x = 0$, so f has a local minimum at $x = 0$.
If m is odd, then $f'(x)$ is positive to both the left and right of 0, so $x = 0$ is an inflection point of f.
At $x = m/(m+n)$, the derivative $f'(x)$ changes from positive to negative, so $x = m/(m+n)$ is a local maximum of f.
If n is even, then $f'(x)$ changes from negative to positive at $x = 1$, so f has a local minimum at $x = 1$. If n is odd, then $f'(x)$ is negative to both the left and right of 1, so $x = 1$ is an inflection point of f.

23. A function may have any number of critical points or none at all. (See Figures 4.14–4.16.)

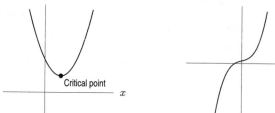

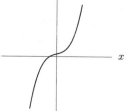

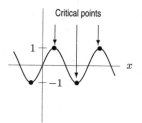

Figure 4.14: A quadratic:
One critical point

Figure 4.15: $f(x) = x^3 + x + 1$:
No critical points

Figure 4.16: $f(x) = \sin x$:
Infinitely many critical points

24. (a) A critical point occurs when $f'(x) = 0$. Since $f'(x)$ changes sign between $x = 2$ and $x = 3$, between $x = 6$ and $x = 7$, and between $x = 9$ and $x = 10$, we expect critical points at around $x = 2.5$, $x = 6.5$, and $x = 9.5$.
   (b) Since $f'(x)$ goes from positive to negative at $x \approx 2.5$, a local maximum should occur there. Similarly, $x \approx 6.5$ is a local minimum and $x \approx 9.5$ a local maximum.

25. (a) It appears that this function has a local maximum at about $x = 1$, a local minimum at about $x = 4$, and a local maximum at about $x = 8$.
   (b) The table now gives values of the derivative, so critical points occur where $f'(x) = 0$. Since f' is continuous, this occurs between 2 and 3, so there is a critical point somewhere around 2.5. Since f' is positive for values less than 2.5 and negative for values greater than 2.5, it appears that f has a local maximum at about $x = 2.5$. Similarly, it appears that f has a local minimum at about $x = 6.5$ and another local maximum at about $x = 9.5$.

26. (a) Since $P = 1/(1 + 10e^{-t}) = (1 + 10e^{-t})^{-1}$, we have

$$\frac{dP}{dt} = -(1 + 10e^{-t})^{-2} \cdot (-10e^{-t}) = \frac{10e^{-t}}{(1 + 10e^{-t})^2}$$

$$\frac{d^2P}{dt^2} = -10e^{-t}(1 + 10e^{-t})^{-2} + 10e^{-t}(-2(1 + 10e^{-t})^{-3} \cdot (-10e^{-t})) = \frac{10e^{-t}(10e^{-t} - 1)}{(1 + 10e^{-t})^3}.$$

   (b) See Figures 4.17 and 4.18.

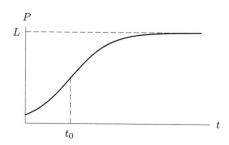

Figure 4.17

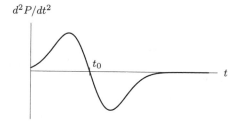

Figure 4.18

27. First, we wish to have $f'(6) = 0$, since $f(6)$ should be a local minimum:

$$f'(x) = 2x + a = 0$$
$$x = -\frac{a}{2} = 6$$
$$a = -12.$$

Next, we need to have $f(6) = -5$, since the point $(6, -5)$ is on the graph of $f(x)$. We can substitute $a = -12$ into our equation for $f(x)$ and solve for b:

$$f(x) = x^2 - 12x + b$$
$$f(6) = 36 - 72 + b = -5$$
$$b = 31.$$

Thus, $f(x) = x^2 - 12x + 31$.

28. We wish to have $f'(3) = 0$. Differentiating to find $f'(x)$ and then solving $f'(3) = 0$ for a gives:

$$f'(x) = x(ae^{ax}) + 1(e^{ax}) = e^{ax}(ax + 1)$$
$$f'(3) = e^{3a}(3a + 1) = 0$$
$$3a + 1 = 0$$
$$a = -\frac{1}{3}.$$

Thus, $f(x) = xe^{-x/3}$.

29. Using the product rule on the function $f(x) = axe^{bx}$, we have $f'(x) = ae^{bx} + abxe^{bx} = ae^{bx}(1 + bx)$. We want $f(\frac{1}{3}) = 1$, and since this is to be a maximum, we require $f'(\frac{1}{3}) = 0$. These conditions give

$$f(1/3) = a(1/3)e^{b/3} = 1,$$
$$f'(1/3) = ae^{b/3}(1 + b/3) = 0.$$

Since $ae^{(1/3)b}$ is non-zero, we can divide both sides of the second equation by $ae^{(1/3)b}$ to obtain $0 = 1 + \frac{b}{3}$. This implies $b = -3$. Plugging $b = -3$ into the first equation gives us $a(\frac{1}{3})e^{-1} = 1$, or $a = 3e$. How do we know we have a maximum at $x = \frac{1}{3}$ and not a minimum? Since $f'(x) = ae^{bx}(1 + bx) = (3e)e^{-3x}(1 - 3x)$, and $(3e)e^{-3x}$ is always positive, it follows that $f'(x) > 0$ when $x < \frac{1}{3}$ and $f'(x) < 0$ when $x > \frac{1}{3}$. Since f' is positive to the left of $x = \frac{1}{3}$ and negative to the right of $x = \frac{1}{3}$, $f(\frac{1}{3})$ is a local maximum.

30. Figure 4.19 contains the graph of $f(x) = x^2 + \cos x$.

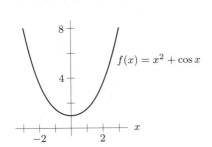

Figure 4.19

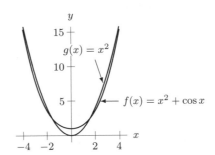

Figure 4.20

The graph looks like a parabola with no waves because $f''(x) = 2 - \cos x$, which is always positive. Thus, the graph of f is concave up everywhere; there are no waves. If you plot the graph of $f(x)$ together with the graph of $g(x) = x^2$, you see that the graph of f does wave back and forth across the graph of g, but never enough to change the concavity of f. See Figure 4.20.

31. (a) From the graph of $P(t) = \dfrac{2000}{1 + e^{(5.3 - 0.4t)}}$ in Figure 4.21, we see that the population levels off at about 2000 rabbits.

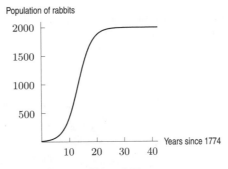

Figure 4.21

(b) The population appears to have been growing fastest when there were about 1000 rabbits, about 13 years after Captain Cook left them there.

(c) The rabbits reproduce quickly, so their population initially grew very rapidly. Limited food and space availability and perhaps predators on the island probably account for the population being unable to grow past 2000.

32. (a) Since the volume of water in the container is proportional to its depth, and the volume is increasing at a constant rate,

$$d(t) = \text{Depth at time } t = Kt,$$

where K is some positive constant. So the graph is linear, as shown in Figure 4.22. Since initially no water is in the container, we have $d(0) = 0$, and the graph starts from the origin.

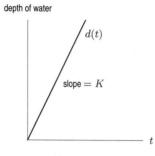

Figure 4.22

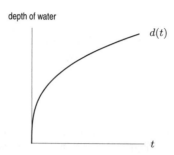

Figure 4.23

(b) As time increases, the additional volume needed to raise the water level by a fixed amount increases. Thus, although the depth, $d(t)$, of water in the cone at time t, continues to increase, it does so more and more slowly. This means $d'(t)$ is positive but decreasing, i.e., $d(t)$ is concave down. See Figure 4.23.

33. See Figure 4.24.

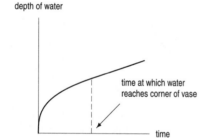

Figure 4.24

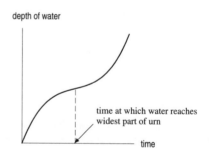

Figure 4.25

34. See Figure 4.25.

35. From the first condition, we get that $x = 2$ is a local minimum for f. From the second condition, it follows that $x = 4$ is an inflection point. A possible graph is shown in Figure 4.26.

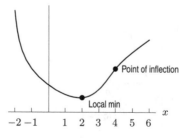

Figure 4.26

36. Since f is differentiable everywhere, f' must be zero (not undefined) at any critical points; thus, $f'(3) = 0$. Since f has exactly one critical point, f' may change sign only at $x = 3$. Thus f is always increasing or always decreasing for $x < 3$ and for $x > 3$. Using the information in parts (a) through (d), we determine whether $x = 3$ is a local minimum, local maximum, or neither.

(a) $x = 3$ is a local maximum because $f(x)$ is increasing when $x < 3$ and decreasing when $x > 3$. See Figure 4.27.

Figure 4.27

Figure 4.28

(b) $x = 3$ is a local minimum because $f(x)$ heads to infinity to either side of $x = 3$. See Figure 4.28.
(c) $x = 3$ is neither a local minimum nor maximum, as $f(1) < f(2) < f(4) < f(5)$. See Figure 4.29.

Figure 4.29

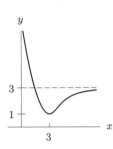

Figure 4.30

(d) $x = 3$ is a local minimum because $f(x)$ is decreasing to the left of $x = 3$ and must increase to the right of $x = 3$, as $f(3) = 1$ and eventually $f(x)$ must become close to 3. See Figure 4.30.

37. (a)

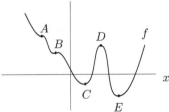

(b)

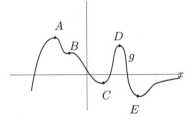

38. Neither B nor C is 0 where A has its maxima and minimum. Therefore neither B nor C is the derivative of A, so $A = f''$. We can see B could be the derivative of C because where C has a maximum, B is 0. However, C is not the derivative of B because B is decreasing for some x-values and C is never negative. Thus, $C = f$, $B = f'$, and $A = f''$.

39. A has zeros where B has maxima and minima, so A could be a derivative of B. This is confirmed by comparing intervals on which B is increasing and A is positive. (They are the same.) So, C is either the derivative of A or the derivative of C is B. However, B does not have a zero at the point where C has a minimum, so B cannot be the derivative of C. Therefore, C is the derivative of A. So $B = f$, $A = f'$, and $C = f''$.

40. Since the derivative of an even function is odd and the derivative of an odd function is even, f and f'' are either both odd or both even, and f' is the opposite. Graphs I and III represent even functions; II represents an odd function, so II is f'. Since the maxima and minima of II occur where I crosses the x-axis, I must be the derivative of f', that is, f''. In addition, the maxima and minima of III occur where II crosses the x-axis, so III is f.

41. Since the derivative of an even function is odd and the derivative of an odd function is even, f and f'' are either both odd or both even, and f' is the opposite. Graphs I and II represent odd functions; III represents an even function, so III is f'. Since the maxima and minima of III occur where I crosses the x-axis, I must be the derivative of f', that is, f''. In addition, the maxima and minima of II occur where III crosses the x-axis, so II is f.

42. See Figure 4.31.

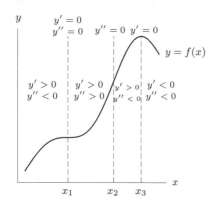

Figure 4.31

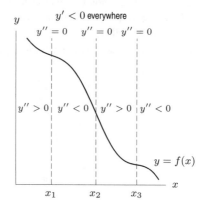

Figure 4.32

43. See Figure 4.32.
44. See Figure 4.33.

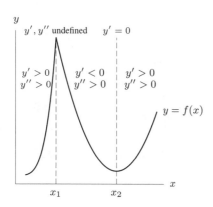

Figure 4.33

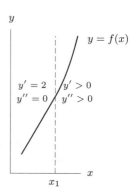

Figure 4.34

45. See Figure 4.34.
46. (a) This is one of many possible graphs.

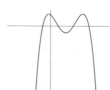

(b) Since f must have a bump between each pair of zeros, f could have at most four zeros.
(c) f could well have no zeros at all. To see this, consider the graph of the above function shifted vertically downward.
(d) f must have at least two inflection points. Since f has 3 maxima or minima, it has 3 critical points. Consequently f' will have 3 corresponding zeros. Between each consecutive pair of these zeroes f' must have a local maximum or minimum. Thus f' will have one local maximum and one local minimum, which implies that f'' will have two zeros. These values, where the second derivative is zero, correspond to points of inflection on the graph of f.
(e) The 3 critical points are zeros of f', so degree(f') $\geq$ 3. Thus degree(f) $\geq$ 4.
(f) For example:
$$f(x) = -(x+1)(x-1)(x-3)(x-5)$$
will look something like the graph in part (a). Many other answers are possible.

47. (a) When a number grows larger, its reciprocal grows smaller. Therefore, since f is increasing near x_0, we know that g (its reciprocal) must be decreasing. Another argument can be made using derivatives. We know that (since f is increasing) $f'(x) > 0$ near x_0. We also know (by the chain rule) that $g'(x) = (f(x)^{-1})' = -\frac{f'(x)}{f(x)^2}$. Since both $f'(x)$ and $f(x)^2$ are positive, this means $g'(x)$ is negative, which in turn means $g(x)$ is decreasing near $x = x_0$.

(b) Since f has a local maximum near x_1, $f(x)$ increases as x nears x_1, and then $f(x)$ decreases as x exceeds x_1. Thus the reciprocal of f, g, decreases as x nears x_1 and then increases as x exceeds x_1. Thus g has a local minimum at $x = x_1$. To put it another way, since f has a local maximum at $x = x_1$, we know $f'(x_1) = 0$. Since $g'(x) = -\frac{f'(x)}{f(x)^2}$, $g'(x_1) = 0$. To the left of x_1, $f'(x_1)$ is positive, so $g'(x)$ is negative. To the right of x_1, $f'(x_1)$ is negative, so $g'(x)$ is positive. Therefore, g has a local minimum at x_1.

(c) Since f is concave down at x_2, we know $f''(x_2) < 0$. We also know (from above) that

$$g''(x_2) = \frac{2f'(x_2)^2}{f(x_2)^3} - \frac{f''(x_2)}{f(x_2)^2} = \frac{1}{f(x_2)^2}\left(\frac{2f'(x_2)^2}{f(x_2)} - f''(x_2)\right).$$

Since $\frac{1}{f(x_2)^2} > 0$, $2f'(x_2)^2 > 0$, and $f(x_2) > 0$ (as f is assumed to be everywhere positive), we see that $g''(x_2)$ is positive. Thus g is concave up at x_2.

Note that for the first two parts of the problem, we did not need to require f to be positive (only non-zero). However, it was necessary here.

48. (a) Since $f''(x) > 0$ and $g''(x) > 0$ for all x, then $f''(x) + g''(x) > 0$ for all x, so $f(x) + g(x)$ is concave up for all x.

(b) Nothing can be concluded about the concavity of $(f + g)(x)$. For example, if $f(x) = ax^2$ and $g(x) = bx^2$ with $a > 0$ and $b < 0$, then $(f + g)''(x) = a + b$. So $f + g$ is either always concave up, always concave down, or a straight line, depending on whether $a > |b|$, $a < |b|$, or $a = |b|$. More generally, it is even possible that $(f + g)(x)$ may have one or more changes in concavity.

(c) It is possible to have infinitely many changes in concavity. Consider $f(x) = x^2 + \cos x$ and $g(x) = -x^2$. Since $f''(x) = 2 - \cos x$, we see that $f(x)$ is concave up for all x. Clearly $g(x)$ is concave down for all x. However, $f(x) + g(x) = \cos x$, which changes concavity an infinite number of times.

Solutions for Section 4.2

Exercises

1. The line of slope m through the point (x_0, y_0) has equation

$$y - y_0 = m(x - x_0),$$

so the line we want is

$$y - 0 = 2(x - 5)$$
$$y = 2x - 10.$$

2. We want a function of the form $y = a(x - h)^2 + k$, with $a < 0$ because the parabola opens downward. Since (h, k) is the vertex, we must take $h = 2$, $k = 5$, but we can take any negative value of a. Figure 4.35 shows the graph with $a = -1$, namely $y = -(x - 2)^2 + 5$.

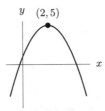

Figure 4.35: Graph of $y = -(x - 2)^2 + 5$

3. A parabola with x-intercepts ± 1 has an equation of the form

$$y = k(x-1)(x+1).$$

Substituting the point $x = 0, y = 3$ gives

$$3 = k(-1)(1) \quad \text{so} \quad k = -3.$$

Thus, the equation we want is

$$y = -3(x-1)(x+1)$$
$$y = -3x^2 + 3.$$

4. The equation of the whole circle is

$$x^2 + y^2 = 5^2,$$

so the top half is

$$y = \sqrt{25 - x^2}.$$

5. The equation of the whole circle is

$$x^2 + y^2 = (\sqrt{2})^2,$$

so the bottom half is

$$y = -\sqrt{2 - x^2}.$$

6. A circle with center (h, k) and radius r has equation $(x-h)^2 + (y-k)^2 = r^2$. Thus $h = -1$, $k = 2$, and $r = 3$, giving

$$(x+1)^2 + (y-2)^2 = 9.$$

Solving for y, and taking the positive square root gives the top half, so

$$(y-2)^2 = 9 - (x+1)^2$$
$$y = 2 + \sqrt{9 - (x+1)^2}.$$

See Figure 4.36.

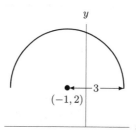

Figure 4.36: Graph of $y = 2 + \sqrt{9 - (x+1)^2}$

7. Since the horizontal asymptote is $y = 5$, we know $a = 5$. The value of b can be any number. Thus $y = 5(1 - e^{-bx})$ for any $b > 0$.

8. Since the vertical asymptote is $x = 2$, we have $b = -2$. The fact that the horizontal asymptote is $y = -5$ gives $a = -5$. So

$$y = \frac{-5x}{x-2}.$$

9. Since the maximum is $y = 2$ and the minimum is $y = 1.5$, the amplitude is $A = (2 - 1.5)/2 = 0.25$. Between the maximum and the minimum, the x-value changes by 10. There is half a period between a maximum and the next minimum, so the period is 20. Thus

$$\frac{2\pi}{B} = 20 \quad \text{so} \quad B = \frac{\pi}{10}.$$

The mid-line is $y = C = (2 + 1.5)/2 = 1.75$. Figure 4.37 shows a graph of the function

$$y = 0.25 \sin\left(\frac{\pi x}{10}\right) + 1.75.$$

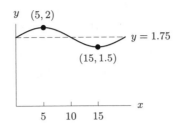

Figure 4.37: Graph of $y = 0.25 \sin(\pi x/10) + 1.75$

10. Since the maximum is on the y-axis, $a = 0$. At that point, $y = be^{-0^2/2} = b$, so $b = 3$.

11. The maximum of $y = e^{-(x-a)^2/b}$ occurs at $x = a$. (This is because the exponent $-(x-a)^2/b$ is zero when $x = a$ and negative for all other x-values. The same result can be obtained by taking derivatives.) Thus we know that $a = 2$.
  Points of inflection occur where d^2y/dx^2 changes sign, that is, where $d^2y/dx^2 = 0$. Differentiating gives

$$\frac{dy}{dx} = -\frac{2(x-2)}{b}e^{-(x-2)^2/b}$$

$$\frac{d^2y}{dx^2} = -\frac{2}{b}e^{-(x-2)^2/b} + \frac{4(x-2)^2}{b^2}e^{-(x-2)^2/b} = \frac{2}{b}e^{-(x-2)^2/b}\left(-1 + \frac{2}{b}(x-2)^2\right).$$

Since $e^{-(x-2)^2/b}$ is never zero, $d^2y/dx^2 = 0$ where

$$-1 + \frac{2}{b}(x-2)^2 = 0.$$

We know $d^2y/dx^2 = 0$ at $x = 1$, so substituting $x = 1$ gives

$$-1 + \frac{2}{b}(1-2)^2 = 0.$$

Solving for b gives

$$-1 + \frac{2}{b} = 0$$
$$b = 2.$$

Since $a = 2$, the function is

$$y = e^{-(x-2)^2/2}.$$

You can check that at $x = 2$, we have

$$\frac{d^2y}{dx^2} = \frac{2}{2}e^{-0}(-1 + 0) < 0$$

so the point $x = 2$ does indeed give a maximum. See Figure 4.38.

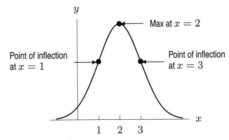

Figure 4.38: Graph of $y = e^{-(x-2)^2/2}$

12. Differentiating $y = ax^b \ln x$, we have

$$\frac{dy}{dx} = abx^{b-1} \ln x + ax^b \cdot \frac{1}{x} = ax^{b-1}(b \ln x + 1).$$

Since the maximum occurs at $x = e^2$, we know that

$$a(e^2)^{b-1}(b \ln(e^2) + 1) = 0.$$

Since $a \neq 0$ and $(e^2)^{b-1} \neq 0$ for all b, we have

$$b \ln(e^2) + 1 = 0.$$

Since $\ln(e^2) = 2$, the equation becomes

$$2b + 1 = 0$$
$$b = -\frac{1}{2}.$$

Thus $y = ax^{-1/2} \ln x$. When $x = e^2$, we know $y = 6e^{-1}$, so

$$y = a(e^2)^{-1/2} \ln e^2 = ae^{-1}(2) = 6e^{-1}$$
$$a = 3.$$

Thus $y = 3x^{-1/2} \ln x$. To check that $x = e^2$ gives a local maximum, we differentiate twice

$$\frac{dy}{dx} = -\frac{3}{2}x^{-3/2} \ln x + 3x^{-1/2} \cdot \frac{1}{x} = -\frac{3}{2}x^{-3/2} \ln x + 3x^{-3/2},$$
$$\frac{d^2y}{dx^2} = \frac{9}{4}x^{-5/2} \ln x - \frac{3}{2}x^{-3/2} \cdot \frac{1}{x} - \frac{3}{2} \cdot 3x^{-5/2}$$
$$= \frac{9}{4}x^{-5/2} \ln x - 6x^{-5/2} = \frac{3}{4}x^{-5/2}(3 \ln x - 8).$$

At $x = e^2$, since $\ln(e^2) = 2$, we have a maximum because

$$\frac{d^2y}{dx^2} = \frac{3}{4}(e^2)^{-5/2}\left(3 \ln(e^2) - 8\right) = \frac{3}{4}e^{-5}(3 \cdot 2 - 8) < 0.$$

See Figure 4.39.

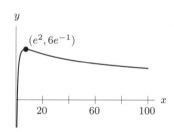

Figure 4.39: Graph of $y = 3x^{-1/2} \ln x$

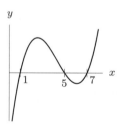

Figure 4.40: Graph of $y = (x - 1)(x - 5)(x - 7)$

13. A cubic polynomial of the form $y = a(x-1)(x-5)(x-7)$ has the correct intercepts for any value of $a \neq 0$. Figure 4.40 shows the graph with $a = 1$, namely $y = (x - 1)(x - 5)(x - 7)$.

14. Since the x^3 term has coefficient of 1, the cubic polynomial is of the form $y = x^3 + ax^2 + bx + c$. We now find a, b, and c. Differentiating gives

$$\frac{dy}{dx} = 3x^2 + 2ax + b.$$

The derivative is 0 at local maxima and minima, so

$$\left. \frac{dy}{dx} \right|_{x=1} = 3(1)^2 + 2a(1) + b = 3 + 2a + b = 0$$

$$\left. \frac{dy}{dx} \right|_{x=3} = 3(3)^2 + 2a(3) + b = 27 + 6a + b = 0$$

Subtracting the first equation from the second and solving for a and b gives

$$24 + 4a = 0 \qquad \text{so} \qquad a = -6$$
$$b = -3 - 2(-6) = 9.$$

Since the y-intercept is 5, the cubic is

$$y = x^3 - 6x^2 + 9x + 5.$$

Since the coefficient of x^3 is positive, $x = 1$ is the maximum and $x = 3$ is the minimum. See Figure 4.41. To confirm that $x = 1$ gives a maximum and $x = 3$ gives a minimum, we calculate

$$\frac{d^2y}{dx^2} = 6x + 2a = 6x - 12.$$

At $x = 1$, $\dfrac{d^2y}{dx^2} = -6 < 0$, so we have a maximum.

At $x = 3$, $\dfrac{d^2y}{dx^2} = 6 > 0$, so we have a minimum.

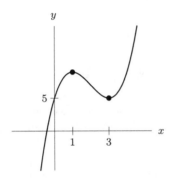

Figure 4.41: Graph of $y = x^3 - 6x^2 + 9x + 5$

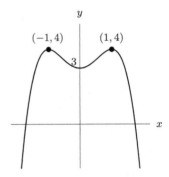

Figure 4.42: Graph of $y = -x^4 + 2x^2 + 3$

15. Since the graph of the quartic polynomial is symmetric about the y-axis, the quartic must have only even powers and be of the form

$$y = ax^4 + bx^2 + c.$$

The y-intercept is 3, so $c = 3$. Differentiating gives

$$\frac{dy}{dx} = 4ax^3 + 2bx.$$

Since there is a maximum at $(1, 4)$, we have $dy/dx = 0$ if $x = 1$, so

$$4a(1)^3 + 2b(1) = 4a + 2b = 0 \qquad \text{so} \qquad b = -2a.$$

The fact that $dy/dx = 0$ if $x = -1$ gives us the same relationship

$$-4a - 2b = 0 \qquad \text{so} \qquad b = -2a.$$

We also know that $y = 4$ if $x = \pm 1$, so

$$a(1)^4 + b(1)^2 + 3 = a + b + 3 = 4 \qquad \text{so} \qquad a + b = 1.$$

Solving for a and b gives

$$a - 2a = 1 \qquad \text{so} \qquad a = -1 \text{ and } b = 2.$$

Finding d^2y/dx^2 so that we can check that $x = \pm 1$ are maxima, not minima, we see

$$\frac{d^2y}{dx^2} = 12ax^2 + 2b = -12x^2 + 4.$$

Thus $\dfrac{d^2y}{dx^2} = -8 < 0$ for $x = \pm 1$, so $x = \pm 1$ are maxima. See Figure 4.42.

Problems

16. (a) Let $p(x) = x^3 - ax$, and suppose $a < 0$. Then $p'(x) = 3x^2 - a > 0$ for all x, so $p(x)$ is always increasing.

(b) Now suppose $a > 0$. We have $p'(x) = 3x^2 - a = 0$ when $x^2 = a/3$, i.e., when $x = \sqrt{a/3}$ and $x = -\sqrt{a/3}$. We also have $p''(x) = 6x$; so $x = \sqrt{a/3}$ is a local minimum since $6\sqrt{a/3} > 0$, and $x = -\sqrt{a/3}$ is a local maximum since $-6\sqrt{a/3} < 0$.

(c) <u>Case 1:</u> $a < 0$

In this case, $p(x)$ is always increasing. We have $p''(x) = 6x > 0$ if $x > 0$, meaning the graph is concave up for $x > 0$. Furthermore, $6x < 0$ if $x < 0$, meaning the graph is concave down for $x < 0$. Thus, $x = 0$ is an inflection point.

<u>Case 2:</u> $a > 0$

We have

$$p\left(\sqrt{\frac{a}{3}}\right) = \left(\sqrt{\frac{a}{3}}\right)^3 - a\sqrt{\frac{a}{3}} = \frac{a\sqrt{a}}{\sqrt{27}} - \frac{a\sqrt{a}}{\sqrt{3}} = -\frac{2a\sqrt{a}}{3\sqrt{3}} < 0,$$

$$\text{and} \quad p\left(-\sqrt{\frac{a}{3}}\right) = -\frac{a\sqrt{a}}{\sqrt{27}} + \frac{a\sqrt{a}}{\sqrt{3}} = -p\left(\sqrt{\frac{a}{3}}\right) > 0.$$

$$p'(x) = 3x^2 - a \begin{cases} = 0 & \text{if } |x| = \sqrt{\frac{a}{3}}; \\ > 0 & \text{if } |x| > \sqrt{\frac{a}{3}}; \\ < 0 & \text{if } |x| < \sqrt{\frac{a}{3}}. \end{cases}$$

So p is increasing for $x < -\sqrt{a/3}$, decreasing for $-\sqrt{a/3} < x < \sqrt{a/3}$, and increasing for $x > \sqrt{a/3}$. Since $p''(x) = 6x$, the graph of $p(x)$ is concave down for values of x less than zero and concave up for values greater than zero. Graphs of $p(x)$ for $a < 0$ and $a > 0$ are found in Figures 4.43 and 4.44, respectively.

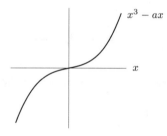

Figure 4.43: $p(x)$ for $a < 0$

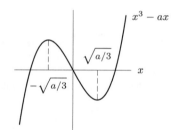

Figure 4.44: $p(x)$ for $a > 0$

17. (a) We have $p'(x) = 3x^2 - a$, so

$$p \text{ increasing} \quad | \quad p \text{ decreasing} \quad | \quad p \text{ increasing}$$
$$x = -\sqrt{\frac{a}{3}} \qquad x = \sqrt{\frac{a}{3}}$$

Local maximum: $p(-\sqrt{\frac{a}{3}}) = \frac{-a\sqrt{a}}{\sqrt{27}} + \frac{a\sqrt{a}}{\sqrt{3}} = +\frac{2a\sqrt{a}}{3\sqrt{3}}$

Local minimum: $p(\sqrt{\frac{a}{3}}) = -p(-\sqrt{\frac{a}{3}}) = -\frac{2a\sqrt{a}}{3\sqrt{3}}$

(b) Increasing the value of a moves the critical points of p away from the y-axis, and moves the critical values away from the x-axis. Thus, the "bumps" get further apart and higher. At the same time, increasing the value of a spreads the zeros of p further apart (while leaving the one at the origin fixed).

(c) See Figure 4.45

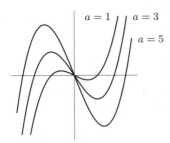

Figure 4.45

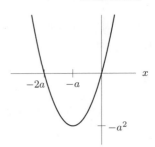

Figure 4.46

18. We have $f(x) = x^2 + 2ax = x(x + 2a) = 0$ when $x = 0$ or $x = -2a$.

$$f'(x) = 2x + 2a = 2(x + a) \begin{cases} = 0 & \text{when } x = -a \\ > 0 & \text{when } x > -a \\ < 0 & \text{when } x < -a. \end{cases}$$

See Figure 4.46. Furthermore, $f''(x) = 2$, so that $f(-a) = -a^2$ is a global minimum, and the graph is always concave up. Increasing $|a|$ stretches the graph horizontally. Also, the critical value (the value of f at the critical point) drops further beneath the x-axis. Letting $a < 0$ would reflect the graph shown through the y-axis.

19. (a) See Figure 4.47.
  (b) The function $f(x) = x + a \sin x$ is increasing for all x if $f'(x) > 0$ for all x. We have $f'(x) = 1 + a \cos x$. Because $\cos x$ varies between -1 and 1, we have $1 + a \cos x > 0$ for all x if $-1 < a < 1$ but not otherwise. When $a = 1$, the function $f(x) = x + \sin x$ is increasing for all x, as is $f(x) = x - \sin x$, obtained when $a = -1$. Thus $f(x)$ is increasing for all x if $-1 \le a \le 1$.

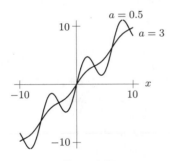

Figure 4.47

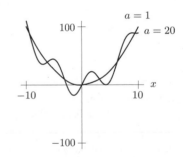

Figure 4.48

20. (a) See Figure 4.48.
  (b) The function $f(x) = x^2 + a \sin x$ is concave up for all x if $f''(x) > 0$ for all x. We have $f''(x) = 2 - a \sin x$. Because $\sin x$ varies between -1 and 1, we have $2 - a \sin x > 0$ for all x if $-2 < a < 2$ but not otherwise. Thus $f(x)$ is concave up for all x if $-2 < a < 2$.

21. Since $\lim_{t \to \infty} N = a$, we have $a = 200{,}000$. Note that while $N(t)$ will never actually reach $200{,}000$, it will become arbitrarily close to $200{,}000$. Since N represents the number of people, it makes sense to round up long before $t \to \infty$. When $t = 1$, we have $N = 0.1(200{,}000) = 20{,}000$ people, so plugging into our formula gives

$$N(1) = 20{,}000 = 200{,}000 \left(1 - e^{-k(1)}\right).$$

Solving for k gives

$$0.1 = 1 - e^{-k}$$
$$e^{-k} = 0.9$$
$$k = -\ln 0.9 \approx 0.105.$$

22. $T(t) =$ the temperature at time $t = a(1 - e^{-kt}) + b$.

(a) Since at time $t = 0$ the yam is at $20°$C, we have

$$T(0) = 20° = a\left(1 - e^0\right) + b = a(1 - 1) + b = b.$$

Thus $b = 20°$C. Now, common sense tells us that after a period of time, the yam will heat up to about $200°$, or oven temperature. Thus the temperature T should approach $200°$ as the time t grows large:

$$\lim_{t \to \infty} T(t) = 200°\text{C} = a(1 - 0) + b = a + b.$$

Since $a + b = 200°$, and $b = 20°$C, this means $a = 180°$C.

(b) Since we're talking about how quickly the yam is heating up, we need to look at the derivative, $T'(t) = ake^{-kt}$:

$$T'(t) = (180)ke^{-kt}.$$

We know $T'(0) = 2°$C/min, so

$$2 = (180)ke^{-k(0)} = (180)(k).$$

So $k = (2°\text{C/min})/180°\text{C} = \frac{1}{90}\text{min}^{-1}$.

23. We begin by finding the intercepts, which occur where $f(x) = 0$, that is

$$x - k\sqrt{x} = 0$$
$$\sqrt{x}(\sqrt{x} - k) = 0$$

$$\text{so} \quad x = 0 \quad \text{or} \quad \sqrt{x} = k, \quad x = k^2.$$

So 0 and k^2 are the x-intercepts. Now we find the location of the critical points by setting $f'(x)$ equal to 0:

$$f'(x) = 1 - k\left(\frac{1}{2}x^{-(1/2)}\right) = 1 - \frac{k}{2\sqrt{x}} = 0.$$

This means

$$1 = \frac{k}{2\sqrt{x}}, \quad \text{so} \quad \sqrt{x} = \frac{1}{2}k, \quad \text{and} \quad x = \frac{1}{4}k^2.$$

We can use the second derivative to verify that $x = \frac{k^2}{4}$ is a local minimum. $f''(x) = 1 + \frac{k}{4x^{3/2}}$ is positive for all $x > 0$. So the critical point, $x = \frac{1}{4}k^2$, is $1/4$ of the way between the x-intercepts, $x = 0$ and $x = k^2$. Since $f''(x) = \frac{1}{4}kx^{-3/2}$, $f''(\frac{1}{4}k^2) = 2/k^2 > 0$, this critical point is a minimum.

24. Graphs of $y = xe^{-bx}$ for $b = 1, 2, 3, 4$ are shown below. All the graphs rise at first, passing through the origin, reach a maximum and then decay toward 0. If b is small, the graph rises longer and to a higher maximum before the decay begins.

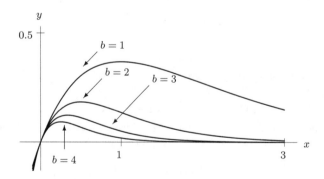

25. Since

$$\frac{dy}{dx} = (1 - bx)e^{-bx},$$

we see

$$\frac{dy}{dx} = 0 \quad \text{at} \quad x = \frac{1}{b}.$$

The critical point has coordinates $(1/b, 1/(be))$. If b is small, the x and y-coordinates of the critical point are both large, indicating a higher maximum further to the right. See figure below.

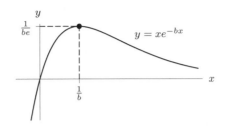

26. (a) $f'(x) = 4x^3 + 2ax = 2x(2x^2 + a)$; so $x = 0$ and $x = \pm\sqrt{-a/2}$ (if $\pm\sqrt{-a/2}$ is real, i.e. if $-a/2 \geq 0$) are critical points.

(b) $x = 0$ is a critical point for any value of a. In order to guarantee that $x = 0$ is the only critical point, the factor $2x^2 + a$ should not have a root other than possibly $x = 0$. This means $a \geq 0$, since $2x^2 + a$ has only one root ($x = 0$) for $a = 0$, and no roots for $a > 0$. There is no restriction on the constant b.

Now $f''(x) = 12x^2 + 2a$ and $f''(0) = 2a$.

If $a > 0$, then by the second derivative test, $f(0)$ is a local minimum.

If $a = 0$, then $f(x) = x^4 + b$, which has a local minimum at $x = 0$.

So $x = 0$ is a local minimum when $a \geq 0$.

(c) Again, b will have no effect on the location of the critical points. In order for $f'(x) = 2x(2x^2 + a)$ to have three different roots, the constant a has to be negative. Let $a = -2c^2$, for some $c > 0$. Then

$$f'(x) = 4x(x^2 - c^2) = 4x(x - c)(x + c).$$

The critical points of f are $x = 0$ and $x = \pm c = \pm\sqrt{-a/2}$.

To the left of $x = -c$, $f'(x) < 0$.

Between $x = -c$ and $x = 0$, $f'(x) > 0$.

Between $x = 0$ and $x = c$, $f'(x) < 0$.

To the right of $x = c$, $f'(x) > 0$.

So, $f(-c)$ and $f(c)$ are local minima and $f(0)$ is a local maximum.

(d) For $a \geq 0$, there is exactly one critical point, $x = 0$. For $a < 0$ there are exactly three different critical points. These exhaust all the possibilities. (Notice that the value of b is irrelevant here.)

27. Since $f'(x) = abe^{-bx}$, we have $f'(x) > 0$ for all x. Therefore, f is increasing for all x. Since $f''(x) = -ab^2e^{-bx}$, we have $f''(x) < 0$ for all x. Therefore, f is concave down for all x.

28. (a) The graph of r has a vertical asymptote if the denominator is zero. Since $(x - b)^2$ is nonnegative, the denominator can only be zero if $a \leq 0$. Then

$$a + (x - b)^2 = 0$$
$$(x - b)^2 = -a$$
$$x - b = \pm\sqrt{-a}$$
$$x = b \pm \sqrt{-a}.$$

In order for there to be a vertical asymptote, a must be less than or equal to zero. There are no restrictions on b.

(b) Differentiating gives

$$r'(x) = \frac{-1}{(a + (x - b)^2)^2} \cdot 2(x - b),$$

so $r' = 0$ when $x = b$. If $a \leq 0$, then r' is undefined at the same points at which r is undefined. Thus the only critical point is $x = b$. Since we want $r(x)$ to have a maximum at $x = 3$, we choose $b = 3$. Also, since $r(3) = 5$, we have

$$r(3) = \frac{1}{a + (3 - 3)^2} = \frac{1}{a} = 5 \qquad \text{so} \qquad a = \frac{1}{5}.$$

29. (a) The x-intercept occurs where $f(x) = 0$, so

$$ax - x\ln x = 0$$
$$x(a - \ln x) = 0.$$

Since $x > 0$, we must have

$$a - \ln x = 0$$
$$\ln x = a$$
$$x = e^a.$$

(b) See Figures 4.49 and 4.50.

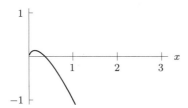

Figure 4.49: Graph of $f(x)$ with $a = -1$

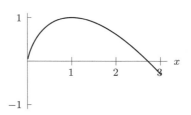

Figure 4.50: Graph of $f(x)$ with $a = 1$

(c) Differentiating gives $f'(x) = a - \ln x - 1$. Critical points are obtained by solving

$$a - \ln x - 1 = 0$$
$$\ln x = a - 1$$
$$x = e^{a-1}.$$

Since $e^{a-1} > 0$ for all a, there is no restriction on a. Now,

$$f(e^{a-1}) = ae^{a-1} - e^{a-1} \ln(e^{a-1}) = ae^{a-1} - (a-1)e^{a-1} = e^{a-1},$$

so the coordinates of the critical point are (e^{a-1}, e^{a-1}). From the graphs, we see that this critical point is a local maximum; this can be confirmed using the second derivative:

$$f''(x) = -\frac{1}{x} < 0 \qquad \text{for } x = e^{a-1}.$$

30. (a) Figures 4.51- 4.54 show graphs of $f(x) = x^2 + \cos(kx)$ for various values of k. For $k = 0.5$ and $k = 1$, the graphs look like parabolas. For $k = 3$, there is some waving in the parabola, which becomes more noticeable if $k = 5$. The waving begins to happen at about $k = 1.5$.

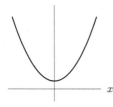

Figure 4.51: $k = 0.5$

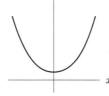

Figure 4.52: $k = 1$

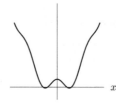

Figure 4.53: $k = 3$

Figure 4.54: $k = 5$

(b) Differentiating, we have

$$f'(x) = 2x - k \sin(kx)$$
$$f''(x) = 2 - k^2 \cos(kx).$$

If $k^2 \leq 2$, then $f''(x) \geq 2 - 2\cos(kx) \geq 0$, since $\cos(kx) \leq 1$. Thus, the graph is always concave up if $k \leq \sqrt{2}$. If $k^2 > 2$, then $f''(x)$ changes sign whenever $\cos(kx) = 2/k^2$, which occurs for infinitely many values of x, since $0 < 2/k^2 < 1$.

(c) Since $f'(x) = 2x - k \sin(kx)$, we want to find all points where

$$2x - k \sin(kx) = 0.$$

Since

$$-1 \leq \sin(kx) \leq 1,$$

$f'(x) \neq 0$ if $x > k/2$ or $x < -k/2$. Thus, all the roots of $f'(x)$ must be in the interval $-k/2 \leq x \leq k/2$. The roots occur where the line $y = 2x$ intersects the curve $y = k \sin(kx)$, and there are only a finite number of such points for $-k/2 \leq x \leq k/2$.

31. (a) Figure 4.55 suggests that each graph decreases to a local minimum and then increases sharply. The local minimum appears to move to the right as k increases. It appears to move up until $k = 1$, and then to move back down.

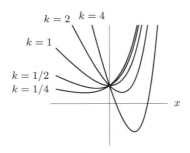

$k = 2$ $k = 4$
$k = 1$
$k = 1/2$
$k = 1/4$
x

Figure 4.55

(b) $f'(x) = e^x - k = 0$ when $x = \ln k$. Since $f'(x) < 0$ for $x < \ln k$ and $f'(x) > 0$ for $x > \ln k$, f is decreasing to the left of $x = \ln k$ and increasing to the right, so f reaches a local minimum at $x = \ln k$.

(c) The minimum value of f is
$$f(\ln k) = e^{\ln k} - k(\ln k) = k - k\ln k.$$

Since we want to maximize the expression $k - k\ln k$, we can imagine a function $g(k) = k - k\ln k$. To maximize this function we simply take its derivative and find the critical points. Differentiating, we obtain
$$g'(k) = 1 - \ln k - k(1/k) = -\ln k.$$

Thus $g'(k) = 0$ when $k = 1$, $g'(k) > 0$ for $k < 1$, and $g'(k) < 0$ for $k > 1$. Thus $k = 1$ is a local maximum for $g(k)$. That is, the largest global minimum for f occurs when $k = 1$.

32. Let $f(x) = Ae^{-Bx^2}$. Since
$$f(x) = Ae^{-Bx^2} = Ae^{-\frac{(x-0)^2}{(1/B)}},$$

this is just the family of curves $y = e^{\frac{(x-a)^2}{b}}$ multiplied by a constant A. This family of curves is discussed in the text; here, $a = 0$, $b = \frac{1}{B}$. When $x = 0$, $y = Ae^0 = A$, so A determines the y-intercept. A also serves to flatten or stretch the graph of e^{-Bx^2} vertically. Since $f'(x) = -2ABxe^{-Bx^2}$, $f(x)$ has a critical point at $x = 0$. For $B > 0$, the graphs are bell-shaped curves centered at $x = 0$, and $f(0) = A$ is a global maximum.

To find the inflection points of f, we solve $f''(x) = 0$. Since $f'(x) = -2ABxe^{-Bx^2}$,
$$f''(x) = -2ABe^{-Bx^2} + 4AB^2x^2e^{-Bx^2}.$$

Since e^{-Bx^2} is always positive, $f''(x) = 0$ when
$$-2AB + 4AB^2x^2 = 0$$
$$x^2 = \frac{2AB}{4AB^2}$$
$$x = \pm\sqrt{\frac{1}{2B}}.$$

These are points of inflection, since the second derivative changes sign here. Thus for large values of B, the inflection points are close to $x = 0$, and for smaller values of B the inflection points are further from $x = 0$. Therefore B affects the width of the graph.

In the graphs in Figure 4.56, A is held constant, and variations in B are shown.

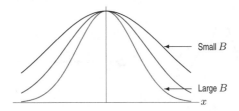

Small B
Large B
x

Figure 4.56: $f(x) = Ae^{-Bx^2}$ for varying B

33. (a) Let $f(x) = axe^{-bx}$. To find the local maxima and local minima of f, we solve

$$f'(x) = ae^{-bx} - abxe^{-bx} = ae^{-bx}(1 - bx) \begin{cases} = 0 & \text{if } x = 1/b \\ < 0 & \text{if } x > 1/b \\ > 0 & \text{if } x < 1/b. \end{cases}$$

Therefore, f is increasing ($f' > 0$) for $x < 1/b$ and decreasing ($f' > 0$) for $x > 1/b$. A local maximum occurs at $x = 1/b$. There are no local minima. To find the points of inflection, we write

$$\begin{aligned} f''(x) &= -abe^{-bx} + ab^2xe^{-bx} - abe^{-bx} \\ &= -2abe^{-bx} + ab^2xe^{-bx} \\ &= ab(bx - 2)e^{-bx}, \end{aligned}$$

so $f'' = 0$ at $x = 2/b$. Therefore, f is concave up for $x < 2/b$ and concave down for $x > 2/b$, and the inflection point is $x = 2/b$.

(b) Varying a stretches or flattens the graph but does not affect the critical point $x = 1/b$ and the inflection point $x = 2/b$. Since the critical and inflection points are depend on b, varying b will change these points, as well as the maximum $f(1/b) = a/be$. For example, an increase in b will shift the critical and inflection points to the left, and also lower the maximum value of f.

(c)

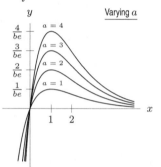 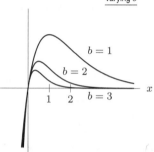

34. Graphs of $y = e^{-ax}\sin(bx)$ for $b = 1$ and various values of a are shown in Figure 4.57. The parameter a controls the amplitude of the oscillations.

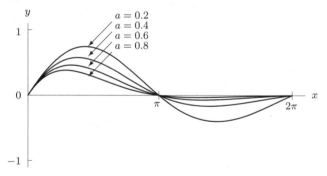

Figure 4.57

35.

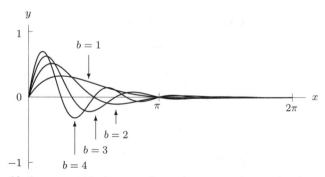

The larger the value of b, the narrower the humps and more humps per given region there are in the graph.

36. (a) The larger the value of $|A|$, the steeper the graph (for the same x-value).
   (b) The graph is shifted horizontally by B. The shift is to the left for positive B, to the right for negative B. There is a
       vertical asymptote at $x = -B$. See Figure 4.58.
   (c)

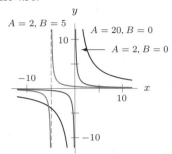

Figure 4.58

37. (a) Since
$$U = b\left(\frac{a^2 - ax}{x^2}\right) = 0 \quad \text{when} \quad x = a,$$
the x-intercept is $x = a$. There is a vertical asymptote at $x = 0$ and a horizontal asymptote at $U = 0$.
   (b) Setting $dU/dx = 0$, we have
$$\frac{dU}{dx} = b\left(-\frac{2a^2}{x^3} + \frac{a}{x^2}\right) = b\left(\frac{-2a^2 + ax}{x^3}\right) = 0.$$

So the critical point is
$$x = 2a.$$

When $x = 2a$,
$$U = b\left(\frac{a^2}{4a^2} - \frac{a}{2a}\right) = -\frac{b}{4}.$$

The second derivative of U is
$$\frac{d^2U}{dx^2} = b\left(\frac{6a^2}{x^4} - \frac{2a}{x^3}\right).$$

When we evaluate this at $x = 2a$, we get
$$\frac{d^2U}{dx^2} = b\left(\frac{6a^2}{(2a)^4} - \frac{2a}{(2a)^3}\right) = \frac{b}{8a^2} > 0.$$

Since $d^2U/dx^2 > 0$ at $x = 2a$, we see that the point $(2a, -b/4)$ is a local minimum.
   (c)

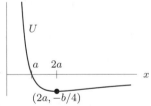

38. Both U and F have asymptotes at $x = 0$ and the x-axis. In Problem 37 we saw that U has intercept $(a, 0)$ and local
minimum $(2a, -b/4)$. Differentiating U gives
$$F = b\left(\frac{2a^2}{x^3} - \frac{a}{x^2}\right).$$

Since
$$F = b\left(\frac{2a^2 - ax}{x^3}\right) = 0 \quad \text{for} \quad x = 2a,$$

F has one intercept: $(2a, 0)$. Differentiating again to find the critical points:

$$\frac{dF}{dx} = b\left(-\frac{6a^2}{x^4} + \frac{2a}{x^3}\right) = b\left(\frac{-6a^2 + 2ax}{x^4}\right) = 0,$$

so $x = 3a$. When $x = 3a$,

$$F = b\left(\frac{2a^2}{27a^3} - \frac{a}{9a^2}\right) = -\frac{b}{27a}.$$

By the first or second derivative test, $x = 3a$ is a local minimum of F. See figure below.

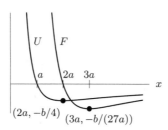

39. (a) The force is zero where

$$f(r) = -\frac{A}{r^2} + \frac{B}{r^3} = 0$$
$$Ar^3 = Br^2$$
$$r = \frac{B}{A}.$$

The vertical asymptote is $r = 0$ and the horizontal asymptote is the r-axis.

(b) To find critical points, we differentiate and set $f'(r) = 0$:

$$f'(r) = \frac{2A}{r^3} - \frac{3B}{r^4} = 0$$
$$2Ar^4 = 3Br^3$$
$$r = \frac{3B}{2A}.$$

Thus, $r = 3B/(2A)$ is the only critical point. Since $f'(r) < 0$ for $r < 3B/(2A)$ and $f'(r) > 0$ for $r > 3B/(2A)$, we see that $r = 3B/(2A)$ is a local minimum. At that point,

$$f\left(\frac{3B}{2A}\right) = -\frac{A}{9B^2/4A^2} + \frac{B}{27B^3/8A^3} = -\frac{4A^3}{27B^2}.$$

Differentiating again, we have

$$f''(r) = -\frac{6A}{r^4} + \frac{12B}{r^5} = -\frac{6}{r^5}(Ar - 2B).$$

So $f''(r) < 0$ where $r > 2B/A$ and $f''(r) > 0$ when $r < 2B/A$. Thus, $r = 2B/A$ is the only point of inflection. At that point

$$f\left(\frac{2B}{A}\right) = -\frac{A}{4B^2/A^2} + \frac{B}{8B^3/A^3} = -\frac{A^3}{8B^2}.$$

(c)

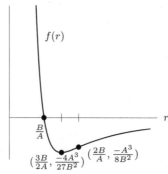

(d) (i) Increasing B means that the r-values of the zero, the minimum, and the inflection point increase, while the $f(r)$ values of the minimum and the point of inflection decrease in magnitude. See Figure 4.59.

(ii) Increasing A means that the r-values of the zero, the minimum, and the point of inflection decrease, while the $f(r)$ values of the minimum and the point of inflection increase in magnitude. See Figure 4.60.

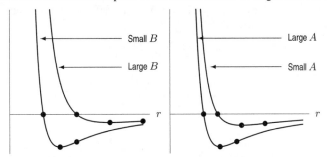

Figure 4.59: Increasing B **Figure 4.60**: Increasing A

40. For $-5 \le x \le 5$, we have the graphs of $y = a\cosh(x/a)$ shown below.

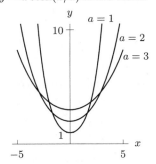

Increasing the value of a makes the graph flatten out and raises the minimum value. The minimum value of y occurs at $x = 0$ and is given by

$$y = a\cosh\left(\frac{0}{a}\right) = a\left(\frac{e^{0/a} + e^{-0/a}}{2}\right) = a.$$

41. (a) The graphs are shown in Figures 4.61–4.66.

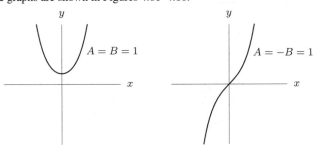

Figure 4.61: $A > 0, B > 0$ **Figure 4.62**: $A > 0, B < 0$ **Figure 4.63**: $A > 0, B > 0$

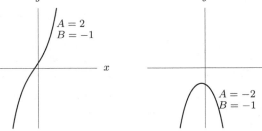

Figure 4.64: $A > 0, B < 0$ **Figure 4.65**: $A < 0, B < 0$ **Figure 4.66**: $A < 0, B > 0$

(b) If A and B have the same sign, the graph is U-shaped. If A and B are both positive, the graph opens upward. If A and B are both negative, the graph opens downward.

(c) If A and B have different signs, the graph appears to be everywhere increasing (if $A > 0, B < 0$) or decreasing (if $A < 0, B > 0$).

(d) The function appears to have a local maximum if $A < 0$ and $B < 0$, and a local minimum if $A > 0$ and $B > 0$.

To justify this, calculate the derivative

$$\frac{dy}{dx} = Ae^x - Be^{-x}.$$

Setting $dy/dx = 0$ gives

$$Ae^x - Be^{-x} = 0$$
$$Ae^x = Be^{-x}$$
$$e^{2x} = \frac{B}{A}.$$

This equation has a solution only if B/A is positive, that is, if A and B have the same sign. In that case,

$$2x = \ln\left(\frac{B}{A}\right)$$
$$x = \frac{1}{2}\ln\left(\frac{B}{A}\right).$$

This value of x gives the only critical point.

To determine whether the critical point is a local maximum or minimum, we use the first derivative test. Since

$$\frac{dy}{dx} = Ae^x - Be^{-x},$$

we see that:

If $A > 0, B > 0$, we have $dy/dx > 0$ for large positive x and $dy/dx < 0$ for large negative x, so there is a local minimum.

If $A < 0, B < 0$, we have $dy/dx < 0$ for large positive x and $dy/dx > 0$ for large negative x, so there is a local maximum.

42. (a) See Figure 4.67.

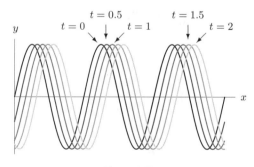

Figure 4.67

(b) (i) For fixed t, the function represents the surface of the water at time t. The shape of the surface is a sine wave of period 2π.

(ii) For fixed x, the function represents the vertical (up-and-down) motion of a particle at position x.

(c) For fixed t, the derivative dy/dx represents the slope of the surface of the wave at position x and time t.

(d) For fixed x, the derivative dy/dt represents the vertical velocity of a particle of water at position x and time t.

43. (a) The vertical intercept is $W = Ae^{-e^{b-c\cdot 0}} = Ae^{-e^b}$. There is no horizontal intercept since the exponential function is always positive. There is a horizontal asymptote. As $t \to \infty$, we see that $e^{b-ct} = e^b/e^{ct} \to 0$, since t is positive. Therefore $W \to Ae^0 = A$, so there is a horizontal asymptote at $W = A$.

(b) The derivative is

$$\frac{dW}{dt} = Ae^{-e^{b-ct}}(-e^{b-ct})(-c) = Ace^{-e^{b-ct}}e^{b-ct}.$$

Thus, dW/dt is always positive, so W is always increasing and has no critical points. The second derivative is

$$\frac{d^2W}{dt^2} = \frac{d}{dt}(Ace^{-e^{b-ct}})e^{b-ct} + Ace^{-e^{b-ct}}\frac{d}{dt}(e^{b-ct})$$

$$= Ac^2e^{-e^{b-ct}}e^{b-ct}e^{b-ct} + Ace^{-e^{b-ct}}(-c)e^{b-ct}$$

$$= Ac^2e^{-e^{b-ct}}e^{b-ct}(e^{b-ct} - 1).$$

Now e^{b-ct} decreases from $e^b > 1$ when $t = 0$ toward 0 as $t \to \infty$. The second derivative changes sign from positive to negative when $e^{b-ct} = 1$, i.e., when $b - ct = 0$, or $t = b/c$. Thus the curve has an inflection point at $t = b/c$, where $W = Ae^{-e^{b-(b/c)c}} = Ae^{-1}$.

(c) See Figure 4.68.

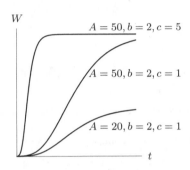

Figure 4.68

(d) The final size of the organism is given by the horizontal asymptote $W = A$. The curve is steepest at its inflection point, which occurs at $t = b/c$, $W = Ae^{-1}$. Since $e = 2.71828\ldots \approx 3$, the size the organism when it is growing fastest is about $A/3$, one third its final size. So yes, the Gompertz growth function is useful in modeling such growth.

Solutions for Section 4.3

Exercises

1. See Figure 4.69.

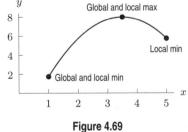

Figure 4.69

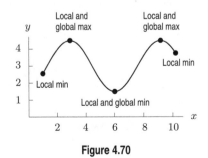

Figure 4.70

2. The global maximum is achieved at the two local maxima, which are at the same height. See Figure 4.70.

3. (a) Setting the derivative of $p(1-p)^4$ equal to 0

$$\frac{d}{dp}(p(1-p)^4) = (1-p)^4 - 4p(1-p)^3 = 0$$

$$(1-p)^3(1-p-4p) = 0$$

$$(1-p)^3(1-5p) = 0$$

$$p = 1/5, 1.$$

Thus, the critical points are $p = 1/5$ and $p = 1$.

(b) Since

$$\frac{d^2}{dp^2}(p(1-p)^4) = \frac{d}{dp}((1-p)^4 - 4p(1-p)^3)$$

$$= -4(1-p)^3 - 4(1-p)^3 + 12p(1-p)^2$$

$$= 4(1-p)^2(-2(1-p) + 3p)$$

$$= 4(1-p)^2(-2 + 5p),$$

substituting $p = 1/5$ and $p = 1$, we have

$$\frac{d^2}{dp^2}(p(1-p)^4)\bigg|_{p=1/5} = 4\left(\frac{4}{5}\right)^2(-1) < 0 \quad \text{and} \quad \frac{d^2}{dp^2}(p(1-p)^4)\bigg|_{p=1} = 0$$

Thus $p = 1/5$ is a local maximum. The second derivative test does not enable us to classify $p = 1$. However, $p(1-p)^4$ is positive everywhere except at $p = 0$ and $p = 1$, where it is 0. Thus, $p = 1$ is a local minimum.

(c) The global maximum occurs at the local maximum, at $p = 1/5$, so

$$\text{Maximum} = \frac{1}{5}\left(1 - \frac{1}{5}\right)^4 = \frac{4^4}{5^5} = \frac{256}{3125}.$$

The global minimum occurs at the end points, so

$$\text{Minimum} = 0(1-0)^4 = 1(1-1)^4 = 0.$$

4. (a) We have $f'(x) = 10x^9 - 10 = 10(x^9 - 1)$. This is zero when $x = 1$, so $x = 1$ is a critical point of f. For values of x less than 1, x^9 is less than 1, and thus $f'(x)$ is negative when $x < 1$. Similarly, $f'(x)$ is positive for $x > 1$. Thus $f(1) = -9$ is a local minimum.

We also consider the endpoints $f(0) = 0$ and $f(2) = 1004$. Since $f'(0) < 0$ and $f'(2) > 0$, we see $x = 0$ and $x = 2$ are local maxima.

(b) Comparing values of f shows that the global minimum is at $x = 1$, and the global maximum is at $x = 2$.

5. (a) $f'(x) = 1 - 1/x$. This is zero only when $x = 1$. Now $f'(x)$ is positive when $1 < x \le 2$, and negative when $0.1 < x < 1$. Thus $f(1) = 1$ is a local minimum. The endpoints $f(0.1) \approx 2.4026$ and $f(2) \approx 1.3069$ are local maxima.

(b) Comparing values of f shows that $x = 0.1$ gives the global maximum and $x = 1$ gives the global minimum.

6. (a) Differentiating

$$f(x) = \sin^2 x - \cos x \quad \text{for } 0 \le x \le \pi$$

$$f'(x) = 2\sin x \cos x + \sin x = (\sin x)(2\cos x + 1)$$

$f'(x) = 0$ when $\sin x = 0$ or when $2\cos x + 1 = 0$. Now, $\sin x = 0$ when $x = 0$ or when $x = \pi$. On the other hand, $2\cos x + 1 = 0$ when $\cos x = -1/2$, which happens when $x = 2\pi/3$. So the critical points are $x = 0$, $x = 2\pi/3$, and $x = \pi$.

Note that $\sin x > 0$ for $0 < x < \pi$. Also, $2\cos x + 1 < 0$ if $2\pi/3 < x \le \pi$ and $2\cos x + 1 > 0$ if $0 < x < 2\pi/3$. Therefore,

$$f'(x) < 0 \quad \text{for} \quad \frac{2\pi}{3} < x < \pi$$

$$f'(x) > 0 \quad \text{for} \quad 0 < x < \frac{2\pi}{3}.$$

Thus f has a local maximum at $x = 2\pi/3$ and local minima at $x = 0$ and $x = \pi$.

(b) We have

$$f(0) = [\sin(0)]^2 - \cos(0) = -1$$

$$f\left(\frac{2\pi}{3}\right) = \left[\sin\left(\frac{2\pi}{3}\right)\right]^2 - \cos\frac{2\pi}{3} = 1.25$$

$$f(\pi) = [\sin(\pi)]^2 - \cos(\pi) = 1.$$

Thus the global maximum is at $x = 2\pi/3$, and the global minimum is at $x = 0$.

7. This is a parabola opening downward. We find the critical points by setting $g'(x) = 0$:

$$g'(x) = 4 - 2x = 0$$

$$x = 2.$$

Since $g'(x) > 0$ for $x < 2$ and $g'(x) < 0$ for $x > 2$, the critical point at $x = 2$ is a local maximum.

As $x \to \pm\infty$, the value of $g(x) \to -\infty$. Thus, the local maximum at $x = 2$ is a global maximum of $g(2) = 4 \cdot 2 - 2^2 - 5 = -1$. There is no global minimum. See Figure 4.71.

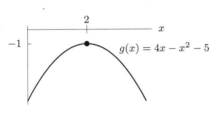

Figure 4.71

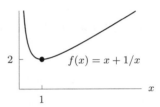

Figure 4.72

8. Differentiating gives

$$f'(x) = 1 - \frac{1}{x^2},$$

so the critical points satisfy

$$1 - \frac{1}{x^2} = 0$$

$$x^2 = 1$$

$$x = 1 \quad \text{(We want } x > 0\text{)}.$$

Since f' is negative for $0 < x < 1$ and f' is positive for $x > 1$, there is a local minimum at $x = 1$.

Since $f(x) \to \infty$ as $x \to 0^+$ and as $x \to \infty$, the local minimum at $x = 1$ is a global minimum; there is no global maximum. See Figure 4.72. The the global minimum is $f(1) = 2$.

9. Differentiating using the product rule gives

$$g'(t) = 1 \cdot e^{-t} - te^{-t} = (1 - t)e^{-t},$$

so the critical point is $t = 1$.

Since $g'(t) > 0$ for $0 < t < 1$ and $g'(t) < 0$ for $t > 1$, the critical point is a local maximum.

As $t \to \infty$, the value of $g(t) \to 0$, and as $t \to 0^+$, the value of $g(t) \to 0$. Thus, the local maximum at $x = 1$ is a global maximum of $g(1) = 1e^{-1} = 1/e$. In addition, the value of $g(t)$ is positive for all $t > 0$; it tends to 0 but never reaches 0. Thus, there is no global minimum. See Figure 4.73.

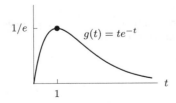

Figure 4.73

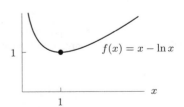

Figure 4.74

10. Differentiating gives

$$f'(x) = 1 - \frac{1}{x},$$

so the critical points satisfy

$$1 - \frac{1}{x} = 0$$
$$\frac{1}{x} = 1$$
$$x = 1.$$

Since f' is negative for $0 < x < 1$ and f' is positive for $x > 1$, there is a local minimum at $x = 1$.

Since $f(x) \to \infty$ as $x \to 0^+$ and as $x \to \infty$, the local minimum at $x = 1$ is a global minimum; there is no global maximum. See Figure 4.74. Thus, the global minimum is $f(1) = 1$.

11. Differentiating using the quotient rule gives

$$f'(t) = \frac{1(1+t^2) - t(2t)}{(1+t^2)^2} = \frac{1-t^2}{(1+t^2)^2}.$$

The critical points are the solutions to

$$\frac{1-t^2}{(1+t^2)^2} = 0$$
$$t^2 = 1$$
$$t = \pm 1.$$

Since $f'(t) > 0$ for $-1 < t < 1$ and $f'(t) < 0$ otherwise, there is a local minimum at $t = -1$ and a local maximum at $t = 1$.

As $t \to \pm\infty$, we have $f(t) \to 0$. Thus, the local maximum at $t = 1$ is a global maximum of $f(1) = 1/2$, and the local minimum at $t = -1$ is a global minimum of $f(-1) = -1/2$. See Figure 4.75.

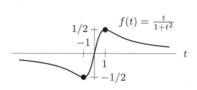

Figure 4.75

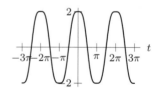

Figure 4.76

12. Differentiating using the product rule gives

$$f'(t) = 2\sin t \cos t \cdot \cos t - (\sin^2 t + 2)\sin t = 0$$
$$\sin t(2\cos^2 t - \sin^2 t - 2) = 0$$
$$\sin t(2(1 - \sin^2 t) - \sin^2 t - 2) = 0$$
$$\sin t(-3\sin^2 t) = -3\sin^3 t = 0.$$

Thus, the critical points are where $\sin t = 0$, so

$$t = 0, \pm\pi, \pm 2\pi, \pm 3\pi, \ldots.$$

Since $f'(t) = -3\sin^3 t$ is negative for $-\pi < t < 0$, positive for $0 < t < \pi$, negative for $\pi < t < 2\pi$, and so on, we find that $t = 0, \pm 2\pi, \ldots$ give local minima, while $t = \pm\pi, \pm 3\pi, \ldots$ give local maxima. Evaluating gives

$$f(0) = f(\pm 2\pi) = (0 + 2)1 = 2$$
$$f(\pm\pi) = f(\pm 3\pi) = (0 + 2)(-1) = -2.$$

Thus, the global maximum of $f(t)$ is 2, occurring at $t = 0, \pm 2\pi, \ldots$, and the global minimum of $f(t)$ is -2, occurring at $t = \pm\pi, \pm 3\pi, \ldots$. See Figure 4.76.

13. Let $y = x^3 - 4x^2 + 4x$. To locate the critical points, we solve $y' = 0$. Since $y' = 3x^2 - 8x + 4 = (3x - 2)(x - 2)$, the critical points are $x = 2/3$ and $x = 2$. To find the global minimum and maximum on $0 \le x \le 4$, we check the critical points and the endpoints: $y(0) = 0$; $y(2/3) = 32/27$; $y(2) = 0$; $y(4) = 16$. Thus, the global minimum is at $x = 0$ and $x = 2$, the global maximum is at $x = 4$, and $0 \le y \le 16$.

14. Let $y = e^{-x^2}$. Since $y' = -2xe^{-x^2}$, y is increasing for $x < 0$ and decreasing for $x > 0$. Hence $y = e^0 = 1$ is a global maximum.

When $x = \pm 0.3$, $y = e^{-0.09} \approx 0.9139$, which is a global minimum on the given interval. Thus $e^{-0.09} \le y \le 1$ for $|x| \le 0.3$.

15. Examination of the graph suggests that $0 \le x^3 e^{-x} \le 2$. The lower bound of 0 is the best possible lower bound since

$$f(0) = (0)^3 e^{-0} = 0.$$

To find the best possible upper bound, we find the critical points. Differentiating, using the product rule, yields

$$f'(x) = 3x^2 e^{-x} - x^3 e^{-x}$$

Setting $f'(x) = 0$ and factoring gives

$$3x^2 e^{-x} - x^3 e^{-x} = 0$$
$$x^2 e^{-x}(3 - x) = 0$$

So the critical points are $x = 0$ and $x = 3$. Note that $f'(x) < 0$ for $x > 3$ and $f'(x) > 0$ for $x < 3$, so $f(x)$ has a local maximum at $x = 3$. Examination of the graph tells us that this is the global maximum. So $0 \le x^3 e^{-x} \le f(3)$.

$$f(3) = 3^3 e^{-3} \approx 1.34425$$

So $0 \le x^3 e^{-x} \le 3^3 e^{-3} \approx 1.34425$ are the best possible bounds for the function.

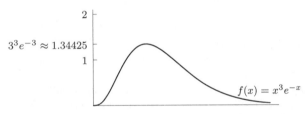

Figure 4.77

16. The graph of $y = x + \sin x$ in Figure 4.78 suggests that the function is nondecreasing over the entire interval. You can confirm this by looking at the derivative:

$$y' = 1 + \cos x$$

Figure 4.78: Graph of $y = x + \sin x$

Since $\cos x \ge -1$, we have $y' \ge 0$ everywhere, so y never decreases. This means that a lower bound for y is 0 (its value at the left endpoint of the interval) and an upper bound is 2π (its value at the right endpoint). That is, if $0 \le x \le 2\pi$:

$$0 \le y \le 2\pi.$$

These are the best bounds for y over the interval.

17. Let $y = \ln(1 + x)$. Since $y' = 1/(1 + x)$, y is increasing for all $x \geq 0$. The lower bound is at $x = 0$, so, $\ln(1) = 0 \leq y$. There is no upper bound.

18. Let $y = \ln(1 + x^2)$. Then $y' = 2x/(1 + x^2)$. Since the denominator is always positive, the sign of y' is determined by the numerator $2x$. Thus $y' > 0$ when $x > 0$, and $y' < 0$ when $x < 0$, and we have a local (and global) minimum for y at $x = 0$. Since $y(-1) = \ln 2$ and $y(2) = \ln 5$, the global maximum is at $x = 2$. Thus $0 \leq y \leq \ln 5$, or (in decimals) $0 \leq y < 1.61$. (Note that our upper bound has been rounded *up* from 1.6094.)

Problems

19. We want to maximize the height, y, of the grapefruit above the ground, as shown in the figure below. Using the derivative we can find exactly when the grapefruit is at the highest point. We can think of this in two ways. By common sense, at the peak of the grapefruit's flight, the velocity, dy/dt, must be zero. Alternately, we are looking for a global maximum of y, so we look for critical points where $dy/dt = 0$. We have

$$\frac{dy}{dt} = -32t + 50 = 0 \qquad \text{and so} \qquad t = \frac{-50}{-32} \approx 1.56 \text{ sec.}$$

Thus, we have the time at which the height is a maximum; the maximum value of y is then

$$y \approx -16(1.56)^2 + 50(1.56) + 5 = 44.1 \text{ feet.}$$

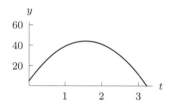

20. The speed is given for r in the interval $0 \leq r \leq R$. We have $v(r) = a(R - r)r^2 = aRr^2 - ar^3$, and $v'(r) = 2aRr - 3ar^2 = 2ar(R - \frac{3}{2}r)$, which is zero if $r = \frac{2}{3}R$, or if $r = 0$, and so $v(r)$ has critical points there.

Since $r = \frac{2}{3}R$ is the only critical point in the interval $0 < r < R$ and $v(0) = v(R) = 0$, we know that $r = \frac{2}{3}R$ is the global maximum.

21. (a) We have

$$T(D) = \left(\frac{C}{2} - \frac{D}{3}\right) D^2 = \frac{CD^2}{2} - \frac{D^3}{3},$$

and

$$\frac{dT}{dD} = CD - D^2 = D(C - D).$$

Since, by this formula, dT/dD is zero when $D = 0$ or $D = C$, negative when $D > C$, and positive when $D < C$, we have (by the first derivative test) that the temperature change is maximized when $D = C$.

(b) The sensitivity is $dT/dD = CD - D^2$; its derivative is $d^2T/dD^2 = C - 2D$, which is zero if $D = C/2$, negative if $D > C/2$, and positive if $D < C/2$. Thus by the first derivative test the sensitivity is maximized at $D = C/2$.

22. (a) Since a/q decreases with q, this term represents the ordering cost. Since bq increases with q, this term represents the storage cost.

(b) At the minimum,

$$\frac{dC}{dq} = \frac{-a}{q^2} + b = 0$$

giving

$$q^2 = \frac{a}{b} \qquad \text{so} \qquad q = \sqrt{\frac{a}{b}}.$$

Since

$$\frac{d^2C}{dq^2} = \frac{2a}{q^3} > 0 \quad \text{for} \quad q > 0,$$

we know that $q = \sqrt{a/b}$ gives a local minimum. Since $q = \sqrt{a/b}$ is the only critical point, this must be the global minimum.

23. (a) If we expect the rate to be nonnegative, then we must have $0 \le y \le a$. See Figure 4.79.

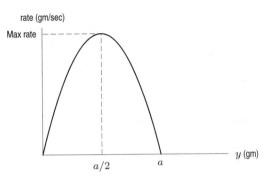

Figure 4.79

(b) The maximum value of the rate occurs at $y = a/2$, as can be seen from Figure 4.79, or by setting

$$\frac{d}{dy}(\text{rate}) = 0$$

$$\frac{d}{dy}(\text{rate}) = \frac{d}{dy}(kay - ky^2) = ka - 2ky = 0$$

$$y = \frac{a}{2}.$$

From the graph, we see that $y = a/2$ gives the global maximum.

24. We set $f'(r) = 0$ to find the critical points:

$$\frac{2A}{r^3} - \frac{3B}{r^4} = 0$$

$$\frac{2Ar - 3B}{r^4} = 0$$

$$2Ar - 3B = 0$$

$$r = \frac{3B}{2A}.$$

The only critical point is at $r = 3B/(2A)$. If $r > 3B/(2A)$, we have $f' > 0$ and if $r < 3B/(2A)$, we have $f' < 0$. Thus, the force between the atoms is minimized at $r = 3B/(2A)$.

25. (a) To show that R is an increasing function of r_1, we show that $dR/dr_1 > 0$ for all values of r_1. We first solve for R:

$$\frac{1}{R} = \frac{1}{r_1} + \frac{1}{r_2}$$

$$\frac{1}{R} = \frac{r_2 + r_1}{r_1 r_2}$$

$$R = \frac{r_1 r_2}{r_2 + r_1}.$$

We use the quotient rule (and remember that r_2 is a constant) to find dR/dr_1:

$$\frac{dR}{dr_1} = \frac{(r_2 + r_1)(r_2) - (r_1 r_2)(1)}{(r_2 + r_1)^2} = \frac{(r_2)^2}{(r_2 + r_1)^2}.$$

Since dR/dr_1 is the square of a number, we have $dR/dr_1 > 0$ for all values of r_1, and thus R is increasing for all r_1.

(b) Since R is increasing on any interval $a \le r_1 \le b$, the maximum value of R occurs at the right endpoint $r_1 = b$.

26. (a) We want the maximum value of I. Using the properties of logarithms, we rewrite the expression for I as

$$I = k(\ln S - \ln S_0) - S + S_0 + I_0.$$

Since k and S_0 are constant, differentiating with respect to S gives

$$\frac{dI}{dS} = \frac{k}{S} - 1.$$

Thus, the critical point is at $S = k$. Since dI/dS is positive for $S < k$ and dI/dS is negative for $S > k$, we see that $S = k$ is a local maximum.

We only consider positive values of S. Since $S = k$ is the only critical point, it gives the global maximum value for I, which is

$$I = k(\ln k - \ln S_0) - k + S_0 + I_0.$$

(b) Since both k and S_0 are in the expression for the maximum value of I, both the particular disease and how it starts influence the maximum.

27. (a) For a point (t, s), the line from the origin has rise $= s$ and run $= t$; See Figure 4.80. Thus, the slope of the line OP is s/t.

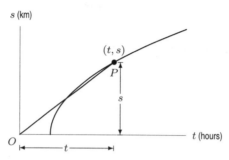

Figure 4.80

(b) Sketching several lines from the origin to points on the curve, we see that the maximum slope occurs at the point P, where the line to the origin is tangent to the graph. Reading from the graph, we see $t \approx 2$ hours at this point.

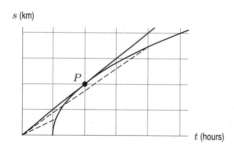

(c) The instantaneous speed of the cyclist at any time is given by the slope of the corresponding point on the curve. At the point P, the line from the origin is tangent to the curve, so the quantity s/t equals the cyclist's speed at the point P.

28. For $x > 0$, the line in Figure 4.81 has

$$\text{Slope} = \frac{y}{x} = \frac{x^2 e^{-3x}}{x} = xe^{-3x}.$$

If the slope has a maximum, it occurs where

$$\frac{d}{dx} (\text{Slope}) = 1 \cdot e^{-3x} - 3xe^{-3x} = 0$$

$$e^{-3x} (1 - 3x) = 0$$

$$x = \frac{1}{3}.$$

For this x-value,

$$\text{Slope} = \frac{1}{3} e^{-3(1/3)} = \frac{1}{3} e^{-1} = \frac{1}{3e}.$$

Figure 4.81 shows that the slope tends toward 0 as $x \to \infty$; the formula for the slope shows that the slope tends toward 0 as $x \to 0$. Thus the only critical point, $x = 1/3$, must give a local and global maximum.

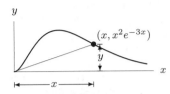

Figure 4.81

29. Suppose the points are given by x and $-x$, where $x \geq 0$. The function is odd, since

$$y = \frac{(-x)^3}{1 + (-x)^4} = -\frac{x^3}{1 + x^4},$$

so the corresponding y-coordinates are also opposite. See Figure 4.82. For $x > 0$, we have

$$m = \frac{\frac{x^3}{1+x^4} - \left(-\frac{x^3}{1+x^4}\right)}{x - (-x)} = \frac{1}{2x} \cdot \frac{2x^3}{1 + x^4} = \frac{x^2}{1 + x^4}.$$

For the maximum slope,

$$\frac{dm}{dx} = \frac{2x}{1 + x^4} - \frac{x^2(4x^3)}{(1 + x^4)^2} = 0$$

$$\frac{2x(1 + x^4) - 4x^5}{(1 + x^4)^2} = 0$$

$$\frac{2x(1 - x^4)}{(1 + x^4)^2} = 0$$

$$x\left(1 - x^4\right) = 0$$

$$x = 0, \pm 1.$$

For $x > 0$, there is one critical point, $x = 1$. Since m tends to 0 when $x \to 0$ and when $x \to \infty$, the critical point $x = 1$ gives the maximum slope. Thus, the maximum slope occurs when the line has endpoints

$$\left(-1, -\frac{1}{2}\right) \quad \text{and} \quad \left(1, \frac{1}{2}\right).$$

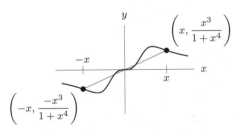

Figure 4.82

30. (a) To maximize benefit (surviving young), we pick 10, because that's the highest point of the benefit graph.
(b) To optimize the vertical distance between the curves, we can either do it by inspection or note that the slopes of the two curves will be the same where the difference is maximized. Either way, one gets approximately 9.

31. (a) At higher speeds, more energy is used so the graph rises to the right. The initial drop is explained by the fact that the energy it takes a bird to fly at very low speeds is greater than that needed to fly at a slightly higher speed. When it flies slightly faster, the amount of energy consumed decreases. But when it flies at very high speeds, the bird consumes a lot more energy (this is analogous to our swimming in a pool).

(b) $f(v)$ measures energy per second; $a(v)$ measures energy per meter. A bird traveling at rate v will in 1 second travel v meters, and thus will consume $v \cdot a(v)$ joules of energy in that 1 second period. Thus $v \cdot a(v)$ represents the energy consumption per second, and so $f(v) = v \cdot a(v)$.

(c) Since $v \cdot a(v) = f(v)$, $a(v) = f(v)/v$. But this ratio has the same value as the slope of a line passing from the origin through the point $(v, f(v))$ on the curve (see figure). Thus $a(v)$ is minimal when the slope of this line is minimal. To find the value of v minimizing $a(v)$, we solve $a'(v) = 0$. By the quotient rule,

$$a'(v) = \frac{vf'(v) - f(v)}{v^2}.$$

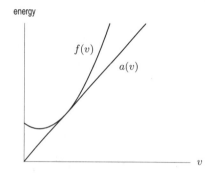

Thus $a'(v) = 0$ when $vf'(v) = f(v)$, or when $f'(v) = f(v)/v = a(v)$. Since $a(v)$ is represented by the slope of a line through the origin and a point on the curve, $a(v)$ is minimized when this line is tangent to $f(v)$, so that the slope $a(v)$ equals $f'(v)$.

(d) The bird should minimize $a(v)$ assuming it wants to go from one particular point to another, i.e. where the distance is set. Then minimizing $a(v)$ minimizes the total energy used for the flight.

32. (a) Figure 4.83 contains the graph of total drag, plotted on the same coordinate system with induced and parasite drag. It was drawn by adding the vertical coordinates of Induced and Parasite drag.

(b) Airspeeds of approximately 160 mph and 320 mph each result in a total drag of 1000 pounds. Since two distinct airspeeds are associated with a single total drag value, the total drag function does not have an inverse. The parasite and induced drag functions do have inverses, because they are strictly increasing and strictly decreasing functions, respectively.

(c) To conserve fuel, fly the at the airspeed which minimizes total drag. This is the airspeed corresponding to the lowest point on the total drag curve in part (a): that is, approximately 220 mph.

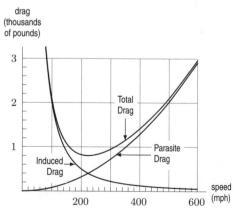

Figure 4.83

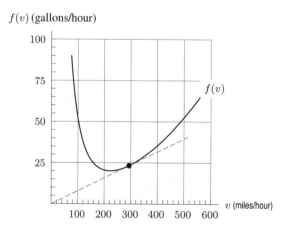

Figure 4.84

33. (a) To obtain $g(v)$, which is in gallons per mile, we need to divide $f(v)$ (in gallons per hour) by v (in miles per hour). Thus, $g(v) = f(v)/v$.

(b) By inspecting the graph, we see that $f(v)$ is minimized at approximately 220 mph.

(c) Note that a point on the graph of $f(v)$ has the coordinates $(v, f(v))$. The line passing through this point and the origin $(0, 0)$ has

$$\text{Slope} = \frac{f(v) - 0}{v - 0} = \frac{f(v)}{v} = g(v).$$

So minimizing $g(v)$ corresponds to finding the line of minimum slope from the family of lines which pass through the origin $(0, 0)$ and the point $(v, f(v))$ on the graph of $f(v)$. This line is the unique member of the family which is tangent to the graph of $f(v)$. The value of v corresponding to the point of tangency will minimize $g(v)$. This value of v will satisfy $f(v)/v = f'(v)$. From the graph in Figure 4.84, we see that $v \approx 300$ mph.

(d) The pilot's goal with regard to $f(v)$ and $g(v)$ would depend on the purpose of the flight, and might even vary within a given flight. For example, if the mission involved aerial surveillance or banner-towing over some limited area, or if the plane was flying a holding pattern, then the pilot would want to minimize $f(v)$ so as to remain aloft as long as possible. In a more normal situation where the purpose was economical travel between two fixed points, then the minimum net fuel expenditure for the trip would result from minimizing $g(v)$.

34. Since the function is positive, the graph lies above the x-axis. If there is a global maximum at $x = 3$, $t'(x)$ must be positive, then negative. Since $t'(x)$ and $t''(x)$ have the same sign for $x < 3$, they must both be positive, and thus the graph must be increasing and concave up. Since $t'(x)$ and $t''(x)$ have opposite signs for $x > 3$ and $t'(x)$ is negative, $t''(x)$ must again be positive and the graph must be decreasing and concave up. A possible sketch of $y = t(x)$ is shown in Figure 4.85.

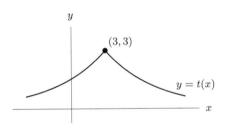

Figure 4.85

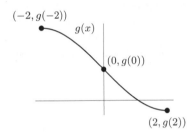

Figure 4.86

35. One possible graph of g is in Figure 4.86.

(a) From left to right, the graph of $g(x)$ starts "flat", decreases slowly at first then more rapidly, most rapidly at $x = 0$. The graph then continues to decrease but less and less rapidly until flat again at $x = 2$. The graph should exhibit symmetry about the point $(0, g(0))$.

(b) The graph has an inflection point at $(0, g(0))$ where the slope changes from negative and decreasing to negative and increasing.

(c) The function has a global maximum at $x = -2$ and a global minimum at $x = 2$.

(d) Since the function is decreasing over the interval $-2 \leq x \leq 2$

$$g(-2) = 5 > g(0) > g(2).$$

Since the function appears symmetric about $(0, g(0))$, we have

$$g(-2) - g(0) = g(0) - g(2).$$

36. (a) We know that $h''(x) < 0$ for $-2 \leq x < -1$, $h''(-1) = 0$, and $h''(x) > 0$ for $x > -1$. Thus, $h'(x)$ decreases to its minimum value at $x = -1$, which we know to be zero, and then increases; it is never negative.

(b) Since $h'(x)$ is non-negative for $-2 \leq x \leq 1$, we know that $h(x)$ is never decreasing on $[-2, 1]$. So a global maximum must occur at the right hand endpoint of the interval.

(c) The graph below shows a function that is increasing on the interval $-2 \leq x \leq 1$ with a horizontal tangent and an inflection point at $(-1, 2)$.

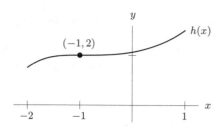

37. False. For example, if $f(x) = x^3$, then $f'(0) = 0$, so $x = 0$ is a critical point, but $x = 0$ is neither a local maximum nor a local minimum.

38. False, since $f(x) = 1/x$ takes on arbitrarily large values as $x \to 0^+$. The Extreme Value Theorem requires the interval to be closed as well as bounded.

39. False. The Extreme Value Theorem says that continuous functions have global maxima and minima on every closed, bounded interval. It does not say that only continuous functions have such maxima and minima.

40. Suppose f has critical points $x = a$ and $x = b$. Suppose $a < b$. By the Extreme Value Theorem, we know that the derivative function, $f'(x)$, has global extrema on $[a, b]$. If both the maximum and minimum of $f'(x)$ occur at the endpoints of $[a, b]$, then $f'(a) = 0 = f'(b)$, so $f'(x) = 0$ for all x in $[a, b]$. In this case, f would have more than two critical points. Since f has only two critical points, there is a local maximum or minimum of f' inside the interval $[a, b]$.

41. (a) If both the global minimum and the global maximum are at the endpoints, then $f(x) = 0$ everywhere in $[a, b]$, since $f(a) = f(b) = 0$. In that case $f'(x) = 0$ everywhere as well, so any point in (a, b) will do for c.

    (b) Suppose that either the global maximum or the global minimum occurs at an interior point of the interval. Let c be that point. Then c must be a local extremum of f, so, by the theorem concerning local extrema on page 168, we have $f'(c) = 0$, as required.

42. (a) The equation of the secant line between $x = a$ and $x = b$ is

$$y = f(a) + \frac{f(b) - f(a)}{b - a}(x - a)$$

and

$$g(x) = f(x) - f(a) - \frac{f(b) - f(a)}{b - a}(x - a),$$

so $g(x)$ is the difference, or distance, between the graph of $f(x)$ and the secant line. See Figure 4.87.

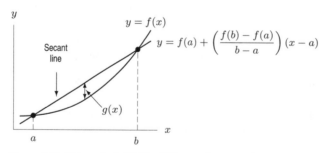

Figure 4.87: Value of $g(x)$ is the difference between the secant line and the graph of $f(x)$

    (b) Figure 4.87 shows that $g(a) = g(b) = 0$. You can also easily check this from the formula for $g(x)$. By Rolle's Theorem, there must be a point c in (a, b) where $g'(c) = 0$.

    (c) Differentiating the formula for $g(x)$, we have

$$g'(x) = f'(x) - \frac{f(b) - f(a)}{b - a}.$$

So from $g'(c) = 0$, we get

$$f'(c) = \frac{f(b) - f(a)}{b - a},$$

as required.

Solutions for Section 4.4

Exercises

1. The fixed costs are $5000, the marginal cost per item is $2.40, and the price per item is $4.

2. (a) Total cost, in millions of dollars, $C(q) = 3 + 0.4q$.
   (b) Revenue, in millions of dollars, $R(q) = 0.5q$.
   (c) Profit, in millions of dollars, $\pi(q) = R(q) - C(q) = 0.5q - (3 + 0.4q) = 0.1q - 3$.

3. The profit $\pi(q)$ is given by

$$\pi(q) = R(q) - C(q) = 500q - q^2 - (150 + 10q) = 490q - q^2 - 150.$$

The maximum profit occurs when

$$\pi'(q) = 490 - 2q = 0 \quad \text{so} \quad q = 245 \text{ items.}$$

Since $\pi''(q) = -2$, this critical point is a maximum. Alternatively, we obtain the same result from the fact that the graph of π is a parabola opening downward.

4. First find marginal revenue and marginal cost.

$$MR = R'(q) = 450$$

$$MC = C'(q) = 6q$$

Setting $MR = MC$ yields $6q = 450$, so marginal cost is equal to marginal revenue when

$$q = \frac{450}{6} = 75 \text{ units.}$$

Is profit maximized at $q = 75$? Profit $= R(q) - C(q)$;

$$R(75) - C(75) = 450(75) - (10{,}000 + 3(75)^2)$$
$$= 33{,}750 - 26{,}875 = \$6875.$$

Testing $q = 74$ and $q = 76$:

$$R(74) - C(74) = 450(74) - (10{,}000 + 3(74)^2)$$
$$= 33{,}300 - 26{,}428 = \$6872.$$

$$R(76) - C(76) = 450(76) - (10{,}000 + 3(76)^2)$$
$$= 34{,}200 - 27{,}328 = \$6872.$$

Since profit at $q = 75$ is more than profit at $q = 74$ and $q = 76$, we conclude that profit is maximized locally at $q = 75$. The only endpoint we need to check is $q = 0$.

$$R(0) - C(0) = 450(0) - (10{,}000 + 3(0)^2)$$
$$= -\$10{,}000.$$

This is clearly not a maximum, so we conclude that the profit is maximized globally at $q = 75$, and the total profit at this production level is $6,875.

5. The profit function is positive when $R(q) > C(q)$, and negative when $C(q) > R(q)$. It's positive for $5.5 < q < 12.5$, and negative for $0 < q < 5.5$ and $12.5 < q$. Profit is maximized when $R(q) > C(q)$ and $R'(q) = C'(q)$ which occurs at about $q = 9.5$. See Figure 4.88.

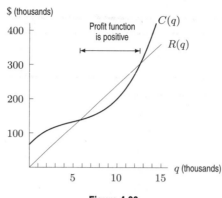

Figure 4.88

6. Since for $q = 500$, we have $MC(500) = C'(500) = 75$ and $MR(500) = R'(500) = 100$, so $MR(500) > MC(500)$. Thus, increasing production from $q = 500$ increases profit.

7. Since marginal revenue is larger than marginal cost around $q = 2000$, as you produce more of the product your revenue increases faster than your costs, so profit goes up, and maximal profit will occur at a production level above 2000.

8. Since fixed costs are represented by the vertical intercept, they are \$1.1 million. The quantity that maximizes profit is about $q = 70$, and the profit achieved is $\$(3.7 - 2.5) = \$1.2$ million

9. (a) Profit is maximized when $R(q) - C(q)$ is as large as possible. This occurs at $q = 2500$, where profit $= 7500 - 5500 = \$2000$.
   (b) We see that $R(q) = 3q$ and so the price is $p = 3$, or \$3 per unit.
   (c) Since $C(0) = 3000$, the fixed costs are \$3000.

10. (a) At $q = 5000$, $MR > MC$, so the marginal revenue to produce the next item is greater than the marginal cost. This means that the company will make money by producing additional units, and production should be increased.
   (b) Profit is maximized where $MR = MC$, and where the profit function is going from increasing ($MR > MC$) to decreasing ($MR < MC$). This occurs at $q = 8000$.

Problems

11.

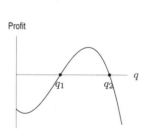

12. (a) $\pi(q)$ is maximized when $R(q) > C(q)$ and they are as far apart as possible. See Figure 4.89.
   (b) $\pi'(q_0) = R'(q_0) - C'(q_0) = 0$ implies that $C'(q_0) = R'(q_0) = p$.
      Graphically, the slopes of the two curves at q_0 are equal. This is plausible because if $C'(q_0)$ were greater than p or less than p, the maximum of $\pi(q)$ would be to the left or right of q_0, respectively. In economic terms, if the cost were rising more quickly than revenues, the profit would be maximized at a lower quantity (and if the cost were rising more slowly, at a higher quantity).
   (c) See Figure 4.90.

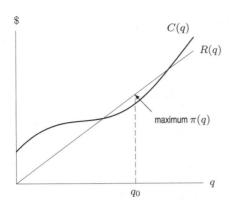

Figure 4.89

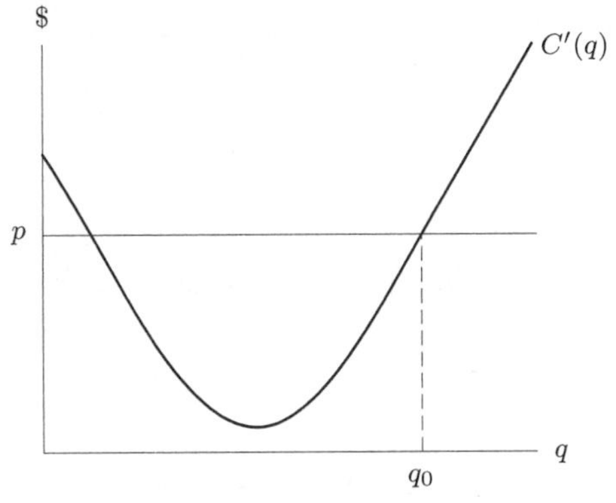

Figure 4.90

13. (a) We know that Profit = Revenue − Cost, so differentiating with respect to q gives:

$$\text{Marginal Profit} = \text{Marginal Revenue} - \text{Marginal Cost}.$$

We see from the figure in the problem that just to the left of $q = a$, marginal revenue is less than marginal cost, so marginal profit is negative there. To the right of $q = a$ marginal revenue is greater than marginal cost, so marginal profit is positive there. At $q = a$ marginal profit changes from negative to positive. This means that profit is decreasing to the left of a and increasing to the right. The point $q = a$ corresponds to a local minimum of profit, and does not maximize profit. It would be a terrible idea for the company to set its production level at $q = a$.

(b) We see from the figure in the problem that just to the left of $q = b$ marginal revenue is greater than marginal cost, so marginal profit is positive there. Just to the right of $q = b$ marginal revenue is less than marginal cost, so marginal profit is negative there. At $q = b$ marginal profit changes from positive to negative. This means that profit is increasing to the left of b and decreasing to the right. The point $q = b$ corresponds to a local maximum of profit. In fact, since the area between the MC and MR curves in the figure in the text between $q = a$ and $q = b$ is bigger than the area between $q = 0$ and $q = a$, $q = b$ is in fact a global maximum.

14. (a) The value of $C(0)$ represents the fixed costs before production, that is, the cost of producing zero units, incurred for initial investments in equipment, and so on.

(b) The marginal cost decreases slowly, and then increases as quantity produced increases. See Problem 11, graph (b).

(c) Concave down implies decreasing marginal cost, while concave up implies increasing marginal cost.

(d) An inflection point of the cost function is (locally) the point of maximum or minimum marginal cost.

(e) One would think that the more of an item you produce, the less it would cost to produce extra items. In economic terms, one would expect the marginal cost of production to decrease, so we would expect the cost curve to be concave down. In practice, though, it eventually becomes more expensive to produce more items, because workers and resources may become scarce as you increase production. Hence after a certain point, the marginal cost may rise again. This happens in oil production, for example.

15. (a) The fixed cost is 0 because $C(0) = 0$.

(b) Profit, $\pi(q)$, is equal to money from sales, $7q$, minus total cost to produce those items, $C(q)$.

$$\pi = 7q - 0.01q^3 + 0.6q^2 - 13q$$
$$\pi' = -0.03q^2 + 1.2q - 6$$

$$\pi' = 0 \quad \text{if} \quad q = \frac{-1.2 \pm \sqrt{(1.2)^2 - 4(0.03)(6)}}{-0.06} \approx 5.9 \quad \text{or} \quad 34.1.$$

Now $\pi'' = -0.06q + 1.2$, so $\pi''(5.9) > 0$ and $\pi''(34.1) < 0$. This means $q = 5.9$ is a local min and $q = 34.1$ a local max. We now evaluate the endpoint, $\pi(0) = 0$, and the points nearest $q = 34.1$ with integer q-values:

$$\pi(35) = 7(35) - 0.01(35)^3 + 0.6(35)^2 - 13(35) = 245 - 148.75 = 96.25,$$

$$\pi(34) = 7(34) - 0.01(34)^3 + 0.6(34)^2 - 13(34) = 238 - 141.44 = 96.56.$$

So the (global) maximum profit is $\pi(34) = 96.56$. The money from sales is $238, the cost to produce the items is $141.44, resulting in a profit of $96.56.

(c) The money from sales is equal to price×quantity sold. If the price is raised from \$7 by \$$x$ to \$$(7 + x)$, the result is a reduction in sales from 34 items to $(34 - 2x)$ items. So the result of raising the price by \$$x$ is to change the money from sales from $(7)(34)$ to $(7 + x)(34 - 2x)$ dollars. If the production level is fixed at 34, then the production costs are fixed at \$141.44, as found in part (b), and the profit is given by:

$$\pi(x) = (7 + x)(34 - 2x) - 141.44$$

This expression gives the profit as a function of change in price x, rather than as a function of quantity as in part (b). We set the derivative of π with respect to x equal to zero to find the change in price that maximizes the profit:

$$\frac{d\pi}{dx} = (1)(34 - 2x) + (7 + x)(-2) = 20 - 4x = 0$$

So $x = 5$, and this must give a maximum for $\pi(x)$ since the graph of π is a parabola which opens downward. The profit when the price is \$12 $(= 7 + x = 7 + 5)$ is thus $\pi(5) = (7 + 5)(34 - 2(5)) - 141.44 = \$146.56$. This is indeed higher than the profit when the price is \$7, so the smart thing to do is to raise the price by \$5.

16. (a) Say n passengers sign up for the cruise. If $n \leq 100$, then the cruise's revenue is $R = 1000n$, and so the maximum revenue if $n \leq 100$ is $R = 1000 \cdot 100 = 100{,}000$. If $n \geq 100$, then the price is

$$p = 1000 - 5(n - 100)$$

and hence revenue is

$$R = n(1000 - 5(n - 100)) = 1500n - 5n^2.$$

To find the maximum of this, we set $dR/dn = 0$, or $10n = 1500$, or $n = 150$, yielding revenue of $(1000 - 5 \cdot 50) \cdot 150 = 112500$. Since this is more than the maximum revenue when $n \leq 100$, we see that the boat maximizes its revenue with 150 passengers, each paying \$750.

(b) We approach this problem in a similar way to part (a), except now we are dealing with the profit function π. If $n \leq 100$, we have that $\pi = 1000n - 40{,}000 - 200n$, and thus π would be maximized with 100 passengers yielding a profit of $\pi = 800 \cdot 100 - 40{,}000 = \$40{,}000$. If $n > 100$, we have the formula $\pi = n(1000 - 5(n - 100)) - (40{,}000 + 200n)$. We again wish to set $d\pi/dn = 0$, or $1300 = 10n$, or $n = 130$, yielding profit of \$44,500. So the boat will maximize profit by boarding 130 passengers, each paying \$850. This gives the boat \$44,500 in profit.

17. For each month,

$$\text{Profit} = \text{Revenue} - \text{Cost}$$
$$\pi = pq - wL = pcK^\alpha L^\beta - wL$$

The variable on the right is L, so at the maximum

$$\frac{d\pi}{dL} = \beta pcK^\alpha L^{\beta-1} - w = 0$$

Now $\beta - 1$ is negative, since $0 < \beta < 1$, so $1 - \beta$ is positive and we can write

$$\frac{\beta pcK^\alpha}{L^{1-\beta}} = w$$

giving

$$L = \left(\frac{\beta pcK^\alpha}{w}\right)^{\frac{1}{1-\beta}}$$

Since $\beta - 1$ is negative, when L is just above 0, the quantity $L^{\beta-1}$ is huge and positive, so $d\pi/dL > 0$. When L is large, $L^{\beta-1}$ is small, so $d\pi/dL < 0$. Thus the value of L we have found gives a global maximum, since it is the only critical point.

18. (a) $N = 100 + 20x$, graphed in Figure 4.91.

(b) $N'(x) = 20$ and its graph is just a horizontal line. This means that rate of increase of the number of bees with acres of clover is constant — each acre of clover brings 20 more bees.

On the other hand, $N(x)/x = 100/x + 20$ means that the average number of bees per acre of clover approaches 20 as more acres are put under clover. See Figure 4.92. As x increases, $100/x$ decreases to 0, so $N(x)/x$ approaches 20 (i.e. $N(x)/x \to 20$). Since the total number of bees is 20 per acre plus the original 100, the average number of bees per acre is 20 plus the 100 shared out over x acres. As x increases, the 100 are shared out over more acres, and so its contribution to the average becomes less. Thus the average number of bees per acre approaches 20 for large x.

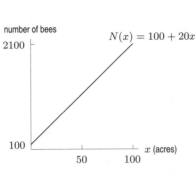

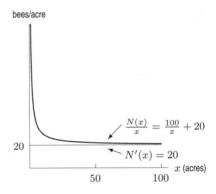

Figure 4.91

Figure 4.92

19. This question implies that the line from the origin to the point $(x, R(x))$ has some relationship to $r(x)$. The slope of this line is $R(x)/x$, which is $r(x)$. So the point x_0 at which $r(x)$ is maximal will also be the point at which the slope of this line is maximal. The question claims that the line from the origin to $(x_0, R(x_0))$ will be tangent to the graph of $R(x)$. We can understand this by trying to see what would happen if it were otherwise.

If the line from the origin to $(x_0, R(x_0))$ intersects the graph of $R(x)$, but is not tangent to the graph of $R(x)$ at x_0, then there are points of this graph on both sides of the line — and, in particular, there is some point x_1 such that the line from the origin to $(x_1, R(x_1))$ has larger slope than the line to $(x_0, R(x_0))$. (See the graph below.) But we picked x_0 so that no other line had larger slope, and therefore no such x_1 exists. So the original supposition is false, and the line from the origin to $(x_0, R(x_0))$ is tangent to the graph of $R(x)$.

(a) See (b).

(b)

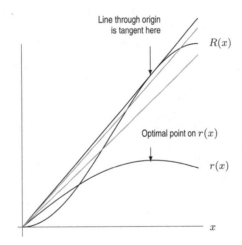

(c)

$$r(x) = \frac{R(x)}{x}$$

$$r'(x) = \frac{xR'(x) - R(x)}{x^2}$$

So when $r(x)$ is maximized $0 = xR'(x) - R(x)$, the numerator of $r'(x)$, or $R'(x) = R(x)/x = r(x)$. i.e. when $r(x)$ is maximized, $r(x) = R'(x)$.

Let us call the x-value at which the maximum of r occurs x_m. Then the line passing through $R(x_m)$ and the origin is $y = x \cdot R(x_m)/x_m$. Its slope is $R(x_m)/x_m$, which also happens to be $r(x_m)$. In the previous paragraph, we showed that at x_m, this is also equal to the slope of the tangent to $R(x)$. So, the line through the origin is the tangent line.

20. (a) The value of MC is the slope of the tangent to the curve at q_0. See Figure 4.93.

(b) The line from the curve to the origin joins $(0, 0)$ and $(q_0, C(q_0))$, so its slope is $C(q_0)/q_0 = a(q_0)$.

(c) Figure 4.94 shows that the line whose slope is the minimum $a(q)$ is tangent to the curve $C(q)$. This line, therefore, also has slope MC, so $a(q) = MC$ at the q making $a(q)$ minimum.

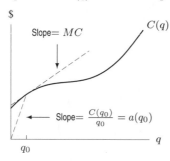

Figure 4.93   **Figure 4.94**

21. (a) $a(q) = C(q)/q$, so $C(q) = 0.01q^3 - 0.6q^2 + 13q$.
    (b) Taking the derivative of $C(q)$ gives an expression for the marginal cost:

    $$C'(q) = MC(q) = 0.03q^2 - 1.2q + 13.$$

    To find the smallest MC we take its derivative and find the value of q that makes it zero. So: $MC'(q) = 0.06q - 1.2 = 0$ when $q = 1.2/0.06 = 20$. This value of q must give a minimum because the graph of $MC(q)$ is a parabola opening upward. Therefore the minimum marginal cost is $MC(20) = 1$. So the marginal cost is at a minimum when the additional cost per item is \$1.
    (c) $a'(q) = 0.02q - 0.6$
    Setting $a'(q) = 0$ and solving for q gives $q = 30$ as the quantity at which the average is minimized, since the graph of a is a parabola which opens upward. The minimum average cost is $a(30) = 4$ dollars per item.
    (d) The marginal cost at $q = 30$ is $MC(30) = 0.03(30)^2 - 1.2(30) + 13 = 4$. This is the same as the average cost at this quantity. Note that since $a(q) = C(q)/q$, we have $a'(q) = (qC'(q) - C(q))/q^2$. At a critical point, q_0, of $a(q)$, we have

    $$0 = a'(q_0) = \frac{q_0 C'(q_0) - C(q_0)}{q_0^2},$$

    so $C'(q_0) = C(q_0)/q_0 = a(q_0)$. Therefore $C'(30) = a(30) = 4$ dollars per item.
         Another way to see why the marginal cost at $q = 30$ must equal the minimum average cost $a(30) = 4$ is to view $C'(30)$ as the approximate cost of producing the 30th or 31st good. If $C'(30) < a(30)$, then producing the 31st good would lower the average cost, i.e. $a(31) < a(30)$. If $C'(30) > a(30)$, then producing the 30th good would raise the average cost, i.e. $a(30) > a(29)$. Since $a(30)$ is the global minimum, we must have $C'(30) = a(30)$.

22. (a) Differentiating $C(q)$ gives

    $$C'(q) = \frac{K}{a} q^{(1/a)-1}, \quad C''(q) = \frac{K}{a}\left(\frac{1}{a} - 1\right) q^{(1/a)-2}.$$

    If $a > 1$, then $C''(q) < 0$, so C is concave down.
    (b) We have

    $$a(q) = \frac{C(q)}{q} = \frac{Kq^{1/a} + F}{q}$$

    $$C'(q) = \frac{K}{a} q^{(1/a)-1}$$

    so $a(q) = C'(q)$ means

    $$\frac{Kq^{1/a} + F}{q} = \frac{K}{a} q^{(1/a)-1}.$$

    Solving,

    $$Kq^{1/a} + F = \frac{K}{a} q^{1/a}$$

    $$K\left(\frac{1}{a} - 1\right) q^{1/a} = F$$

    $$q = \left[\frac{Fa}{K(1-a)}\right]^a.$$

23. (a) Since the company can produce more goods if it has more raw materials to use, the function $f(x)$ is increasing. Thus, we expect the derivative $f'(x)$ to be positive.

(b) The cost to the company of acquiring x units of raw material is wx, and the revenue from the sale of $f(x)$ units of the product is $pf(x)$. The company's profit $\pi(x) = \text{Revenue} - \text{Cost} = pf(x) - wx$.

(c) Since profit $\pi(x)$ is maximized at $x = x^*$, we have $\pi'(x^*) = 0$. From $\pi'(x) = pf'(x) - w$, we have $pf'(x^*) - w = 0$. Thus $f'(x^*) = w/p$.

(d) Computing the second derivative of $\pi(x)$ gives $\pi''(x) = pf''(x)$. Since $\pi(x)$ has a maximum at $x = x^*$, the second derivative $\pi''(x^*) = pf''(x^*)$ is negative. Thus $f''(x^*)$ is negative.

(e) Differentiate both sides of $pf'(x^*) - w = 0$ with respect to w. The chain rule gives

$$p\frac{d}{dw}f'(x^*) - 1 = 0$$

$$pf''(x^*)\frac{dx^*}{dw} - 1 = 0$$

$$\frac{dx^*}{dw} = \frac{1}{pf''(x^*)}.$$

Since $f''(x^*) < 0$, we see dx^*/dw is negative.

(f) Since $dx^*/dw < 0$, the quantity x^* is a decreasing function of w. If the price w of the raw material goes up, the company should buy less.

Solutions for Section 4.5

Exercises

1. We look for critical points of M:

$$\frac{dM}{dx} = \frac{1}{2}wL - wx.$$

Now $dM/dx = 0$ when $x = L/2$. At this point $d^2M/dx^2 = -w$ so this point is a local maximum. The graph of $M(x)$ is a parabola opening downward, so the local maximum is also the global maximum.

2. We set $dU/dx = 0$ to find the critical points:

$$b\left(\frac{-2a^2}{x^3} + \frac{a}{x^2}\right) = 0$$

$$-2a^2 + ax = 0$$

$$x = 2a.$$

The only critical point is at $x = 2a$. When $x < 2a$ we have $dU/dx < 0$, and when $x > 2a$ we have $dU/dx > 0$. The potential energy, U, is minimized at $x = 2a$.

3. Since $I(t)$ is a periodic function with period $2\pi/w$, it is enough to consider $I(t)$ for $0 \leq wt \leq 2\pi$. Differentiating, we find

$$\frac{dI}{dt} = -w\sin(wt) + \sqrt{3}w\cos(wt).$$

At a critical point

$$-w\sin(wt) + \sqrt{3}w\cos(wt) = 0$$

$$\sin(wt) = \sqrt{3}\cos(wt)$$

$$\tan(wt) = \sqrt{3}.$$

So $wt = \pi/3$ or $4\pi/3$, or these values plus multiples of 2π. Substituting into I, we see

$$\text{At } wt = \frac{\pi}{3}: \quad I = \cos\left(\frac{\pi}{3}\right) + \sqrt{3}\sin\left(\frac{\pi}{3}\right) = \frac{1}{2} + \sqrt{3}\cdot\left(\frac{\sqrt{3}}{2}\right) = 2.$$

$$\text{At } wt = \frac{4\pi}{3}: \quad I = \cos\left(\frac{4\pi}{3}\right) + \sqrt{3}\sin\left(\frac{4\pi}{3}\right) = -\frac{1}{2} - \sqrt{3}\cdot\left(\frac{\sqrt{3}}{2}\right) = -2.$$

Thus, the maximum value is 2 amps and the minimum is -2 amps.

4. Call the stacks A and B. (See below.) Assume that A corresponds to k_1, and B corresponds to k_2.

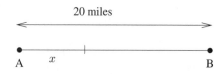

20 miles

A x B

Suppose the point where the concentration of deposit is a minimum occurs at a distance of x miles from stack A. We want to find x such that

$$S = \frac{k_1}{x^2} + \frac{k_2}{(20-x)^2} = k_2 \left(\frac{7}{x^2} + \frac{1}{(20-x)^2} \right)$$

is a minimum, which is the same thing as minimizing $f(x) = 7x^{-2} + (20-x)^{-2}$ since k_2 is nonnegative.

We have

$$f'(x) = -14x^{-3} - 2(20-x)^{-3}(-1) = \frac{-14}{x^3} + \frac{2}{(20-x)^3} = \frac{-14(20-x)^3 + 2x^3}{x^3(20-x)^3}.$$

Thus we want to find x such that $-14(20-x)^3 + 2x^3 = 0$, which implies $2x^3 = 14(20-x)^3$. That's equivalent to $x^3 = 7(20-x)^3$, or $\frac{20-x}{x} = (1/7)^{1/3} \approx 0.523$. Solving for x, we have $20 - x = 0.523x$, whence $x = 20/1.523 \approx 13.13$.

To verify that this minimizes f, we take the second derivative:

$$f''(x) = 42x^{-4} + 6(20-x)^{-4} = \frac{42}{x^4} + \frac{6}{(20-x)^4} > 0$$

for any $0 < x < 20$, so by the second derivative test the concentration is minimized 13.13 miles from A.

5. (a) If we expect the rate to be nonnegative, we must have $0 \le y \le a$ and $0 \le y \le b$. Since we assume $a < b$, we restrict y to $0 \le y \le a$.

In fact, the expression for the rate is nonnegative for y greater than b, but these values of y are not meaningful for the reaction. See Figure 4.95.

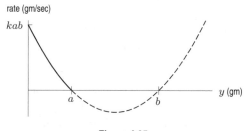

rate (gm/sec)

kab

a b y (gm)

Figure 4.95

(b) From the graph, we see that the maximum rate occurs when $y = 0$; that is, at the start of the reaction.

6. We only consider $\lambda > 0$. For such λ, the value of $v \to \infty$ as $\lambda \to \infty$ and as $\lambda \to 0^+$. Thus, v does not have a maximum velocity. It will have a minimum velocity. To find it, we set $dv/d\lambda = 0$:

$$\frac{dv}{d\lambda} = k\frac{1}{2} \left(\frac{\lambda}{c} + \frac{c}{\lambda} \right)^{-1/2} \left(\frac{1}{c} - \frac{c}{\lambda^2} \right) = 0.$$

Solving, and remembering that $\lambda > 0$, we obtain

$$\frac{1}{c} - \frac{c}{\lambda^2} = 0$$
$$\frac{1}{c} = \frac{c}{\lambda^2}$$
$$\lambda^2 = c^2,$$

so

$$\lambda = c.$$

Thus, we have one critical point. Since

$$\frac{dv}{d\lambda} < 0 \quad \text{for } \lambda < c$$

and

$$\frac{dv}{d\lambda} > 0 \quad \text{for } \lambda > c,$$

the first derivative test tells us that we have a local minimum of v at $x = c$. Since $\lambda = c$ is the only critical point, it gives the global minimum. Thus the minimum value of v is

$$v = k\sqrt{\frac{c}{c} + \frac{c}{c}} = \sqrt{2}k.$$

7.

$$\frac{dE}{d\theta} = \frac{(\mu + \theta)(1 - 2\mu\theta) - (\theta - \mu\theta^2)}{(\mu + \theta)^2} = \frac{\mu(1 - 2\mu\theta - \theta^2)}{(\mu + \theta)^2}.$$

Now $dE/d\theta = 0$ when $\theta = -\mu \pm \sqrt{1 + \mu^2}$. Since $\theta > 0$, the only possible critical point is when $\theta = -\mu + \sqrt{\mu^2 + 1}$. Differentiating again gives $E'' < 0$ at this point and so it is a local maximum. Since $E(\theta)$ is continuous for $\theta > 0$ and $E(\theta)$ has only one critical point, the local maximum is the global maximum.

8. A graph of F against θ is shown below.

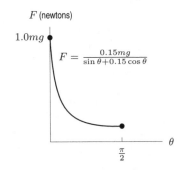

Taking the derivative:

$$\frac{dF}{d\theta} = -\frac{mg\mu(\cos\theta - \mu\sin\theta)}{(\sin\theta + \mu\cos\theta)^2}.$$

At a critical point, $dF/d\theta = 0$, so

$$\cos\theta - \mu\sin\theta = 0$$
$$\tan\theta = \frac{1}{\mu}$$
$$\theta = \arctan\left(\frac{1}{\mu}\right).$$

If $\mu = 0.15$, then $\theta = \arctan(1/0.15) = 1.422 \approx 81.5°$. To calculate the maximum and minimum values of F, we evaluate at this critical point and the endpoints:

$$\text{At } \theta = 0, \quad F = \frac{0.15mg}{\sin 0 + 0.15\cos 0} = 1.0mg \text{ newtons.}$$

$$\text{At } \theta = 1.422, \quad F = \frac{0.15mg}{\sin(1.422) + 0.15\cos(1.422)} = 0.148mg \text{ newtons.}$$

$$\text{At } \theta = \pi/2, \quad F = \frac{0.15mg}{\sin(\frac{\pi}{2}) + 0.15\cos(\frac{\pi}{2})} = 0.15mg \text{ newtons.}$$

Thus, the maximum value of F is $1.0mg$ newtons when $\theta = 0$ (her arm is vertical) and the minimum value of F is $0.148mg$ newtons is when $\theta = 1.422$ (her arm is close to horizontal). See Figure 4.96.

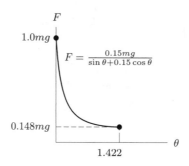

Figure 4.96

9. The domain for E is all real x. Note $E \to 0$ as $x \to \pm\infty$. The critical points occur where $dE/dx = 0$. The derivative is

$$\frac{dE}{dx} = \frac{k}{(x^2 + r_0^2)^{3/2}} - \frac{3}{2} \cdot \frac{kx(2x)}{(x^2 + r_0^2)^{5/2}}$$

$$= \frac{k\left(x^2 + r_0^2 - 3x^2\right)}{(x^2 + r_0^2)^{5/2}}$$

$$= \frac{k\left(r_0^2 - 2x^2\right)}{(x^2 + r_0^2)^{5/2}}.$$

So $dE/dx = 0$ where

$$r_0^2 - 2x^2 = 0$$
$$x = \pm\frac{r_0}{\sqrt{2}}.$$

Looking at the formula for dE/dx shows

$$\frac{dE}{dx} > 0 \text{ for } -\frac{r_0}{\sqrt{2}} < x < \frac{r_0}{\sqrt{2}}$$

$$\frac{dE}{dx} < 0 \text{ for } x < -\frac{r_0}{\sqrt{2}}$$

$$\frac{dE}{dx} < 0 \text{ for } x > \frac{r_0}{\sqrt{2}}.$$

Therefore, $x = -r_0/\sqrt{2}$ gives the minimum value of E and $x = r_0/\sqrt{2}$ gives the maximum value of E.

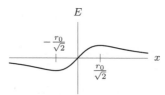

10. We take the derivative, set it equal to 0, and solve for x:

$$\frac{dt}{dx} = \frac{1}{6} - \frac{1}{4} \cdot \frac{1}{2}\left((2000 - x)^2 + 600^2\right)^{-1/2} \cdot 2(2000 - x) = 0$$

$$(2000 - x) = \frac{2}{3}\left((2000 - x)^2 + 600^2\right)^{1/2}$$

$$(2000 - x)^2 = \frac{4}{9}\left((2000 - x)^2 + 600^2\right)$$

$$\frac{5}{9}(2000 - x)^2 = \frac{4}{9} \cdot 600^2$$

$$2000 - x = \sqrt{\frac{4}{5} \cdot 600^2} = \frac{1200}{\sqrt{5}}$$

$$x = 2000 - \frac{1200}{\sqrt{5}} \text{ feet.}$$

Note that $2000 - (1200/\sqrt{5}) \approx 1463$ feet, as given in the example.

Problems

11. We wish to choose a to maximize the area of the rectangle with corners at $(a, \sqrt{a})$ and $(9, \sqrt{a})$. The area of this rectangle will be given by the formula

$$R = h \cdot l = \sqrt{a}(9 - a) = 9a^{1/2} - a^{3/2}.$$

We are restricted to $0 \le a \le 9$. To maximize this area, we set $dR/da = 0$, and then check that the resulting area is greater than the area if $a = 0$ or $a = 9$. Since $R = 0$ if $a = 0$ or $a = 9$, all we need to do is to find where $dR/da = 0$:

$$\frac{dR}{da} = \frac{9}{2}a^{-1/2} - \frac{3}{2}a^{1/2} = 0$$

$$\frac{9}{2\sqrt{a}} = \frac{3\sqrt{a}}{2}$$

$$18 = 6a$$

$$a = 3.$$

Thus, the dimensions of the maximal rectangle are 6 by $\sqrt{3}$.

12. The triangle in Figure 4.97 has area, A, given by

$$A = \frac{1}{2}x \cdot y = \frac{1}{2}x^3 e^{-3x}.$$

If the area has a maximum, it occurs where

$$\frac{dA}{dx} = \frac{3}{2}x^2 e^{-3x} - \frac{3}{2}x^3 e^{-3x} = 0$$

$$\frac{3}{2}x^2\left(1 - x\right)e^{-3x} = 0$$

$$x = 0, 1.$$

The value $x = 0$ gives the minimum area, $A = 0$, for $x \ge 0$. Since

$$\frac{dA}{dx} = \frac{3}{2}x^2(1 - x)e^{-3x},$$

we see that

$$\frac{dA}{dx} > 0 \text{ for } 0 < x < 1 \quad \text{and} \quad \frac{dA}{dx} < 0 \text{ for } x > 1.$$

Thus, $x = 1$ gives the local and global maximum of

$$A = \frac{1}{2}1^3 e^{-3 \cdot 1} = \frac{1}{2e^3}.$$

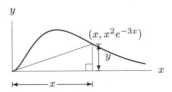

Figure 4.97

13. The rectangle in Figure 4.98 has area, A, given by

$$A = 2xy = \frac{2x}{1 + x^2} \qquad \text{for } x \geq 0.$$

At a critical point,

$$\frac{dA}{dx} = \frac{2}{1 + x^2} + 2x \left(\frac{-2x}{(1 + x^2)^2} \right) = 0$$

$$\frac{2(1 + x^2 - 2x^2)}{(1 + x^2)^2} = 0$$

$$1 - x^2 = 0$$

$$x = \pm 1.$$

Since $A = 0$ for $x = 0$ and $A \to 0$ as $x \to \infty$, the critical point $x = 1$ is a local and global maximum for the area. Then $y = 1/2$, so the vertices are

$$(-1, 0), \; (1, 0), \; \left(1, \frac{1}{2} \right), \; \left(-1, \frac{1}{2} \right).$$

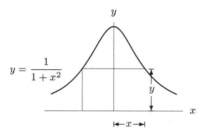

Figure 4.98

14. (a) The rectangle in Figure 4.99 has area, A, given by

$$A = xy = xe^{-2x}.$$

At a critical point, we have

$$\frac{dA}{dx} = 1 \cdot e^{-2x} - 2xe^{-2x} = 0$$

$$e^{-2x} (1 - 2x) = 0$$

$$x = \frac{1}{2}.$$

Since $A = 0$ when $x = 0$ and $A \to 0$ as $x \to \infty$, the critical point $x = 1/2$ is a local and global maximum. Thus the maximum area is

$$A = \frac{1}{2} e^{-2(1/2)} = \frac{1}{2e}.$$

(b) The rectangle in Figure 4.99 has perimeter, P, given by

$$P = 2x + 2y = 2x + 2e^{-2x}.$$

At a critical point, we have

$$\frac{dP}{dx} = 2 - 4e^{-2x} = 0$$

$$e^{-2x} = \frac{1}{2}$$

$$-2x = \ln \frac{1}{2}$$

$$x = -\frac{1}{2} \ln \frac{1}{2} = \frac{1}{2} \ln 2.$$

To see if this critical point gives a maximum or minimum, we find

$$\frac{d^2P}{dx^2} = 8e^{-2x}.$$

Since $d^2P/dx^2 > 0$ for all x, including $x = \frac{1}{2}\ln 2$, the critical point is a local and global minimum. Thus, the minimum perimeter is

$$P = 2\left(\frac{1}{2}\ln 2\right) + 2e^{-2\left(\frac{1}{2}\ln 2\right)} = \ln 2 + 2e^{-\ln 2} = \ln 2 + 2 \cdot \frac{1}{2} = \ln 2 + 1.$$

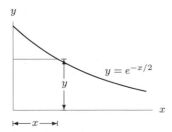

Figure 4.99

15. Figure 4.100 shows the vertical cross section through the cylinder and sphere. The circle has equation $y = \sqrt{1-x^2}$, so if the cylinder has radius x and height y, its volume, V, is given by

$$V = \pi x^2 y = \pi x^2 \sqrt{1-x^2} \qquad \text{for } 0 \le x \le 1.$$

At a critical point, $dV/dx = 0$, so

$$\frac{dV}{dx} = 2\pi x\sqrt{1-x^2} + \pi x^2\left(\frac{1}{2}(1-x^2)^{-1/2}(-2x)\right) = 0$$

$$2\pi x\sqrt{1-x^2} - \frac{\pi x^3}{\sqrt{1-x^2}} = 0$$

$$\frac{\pi x}{\sqrt{1-x^2}}\left(2\left(\sqrt{1-x^2}\right)^2 - x^2\right) = 0$$

$$x(2 - 3x^2) = 0$$

$$x = 0, \; \pm\sqrt{\frac{2}{3}}.$$

Since $V = 0$ at the endpoints $x = 0$ and $x = 1$, and V is positive at the only critical point, $x = \sqrt{2/3}$, in the interval, the critical point $x = \sqrt{2/3}$ is a local and global maximum. Thus, the cylinder with maximum volume has

$$\text{Radius} = x = \sqrt{\frac{2}{3}}$$

$$\text{Height} = y = \sqrt{1 - \left(\sqrt{\frac{2}{3}}\right)^2} = \sqrt{\frac{1}{3}}.$$

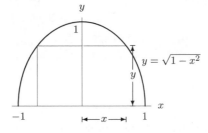

Figure 4.100

16. (a) Suppose the height of the box is h. The box has six sides, four with area xh and two, the top and bottom, with area x^2. Thus,

$$4xh + 2x^2 = A.$$

So

$$h = \frac{A - 2x^2}{4x}.$$

Then, the volume, V, is given by

$$V = x^2 h = x^2 \left(\frac{A - 2x^2}{4x} \right) = \frac{x}{4} \left(A - 2x^2 \right)$$

$$= \frac{A}{4} x - \frac{1}{2} x^3.$$

(b) The graph is shown in Figure 4.101. We are assuming A is a positive constant. Also, we have drawn the whole graph, but we should only consider $V > 0$, $x > 0$ as V and x are lengths.

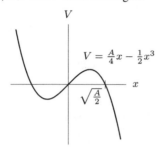

$$V = \frac{A}{4}x - \frac{1}{2}x^3$$

$$\sqrt{\frac{A}{2}}$$

Figure 4.101

(c) To find the maximum, we differentiate, regarding A as a constant:

$$\frac{dV}{dx} = \frac{A}{4} - \frac{3}{2} x^2.$$

So $dV/dx = 0$ if

$$\frac{A}{4} - \frac{3}{2} x^2 = 0$$

$$x = \pm \sqrt{\frac{A}{6}}.$$

For a real box, we must use $x = \sqrt{A/6}$. Figure 4.101 makes it clear that this value of x gives the maximum. Evaluating at $x = \sqrt{A/6}$, we get

$$V = \frac{A}{4} \sqrt{\frac{A}{6}} - \frac{1}{2} \left(\sqrt{\frac{A}{6}} \right)^3 = \frac{A}{4} \sqrt{\frac{A}{6}} - \frac{1}{2} \cdot \frac{A}{6} \sqrt{\frac{A}{6}} = \left(\frac{A}{6} \right)^{3/2}.$$

17. Let w and l be the width and length, respectively, of the rectangular area you wish to enclose. Then

$$w + w + l = 100 \text{ feet}$$

$$l = 100 - 2w$$

$$\text{Area} = w \cdot l = w(100 - 2w) = 100w - 2w^2$$

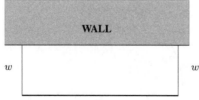

To maximize area, we solve $A' = 0$ to find critical points. This gives $A' = 100 - 4w = 0$, so $w = 25$, $l = 50$. So the area is $25 \cdot 50 = 1250$ square feet. This is a local maximum by the second derivative test because $A'' = -4 < 0$. Since the graph of A is a parabola, the local maximum is in fact a global maximum.

18. From the triangle shown in Figure 4.102, we see that

$$\left(\frac{w}{2}\right)^2 + \left(\frac{h}{2}\right)^2 = 30^2$$
$$w^2 + h^2 = 4(30)^2 = 3600.$$

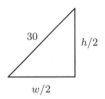

$$30 \qquad h/2$$
$$w/2$$

Figure 4.102

The strength, S, of the beam is given by

$$S = kwh^2,$$

for some constant k. To make S a function of only one variable, substitute for h^2, giving

$$S = kw(3600 - w^2) = k(3600w - w^3).$$

Differentiating and setting $dS/dw = 0$,

$$\frac{dS}{dw} = k(3600 - 3w^2) = 0.$$

Solving for w gives

$$w = \sqrt{1200} = 34.64 \text{ cm},$$

so

$$h^2 = 3600 - w^2 = 3600 - 1200 = 2400$$
$$h = \sqrt{2400} = 48.99 \text{ cm}.$$

Thus, $w = 34.64$ cm and $h = 48.99$ cm give a critical point. To check that this is a local maximum, we compute

$$\frac{d^2S}{dw^2} = -6w < 0 \quad \text{for} \quad w > 0.$$

Since $d^2S/dw^2 < 0$, we see that $w = 34.64$ cm is a local maximum. It is the only critical point, so it is a global maximum.

19. Consider the rectangle of sides x and y shown in the figure below.

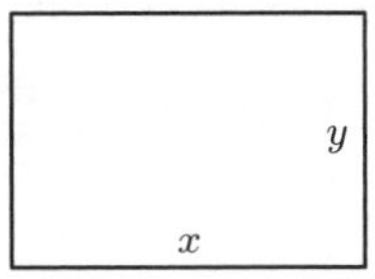

$$y$$
$$x$$

The total area is $xy = 3000$, so $y = 3000/x$. Suppose the left and right edges and the lower edge have the shrubs and the top edge has the fencing. The total cost is

$$C = 25(x + 2y) + 10(x)$$
$$= 35x + 50y.$$

Since $y = 3000/x$, this reduces to

$$C(x) = 35x + 50(3000/x) = 35x + 150{,}000/x.$$

Therefore, $C'(x) = 35 - 150{,}000/x^2$. We set this to 0 to find the critical points:

$$35 - \frac{150{,}000}{x^2} = 0$$

$$\frac{150{,}000}{x^2} = 35$$

$$x^2 = 4285.71$$

$$x \approx 65.5 \text{ ft}$$

so that

$$y = 3000/x \approx 45.8 \text{ ft}.$$

Since $C(x) \to \infty$ as $x \to 0^+$ and $x \to \infty$, $x = 65.5$ is a minimum. The minimum total cost is then

$$C(65.5) \approx \$4583.$$

20. Figure 4.103 shows the the pool has dimensions x by y and the deck extends 5 feet at either side and 10 feet at the ends of the pool.

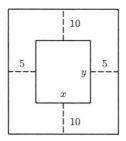

Figure 4.103

The dimensions of the plot of land containing the pool are then $(x + 5 + 5)$ by $(y + 10 + 10)$. The area of the land is then

$$A = (x + 10)(y + 20),$$

which is to be minimized. We also are told that the area of the pool is $xy = 1800$, so

$$y = 1800/x$$

and

$$A = (x + 10)\left(\frac{1800}{x} + 20\right)$$

$$= 1800 + 20x + \frac{18000}{x} + 200.$$

We find dA/dx and set it to zero to get

$$\frac{dA}{dx} = 20 - \frac{18000}{x^2} = 0$$

$$20x^2 = 18000$$

$$x^2 = 900$$

$$x = 30 \text{ feet.}$$

Since $A \to \infty$ as $x \to 0^+$ and as $x \to \infty$, this critical point must be a global minimum. Also, $y = 1800/30 = 60$ feet. The plot of land is therefore $(30 + 10) = 40$ by $(60 + 20) = 80$ feet.

21. Volume: $V = x^2 y$,
Surface: $S = x^2 + 4xy = x^2 + 4xV/x^2 = x^2 + 4V/x$.
To find the dimensions which minimize the area, find x such that $dS/dx = 0$.

$$\frac{dS}{dx} = 2x - \frac{4V}{x^2} = 0,$$

so

$$x^3 = 2V,$$

and solving for x gives $x = \sqrt[3]{2V}$. To see that this gives a minimum, note that for small x, $S \approx 4V/x$ is decreasing. For large x, $S \approx x^2$ is increasing. Since there is only one critical point, this must give a global minimum. Using x to find y gives $y = V/x^2 = V/(2V)^{2/3} = \sqrt[3]{V/4}$.

22. If the illumination is represented by I, then we know that

$$I = \frac{k \cos \theta}{r^2}.$$

See Figure 4.104.

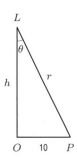

Figure 4.104

Since $r^2 = h^2 + 10^2$ and $\cos \theta = h/r = h/\sqrt{h^2 + 10^2}$, we have

$$I = \frac{kh}{(h^2 + 10^2)^{3/2}}.$$

To find the height at which I is maximized, we differentiate

$$\frac{dI}{dh} = \frac{k}{(h^2 + 10^2)^{3/2}} - \frac{3kh(2h)}{2(h^2 + 10^2)^{5/2}} = \frac{k(h^2 + 10^2) - 3kh^2}{(h^2 + 10^2)^{5/2}} = \frac{k(10^2 - 2h^2)}{(h^2 + 10^2)^{5/2}}.$$

Setting $dI/dh = 0$ gives

$$10^2 - 2h^2 = 0$$
$$h = \sqrt{50} \text{ meters.}$$

Since $dI/dh > 0$ for $0 \le h < \sqrt{50}$ and $dI/dh < 0$ for $h > \sqrt{50}$, we know that I is a maximum when $h = \sqrt{50}$ meters.

23. The distance from a given point on the parabola (x, x^2) to $(1, 0)$ is given by

$$D = \sqrt{(x-1)^2 + (x^2 - 0)^2}.$$

Minimizing this is equivalent to minimizing $d = (x-1)^2 + x^4$. (We can ignore the square root if we are only interested in minimizing because the square root is smallest when the thing it is the square root of is smallest.) To minimize d, we find its critical points by solving $d' = 0$. Since $d = (x-1)^2 + x^4 = x^2 - 2x + 1 + x^4$,

$$d' = 2x - 2 + 4x^3 = 2(2x^3 + x - 1).$$

By graphing $d' = 2(2x^3 + 2x - 1)$ on a calculator, we see that it has only 1 root, $x \approx 0.59$. This must give a minimum because $d \to \infty$ as $x \to -\infty$ and as $x \to +\infty$, and d has only one critical point. This is confirmed by the second derivative test: $d'' = 12x^2 + 2 = 2(6x^2 + 1)$, which is always positive. Thus the point $(0.59, 0.59^2) \approx (0.59, 0.35)$ is approximately the closest point of $y = x^2$ to $(1, 0)$.

24. Any point on the curve can be written (x, x^2). The distance between such a point and $(3, 0)$ is given by

$$s(x) = \sqrt{(3 - x)^2 + (0 - x^2)^2} = \sqrt{(3 - x)^2 + x^4}.$$

Plotting this function in Figure 4.105, we see that there is a minimum near $x = 1$.

To find the value of x that minimizes the distance we can instead minimize the function $Q = s^2$ (the derivative is simpler). Then we have

$$Q(x) = (3 - x)^2 + x^4.$$

Differentiating $Q(x)$ gives

$$\frac{dQ}{dx} = -6 + 2x + 4x^3.$$

Plotting the function $4x^3 + 2x - 6$ shows that there is one real solution at $x = 1$, which can be verified by substitution; the required coordinates are therefore $(1, 1)$. Because $Q''(x) = 2 + 12x^2$ is always positive, $x = 1$ is indeed the minimum. See Figure 4.106.

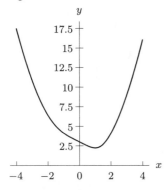

Figure 4.105

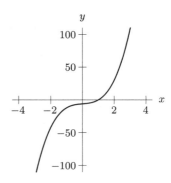

Figure 4.106

25. We see that the width of the tunnel is $2r$. The area of the rectangle is then $(2r)h$. The area of the semicircle is $(\pi r^2)/2$. The cross-sectional area, A, is then

$$A = 2rh + \frac{1}{2}\pi r^2$$

and the perimeter, P, is

$$P = 2h + 2r + \pi r.$$

From $A = 2rh + (\pi r^2)/2$ we get

$$h = \frac{A}{2r} - \frac{\pi r}{4}.$$

Thus,

$$P = 2\left(\frac{A}{2r} - \frac{\pi r}{4}\right) + 2r + \pi r = \frac{A}{r} + 2r + \frac{\pi r}{2}.$$

We now have the perimeter in terms of r and the constant A. Differentiating, we obtain

$$\frac{dP}{dr} = -\frac{A}{r^2} + 2 + \frac{\pi}{2}.$$

To find the critical points we set $P' = 0$:

$$-\frac{A}{r^2} + \frac{\pi}{2} + 2 = 0$$

$$\frac{r^2}{A} = \frac{2}{4 + \pi}$$

$$r = \sqrt{\frac{2A}{4 + \pi}}.$$

Substituting this back into our expression for h, we have

$$h = \frac{A}{2} \cdot \frac{\sqrt{4 + \pi}}{\sqrt{2A}} - \frac{\pi}{4} \cdot \frac{\sqrt{2A}}{\sqrt{4 + \pi}}.$$

Since $P \to \infty$ as $r \to 0^+$ and as $r \to \infty$, this critical point must be a global minimum. Notice that the h-value simplifies to

$$h = \sqrt{\frac{2A}{4 + \pi}} = r.$$

26. Let the sides of the rectangle have lengths a and b. We shall look for the minimum of the square s of the length of either diagonal, i.e. $s = a^2 + b^2$. The area is $A = ab$, so $b = A/a$. This gives

$$s(a) = a^2 + \frac{A^2}{a^2}.$$

To find the minimum squared length we need to find the critical points of s. Differentiating s with respect to a gives

$$\frac{ds}{da} = 2a + (-2)A^2 a^{-3} = 2a\left(1 - \frac{A^2}{a^4}\right)$$

The derivative $ds/da = 0$ when $a = \sqrt{A}$, that is when $a = b$ and so the rectangle is a square. Because $\dfrac{d^2 s}{da^2} = 2\left(1 + \dfrac{3A^2}{a^4}\right) > 0$, this is a minimum.

27. Let x equal the number of chairs ordered in excess of 300, so $0 \le x \le 100$.

$$\text{Revenue} = R = (90 - 0.25x)(300 + x)$$
$$= 27,000 - 75x + 90x - 0.25x^2 = 27,000 + 15x - 0.25x^2$$

At a critical point $dR/dx = 0$. Since $dR/dx = 15 - 0.5x$, we have $x = 30$, and the maximum revenue is $\$27,225$ since the graph of R is a parabola which opens downward. The minimum is $\$0$ (when no chairs are sold).

28. If v is the speed of the boat in miles per hour, then

$$\text{Cost of fuel per hour (in \$/hour)} = kv^3,$$

where k is the constant of proportionality. To find k, use the information that the boat uses $\$100$ worth of fuel per hour when cruising at 10 miles per hour: $100 = k10^3$, so $k = 100/10^3 = 0.1$. Thus,

$$\text{Cost of fuel per hour (in \$/hour)} = 0.1v^3.$$

From the given information, we also have

$$\text{Cost of other operations (labor, maintenance, etc.) per hour (in \$/hour)} = 675.$$

So

$$\text{Total Cost per hour (in \$/hour)} = \text{Cost of fuel (in \$/hour)} + \text{Cost of other (in \$/hour)}$$
$$= 0.1v^3 + 675.$$

However, we want to find the Cost per *mile*, which is the Total Cost per *hour* divided by the number of miles that the ferry travels in one hour. Since v is the speed in miles/hour at which the ferry travels, the number of miles that the ferry travels in one hour is simply v miles. Let C = Cost per *mile*. Then

$$\text{Cost per \emph{mile} (in \$/mile)} = \frac{\text{Total Cost per \emph{hour} (in \$/hour)}}{\text{Distance traveled per hour (in miles/hour)}}$$

$$C = \frac{0.1v^3 + 675}{v} = 0.1v^2 + \frac{675}{v}.$$

We also know that $0 < v < \infty$. To find the speed at which Cost per *mile* is minimized, set

$$\frac{dC}{dv} = 2(0.1)v - \frac{675}{v^2} = 0$$

so

$$2(0.1)v = \frac{675}{v^2}$$
$$v^3 = \frac{675}{2(0.1)} = 3375$$
$$v = 15 \text{ miles/hour.}$$

Since

$$\frac{d^2 C}{dv^2} = 0.2 + \frac{2(675)}{v^3} > 0$$

for $v > 0$, $v = 15$ gives a local minimum for C by the second-derivative test. Since this is the only critical point for $0 < v < \infty$, it must give a global minimum.

29. (a) We have

$$x^{1/x} = e^{\ln(x^{1/x})} = e^{(1/x)\ln x}.$$

Thus

$$\frac{d(x^{1/x})}{dx} = \frac{d(e^{(1/x)\ln x})}{dx} = \frac{d(\frac{1}{x}\ln x)}{dx}e^{(1/x)\ln x}$$

$$= \left(-\frac{\ln x}{x^2} + \frac{1}{x^2}\right)x^{1/x}$$

$$= \frac{x^{1/x}}{x^2}(1 - \ln x)\begin{cases} = 0 & \text{when } x = e \\ < 0 & \text{when } x > e \\ > 0 & \text{when } x < e. \end{cases}$$

Hence $e^{1/e}$ is the global maximum for $x^{1/x}$, by the first derivative test.

(b) Since $x^{1/x}$ is increasing for $0 < x < e$ and decreasing for $x > e$, and 2 and 3 are the closest integers to e, either $2^{1/2}$ or $3^{1/3}$ is the maximum for $n^{1/n}$. We have $2^{1/2} \approx 1.414$ and $3^{1/3} \approx 1.442$, so $3^{1/3}$ is the maximum.

(c) Since $e < 3 < \pi$, and $x^{1/x}$ is decreasing for $x > e$, $3^{1/3} > \pi^{1/\pi}$.

30. (a) If, following the hint, we set $f(x) = (a + x)/2 - \sqrt{ax}$, then $f(x)$ represents the difference between the arithmetic and geometric means for some fixed a and any $x > 0$. We can find where this difference is minimized by solving $f'(x) = 0$. Since $f'(x) = \frac{1}{2} - \frac{1}{2}\sqrt{a}x^{-1/2}$, if $f'(x) = 0$ then $\frac{1}{2}\sqrt{a}x^{-1/2} = \frac{1}{2}$, or $x = a$. Since $f''(x) = \frac{1}{4}\sqrt{a}x^{-3/2}$ is positive for all positive x, by the second derivative test $f(x)$ has a minimum at $x = a$, and $f(a) = 0$. Thus $f(x) = (a + x)/2 - \sqrt{ax} \geq 0$ for all $x > 0$, which means $(a + x)/2 \geq \sqrt{ax}$. This means that the arithmetic mean is greater than the geometric mean unless $a = x$, in which case the two means are equal.

Alternatively, and without using calculus, we obtain

$$\frac{a + b}{2} - \sqrt{ab} = \frac{a - 2\sqrt{ab} + b}{2}$$

$$= \frac{(\sqrt{a} - \sqrt{b})^2}{2} \geq 0,$$

and again we have $(a + b)/2 \geq \sqrt{ab}$.

(b) Following the hint, set $f(x) = \frac{a+b+x}{3} - \sqrt[3]{abx}$. Then $f(x)$ represents the difference between the arithmetic and geometric means for some fixed a, b and any $x > 0$. We can find where this difference is minimized by solving $f'(x) = 0$. Since $f'(x) = \frac{1}{3} - \frac{1}{3}\sqrt[3]{ab}x^{-2/3}$, $f'(x) = 0$ implies that $\frac{1}{3}\sqrt[3]{ab}x^{-2/3} = \frac{1}{3}$, or $x = \sqrt{ab}$. Since $f''(x) = \frac{2}{9}\sqrt[3]{ab}x^{-5/3}$ is positive for all positive x, by the second derivative test $f(x)$ has a minimum at $x = \sqrt{ab}$. But

$$f(\sqrt{ab}) = \frac{a + b + \sqrt{ab}}{3} - \sqrt[3]{ab\sqrt{ab}} = \frac{a + b + \sqrt{ab}}{3} - \sqrt{ab} = \frac{a + b - 2\sqrt{ab}}{3}.$$

By the first part of this problem, we know that $\frac{a+b}{2} - \sqrt{ab} \geq 0$, which implies that $a + b - 2\sqrt{ab} \geq 0$. Thus $f(\sqrt{ab}) = \frac{a+b-2\sqrt{ab}}{3} \geq 0$. Since f has a maximum at $x = \sqrt{ab}$, $f(x)$ is always nonnegative. Thus $f(x) = \frac{a+b+x}{3} - \sqrt[3]{abx} \geq 0$, so $\frac{a+b+c}{3} \geq \sqrt[3]{abc}$. Note that equality holds only when $a = b = c$. (Part (b) may also be done without calculus, but it's harder than (a).)

31. (a) The line in the left-hand figure has slope equal to the rate worms arrive. To understand why, see line (1) in the right-hand figure. (This is the same line.) For any point Q on the loading curve, the line PQ has slope

$$\frac{QT}{PT} = \frac{QT}{PO + OT} = \frac{\text{load}}{\text{traveling time} + \text{searching time}}.$$

(b) The slope of the line PQ is maximized when the line is tangent to the loading curve, which happens with line (2). The load is then approximately 7 worms.

(c) If the traveling time is increased, the point P moves to the left, to point P', say. If line (3) is tangent to the curve, it will be tangent to the curve further to the right than line (2), so the optimal load is larger. This makes sense: if the bird has to fly further, you'd expect it to bring back more worms each time.

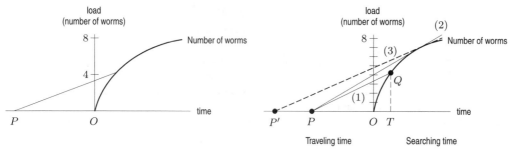

32. Let x be as indicated in the figure in the text. Then the distance from S to Town 1 is $\sqrt{1+x^2}$ and the distance from S to Town 2 is $\sqrt{(4-x)^2+4^2} = \sqrt{x^2-8x+32}$.

$$\text{Total length of pipe} = f(x) = \sqrt{1+x^2} + \sqrt{x^2-8x+32}.$$

We want to look for critical points of f. The easiest way is to graph f and see that it has a local minimum at about $x = 0.8$ miles. Alternatively, we can use the formula:

$$
\begin{aligned}
f'(x) &= \frac{2x}{2\sqrt{1+x^2}} + \frac{2x-8}{2\sqrt{x^2-8x+32}} \\
&= \frac{x}{\sqrt{1+x^2}} + \frac{x-4}{\sqrt{x^2-8x+32}} \\
&= \frac{x\sqrt{x^2-8x+32} + (x-4)\sqrt{1+x^2}}{\sqrt{1+x^2}\sqrt{x^2-8x+32}} = 0.
\end{aligned}
$$

$f'(x)$ is equal to zero when the numerator is equal to zero.

$$
\begin{aligned}
x\sqrt{x^2-8x+32} + (x-4)\sqrt{1+x^2} &= 0 \\
x\sqrt{x^2-8x+32} &= (4-x)\sqrt{1+x^2}.
\end{aligned}
$$

Squaring both sides and simplifying, we get

$$
\begin{aligned}
x^2(x^2-8x+32) &= (x^2-8x+16)(14x^2) \\
x^4 - 8x^3 + 32x^2 &= x^4 - 8x^3 + 17x^2 - 8x + 16 \\
15x^2 + 8x - 16 &= 0, \\
(3x+4)(5x-4) &= 0.
\end{aligned}
$$

So $x = 4/5$. (Discard $x = -4/3$ since we are only interested in x between 0 and 4, between the two towns.) Using the second derivative test, we can verify that $x = 4/5$ is a local minimum.

33. (a) The distance the pigeon flies over water is

$$\overline{BP} = \frac{\overline{AB}}{\sin\theta} = \frac{500}{\sin\theta},$$

and over land is

$$\overline{PL} = \overline{AL} - \overline{AP} = 2000 - \frac{500}{\tan\theta} = 2000 - \frac{500\cos\theta}{\sin\theta}.$$

Therefore the energy required is

$$
\begin{aligned}
E &= 2e\left(\frac{500}{\sin\theta}\right) + e\left(2000 - \frac{500\cos\theta}{\sin\theta}\right) \\
&= 500e\left(\frac{2-\cos\theta}{\sin\theta}\right) + 2000e, \quad \text{for} \quad \arctan\left(\frac{500}{2000}\right) \le \theta \le \frac{\pi}{2}.
\end{aligned}
$$

(b) Notice that E and the function $f(\theta) = \dfrac{2-\cos\theta}{\sin\theta}$ must have the same critical points since the graph of E is just a stretch and a vertical shift of the graph of f. The graph of $\dfrac{2-\cos\theta}{\sin\theta}$ for $\arctan(\frac{500}{2000}) \le \theta \le \frac{\pi}{2}$ in Figure 4.107 shows that E has precisely one critical point, and that a minimum for E occurs at this point.

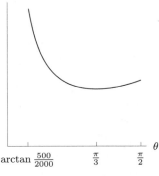

$$\text{arctan}\frac{500}{2000} \qquad \frac{\pi}{3} \qquad \frac{\pi}{2}$$

Figure 4.107: Graph of $f(\theta) = \frac{2-\cos\theta}{\sin\theta}$ for $\arctan(\frac{500}{2000}) \le \theta \le \frac{\pi}{2}$

To find the critical point θ, we solve $f'(\theta) = 0$ or

$$E' = 0 = 500e \left(\frac{\sin\theta \cdot \sin\theta - (2 - \cos\theta) \cdot \cos\theta}{\sin^2\theta} \right)$$

$$= 500e \left(\frac{1 - 2\cos\theta}{\sin^2\theta} \right).$$

Therefore $1 - 2\cos\theta = 0$ and so $\theta = \pi/3$.

(c) Letting $a = \overline{AB}$ and $b = \overline{AL}$, our formula for E becomes

$$E = 2e\left(\frac{a}{\sin\theta}\right) + e\left(b - \frac{a\cos\theta}{\sin\theta}\right)$$

$$= ea\left(\frac{2 - \cos\theta}{\sin\theta}\right) + eb, \quad \text{for} \quad \arctan\left(\frac{a}{b}\right) \le \theta \le \frac{\pi}{2}.$$

Again, the graph of E is just a stretch and a vertical shift of the graph of $\dfrac{2 - \cos\theta}{\sin\theta}$. Thus, the critical point $\theta = \pi/3$ is independent of e, a, and b. But the maximum of E *on the domain* $\arctan(a/b) \le \theta \le \frac{\pi}{2}$ is dependent on the ratio $a/b = \dfrac{\overline{AB}}{\overline{AL}}$. In other words, the optimal angle is $\theta = \pi/3$ provided $\arctan(a/b) \le \frac{\pi}{3}$; otherwise, the optimal angle is $\arctan(a/b)$, which means the pigeon should fly over the lake for the entire trip—this occurs when $a/b > 1.733$.

34. We want to maximize the viewing angle, which is $\theta = \theta_1 - \theta_2$.

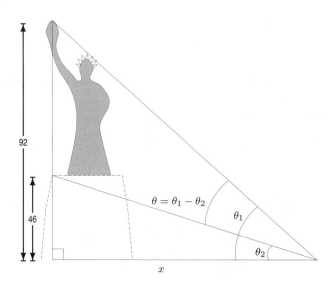

Now

$$\tan(\theta_1) = \frac{92}{x} \quad \text{so } \theta_1 = \arctan\left(\frac{92}{x}\right)$$

$$\tan(\theta_2) = \frac{46}{x} \quad \text{so } \theta_2 = \arctan\left(\frac{46}{x}\right).$$

Then

$$\theta = \arctan\left(\frac{92}{x}\right) - \arctan\left(\frac{46}{x}\right) \quad \text{for} \quad x > 0.$$

We look for critical points of the function by computing $d\theta/dx$:

$$\frac{d\theta}{dx} = \frac{1}{1 + (92/x)^2}\left(\frac{-92}{x^2}\right) - \frac{1}{1 + (46/x)^2}\left(\frac{-46}{x^2}\right)$$

$$= \frac{-92}{x^2 + 92^2} - \frac{-46}{x^2 + 46^2}$$

$$= \frac{-92(x^2 + 46^2) + 46(x^2 + 92^2)}{(x^2 + 92^2) \cdot (x^2 + 46^2)}$$

$$= \frac{46(4232 - x^2)}{(x^2 + 92^2) \cdot (x^2 + 46^2)}.$$

Setting $d\theta/dx = 0$ gives

$$x^2 = 4232$$
$$x = \pm\sqrt{4232}.$$

Since $x > 0$, the critical point is $x = \sqrt{4232} \approx 65.1$ meters. To verify that this is indeed where θ attains a maximum, we note that $d\theta/dx > 0$ for $0 < x < \sqrt{4232}$ and $d\theta/dx < 0$ for $x > \sqrt{4232}$. By the First Derivative Test, θ attains a maximum at $x = \sqrt{4232} \approx 65.1$.

35. (a) Since the speed of light is a constant, the time of travel is minimized when the distance of travel is minimized. From Figure 4.108,

$$\text{Distance } \overrightarrow{OP} = \sqrt{x^2 + 1^2} = \sqrt{x^2 + 1}$$
$$\text{Distance } \overrightarrow{PQ} = \sqrt{(2 - x)^2 + 1^2} = \sqrt{(2 - x)^2 + 1}$$

Thus,

$$\text{Total distance traveled } = s = \sqrt{x^2 + 1} + \sqrt{(2 - x)^2 + 1}.$$

The total distance is a minimum if

$$\frac{ds}{dx} = \frac{1}{2}(x^2 + 1)^{-1/2} \cdot 2x + \frac{1}{2}((2 - x)^2 + 1)^{-1/2} \cdot 2(2 - x)(-1) = 0,$$

giving

$$\frac{x}{\sqrt{x^2 + 1}} - \frac{2 - x}{\sqrt{(2 - x)^2 + 1}} = 0$$
$$\frac{x}{\sqrt{x^2 + 1}} = \frac{2 - x}{\sqrt{(2 - x)^2 + 1}}$$

Squaring both sides gives

$$\frac{x^2}{x^2 + 1} = \frac{(2 - x)^2}{(2 - x)^2 + 1}.$$

Cross multiplying gives

$$x^2((2 - x)^2 + 1) = (2 - x)^2(x^2 + 1).$$

Multiplying out

$$x^2(4 - 4x + x^2 + 1) = (4 - 4x + x^2)(x^2 + 1)$$
$$4x^2 - 4x^3 + x^4 + x^2 = 4x^2 - 4x^3 + x^4 + 4 - 4x + x^2.$$

Collecting terms and canceling gives

$$0 = 4 - 4x$$
$$x = 1.$$

We can see that this value of x gives a minimum by comparing the value of s at this point and at the endpoints, $x = 0, x = 2$.
At $x = 1$,

$$s = \sqrt{1^2 + 1} + \sqrt{(2 - 1)^2 + 1} = 2.83.$$

At $x = 0$,

$$s = \sqrt{0^2 + 1} + \sqrt{(2 - 0)^2 + 1} = 3.24.$$

At $x = 2$,

$$s = \sqrt{2^2 + 1} + \sqrt{(2 - 2)^2 + 1} = 3.24.$$

Thus the shortest travel time occurs when $x = 1$; that is, when P is at the point $(1, 1)$.
(b) Since $x = 1$ is halfway between $x = 0$ and $x = 2$, the angles θ_1 and θ_2 are equal.

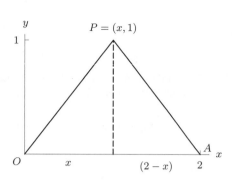

Figure 4.108

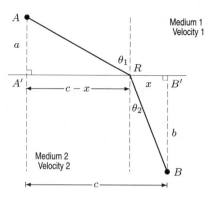

Figure 4.109

36. (a) Since $RB' = x$ and $A'R = c - x$, we have

$$AR = \sqrt{a^2 + (c - x)^2} \quad \text{and} \quad RB = \sqrt{b^2 + x^2}.$$

See Figure 4.109.

The time traveled, T, is given by

$$T = \text{Time } AR + \text{Time } RB = \frac{\text{Distance } AR}{v_1} + \frac{\text{Distance } RB}{v_2}$$

$$= \frac{\sqrt{a^2 + (c - x)^2}}{v_1} + \frac{\sqrt{b^2 + x^2}}{v_2}.$$

(b) Let us calculate dT/dx:

$$\frac{dT}{dx} = \frac{-2(c - x)}{2v_1\sqrt{a^2 + (c - x)^2}} + \frac{2x}{2v_2\sqrt{b^2 + x^2}}.$$

At the minimum $dT/dx = 0$, so

$$\frac{c - x}{v_1\sqrt{a^2 + (c - x)^2}} = \frac{x}{v_2\sqrt{b^2 + x^2}}.$$

But we have

$$\sin\theta_1 = \frac{c - x}{\sqrt{a^2 + (c - x)^2}} \quad \text{and} \quad \sin\theta_2 = \frac{x}{\sqrt{b^2 + x^2}}.$$

Therefore, setting $dT/dx = 0$ tells us that

$$\frac{\sin\theta_1}{v_1} = \frac{\sin\theta_2}{v_2}$$

which gives

$$\frac{\sin\theta_1}{\sin\theta_2} = \frac{v_1}{v_2}.$$

37. We know that the time taken is given by

$$T = \frac{\sqrt{a^2 + (c - x)^2}}{v_1} + \frac{\sqrt{b^2 + x^2}}{v_2}$$

$$\frac{dT}{dx} = \frac{-(c - x)}{v_1\sqrt{a^2 + (c - x)^2}} + \frac{x}{v_2\sqrt{b^2 + x^2}}.$$

Differentiating again gives

$$\frac{d^2T}{dx^2} = \frac{1}{v_1\sqrt{a^2 + (c - x)^2}} + \frac{(c - x)(-2(c - x))}{2v_1(a^2 + (c - x)^2)^{3/2}} + \frac{1}{v_2\sqrt{b^2 + x^2}} - \frac{x(2x)}{2v_2(b^2 + x^2)^{3/2}}$$

$$= \frac{a^2 + (c - x)^2 - (c - x)^2}{v_1(a^2 + (c - x)^2)^{3/2}} + \frac{b^2 + x^2 - x^2}{v_2(b^2 + x^2)^{3/2}}$$

$$= \frac{a^2}{v_1(a^2 + (c - x)^2)^{3/2}} + \frac{b^2}{v_2(b^2 + x^2)^{3/2}}.$$

This expression for d^2T/dx^2 shows that for any value of x, a, c, v_1, and v_2 with v_1, $v_2 > 0$, we have $d^2T/dx^2 > 0$. Thus, any critical point must be a local minimum. Since there is only one critical point, it must be a global minimum.

38. (a) See Figure 4.110.

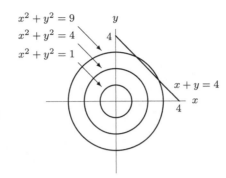

$x^2 + y^2 = 9$
$x^2 + y^2 = 4$
$x^2 + y^2 = 1$
y
4
$x + y = 4$
x
4

Figure 4.110

(b) As C increases in the equation $x^2 + y^2 = C$, the circle expands outward. For $C = 4$, the circle does not intersect the line. As C increases from 4, the circle expands until it touches the line. At $C = 9$, the circle cuts the line twice.

The minimum value of $C = x^2 + y^2$ occurs where a circle tangent to the line. For larger C-values, $x^2 + y^2 = C$ cuts the line twice, for smaller C-values, the circle does not touch the line.

(c) At the point at when the circle touches the line, the slope of the circle equals the slope of the line, namely -1. Implicit differentiation gives the slope of $x^2 + y^2 = C$:

$$2x + 2y \cdot y' = 0$$
$$y' = \frac{-x}{y}.$$

Thus, at the point where a circle touches the line, we have

$$-\frac{x}{y} = -1$$
$$x = y.$$

Substitution into $x + y = 4$ gives $2x = 4$, so $x = 2$ and $y = 2$. Thus, the minimum is $x^2 + y^2 = 2^2 + 2^2 = 8$.

39. (a) See Figure 4.111.

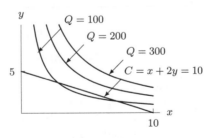

y
$Q = 100$
$Q = 200$
$Q = 300$
$C = x + 2y = 10$
5
x
10

Figure 4.111

(b) Comparing the curves $Q = 100$, $Q = 200$, and $Q = 300$, we see that production increases as we move away from the origin. The curve $Q = 100$ cuts the line $C = x + 2y = 10$ twice while the curves $Q = 200$ and $Q = 300$ do not cut the line.

The maximum possible Q occurs where a curve touches the line. At this point, the slope of the production curve equals the slope of the budget line, namely $-1/2$.

(c) Using implicit differentiation, the slope of the curve $10xy = C$ is given by

$$10y + 10xy' = 0$$
$$y' = -\frac{y}{x}.$$

Thus, at the point where the curve touches the line, whose slope is $-1/2$, we have

$$-\frac{y}{x} = -\frac{1}{2}$$
$$y = \frac{x}{2}.$$

Substituting into $C = x + 2y = 10$ gives $2x = 10$, so $x = 5$ and $y = 5/2$. Thus, the maximum production is

$$Q = 10 \cdot 5 \cdot \frac{5}{2} = 125.$$

40. (a) See Figure 4.112.

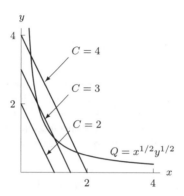

Figure 4.112

(b) Comparing the lines $C = 2$, $C = 3$, $C = 4$, we see that the cost increases as we move away from the origin. The line $C = 2$ does not cut the curve $Q = 1$; the lines $C = 3$ and $C = 4$ cut twice.

The minimum cost occurs where a cost line is tangent to the production curve.

(c) Using implicit differentiation, the slope of $x^{1/2}y^{1/2} = 1$ is given by

$$\frac{1}{2}x^{-1/2}y^{1/2} + \frac{1}{2}x^{1/2}y^{-1/2}y' = 0$$
$$y' = \frac{-x^{-1/2}y^{1/2}}{x^{1/2}y^{-1/2}} = -\frac{y}{x}.$$

The cost lines all have slope -2. Thus, if the curve is tangent to a line, we have

$$-\frac{y}{x} = -2$$
$$y = 2x.$$

Substituting into $Q = x^{1/2}y^{1/2} = 1$ gives

$$x^{1/2}(2x)^{1/2} = 1$$
$$\sqrt{2}x = 1$$
$$x = \frac{1}{\sqrt{2}}$$
$$y = 2 \cdot \frac{1}{\sqrt{2}} = \sqrt{2}.$$

Thus the minimum cost is

$$C = 2\frac{1}{\sqrt{2}} + \sqrt{2} = 2\sqrt{2}.$$

Solutions for Section 4.6

Exercises

1. The rate of growth, in billions of people per year, is

$$\frac{dP}{dt} = 6.342(0.011)e^{0.011t}.$$

On January 1, 2004, we have $t = 0$, so

$$\frac{dP}{dt} = 6.342(0.011)e^0 = 0.0698 \text{ billion/year} = 69.8 \text{ million/year}.$$

2. The rate of change of temperature is

$$\frac{dH}{dt} = 16(-0.02)e^{-0.02t} = -0.32e^{-0.02t}.$$

When $t = 0$,

$$\frac{dH}{dt} = -0.32e^0 = -0.32°\text{C/min}.$$

When $t = 10$,

$$\frac{dH}{dt} = -0.32e^{-0.02(10)} = -0.262°\text{C/min}.$$

3. The rate of change of the power dissipated is given by

$$\frac{dP}{dR} = -\frac{81}{R^2}.$$

4. (a) The rate of change of the period is given by

$$\frac{dT}{dl} = \frac{2\pi}{\sqrt{9.8}}\frac{d}{dl}(\sqrt{l}) = \frac{2\pi}{\sqrt{9.8}}\cdot\frac{1}{2}l^{-1/2} = \frac{\pi}{\sqrt{9.8}}\cdot\frac{1}{\sqrt{l}} = \frac{\pi}{\sqrt{9.8l}}.$$

(b) The rate decreases since $\sqrt{l}$ is in the denominator.

5. (a) The rate of change of thickness of ice is

$$\frac{dy}{dt} = 0.2(1.5)t^{0.5} = 0.3t^{0.5} \text{ cm/hr}.$$

Thus, at $t = 1$

$$\left.\frac{dy}{dt}\right|_{t=1} = 0.3(1)^{0.5} = 0.3 \text{ cm/hr}.$$

At $t = 2$,

$$\left.\frac{dy}{dt}\right|_{t=2} = 0.3(2)^{0.5} = 0.424 \text{ cm/hr}.$$

(b) Since both $y = 0.2t^{1.5}$ and $dy/dt = 0.3t^{0.5}$ increase as t increase on the interval $0 \leq t \leq 3$, the thickness, y, and the rate, dy/dt, are both greatest when $t = 3$.

6. (a) The rate of change of temperature change is

$$\frac{dT}{dD} = \frac{d}{dD}\left(\frac{C}{2}D^3 - \frac{D^4}{3}\right) = \frac{3C}{2}D^2 - \frac{4D^3}{3}.$$

(b) We want to know for what values of D the value of dT/dD is positive. This occurs when

$$\frac{dT}{dD} = \left(\frac{3C}{2} - \frac{4D}{3}\right)D^2 > 0$$

Since $D^2 \geq 0$ for all D, we have

$$\frac{3C}{2} - \frac{4}{3}D > 0 \quad \text{so} \quad \frac{3C}{2} > \frac{4}{3}D \quad \text{so} \quad D < \frac{9C}{8}.$$

So the rate of change of temperature change is positive for doses less than $9C/8$.

7. The rate of change of velocity is given by

$$\frac{dv}{dt} = -\frac{mg}{k} \left(-\frac{k}{m} e^{-kt/m} \right) = ge^{-kt/m}.$$

When $t = 0$,

$$\left. \frac{dv}{dt} \right|_{t=0} = g.$$

When $t = 1$,

$$\left. \frac{dv}{dt} \right|_{t=1} = ge^{-k/m}.$$

These answers give the acceleration at $t = 0$ and $t = 1$. The acceleration at $t = 0$ is g, the acceleration due to gravity, and at $t = 1$, the acceleration is $ge^{-k/m}$, a smaller value.

8. (a) The rate of change of average cost as quantity increases is

$$\frac{dC}{dq} = -\frac{a}{q^2} \text{ dollars/cell phone.}$$

(b) We are told that $dq/dt = 100$, and we want dC/dt. The chain rule gives

$$\frac{dC}{dt} = \frac{dC}{dq} \cdot \frac{dq}{dt} = -\frac{a}{q^2} \cdot 100 = -\frac{100a}{q^2} \text{ dollars/week.}$$

Since a is positive, dC/dt is negative, so C is decreasing.

9. (a) The rate of change of force with respect to distance is

$$\frac{dF}{dr} = \frac{2A}{r^3} - \frac{3B}{r^4}.$$

The units are units of force per units of distance.

(b) We are told that $dr/dt = k$ and we want dF/dt. By the chain rule

$$\frac{dF}{dt} = \frac{dF}{dr} \cdot \frac{dr}{dt} = \left(\frac{2A}{r^3} - \frac{3B}{r^4} \right) k.$$

The units are units of force per unit time.

10. (a) (i) Differentiating thinking of r as a constant gives

$$\frac{dP}{dt} = 500e^{rt/100} \cdot \frac{r}{100} = 5re^{rt/100}.$$

Substituting $t = 0$ gives

$$\frac{dP}{dt} = 5re^{r \cdot 0/100} = 5r \text{ dollars/yr.}$$

(ii) Substituting $t = 2$ gives

$$\frac{dP}{dt} = 5re^{r \cdot 2/100} = 5re^{0.02r} \text{ dollars/yr.}$$

(b) To differentiate thinking of r as variable, think of the function as

$$P = 500e^{r(t) \cdot t/100},$$

and use the chain rule (for $e^{rt/100}$) and the product rule (for $r(t) \cdot t$):

$$\frac{dP}{dt} = 500e^{r(t) \cdot t/100} \cdot \frac{1}{100} \cdot \frac{d}{dt}(r(t) \cdot t) = 5e^{r(t) \cdot t/100} \left(r(t) \cdot 1 + r'(t) \cdot t \right).$$

Substituting $t = 2$, $r = 4$, and $r'(2) = 0.3$ gives

$$\frac{dP}{dt} = 5e^{4 \cdot 2/100} (4 + 0.3 \cdot 2) = 24.916 \text{ dollars/year}$$

Thus, the price is increasing by about \$25 per year at that time.

11. We know $dR/dt = 0.2$ when $R = 5$ and $V = 9$ and we want to know dI/dt. Differentiating $I = V/R$ with V constant gives

$$\frac{dI}{dt} = V\left(-\frac{1}{R^2}\frac{dR}{dt}\right),$$

so substituting gives

$$\frac{dI}{dt} = 9\left(-\frac{1}{5^2}\cdot 0.2\right) = -0.072 \text{ ohms per second.}$$

12. We differentiate $F = k/r^2$ with respect to t using the chain rule to give

$$\frac{dF}{dt} = -\frac{2k}{r^3}\cdot\frac{dr}{dt}.$$

We know that $k = 10^{13}$ newton $\cdot$ km^2 and that the rocket is moving at 0.2 km/sec when $r = 10^4$ km. In other words, $dr/dt = 0.2$ km/sec when $r = 10^4$. Substituting gives

$$\frac{dF}{dt} = -\frac{2\cdot 10^{13}}{(10^4)^3}\cdot 0.2 = -4\,\text{newtons/sec.}$$

Problems

13. (a) From the second figure in the problem, we see that $\theta \approx 3.3$ when $t = 2$. The coordinates of P are given by $x = \cos\theta$, $y = \sin\theta$. When $t = 2$, the coordinates of P are

$$(x, y) \approx (\cos 3.3, \sin 3.3) = (-0.99, -0.16).$$

(b) Using the chain rule, the velocity in the x-direction is given by

$$v_x = \frac{dx}{dt} = \frac{dx}{d\theta}\cdot\frac{d\theta}{dt} = -\sin\theta\cdot\frac{d\theta}{dt}.$$

From Figure 4.113, we estimate that when $t = 2$,

$$\left.\frac{d\theta}{dt}\right|_{t=2} \approx 2.$$

So

$$v_x = \frac{dx}{dt} \approx -(-0.16)\cdot(2) = 0.32.$$

Similarly, the velocity in the y-direction is given by

$$v_y = \frac{dy}{dt} = \frac{dy}{d\theta}\cdot\frac{d\theta}{dt} = \cos\theta\cdot\frac{d\theta}{dt}.$$

When $t = 2$

$$v_y = \frac{dy}{dt} \approx (-0.99)\cdot(2) = -1.98.$$

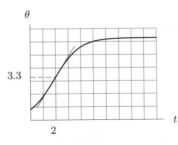

Figure 4.113

14. (a) On the interval $0 < M < 70$, we have

$$\text{Slope} = \frac{\Delta G}{\Delta M} = \frac{2.8}{70} = 0.04 \text{ gallons per mile.}$$

On the interval $70 < M < 100$, we have

$$\text{Slope} = \frac{\Delta G}{\Delta M} = \frac{4.6 - 2.8}{100 - 70} = \frac{1.8}{30} = 0.06 \text{ gallons per mile.}$$

(b) Gas consumption, in miles per gallon, is the reciprocal of the slope, in gallons per mile. On the interval $0 < M < 70$, gas consumption is $1/(0.04) = 25$ miles per gallon. On the interval $70 < M < 100$, gas consumption is $1/(0.06) = 16.667$ miles per gallon.

(c) In Figure 4.85 in the text, we see that the velocity for the first hour of this trip is 70 mph and the velocity for the second hour is 30 mph. The first hour may have been spent driving on an interstate highway and the second hour may have been spent driving in a city. The answers to part (b) would then tell us that this car gets 25 miles to the gallon on the highway and about 16 miles to the gallon in the city.

(d) Since $M = h(t)$, we have $G = f(M) = f(h(t)) = k(t)$. The function k gives the total number of gallons of gas used t hours into the trip. We have

$$G = k(0.5) = f(h(0.5)) = f(35) = 1.4 \text{ gallons.}$$

The car consumes 1.4 gallons of gas during the first half hour of the trip.

(e) Since $k(t) = f(h(t))$, by the chain rule, we have

$$\frac{dG}{dt} = k'(t) = f'(h(t)) \cdot h'(t).$$

Therefore:

$$\frac{dG}{dt}\bigg|_{t=0.5} = k'(0.5) = f'(h(0.5)) \cdot h'(0.5) = f'(35) \cdot 70 = 0.04 \cdot 70 = 2.8 \text{ gallons per hour,}$$

and

$$\frac{dG}{dt}\bigg|_{t=1.5} = k'(1.5) = f'(h(1.5)) \cdot h'(1.5) = f'(85) \cdot 30 = 0.06 \cdot 30 = 1.8 \text{ gallons per hour.}$$

Gas is being consumed at a rate of 2.8 gallons per hour at time $t = 0.5$ and is being consumed at a rate of 1.8 gallons per hour at time $t = 1.5$. Notice that gas is being consumed more quickly on the highway, even though the gas mileage is significantly better there.

15. (a) Assuming that $T(1) = 98.6 - 2 = 96.6$, we get

$$96.6 = 68 + 30.6e^{-k \cdot 1}$$
$$28.6 = 30.6e^{-k}$$
$$0.935 = e^{-k}.$$

So

$$k = -\ln(0.935) \approx 0.067.$$

(b) We're looking for a value of t which gives $T'(t) = -1$. First we find $T'(t)$:

$$T(t) = 68 + 30.6e^{-0.067t}$$
$$T'(t) = (30.6)(-0.067)e^{-0.067t} \approx -2e^{-0.067t}.$$

Setting this equal to -1 per hour gives

$$-1 = -2e^{-0.067t}$$
$$\ln(0.5) = -0.067t$$
$$t = -\frac{\ln(0.5)}{0.067} \approx 10.3.$$

Thus, when $t \approx 10.3$ hours, we have $T'(t) \approx -1°$F per hour.

(c) The coroner's rule of thumb predicts that in 24 hours the body temperature will decrease 25°F, to about 73.6°F. The formula predicts a temperature of

$$T(24) = 68 + 30.6e^{-0.067 \cdot 24} \approx 74.1°\text{F.}$$

16. (a) Since $P = 1$ when $V = 20$, we have

$$k = 1 \cdot (20^{1.4}) = 66.29.$$

Thus, we have

$$P = 66.29V^{-1.4}.$$

Differentiating gives

$$\frac{dP}{dV} = 66.29(-1.4V^{-2.4}) = -92.8V^{-2.4} \text{ atmospheres/cm}^3.$$

(b) We are given that $dV/dt = 2 \text{ cm}^3/\text{min}$ when $V = 30 \text{ cm}^3$. Using the chain rule, we have

$$\frac{dP}{dt} = \frac{dP}{dV} \cdot \frac{dV}{dt} = \left(-92.8V^{-2.4}\frac{\text{atm}}{\text{cm}^3}\right)\left(2\frac{\text{cm}^3}{\text{min}}\right)$$

$$= -92.8\left(30^{-2.4}\right)2\frac{\text{atm}}{\text{min}}$$

$$= -0.0529 \text{ atmospheres/min}$$

Thus, the pressure is decreasing at 0.0529 atmospheres per minute.

17. (a) The surface of the water is circular with radius r cm. Applying Pythagoras' Theorem to the triangle in Figure 4.114 shows that

$$(10 - h)^2 + r^2 = 10^2$$

so

$$r = \sqrt{10^2 - (10 - h)^2} = \sqrt{20h - h^2} \text{ cm}.$$

(b) We know $dh/dt = -0.1$ cm/hr and we want to know dr/dt when $h = 5$ cm. Differentiating

$$r = \sqrt{20h - h^2}$$

gives

$$\frac{dr}{dt} = \frac{1}{2}(20h - h^2)^{-1/2}\left(20\frac{dh}{dt} - 2h\frac{dh}{dt}\right) = \frac{10 - h}{\sqrt{20h - h^2}} \cdot \frac{dh}{dt}.$$

Substituting $dh/dt = -0.1$ and $h = 5$ gives

$$\left.\frac{dr}{dt}\right|_{h=5} = \frac{5}{\sqrt{20 \cdot 5 - 5^2}} \cdot (-0.1) = -\frac{1}{2\sqrt{75}} = -0.0577 \text{ cm/hr}.$$

Thus, the radius is decreasing at 0.0577 cm per hour.

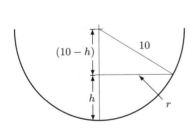

Figure 4.114

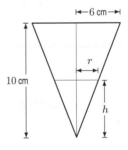

Figure 4.115

18. (a) When full

$$\text{Volume of water in filter} = \frac{1}{3}\pi r^2 h = \frac{1}{3}\pi 6^2 \cdot 10 = 120\pi.$$

Water flows out at a rate of 1.5 cm^3 per second, so

$$\text{Time to empty} = \frac{120\pi}{1.5} = 80\pi = 251.327 \text{ secs}.$$

The time taken is 251.327 sec or just over 4 minutes.

(b) Let the radius of the surface of the water be r cm when the depth is h cm. See Figure 4.115. Then by similar triangles

$$\frac{6}{10} = \frac{r}{h}$$

$$r = \frac{3}{5}h.$$

Thus, when the depth of the water is h,

$$\text{Volume of water } = V = \frac{1}{3}\pi r^2 h = \frac{1}{3}\pi \left(\frac{3}{5}h\right)^2 h = \frac{3}{25}\pi h^3 \text{ cm}^3.$$

(c) We know that water is flowing out at 1.5 cm^3 per second, so $dV/dt = -1.5$. We want to know dh/dt when $h = 8$. Differentiating the answer to part (b), we have

$$\frac{dV}{dt} = \frac{3}{25}\pi 3h^2 \frac{dh}{dt} = \frac{9}{25}\pi h^2 \frac{dh}{dt}.$$

Substituting $dV/dt = -1.5$ and $h = 8$ gives

$$-1.5 = \frac{9}{25}\pi 8^2 \cdot \frac{dh}{dt}$$

$$\frac{dh}{dt} = -\frac{1.5 \cdot 25}{9\pi 8^2} = -0.0207 \text{ cm/sec.}$$

Thus, the water level is dropping by 0.0207 cm per second.

19. When the radius is r, the volume V of the snowball is

$$V = \frac{4}{3}\pi r^3.$$

We know that $dr/dt = -0.2$ when $r = 15$ and we want to know dV/dt at that time. Differentiating, we have

$$\frac{dV}{dt} = \frac{4}{3}\pi 3r^2 \frac{dr}{dt} = 4\pi r^2 \frac{dr}{dt}.$$

Substituting $dr/dt = -0.2$ gives

$$\left.\frac{dV}{dt}\right|_{r=15} = 4\pi(15)^2(-0.2) = -180\pi = -565.487 \text{ cm}^3/\text{hr.}$$

Thus, the volume is decreasing at 565.487 cm^3 per hour.

20. (a) Since the slick is circular, if its radius is r meters, its area, A, is $A = \pi r^2$. Differentiating with respect to time using the chain rule gives

$$\frac{dA}{dt} = 2\pi r \frac{dr}{dt}.$$

We know $dr/dt = 0.1$ when $r = 150$, so

$$\frac{dA}{dt} = 2\pi 150(0.1) = 30\pi = 94.248 \text{ m}^2/\text{min.}$$

(b) If the thickness of the slick is h, its volume, V, is given by

$$V = Ah.$$

Differentiating with respect to time using the product rule gives

$$\frac{dV}{dt} = \frac{dA}{dt}h + A\frac{dh}{dt}.$$

We know $h = 0.02$ and $A = \pi(150)^2$ and $dA/dt = 30\pi$. Since V is fixed, $dV/dt = 0$, so

$$0 = 0.02(30\pi) + \pi(150)^2\frac{dh}{dt}.$$

Thus

$$\frac{dh}{dt} = -\frac{0.02(30\pi)}{\pi(150)^2} = -0.0000267 \text{ m/min,}$$

so the thickness is decreasing at 0.0000267 meters per minute.

21. Let the volume of clay be V. The clay is in the shape of a cylinder, so $V = \pi r^2 L$. We know $dL/dt = 0.1$ cm/sec and we want to know dr/dt when $r = 1$ cm and $L = 5$ cm. Differentiating with respect to time t gives

$$\frac{dV}{dt} = \pi 2rL\frac{dr}{dt} + \pi r^2\frac{dL}{dt}.$$

However, the amount of clay is unchanged, so $dV/dt = 0$ and

$$2rL\frac{dr}{dt} = -r^2\frac{dL}{dt},$$

therefore

$$\frac{dr}{dt} = -\frac{r}{2L}\frac{dL}{dt}.$$

When the radius is 1 cm and the length is 5 cm, and the length is increasing at 0.1 cm per second, the rate at which the radius is changing is

$$\frac{dr}{dt} = -\frac{1}{2 \cdot 5} \cdot 0.1 = -0.01 \text{ cm/sec}.$$

Thus, the radius is decreasing at 0.01 cm/sec.

22. Let the origin be at the center of the wheel and (x, y) be the coordinates of a point on the wheel. Then $x^2 + y^2 = R^2$, where $R = 62.5$ meters is the radius of the wheel. One minute into the ride, we know the passenger is rising at 0.1 meters per second, so $dy/dt = 0.1$. We want to know dx/dt. Differentiating with respect to time, t, gives

$$2x\frac{dx}{dt} + 2y\frac{dy}{dt} = 0,$$

so

$$\frac{dx}{dt} = -\frac{y}{x}\frac{dy}{dt}.$$

Suppose we are looking at the wheel in such a way that it appears to be rotating counter clockwise. In one minute, the wheel travels through $360°/20 = 18°$. From Figure 4.116, we see that at this time the coordinates of the passenger are $x = R\sin 18°$ and $y = -R\cos 18°$. Since the vertical speed of the cabin is $dy/dt = 0.1$ meters per second, the horizontal speed of the wheel, dx/dt, is

$$\frac{dx}{dt} = -\frac{-R\cos 18°}{R\sin 18°}0.1 = 0.308 \text{ meters/second}.$$

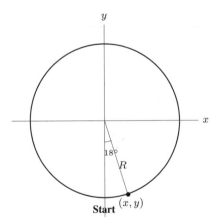

Figure 4.116

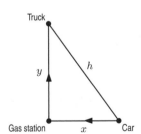

Figure 4.117

23. (a) Let x, y be the distances, in miles, of the car and truck respectively, from the gas station. See Figure 4.117. If the car and truck are h miles apart, Pythagoras' Theorem gives

$$h^2 = x^2 + y^2.$$

We know that when $x = 3$, $dx/dt = -100$ (the negative sign represents the fact that the distance from the gas station is decreasing), and $y = 4$, $dy/dt = 80$. Thus

$$h^2 = 3^2 + 4^2 = 25 \quad \text{so} \quad h = 5 \text{ miles.}$$

We want to find dh/dt. Differentiating $h^2 = x^2 + y^2$ gives

$$2h\frac{dh}{dt} = 2x\frac{dx}{dt} + 2y\frac{dy}{dt}$$

$$5\frac{dh}{dt} = 3(-100) + 4(80)$$

$$\frac{dh}{dt} = \frac{-300 + 320}{5} = 4 \text{ mph.}$$

Thus, the distance is increasing at 4 mph.

(b) If $dy/dt = 70$, we have

$$5\frac{dh}{dt} = 3(-100) + 4(70)$$

$$\frac{dh}{dt} = \frac{-300 + 280}{5} = -4 \text{ mph.}$$

Thus, the distance is decreasing at 4 mph.

24. (a) Using Pythagoras' theorem, we see

$$z^2 = 0.5^2 + x^2$$

so

$$z = \sqrt{0.25 + x^2}.$$

(b) We want to calculate dz/dt. Using the chain rule, we have

$$\frac{dz}{dt} = \frac{dz}{dx} \cdot \frac{dx}{dt} = \frac{2x}{2\sqrt{0.25 + x^2}}\frac{dx}{dt}.$$

Because the train is moving at 0.8 km/hr, we know that

$$\frac{dx}{dt} = 0.8 \text{ km/hr.}$$

At the moment we are interested in $z = 1$ km so

$$1^2 = 0.25 + x^2$$

giving

$$x = \sqrt{0.75} = 0.866 \text{ km.}$$

Therefore

$$\frac{dz}{dt} = \frac{2(0.866)}{2\sqrt{0.25 + 0.75}} \cdot 0.8 = 0.866 \cdot 0.8 = 0.693 \text{ km/min.}$$

(c) We want to know $d\theta/dt$, where θ is as shown in Figure 4.118. Since

$$\frac{x}{0.5} = \tan\theta$$

we know

$$\theta = \arctan\left(\frac{x}{0.5}\right),$$

so

$$\frac{d\theta}{dt} = \frac{1}{1 + (x/0.5)^2} \cdot \frac{1}{0.5}\frac{dx}{dt}.$$

We know that $dx/dt = 0.8$ km/min and, at the moment we are interested in, $x = \sqrt{0.75}$. Substituting gives

$$\frac{d\theta}{dt} = \frac{1}{1 + 0.75/0.25} \cdot \frac{1}{0.5} \cdot 0.8 = 0.4 \text{ radians/min.}$$

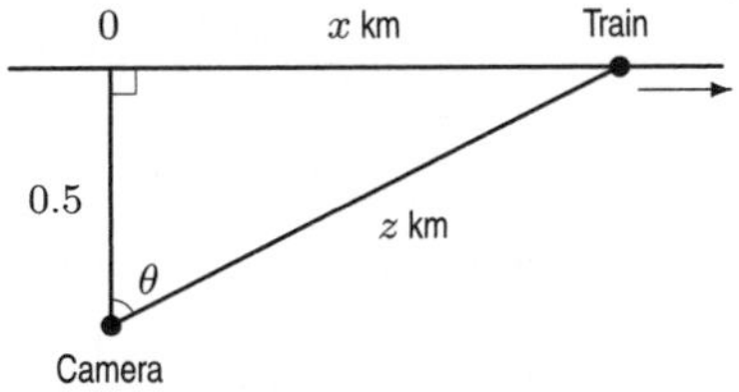

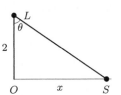

Figure 4.118

Figure 4.119

25. Using the triangle OSL in Figure 4.119, we label the distance x.

We want to calculate $dx/d\theta$. First we must find x as a function of θ. From the triangle, we see

$$\frac{x}{2} = \tan\theta \quad \text{so} \quad x = 2\tan\theta.$$

Thus,

$$\frac{dx}{d\theta} = \frac{2}{\cos^2\theta}.$$

26. From Figure 4.120, Pythagoras' Theorem shows that the ground distance, d, between the train and the point, B, vertically below the plane is given by

$$d^2 = x^2 + y^2.$$

Figure 4.121 shows that

$$z^2 = d^2 + 4^2$$

so

$$z^2 = x^2 + y^2 + 4^2.$$

We know that when $x = 1$, $dx/dt = 80$, $y = 5$, $dy/dt = 500$, and we want to know dz/dt. First, we find z:

$$z^2 = 1^2 + 5^2 + 4^2 = 42, \quad \text{so} \quad z = \sqrt{42}.$$

Differentiating $z^2 = x^2 + y^2 + 4^2$ gives

$$2z\frac{dz}{dt} = 2x\frac{dx}{dt} + 2y\frac{dy}{dt}.$$

Canceling 2s and substituting gives

$$\sqrt{42}\frac{dz}{dt} = 1(80) + 5(500)$$

$$\frac{dz}{dt} = \frac{2580}{\sqrt{42}} = 398.103 \text{ mph.}$$

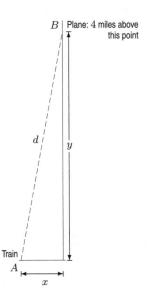

Figure 4.120: View from air

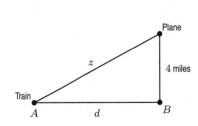

Figure 4.121: Vertical view

27. If V is the volume of the balloon and r is its radius, then

$$V = \frac{4}{3}\pi r^3.$$

We want to know the rate at which air is being blown into the balloon, which is the rate at which the volume is increasing, dV/dt. We are told that

$$\frac{dr}{dt} = 2\,\text{cm/sec} \quad \text{when} \quad r = 10\,\text{cm}.$$

Using the chain rule, we have

$$\frac{dV}{dt} = \frac{dV}{dr} \cdot \frac{dr}{dt} = 4\pi r^2 \frac{dr}{dt}.$$

Substituting gives

$$\frac{dV}{dt} = 4\pi(10)^2 2 = 800\pi = 2513.3\,\text{cm}^3/\text{sec}.$$

28. We are given that the volume is increasing at a constant rate $\frac{dV}{dt} = 400$. The radius r is related to the volume by the formula $V = \frac{4}{3}\pi r^3$. By implicit differentiation, we have

$$\frac{dV}{dt} = \frac{4}{3}\pi 3r^2 \frac{dr}{dt} = 4\pi r^2 \frac{dr}{dt}$$

Plugging in $\frac{dV}{dt} = 400$ and $r = 10$, we have

$$400 = 400\pi \frac{dr}{dt}$$

so $\frac{dr}{dt} = \frac{1}{\pi} \approx 0.32\mu\text{m/day}.$

29. Let r be the radius of the raindrop. Then its volume $V = \frac{4}{3}\pi r^3$ cm^3 and its surface area is $S = 4\pi r^2$ cm^2. It is given that

$$\frac{dV}{dt} = 2S = 8\pi r^2.$$

Furthermore,

$$\frac{dV}{dr} = 4\pi r^2,$$

so from the chain rule,

$$\frac{dV}{dt} = \frac{dV}{dr} \cdot \frac{dr}{dt} \quad \text{and thus} \quad \frac{dr}{dt} = \frac{dV/dt}{dV/dr} = 2.$$

Since dr/dt is a constant, $dr/dt = 2$, the radius is increasing at a constant rate of 2 cm/sec.

30. The volume, V, of a cone of height h and radius r is

$$V = \frac{1}{3}\pi r^2 h.$$

Since the angle of the cone is $\pi/6$, so $r = h\tan(\pi/6) = h/\sqrt{3}$

$$V = \frac{1}{3}\pi \left(\frac{h}{\sqrt{3}}\right)^2 h = \frac{1}{9}\pi h^3.$$

Differentiating gives

$$\frac{dV}{dh} = \frac{1}{3}\pi h^2.$$

To find dh/dt, use the chain rule to obtain

$$\frac{dV}{dt} = \frac{dV}{dh}\frac{dh}{dt}.$$

So,

$$\frac{dh}{dt} = \frac{dV/dt}{dV/dh} = \frac{0.1\text{meters/hour}}{\pi h^2/3} = \frac{0.3}{\pi h^2}\ \text{meters/hour}.$$

Since $r = h\tan(\pi/6) = h/\sqrt{3}$, we have

$$\frac{dr}{dt} = \frac{dh}{dt}\frac{1}{\sqrt{3}} = \frac{1}{\sqrt{3}}\frac{0.3}{\pi h^2}\ \text{meters/hour}.$$

31. (a) The end of the pipe sweeps out a circle of circumference $2\pi \cdot 20 = 40\pi$ meters in 5 minutes, so

$$\text{Speed} = \frac{40\pi}{5} = 8\pi = 25.133 \text{ meters/min}.$$

(b) The distance, h, between P and Q is given by the Law of Cosines:

$$h^2 = 50^2 + 20^2 - 2 \cdot 50 \cdot 20 \cos\theta.$$

When $\theta = \pi/2$, we have

$$h^2 = 50^2 + 20^2 - 2 \cdot 50 \cdot 20 \cdot 0.$$
$$h = \sqrt{2900} = 53.852 \text{ m}.$$

When $\theta = 0$, we have $h = 30$ m.

Since the pipe makes one rotation of 2π radians every 5 minutes, we know

$$\frac{d\theta}{dt} = \frac{2\pi}{5} \text{ radians/minute}.$$

Differentiating the relationship $h^2 = 50^2 + 20^2 - 2 \cdot 50 \cdot 20 \cos\theta$ gives

$$2h\frac{dh}{dt} = 2 \cdot 50 \cdot 20 \sin\theta \frac{d\theta}{dt}.$$

When $\theta = \pi/2$, we have

$$2\sqrt{2900}\frac{dh}{dt} = 2 \cdot 50 \cdot 20 \cdot 1 \cdot \frac{2\pi}{5}$$
$$\frac{dh}{dt} = \frac{50 \cdot 20}{\sqrt{2900}} \cdot \frac{2\pi}{5} = 23.335 \text{ meters/min}.$$

When $\theta = 0$, we have

$$2 \cdot 30\frac{dh}{dt} = 2 \cdot 50 \cdot 20 \cdot 0 \cdot \frac{2\pi}{5}$$
$$\frac{dh}{dt} = 0 \text{ meters/min}.$$

32. The volume, V, of a cone of radius r and height h is

$$V = \frac{1}{3}\pi r^2 h.$$

Figure 4.122 shows that $h/r = 10/8$, thus $r = 8h/10$, so

$$V = \frac{1}{3}\pi\left(\frac{8}{10}h\right)^2 h = \frac{64}{300}\pi h^3.$$

Differentiating V with respect to time, t, gives

$$\frac{dV}{dt} = \frac{64}{100}\pi h^2 \frac{dh}{dt}.$$

Since water is flowing into the tank at 0.1 cubic meters/min but leaking out at a rate of $0.001h^2$ cubic meters/min, we also have

$$\frac{dV}{dt} = 0.1 - 0.001h^2.$$

Equating the two expressions for dV/dt, we have

$$\frac{64}{100}\pi h^2 \frac{dh}{dt} = 0.1 - 0.001h^2.$$

Solving for dh/dt gives

$$\frac{dh}{dt} = \frac{0.1(100 - h^2)}{64\pi h^2}.$$

We conclude that if $h < 10$ then $dh/dt > 0$. Therefore, the depth increases until $h = 10$ when the tank is full. At that point $dh/dt = 0$, so the water level does not continue to rise and the tank does not overflow.

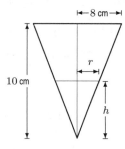

Figure 4.122

33. (a) Since the elevator is descending at 30 ft/sec, its height from the ground is given by $h(t) = 300 - 30t$,   for $0 \le t \le 10$.
    (b) From the triangle in the figure,

    $$\tan\theta = \frac{h(t) - 100}{150} = \frac{300 - 30t - 100}{150} = \frac{200 - 30t}{150}.$$

    Therefore

    $$\theta = \arctan\left(\frac{200 - 30t}{150}\right)$$

    and

    $$\frac{d\theta}{dt} = \frac{1}{1 + \left(\frac{200 - 30t}{150}\right)^2} \cdot \left(\frac{-30}{150}\right) = -\frac{1}{5}\left(\frac{150^2}{150^2 + (200 - 30t)^2}\right).$$

    Notice that $\frac{d\theta}{dt}$ is always negative, which is reasonable since θ decreases as the elevator descends.
    (c) If we want to know when θ changes (decreases) the fastest, we want to find out when $d\theta/dt$ has the largest magnitude. This will occur when the denominator, $150^2 + (200 - 30t)^2$, in the expression for $d\theta/dt$ is the smallest, or when $200 - 30t = 0$. This occurs when $t = \frac{200}{30}$ seconds, and so $h(\frac{200}{30}) = 100$ feet, i.e., when the elevator is at the level of the observer.

34. (a) We differentiate $a^2(t) + b^2(t) = c$ with respect to t to find

    $$\frac{d}{dt}(a^2(t) + b^2(t)) = \frac{d}{dt}c,$$

    or

    $$2a(t) \cdot a'(t) - 2b(t) \cdot b'(t) = 0,$$

    giving

    $$a(t) \cdot a'(t) = -b(t) \cdot b'(t).$$

    (b) (i) If Angela likes Brian, then $a(t) > 0$, so $b'(t) < 0$. This means that $b(t)$ is decreasing, so Brian's affection decreases when Angela likes him.
        (ii) If Angela dislikes Brian, then $a(t) < 0$, so $b'(t) > 0$. This means that $b(t)$ is increasing, so Brian's affection increases when Angela dislikes him.
    (c) Substituting $b'(t) = -a(t)$ into $a(t) \cdot a'(t) = -b(t) \cdot b'(t)$ gives

    $$a(t) \cdot a'(t) = -b(t) \cdot b'(t) = -b(t)(-a(t)),$$

    so

    $$a'(t) = b(t).$$

    (i) If Brian likes Angela, then $b(t) > 0$, so $a'(t) > 0$. This means that $a(t)$ is increasing, so Angela's affection increases when Brian likes her.
    (ii) If Brian dislikes Angela, then $b(t) < 0$, so $a'(t) < 0$. This means that $a(t)$ is decreasing, so Angela's affection decreases when Brian dislikes her.
    (d) When $t = 0$, they both like each other. This means that Angela's affection increases, while Brian's decreases. Eventually $b(t) < 0$, when he dislikes her.

35. (a) We have either $x(0) = 50$ and $y(0) = 40$, or $y(0) = 50$ and $x(0) = 40$. In the first case $c = x^2(0) - y^2(0) = 50^2 - 40^2 = 900$ whereas in the second $c = x^2(0) - y^2(0) = 40^2 - 50^2 = -900$. But $c > 0$, so $c = 900$ and we have $x^2(t) - y^2(t) = 900$.

(b) Because $x^2(t) - y^2(t) = 900$ we have $x^2(3) - y^2(3) = 900$ so $x^2(3) = y^2(3) + 900 = 16^2 + 900 = 1156$, giving $x(3) = \sqrt{1156} = 34$. After 3 hours, y has 16 ships, and x has 34 ships.

(c) The condition $y(T) = 0$ means that there are no more ships on that side, so the battle ends at time T hours.

(d) We have $x^2(T) - y^2(T) = 900$ with $y(T) = 0$ so $x(T) = 30$ ships.

(e) The rate per hour at which y loses ships is $y'(t)$, so $y'(t) = kx$. Because y is decreasing, k is negative.

(f) We differentiate $x^2(t) - y^2(t) = 900$ with respect to t to find

$$\frac{d}{dt}(x^2(t) - y^2(t)) = \frac{d}{dt}900,$$

or

$$2x(t) \cdot x'(t) - 2y(t) \cdot y'(t) = 0,$$

giving

$$x'(t) = \frac{y(t)}{x(t)}y'(t).$$

But $y'(t) = kx(t)$ so

$$x'(t) = \frac{y(t)}{x(t)}kx(t) = ky(t).$$

(g) From part (b), we know that when $t = 3$ we have $x(3) = 34$, $y(3) = 16$; we are now given that $x'(3) = 32$. But $x'(t) = ky(t)$ so $32 = ky(3) = 16k$ giving $k = 2$. In this case $y'(3) = kx(3) = 2 \cdot 34 = 68$ ships/hour.

Solutions for Section 4.7

Exercises

1. Since $f'(a) > 0$ and $g'(a) < 0$, l'Hopital's rule tells us that

$$\lim_{x \to a} \frac{f(x)}{g(x)} = \frac{f'(a)}{g'(a)} < 0.$$

2. Since $f'(a) < 0$ and $g'(a) < 0$, l'Hopital's rule tells us that

$$\lim_{x \to a} \frac{f(x)}{g(x)} = \frac{f'(a)}{g'(a)} > 0.$$

3. Here $f(a) = g(a) = f'(a) = g'(a) = 0$, and $f''(a) > 0$ and $g''(a) < 0$.

$$\lim_{x \to a} \frac{f(x)}{g(x)} = \lim_{x \to a} \frac{f'(x)}{g'(x)} = \frac{f''(a)}{g''(a)} < 0$$

4. Note that $f(0) = g(0) = 0$ and $f'(0) = g'(0)$. Since $x = 0$ looks like a point of inflection for each curve, $f''(0) = g''(0) = 0$. Therefore, applying l'Hopital's rule successively gives us

$$\lim_{x \to 0} \frac{f(x)}{g(x)} = \lim_{x \to 0} \frac{f'(x)}{g'(x)} = \lim_{x \to 0} \frac{f''(x)}{g''(x)} = \lim_{x \to 0} \frac{f'''(x)}{g'''(x)}.$$

Now notice how the concavity of f changes: for $x < 0$, it is concave up, so $f''(x) > 0$, and for $x > 0$ it is concave down, so $f''(x) < 0$. Thus $f''(x)$ is a decreasing function at 0 and so $f'''(0)$ is negative. Similarly, for $x < 0$, we see g is concave down and for $x > 0$ it is concave up, so $g''(x)$ is increasing at 0 and so $g'''(0)$ is positive. Consequently,

$$\lim_{x \to 0} \frac{f(x)}{g(x)} = \lim_{x \to 0} \frac{f'''(0)}{g'''(0)} < 0.$$

5. The denominator approaches zero as x goes to zero and the numerator goes to zero even faster, so you should expect that the limit to be 0. You can check this by substituting several values of x close to zero. Alternatively, using l'Hopital's rule, we have

$$\lim_{x \to 0} \frac{x^2}{\sin x} = \lim_{x \to 0} \frac{2x}{\cos x} = 0.$$

6. The numerator goes to zero faster than the denominator, so you should expect the limit to be zero. Using l'Hopital's rule, we have

$$\lim_{x \to 0} \frac{\sin^2 x}{x} = \lim_{x \to 0} \frac{2 \sin x \cos x}{1} = 0.$$

7. The denominator goes to zero more slowly than x does, so the numerator goes to zero faster than the denominator, so you should expect the limit to be zero. With l'Hopital's rule,

$$\lim_{x \to 0} \frac{\sin x}{x^{1/3}} = \lim_{x \to 0} \frac{\cos x}{\frac{1}{3}x^{-2/3}} = \lim_{x \to 0} 3x^{2/3} \cos x = 0.$$

8. The denominator goes to zero more slowly than x. Therefore, you should expect that the limit to be 0. Using l'Hopital's rule,

$$\lim_{x \to 0} \frac{x}{(\sin x)^{1/3}} = \lim_{x \to 0} \frac{1}{\frac{1}{3}(\sin x)^{-2/3} \cos x} = \lim_{x \to 0} \frac{3(\sin x)^{2/3}}{\cos x} = 0,$$

since $\sin 0 = 0$ and $\cos 0 = 1$.

9. The larger power dominates. Using l'Hopital's rule

$$\lim_{x \to \infty} \frac{x^5}{0.1x^7} = \lim_{x \to \infty} \frac{5x^4}{0.7x^6} = \lim_{x \to \infty} \frac{20x^3}{4.2x^5}$$
$$= \lim_{x \to \infty} \frac{60x^2}{21x^4} = \lim_{x \to \infty} \frac{120x}{84x^3} = \lim_{x \to \infty} \frac{120}{252x^2} = 0$$

so $0.1x^7$ dominates.

10. We apply l'Hopital's rule twice to the ratio $50x^2/0.01x^3$:

$$\lim_{x \to \infty} \frac{50x^2}{0.01x^3} = \lim_{x \to \infty} \frac{100x}{0.03x^2} = \lim_{x \to \infty} \frac{100}{0.06x} = 0.$$

Since the limit is 0, we see that $0.01x^3$ is much larger than $50x^2$ as $x \to \infty$.

11. The power function dominates. Using l'Hopital's rule

$$\lim_{x \to \infty} \frac{\ln(x + 3)}{x^{0.2}} = \lim_{x \to \infty} \frac{\frac{1}{(x+3)}}{0.2x^{-0.8}} = \lim_{x \to \infty} \frac{x^{0.8}}{0.2(x + 3)}.$$

Using l'Hopital's rule again gives

$$\lim_{x \to \infty} \frac{x^{0.8}}{0.2(x + 3)} = \lim_{x \to \infty} \frac{0.8x^{-0.2}}{0.2} = 0,$$

so $x^{0.2}$ dominates.

12. The exponential dominates. After 10 applications of l'Hopital's rule

$$\lim_{x \to \infty} \frac{x^{10}}{e^{0.1x}} = \lim_{x \to \infty} \frac{10x^9}{0.1e^{0.1x}} = \cdots = \lim_{x \to \infty} \frac{10!}{(0.1)^{10}e^{0.1x}} = 0.$$

so $e^{0.1x}$ dominates.

13. Let $f(x) = \ln x$ and $g(x) = 1/x$ so $f'(x) = 1/x$ and $g'(x) = -1/x^2$ and

$$\lim_{x \to 0^+} \frac{\ln x}{1/x} = \lim_{x \to 0^+} \frac{1/x}{-1/x^2} = \lim_{x \to 0^+} \frac{x}{-1} = 0.$$

Problems

14. We want to find $\lim\limits_{x \to \infty} f(x)$, which we do by three applications of l'Hopital's rule:

$$\lim_{x \to \infty} \frac{2x^3 + 5x^2}{3x^3 - 1} = \lim_{x \to \infty} \frac{6x^2 + 10x}{9x^2} = \lim_{x \to \infty} \frac{12x + 10}{18x} = \lim_{x \to \infty} \frac{12}{18} = \frac{2}{3}.$$

So the line $y = 2/3$ is the horizontal asymptote.

15. Observe that both $f(4)$ and $g(4)$ are zero. Also, $f'(4) = 1.4$ and $g'(4) = -0.7$, so by l'Hopital's rule,

$$\lim_{x \to 4} \frac{f(x)}{g(x)} = \frac{f'(4)}{g'(4)} = \frac{1.4}{-0.7} = -2.$$

16. (a) Since $f'(x) = 3\cos(3x)$, we have $f'(0) = 3$.
  (b) Since $g'(x) = 5$, we have $g'(0) = 5$.
  (c) Since $f(x) = \sin 3x$ and $g(x) = 5x$ are both 0 at $x = 0$, we apply l'Hopital's rule to obtain

$$\lim_{x \to 0} \frac{\sin(3x)}{5x} = \frac{f'(0)}{g'(0)} = \frac{3}{5}.$$

17. Let $f(x) = \ln x$ and $g(x) = x^2 - 1$, so $f(1) = 0$ and $g(1) = 0$ and l'Hopital's rule can be used. To apply l'Hopital's rule, we first find $f'(x) = 1/x$ and $g'(x) = 2x$, then

$$\lim_{x \to 1} \frac{\ln x}{x^2 - 1} = \lim_{x \to 1} \frac{1/x}{2x} = \lim_{x \to 1} \frac{1}{2x^2} = \frac{1}{2}.$$

18. Let $f(t) = \sin^2 t$ and $g(t) = t - \pi$, then $f(\pi) = 0$ and $g(\pi) = 0$ but $f'(t) = 2\sin t \cos t$ and $g'(t) = 1$, so $f'(\pi) = 0$ and $g'(\pi) = 1$. L'Hopital's rule can be used, giving

$$\lim_{t \to \pi} \frac{\sin^2 t}{t - \pi} = \frac{0}{1} = 0.$$

19. If $f(x) = \sinh(2x)$ and $g(x) = x$, then $f(0) = g(0) = 0$, so we use l'Hopital's Rule:

$$\lim_{x \to 0} \frac{\sinh 2x}{x} = \lim_{x \to 0} \frac{2\cosh 2x}{1} = 2.$$

20. If $f(x) = 1 - \cosh(3x)$ and $g(x) = x$, then $f(0) = g(0) = 0$, so we use l'Hopital's Rule:

$$\lim_{x \to 0} \frac{1 - \cosh 3x}{x} = \lim_{x \to 0} \frac{-3\sinh 3x}{1} = 0.$$

21. To get this expression in a form in which l'Hopital's rule applies, we rewrite it as a fraction:

$$x^a \ln x = \frac{\ln x}{x^{-a}}.$$

Letting $f(x) = \ln x$ and $g(x) = x^{-a}$, we have

$$\lim_{x \to 0^+} f(x) = \lim_{x \to 0^+} \ln x = -\infty, \quad \text{and} \quad \lim_{x \to 0^+} g(x) = \lim_{x \to 0^+} \frac{1}{x^a} = \infty.$$

So l'Hopital's rule can be used. To apply l'Hopital's rule we differentiate to get $f'(x) = 1/x$ and $g'(x) = -ax^{-a-1}$. Then

$$\lim_{x \to 0^+} x^a \ln x = \lim_{x \to 0^+} \frac{\ln x}{x^{-a}}$$
$$= \lim_{x \to 0^+} \frac{1/x}{-ax^{-a-1}}$$
$$= -\frac{1}{a} \lim_{x \to 0^+} x^a$$
$$= 0.$$

22. Since $\cos 0 = 1$, we have $\cos^{-1}(1) = 0$ and $\lim\limits_{x \to 1^{-1}} \cos^{-1} x = 0$. Therefore, both $\cos^{-1} x$ and $(x - 1)$ tend to 0 as $x \to 1^-$, so l'Hopital's rule can be applied. Let $f(x) = \cos^{-1} x$ and $g(x) = x - 1$, and differentiate to get $f'(x) = -1/\sqrt{1 - x^2}$ and $g'(x) = 1$. Applying l'Hopital's rule gives

$$\lim_{x \to 1^-} \frac{\cos^{-1} x}{x - 1} = \lim_{x \to 1^-} \frac{-1/\sqrt{1 - x^2}}{1}$$
$$= \lim_{x \to 1^-} \frac{-1}{\sqrt{1 - x^2}}.$$

However, $\sqrt{1 - x^2} \to 0$ as $x \to 1^-$, so the limit does not exist.

23. Let $f(t) = 3 \sin t - \sin 3t$ and $g(t) = 3 \tan t - \tan 3t$, then $f(0) = 0$ and $g(0) = 0$. Similarly,

$$f'(t) = 3 \cos t - 3 \cos 3t \qquad\qquad f'(0) = 0$$
$$f''(t) = -3 \sin t + 9 \sin 3t \qquad\qquad f''(0) = 0$$
$$f'''(t) = -3 \cos t + 27 \cos 3t \qquad\qquad f'''(0) = 24$$
$$g'(t) = 3\sec^2 t - 3\sec^2 3t \qquad\qquad g'(0) = 0$$
$$g''(t) = 6 \sec^2 t \tan t - 18 \sec^2 3t \tan 3t \qquad\qquad g''(0) = 0$$
$$g'''(t) = -54 \sec^4 3t - 108 \sec^2 37 \tan^2 3t + 6 \sec^4 t + 12 \sec^2 t \tan^2 t \quad g'''(0) = -48$$

Since the first and second derivatives of f and g are both 0 at $t = 0$, we have to go as far as the third derivative to use l'Hopital's rule. Applying l'Hopital's rule gives

$$\lim_{t \to 0^+} \frac{3 \sin t - \sin 3t}{3 \tan t - \tan 3t} = \lim_{t \to 0^+} \frac{f'(t)}{g'(t)} = \lim_{t \to 0^+} \frac{f''(t)}{g''(t)} = \lim_{t \to 0^+} \frac{f'''(t)}{g'''(t)} = \frac{24}{-48} = -\frac{1}{2}.$$

24. To get this expression in a form in which l'Hopital's rule applies, we combine the fractions:

$$\frac{1}{x} - \frac{1}{\sin x} = \frac{\sin x - x}{x \sin x}.$$

Letting $f(x) = \sin x - x$ and $g(x) = x \sin x$, we have $f(0) = 0$ and $g(0) = 0$ so l'Hopital's rule can be used. Differentiating gives $f'(x) = \cos x - 1$ and $g'(x) = x \cos x + \sin x$, so $f'(0) = 0$ and $g'(0) = 0$, so $f'(0)/g'(0)$ is undefined. Therefore, to apply l'Hopital's rule we differentiate again to obtain $f''(x) = -\sin x$ and $g''(x) = 2 \cos x - x \sin x$, for which $f''(0) = 0$ and $g''(0) = 2 \neq 0$. Then

$$\lim_{x \to 0} \left(\frac{1}{x} - \frac{1}{\sin x} \right) = \lim_{x \to 0} \left(\frac{\sin x - x}{x \sin x} \right)$$
$$= \lim_{x \to 0} \left(\frac{\cos x - 1}{x \cos x + \sin x} \right)$$
$$= \lim_{x \to 0} \left(\frac{-\sin x}{2 \cos x - x \sin x} \right)$$
$$= \frac{0}{2} = 0.$$

25. Let $y = (1 + \sin 3/x)^x$. Taking logs gives

$$\ln y = x \ln \left(1 + \sin \frac{3}{x} \right).$$

To use l'Hopital's rule, we rewrite $\ln y$ as a fraction:

$$\lim_{x \to \infty} \ln y = \lim_{x \to \infty} x \ln \left(1 + \sin \left(\frac{3}{x} \right) \right)$$
$$= \lim_{x \to \infty} \frac{\ln(1 + \sin(3/x))}{1/x}.$$

Let $f(x) = \ln(1 + \sin(3/x))$ and $g(x) = 1/x$ then

$$f'(x) = \frac{\cos(3/x)(-3/x^2)}{(1 + \sin(3/x))} \quad \text{and} \quad g'(x) = -\frac{1}{x^2}.$$

Now apply l'Hopital's rule to get

$$\lim_{x \to \infty} \ln y = \lim_{x \to \infty} \frac{f(x)}{g(x)}$$

$$= \lim_{x \to \infty} \frac{f'(x)}{g'(x)}$$

$$= \lim_{x \to \infty} \frac{\cos(3/x)(-3/x^2)/(1 + \sin(3/x))}{-1/x^2}$$

$$= \lim_{x \to \infty} \frac{3 \cos(3/x)}{1 + \sin(3/x)} = \frac{3 \cos 0}{1 + \sin 0}$$

$$= 3.$$

Since $\lim_{x \to \infty} \ln y = 3$, we have

$$\lim_{x \to \infty} y = e^3.$$

Thus,

$$\lim_{x \to \infty} \left(1 + \sin \frac{3}{x}\right)^x = e^3.$$

26. Let $f(x) = \sin(2x)$ and $g(x) = x$. Observe that $f(1) = \sin 2 \neq 0$ and $g(1) = 1 \neq 0$. Therefore l'Hopital's rule does not apply. However,

$$\lim_{x \to 1} \frac{\sin 2x}{x} = \frac{\sin 2}{1} = 0.909297.$$

27. Let $f(x) = \cos x$ and $g(x) = x$. Observe that since $f(0) = 1$, l'Hopital's rule does not apply. But since $g(0) = 0$,

$$\lim_{x \to 0} \frac{\cos x}{x} \quad \text{does not exist.}$$

28. Let $f(x) = e^{-x}$ and $g(x) = \sin x$. Observe that as x increases, $f(x)$ approaches 0 but $g(x)$ oscillates between -1 and 1. Since $g(x)$ does not approach 0 in the limit, l'Hopital's rule does not apply. Because $g(x)$ is in the denominator and oscillates through 0 forever, the limit does not exist.

29. (a) Since $a + b = 1$, as $p \to 0$, we have

$$\ln(ax^p + by^p) \to \ln(ax^0 + by^0) = \ln(a + b) = \ln 1 = 0.$$

Thus, the limit is of the form $0/0$, so l'Hopital's rule applies. Since $d(x^p)/dp = (\ln x)x^p$,

$$\frac{d \ln(ax^p + by^p)}{dp} = \frac{a(\ln x)x^p + b(\ln y)y^p}{ax^p + by^p}$$

and $dp/dp = 1$ we have

$$\lim_{p \to 0} \frac{\ln(ax^p + by^p)}{p} = \lim_{p \to 0} \frac{a(\ln x)x^p + b(\ln y)y^p}{(ax^p + by^p) \cdot 1} = \frac{a(\ln x)x^0 + b(\ln y)y^0}{ax^0 + by^0} = \frac{a(\ln x) + b(\ln y)}{a + b} = a \ln x + b \ln y.$$

(b) Because

$$(ax^p + by^p)^{1/p} = e^{(\ln(ax^p + by^p))/p}$$

and the exponential function is continuous, using part (a), we have

$$\lim_{p \to 0} (ax^p + by^p)^{1/p} = \lim_{p \to 0} e^{(\ln(ax^p + by^p))/p} = e^{\lim_{p \to 0} (\ln(ax^p + by^p))/p} = e^{a \ln x + b \ln y} = x^a y^b.$$

30. (a) Let $f(x) = \pi - 2 \tan^{-1} x$ and $g(x) = e^{-x}$, so $\lim_{x \to \infty} g(x) = 0$. Since $\lim_{x \to \pi/2} \tan x = \infty$, we have $\lim_{x \to \infty} \tan^{-1} x = \pi/2$ so

$$\lim_{x \to \infty} (\pi - 2 \tan^{-1} x) = \pi - 2\frac{\pi}{2} = 0$$

To apply l'Hopital's rule we differentiate to get

$$f'(x) = \frac{-2}{1 + x^2} \quad \text{and} \quad g'(x) = -e^{-x}$$

so $\lim_{x \to \infty} f'(x) = 0$ and $\lim_{x \to \infty} g'(x) = 0$. Therefore, to apply l'Hopital's rule we must differentiate again, getting

$$f''(x) = \frac{4x}{(1 + x^2)^2} \quad \text{and} \quad g''(x) = e^{-x}$$

and find $\lim_{x\to\infty} f''(x) = 0$ and $\lim_{x\to\infty} g''(x) = 0$. No matter how many times we repeat this process we end up with the $\lim_{x\to\infty} f^{(n)}(x) = 0$ and $\lim_{x\to\infty} g^{(n)}(x) = 0$ so l'Hopital's rule does not give a limit.

(b) Figure 4.123 shows $\lim_{t\to\infty} \dfrac{\pi - 2\tan^{-1} x}{e^{-x}}$ does not exist.

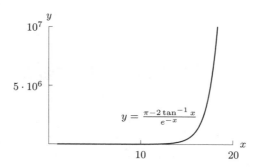

Figure 4.123

31. Let $n = 1/x$, so $n \to \infty$ as $x \to 0^+$. Thus

$$\lim_{x\to 0^+} (1 + x)^{1/x} = \lim_{n\to\infty} \left(1 + \frac{1}{n}\right)^n = e.$$

32. Let $k = n/2$, so $k \to \infty$ as $n \to \infty$. Thus,

$$\lim_{n\to\infty} \left(1 + \frac{2}{n}\right)^n = \lim_{k\to\infty} \left(1 + \frac{1}{k}\right)^{2k} = \lim_{k\to\infty} \left(\left(1 + \frac{1}{k}\right)^k\right)^2 = e^2.$$

33. Let $n = 1/(kx)$, so $n \to \infty$ as $x \to 0^+$. Thus

$$\lim_{x\to 0^+} (1 + kx)^{t/x} = \lim_{n\to\infty} \left(1 + \frac{1}{n}\right)^{nkt} = \lim_{n\to\infty} \left(\left(1 + \frac{1}{n}\right)^n\right)^{kt} = e^{kt}.$$

34. Let

$$y = \left(1 - \frac{1}{n}\right)^n.$$

Then

$$\ln y = \ln \left(1 - \frac{1}{n}\right)^n = n \ln \left(1 - \frac{1}{n}\right) = \frac{\ln(1 - 1/n)}{1/n}.$$

As $n \to \infty$, both the numerator and the denominator of the last fraction tend to 0. Thus, applying L'Hopital's rule, we have

$$\lim_{n\to\infty} \frac{\ln(1 - 1/n)}{1/n} = \lim_{n\to\infty} \frac{\frac{1}{1-1/n} \cdot \frac{1}{n^2}}{-1/n^2} = \lim_{n\to\infty} -\frac{1}{1 - 1/n} = -1.$$

Thus,

$$\lim_{n\to\infty} \ln y = -1$$

$$\lim_{n\to\infty} y = e^{-1},$$

so

$$\lim_{n\to\infty} \left(1 - \frac{1}{n}\right) = e^{-1}.$$

35. Let $k = n/\lambda$, so $k \to \infty$ as $n \to \infty$. Thus

$$\lim_{n\to\infty} \left(1 - \frac{\lambda}{n}\right)^n = \lim_{k\to\infty} \left(1 - \frac{1}{k}\right)^{k\lambda} = \lim_{k\to\infty} \left(\left(1 - \frac{1}{k}\right)^k\right)^\lambda = (e^{-1})^\lambda = e^{-\lambda}.$$

36. This limit is of the form 0^0 so we apply l'Hopital's rule to

$$\ln f(t) = \frac{\ln\left((3^t + 5^t)/2\right)}{t}.$$

We have

$$\lim_{t\to-\infty} \ln f(t) = \lim_{t\to-\infty} \frac{\left((\ln 3)3^t + (\ln 5)5^t\right)/\left(3^t + 5^t\right)}{1}$$

$$= \lim_{t\to-\infty} \frac{(\ln 3)3^t + (\ln 5)5^t}{3^t + 5^t}$$

$$= \lim_{t\to-\infty} \frac{\ln 3 + (\ln 5)(5/3)^t}{1 + (5/3)^t}$$

$$= \frac{\ln 3 + 0}{1 + 0} = \ln 3.$$

Thus

$$\lim_{t\to-\infty} f(t) = \lim_{t\to-\infty} e^{\ln f(t)} = e^{\lim_{t\to-\infty} \ln f(t)} = e^{\ln 3} = 3.$$

37. This limit is of the form ∞^0 so we apply l'Hopital's rule to

$$\ln f(t) = \frac{\ln\left((3^t + 5^t)/2\right)}{t}.$$

We have

$$\lim_{t\to+\infty} \ln f(t) = \lim_{t\to+\infty} \frac{\left((\ln 3)3^t + (\ln 5)5^t\right)/\left(3^t + 5^t\right)}{1}$$

$$= \lim_{t\to+\infty} \frac{(\ln 3)3^t + (\ln 5)5^t}{3^t + 5^t}$$

$$= \lim_{t\to+\infty} \frac{(\ln 3)(3/5)^t + \ln 5}{(3/5)^t + 1}$$

$$= \lim_{t\to+\infty} \frac{0 + \ln 5}{0 + 1} = \ln 5.$$

Thus

$$\lim_{t\to-\infty} f(t) = \lim_{t\to-\infty} e^{\ln f(t)} = e^{\lim_{t\to-\infty} \ln f(t)} = e^{\ln 5} = 5.$$

38. This limit is of the form 1^∞ so we apply l'Hopital's rule to

$$\ln f(t) = \frac{\ln\left((3^t + 5^t)/2\right)}{t}.$$

We have

$$\lim_{t\to 0} \ln f(t) = \lim_{t\to 0} \frac{\left((\ln 3)3^t + (\ln 5)5^t\right)/\left(3^t + 5^t\right)}{1}$$

$$= \lim_{t\to 0} \frac{(\ln 3)3^t + (\ln 5)5^t}{3^t + 5^t}$$

$$= \frac{\ln 3 + \ln 5}{1 + 1} = \frac{\ln 15}{2}.$$

Thus

$$\lim_{t\to-\infty} f(t) = \lim_{t\to-\infty} e^{\ln f(t)} = e^{\lim_{t\to-\infty} \ln f(t)} = e^{(\ln 15)/2} = \sqrt{15}.$$

39. (a) The graphs in Figure 4.124 are almost indistinguishable.

(b) Since $\lim_{a \to 1} \ln\left(\dfrac{x-a}{x-1}\right) = 0$ and $\lim_{a \to 1}(a-1) = 0$ we can use l'Hopital's rule. The variable is a, so we differentiate with respect to a.

$$\lim_{a \to 1} \frac{\ln(\frac{x-a}{x-1})}{a-1} = \lim_{a \to 1} \frac{\frac{d}{da}\ln(\frac{x-a}{x-1})}{\frac{d}{da}(a-1)} = \lim_{a \to 1} \frac{\frac{x-1}{x-a}\frac{d}{da}(\frac{x-a}{x-1})}{1} = \lim_{a \to 1} \frac{\frac{x-1}{x-a}\frac{-1}{x-1}}{1} = \frac{1}{1-x}.$$

(c) Part (b) tells us that as a gets closer and closer to 1, the function $\dfrac{\ln((x-a)/(x-1))}{a-1}$ gets closer and closer to $\dfrac{1}{1-x}$, which is what part (a) is saying graphically.

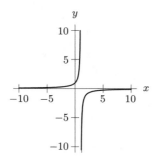

Figure 4.124

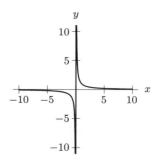

Figure 4.125

40. (a) The graphs in Figure 4.125 are almost indistinguishable.

(b) Since $\lim_{a \to 0} \ln\left(\dfrac{x+a}{x-a}\right) = 0$ and $\lim_{a \to 1} a = 0$ we can use l'Hopital's rule. The variable is a, so we differentiate with respect to a.

$$\lim_{a \to 0} \frac{\ln(\frac{x+a}{x-a})}{2a} = \lim_{a \to 0} \frac{\frac{d}{da}\ln(\frac{x+a}{x-a})}{\frac{d}{da}(2a)} = \lim_{a \to 0} \frac{\frac{x-a}{x+a}\frac{d}{da}(\frac{x+a}{x-a})}{2} = \lim_{a \to 0} \frac{\frac{x-a}{x+a}\frac{2x}{(x-a)^2}}{2} = \frac{1}{x}.$$

(c) Part (b) tells us that as a gets closer and closer to 0, the function $\dfrac{\ln((x+a)/(x-a))}{2a}$ gets closer and closer to $\dfrac{1}{x}$, which is what part (a) is saying graphically.

41. (a) Let $f(r) = x^r - 1$ and $g(r) = r$, where we are to compute $\lim_{r \to 0} f(r)/g(r)$. Since $f(0) = g(0) = 0$, the limit is of the form $0/0$ and l'Hopital's rule applies. Then $f'(r) = (\ln x)x^r$ and $g'(r) = 1$. Thus

$$h_0(x) = \lim_{r \to 0} \frac{x^r - 1}{r} = \frac{(\ln x)x^0}{1} = \ln x.$$

(b) See Figure 4.126.

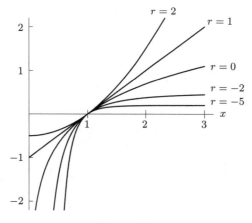

Figure 4.126

Solutions for Section 4.8

Exercises

1. Between times $t = 0$ and $t = 1$, x goes at a constant rate from 0 to 1 and y goes at a constant rate from 1 to 0. So the particle moves in a straight line from $(0, 1)$ to $(1, 0)$. Similarly, between times $t = 1$ and $t = 2$, it goes in a straight line to $(0, -1)$, then to $(-1, 0)$, then back to $(0, 1)$. So it traces out the diamond shown in Figure 4.127.

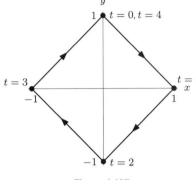

Figure 4.127

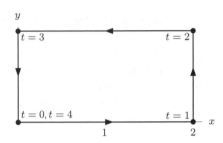

Figure 4.128

2. This is like Example 2, except that the x-coordinate goes all the way to 2 and back. So the particle traces out the rectangle shown in Figure 4.128.

3. As the x-coordinate goes at a constant rate from 2 to 0, the y-coordinate goes from 0 to 1, then down to -1, then back to 0. So the particle zigs and zags from $(2, 0)$ to $(1.5, 1)$ to $(1, 0)$ to $(.5, -1)$ to $(0, 0)$. Then it zigs and zags back again, forming the shape in Figure 4.129.

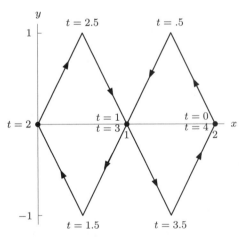

Figure 4.129

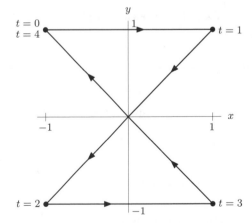

Figure 4.130

4. Between times $t = 0$ and $t = 1$, x goes from -1 to 1, while y stays fixed at 1. So the particle goes in a straight line from $(-1, 1)$ to $(1, 1)$. Then both the x- and y-coordinates decrease at a constant rate from 1 to -1. So the particle goes in a straight line from $(1, 1)$ to $(-1, -1)$. Then it moves across to $(1, -1)$, then back diagonally to $(-1, 1)$. See Figure 4.130.

5. For $0 \leq t \leq \frac{\pi}{2}$, we have $x = \sin t$ increasing and $y = \cos t$ decreasing, so the motion is clockwise for $0 \leq t \leq \frac{\pi}{2}$. Similarly, we see that the motion is clockwise for the time intervals $\frac{\pi}{2} \leq t \leq \pi, \pi \leq t \leq \frac{3\pi}{2}$, and $\frac{3\pi}{2} \leq t \leq 2\pi$.

6. The particle moves clockwise: For $0 \leq t \leq \frac{\pi}{2}$, we have $x = \cos t$ decreasing and $y = -\sin t$ decreasing. Similarly, for the time intervals $\frac{\pi}{2} \leq t \leq \pi, \pi \leq t \leq \frac{3\pi}{2}$, and $\frac{3\pi}{2} \leq t \leq 2\pi$, we see that the particle moves clockwise.

7. Let $f(t) = t^2$. The particle is moving clockwise when $f(t)$ is decreasing, that is, when $f'(t) = 2t < 0$, so when $t < 0$. The particle is moving counterclockwise when $f'(t) = 2t > 0$, so when $t > 0$.

8. Let $f(t) = t^3 - t$. The particle is moving clockwise when $f(t)$ is decreasing, that is, when $f'(t) = 3t^2 - 1 < 0$, and counterclockwise when $f'(t) = 3t^2 - 1 > 0$. That is, it moves clockwise when $-\sqrt{\frac{1}{3}} < t < \sqrt{\frac{1}{3}}$, between $(\cos((-\sqrt{\frac{1}{3}})^3 + \sqrt{\frac{1}{3}}), \sin((-\sqrt{\frac{1}{3}})^3 + \sqrt{\frac{1}{3}}))$ and $(\cos((\sqrt{\frac{1}{3}})^3 - \sqrt{\frac{1}{3}}), \sin((\sqrt{\frac{1}{3}})^3 - \sqrt{\frac{1}{3}}))$, and counterclockwise when $t < -\sqrt{\frac{1}{3}}$ or $t > \sqrt{\frac{1}{3}}$.

9. Let $f(t) = \ln t$. Then $f'(t) = \frac{1}{t}$. The particle is moving counterclockwise when $f'(t) > 0$, that is, when $t > 0$. Any other time, when $t \leq 0$, the position is not defined.

10. Let $f(t) = \cos t$. Then $f'(t) = -\sin t$. The particle is moving clockwise when $f'(t) < 0$, or $-\sin t < 0$, that is, when

$$2k\pi < t < (2k + 1)\pi,$$

where k is an integer. The particle is otherwise moving counterclockwise, that is, when

$$(2k - 1)\pi < t < 2k\pi,$$

where k is an integer. Actually, the particle does not fully trace out a circle. The range of $f(t)$ is $[-1, 1]$ so the particle oscillates between the points $(\cos(-1), \sin(-1))$ and $(\cos 1, \sin 1)$.

11. We have $dx/dt = 2t$ and $dy/dt = 3t^2$. Therefore, the speed of the particle is

$$v = \sqrt{\left(\frac{dx}{dt}\right)^2 + \left(\frac{dy}{dt}\right)^2} = \sqrt{((2t)^2 + (3t^2)^2)} = |t| \cdot \sqrt{(4 + 9t^2)}.$$

The particle comes to a complete stop when its speed is 0, that is, if $t\sqrt{4 + 9t^2} = 0$, and so when $t = 0$.

12. We have $dx/dt = -2t \sin(t^2)$ and $dy/dt = 2t \cos(t^2)$. Therefore, the speed of the particle is given by

$$v = \sqrt{(-2t \sin(t^2))^2 + (2t \cos(t^2))^2}$$
$$= \sqrt{4t^2 (\sin(t^2))^2 + 4t^2 (\cos(t^2))^2}$$
$$= 2|t| \sqrt{\sin^2(t^2) + \cos^2(t^2)}$$
$$= 2|t|.$$

The particle comes to a complete stop when speed is 0, that is, if $2|t| = 0$, and so when $t = 0$.

13. We have

$$\frac{dx}{dt} = -2 \sin 2t, \quad \frac{dy}{dt} = \cos t.$$

The speed is

$$v = \sqrt{4 \sin^2(2t) + \cos^2 t}.$$

Thus, $v = 0$ when $\sin(2t) = \cos t = 0$, and so the particle stops when $t = \pm\pi/2, \pm 3\pi/2, \ldots$ or $t = (2n + 1)\frac{\pi}{2}$, for any integer n.

14. We have

$$\frac{dx}{dt} = (2t - 2), \quad \frac{dy}{dt} = (3t^2 - 3).$$

The speed is given by:

$$v = \sqrt{(2t - 2)^2 + (3t^2 - 3)^2}.$$

The particle stops when $2t - 2 = 0$ and $3t^2 - 3 = 0$. Since these are both satisfied only by $t = 1$, this is the only time that the particle stops.

15. At $t = 2$, the position is $(2^2, 2^3) = (4, 8)$, the velocity in the x-direction is $2 \cdot 2 = 4$, and the velocity in the y-direction is $3 \cdot 2^2 = 12$. So we want the line going through the point $(4, 8)$ at the time $t = 2$, with the given x- and y-velocities:

$$x = 4 + 4(t - 2), \quad y = 8 + 12(t - 2).$$

16. One possible answer is $x = 3 \cos t, y = -3 \sin t, 0 \leq t \leq 2\pi$.

17. One possible answer is $x = -2, y = t$.

18. One possible answer is $x = 2 + 5 \cos t, y = 1 + 5 \sin t, 0 \leq t \leq 2\pi$.

19. The parameterization $x = 2\cos t$, $y = 2\sin t$, $0 \le t \le 2\pi$, is a circle of radius 2 traced out counterclockwise starting at the point $(2, 0)$. To start at $(-2, 0)$, put a negative in front of the first coordinate

$$x = -2\cos t \quad y = 2\sin t, \qquad 0 \le t \le 2\pi.$$

Now we must check whether this parameterization traces out the circle clockwise or counterclockwise. Since when t increases from 0, $\sin t$ is positive, the point (x, y) moves from $(-2, 0)$ into the second quadrant. Thus, the circle is traced out clockwise and so this is one possible parameterization.

20. The slope of the line is

$$m = \frac{3 - (-1)}{1 - 2} = -4.$$

The equation of the line with slope -4 through the point $(2, -1)$ is $y - (-1) = (-4)(x - 2)$, so one possible parameterization is $x = t$ and $y = -4t + 8 - 1 = -4t + 7$.

21. The ellipse $x^2/25 + y^2/49 = 1$ can be parameterized by $x = 5\cos t$, $y = 7\sin t$, $0 \le t \le 2\pi$.

22. The parameterization $x = -3\cos t$, $y = 7\sin t$, $0 \le t \le 2\pi$, starts at the right point but sweeps out the ellipse in the wrong direction (the y-coordinate becomes positive as t increases). Thus, a possible parameterization is $x = -3\cos(-t) = -3\cos t$, $y = 7\sin(-t) = -7\sin t$, $0 \le t \le 2\pi$.

23. We have

$$\frac{dy}{dx} = \frac{dy/dt}{dx/dt} = \frac{2t}{3t^2 - 1}.$$

Thus when $t = 2$, the slope of the tangent line is $4/11$. Also when $t = 2$, we have

$$x = 2^3 - 2 = 6, \quad y = 2^2 = 4.$$

Therefore the equation of the tangent line is

$$(y - 4) = \frac{4}{11}(x - 6).$$

24. We have

$$\frac{dy}{dx} = \frac{dy/dt}{dx/dt} = \frac{2t + 2}{2t - 2}.$$

When $t = 1$, the denominator is zero and the numerator is nonzero, so the tangent line is vertical. Since $x = -1$ when $t = 1$, the equation of the tangent line is $x = -1$.

25. We have

$$\frac{dy}{dx} = \frac{dy/dt}{dx/dt} = \frac{4\cos(4t)}{3\cos(3t)}.$$

Thus when $t = \pi$, the slope of the tangent line is $-4/3$. Since $x = 0$ and $y = 0$ when $t = \pi$, the equation of the tangent line is $y = -(4/3)x$.

Problems

26. (a) We get the part of the line with $x < 10$ and $y < 0$.
(b) We get the part of the line between the points $(10, 0)$ and $(11, 2)$.

27. (a) If $t \ge 0$, we have $x \ge 2$, $y \ge 4$, so we get the part of the line to the right of and above the point $(2, 4)$.
(b) When $t = 0$, $(x, y) = (2, 4)$. When $t = -1$, $(x, y) = (-1, -3)$. Restricting t to the interval $-1 \le t \le 0$ gives the part of the line between these two points.
(c) If $x < 0$, giving $2 + 3t < 0$ or $t < -2/3$. Thus $t < -2/3$ gives the points on the line to the left of the y-axis.

28. (a) Eliminating t between

$$x = 2 + t, \quad y = 4 + 3t$$

gives

$$y - 4 = 3(x - 2),$$
$$y = 3x - 2.$$

Eliminating t between

$$x = 1 - 2t, \quad y = 1 - 6t$$

gives

$$y - 1 = 3(x - 1),$$
$$y = 3x - 2.$$

Since both parametric equations give rise to the same equation in x and y, they both parameterize the same line.
(b) Slope $= 3$, y-intercept $= -2$.

29. In all three cases, $y = x^2$, so that the motion takes place on the parabola $y = x^2$.

In case (a), the x-coordinate always increases at a constant rate of one unit distance per unit time, so the equations describe a particle moving to the right on the parabola at constant horizontal speed.

In case (b), the x-coordinate is never negative, so the particle is confined to the right half of the parabola. As t moves from $-\infty$ to $+\infty$, $x = t^2$ goes from ∞ to 0 to ∞. Thus the particle first comes down the right half of the parabola, reaching the origin $(0, 0)$ at time $t = 0$, where it reverses direction and goes back up the right half of the parabola.

In case (c), as in case (a), the particle traces out the entire parabola $y = x^2$ from left to right. The difference is that the horizontal speed is not constant. This is because a unit change in t causes larger and larger changes in $x = t^3$ as t approaches $-\infty$ or ∞. The horizontal motion of the particle is faster when it is farther from the origin.

30. (a) C_1 has center at the origin and radius 5, so $a = b = 0, k = 5$ or -5.
(b) C_2 has center at $(0, 5)$ and radius 5, so $a = 0, b = 5, k = 5$ or -5.
(c) C_3 has center at $(10, -10)$, so $a = 10, b = -10$. The radius of C_3 is $\sqrt{10^2 + (-10)^2} = \sqrt{200}$, so $k = \sqrt{200}$ or $k = -\sqrt{200}$.

31. (I) has a positive slope and so must be l_1 or l_2. Since its y-intercept is negative, these equations must describe l_2. (II) has a negative slope and positive x-intercept, so these equations must describe l_3.

32. It is a straight line through the point $(3, 5)$ with slope -1. A linear parameterization of the same line is $x = 3 + t$, $y = 5 - t$.

33. (a) The curve is a spiral as shown in Figure 4.131.
(b) At $t = 2$, the position is $(2 \cos 2, 2 \sin 2) = (-0.8323, 1.8186)$, and at $t = 2.01$ the position is $(2.01 \cos 2.01, 2.01 \sin 2.01) = (-0.8546, 1.8192)$. The distance between these points is

$$\sqrt{(-0.8546 - (-0.8323))^2 + (1.8192 - 1.8186)^2} \approx 0.022.$$

Thus the speed is approximately $0.022/0.01 \approx 2.2$. See Figure 4.132.

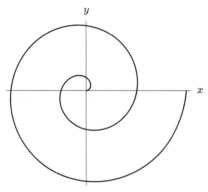

Figure 4.131: The spiral
$x = t \cos t, y = t \sin t$ for $0 \le t \le 4\pi$

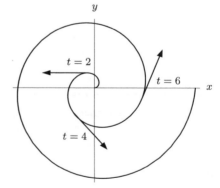

Figure 4.132: The spiral $x = t \cos t, y = t \sin t$ and three velocity vectors

(c) Evaluating the exact formula

$$v = \sqrt{(\cos t - t \sin t)^2 + (\sin t + t \cos t)^2}$$

gives :

$$v(2) = \sqrt{(-2.235)^2 + (0.077)^2} = 2.2363.$$

34. (a) The chain rule gives

$$\frac{dy}{dx} = \frac{dy/dt}{dx/dt} = \frac{4e^{2t}}{e^t} = 4e^t.$$

(b) We are given $y = 2e^{2t}$ so $y = 2(e^t)^2$. Since $x = e^t$, we can substitute x for e^t. Thus $y = 2x^2$.

(c) Differentiating $y = 2x^2$ with respect to x, we get $dy/dx = 4x$. Notice that, since $x = e^t$, this is equivalent to the answer that we obtained in part (a).

35. (a) In order for the particle to stop, its velocity both dx/dt and dy/dt must be zero,

$$\frac{dx}{dt} = 3t^2 - 3 = 3(t-1)(t+1) = 0,$$
$$\frac{dy}{dt} = 2t - 2 = 2(t-1) = 0.$$

The value $t = 1$ is the only solution. Therefore, the particle stops when $t = 1$ at the point $(t^3 - 3t, \; t^2 - 2t)|_{t=1} = (-2, -1)$.

(b) In order for the particle to be traveling straight up or down, the velocity in the x-direction must be 0. Thus, we solve $dx/dt = 3t^2 - 3 = 0$ and obtain $t = \pm 1$. However, at $t = 1$ the particle has no vertical motion, as we saw in part (a). Thus, the particle is moving straight up or down only when $t = -1$. The position at that time is $(t^3 - 3t, \; t^2 - 2t)|_{t=-1} = (2, 3)$.

(c) For horizontal motion we need $dy/dt = 0$. That happens when $dy/dt = 2t - 2 = 0$, and so $t = 1$. But from part (a) we also have $dx/dt = 0$ also at $t = 1$, so the particle is not moving at all when $t = 1$. Thus, there is no time when the motion is horizontal.

36. (a) (i) A horizontal tangent occurs when $dy/dt = 0$ and $dx/dt \neq 0$. Thus,

$$\frac{dy}{dt} = 6e^{2t} - 2e^{-2t} = 0$$
$$6e^{2t} = 2e^{-2t}$$
$$e^{4t} = \frac{1}{3}$$
$$4t = \ln\frac{1}{3}$$
$$t = \frac{1}{4}\ln\frac{1}{3} = -0.25\ln 3 = -0.275.$$

We need to check that $dx/dt \neq 0$ when $t = -0.25\ln 3$. Since $dx/dt = 2e^{2t} + 2e^{-2t}$ is always positive, dx/dt is never zero.

(ii) A vertical tangent occurs when $dx/dt = 0$ and $dy/dt \neq 0$. Since $dx/dt = 2e^{2t} + 2e^{-2t}$ is always positive, there is no vertical tangent.

(b) The chain rule gives

$$\frac{dy}{dx} = \frac{dy/dt}{dx/dt} = \frac{6e^{2t} - 2e^{-2t}}{2e^{2t} + 2e^{-2t}} = \frac{3e^{2t} - e^{-2t}}{e^{2t} + e^{-2t}}.$$

(c) As $t \to \infty$, we have $e^{-2t} \to 0$. Thus,

$$\lim_{t\to\infty}\frac{dy}{dx} = \lim_{t\to\infty}\frac{3e^{2t} - e^{-2t}}{e^{2t} + e^{-2t}} = \lim_{t\to\infty}\frac{3e^{2t}}{e^{2t}} = 3.$$

As $t \to \infty$, the fraction gets closer and closer to 3.

37. (a) Figure 4.133 shows the path and the clockwise direction of motion. (The curve is an ellipse.)

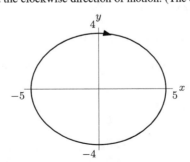

Figure 4.133

(b) At $t = \pi/4$, the position is given by

$$x(\pi/4) = 5\sin\frac{2\pi}{4} = 5\sin\frac{\pi}{2} = 5 \quad\text{and}\quad y(\pi/4) = 4\cos\frac{2\pi}{4} = 4\cos\frac{\pi}{2} = 0.$$

Differentiating, we get $x'(t) = 10\cos(2t)$ and $y'(t) = -8\sin(2t)$. At $t = \pi/4$, the velocity is given by

$$x'(\pi/4) = 10\cos\frac{2\pi}{4} = 10\cos\frac{\pi}{2} = 0 \quad\text{and}\quad y'(\pi/4) = -8\sin\frac{2\pi}{4} = -8\sin\frac{\pi}{2} = -8.$$

(c) As t increases from 0 to 2π, the ellipse is traced out twice. Thus, the particle passes through the point $(5, 0)$ twice.

(d) Since $x'(\pi/4) = 0$ and $y'(\pi/4) = -8$, when $t = \pi/4$, the particle is moving in the negative y-direction, parallel to the y-axis.

(e) At time t,

$$\text{Speed} = \sqrt{(x'(t))^2 + (y'(t))^2} = \sqrt{(10\cos(2t))^2 + (-8\sin(2t))^2}.$$

When $t = \pi$,

$$\text{Speed} = \sqrt{(10\cos(2\pi))^2 + (-8\sin(2\pi))^2} = \sqrt{(10\cdot 1)^2 + (-8\cdot 0)^2} = 10.$$

38. (a) Substituting $\alpha = 36° = \pi/5$ and $v_0 = 60$ into $x(t) = (v_0\cos\alpha)t$ and $y(t) = (v_0\sin\alpha)t - \frac{1}{2}gt^2$, we get

$$x(t) = \left(60\cos\frac{\pi}{5}\right)t \quad\text{and}\quad y(t) = \left(60\sin\frac{\pi}{5}\right)t - \frac{1}{2}(32)t^2 = \left(60\sin\frac{\pi}{5}\right)t - 16t^2.$$

(b) Figure 4.134 shows the path and the direction of motion.

Figure 4.134

(c) When the football hits the ground, $y(t) = 0$, so

$$\left(60\sin\frac{\pi}{5}\right)t - 16t^2 = 0$$

$$4t\left(15\sin\frac{\pi}{5} - 4t\right) = 0$$

$$t = 0 \quad\text{or}\quad t = \frac{15\sin(\pi/5)}{4} = 2.204 \text{ seconds.}$$

The ball hits the ground in approximately 2.204 seconds. The ball's distance from the spot where it was kicked is $x(2.204) = 106.994$ feet.

(d) At its highest point, the football is moving neither upward nor downward, so $y'(t)$ is zero. To find the time when the football reaches its maximum height, we set $y'(t) = 0$, giving

$$y'(t) = \left(60\sin\frac{\pi}{5}\right) - 32t = 0$$

$$t = \frac{60\sin(\pi/5)}{32} = 1.102 \text{ seconds.}$$

This makes sense since this is half the time it took the football to reach the ground. The maximum height is $y(1.102) = 19.434$ feet. Thus the football reaches 19.434 feet.

(e) Since $x(t) = \left(60\cos\frac{\pi}{5}\right)t$ and $y(t) = \left(60\sin\frac{\pi}{5}\right)t - 16t^2$, we have

$$x'(t) = 60\cos\frac{\pi}{5} \quad\text{and}\quad y'(t) = 60\sin\frac{\pi}{5} - 32t.$$

Thus,

$$\text{Speed} = \sqrt{(x'(t))^2 + (y'(t))^2} = \sqrt{\left(60\cos\frac{\pi}{5}\right)^2 + \left(60\sin\frac{\pi}{5} - 32t\right)^2}.$$

At $t = 1$,

$$\text{Speed} = \sqrt{\left(60\cos\frac{\pi}{5}\right)^2 + \left(60\sin\frac{\pi}{5} - 32\right)^2} = 48.651 \text{ feet/sec.}$$

39. (a) To determine if the particles collide, we check whether they are ever at the same point at the same time. We first set the two x-coordinates equal to each other:

$$4t - 4 = 3t$$
$$t = 4.$$

When $t = 4$, both x-coordinates are 12. Now we check whether the y-coordinates are also equal at $t = 4$:

$$y_A(4) = 2 \cdot 4 - 5 = 3$$
$$y_B(4) = 4^2 - 2 \cdot 4 - 1 = 7.$$

Thus, the particles do not collide since they are not at the same point at the same time.

(b) For the particles to collide, we need both x- and y-coordinates to be equal. Since the x-coordinates are equal at $t = 4$, we find the k value making $y_A(4) = y_B(4)$.

Substituting $t = 4$ into $y_A(t) = 2t - k$ and $y_B(t) = t^2 - 2t - 1$, we have

$$8 - k = 16 - 8 - 1$$
$$k = 1.$$

(c) To find the speed of the particles, we differentiate.

For particle A,

$x(t) = 4t - 4$, so $x'(t) = 4$, and $x'(4) = 4$
$y(t) = 2t - 1$, so $y'(t) = 2$, and $y'(4) = 2$

$$\text{Speed}_A = \sqrt{(x'(t))^2 + (y'(t))^2} = \sqrt{4^2 + 2^2} = \sqrt{20}.$$

For particle B,

$x(t) = 3t$, so $x'(t) = 3$, and $x'(4) = 3$
$y(t) = t^2 - 2t - 1$, so $y'(t) = 2t - 2$, and $y'(4) = 6$

$$\text{Speed}_B = \sqrt{(x'(t))^2 + (y'(t))^2} = \sqrt{3^2 + 6^2} = \sqrt{45}.$$

Thus, when $t = 4$, particle B is moving faster.

40. (a) Since $x = t^3 + t$ and $y = t^2$, we have

$$w = \frac{dy}{dx} = \frac{dy/dt}{dx/dt} = \frac{2t}{3t^2 + 1}.$$

Differentiating w with respect to t, we get

$$\frac{dw}{dt} = \frac{(3t^2 + 1)2 - (2t)(6t)}{(3t^2 + 1)^2} = \frac{-6t^2 + 2}{(3t^2 + 1)^2},$$

so

$$\frac{d^2y}{dx^2} = \frac{dw}{dx} = \frac{dw/dt}{dx/dt} = \frac{-6t^2 + 2}{(3t^2 + 1)^3}.$$

(b) When $t = 1$, we have $d^2y/dx^2 = -1/16 < 0$, so the curve is concave down.

41. (a) The x and y-coordinates of the point on the graph when $t = \pi/3$ are given by

$$x = 3 \cdot \frac{\pi}{3} = \pi \quad \text{and} \quad y = \cos\left(\frac{2\pi}{3}\right) = -\frac{1}{2}.$$

Thus when $t = \pi/3$, the particle is at the point $(\pi, -1/2)$.

To find the slope, we find dy/dx

$$\frac{dy}{dx} = \frac{dy/dt}{dx/dt} = \frac{-2\sin(2t)}{3}.$$

When $t = \pi/3$,

$$\frac{dy}{dx} = \frac{-2\sin(2\pi/3)}{3} = -\frac{\sqrt{3}}{3}.$$

The equation of the tangent line when $t = \pi/3$ is:

$$y + \frac{1}{2} = -\frac{\sqrt{3}}{3}(x - \pi).$$

(b) To find the smallest positive value of t for which the y-coordinate is a local maximum, we set $dy/dt = 0$. We have

$$\frac{dy}{dt} = -2\sin(2t) = 0$$

$$2t = \pi \quad \text{or} \quad 2t = 2\pi$$

$$t = \frac{\pi}{2} \quad \text{or} \quad t = \pi.$$

There is a minimum of $y = \cos(2t)$ at $t = \pi/2$, and a maximum at $t = \pi$.

(c) To find d^2y/dx^2 when $t = 2$, we use the formula:

$$\frac{d^2y}{dx^2} = \frac{dw/dt}{dx/dt} \quad \text{where} \quad w = \frac{dy}{dx}.$$

Since $w = -2\sin(2t)/3$ from part (a), we have

$$\frac{d^2y}{dx^2} = \frac{-4\cos(2t)/3}{3}.$$

When $t = 2$, we have

$$\frac{d^2y}{dx^2} = \frac{-4\cos(4)/3}{3} = 0.291.$$

Since the second derivative is positive, the graph is concave up when $t = 2$.

42. (a) We differentiate for both x and y in terms of t, giving us:

$$\frac{dy}{dx} = \frac{dy/dt}{dx/dt} = \frac{2e^{2t} + 6e^t}{e^t} = 2e^t + 6.$$

(b) To find d^2y/dx^2, we use the formula:

$$\frac{d^2y}{dx^2} = \frac{dw/dt}{dx/dt} \quad \text{where} \quad w = \frac{dy}{dx}$$

$$\frac{d^2y}{dx^2} = \frac{2e^t}{e^t} = 2.$$

Since the second derivative is always positive, the graph is concave up everywhere.

(c) We are given $y = e^{2t} + 6e^t + 9$. We can factor this to $y = (e^t + 3)^2$. Since $x = e^t + 3$, we can substitute x for $e^t + 3$. Thus, $y = x^2$ for $x > 3$.

(d) Since $y = x^2$, $dy/dx = 2x$ and $d^2y/dx^2 = 2$.
From part (a), we have $dy/dx = 2e^t + 6$. We can factor this to $dy/dx = 2(e^t + 3) = 2x$.
Part (b) tells us that $d^2y/dx^2 = 2$, which is what we have just determined.
Our graph is a parabola that is concave up everywhere.

43. (a) The particle touches the x-axis when $y = 0$. Since $y = \cos(2t) = 0$ for the first time when $2t = \pi/2$, we have $t = \pi/4$. To find the speed of the particle at that time, we use the formula

$$\text{Speed} = \sqrt{\left(\frac{dx}{dt}\right)^2 + \left(\frac{dy}{dt}\right)^2} = \sqrt{(\cos t)^2 + (-2\sin(2t))^2}.$$

When $t = \pi/4$,

$$\text{Speed} = \sqrt{(\cos(\pi/4))^2 + (-2\sin(\pi/2))^2} = \sqrt{(\sqrt{2}/2)^2 + (-2 \cdot 1)^2} = \sqrt{9/2}.$$

(b) The particle is at rest when its speed is zero. Since $\sqrt{(\cos t)^2 + (-2\sin(2t))^2} \geq 0$, the speed is zero when

$$\cos t = 0 \quad \text{and} \quad -2\sin(2t) = 0.$$

Now $\cos t = 0$ when $t = \pi/2$ or $t = 3\pi/2$. Since $-2\sin(2t) = -4\sin t \cos t$, we see that this expression also equals zero when $t = \pi/2$ or $t = 3\pi/2$.

(c) We need to find d^2y/dx^2. First, we must determine dy/dx. We know

$$\frac{dy}{dx} = \frac{dy/dt}{dx/dt} = \frac{-2\sin 2t}{\cos t} = \frac{-4\sin t \cos t}{\cos t} = -4\sin t.$$

Since $dy/dx = -4\sin t$, we can now use the formula:

$$\frac{d^2y}{dx^2} = \frac{dw/dt}{dx/dt} \quad \text{where} \quad w = \frac{dy}{dx}$$

$$\frac{d^2y}{dx^2} = \frac{-4\cos t}{\cos t} = -4.$$

Since d^2y/dx^2 is always negative, our graph is concave down everywhere.

Using the identity $y = \cos(2t) = 1 - 2\sin^2 t$, we can eliminate the parameter and write the original equation as $y = 1 - 2x^2$, which is a parabola that is concave down everywhere.

44. Let

$$w = \frac{dy}{dx} = \frac{dy/dt}{dx/dt}.$$

We want to find

$$\frac{d^2y}{dx^2} = \frac{dw}{dx} = \frac{dw/dt}{dx}dt.$$

To find dw/dt, we use the quotient rule:

$$\frac{dw}{dt} = \frac{(dx/dt)(d^2y/dt^2) - (dy/dt)(d^2x/dt^2)}{(dx/dt)^2}.$$

We then divide this by dx/dt again to get the required formula, since

$$\frac{d^2y}{dx^2} = \frac{dw}{dx} = \frac{dw/dt}{dx/dt}.$$

45. For $0 \le t \le 2\pi$, we get Figure 4.135.

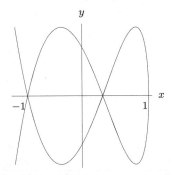

Figure 4.135

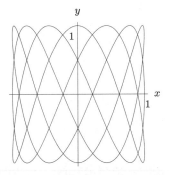

Figure 4.136

46. For $0 \le t \le 2\pi$, we get Figure 4.136.

47. For $0 \le t \le 2\pi$, we get Figure 4.137.

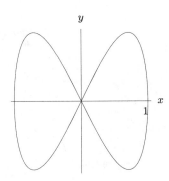

Figure 4.137

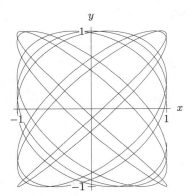

Figure 4.138

48. This curve never closes on itself. The plot for $0 \le t \le 8\pi$ is in Figure 4.138.

49. (a) To find the equations of the moon's motion relative to the star, you must first calculate the equation of the planet's motion relative to the star, and then the moon's motion relative to the planet, and then add the two together.

The distance from the planet to the star is R, and the time to make one revolution is one unit, so the parametric equations for the planet relative to the star are $x = R \cos t$, $y = R \sin t$.

The distance from the moon to the planet is 1, and the time to make one revolution is twelve units, therefore, the parametric equations for the moon relative to the planet are $x = \cos 12t$, $y = \sin 12t$.

Adding these together, we get:

$$x = R \cos t + \cos 12t,$$
$$y = R \sin t + \sin 12t.$$

(b) For the moon to stop completely at time t, the velocity of the moon must be equal to zero. Therefore,

$$\frac{dx}{dt} = -R \sin t - 12 \sin 12t = 0,$$
$$\frac{dy}{dt} = R \cos t + 12 \cos 12t = 0.$$

There are many possible values to choose for R and t that make both of these equations equal to zero. We choose $t = \pi$, and $R = 12$.

(c) The graph with $R = 12$ is shown below.

Solutions for Chapter 4 Review

Exercises

1. See Figure 4.139.

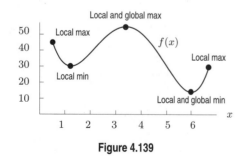

Figure 4.139

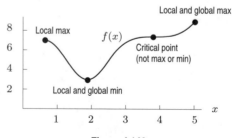

Figure 4.140

2. See Figure 4.140.

3. (a) We wish to investigate the behavior of $f(x) = x^3 - 3x^2$ on the interval $-1 \le x \le 3$. We find:

$$f'(x) = 3x^2 - 6x = 3x(x - 2)$$
$$f''(x) = 6x - 6 = 6(x - 1)$$

(b) The critical points of f are $x = 2$ and $x = 0$ since $f'(x) = 0$ at those points. Using the second derivative test, we find that $x = 0$ is a local maximum since $f'(0) = 0$ and $f''(0) = -6 < 0$, and that $x = 2$ is a local minimum since $f'(2) = 0$ and $f''(2) = 6 > 0$.

(c) There is an inflection point at $x = 1$ since f'' changes sign at $x = 1$.

(d) At the critical points, $f(0) = 0$ and $f(2) = -4$.
At the endpoints: $f(-1) = -4$, $f(3) = 0$.
So the global maxima are $f(0) = 0$ and $f(3) = 0$, while the global minima are $f(-1) = -4$ and $f(2) = -4$.

(e) See Figure 4.141.

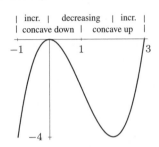

Figure 4.141

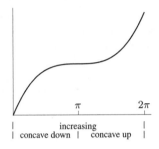

Figure 4.142

4. (a) First we find f' and f''; $f'(x) = 1 + \cos x$ and $f''(x) = -\sin x$.

(b) The critical point of f is $x = \pi$, since $f'(\pi) = 0$.

(c) Since f'' changes sign at $x = \pi$, it means that $x = \pi$ is an inflection point.

(d) Evaluating f at the critical point and endpoints, we find $f(0) = 0$, $f(\pi) = \pi$, $f(2\pi) = 2\pi$,. Therefore, the global maximum is $f(2\pi) = 2\pi$, and the global minimum is $f(0) = 0$. Note that $x = \pi$ is not a local maximum or minimum of f, and that the second derivative test is inconclusive here.

(e) See Figure 4.142.

5. (a) First we find f' and f'':

$$f'(x) = -e^{-x} \sin x + e^{-x} \cos x$$
$$f''(x) = e^{-x} \sin x - e^{-x} \cos x$$
$$-e^{-x} \cos x - e^{-x} \sin x$$
$$= -2e^{-x} \cos x$$

(b) The critical points are $x = \pi/4, 5\pi/4$, since $f'(x) = 0$ here.

(c) The inflection points are $x = \pi/2, 3\pi/2$, since f'' changes sign at these points.

(d) At the endpoints, $f(0) = 0$, $f(2\pi) = 0$. So we have $f(\pi/4) = (e^{-\pi/4})(\sqrt{2}/2)$ as the global maximum; $f(5\pi/4) = -e^{-5\pi/4}(\sqrt{2}/2)$ as the global minimum.

(e) See Figure 4.143.

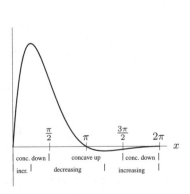

Figure 4.143

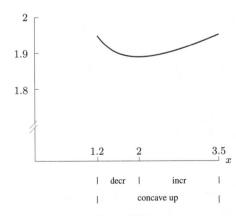

Figure 4.144

6. (a) We first find f' and f'':

$$f'(x) = -\frac{2}{3}x^{-\frac{5}{3}} + \frac{1}{3}x^{-\frac{2}{3}} = \frac{1}{3}x^{-\frac{5}{3}}(x-2)$$

$$f''(x) = \frac{10}{9}x^{-\frac{8}{3}} - \frac{2}{9}x^{-\frac{5}{3}} = -\frac{2}{9}x^{-\frac{8}{3}}(x-5)$$

(b) Critical point: $x = 2$.

(c) There are no inflection points, since f'' does not change sign on the interval $1.2 \le x \le 3.5$.

(d) At the endpoints, $f(1.2) \approx 1.94821$ and $f(3.5) \approx 1.95209$. So, the global minimum is $f(2) \approx 1.88988$ and the global maximum is $f(3.5) \approx 1.95209$.

(e) See Figure 4.144.

7. The polynomial $f(x)$ behaves like $2x^3$ as x goes to ∞. Therefore, $\lim\limits_{x \to \infty} f(x) = \infty$ and $\lim\limits_{x \to -\infty} f(x) = -\infty$.

We have $f'(x) = 6x^2 - 18x + 12 = 6(x-2)(x-1)$, which is zero when $x = 1$ or $x = 2$.

Also, $f''(x) = 12x - 18 = 6(2x - 3)$, which is zero when $x = 3/2$. For $x < 3/2$, $f''(x) < 0$; for $x > 3/2$, $f''(x) > 0$. Thus $x = 3/2$ is an inflection point.

The critical points are $x = 1$ and $x = 2$, and $f(1) = 6$, $f(2) = 5$. By the second derivative test, $f''(1) = -6 < 0$, so $x = 1$ is a local maximum; $f''(2) = 6 > 0$, so $x = 2$ is a local minimum.

Now we can draw the diagrams below.

$y' > 0$	$y' < 0$	$y' > 0$
increasing $\quad x = 1 \quad$	decreasing $\quad x = 2 \quad$	increasing

$y'' < 0$	$y'' > 0$
concave down $\quad x = 3/2 \quad$	concave up

The graph of $f(x) = 2x^3 - 9x^2 + 12x + 1$ is shown in Figure 4.145. It has no global maximum or minimum.

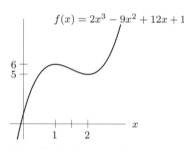

$f(x) = 2x^3 - 9x^2 + 12x + 1$

Figure 4.145

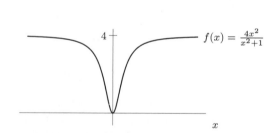

$f(x) = \frac{4x^2}{x^2+1}$

Figure 4.146

8. If we divide the denominator and numerator of $f(x)$ by x^2 we have

$$\lim_{x \to \pm\infty} \frac{4x^2}{x^2 + 1} = \lim_{x \to \pm\infty} \frac{4}{1 + \frac{1}{x^2}} = 4$$

since

$$\lim_{x \to \pm\infty} \frac{1}{x^2} = 0.$$

Using the quotient rule we get

$$f'(x) = \frac{(x^2 + 1)8x - 4x^2(2x)}{(x^2 + 1)^2} = \frac{8x}{(x^2 + 1)^2},$$

which is zero when $x = 0$, positive when $x > 0$, and negative when $x < 0$. Thus $f(x)$ has a local minimum when $x = 0$, with $f(0) = 0$.

Because $f'(x) = 8x/(x^2 + 1)^2$, the quotient rule implies that

$$f''(x) = \frac{(x^2 + 1)^2 8 - 8x[2(x^2 + 1)2x]}{(x^2 + 1)^4}$$

$$= \frac{8x^2 + 8 - 32x^2}{(x^2 + 1)^3} = \frac{8(1 - 3x^2)}{(x^2 + 1)^3}.$$

The denominator is always positive, so $f''(x) = 0$ when $x = \pm\sqrt{1/3}$, positive when $-\sqrt{1/3} < x < \sqrt{1/3}$, and negative when $x > \sqrt{1/3}$ or $x < -\sqrt{1/3}$. This gives the diagram

$$\begin{array}{ccc} y' < 0 & & y' > 0 \\ \text{decreasing} & x = 0 & \text{increasing} \end{array}$$

$$\begin{array}{ccccc} y'' < 0 & & y'' > 0 & & y'' < 0 \\ \text{concave down} & & \text{concave up} & & \text{concave down} \\ & x = -\sqrt{1/3} & & x = \sqrt{1/3} & \end{array}$$

and the graph of f looks Figure 4.146. with inflection points $x = \pm\sqrt{1/3}$, a global minimum at $x = 0$, and no local or global maxima (since $f(x)$ never equals 4).

9. As $x \to -\infty$, $e^{-x} \to \infty$, so $xe^{-x} \to -\infty$. Thus $\lim_{x \to -\infty} xe^{-x} = -\infty$.

As $x \to \infty$, $\frac{x}{e^x} \to 0$, since e^x grows much more quickly than x. Thus $\lim_{x \to \infty} xe^{-x} = 0$.

Using the product rule,

$$f'(x) = e^{-x} - xe^{-x} = (1 - x)e^{-x},$$

which is zero when $x = 1$, negative when $x > 1$, and positive when $x < 1$. Thus $f(1) = 1/e^1 = 1/e$ is a local maximum.

Again, using the product rule,

$$f''(x) = -e^{-x} - e^{-x} + xe^{-x}$$

$$= xe^{-x} - 2e^{-x}$$

$$= (x - 2)e^{-x},$$

which is zero when $x = 2$, positive when $x > 2$, and negative when $x < 2$, giving an inflection point at $(2, \frac{2}{e^2})$. With the above, we have the following diagram:

$$\begin{array}{ccc} y' > 0 & & y' < 0 \\ \text{increasing} & x = 1 & \text{decreasing} \end{array}$$

$$\begin{array}{ccc} y'' < 0 & & y'' > 0 \\ \text{concave down} & x = 2 & \text{concave up} \end{array}$$

The graph of f is shown in Figure 4.147. and $f(x)$ has one global maximum at $1/e$ and no local or global minima.

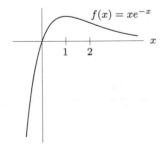

Figure 4.147

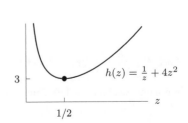

Figure 4.148

10. We rewrite $h(z)$ as $h(z) = z^{-1} + 4z^2$.

Differentiating gives

$$h'(z) = -z^{-2} + 8z,$$

so the critical points satisfy

$$
\begin{aligned}
-z^{-2} + 8z &= 0 \\
z^{-2} &= 8z \\
8z^3 &= 1 \\
z^3 &= \frac{1}{8} \\
z &= \frac{1}{2}.
\end{aligned}
$$

Since h' is negative for $0 < z < 1/2$ and h' is positive for $z > 1/2$, there is a local minimum at $z = 1/2$.

Since $h(z) \to \infty$ as $z \to 0^+$ and as $z \to \infty$, the local minimum at $z = 1/2$ is a global minimum; there is no global maximum. See Figure 4.148. Thus, the global minimum is $h(1/2) = 3$.

11. Since $g(t)$ is always decreasing for $t \geq 0$, we expect it to a global maximum at $t = 0$ but no global minimum. At $t = 0$, we have $g(0) = 1$, and as $t \to \infty$, we have $g(t) \to 0$.

Alternatively, rewriting as $g(t) = (t^3 + 1)^{-1}$ and differentiating using the chain rule gives

$$g'(t) = -(t^3 + 1)^{-2} \cdot 3t^2.$$

Since $3t^2 = 0$ when $t = 0$, there is a critical point at $t = 0$, and g decreases for all $t > 0$. See Figure 4.149.

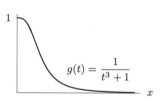

Figure 4.149

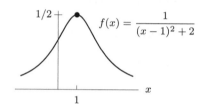

Figure 4.150

12. We begin by rewriting $f(x)$:

$$f(x) = \frac{1}{(x-1)^2 + 2} = ((x-1)^2 + 2)^{-1} = (x^2 - 2x + 3)^{-1}.$$

Differentiating using the chain rule gives

$$f'(x) = -(x^2 - 2x + 3)^{-2}(2x - 2) = \frac{2 - 2x}{(x^2 - 2x + 3)^2},$$

so the critical points satisfy

$$
\begin{aligned}
\frac{2 - 2x}{(x^2 - 2x + 3)^2} &= 0 \\
2 - 2x &= 0 \\
2x &= 2 \\
x &= 1.
\end{aligned}
$$

Since f' is positive for $x < 1$ and f' is negative for $x > 1$, there is a local maximum at $x = 1$.

Since $f(x) \to 0$ as $x \to \infty$ and as $x \to -\infty$, the local maximum at $x = 1$ is a global maximum; there is no global minimum. See Figure 4.150. Thus, the global maximum is $f(1) = 1/2$.

13. $\lim\limits_{x \to \infty} f(x) = +\infty$, and $\lim\limits_{x \to -\infty} f(x) = -\infty$.

There are no asymptotes.

$f'(x) = 3x^2 + 6x - 9 = 3(x+3)(x-1)$. Critical points are $x = -3$, $x = 1$.

$f''(x) = 6(x+1)$.

x		-3		-1		1	
f'	+	0	−	−	−	0	+
f''	−	−	−	0	+	+	+
f	⟋⌢		⟍⌢		⟍⌣		⟋⌣

Thus, $x = -1$ is an inflection point. $f(-3) = 12$ is a local maximum; $f(1) = -20$ is a local minimum. There are no global maxima or minima.

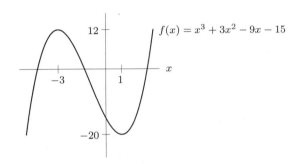

$f(x) = x^3 + 3x^2 - 9x - 15$

14. $\lim\limits_{x \to +\infty} f(x) = +\infty$, and $\lim\limits_{x \to -\infty} f(x) = -\infty$.

There are no asymptotes.

$f'(x) = 5x^4 - 45x^2 = 5x^2(x^2 - 9) = 5x^2(x+3)(x-3)$.

The critical points are $x = 0$, $x = \pm 3$. f' changes sign at 3 and -3 but not at 0.

$f''(x) = 20x^3 - 90x = 10x(2x^2 - 9)$. f'' changes sign at $0, \pm 3/\sqrt{2}$.

So, inflection points are at $x = 0$, $x = \pm 3/\sqrt{2}$.

x		-3		$-3/\sqrt{2}$		0		$3/\sqrt{2}$		3	
f'	+	0	−		−	0	−		−	0	+
f''	−	−	−	0	+	0	−	0	+	+	+
f	⟋⌢		⟍⌢		⟍⌣		⟍⌢		⟍⌣		⟋⌣

Thus, $f(-3)$ is a local maximum; $f(3)$ is a local minimum. There are no global maxima or minima.

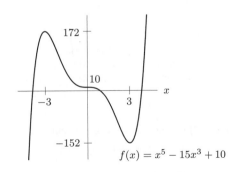

$f(x) = x^5 - 15x^3 + 10$

15. $\lim_{x \to +\infty} f(x) = +\infty$, and $\lim_{x \to 0^+} f(x) = +\infty$.

Hence, $x = 0$ is a vertical asymptote.

$f'(x) = 1 - \dfrac{2}{x} = \dfrac{x-2}{x}$, so $x = 2$ is the only critical point.

$f''(x) = \dfrac{2}{x^2}$, which can never be zero. So there are no inflection points.

x		2	
f'	$-$	0	$+$
f''	$+$	$+$	$+$
f	$\searrow\smile$		$\nearrow\smile$

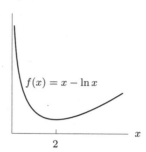

$f(x) = x - \ln x$

2

Thus, $f(2)$ is a local and global minimum.

16. $\lim_{x \to +\infty} f(x) = +\infty$, $\lim_{x \to -\infty} f(x) = 0$.

$y = 0$ is the horizontal asymptote.

$f'(x) = 2xe^{5x} + 5x^2e^{5x} = xe^{5x}(5x + 2)$.

Thus, $x = -\dfrac{2}{5}$ and $x = 0$ are the critical points.

$$f''(x) = 2e^{5x} + 2xe^{5x} \cdot 5 + 10xe^{5x} + 25x^2e^{5x}$$
$$= e^{5x}(25x^2 + 20x + 2).$$

So, $x = \dfrac{-2 \pm \sqrt{2}}{5}$ are inflection points.

x		$\frac{-2-\sqrt{2}}{5}$		$-\frac{2}{5}$		$\frac{-2+\sqrt{2}}{5}$		0	
f'	$+$	$+$	$+$	0	$-$	$-$	$-$	0	$+$
f''	$+$	0	$-$	$-$	$-$	0	$+$	$+$	$+$
f	$\nearrow\smile$		$\nearrow\frown$		$\searrow\frown$		$\searrow\smile$		$\nearrow\smile$

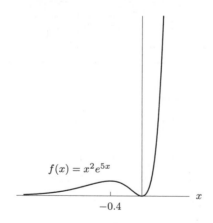

$f(x) = x^2 e^{5x}$

-0.4

So, $f(-\dfrac{2}{5})$ is a local maximum; $f(0)$ is a local and global minimum.

17. Since $\lim_{x \to -\infty} f(x) = \lim_{x \to +\infty} f(x) = 0$, $y = 0$ is a horizontal asymptote.

$f'(x) = -2xe^{-x^2}$. So, $x = 0$ is the only critical point.

$f''(x) = -2(e^{-x^2} + x(-2x)e^{-x^2}) = 2e^{-x^2}(2x^2 - 1) = 2e^{-x^2}(\sqrt{2}x - 1)(\sqrt{2}x + 1).$

Thus, $x = \pm 1/\sqrt{2}$ are inflection points.

Table 4.1

x		$-1/\sqrt{2}$		0		$1/\sqrt{2}$	
f'	+	+	+	0	−	−	−
f''	+	0	−	−	−	0	+
f	↗◡		↗◠		↘◠		↘◡

Thus, $f(0) = 1$ is a local and global maximum.

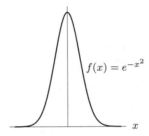

18. $\displaystyle\lim_{x \to +\infty} f(x) = \lim_{x \to -\infty} f(x) = 1.$

Thus, $y = 1$ is a horizontal asymptote. Since $x^2 + 1$ is never 0, there are no vertical asymptotes.

$$f'(x) = \frac{2x(x^2 + 1) - x^2(2x)}{(x^2 + 1)^2} = \frac{2x}{(x^2 + 1)^2}.$$

So, $x = 0$ is the only critical point.

$$f''(x) = \frac{2(x^2 + 1)^2 - 2x \cdot 2(x^2 + 1) \cdot 2x}{(x^2 + 1)^4}$$

$$= \frac{2(x^2 + 1 - 4x^2)}{(x^2 + 1)^3}$$

$$= \frac{2(1 - 3x^2)}{(x^2 + 1)^3}.$$

So, $x = \pm \frac{1}{\sqrt{3}}$ are inflection points.

Table 4.2

x		$\frac{-1}{\sqrt{3}}$		0		$\frac{1}{\sqrt{3}}$	
f'	−	−	−	0	+	+	+
f''	−	0	+	+	+	0	−
f	↘◠		↘◡		↗◡		↗◠

Thus, $f(0) = 0$ is a local and global minimum. A graph of $f(x)$ can be found in Figure 4.151.

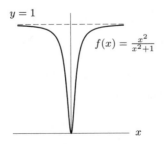

Figure 4.151

19.

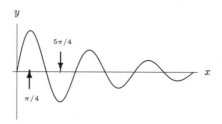

Letting $f(x) = e^{-x} \sin x$, we have

$$f'(x) = -e^{-x} \sin x + e^{-x} \cos x.$$

Solving $f'(x) = 0$, we get $\sin x = \cos x$. This means $x = \arctan(1) = \pi/4$, and $\pi/4$ plus multiples of π, are the critical points of $f(x)$. By evaluating $f(x)$ at the points $k\pi + \pi/4$, where k is an integer, we can find:

$$e^{-5\pi/4} \sin(5\pi/4) \le e^{-x} \sin x \le e^{-\pi/4} \sin(\pi/4),$$

since $f(0) = 0$ at the endpoint. So

$$-0.014 \le e^{-x} \sin x \le 0.322.$$

20. Let $f(x) = x \sin x$. Then $f'(x) = x \cos x + \sin x$.

$f'(x) = 0$ when $x = 0, x \approx 2$, and $x \approx 5$. The latter two estimates we can get from the graph of $f'(x)$.

Zooming in (or using some other approximation method), we can find the zeros of $f'(x)$ with more precision. They are (approximately) $0, 2.029$, and 4.913. We check the endpoints and critical points for the global maximum and minimum.

$$f(0) = 0, \qquad f(2\pi) = 0,$$
$$f(2.029) \approx 1.8197, \quad f(4.914) \approx -4.814.$$

Thus for $0 \le x \le 2\pi$, $-4.81 \le f(x) \le 1.82$.

21. To find the best possible bounds for $f(x) = x^3 - 6x^2 + 9x + 5$ on $0 \le x \le 5$, we find the global maximum and minimum for the function on the interval. First, we find the critical points. Differentiating yields

$$f'(x) = 3x^2 - 12x + 9$$

Letting $f'(x) = 0$ and factoring yields

$$3x^2 - 12x + 9 = 0$$
$$3(x^2 - 4x + 3) = 0$$
$$3(x - 3)(x - 1) = 0$$

So $x = 1$ and $x = 3$ are critical points for the function on $0 \le x \le 5$. Evaluating the function at the critical points and endpoints gives us

$$f(0) = (0)^3 - 6(0)^2 + 9(0) + 5 = 5$$
$$f(1) = (1)^3 - 6(1)^2 + 9(1) + 5 = 9$$
$$f(3) = (3)^3 - 6(3)^2 + 9(3) + 5 = 5$$
$$f(5) = (5)^3 - 6(5)^2 + 9(5) + 5 = 25$$

So the global minimum on this interval is $f(0) = f(3) = 5$ and the global maximum is $f(5) = 25$. From this we conclude

$$5 \le x^3 - 6x^2 + 9x + 5 \le 25$$

are the best possible bounds for the function on the interval $0 \le x \le 5$.

Problems

22. (a)

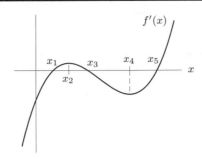

    (b) $f'(x)$ changes sign at x_1, x_3, and x_5.

    (c) $f'(x)$ has local extrema at x_2 and x_4.

23. The local maxima and minima of f correspond to places where f' is zero and changes sign or, possibly, to the endpoints of intervals in the domain of f. The points at which f changes concavity correspond to local maxima and minima of f'. The change of sign of f', from positive to negative corresponds to a maximum of f and change of sign of f' from negative to positive corresponds to a minimum of f.

24. The function f has critical points at $x = 1$, $x = 3$, $x = 5$.

    By the first derivative test, since f' is positive to the left of $x = 1$ and negative to the right, $x = 1$ is a local maximum.

    Since f' is negative to the left of $x = 3$ and positive to the right, $x = 3$ is a local minimum.

    Since f' does not change sign at $x = 5$, this point is neither a local maximum nor a local minimum.

25. The critical points of f occur where f' is zero. These two points are indicated in the figure below.

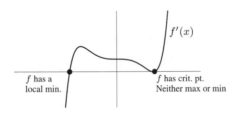

    Note that the point labeled as a local minimum of f is not a critical point of f'.

26. (a) The function f is a local maximum where $f'(x) = 0$ and $f' > 0$ to the left, $f' < 0$ to the right. This occurs at the point x_3.

    (b) The function f is a local minimum where $f'(x) = 0$ and $f' < 0$ to the left, $f' > 0$ to the right. This occurs at the points x_1 and x_5.

    (c) The graph of f is climbing fastest where f' is a maximum, which is at the point x_2.

    (d) The graph of f is falling most steeply where f' is the most negative, which is at the point 0.

27. (a) Increasing for $x > 0$, decreasing for $x < 0$.

    (b) $f(0)$ is a local and global minimum, and f has no global maximum.

28. (a) Increasing for all x.

    (b) No maxima or minima.

29. (a) Decreasing for $x < 0$, increasing for $0 < x < 4$, and decreasing for $x > 4$.

    (b) $f(0)$ is a local minimum, and $f(4)$ is a local maximum.

30. (a) Decreasing for $x < -1$, increasing for $-1 < x < 0$, decreasing for $0 < x < 1$, and increasing for $x > 1$.

    (b) $f(-1)$ and $f(1)$ are local minima, $f(0)$ is a local maximum.

31. Differentiating gives

$$\frac{dy}{dx} = a(e^{-bx} - bxe^{-bx}) = ae^{-bx}(1 - bx).$$

Thus, $dy/dx = 0$ when $x = 1/b$. Then

$$y = a\frac{1}{b}e^{-b \cdot 1/b} = \frac{a}{b}e^{-1}.$$

Differentiating again gives

$$\frac{d^2y}{dx^2} = -abe^{-bx}(1 - bx) - abe^{-bx}$$
$$= -abe^{-bx}(2 - bx)$$

When $x = 1/b$,

$$\frac{d^2y}{dx^2} = -abe^{-b\cdot 1/b}\left(2 - b\cdot\frac{1}{b}\right) = -abe^{-1}.$$

Therefore the point $\left(\frac{1}{b}, \frac{a}{b}e^{-1}\right)$ is a maximum if a and b are positive. We can make $(2, 10)$ a maximum by setting

$$\frac{1}{b} = 2 \quad \text{so} \quad b = \frac{1}{2}$$

and

$$\frac{a}{b}e^{-1} = \frac{a}{1/2}e^{-1} = 2ae^{-1} = 10 \quad \text{so} \quad a = 5e.$$

Thus $a = 5e$, $b = 1/2$.

32. We want the maximum value of $r(t) = ate^{-bt}$ to be 0.3 ml/sec and to occur at $t = 0.5$ sec. Differentiating gives

$$r'(t) = ae^{-bt} - abte^{-bt},$$

so $r'(t) = 0$ when

$$ae^{-bt}(1 - bt) = 0 \quad \text{or} \quad t = \frac{1}{b}.$$

Since the maximum occurs at $t = 0.5$, we have

$$\frac{1}{b} = 0.5 \quad \text{so} \quad b = 2.$$

Thus, $r(t) = ate^{-2t}$. The maximum value of r is given by

$$r(0.5) = a(0.5)e^{-2(0.5)} = 0.5ae^{-1}.$$

Since the maximum value of r is 0.3, we have

$$0.5ae^{-1} = 0.3 \quad \text{so} \quad a = \frac{0.3e}{0.5} = 1.63.$$

Thus, $r(t) = 1.63te^{-2t}$ ml/sec.

33.

$$r(\lambda) = a(\lambda)^{-5}(e^{b/\lambda} - 1)^{-1}$$
$$r'(\lambda) = a(-5\lambda^{-6})(e^{b/\lambda} - 1)^{-1} + a(\lambda^{-5})\left(\frac{b}{\lambda^2}e^{b/\lambda}\right)(e^{b/\lambda} - 1)^{-2}$$

$(0.96, 3.13)$ is a maximum, so $r'(0.96) = 0$ implies that the following holds, with $\lambda = 0.96$:

$$5\lambda^{-6}(e^{b/\lambda} - 1)^{-1} = \lambda^{-5}\left(\frac{b}{\lambda^2}e^{b/\lambda}\right)(e^{b/\lambda} - 1)^{-2}$$
$$5\lambda(e^{b/\lambda} - 1) = be^{b/\lambda}$$
$$5\lambda e^{b/\lambda} - 5\lambda = be^{b/\lambda}$$
$$5\lambda e^{b/\lambda} - be^{b/\lambda} = 5\lambda$$
$$\left(\frac{5\lambda - b}{5\lambda}\right)e^{b/\lambda} = 1$$
$$\frac{4.8 - b}{4.8}e^{b/0.96} - 1 = 0.$$

Using Newton's method, or some other approximation method, we search for a root. The root should be near 4.8. Using our initial guess, we get $b \approx 4.7665$. At $\lambda = 0.96$, $r = 3.13$, so

$$3.13 = \frac{a}{0.96^5 \left(e^{b/0.96} - 1\right)} \qquad \text{or}$$

$$a = 3.13(0.96)^5 \left(e^{b/0.96} - 1\right)$$

$$\approx 363.23.$$

As a check, we try $r(4) \approx 0.155$, which looks about right on the given graph.

34.

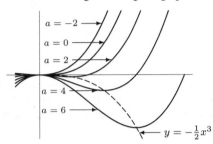

To solve for the critical points, we set $\frac{dy}{dx} = 0$. Since $\frac{d}{dx}\left(x^3 - ax^2\right) = 3x^2 - 2ax$, we want $3x^2 - 2ax = 0$, so $x = 0$ or $x = \frac{2}{3}a$. At $x = 0$, we have $y = 0$. This first critical point is independent of a and lies on the curve $y = -\frac{1}{2}x^3$. At $x = \frac{2}{3}a$, we calculate $y = -\frac{4}{27}a^3 = -\frac{1}{2}\left(\frac{2}{3}a\right)^3$. Thus the second critical point also lies on the curve $y = -\frac{1}{2}x^3$.

35. The triangle in Figure 4.152 has area, A, given by

$$A = \frac{1}{2}xy = \frac{x}{2}e^{-x/3}.$$

At a critical point,

$$\frac{dA}{dx} = \frac{1}{2}e^{-x/3} - \frac{x}{6}e^{-x/3} = 0$$

$$\frac{1}{6}e^{-x/3}(3 - x) = 0$$

$$x = 3.$$

Substituting the critical point and the endpoints into the formula for the area gives:
For $x = 1$, we have $A = \frac{1}{2}e^{-1/3} = 0.358$
For $x = 3$, we have $A = \frac{3}{2}e^{-1} = 0.552$
For $x = 5$, we have $A = \frac{5}{2}e^{-5/3} = 0.472$
Thus, the maximum area is 0.552 and the minimum area is 0.358.

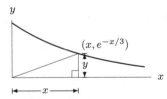

Figure 4.152

36. The top half of the circle has equation $y = \sqrt{1 - x^2}$. The rectangle in Figure 4.153 has area, A, given by

$$A = 2xy = 2x\sqrt{1 - x^2}, \qquad \text{for } 0 \le x \le 1.$$

At a critical point,

$$\frac{dA}{dt} = 2\sqrt{1 - x^2} + 2x \left(\frac{1}{2} \left(1 - x^2 \right)^{-1/2} (-2x) \right) = 0$$

$$2\sqrt{1 - x^2} - \frac{2x^2}{\sqrt{1 - x^2}} = 0$$

$$\frac{2 \left(\sqrt{1 - x^2} \right)^2 - 2x^2}{\sqrt{1 - x^2}} = 0$$

$$\frac{2(1 - x^2 - x^2)}{\sqrt{1 - x^2}} = 0$$

$$2(1 - 2x^2) = 0$$

$$x = \pm \frac{1}{\sqrt{2}}.$$

Since $A = 0$ at the endpoints $x = 0$ and $x = 1$, and since A is positive at the only critical point, $x = 1/\sqrt{2}$, in the interval $0 \le x \le 1$, the critical point is a local and global maximum. The vertices on the circle have $y = \sqrt{1 - (1/2)^2} = 1/\sqrt{2}$. Thus the coordinates of the rectangle with maximum area are

$$\left(\frac{1}{\sqrt{2}}, 0 \right); \quad \left(\frac{1}{\sqrt{2}}, \frac{1}{\sqrt{2}} \right); \quad \left(-\frac{1}{\sqrt{2}}, 0 \right); \quad \left(-\frac{1}{\sqrt{2}}, \frac{1}{\sqrt{2}} \right)$$

and the maximum area is

$$A = 2 \frac{1}{\sqrt{2}} \cdot \frac{1}{\sqrt{2}} = 1.$$

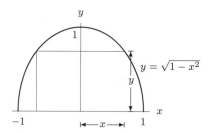

Figure 4.153

37. The volume is given by $V = x^2 y$. The surface area is given by

$$S = 2x^2 + 4xy$$
$$= 2x^2 + 4xV/x^2 = 2x^2 + 4V/x.$$

To find the dimensions which minimize the area, find x such that $dS/dx = 0$:

$$\frac{dS}{dx} = 4x - \frac{4V}{x^2} = 0$$
$$x^3 = V.$$

Solving for x gives $x = \sqrt[3]{V} = y$. To see that this gives a minimum, note that for small x, $S \approx 4V/x$ is decreasing. For large x, $S \approx 2x^2$ is increasing. Since there is only one critical point, it must give a global minimum. Therefore, when the width equals the height, the surface area is minimized.

38. (a) The business must reorder often enough to keep pace with sales. If reordering is done every t months, then,

$$\text{Quantity sold in } t \text{ months} = \text{Quantity reordered in each batch}$$
$$rt = q$$
$$t = \frac{q}{r} \text{ months.}$$

(b) The amount spent on each order is $a + bq$, which is spent every q/r months. To find the monthly expenditures, divide by q/r. Thus, on average,

$$\text{Amount spent on ordering per month} = \frac{a + bq}{q/r} = \frac{ra}{q} + rb \text{ dollars.}$$

(c) The monthly cost of storage is $kq/2$ dollars, so

$$C = \text{Ordering costs} + \text{Storage costs}$$

$$C = \frac{ra}{q} + rb + \frac{kq}{2} \text{ dollars.}$$

(d) The optimal batch size minimizes C, so

$$\frac{dC}{dq} = \frac{-ra}{q^2} + \frac{k}{2} = 0$$

$$\frac{ra}{q^2} = \frac{k}{2}$$

$$q^2 = \frac{2ra}{k}$$

so

$$q = \sqrt{\frac{2ra}{k}} \text{ items per order.}$$

39.

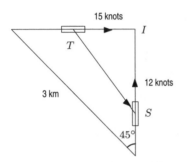

Figure 4.154: Position of the tanker and ship

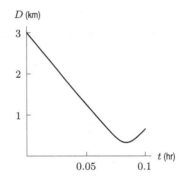

Figure 4.155: Distance between the ship at S and the tanker at T

Suppose t is the time, in hours, since the ships were 3 km apart. Then $\overline{TI} = \frac{3\sqrt{2}}{2} - (15)(1.85)t$ and $\overline{SI} = \frac{3\sqrt{2}}{2} - (12)(1.85)t$. So the distance, $D(t)$, in km, between the ships at time t is

$$D(t) = \sqrt{\left(\frac{3\sqrt{2}}{2} - 27.75t\right)^2 + \left(\frac{3\sqrt{2}}{2} - 22.2t\right)^2}.$$

Differentiating gives

$$\frac{dD}{dt} = \frac{-55.5\left(\frac{3}{\sqrt{2}} - 27.75\,t\right) - 44.4\left(\frac{3}{\sqrt{2}} - 22.2\,t\right)}{2\sqrt{\left(\frac{3}{\sqrt{2}} - 27.75\,t\right)^2 + \left(\frac{3}{\sqrt{2}} - 22.2\,t\right)^2}}.$$

Solving $dD/dt = 0$ gives a critical point at $t = 0.0839$ hours when the ships will be approximately 331 meters apart. So the ships do not need to change course. Alternatively, tracing along the curve in Figure 4.155 gives the same result. Note that this is after the eastbound ship crosses the path of the northbound ship.

40. (a) Consider Figure 4.156. The company wants to truck its potatoes to some point, P, along the coast before transferring them to a ship. Let x represent the distance between that point and the point C. The distance covered by truck is the hypotenuse of the right triangle (provided that it is covered by highway)whose sides have lengths of x and 300 (in miles). This distance is given by

$$\text{Distance in miles covered by truck} = \sqrt{x^2 + 300^2}.$$

The cost of transporting by truck is 2 cents per mile, or $2\sqrt{x^2 + 300^2}$ cents while the cost of transporting by ship is 1 cent per mile, or $1(1000 - x)$ cents. The cost function which we want to minimize, in cents, is therefore

$$C(x) = 2\sqrt{x^2 + 300^2} + (1000 - x).$$

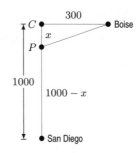

Figure 4.156

(b) To minimize the cost function C, we compute its derivative,

$$C'(x) = (x^2 + 300^2)^{-1/2} \cdot (2x) + (-1)$$
$$= \frac{2x}{\sqrt{x^2 + 300^2}} - 1.$$

When we set $C'(x)$ to 0 to determine the critical point, we get

$$\frac{2x}{\sqrt{x^2 + 300^2}} = 1$$
$$2x = \sqrt{x^2 + 300^2}$$
$$4x^2 = x^2 + 300^2$$
$$3x^2 = 300^2$$
$$x^2 = \frac{300^2}{3} = \frac{90000}{3} = 30000$$
$$x = \sqrt{30000} = 173.21 \text{ miles}$$

Taking the second derivative, we see that

$$C''(x) = \frac{2}{\sqrt{x^2 + 300^2}} - 2x^2(x^2 + 300^2)^{-3/2},$$

which is positive at $x = 173.21$, so the critical point is a minimum. Since there is only one critical point, this must be the global minimum.

41. Since the volume is fixed at 200 ml (i.e. 200 cm^3), we can solve the volume expression for h in terms of r to get (with h and r in centimeters)

$$h = \frac{200 \cdot 3}{7\pi r^2}.$$

Using this expression in the surface area formula we arrive at

$$S = 3\pi r\sqrt{r^2 + \left(\frac{600}{7\pi r^2}\right)^2}$$

By plotting $S(r)$ we see that there is a minimum value near $r = 2.7$ cm.

42. To find the critical points, set $dD/dx = 0$:

$$\frac{dD}{dx} = 2(x - a_1) + 2(x - a_2) + 2(x - a_3) + \cdots + 2(x - a_n) = 0.$$

Dividing by 2 and solving for x gives

$$x + x + x + \cdots + x = a_1 + a_2 + a_3 + \cdots + a_n.$$

Since there are n terms on the left,

$$nx = a_1 + a_2 + a_3 + \cdots + a_n$$

$$x = \frac{a_1 + a_2 + a_3 + \cdots + a_n}{n} = \frac{1}{n}\sum_{i=1}^{n} a_i.$$

The expression on the right is the average of $a_1, a_2, a_3, \cdots, a_n$.

Since D is a quadratic with positive leading coefficient, this critical point is a minimum.

43. (a) We have $g'(t) = \frac{t(1/t) - \ln t}{t^2} = \frac{1 - \ln t}{t^2}$, which is zero if $t = e$, negative if $t > e$, and positive if $t < e$, since $\ln t$ is increasing. Thus $g(e) = \frac{1}{e}$ is a global maximum for g. Since $t = e$ was the only point at which $g'(t) = 0$, there is no minimum.

(b) Now $\ln t/t$ is increasing for $0 < t < e$, $\ln 1/1 = 0$, and $\ln 5/5 \approx 0.322 < \ln(e)/e$. Thus, for $1 < t < e$, $\ln t/t$ increases from 0 to above $\ln 5/5$, so there must be a t between 1 and e such that $\ln t/t = \ln 5/5$. For $t > e$, there is only one solution to $\ln t/t = \ln 5/5$, namely $t = 5$, since $\ln t/t$ is decreasing for $t > e$. For $0 < t < 1$, $\ln t/t$ is negative and so cannot equal $\ln 5/5$. Thus $\ln x/x = \ln t/t$ has exactly two solutions.

(c) The graph of $\ln t/t$ intersects the horizontal line $y = \ln 5/5$, at $x = 5$ and $x \approx 1.75$.

44. (a) x-intercept: $(a, 0)$, y-intercept: $(0, \frac{1}{a^2 + 1})$

(b) Area $= \frac{1}{2}(a)(\frac{1}{a^2 + 1}) = \frac{a}{2(a^2 + 1)}$

(c)

$$A = \frac{a}{2(a^2 + 1)}$$

$$A' = \frac{2(a^2 + 1) - a(4a)}{4(a^2 + 1)^2}$$

$$= \frac{2(1 - a^2)}{4(a^2 + 1)^2}$$

$$= \frac{(1 - a^2)}{2(a^2 + 1)^2}.$$

If $A' = 0$, then $a = \pm 1$. We only consider positive values of a, and we note that A' changes sign from positive to negative at $a = 1$. Hence $a = 1$ is a local maximum of A which is a global maximum because $A' < 0$ for all $a > 1$ and $A' > 0$ for $0 < a < 1$.

(d) $A = \frac{1}{2}(1)(\frac{1}{2}) = \frac{1}{4}$

(e) Set $\frac{a}{2(a^2 + a)} = \frac{1}{3}$ and solve for a:

$$5a = 2a^2 + 2$$

$$2a^2 - 5a + 2 = 0$$

$$(2a - 1)(a - 2) = 0.$$

45. (a) The length of the piece of wire made into a circle is x cm, so the length of the piece made into a square is $(L - x)$ cm. See Figure 4.157.

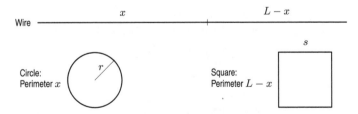

Figure 4.157

The circumference of the circle is x, so its radius, r cm, is given by

$$r = \frac{x}{2\pi} \text{ cm.}$$

The perimeter of the square is $(L - x)$, so the side length, s cm, is given by

$$s = \frac{L - x}{4} \text{ cm.}$$

Thus, the sum of areas is given by

$$A = \pi r^2 + s^2 = \pi \left(\frac{x}{2\pi}\right)^2 + \left(\frac{L - x}{4}\right)^2 = \frac{x^2}{4\pi} + \frac{(L - x)^2}{16}, \quad \text{for } 0 \leq x \leq L.$$

Setting $dA/dx = 0$ to find the critical points gives

$$\frac{dA}{dx} = \frac{x}{2\pi} - \frac{(L - x)}{8} = 0$$

$$8x = 2\pi L - 2\pi x$$

$$(8 + 2\pi)x = 2\pi L$$

$$x = \frac{2\pi L}{8 + 2\pi} = \frac{\pi L}{4 + \pi} \approx 0.44L.$$

To find the maxima and minima, we substitute the critical point and the endpoints, $x = 0$ and $x = L$, into the area function.

For $x = 0$, we have $A = \dfrac{L^2}{16}$.

For $x = \dfrac{\pi L}{4 + \pi}$, we have $L - x = L - \dfrac{\pi L}{4 + \pi} = \dfrac{4L}{4 + \pi}$. Then

$$A = \frac{\pi^2 L^2}{4\pi(4 + \pi)^2} + \frac{1}{16}\left(\frac{4L}{4 + \pi}\right)^2 = \frac{\pi L^2}{4(4 + \pi)^2} + \frac{L^2}{(4 + \pi)^2}$$

$$= \frac{\pi L^2 + 4L^2}{4(4 + \pi)^2} = \frac{L^2}{4(4 + \pi)} = \frac{L^2}{16 + 4\pi}.$$

For $x = L$, we have $A = \dfrac{L^2}{4\pi}$.

Thus, $x = \dfrac{\pi L}{4 + \pi}$ gives the minimum value of $A = \dfrac{L^2}{16 + 4\pi}$.

Since $4\pi < 16$, we see that $x = L$ gives the maximum value of $A = \dfrac{L^2}{4\pi}$.

This corresponds to the situation in which we do not cut the wire at all and use the single piece to make a circle.

(b) At the maximum, $x = L$, so

$$\frac{\text{Length of wire in square}}{\text{Length of wire in circle}} = \frac{0}{L} = 0.$$

$$\frac{\text{Area of square}}{\text{Area of circle}} = \frac{0}{L^2/4\pi} = 0.$$

At the minimum, $x = \dfrac{\pi L}{4 + \pi}$, so $L - x = L - \dfrac{\pi L}{4 + \pi} = \dfrac{4L}{4 + \pi}$.

$$\frac{\text{Length of wire in square}}{\text{Length of wire in circle}} = \frac{4L/(4 + \pi)}{\pi L/(4 + \pi)} = \frac{4}{\pi}.$$

$$\frac{\text{Area of square}}{\text{Area of circle}} = \frac{L^2/(4 + \pi)^2}{\pi L^2/(4(4 + \pi)^2)} = \frac{4}{\pi}.$$

(c) For a general value of x,

$$\frac{\text{Length of wire in square}}{\text{Length of wire in circle}} = \frac{L - x}{x}.$$

$$\frac{\text{Area of square}}{\text{Area of circle}} = \frac{(L - x)^2/16}{x^2/(4\pi)} = \frac{\pi}{4} \cdot \frac{(L - x)^2}{x^2}.$$

If the ratios are equal, we have

$$\frac{L - x}{x} = \frac{\pi}{4} \cdot \frac{(L - x)^2}{x^2}.$$

So either $L - x = 0$, giving $x = L$, or we can cancel $(L - x)$ and multiply through by $4x^2$, giving

$$4x = \pi(L - x)$$
$$x = \frac{\pi L}{4 + \pi}.$$

Thus, the two values of x found in part (a) are the only values of x in $0 \leq x \leq L$ making the ratios in part (b) equal. (The ratios are not defined if $x = 0$.)

46. (a) The concavity changes at t_1 and t_3, as shown in Figure 4.158.

(b) $f(t)$ grows most quickly where the vase is skinniest (at y_3) and most slowly where the vase is widest (at y_1). The diameter of the widest part of the vase looks to be about 4 times as large as the diameter at the skinniest part. Since the area of a cross section is given by πr^2, where r is the radius, the ratio between areas of cross sections at these two places is about 4^2, so the growth rates are in a ratio of about 1 to 16 (the wide part being 16 times slower).

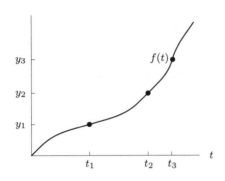

Figure 4.158

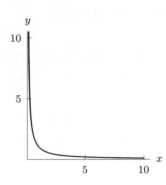

Figure 4.159

47. (a) For $x > 0$ the graphs in Figure 4.159 are almost indistinguishable.

(b) Since $\lim\limits_{a \to 0} \left(\arctan\left(\frac{x}{a}\right) - \frac{\pi}{2} \right) = 0$ and $\lim\limits_{a \to 1} a = 0$ we can use l'Hopital's rule. The variable is a, so we differentiate with respect to a.

$$\lim_{a \to 0^+} \frac{\left(\arctan\left(\frac{x}{a}\right) - \frac{\pi}{2} \right)}{a} = \lim_{a \to 0^+} \frac{\frac{d}{da}\left(\arctan\left(\frac{x}{a}\right) - \frac{\pi}{2} \right)}{\frac{d}{da}(a)} = \lim_{a \to 0^+} \frac{\frac{1}{1+(x/a)^2} \frac{d}{da}\left(\frac{x}{a}\right)}{1} = \lim_{a \to 0^+} \frac{\frac{1}{1+(x/a)^2} \frac{-x}{a^2}}{1} = -\frac{1}{x}.$$

(c) Part (b) tells us that as a gets closer and closer to 0 through positive values of a, the function $\frac{1}{a}\left(\arctan\left(\frac{x}{a}\right) - \frac{\pi}{2} \right)$ gets closer and closer to $-\frac{1}{x}$, which is what part (a) is saying graphically.

48. If $f(x) = 1 - \cosh(5x)$ and $g(x) = x^2$, then $f(0) = g(0) = 0$, so we use l'Hopital's Rule:

$$\lim_{x \to 0} \frac{1 - \cosh 5x}{x^2} = \lim_{x \to 0} \frac{-5\sinh 5x}{2x} = \lim_{x \to 0} \frac{-25\cosh 5x}{2} = -\frac{25}{2}.$$

49. If $f(x) = x - \sinh x$ and $g(x) = x^3$, then $f(0) = g(0) = 0$. However, $f'(0) = g'(0) = f''(0) = g''(0) = 0$ also, so we use l'Hopital's Rule three times. Since $f'''(x) = -\cosh x$ and $g'''(x) = 6$:

$$\lim_{x \to 0} \frac{x - \sinh x}{x^3} = \lim_{x \to 0} \frac{1 - \cosh x}{3x^2} = \lim_{x \to 0} \frac{-\sinh x}{6x} = \lim_{x \to 0} \frac{-\cosh x}{6} = -\frac{1}{6}.$$

50. (a) The population is increasing if $dP/dt > 0$, that is, if

$$kP(L - P) > 0.$$

Since $P \geq 0$ and $k, L > 0$, we must have $P > 0$ and $L - P > 0$ for this to be true. Thus, the population is increasing if $0 < P < L$.

The population is decreasing if $dP/dt < 0$, that is, if $P > L$.

The population remains constant if $dP/dt = 0$, so $P = 0$ or $P = L$.

(b) Differentiating with respect to t using the chain rule gives

$$\frac{d^2P}{dt^2} = \frac{d}{dt}\left(kP(L-P)\right) = \frac{d}{dP}(kLP - kP^2) \cdot \frac{dP}{dt} = (kL - 2kP)(kP(L-P))$$
$$= k^2P(L - 2P)(L - P).$$

51. Let r be the radius of the balloon. Then its volume, V, is

$$V = \frac{4}{3}\pi r^3.$$

We need to find the rate of change of V with respect to time, that is dV/dt. Since $V = V(r)$,

$$\frac{dV}{dr} = 4\pi r^2$$

so that by the chain rule,

$$\frac{dV}{dt} = \frac{dV}{dr}\frac{dr}{dt} = 4\pi r^2 \cdot 1.$$

When $r = 5$, $dV/dt = 100\pi$ cm³/sec.

52. The radius r is related to the volume by the formula $V = \frac{4}{3}\pi r^3$. By implicit differentiation, we have

$$\frac{dV}{dt} = \frac{4}{3}\pi 3r^2\frac{dr}{dt} = 4\pi r^2\frac{dr}{dt}.$$

The surface area of a sphere is $4\pi r^2$, so we have

$$\frac{dV}{dt} = s \cdot \frac{dr}{dt},$$

but since $\dfrac{dV}{dt} = \dfrac{1}{3}s$ was given, we have

$$\frac{dr}{dt} = \frac{1}{3}.$$

53. (a) Since $d\theta/dt$ represents the rate of change of θ with time, $d\theta/dt$ represents the angular velocity of the disk.
(b) Suppose P is the point on the rim shown in Figure 4.160.

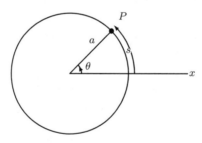

Figure 4.160

Any other point on the rim is moving at the same speed, though in a different direction. We know that since θ is in radians,

$$s = a\theta.$$

Since a is a constant, we know

$$\frac{ds}{dt} = a\frac{d\theta}{dt}.$$

But $ds/dt = v$, the speed of the point on the rim, so

$$v = a\frac{d\theta}{dt}.$$

54. The volume, V, of a cone of radius r and height h is

$$V = \frac{1}{3}\pi r^2 h.$$

However, Figure 4.161 shows that $h/r = 12/5$, thus $r = 5h/12$, so

$$V = \frac{1}{3}\pi \left(\frac{5}{12}h\right)^2 h = \frac{25}{432}\pi h^3.$$

Differentiating with respect to time, t, gives

$$\frac{dV}{dt} = \frac{25}{144}\pi h^2 \frac{dh}{dt}.$$

When the depth of chemical in the tank is 1 meter, the level is falling at 0.1 meter/min so $h = 1$ and $dh/dt = -0.1$. Thus

$$\frac{dV}{dt} = -\frac{25}{144} \cdot \pi \cdot 1^2 \cdot 0.1 = -0.0545 \text{ m}^3/\text{min}.$$

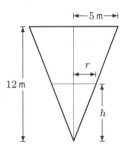

Figure 4.161

55. The rate at which the voltage, V, is changing is obtained by differentiating $V = IR$ to get

$$\frac{dV}{dt} = I\frac{dR}{dt} + R\frac{dI}{dt}.$$

Since the voltage remains constant, $dV/dt = 0$. Thus

$$\frac{dR}{dt} = -\frac{R}{I}\frac{dI}{dt},$$

and the rate at which the resistance is changing is

$$\frac{dR}{dt} = -\frac{1000}{0.1}(0.001) = -10 \text{ ohms/min}.$$

We conclude that the resistance is falling by 10 ohms/min.

56. Using Pythagoras' theorem, we see that the distance x between the aircraft's current position and the point 2 miles directly above the ground station are related to s by the formula $x = (s^2 - 2^2)^{1/2}$. See Figure 4.162. The speed along the aircraft's constant altitude flight path is

$$\frac{dx}{dt} = \left(\frac{1}{2}\right)(s^2 - 4)^{-1/2}(2s)\left(\frac{ds}{dt}\right) = \frac{s}{x}\frac{ds}{dt}.$$

When $s = 4.6$ and $ds/dt = 210$,

$$\frac{dx}{dt} = \frac{4.6}{\sqrt{(4.6)^2 - 4}}210$$

$$= \frac{966}{\sqrt{21.16 - 4}}$$

$$= \frac{966}{4.14} \approx 233.2 \text{ miles/hour}.$$

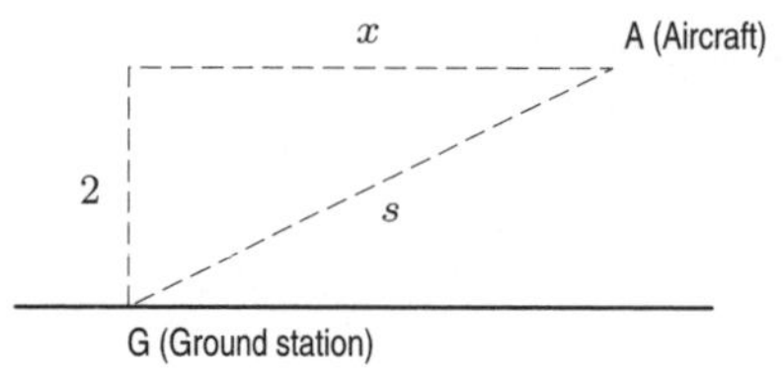

Figure 4.162

57. We want to find dP/dV. Solving $PV = k$ for P gives

$$P = k/V$$

so,

$$\frac{dP}{dV} = -\frac{k}{V^2}.$$

58. (a) Since $V = k/P$, the volume decreases.
 (b) Since $PV = k$ and $P = 2$ when $V = 10$, we have $k = 20$, so

$$V = \frac{20}{P}.$$

We think of both P and V as functions of time, so by the chain rule

$$\frac{dV}{dt} = \frac{dV}{dP}\frac{dP}{dt},$$
$$\frac{dV}{dt} = -\frac{20}{P^2}\frac{dP}{dt}.$$

We know that $dP/dt = 0.05$ atm/min when $P = 2$ atm, so

$$\frac{dV}{dt} = -\frac{20}{2^2} \cdot (0.05) = -0.25 \text{ cm}^3/\text{min}.$$

CAS Challenge Problems

59. (a) Since $k > 0$, we have $\lim\limits_{t \to \infty} e^{-kt} = 0$. Thus

$$\lim_{t \to \infty} P = \lim_{t \to \infty} \frac{L}{1 + Ce^{-kt}} = \frac{L}{1 + C \cdot 0} = L.$$

The constant L is called the carrying capacity of the environment because it represents the long-run population in the environment.
 (b) Using a CAS, we find

$$\frac{d^2P}{dt^2} = -\frac{LCk^2e^{-kt}(1 - Ce^{-kt})}{(1 + Ce^{-kt})^3}.$$

Thus, $d^2P/dt^2 = 0$ when

$$1 - Ce^{-kt} = 0$$
$$t = -\frac{\ln(1/C)}{k}.$$

Since e^{-kt} and $(1 + Ce^{-kt})$ are both always positive, the sign of d^2P/dt^2 is negative when $(1 - Ce^{-kt}) > 0$, that is, for $t > -\ln(1/C)/k$. Similarly, the sign of d^2P/dt^2 is positive when $(1 - Ce^{-kt}) < 0$, that is, for $t < -\ln(1/C)/k$. Thus, there is an inflection point at $t = -\ln(1/C)/k$.
  For $t = -\ln(1/C)/k$,

$$P = \frac{L}{1 + Ce^{\ln(1/C)}} = \frac{L}{1 + C(1/C)} = \frac{L}{2}.$$

Thus, the inflection point occurs where $P = L/2$.

60. (a) The graph has a jump discontinuity whose position depends on a. The function is increasing, and the slope at a given x-value seems to be the same for all values of a. See Figure 4.163.

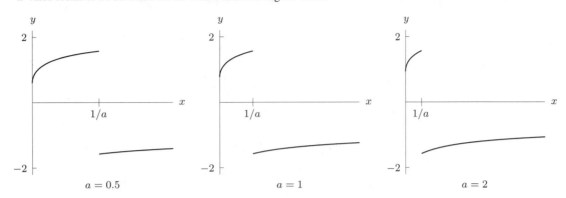

Figure 4.163

(b) Most computer algebra systems will give a fairly complicated answer for the derivative. Here is one example; others may be different.
$$\frac{dy}{dx} = \frac{\sqrt{x} + \sqrt{a}\,\sqrt{a\,x}}{2\,x\,\left(1 + a + 2\,\sqrt{a}\,\sqrt{x} + x + a\,x - 2\,\sqrt{a\,x}\right)}.$$
When we graph the derivative, it appears that we get the same graph for all values of a. See Figure 4.164.

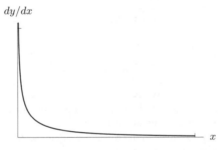

dy/dx

Figure 4.164

(c) Since a and x are positive, we have $\sqrt{ax} = \sqrt{a}\sqrt{x}$. We can use this to simplify the expression we found for the derivative:
$$\frac{dy}{dx} = \frac{\sqrt{x} + \sqrt{a}\sqrt{ax}}{2x\left(1 + a + 2\sqrt{a}\sqrt{x} + x + ax - 2\sqrt{ax}\right)}$$
$$= \frac{\sqrt{x} + \sqrt{a}\sqrt{a}\sqrt{x}}{2x\left(1 + a + 2\sqrt{a}\sqrt{x} + x + ax - 2\sqrt{a}\sqrt{x}\right)}$$
$$= \frac{\sqrt{x} + a\sqrt{x}}{2x\left(1 + a + x + ax\right)} = \frac{(1+a)\sqrt{x}}{2x(1+a)(1+x)} = \frac{\sqrt{x}}{2x(1+x)}.$$

Since a has canceled out, the derivative is independent of a. This explains why all the graphs look the same in part (b). (In fact they are not exactly the same, because $f'(x)$ is undefined where $f(x)$ has its jump discontinuity. The point at which this happens changes with a.)

61. (a) A CAS gives
$$\frac{d}{dx}\operatorname{arcsinh} x = \frac{1}{\sqrt{1 + x^2}}$$

(b) Differentiating both sides of $\sinh(\operatorname{arcsinh} x) = x$, we get
$$\cosh(\operatorname{arcsinh} x)\frac{d}{dx}(\operatorname{arcsinh} x) = 1$$
$$\frac{d}{dx}(\operatorname{arcsinh} x) = \frac{1}{\cosh(\operatorname{arcsinh} x)}.$$

Since $\cosh^2 x - \sinh^2 x = 1$, $\cosh x = \pm\sqrt{1 + \sinh^2 x}$. Furthermore, since $\cosh x > 0$ for all x, we take the positive square root, so $\cosh x = \sqrt{1 + \sinh^2 x}$. Therefore, $\cosh(\text{arcsinh}\, x) = \sqrt{1 + (\sinh(\text{arcsinh}\, x))^2} = \sqrt{1 + x^2}$. Thus

$$\frac{d}{dx}\text{arcsinh}\, x = \frac{1}{\sqrt{1 + x^2}}.$$

62. (a) A CAS gives

$$\frac{d}{dx}\text{arccosh}\, x = \frac{1}{\sqrt{x^2 - 1}}, \quad x \geq 1.$$

(b) Differentiating both sides of $\cosh(\text{arccosh}\, x) = x$, we get

$$\sinh(\text{arccosh}\, x)\frac{d}{dx}(\text{arccosh}\, x) = 1$$

$$\frac{d}{dx}(\text{arccosh}\, x) = \frac{1}{\sinh(\text{arccosh}\, x)}.$$

Since $\cosh^2 x - \sinh^2 x = 1$, $\sinh x = \pm\sqrt{\cosh^2 x - 1}$. If $x \geq 0$, then $\sinh x \geq 0$, so we take the positive square root. So $\sinh x = \sqrt{\cosh^2 x - 1}$, $x \geq 0$. Therefore, $\sinh(\text{arccosh}\, x) = \sqrt{(\cosh(\text{arccosh}\, x))^2 - 1} = \sqrt{x^2 - 1}$, for $x \geq 1$. Thus

$$\frac{d}{dx}\text{arccosh}\, x = \frac{1}{\sqrt{x^2 - 1}}.$$

63. (a) Using a computer algebra system or differentiating by hand, we get

$$f'(x) = \frac{1}{2\sqrt{a + x}(\sqrt{a} + \sqrt{x})} - \frac{\sqrt{a + x}}{2\sqrt{x}(\sqrt{a} + \sqrt{x})^2}.$$

Simplifying gives

$$f'(x) = \frac{-a + \sqrt{a}\sqrt{x}}{2\left(\sqrt{a} + \sqrt{x}\right)^2 \sqrt{x}\sqrt{a + x}}.$$

The denominator of the derivative is always positive if $x > 0$, and the numerator is zero when $x = a$. Writing the numerator as $\sqrt{a}(\sqrt{x} - \sqrt{a})$, we see that the derivative changes from negative to positive at $x = a$. Thus, by the first derivative test, the function has a local minimum at $x = a$.

(b) As a increases, the local minimum moves to the right. See Figure 4.165. This is consistent with what we found in part (a), since the local minimum is at $x = a$.

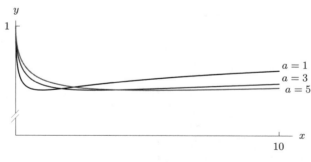

Figure 4.165

(c) Using a computer algebra system to find the second derivative when $a = 2$, we get

$$f''(x) = \frac{4\sqrt{2} + 12\sqrt{x} + 6\,x^{3/2} - 3\sqrt{2}\,x^2}{4\left(\sqrt{2} + \sqrt{x}\right)^3 x^{3/2}\,(2 + x)^{3/2}}.$$

Using the computer algebra system again to solve $f''(x) = 0$, we find that it has one zero at $x = 4.6477$. Graphing the second derivative, we see that it goes from positive to negative at $x = 4.6477$, so this is an inflection point.

64. (a) Different CASs give different answers. (In fact, their answers could be more complicated than what you get by hand.) One possible answer is

$$\frac{dy}{dx} = \frac{\tan\left(\frac{x}{2}\right)}{2\sqrt{\frac{1-\cos x}{1+\cos x}}}.$$

(b) The graph in Figure 4.166 is a step function:

$$f(x) = \begin{cases} 1/2 & 2n\pi < x < (2n+1)\pi \\ -1/2 & (2n+1)\pi < x < (2n+2)\pi. \end{cases}$$

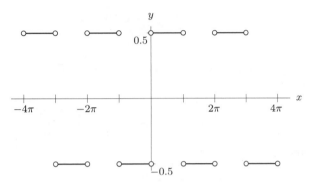

Figure 4.166

Figure 4.166, which shows the graph in disconnected line segments, is correct. However, unless you select certain graphing options in your CAS, it may join up the segments. Use the double angle formula $\cos(x) = \cos^2(x/2) - \sin^2(x/2)$ to simplify the answer in part (a). We find

$$\frac{dy}{dx} = \frac{\tan(x/2)}{2\sqrt{\frac{1-\cos x}{1+\cos x}}} = \frac{\tan(x/2)}{2\sqrt{\frac{1-\cos(2\cdot(x/2))}{1+\cos(2\cdot(x/2))}}} = \frac{\tan(x/2)}{2\sqrt{\frac{1-\cos^2(x/2)+\sin^2(x/2)}{1+\cos^2(x/2)-\sin^2(x/2)}}}$$

$$= \frac{\tan(x/2)}{2\sqrt{\frac{2\sin^2(x/2)}{2\cos^2(x/2)}}} = \frac{\tan(x/2)}{2\sqrt{\tan^2(x/2)}} = \frac{\tan(x/2)}{2\left|\tan(x/2)\right|}$$

Thus, $dy/dx = 1/2$ when $\tan(x/2) > 0$, i.e. when $0 < x < \pi$ (more generally, when $2n\pi < x < (2n+1)\pi$), and $dy/dx = -1/2$ when $\tan(x/2) < 0$, i.e., when $\pi < x < 2\pi$ (more generally, when $(2n+1)\pi < x < (2n+2)\pi$, where n is any integer).

65. (a)

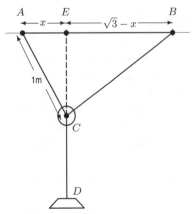

Figure 4.167

We want to maximize the sum of the lengths EC and CD in Figure 4.167. Let x be the distance AE. Then x can be between 0 and 1, the length of the left rope. By the Pythagorean theorem,

$$EC = \sqrt{1 - x^2}.$$

The length of the rope from B to C can also be found by the Pythagorean theorem:

$$BC = \sqrt{EC^2 + EB^2} = \sqrt{1 - x^2 + (\sqrt{3} - x)^2} = \sqrt{4 - 2\sqrt{3}x}.$$

Since the entire rope from B to D has length 3 m, the length from C to D is

$$CD = 3 - \sqrt{4 - 2\sqrt{3}x}.$$

The distance we want to maximize is

$$f(x) = EC + CD = \sqrt{1 - x^2} + 3 - \sqrt{4 - 2\sqrt{3}x}, \quad \text{for} \quad 0 \le x \le 1.$$

Differentiating gives

$$f'(x) = \frac{-2x}{2\sqrt{1 - x^2}} - \frac{-2\sqrt{3}}{2\sqrt{4 - 2\sqrt{3}x}}.$$

Setting $f'(x) = 0$ gives the cubic equation

$$2\sqrt{3}x^3 - 7x^2 + 3 = 0.$$

Using a computer algebra system to solve the equation gives three roots: $x = -1/\sqrt{3}, x = \sqrt{3}/2, x = \sqrt{3}$. We discard the negative root. Since x cannot be larger than 1 meter (the length of the left rope), the only critical point of interest is $x = \sqrt{3}/2$, that is, halfway between A and B.

To find the global maximum, we calculate the distance of the weight from the ceiling at the critical point and at the endpoints:

$$f(0) = \sqrt{1} + 3 - \sqrt{4} = 2$$

$$f\left(\frac{\sqrt{3}}{2}\right) = \sqrt{1 - \frac{3}{4}} + 3 - \sqrt{4 - 2\sqrt{3} \cdot \frac{\sqrt{3}}{2}} = 2.5$$

$$f(1) = \sqrt{0} + 3 - \sqrt{4 - 2\sqrt{3}} = 4 - \sqrt{3} = 2.27.$$

Thus, the weight is at the maximum distance from the ceiling when $x = \sqrt{3}/2$; that is, the weight comes to rest at a point halfway between points A and B.

(b) No, the equilibrium position depends on the length of the rope. For example, suppose that the left-hand rope was 1 cm long. Then there is no way for the pulley at its end to move to a point halfway between the anchor points.

CHECK YOUR UNDERSTANDING

1. True. Since the domain of f is all real numbers, all local minima occur at critical points.

2. True. Since the domain of f is all real numbers, all local maxima occur at critical points. Thus, if $x = p$ is a local maximum, $x = p$ must be a critical point.

3. False. A local maximum of f might occur at a point where f' does not exist. For example, $f(x) = -|x|$ has a local maximum at $x = 0$, but the derivative is not 0 (or defined) there.

4. False, because $x = p$ could be a local minimum of f. For example, if $f(x) = x^2$, then $f'(0) = 0$, so $x = 0$ is a critical point, but $x = 0$ is not a local maximum of f.

5. False. For example, if $f(x) = x^3$, then $f'(0) = 0$, but $f(x)$ does not have either a local maximum or a local minimum at $x = 0$.

6. True. Suppose f is increasing at some points and decreasing at others. Then $f'(x)$ takes both positive and negative values. Since $f'(x)$ is continuous, by the Intermediate Value Theorem, there would be some point where $f'(x)$ is zero, so that there would be a critical point. Since we are told there are no critical points, f must be increasing everywhere or decreasing everywhere.

7. False. For example, if $f(x) = x^4$, then $f''(x) = 12x^2$, and hence $f''(0) = 0$. But f does not have an inflection point at $x = 0$ because the second derivative does not change sign at 0.

8. True. Since f'' changes sign at the inflection point $x = p$, by the Intermediate Value Theorem, $f''(p) = 0$.

9. Let $f(x) = ax^2$, with $a \neq 0$. Then $f'(x) = 2ax$, so f has a critical point only at $x = 0$.

10. Let $g(x) = ax^3 + bx^2$, where neither a nor b are allowed to be zero. Then

$$g'(x) = 3ax^2 + 2bx = x(3ax + 2b).$$

Then $g(x)$ has two distinct critical points, at $x = 0$ and at $x = -2b/3a$. Since

$$g''(x) = 6ax + 2b,$$

there is exactly one point of inflection, $x = -2b/6a = -b/3a$.

11. (a) True, $f(x) \leq 4$ on the interval $(0, 2)$
   (b) False. The values of $f(x)$ get arbitrarily close to 4, but $f(x) < 4$ for all x in the interval $(0, 2)$.
   (c) True. The values of $f(x)$ get arbitrarily close to 0, but $f(x) > 0$ for all x in the interval $(0, 2)$.
   (d) False. On the interval $(-1, 1)$, the global minimum is 0.
   (e) True, by the Extreme Value Theorem, Theorem 4.2.

12. (a) This is not implied; just because a function satisfies the conclusions of the statement, that does not mean it has to satisfy the conditions.
   (b) This is not implied; if a function fails to satisfy the conditions of the statement, then the statement does not tell us anything about it.
   (c) This is implied; if a function fails to satisfy the conclusions of the statement, then it could not satisfy the conditions of the statement, because if it did the statement would imply it also satisfied the conclusions.

13. True. If the maximum is not at an endpoint, then it must be at critical point of f. But $x = 0$ is the only critical point of $f(x) = x^2$ and it gives a minimum, not a maximum.

14. True. For example, $A = 1$ and $A = 2$ are both upper bounds for $f(x) = \sin x$.

15. True. If $f'(0) > 0$, then f would be increasing at 0 and so $f(0) < f(x)$ for x just to the right of 0. Then $f(0)$ would not be a maximum for f on the interval $0 \leq x \leq 10$.

16. True. The circumference C and radius r are related by $C = 2\pi r$, so $dC/dt = 2\pi dr/dt$. Thus if dr/dt is constant, so is dC/dt.

17. False. The circumference A and radius r are related by $A = \pi r^2$, so $dA/dt = 2\pi r dr/dt$. Thus dA/dt depends on r and since r is not constant, neither is dA/dt.

18. False. If the particle tracing out the curve comes to a complete stop, it can then head off in a completely new direction. For example, the curve given parametrically by $x = t^3$ and $y = t^2$ is the same as the graph of $y = x^{2/3}$ which has a cusp at $x = 0$.

19. False. The slope is given by

$$\frac{dy}{dx} = \frac{dy/dt}{dx/dt} = \frac{2t\cos(t^2)}{-2t\sin(t^2)} = -\frac{\cos(t^2)}{\sin(t^2)}.$$

20. False. To use l'Hopital's rule, we need $f(a) = g(a) = 0$. For example, if $f(x) = 3$ and $g(x) = x$, then $g(1) = 1$ and $f'(1)/g'(1) = 0/1 = 0$, but $\lim_{x\to 1}(f(x)/g(x)) = 3/1 = 3$.

21. $f(x) = x^2 + 1$ is positive for all x and concave up.

22. This is impossible. If $f(a) > 0$, then the downward concavity forces the graph of f to cross the x-axis to the right or left of $x = a$, which means $f(x)$ cannot be positive for all values of x. More precisely, suppose that $f(x)$ is positive for all x and f is concave down. Thus there must be some value $x = a$ where $f(a) > 0$ and $f'(a)$ is not zero, since a constant function is not concave down. The tangent line at $x = a$ has nonzero slope and hence must cross the x-axis somewhere to the right or left of $x = a$. Since the graph of f must lie below this tangent line, it must also cross the x-axis, contradicting the assumption that $f(x)$ is positive for all x.

23. $f(x) = -x^2 - 1$ is negative for all x and concave down.

24. This is impossible. If $f(a) < 0$, then the upward concavity forces the graph of f to cross the x-axis to the right or left of $x = a$, which means $f(x)$ cannot be negative for all values of x. More precisely, suppose that $f(x)$ is negative for all x and f is concave up. Thus there must be some value $x = a$ where $f(a) < 0$ and $f'(a)$ is not zero, since a constant function is not concave up. The tangent line at $x = a$ has nonzero slope and hence must cross the x-axis somewhere to the right or left of $x = a$. Since the graph of f must lie above this tangent line, it must also cross the x-axis, contradicting the assumption that $f(x)$ is negative for all x.

25. This is impossible. Since f'' exists, so must f', which means that f is differentiable and hence continuous. If $f(x)$ were positive for some values of x and negative for other values, then by the Intermediate Value Theorem, $f(x)$ would have to be zero somewhere, but this is impossible since $f(x)f''(x) < 0$ for all x. Thus either $f(x) > 0$ for all values of x, in which case $f''(x) < 0$ for all values of x, that is f is concave down. But this is impossible by Problem 22. Or else $f(x) < 0$ for all x, in which case $f''(x) > 0$ for all x, that is f is concave up. But this is impossible by Problem 24.

26. This is impossible. Since f''' exists, f'' must be continuous. By the Intermediate Value Theorem, $f''(x)$ cannot change sign, since $f''(x)$ cannot be zero. In the same way, we can show that $f'(x)$ and $f(x)$ cannot change sign. Since the product of these three with $f'''(x)$ cannot change sign, $f'''(x)$ cannot change sign. Thus $f(x)f''(x)$ and $f'(x)f'''(x)$ cannot change sign. Since their product is negative for all x, one or the other must be negative for all x. By Problem 25, this is impossible.

PROJECTS FOR CHAPTER FOUR

1.

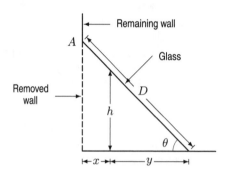

Figure 4.168: A Cross-section of the Projected Greenhouse

Suppose that the glass is at an angle θ (as shown in Figure 4.168), that the length of the wall is l, and that the glass has dimensions D ft by l ft. Since your parents will spend a fixed amount, the area of the glass, say k ft^2, is fixed:

$$Dl = k.$$

The width of the extension is $D\cos\theta$. If h is the height of your tallest parent, he or she can walk in a distance of x, and

$$\frac{h}{y} = \tan\theta, \quad \text{so} \quad y = \frac{h}{\tan\theta}.$$

Thus,

$$x = D\cos\theta - y = D\cos\theta - \frac{h}{\tan\theta} \quad \text{for } 0 < \theta < \frac{\pi}{2}.$$

We maximize x since doing so maximizes the usable area:

$$\frac{dx}{d\theta} = -D\sin\theta + \frac{h}{(\tan\theta)^2} \cdot \frac{1}{(\cos\theta)^2} = 0$$

$$\sin^3\theta = \frac{h}{D}$$

$$\theta = \arcsin\left(\left(\frac{h}{D}\right)^{1/3}\right).$$

This is the only critical point, and $x \to 0$ when $\theta \to 0$ and when $\theta \to \pi/2$. Thus, the critical point is a global maximum. Since

$$\cos\theta = \sqrt{1 - \sin^2\theta} = \sqrt{1 - \left(\frac{h}{D}\right)^{2/3}},$$

the maximum value of x is

$$x = D\cos\theta - \frac{h}{\tan\theta} = D\cos\theta - \frac{h\cos\theta}{\sin\theta}$$

$$= \left(D - \frac{h}{\sin\theta}\right)\cos\theta = \left(D - \frac{h}{(h/D)^{1/3}}\right)\cdot\left(1 - \left(\frac{h}{D}\right)^{2/3}\right)^{1/2}$$

$$= (D - h^{2/3}D^{1/3})\cdot\left(1 - \frac{h^{2/3}}{D^{2/3}}\right)^{1/2}$$

$$= D\left(1 - \frac{h^{2/3}}{D^{2/3}}\right)\cdot\left(1 - \frac{h^{2/3}}{D^{2/3}}\right)^{1/2} = D\left(1 - \frac{h^{2/3}}{D^{2/3}}\right)^{3/2}.$$

This means

$$\text{Maximum Usable Area} = lx$$

$$= lD\left(1 - \frac{h^{2/3}}{D^{2/3}}\right)^{3/2}$$

$$= k\left(1 - \left(\frac{hl}{k}\right)^{2/3}\right)^{3/2}$$

2. (a) The point on the line $y = mx$ corresponding to the point $(2, 3.5)$ has y-coordinate given by $y = m(2) = 2m$. Thus, for the point $(2, 3.5)$

$$\text{Vertical distance to the line} = |2m - 3.5|.$$

We calculate the distance similarly for the other two points. We want to minimize the sum, S, of the squares of these vertical distances

$$S = (2m - 3.5)^2 + (3m - 6.8)^2 + (5m - 9.1)^2.$$

Differentiating with respect to m gives

$$\frac{dS}{dm} = 2(2m - 3.5)\cdot 2 + 2(3m - 6.8)\cdot 3 + 2(5m - 9.1)\cdot 5.$$

Setting $dS/dm = 0$ gives

$$2\cdot 2(2m - 3.5) + 2\cdot 3(3m - 6.8) + 2\cdot 5(5m - 9.1) = 0.$$

Canceling a 2 and multiplying out gives

$$4m - 7 + 9m - 20.4 + 25m - 45.5 = 0$$
$$38m = 72.9$$
$$m = 1.92.$$

Thus, the best fitting line has equation $y = 1.92x$.

(b) To fit a line of the form $y = mx$ to the data, we take $y = V$ and $x = r^3$. Then k will be the slope m. So we make the following table of data:

r	2	5	7	8
$x = r^3$	8	125	343	512
$y = V$	8.7	140.3	355.8	539.2

To find the best fitting line of the form $y = mx$, we minimize the sums of the squares of the vertical distances from the line. For the point $(8, 8.7)$ the corresponding point on the line has $y = 8m$, so

$$\text{Vertical distance} = |8m - 8.7|.$$

We find distances from the other points similarly. Thus we want to minimize

$$S = (8m - 8.7)^2 + (125m - 140.3)^2 + (343m - 355.8)^2 + (512m - 539.2)^2.$$

Differentiating with respect to m, which is the variable, and setting the derivative to zero:

$$\frac{dS}{dm} = 2(8m - 8.7) \cdot 8 + 2(125m - 140.3) \cdot 125 + 2(343m - 355.8) \cdot 343 + 2(512m - 539.2) \cdot 512 = 0.$$

After canceling a 2, solving for m leads to the equation

$$8^2 m + 125^2 m + 343^2 m + 512^2 m = 8 \cdot 8.7 + 125 \cdot 140.3 + 343 \cdot 355.8 + 512 \cdot 539.2$$
$$m = 1.051.$$

Thus, $k = 1.051$ and the relationship between V and r is

$$V = 1.051 r^3.$$

(In fact, the correct relationship is $V = \pi r^3 / 3$, so the exact value of k is $\pi/3 = 1.047$.)

(c) The best fitting line minimizes the sum of the squares of the vertical distances from points to the line. Since the point on the line $y = mx$ corresponding to (x_1, y_1) is the point with $y = mx_1$; for this point we have

$$\text{Vertical distance} = |mx_1 - y_1|.$$

We calculate the distance from the other points similarly. Thus we want to minimize

$$S = (mx_1 - y_1)^2 + (mx_2 - y_2)^2 \cdots + (mx_n - y_n)^2.$$

The variable is m (the x_is and y_is are all constants), so

$$\frac{dS}{dm} = 2(mx_1 - y_1)x_1 + 2(mx_2 - y_2)x_2 + \cdots + 2(mx_n - y_n)x_n = 0$$
$$2(m(x_1^2 + x_2^2 + \cdots + x_n^2) - (x_1 y_1 + x_2 y_2 + \cdots + x_n y_n)) = 0.$$

Solving for m gives

$$m = \frac{x_1 y_1 + x_2 y_2 + \cdots + x_n y_n}{x_1^2 + x_2^2 + \cdots + x_n^2} = \frac{\sum_{i=1}^{n} x_i y_i}{\sum_{i=1}^{n} x_i^2}.$$

3. The optimization problem in part (d) is unusual in that the optimum value is known (55 mph), and the problem is to find the conditions which lead to this optimum. A variant of this project is to ask what group of people in the real world might be interested in each of the questions asked. A possible answer is owners of trucking companies for parts (b) and (c), traffic police for part (d), and Interstate Commerce Commission for parts (e) and (f).

(a) The total cost per mile is the cost of the driver plus the cost of fuel. We let

    w be the driver's hourly wage in dollars/hour,

    v be the average speed in miles/hour,

    m be the weight of the truck in thousands of pounds,

    f the cost of fuel in dollars/gallon.

The cost per mile of the driver's wages is w/v. The cost of fuel per mile will be one over the "mileage per gallon" times the cost of fuel per gallon—i.e. f/mpg. The mileage per gallon is $6 - (m - 25)(0.02) - (v - 45)(0.1)$ for velocities over 45 and $6 - (m - 25)(0.02)$ for velocities under 45. So the total cost per mile, c, is

$$c = \begin{cases} \dfrac{w}{v} + \dfrac{f}{6 - (m - 25)(0.02)} & 0 < v \leq 45 \\[3mm] \dfrac{w}{v} + \dfrac{f}{6 - (m - 25)(0.02) - (v - 45)(0.1)} & 45 < v. \end{cases}$$

Note that there is an upper limit to the velocity in this last expression given when

$$6 - (m - 25)(0.02) - (v - 45)(0.1) = 0.$$

(b) We are now given the values

$$w = 15.00 \text{ dollars/hour}$$
$$m = 75 \text{ thousand pounds}$$
$$f = 1.25 \text{ dollars/gallon.}$$

We have

$$c = \begin{cases} \dfrac{15}{v} + \dfrac{1.25}{6 - (75 - 25)(0.02)} & 0 < v \leq 45 \\[3mm] \dfrac{15}{v} + \dfrac{1}{6 - (75 - 25)(0.02) - (v - 45)(0.1)} & 45 < v, \end{cases}$$

which simplifies to

$$c = \begin{cases} \dfrac{15}{v} + \dfrac{1}{4} & 0 < v \leq 45 \\[3mm] \dfrac{15}{v} + \dfrac{1.25}{5 - (v - 45)(0.1)} & 45 < v < 95. \end{cases}$$

The upper limit for v occurs when $5 - (v - 45)(0.1) = 0$, that is, $v = 95$.

To initiate our search for a minimum, note that the function $c = 15/v + 1/4$ is strictly decreasing. So we only need find the minimum of the function

$$c = \frac{15}{v} + \frac{1.25}{5 - (v - 45)(0.1)}$$

on the interval $45 \leq v < 95$. Rearranging this slightly, we get

$$c = \frac{15}{v} + \frac{1.25}{9.5 - 0.1v}.$$

Then differentiating gives

$$\frac{dc}{dv} = -\frac{15}{v^2} + \frac{(1.25)(0.1)}{(9.5 - 0.1v)^2}.$$

Setting this to zero and solving, we get

$$0 = -\frac{15}{v^2} + \frac{(1.25)(0.1)}{(9.5 - 0.1v)^2}$$
$$15(9.5 - 0.1v)^2 = 0.125v^2$$
$$3.87(9.5 - 0.1v) \approx \pm 0.354v$$
$$36.8 - 0.387v \approx \pm 0.354v$$
$$36.8 \approx 0.741v \text{ or } 36.8 \approx 0.033v$$
$$v \approx 49.7 \text{ or } v \approx 1100.$$

This last value is not in the domain, so we only consider the critical point $v = 49.7$ and the endpoints of $v = 45$ and $v = 95$. We evaluate the cost function:

$$c(45) = 0.333 + 0.25 = 58.3¢/\text{mile}$$
$$c(49.7) = 0.302 + 0.276 = 57.8¢/\text{mile}$$
$$c(95) = \infty.$$

So $v = 49.7$ is a minimum; the cheapest speed is 49.7 mph.

(c) Evaluating the cost at $v = 55$ mph, $v = 60$ mph, and the minimum $v = 49.7$ mph gives

$$c(49.7) = 57.8¢$$
$$c(55) = 58.5¢$$
$$c(60) = 60.7¢.$$

Notice that the cost per mile does not rise very quickly. A produce hauler often gets extra revenue for getting there fast. Increasing speed from 50 to 60 mph decreases the transit time by over 15% but increases the costs by only 5%. Thus, many produce haulers will choose a speed above 49.7 mph.

(d) Now we are not given the price of fuel, but we want the minimum to be at $v = 55$ mph. We find the value of f making $v = 55$ the minimum. The function we want to minimize is

$$c = \frac{15}{v} + \frac{f}{9.5 - 0.1v}.$$

Differentiating gives

$$\frac{dc}{dv} = -\frac{15}{v^2} + \frac{0.1f}{(9.5 - 0.1v)^2}$$

Setting this equal to 0, we have

$$0 = -\frac{15}{v^2} + \frac{0.1f}{(9.5 - 0.1v)^2}$$
$$0 = -15(9.5 - 0.1v)^2 + 0.1fv^2.$$

Substituting $v = 55$ and solving for f gives

$$0 = -15(4)^2 + 0.1(55)^2 f$$
$$f \approx 80¢/\text{gallon}.$$

(e) Now we are not told the driver's wages, w, or the fuel cost, f. We want to find the relationship between w and f making the minimum cost occur at $v = 55$ mph. We have

$$c = \frac{w}{v} + \frac{f}{9.5 - 0.1v}$$
$$\frac{dc}{dv} = -\frac{w}{v^2} + \frac{0.1f}{(9.5 - 0.1v)^2}.$$

We need this to equal 0 when $v = 55$, so

$$0 = -\frac{w}{3025} + \frac{0.1f}{16}.$$

This means

$$\frac{w}{f} = \frac{(3025)(0.1)}{16} = 18.9,$$

that is, the fuel cost per gallon should be $1/18.9$ that of the driver's hourly wage. If the Interstate Commerce Commission wants truck drivers to keep to a speed of 55 mph, they should consider taxing fuel or driver's wages so that they remain in the relation $w = 18.9f$.

(f) Now we assume $w = 18.9f$ and that m is variable. We want to minimize cost, getting a relationship between m and the optimal v. The function we want to minimize is

$$c = \frac{18.9f}{v} + \frac{f}{6 - (m - 25)(0.02) - (v - 45)(0.1)}$$
$$= \frac{18.9f}{v} + \frac{f}{11 - 0.02m - 0.1v}.$$

Differentiating gives

$$\frac{dc}{dv} = \frac{-18.9f}{v^2} + \frac{0.1f}{(11 - 0.02m - 0.1v)^2}.$$

We are interested in when $dc/dv = 0$:

$$-\frac{18.9f}{v^2} + \frac{0.1f}{(11 - 0.02m - 0.1v)^2} = 0.$$

Solving gives

$$v = 63.7 - 0.116m \quad \text{or} \quad v = 403.5 - 0.734m.$$

Only the first gives plausible speeds (and gives $v = 55$ when $m = 75$), so we conclude the optimal speed varies linearly with weight according to the equation $v = 63.7 - 0.116m$. This means that every 10,000 increase in weight reduces the optimal speed by just over 1 mph.

4. (a) (i) We want to minimize A, the total area lost to the forest, which is made up of n firebreaks and 1 stand of trees lying between firebreaks. The area of each firebreak is $(50 \text{ km})(0.01 \text{ km}) = 0.5 \text{ km}^2$, so the total area lost to the firebreaks is $0.5n \text{ km}^2$. There are n total stands of trees between firebreaks. The area of a single stand of trees can be found by subtracting the firebreak area from the forest and dividing by n, so

$$\text{Area of one stand of trees} = \frac{2500 - 0.5n}{n}.$$

Thus, the total area lost is

$$A = \text{Area of one stand} + \text{Area lost to firebreaks}$$
$$= \frac{2500 - 0.5n}{n} + 0.5n = \frac{2500}{n} - 0.5 + 0.5n.$$

We assume that A is a differentiable function of a continuous variable, n. Differentiating this function yields

$$\frac{dA}{dn} = -\frac{2500}{n^2} + 0.5.$$

At critical points, $dA/dn = 0$, so $0.5 = 2500/n^2$ or $n = \sqrt{2500/0.5} \approx 70.7$. Since n must be an integer, we check that when $n = 71$, $A = 70.211$ and when $n = 70$, $A = 70.214$. Thus, $n = 71$ gives a smaller area lost.

We can check that this is a local minimum since the second derivative is positive everywhere

$$\frac{d^2 A}{dn^2} = \frac{5000}{n^3} > 0.$$

Finally, we check the endpoints: $n = 1$ yields the entire forest lost after a fire, since there is only one stand of trees in this case and it all burns. The largest n is 5000, and in this case the firebreaks remove the entire forest. Both of these cases maximize the area of forest lost. Thus, $n = 71$ is a global minimum. So 71 firebreaks minimizes the area of forest lost.

(ii) Repeating the calculation using b for the width gives

$$A = \frac{2500}{n} - 50b + 50bn,$$

and

$$\frac{dA}{dn} = \frac{-2500}{n^2} + 50b,$$

with a critical point when $b = 50/n^2$ so $n = \sqrt{50/b}$. So, for example, if we make the width b four times as large we need half as many firebreaks.

(b) We want to minimize A, the total area lost to the forest, which is made up of n firebreaks in one direction, n firebreaks in the other, and one square of trees surrounded by firebreaks. The area of each firebreak is 0.5 km^2, and there are $2n$ of them, giving a total of $0.5 \cdot 2n$. But this is larger than the total area covered by the firebreaks, since it counts the small intersection squares, of size $(0.01)^2$, twice. Since there are n^2 intersections, we must subtract $(0.01)^2 n^2$ from the total area of the $2n$ firebreaks. Thus,

$$\text{Area covered by the firebreaks} = 0.5 \cdot 2n - (0.01)^2 n^2.$$

To this we must add the area of one square patch of trees lost in a fire. These are squares of side $(50 - 0.01n)/n = 50/n - 0.01$. Thus the total area lost is

$$A = n - 0.0001n^2 + (50/n - 0.01)^2$$

Treating n as a continuous variable and differentiating this function yields

$$\frac{dA}{dn} = 1 - 0.0002n + 2\left(\frac{50}{n} - 0.01\right)\left(\frac{-50}{n^2}\right).$$

Using a computer algebra system to find critical points we find that $dA/dn = 0$ when $n \approx 17$ and $n = 5000$. Thus $n = 17$ gives a minimum lost area, since the endpoints of $n = 1$ and $n = 5000$ both yield $A = 2500$ or the entire forest lost. So we use 17 firebreaks in each direction.

CHAPTER FIVE

Solutions for Section 5.1

Exercises

1. (a) Lower estimate $= (45)(2) + (16)(2) + (0)(2) = 122$ feet.
   Upper estimate $= (88)(2) + (45)(2) + (16)(2) = 298$ feet.

   (b)

   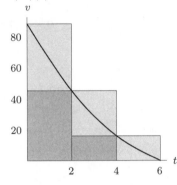

2. (a) Since the velocity is decreasing, for an upper estimate, we use a left sum. With $n = 5$, we have $\Delta t = 2$. Then

   $$\text{Upper estimate } = (44)(2) + (42)(2) + (41)(2) + (40)(2) + (37)(2) = 408.$$

   (b) For a lower estimate, we use a right sum, so

   $$\text{Lower estimate } = (42)(2) + (41)(2) + (40)(2) + (37)(2) + (35)(2) = 390.$$

3. (a) (i) Since the velocity is increasing, for an upper estimate we use a right sum. Using $n = 4$, we have $\Delta t = 3$, so

   $$\text{Upper estimate } = (37)(3) + (38)(3) + (40)(3) + (45)(3) = 480.$$

   (ii) Using $n = 2$, we have $\Delta t = 6$, so

   $$\text{Upper estimate } = (38)(6) + (45)(6) = 498.$$

   (b) The answer using $n = 4$ is more accurate as it uses the values of $v(t)$ when $t = 3$ and $t = 9$.

   (c) Since the velocity is increasing, for a lower estimate we use a left sum. Using $n = 4$, we have $\Delta t = 3$, so

   $$\text{Lower estimate } = (34)(3) + (37)(3) + (38)(3) + (40)(3) = 447.$$

4. (a) With $n = 4$, we have $\Delta t = 2$. Then

   $$t_0 = 15, t_1 = 17, t_2 = 19, t_3 = 21, t_4 = 23 \quad \text{and} \quad f(t_0) = 10, f(t_1) = 13, f(t_2) = 18, f(t_3) = 20, f(t_4) = 30$$

   (b)

   $$\text{Left sum } = (10)(2) + (13)(2) + (18)(2) + (20)(2) = 122$$
   $$\text{Right sum } = (13)(2) + (18)(2) + (20)(2) + (30)(2) = 162.$$

   (c) With $n = 2$, we have $\Delta t = 4$. Then

   $$t_0 = 15, t_1 = 19, t_2 = 23 \quad \text{and} \quad f(t_0) = 10, f(t_1) = 18, f(t_2) = 30$$

   (d)

   $$\text{Left sum } = (10)(4) + (18)(4) = 112$$
   $$\text{Right sum } = (18)(4) + (30)(4) = 192.$$

5. (a) With $n = 4$, we have $\Delta t = 4$. Then

$$t_0 = 0, t_1 = 4, t_2 = 8, t_3 = 12, t_4 = 16 \quad \text{and} \quad f(t_0) = 25, f(t_1) = 23, f(t_2) = 22, f(t_3) = 20, f(t_4) = 17$$

(b)

$$\text{Left sum} = (25)(4) + (23)(4) + (22)(4) + (20)(4) = 360$$
$$\text{Right sum} = (23)(4) + (22)(4) + (20)(4) + (17)(4) = 328.$$

(c) With $n = 2$, we have $\Delta t = 8$. Then

$$t_0 = 0, t_1 = 8, t_2 = 16 \quad \text{and} \quad f(t_0) = 25, f(t_1) = 22, f(t_2) = 17$$

(d)

$$\text{Left sum} = (25)(8) + (22)(8) = 376$$
$$\text{Right sum} = (22)(8) + (17)(8) = 312.$$

6. Using $\Delta t = 2$,

$$\text{Lower estimate} = v(0) \cdot 2 + v(2) \cdot 2 + v(4) \cdot 2$$
$$= 1(2) + 5(2) + 17(2)$$
$$= 46$$
$$\text{Upper estimate} = v(2) \cdot 2 + v(4) \cdot 2 + v(6) \cdot 2$$
$$= 5(2) + 17(2) + 37(2)$$
$$= 118$$
$$\text{Average} = \frac{46 + 118}{2} = 82$$
$$\text{Distance traveled} \approx 82 \text{ meters.}$$

7. Using $\Delta t = 0.2$, our upper estimate is

$$\frac{1}{1 + 0}(0.2) + \frac{1}{1 + 0.2}(0.2) + \frac{1}{1 + 0.4}(0.2) + \frac{1}{1 + 0.6}(0.2) + \frac{1}{1 + 0.8}(0.2) \approx 0.75.$$

The lower estimate is

$$\frac{1}{1 + 0.2}(0.2) + \frac{1}{1 + 0.4}(0.2) + \frac{1}{1 + 0.6}(0.2) + \frac{1}{1 + 0.8}(0.2)\frac{1}{1 + 1}(0.2) \approx 0.65.$$

Since v is a decreasing function, the bug has crawled more than 0.65 meters, but less than 0.75 meters. We average the two to get a better estimate:

$$\frac{0.65 + 0.75}{2} = 0.70 \text{ meters.}$$

8. Just counting the squares (each of which has area 10), and allowing for the broken squares, we can see that the area under the curve from 0 to 6 is between 140 and 150. Hence the distance traveled is between 140 and 150 meters.

9. Figure 5.1 shows the graph of $f(t)$. The region under the graph of $f(t)$ from $t = 0$ to $t = 10$ is a triangle of base 10 seconds and height 50 meter/sec. Then

$$\text{Distance traveled} = \text{Area of triangle} = \frac{1}{2} \cdot 10 \cdot 50 = 250 \text{ meters.}$$

Thus the distance traveled is 250 meters.

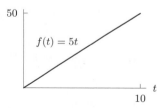

Figure 5.1

10. Since f is increasing, the right-hand sum is the upper estimate and the left-hand sum is the lower estimate. We have $f(a) = 13$, $f(b) = 23$ and $\Delta t = (b-a)/n = 2/100$. Thus,

$$|\text{Difference in estimates}| = |f(b) - f(a)|\Delta t$$
$$= |23 - 13|\frac{1}{50} = \frac{1}{5}.$$

11. Since f is decreasing, the right-hand sum is the lower estimate and the left-hand sum is the upper estimate. We have $f(a) = 24$, $f(b) = 9$ and $\Delta t = (b-a)/n = 3/500$. Thus,

$$|\text{Difference in estimates}| = |f(b) - f(a)|\Delta t$$
$$= |9 - 24|\frac{3}{500} = 0.09.$$

12. Since f is increasing, the right-hand sum is the upper estimate and the left-hand sum is the lower estimate. We have $f(0) = 0$, $f(\pi/2) = 1$ and $\Delta t = (b-a)/n = \pi/200$. Thus,

$$|\text{Difference in estimates}| = |f(b) - f(a)|\Delta t$$
$$= |1 - 0|\frac{\pi}{200} = 0.0157.$$

13. Since f is decreasing, the right-hand sum is the lower estimate and the left-hand sum is the upper estimate. We have $f(0) = 1$, $f(2) = e^{-2}$ and $\Delta t = (b-a)/n = 2/20 = 1/10$. Thus,

$$|\text{Difference in estimates}| = |f(b) - f(a)|\Delta t$$
$$= |e^{-2} - 1|\frac{1}{10} = 0.086.$$

14. Using whole grid squares, we can overestimate the area as $3 + 3 + 3 + 3 + 2 + 1 = 15$, and we can underestimate the area as $1 + 2 + 2 + 1 + 0 + 0 = 6$.

Problems

15. To find the distance the car moved before stopping, we estimate the distance traveled for each two-second interval. Since speed decreases throughout, we know that the left-handed sum will be an overestimate to the distance traveled and the right-hand sum an underestimate. Applying the formulas for these sums with $\Delta t = 2$ gives:

$$\text{LEFT} = 2(100 + 80 + 50 + 25 + 10) = 530 \text{ ft.}$$
$$\text{RIGHT} = 2(80 + 50 + 25 + 10 + 0) = 330 \text{ ft.}$$

(a) The best estimate of the distance traveled will be the average of these two estimates, or

$$\text{Best estimate} = \frac{530 + 330}{2} = 430 \text{ ft.}$$

(b) All we can be sure of is that the distance traveled lies between the upper and lower estimates calculated above. In other words, all the black-box data tells us for sure is that the car traveled between 330 and 530 feet before stopping. So we can't be completely sure about whether it hit the skunk or not.

16. (a) Note that 15 minutes equals 0.25 hours. Lower estimate $= 11(0.25) + 10(0.25) = 5.25$ miles. Upper estimate $= 12(0.25) + 11(0.25) = 5.75$ miles.
(b) Lower estimate $= 11(0.25) + 10(0.25) + 10(0.25) + 8(0.25) + 7(0.25) + 0(0.25) = 11.5$ miles. Upper estimate $= 12(0.25) + 11(0.25) + 10(0.25) + 10(0.25) + 8(0.25) + 7(0.25) = 14.5$ miles.
(c) The difference between Roger's pace at the beginning and the end of his run is 12 mph. If the time between the measurements is h, then the difference between the upper and lower estimates is $12h$. We want $12h < 0.1$, so

$$h < \frac{0.1}{12} \approx 0.0083 \text{ hours} = 30 \text{ seconds}$$

Thus Jeff would have to measure Roger's pace every 30 seconds.

17. The velocity is constant and negative, so the change in position is $-3 \cdot 5$ cm, that is 15 cm to the left.

18. From $t = 0$ to $t = 3$ the velocity is constant and positive, so the change in position is $2 \cdot 3$ cm, that is 6 cm to the right. From $t = 3$ to $t = 5$, the velocity is negative and constant, so the change in position is $-3 \cdot 2$ cm, that is 6 cm to the left. Thus the total change in position is 0. The particle moves 6 cm to the right, followed by 6 cm to the left, and returns to where it started.

19. From $t = 0$ to $t = 5$ the velocity is positive so the change in position is to the right. The area under the velocity graph gives the distance traveled. The region is a triangle, and so has area $(1/2)bh = (1/2)5 \cdot 10 = 25$. Thus the change in position is 25 cm to the right.

20. From $t = 0$ to $t = 4$ the velocity is positive so the change in position is to the right. The area under the velocity graph gives the distance traveled. The region is a triangle, and so has area $(1/2)bh = (1/2)4 \cdot 8 = 16$. Thus the change in position is 16 cm to the right for $t = 0$ to $t = 4$. From $t = 4$ to $t = 5$, the velocity is negative so the change in position is to the left. The distance traveled to the left is given by the area of the triangle, $(1/2)bh = (1/2)1 \cdot 2 = 1$. Thus the total change in position is $16 - 1 = 15$ cm to the right.

21. The change in position is calculated from the area between the velocity graph and the t-axis, with the region below the axis corresponding to negatives velocities and counting negatively.

Figure 5.2 shows the graph of $f(t)$. From $t = 0$ to $t = 3$ the velocity is positive. The region under the graph of $f(t)$ is a triangle with height 6 cm/sec and base 3 seconds. Thus, from $t = 0$ to $t = 3$, the particle moves

$$\text{Distance moved to right} = \frac{1}{2} \cdot 3 \cdot 6 = 9 \text{ centimeters.}$$

From $t = 3$ to $t = 4$, the velocity is negative. The region between the graph of $f(t)$ and the t-axis is a triangle with height 2 cm/sec and base 1 second, so in this interval the particle moves

$$\text{Distance moved to left} = \frac{1}{2} \cdot 1 \cdot 2 = 1 \text{ centimeter.}$$

Thus, the total change in position is $9 - 1 = 8$ centimeters to the right.

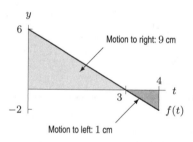

Figure 5.2

22. (a) See Figure 5.3.
   (b) The peak of the flight is when the velocity is 0, namely $t = 3$. The height at $t = 3$ is given by the area under the graph of the velocity from $t = 0$ to $t = 3$; see Figure 5.3. The region is a triangle of base 3 seconds and altitude 96 ft/sec, so the height is $(1/2)3 \cdot 96 = 144$ feet.
   (c) The velocity is negative from $t = 3$ to $t = 5$, so the motion is downward then. The distance traveled downward can be calculated by the area of the triangular region which has base of 2 seconds and altitude of -64 ft/sec. Thus, the baseball travels $(1/2)2 \cdot 64 = 64$ feet downward from its peak height of 144 feet at $t = 3$. Thus, the height at time $t = 5$ is the total change in position, $144 - 64 = 80$ feet.

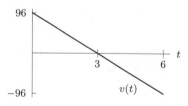

Figure 5.3

23. (a) See Figure 5.4.
  (b) The distance traveled is the area under the graph of the velocity in Figure 5.4. The region is a triangle of base 5 seconds and altitude 50 ft/sec, so the distance traveled is $(1/2)5 \cdot 50 = 125$ feet.
  (c) The slope of the graph of the velocity function is the same, so the triangular region under it has twice the altitude and twice the base (it takes twice as long to stop). See Figure 5.5. Thus, the area is 4 times as large and the car travels 4 times as far.

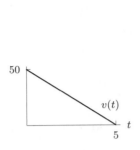

Figure 5.4

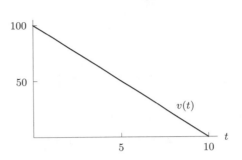

Figure 5.5

24. The graph of her velocity against time is a straight line from 0 mph to 60 mph; see Figure 5.6. Since the distance traveled is the area under the curve, we have

$$\text{Shaded area} = \frac{1}{2} \cdot t \cdot 60 = 10 \text{ miles}$$

Solving for t gives

$$t = \frac{1}{3}\text{hr} = 20 \text{ minutes}.$$

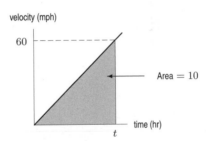

Figure 5.6

25. (a) Car A has the largest maximum velocity because the peak of car A's velocity curve is higher than the peak of B's.
  (b) Car A stops first because the curve representing its velocity hits zero (on the t-axis) first.
  (c) Car B travels farther because the area under car B's velocity curve is the larger.

26. (a) Since car B starts at $t = 2$, the tick marks on the horizontal axis (which we assume are equally spaced) are 2 hours apart. Thus car B stops at $t = 6$ and travels for 4 hours.
  Car A starts at $t = 0$ and stops at $t = 8$, so it travels for 8 hours.
  (b) Car A's maximum velocity is approximately twice that of car B, that is 100 km/hr.
  (c) The distance traveled is given by the area of under the velocity graph. Using the formula for the area of a triangle, the distances are given approximately by

$$\text{Car } A \text{ travels} = \frac{1}{2} \cdot \text{Base} \cdot \text{Height} = \frac{1}{2} \cdot 8 \cdot 100 = 400 \text{ km}$$
$$\text{Car } B \text{ travels} = \frac{1}{2} \cdot \text{Base} \cdot \text{Height} = \frac{1}{2} \cdot 4 \cdot 50 = 100 \text{ km}.$$

Solutions for Section 5.2

Exercises

1.

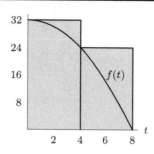

Figure 5.7: Left Sum, $\Delta t = 4$

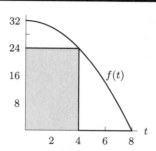

Figure 5.8: Right Sum, $\Delta t = 4$

   (a) Left-hand sum $= 32 \cdot 4 + 24 \cdot 4 = 224$.
   (b) Right-hand sum $= 24 \cdot 4 + 0 \cdot 4 = 96$.

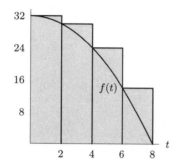

Figure 5.9: Left Sum, $\Delta t = 2$

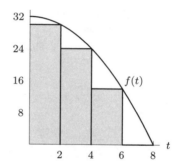

Figure 5.10: Right Sum, $\Delta t = 2$

   (c) Left-hand sum $= 32 \cdot 2 + 30 \cdot 2 + 24 \cdot 2 + 14 \cdot 2 = 200$.
   (d) Right-hand sum $= 30 \cdot 2 + 24 \cdot 2 + 14 \cdot 2 + 0 \cdot 2 = 136$.

2. $\int_0^3 f(x)\,dx$ is equal to the area shaded. We estimate the area by counting shaded rectangles. There are 3 fully shaded and about 4 partially shaded rectangles, for a total of approximately 5 shaded rectangles. Since each rectangle represents 4 square units, our estimated area is $5(4) = 20$. We have

$$\int_0^3 f(x)\,dx \approx 20.$$

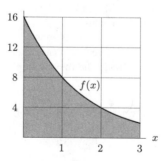

Figure 5.11

3. We know that

$$\int_{-10}^{15} f(x)dx = \text{Area under } f(x) \text{ between } x = -10 \text{ and } x = 15.$$

The area under the curve consists of approximately 14 boxes, and each box has area $(5)(5) = 25$. Thus, the area under the curve is about $(14)(25) = 350$, so

$$\int_{-10}^{15} f(x)dx \approx 350.$$

4. With $\Delta x = 5$, we have

$$\text{Left-hand sum} = 5(0 + 100 + 200 + 100 + 200 + 250 + 275) = 5625,$$

$$\text{Right-hand sum} = 5(100 + 200 + 100 + 200 + 250 + 275 + 300) = 7125.$$

The average of these two sums is our best guess for the value of the integral;

$$\int_{-15}^{20} f(x)\, dx \approx \frac{5625 + 7125}{2} = 6375.$$

5. The graph given shows that f is positive for $0 \le t \le 1$. Since the graph is contained within a rectangle of height 100 and length 1, the answers -98.35 and 100.12 are both either too small or too large to represent $\int_0^1 f(t)dt$. Since the graph of f is above the horizontal line $y = 80$ for $0 \le t \le 0.95$, the best estimate is 93.47 and not 71.84.

6. We estimate $\int_0^{40} f(x)dx$ using left- and right-hand sums:

$$\text{Left sum} = 350 \cdot 10 + 410 \cdot 10 + 435 \cdot 10 + 450 \cdot 10 = 16{,}450.$$

$$\text{Right sum} = 410 \cdot 10 + 435 \cdot 10 + 450 \cdot 10 + 460 \cdot 10 = 17{,}550.$$

We estimate that

$$\int_0^{40} f(x)dx \approx \frac{16450 + 17550}{2} = 17{,}000.$$

In this estimate, we used $n = 4$ and $\Delta x = 10$.

7. We take $\Delta x = 3$. Then:

$$\text{Left-hand sum} = 50(3) + 48(3) + 44(3) + 36(3) + 24(3)$$
$$= 606$$
$$\text{Right-hand sum} = 48(3) + 44(3) + 36(3) + 24(3) + 8(3)$$
$$= 480$$
$$\text{Average} = \frac{606 + 480}{2} = 543.$$

So,

$$\int_0^{15} f(x)\, dx \approx 543.$$

8. With $\Delta x = 3$, we have

$$\text{Left-hand sum} = 3(32 + 22 + 15 + 11) = 240,$$
$$\text{Right-hand sum} = 3(22 + 15 + 11 + 9) = 171.$$

The average of these two sums is our best guess for the value of the integral;

$$\int_0^{12} f(x)\, dx \approx \frac{240 + 171}{2} = 205.5.$$

9. We use a calculator or computer to see that $\int_0^3 2^x dx = 10.0989$.

10. We use a calculator or computer to see that $\int_0^1 \sin(t^2)dt = 0.3103$.

11. We use a calculator or computer to see that $\int_{-1}^{1} e^{-x^2}\, dx = 1.4936.$

12. Since $\cos t \geq 0$ for $0 \leq t \leq \pi/2$, the area is given by

$$\text{Area} = \int_{0}^{\pi/2} \cos t\, dt = 1.$$

The integral was evaluated on a calculator.

13. A graph of $y = 6x^3 - 2$ shows that this function is nonnegative on the interval $x = 5$ to $x = 10$. Thus,

$$\text{Area} = \int_{5}^{10} (6x^3 - 2)\, dx = 14{,}052.5.$$

The integral was evaluated on a calculator.

14. A graph of $y = \ln x$ shows that this function is non-negative on the interval $x = 1$ to $x = 4$. Thus,

$$\text{Area} = \int_{1}^{4} \ln x\, dx = 2.545.$$

The integral was evaluated on a calculator.

15. Since $\cos \sqrt{x} > 0$ for $0 \leq x \leq 2$, the area is given by

$$\text{Area} = \int_{0}^{2} \cos \sqrt{x}\, dx = 1.106.$$

The integral was evaluated on a calculator.

16. A graph of $y = 2\cos t/10$ shows that this function is nonnegative on the interval $t = 5$ to $2 = 10$. Thus,

$$\text{Area} = \int_{1}^{2} 2\cos \frac{t}{10}\, dt = 1.977.$$

The integral was evaluated on a calculator.

17. The graph of $y = 7 - x^2$ has intercepts $x = \pm\sqrt{7}$. See Figure 5.12. Therefore we have

$$\text{Area} = \int_{-\sqrt{7}}^{\sqrt{7}} (7 - x^2)\, dx = 24.694.$$

The integral was evaluated on a calculator.

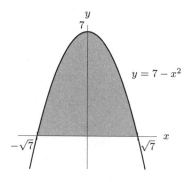

Figure 5.12

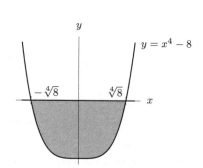

Figure 5.13

18. The graph of $y = x^4 - 8$ has intercepts $x = \pm\sqrt[4]{8}$. See Figure 5.13. Since the region is below the x-axis, the integral is negative, so

$$\text{Area} = -\int_{-\sqrt[4]{8}}^{\sqrt[4]{8}} (x^4 - 8)\, dx = 21.527.$$

The integral was evaluated on a calculator.

Problems

19. (a) See Figure 5.14.

$$\text{Left sum} = f(1)\Delta x + f(1.5)\Delta x = (\ln 1)0.5 + \ln(1.5)0.5 = (\ln 1.5)0.5.$$

(b) See Figure 5.15.

$$\text{Right sum} = f(1.5)\Delta x + f(2)\Delta x = (\ln 1.5)0.5 + (\ln 2)0.5.$$

(c) Right sum is an overestimate, left sum is an underestimate.

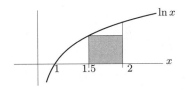

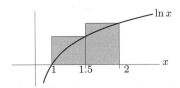

Figure 5.14: Left sum

Figure 5.15: Right sum

20. (a) $\displaystyle\int_0^6 (x^2 + 1)\, dx = 78$

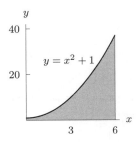

(b) Using $n = 3$, we have

$$\text{Left-hand sum} = f(0) \cdot 2 + f(2) \cdot 2 + f(4) \cdot 2 = 1 \cdot 2 + 5 \cdot 2 + 17 \cdot 2 = 46.$$

This sum is an underestimate. See Figure 5.16.

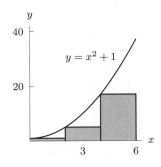

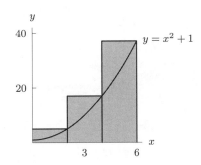

Figure 5.16

Figure 5.17

(c)

$$\text{Right-hand sum} = f(2) \cdot 2 + f(4) \cdot 2 + f(6) \cdot 2 = 5 \cdot 2 + 17 \cdot 2 + 37 \cdot 2 = 118.$$

This sum is an overestimate. See Figure 5.17.

21. Left-hand sum gives: $1^2(1/4) + (1.25)^2(1/4) + (1.5)^2(1/4) + (1.75)^2(1/4) = 1.96875$.
Right-hand sum gives: $(1.25)^2(1/4) + (1.5)^2(1/4) + (1.75)^2(1/4) + (2)^2(1/4) = 2.71875$.

We estimate the value of the integral by taking the average of these two sums, which is 2.34375. Since x^2 is monotonic on $1 \le x \le 2$, the true value of the integral lies between 1.96875 and 2.71875. Thus the most our estimate could be off is 0.375. We expect it to be much closer. (And it is—the true value of the integral is $7/3 \approx 2.333$.)

22. We have $\Delta x = 2/500 = 1/250$. The formulas for the left- and right-hand Riemann sums give us that

$$\text{Left} = \Delta x[f(-1) + f(-1+\Delta x) + ... + f(1-2\Delta x) + f(1-\Delta x)]$$
$$\text{Right} = \Delta x[f(-1+\Delta x) + f(-1+2\Delta x) + ... + f(1-\Delta x) + f(1)].$$

Subtracting these yields

$$\text{Right} - \text{Left} = \Delta x[f(1) - f(-1)] = \frac{1}{250}[6 - 2] = \frac{4}{250} = \frac{2}{125}.$$

23. (a)

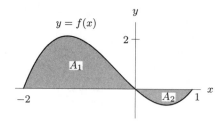

(b) $A_1 = \displaystyle\int_{-2}^{0} f(x)\, dx = 2.667.$

$A_2 = -\displaystyle\int_{0}^{1} f(x)\, dx = 0.417.$

So total area $= A_1 + A_2 \approx 3.084$. Note that while A_1 and A_2 are accurate to 3 decimal places, the quoted value for $A_1 + A_2$ is accurate only to 2 decimal places.

(c) $\displaystyle\int_{-2}^{1} f(x)\, dx = A_1 - A_2 = 2.250.$

24. $\displaystyle\int_{0}^{4} \cos\sqrt{x}\, dx = 0.80 = \text{Area } A_1 - \text{Area } A_2$. See Figure 5.18.

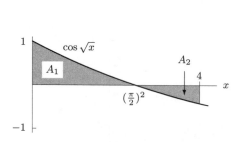

Figure 5.18

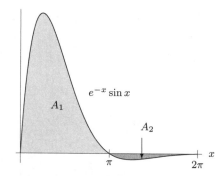

Figure 5.19

25. Looking at the graph of $e^{-x}\sin x$ for $0 \le x \le 2\pi$ in Figure 5.19, we see that the area, A_1, below the curve for $0 \le x \le \pi$ is much greater than the area, A_2, above the curve for $\pi \le x \le 2\pi$. Thus, the integral is

$$\int_{0}^{2\pi} e^{-x}\sin x\, dx = A_1 - A_2 > 0.$$

26. (a) See Figure 5.20.

(b) Since each of the triangular regions in Figure 5.20 have area $1/2$, we have

$$\int_0^2 f(x)\,dx = \frac{1}{2} + \frac{1}{2} = 1.$$

(c) Using $\Delta x = 1/2$ in the 4-term Riemann sum shown in Figure 5.21, we have

$$\text{Left hand sum} = f(0)\Delta x + f(0.5)\Delta x + f(1)\Delta x + f(1.5)\Delta x$$
$$= 1\left(\frac{1}{2}\right) + \frac{1}{2}\left(\frac{1}{2}\right) + 0\left(\frac{1}{2}\right) + \frac{1}{2}\left(\frac{1}{2}\right) = 1.$$

We notice that in this case the approximation is exactly equal to the exact value of the integral.

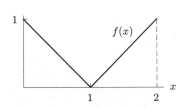

Figure 5.20

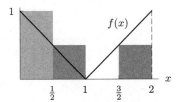

Figure 5.21

27. (a) The area between the graph of f and the x-axis between $x = a$ and $x = b$ is 13, so

$$\int_a^b f(x)\,dx = 13.$$

(b) Since the graph of $f(x)$ is below the x-axis for $b < x < c$,

$$\int_b^c f(x)\,dx = -2.$$

(c) Since the graph of $f(x)$ is above the x-axis for $a < x < b$ and below for $b < x < c$,

$$\int_a^c f(x)\,dx = 13 - 2 = 11.$$

(d) The graph of $|f(x)|$ is the same as the graph of $f(x)$ except that the part below the x-axis is reflected to be above it. See Figure 5.22. Thus

$$\int_a^c |f(x)|\,dx = 13 + 2 = 15.$$

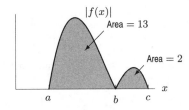

Figure 5.22

28. The region shaded between $x = 0$ and $x = 2$ appears to have approximately the same area as the region shaded between $x = -2$ and $x = 0$, but it lies below the axis. Since $\int_{-2}^0 f(x)dx = 4$, we have the following results:

(a) $\int_0^2 f(x)dx \approx -\int_{-2}^0 f(x)dx = -4.$

(b) $\int_{-2}^2 f(x)dx \approx 4 - 4 = 0.$

(c) The total area shaded is approximately $4 + 4 = 8.$

29. (a) $\displaystyle\int_{-3}^{0} f(x)\,dx = -2.$

(b) $\displaystyle\int_{-3}^{4} f(x)\,dx = \int_{-3}^{0} f(x)\,dx + \int_{0}^{3} f(x)\,dx + \int_{3}^{4} f(x)\,dx = -2 + 2 - \frac{A}{2} = -\frac{A}{2}.$

30. The statement is rarely true. The graph of almost any non-linear monotonic function, such as x^{10} for $0 < x < 1$, should provide convincing geometric evidence. Furthermore, if the statement were true, then (LHS+RHS)/2 would always give the exact value of the definite integral. This is not true.

31. As illustrated in Figure 5.23, the left- and right-hand sums are both equal to $(4\pi) \cdot 3 = 12\pi$, while the integral is smaller. Thus we have:

$$\int_{0}^{4\pi} (2 + \cos x)\,dx < \text{Left-hand sum} = \text{Right-hand sum}.$$

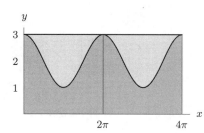

Figure 5.23: Integral vs. Left- and Right-Hand Sums

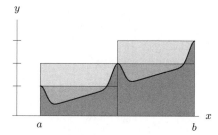

Figure 5.24: Integral vs. Left- and Right-Hand Sums

32. See Figure 5.24.

33. We have

$$\Delta x = \frac{4}{3} = \frac{b-a}{n} \quad \text{and} \quad n = 3, \quad \text{so} \quad b - a = 4 \quad \text{or} \quad b = a + 4.$$

The function, $f(x)$, is squaring something. Since it is a left-hand sum, $f(x)$ could equal x^2 with $a = 2$ and $b = 6$ (note that $2 + 3(\frac{4}{3})$ gives the right-hand endpoint of the last interval). Or, $f(x)$ could possibly equal $(x + 2)^2$ with $a = 0$ and $b = 4$. Other answers are possible.

34. (a) If the interval $1 \leq t \leq 2$ is divided into n equal subintervals of length $\Delta t = 1/n$, the subintervals are given by

$$1 \leq t \leq 1 + \frac{1}{n}, \ 1 + \frac{1}{n} \leq t \leq 1 + \frac{2}{n}, \ \ldots, \ 1 + \frac{n-1}{n} \leq t \leq 2.$$

The left-hand sum is given by

$$\text{Left sum} = \sum_{r=0}^{n-1} f\left(1 + \frac{r}{n}\right) \frac{1}{n} = \sum_{r=0}^{n-1} \frac{1}{1 + r/n} \cdot \frac{1}{n} = \sum_{r=0}^{n-1} \frac{1}{n+r}$$

and the right-hand sum is given by

$$\text{Right sum} = \sum_{r=1}^{n} f\left(1 + \frac{r}{n}\right) \frac{1}{n} = \sum_{r=1}^{n} \frac{1}{n+r}.$$

Since $f(t) = 1/t$ is decreasing in the interval $1 \leq t \leq 2$, we know that the right-hand sum is less than $\int_{1}^{2} 1/t\,dt$ and the left-hand sum is larger than this integral. Thus we have

$$\sum_{r=1}^{n} \frac{1}{n+r} \ < \ \int_{1}^{t} \frac{1}{t}\,dt \ < \ \sum_{r=0}^{n-1} \frac{1}{n+r}.$$

(b) Subtracting the sums gives

$$\sum_{r=0}^{n-1} \frac{1}{n+r} - \sum_{r=1}^{n} \frac{1}{n+r} = \frac{1}{n} - \frac{1}{2n} = \frac{1}{2n}.$$

(c) Here we need to find n such that

$$\frac{1}{2n} \leq 5 \times 10^{-6}, \quad \text{so} \quad n \geq \frac{1}{10} \times 10^{6} = 10^{5}.$$

Solutions for Section 5.3

Exercises

1. The units of measurement are dollars.

2. The units of measurement are meters per second (which are units of velocity).

3. The units of measurement are foot-pounds (which are units of work).

4. The integral $\int_1^3 v(t)\, dt$ represents the change in position between time $t = 1$ and $t = 3$ seconds; it is measured in meters.

5. The integral $\int_0^6 a(t)\, dt$ represents the change in velocity between times $t = 0$ and $t = 6$ seconds; it is measured in km/hr.

6. The integral $\int_{2000}^{2004} f(t)\, dt$ represents the change in the world's population between the years 2000 and 2004. It is measured in billions of people.

7. The integral $\int_0^5 s(x)\, dx$ represents the change in salinity (salt concentration) in the first 5 cm of water; it is measured in gm/liter.

8. (a) One small box on the graph corresponds to moving at 750 ft/min for 15 seconds, which corresponds to a distance of 187.5 ft. Estimating the area beneath the velocity curves, we find:
   Distance traveled by car 1 $\approx$ 5.5 boxes = 1031.25 ft.
   Distance traveled by car 2 $\approx$ 3 boxes = 562.5 ft.

   (b) The two cars will have gone the same distance when the areas beneath their velocity curves are equal. Since the two areas overlap, they are equal when the two shaded regions have equal areas, at $t \approx 1.6$ minutes. See Figure 5.25.

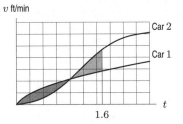

Figure 5.25

9. Average value $= \dfrac{1}{2-0}\int_0^2 (1+t)\, dt = \dfrac{1}{2}(4) = 2.$

10. Average value $= \dfrac{1}{10-0}\int_0^{10} e^t\, dt = \dfrac{1}{10}(22025) = 2202.5$

11. Sketch the graph of f on $1 \le x \le 3$. The integral is the area under the curve, which is a trapezoidal area. So the average value is

$$\frac{1}{3-1}\int_1^3 (4x+7)\, dx = \frac{1}{2}\cdot\frac{11+19}{2}\cdot 2 = \frac{30}{2} = 15.$$

12. Since the average value is given by

$$\text{Average value} = \frac{1}{b-a}\int_a^b f(x)\, dx,$$

the units for dx inside the integral are canceled by the units for $1/(b-a)$ outside the integral, leaving only the units for $f(x)$. This is as it should be, since the average value of f should be measured in the same units as $f(x)$.

13. For any t, consider the interval $[t, t + \Delta t]$. During this interval, oil is leaking out at an approximately constant rate of $f(t)$ gallons/minute. Thus, the amount of oil which has leaked out during this interval can be expressed as

$$\text{Amount of oil leaked} = \text{Rate} \times \text{Time} = f(t)\,\Delta t$$

and the units of $f(t)\,\Delta t$ are gallons/minute $\times$ minutes = gallons. The total amount of oil leaked is obtained by adding all these amounts between $t = 0$ and $t = 60$. (An hour is 60 minutes.) The sum of all these infinitesimal amounts is the integral

$$\begin{array}{c}\text{Total amount of} \\ \text{oil leaked, in gallons}\end{array} = \int_0^{60} f(t)\, dt.$$

14. (a) The amount leaked between $t = 0$ and $t = 2$ is $\displaystyle\int_0^2 R(t)\,dt$.

(b)

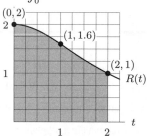

(c) The rectangular boxes on the diagram each have area $\frac{1}{16}$. Of these 45 are wholly beneath the curve, hence the area under the curve is certainly more than $\frac{45}{16} > 2.81$. There are 9 more partially beneath the curve, and so the desired area is completely covered by 54 boxes. Therefore the area is less than $\frac{54}{16} < 3.38$.

These are very safe estimates but far apart. We can do much better by estimating what fractions of the broken boxes are beneath the curve. Using this method, we can estimate the area to be about 3.2, which corresponds to 3.2 gallons leaking over two hours.

Problems

15. (a) An overestimate is 7 tons. An underestimate is 5 tons.

(b) An overestimate is $7 + 8 + 10 + 13 + 16 + 20 = 74$ tons. An underestimate is $5 + 7 + 8 + 10 + 13 + 16 = 59$ tons.

(c) If measurements are made every Δt months, then the error is $|f(6) - f(0)| \cdot \Delta t$. So for this to be less than 1 ton, we need $(20 - 5) \cdot \Delta t < 1$, or $\Delta t < 1/15$. So measurements every 2 days or so will guarantee an error in over- and underestimates of less than 1 ton.

16. (a) Quantity used $= \int_0^5 f(t)\,dt$.

(b) Using a left sum, our approximation is

$$32e^{0.05(0)} + 32e^{0.05(1)} + 32e^{0.05(2)} + 32e^{0.05(3)} + 32e^{0.05(4)} = 177.27.$$

Since f is an increasing function, this represents an underestimate.

(c) Each term is a lower estimate of one year's consumption of oil.

17. (a) The integral $\int_0^{50} f(t)dt$ represents the total emissions of nitrogen oxides, in millions of metric tons, during the period 1940 to 1990.

(b) We estimate the integral using left- and right-hand sums:

$$\text{Left sum} = (6.9)(10) + (9.4)(10) + (13.0)(10) + (18.5)(10) + (20.9)(10) = 687.$$

$$\text{Right sum} = (9.4)(10) + (13.0)(10) + (18.5)(10) + (20.9)(10) + (19.6)(10) = 814.$$

We average the left- and right-hand sums to find the best estimate of the integral:

$$\int_0^{50} f(t)dt \approx \frac{687 + 814}{2} = 750.5 \text{ million metric tons.}$$

Between 1940 and 1990, about 750.5 million metric tons of nitrogen oxides were emitted.

18. The total number of "worker-hours" is equal to the area under the curve. The total area is about 14.5 boxes. Since each box represents $(10 \text{ workers})(8 \text{ hours}) = 80$ worker-hours, the total area is 1160 worker-hours. At \$10 per hour, the total cost is \$11,600.

19. The time period 9am to 5pm is represented by the time $t = 0$ to $t = 8$ and $t = 24$ to $t = 32$. The area under the curve, or total number of worker-hours for these times, is about 9 boxes or $9(80) = 720$ worker-hours. The total cost for 9am to 5pm is $(720)(10) = \$7200$. The area under the rest of the curve is about 5.5 boxes, or $5.5(80) = 440$ worker-hours. The total cost for this time period is $(440)(15) = \$6600$. The total cost is about $7200 + 6600 = \$13,800$.

20. The area under the curve represents the number of cubic feet of storage times the number of days the storage was used. This area is given by

$$\text{Area under graph} = \text{Area of rectangle} + \text{Area of triangle}$$

$$= 30 \cdot 10,000 + \frac{1}{2} \cdot 30(30,000 - 10,000)$$

$$= 600,000.$$

Since the warehouse charges $5 for every 10 cubic feet of storage used for a day, the company will have to pay $(5)(60,000) = \$300,000$.

21. Since W is in tons per week and t is in weeks since January 1, 2000, the integral $\int_0^{52} W \, dt$ gives the amount of waste, in tons, produced during the year 2000.

$$\text{Total waste during the year} = \int_0^{52} 3.75 e^{-0.008t} \, dt = 159.5249 \text{ tons.}$$

Since waste removal costs $15/\text{ton}$, the cost of waste removal for the company is $159.5249 \cdot 15 = \$2392.87$.

22. We know that the the integral of F, and therefore the work, can be obtained by computing the areas in Figure 5.26.

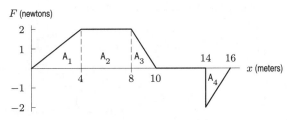

Figure 5.26

$$W = \int_0^{16} F(x) \, dx = \text{Area above } x\text{-axis} - \text{Area below } x\text{-axis}$$

$$= A_1 + A_2 + A_3 - A_4$$
$$= \frac{1}{2} \cdot 4 \cdot 2 + 4 \cdot 2 + \frac{1}{2} \cdot 2 \cdot 2 - \frac{1}{2} \cdot 2 \cdot 2$$
$$= 12 \text{ newton} \cdot \text{meters.}$$

23. (a) (i) Since the triangular region under the graphs of $f(x)$ has area $1/2$, we have

$$\text{Average}(f) = \frac{1}{2-0} \int_0^2 f(x) \, dx = \frac{1}{2} \cdot \frac{1}{2} = \frac{1}{4}.$$

(ii) Similarly,

$$\text{Average}(g) = \frac{1}{2-0} \int_0^2 g(x) \, dx = \frac{1}{2} \cdot \frac{1}{2} = \frac{1}{4}$$

(iii) Since $f(x)$ is nonzero only for $0 \leq x < 1$ and $g(x)$ is nonzero only for $1 < x \leq 2$, the product $f(x)g(x) = 0$ for all x. Thus

$$\text{Average}(f \cdot g) = \frac{1}{2-0} \int_0^2 f(x)g(x) \, dx = \frac{1}{2} \int_0^2 0 \, dx = 0.$$

(b) Since the average values of $f(x)$ and $g(x)$ are nonzero, their product is nonzero. Thus the left side of the statement is nonzero. However, the average of the product $f(x)g(x)$ is zero. Thus, the right side of the statement is zero, so the statement is not true.

24. The integral represents the area below the graph of $f(x)$ but above the x-axis.

(a) Since each square has area 1, by counting squares and half-squares we find

$$\int_1^6 f(x) \, dx = 8.5.$$

(b) The average value is $\dfrac{1}{6-1} \int_1^6 f(x) \, dx = \dfrac{8.5}{5} = \dfrac{17}{10} = 1.7$.

25. (a) The integral is the area above the x-axis minus the area below the x-axis. Thus, we can see that $\int_{-3}^{3} f(x)\,dx$ is about $-6 + 2 = -4$ (the negative of the area from $t = -3$ to $t = 1$ plus the area from $t = 1$ to $t = 3$.)

(b) Since the integral in part (a) is negative, the average value of $f(x)$ between $x = -3$ and $x = 3$ is negative. From the graph, however, it appears that the average value of $f(x)$ from $x = 0$ to $x = 3$ is positive. Hence (ii) is the larger quantity.

26. (a) Average value of $f = \frac{1}{5}\int_{0}^{5} f(x)\,dx$.

(b) Average value of $|f| = \frac{1}{5}\int_{0}^{5} |f(x)|\,dx = \frac{1}{5}(\int_{0}^{2} f(x)\,dx - \int_{2}^{5} f(x)\,dx)$.

27. We'll show that in terms of the average value of f,

$$\text{I} > \text{II} = \text{IV} > \text{III}$$

Using the definition of average value and the fact that f is even, we have

$$\begin{aligned}\frac{\text{Average value}}{\text{of } f \text{ on II}} &= \frac{\int_{0}^{2} f(x)\,dx}{2} = \frac{\frac{1}{2}\int_{-2}^{2} f(x)\,dx}{2} \\ &= \frac{\int_{-2}^{2} f(x)\,dx}{4} \\ &= \text{Average value of } f \text{ on IV.}\end{aligned}$$

Since f is decreasing on $[0,5]$, the average value of f on the interval $[0, c]$, where $0 \le c \le 5$, is decreasing as a function of c. The larger the interval the more low values of f are included. Hence

$$\frac{\text{Average value of } f}{\text{on } [0, 1]} > \frac{\text{Average value of } f}{\text{on } [0, 2]} > \frac{\text{Average value of } f}{\text{on } [0, 5]}$$

28. (a) Since $f(x) = \sin x$ over $[0, \pi]$ is between 0 and 1, the average of $f(x)$ must itself be between 0 and 1. Furthermore, since the graph of $f(x)$ is concave down on this interval, the average value must be greater than the average height of the triangle shown in the figure, namely, 0.5.

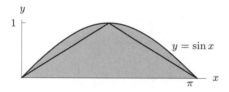

(b) Average $= \dfrac{1}{\pi - 0}\displaystyle\int_{0}^{\pi} \sin x\,dx = 0.64$.

29. (a) Average value $= \displaystyle\int_{0}^{1} \sqrt{1 - x^2}\,dx = 0.79$.

(b) The area between the graph of $y = 1 - x$ and the x-axis is 0.5. Because the graph of $y = \sqrt{1 - x^2}$ is concave down, it lies above the line $y = 1 - x$, so its average value is above 0.5. See figure below.

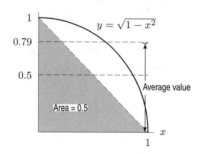

30. Since $t = 0$ in 1965 and $t = 35$ in 2000, we want:

$$\text{Average Value} = \frac{1}{35 - 0} \int_0^{35} 225(1.15)^t \, dt$$
$$= \frac{1}{35}(212{,}787) = \$6080.$$

31. Change in income $= \int_0^{12} r(t) \, dt = \int_0^{12} 40(1.002)^t \, dt = \$485.80$

32. (a) Since $t = 0$ to $t = 31$ covers January:

$$\begin{array}{c}\text{Average number of} \\ \text{daylight hours in January}\end{array} = \frac{1}{31} \int_0^{31} [12 + 2.4\sin(0.0172(t - 80))] \, dt.$$

Using left and right sums with $n = 100$ gives

$$\text{Average} \approx \frac{306}{31} \approx 9.9 \text{ hours.}$$

(b) Assuming it is not a leap year, the last day of May is $t = 151(= 31 + 28 + 31 + 30 + 31)$ and the last day of June is $t = 181(= 151 + 30)$. Again finding the integral numerically:

$$\begin{array}{c}\text{Average number of} \\ \text{daylight hours in June}\end{array} = \frac{1}{30} \int_{151}^{181} [12 + 2.4\sin(0.0172(t - 80))] \, dt$$
$$\approx \frac{431}{30} \approx 14.4 \text{ hours.}$$

(c)

$$\text{Average for whole year} = \frac{1}{365} \int_0^{365} [12 + 2.4\sin(0.0172(t - 80))] \, dt$$
$$\approx \frac{4381}{365} \approx 12.0 \text{ hours.}$$

(d) The average over the whole year should be 12 hours, as computed in (c). Since Madrid is in the northern hemisphere, the average for a winter month, such as January, should be less than 12 hours (it is 9.9 hours) and the average for a summer month, such as June, should be more than 12 hours (it is 14.4 hours).

33. (a) Over the interval $[-1, 3]$, we estimate that the total change of the population is about 1.5, by counting boxes between the curve and the x-axis; we count about 1.5 boxes below the x-axis from $x = -1$ to $x = 1$ and about 3 above from $x = 1$ to $x = 3$. So the average rate of change is just the total change divided by the length of the interval, that is $1.5/4 = 0.375$ thousand/hour.

(b) We can estimate the total change of the algae population by counting boxes between the curve and the x-axis. Here, there is about 1 box above the x-axis from $x = -3$ to $x = -2$, about 0.75 of a box below the x-axis from $x = -2$ to $x = -1$, and a total change of about 1.5 boxes thereafter (as discussed in part (a)). So the total change is about $1 - 0.75 + 1.5 = 1.75$ thousands of algae.

34. Notice that the area of a square on the graph represents $10/6$ miles. At $t = 1/3$ hours, $v = 0$. The area between the curve v and the t-axis over the interval $0 \leq t \leq 1/3$ is $- \int_0^{1/3} v \, dt \approx 5/3$. Since v is negative here, she is moving toward the lake. At $t = 1/3$, she is about $5 - 5/3 = 10/3$ miles from the lake. Then, as she moves away from the lake, v is positive for $1/3 \leq t \leq 1$. At $t = 1$,

$$\int_0^1 v \, dt = \int_0^{1/3} v \, dt + \int_{1/3}^1 v \, dt \approx -\frac{5}{3} + 8 \cdot \frac{10}{6} = \frac{35}{3} = 11.667 \text{ miles,}$$

and the cyclist is about $5 + 35/3 = 50/3 = 16.667$ miles from the lake. Since, starting from the moment $t = 1/3$, she moves away from the lake, the cyclist will be farthest from the lake at $t = 1$. The maximal distance equals 16.667 miles.

35. The car's speed increases by 60 mph in 1/2 hour, that is at a rate of $60/(1/2) = 120$ mph per hour, or $120/60 = 2$ mph per minute. Thus every 5 minutes the speed has increased by 10 mph. At the start of the first 5 minutes, the speed was 10 mph and at the end, the speed was 20 mph. To find the distance traveled, use Distance = Speed × Time. Since 5 min = 5/60 hour, the distance traveled during the first 5 minutes was between

$$10 \cdot \frac{5}{60} \text{ mile} \qquad \text{and} \qquad 20 \cdot \frac{5}{60} \text{ mile.}$$

Since the speed was between 10 and 20 mph during this five minute period, the fuel efficiency during this period is between 15 mpg and 18 mpg. So the fuel used during this period is between

$$\frac{1}{18} \cdot 10 \cdot \frac{5}{60} \text{ gallons} \qquad \text{and} \qquad \frac{1}{15} \cdot 20 \cdot \frac{5}{60} \text{ gallons}.$$

Thus, an underestimate of the fuel used is

$$\text{Fuel} = \left(\frac{1}{18} \cdot 10 + \frac{1}{21} \cdot 20 + \frac{1}{23} \cdot 30 + \frac{1}{24} \cdot 40 + \frac{1}{25} \cdot 50 + \frac{1}{26} \cdot 60 \right) \frac{5}{60} = 0.732 \text{ gallons}.$$

An overestimate of the fuel used is

$$\text{Fuel} = \left(\frac{1}{15} \cdot 20 + \frac{1}{18} \cdot 30 + \frac{1}{21} \cdot 40 + \frac{1}{23} \cdot 50 + \frac{1}{24} \cdot 60 + \frac{1}{25} \cdot 70 \right) \frac{5}{60} = 1.032 \text{ gallons}.$$

36. (a) The black curve is for boys, the colored one for girls. The area under each curve represents the change in growth in centimeters. Since men are generally taller than women, the curve with the larger area under it is the height velocity of the boys.

(b) Each square below the height velocity curve has area 1 cm/yr · 1 yr = 1 cm. Counting squares lying below the black curve gives about 43 cm. Thus, on average, boys grow about 43 cm between ages 3 and 10.

(c) Counting squares lying below the black curve gives about 23 cm growth for boys during their growth spurt. Counting squares lying below the colored curve gives about 18 cm for girls during their growth spurt.

(d) We can measure the difference in growth by counting squares that lie between the two curves. Between ages 2 and 12.5, the average girl grows faster than the average boy. Counting squares yields about 5 cm between the colored and black curves for $2 \le x \le 12.5$. Counting squares between the curves for $12.5 \le x \le 18$ gives about 18 squares. Thus, there is a net increase of boys over girls by about $18 - 5 = 13$ cm.

37. On the interval $a \le t \le b$, we have

$$\begin{array}{c} \text{Average value} \\ \text{of } v(t) \end{array} = \frac{1}{b-a} \int_a^b v(t)\, dt.$$

Since $v(t) = s'(t)$, by the Fundamental Theorem of Calculus, we get:

$$\frac{1}{b-a} \int_a^b v(t)\, dt = \frac{1}{b-a}(s(b) - s(a)) = \text{ Average velocity}.$$

Solutions for Section 5.4

Exercises

1. (a) A graph of $f'(x) = \sin(x^2)$ is shown in Figure 5.27. Since the derivative $f'(x)$ is positive between $x = 0$ and $x = 1$, the change in $f(x)$ is positive, so $f(1)$ is larger than $f(0)$. Between $x = 2$ and $x = 2.5$, we see that $f'(x)$ is negative, so the change in $f(x)$ is negative; thus, $f(2)$ is greater than $f(2.5)$.

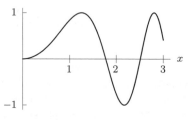

Figure 5.27: Graph of $f'(x) = \sin(x^2)$

(b) The change in $f(x)$ between $x = 0$ and $x = 1$ is given by the Fundamental Theorem of Calculus:

$$f(1) - f(0) = \int_0^1 \sin(x^2)dx = 0.310.$$

Since $f(0) = 2$, we have

$$f(1) = 2 + 0.310 = 2.310.$$

Similarly, since

$$f(2) - f(0) = \int_0^2 \sin(x^2)dx = 0.805,$$

we have

$$f(2) = 2 + 0.805 = 2.805.$$

Since

$$f(3) - f(0) = \int_0^3 \sin(x^2)dx = 0.774,$$

we have

$$f(3) = 2 + 0.774 = 2.774.$$

The results are shown in the table.

x	0	1	2	3
$f(x)$	2	2.310	2.805	2.774

2. We find the changes in $f(x)$ between any two values of x by counting the area between the curve of $f'(x)$ and the x-axis. Since $f'(x)$ is linear throughout, this is quite easy to do. From $x = 0$ to $x = 1$, we see that $f'(x)$ outlines a triangle of area $1/2$ below the x-axis (the base is 1 and the height is 1). By the Fundamental Theorem,

$$\int_0^1 f'(x)\,dx = f(1) - f(0),$$

so

$$f(0) + \int_0^1 f'(x)\,dx = f(1)$$

$$f(1) = 2 - \frac{1}{2} = \frac{3}{2}$$

Similarly, between $x = 1$ and $x = 3$ we can see that $f'(x)$ outlines a rectangle below the x-axis with area -1, so $f(2) = 3/2 - 1 = 1/2$. Continuing with this procedure (note that at $x = 4$, $f'(x)$ becomes positive), we get the table below.

x	0	1	2	3	4	5	6
$f(x)$	2	3/2	1/2	−1/2	−1	−1/2	1/2

3. Since $F(0) = 0$, $F(b) = \int_0^b f(t)\,dt$. For each b we determine $F(b)$ graphically as follows:
$F(0) = 0$
$F(1) = F(0) + \text{Area of } 1 \times 1 \text{ rectangle} = 0 + 1 = 1$
$F(2) = F(1) + \text{Area of triangle } (\frac{1}{2} \cdot 1 \cdot 1) = 1 + 0.5 = 1.5$
$F(3) = F(2) + \text{Negative of area of triangle} = 1.5 - 0.5 = 1$
$F(4) = F(3) + \text{Negative of area of rectangle} = 1 - 1 = 0$
$F(5) = F(4) + \text{Negative of area of rectangle} = 0 - 1 = -1$
$F(6) = F(5) + \text{Negative of area of triangle} = -1 - 0.5 = -1.5$
The graph of $F(t)$, for $0 \le t \le 6$, is shown in Figure 5.28.

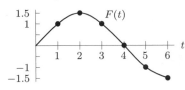

Figure 5.28

4. The graph of $y = e^x$ is above the line $y = 1$ for $0 \leq x \leq 2$. See Figure 5.29. Therefore

$$\text{Area} = \int_0^2 (e^x - 1)\, dx = 4.389.$$

The integral was evaluated on a calculator.

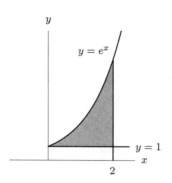

Figure 5.29

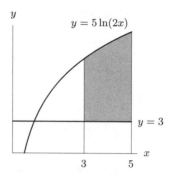

Figure 5.30

5. The graph of $y = 5\ln(2x)$ is above the line $y = 3$ for $3 \leq x \leq 5$. See Figure 5.30. Therefore

$$\text{Area} = \int_3^5 (5\ln(2x) - 3)\, dx = 14.688.$$

The integral was evaluated on a calculator.

6. Since $x^3 \leq x^2$ for $0 \leq x \leq 1$, we have

$$\text{Area} = \int_0^1 (x^2 - x^3)\, dx = 0.083.$$

The integral was evaluated on a calculator.

7. Since $x^{1/2} \leq x^{1/3}$ for $0 \leq x \leq 1$, we have

$$\text{Area} = \int_0^1 (x^{1/3} - x^{1/2})\, dx = 0.0833.$$

The integral was evaluated on a calculator.

8. The graph of $y = \sin x + 2$ is above the line $y = 0.5$ for $6 \leq x \leq 10$. See Figure 5.31. Therefore

$$\text{Area} = \int_6^{10} \sin x + 2 - 0.5\, dx = 7.799.$$

The integral was evaluated on a calculator.

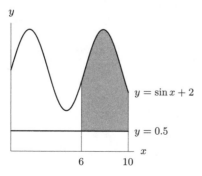

Figure 5.31

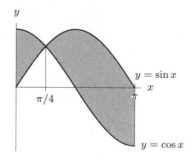

Figure 5.32

9. The graph of $y = \cos t$ is above the graph of $y = \sin t$ for $0 \leq t \leq \pi/4$ and $y = \cos t$ is below $y = \sin t$ for $\pi/4 < t < \pi$. See Figure 5.32. Therefore, we find the area in two pieces:

$$\text{Area} = \int_0^{\pi/4} (\cos t - \sin t)\, dt + \int_{\pi/4}^{\pi} (\sin t - \cos t)\, dt = 2.828.$$

The integral was evaluated on a calculator.

10. We have $f(t) = F'(t) = 2t$, so by the Fundamental Theorem of Calculus,

$$\int_1^3 2t\, dt = F(3) - F(1) = 9 - 1 = 8.$$

11. We have $f(t) = F'(t) = 1/t$, so by the Fundamental Theorem of Calculus,

$$\int_1^5 \frac{1}{t}\, dt = F(5) - F(1) = \ln 5 - \ln 1 = \ln 5.$$

12. We have $f(t) = F'(t) = \cos t$, so by the Fundamental Theorem of Calculus,

$$\int_0^{\pi/2} \cos t\, dt = F(\pi/2) - F(0) = 1 - 0 = 1.$$

13. We have $f(t) = F'(t) = 4t^3$, so by the Fundamental Theorem of Calculus,

$$\int_{-1}^1 4t^3\, dt = F(1) - F(-1) = 1 - 1 = 0.$$

Notice in this case the integral is 0 because the function being integrated, $f(t) = 4t^3$, is odd: the negative contribution to the integral from $a = -1$ to $b = 1$ exactly cancels the positive.

Problems

14. Note that $\int_a^b g(x)\, dx = \int_a^b g(t)\, dt$. Thus, we have

$$\int_a^b (f(x) + g(x))\, dx = \int_a^b f(x)\, dx + \int_a^b g(x)\, dx = 8 + 2 = 10.$$

15. Note that $\int_a^b f(z)\, dz = \int_a^b f(x)\, dx$. Thus, we have

$$\int_a^b cf(z)\, dz = c \int_a^b f(z)\, dz = 8c.$$

16. Note that $\int_a^b (g(x))^2\, dx = \int_a^b (g(t))^2\, dt$. Thus, we have

$$\int_a^b \left((f(x))^2 - (g(x))^2\right)\, dx = \int_a^b (f(x))^2\, dx - \int_a^b (g(x))^2\, dx = 12 - 3 = 9.$$

17. We have

$$\int_a^b (f(x))^2\, dx - \left(\int_a^b f(x)\, dx\right)^2 = 12 - 8^2 = -52.$$

18. We write

$$\int_a^b \left(c_1 g(x) + (c_2 f(x))^2 \right) dx = \int_a^b \left(c_1 g(x) + c_2^2 (f(x))^2 \right) dx$$

$$= \int_a^b c_1 g(x)\, dx + \int_a^b c_2^2 (f(x))^2 \, dx$$

$$= c_1 \int_a^b g(x)\, dx + c_2^2 \int_a^b (f(x))^2 \, dx$$

$$= c_1(2) + c_2^2(12) = 2c_1 + 12c_2^2.$$

19. The graph of $y = f(x - 5)$ is the graph of $y = f(x)$ shifted to the right by 5. Since the limits of integration have also shifted by 5 (to $a + 5$ and $b + 5$), the areas corresponding to $\int_{a+5}^{b+5} f(x - 5)\, dx$ and $\int_a^b f(x)\, dx$ are the same. Thus,

$$\int_{a+5}^{b+5} f(x - 5)\, dx = \int_a^b f(x)\, dx = 8.$$

20. The areas we computed are shaded in Figure 5.33. Since $y = x^2$ and $y = x^{1/2}$ are inverse functions, their graphs are reflections about the line $y = x$. Similarly, $y = x^3$ and $y = x^{1/3}$ are inverse functions and their graphs are reflections about the line $y = x$. Therefore, the two shaded areas in Figure 5.33 are equal.

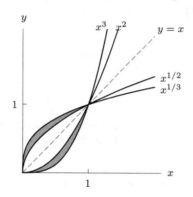

Figure 5.33

21. We have

$$8 = \int_{-2}^5 f(x)\, dx = \int_{-2}^2 f(x)\, dx + \int_2^5 f(x)\, dx.$$

Since f is odd, $\int_{-2}^2 f(x)\, dx = 0$, so $\int_{-2}^5 f(x)\, dx = 8$.

22. Since f is even, $\int_0^2 f(x)\, dx = (1/2)6 = 3$ and $\int_0^5 f(x)\, dx = (1/2)14 = 7$. Therefore

$$\int_2^5 f(x)\, dx = \int_0^5 f(x)\, dx - \int_0^2 f(x)\, dx = 7 - 3 = 4.$$

23. We have

$$18 = \int_2^5 (3f(x) + 4)\, dx = 3 \int_2^5 f(x)\, dx + \int_2^5 4\, dx.$$

Thus, since $\int_2^5 4\, dx = 4(5 - 2) = 12$, we have

$$3 \int_2^5 f(x)\, dx = 18 - 12 = 6,$$

so

$$\int_2^5 f(x)\, dx = 2.$$

24. We have $\int_2^4 f(x)\,dx = 8/2 = 4$ and $\int_4^5 f(x)\,dx = -\int_5^4 f(x)\,dx = -1$. Thus

$$\int_2^5 f(x)\,dx = \int_2^4 f(x)\,dx + \int_4^5 f(x)\,dx = 4 - 1 = 3.$$

25. (a) See Figure 5.34. Since the shaded region lies within a rectangle of area 1, the area is less than 1.
   (b) Since the area is given by the integral

$$\text{Area} = \int_0^1 e^{-x^2/2}\,dx = 0.856.$$

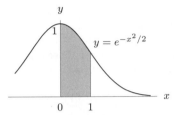

Figure 5.34

26. (a) 0, since the integrand is an odd function and the limits are symmetric around 0.
   (b) 0, since the integrand is an odd function and the limits are symmetric around 0.

27. (a) $\displaystyle\int_{-1}^1 e^{x^2}\,dx > 0$, since $e^{x^2} > 0$, and $\displaystyle\int_{-1}^1 e^{x^2}\,dx$ represents the area below the curve $y = e^{x^2}$.
   (b) Looking at Figure 5.35, we see that $\int_0^1 e^{x^2}\,dx$ represents the area under the curve. This area is clearly greater than zero, but it is less than e since it fits inside a rectangle of width 1 and height e (with room to spare). Thus

$$0 < \int_0^1 e^{x^2}\,dx < e < 3.$$

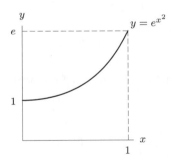

Figure 5.35

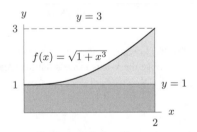

Figure 5.36

28. Notice that $f(x) = \sqrt{1+x^3}$ is increasing for $0 \le x \le 2$, since x^3 gets bigger as x increases. This means that $f(0) \le f(x) \le f(2)$. For this function, $f(0) = 1$ and $f(2) = 3$. Thus, the area under $f(x)$ lies between the area under the line $y = 1$ and the area under the line $y = 3$ on the interval $0 \le x \le 2$. See Figure 5.36. That is,

$$1(2-0) \le \int_0^2 \sqrt{1+x^3}\,dx \le 3(2-0).$$

29. (a) The integrand is positive, so the integral cannot be negative.
   (b) The integrand ≥ 0. If the integral $= 0$, then the integrand must be identically 0, which is not true.

30. We know that we can divide the integral up as follows:

$$\int_0^3 f(x)\,dx = \int_0^1 f(x)\,dx + \int_1^3 f(x)\,dx.$$

The graph suggests that f is an even function for $-1 \le x \le 1$, so $\int_{-1}^1 f(x)\,dx = 2\int_0^1 f(x)\,dx$. Substituting this in to the preceding equation, we have

$$\int_0^3 f(x)\,dx = \frac{1}{2}\int_{-1}^1 f(x)\,dx + \int_1^3 f(x)\,dx.$$

31. (a) For $0 \le x \le 3$, we have

$$\text{Average value} = \frac{1}{3-0}\int_0^3 f(x)dx = \frac{1}{3}(6) = 2.$$

(b) If $f(x)$ is even, the graph is symmetric about the x-axis. For example, see Figure 5.37. By symmetry, the area between $x = -3$ and $x = 3$ is twice the area between $x = 0$ and $x = 3$, so

$$\int_{-3}^3 f(x)dx = 2(6) = 12.$$

Thus for $-3 \le x \le 3$, we have

$$\text{Average value} = \frac{1}{3-(-3)}\int_{-3}^3 f(x)dx = \frac{1}{6}(12) = 2.$$

The graph confirms that the average value between $x = -3$ and $x = 3$ is the same as the average value between $x = 0$ and $x = 3$, which is 2.

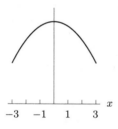

Figure 5.37

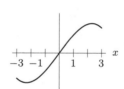

Figure 5.38

(c) If $f(x)$ is odd, then the graph is symmetric about the origin. For example, see Figure 5.38. By symmetry, the area above the x-axis cancels out the area below the x-axis, so

$$\int_{-3}^3 f(x)dx = 0.$$

Thus for $-3 \le x \le 3$, we have

$$\text{Average value} = \frac{1}{3-(-3)}\int_{-3}^3 f(x)dx = \frac{1}{3}(0) = 0.$$

The graph confirms that the average value between $x = -3$ and $x = 3$ is zero.

32. (a) Since the function is odd, the areas above and below the x-axis cancel. Thus,

$$\int_{-3}^0 xe^{-x^2}\,dx = -\int_0^3 xe^{-x^2}\,dx,$$

so

$$\int_{-3}^3 xe^{-x^2}\,dx = \int_{-3}^0 xe^{-x^2}\,dx + \int_0^3 xe^{-x^2}\,dx = 0.$$

(b) For $0 \leq x \leq 3$ with $n = 3$, we have $x_0 = 0$, $x_1 = 1$, $x_2 = 2$, $x_3 = 3$, and $\Delta x = 1$. See Figure 5.39. Thus,

$$\text{Left sum} = f(x_0)\Delta x + f(x_1)\Delta x + f(x_2)\Delta x = 0e^{-0^2} \cdot 1 + 1e^{-1^2} \cdot 1 + 2e^{-2^2} \cdot 1 = 0.4045.$$

(c) For $-3 \leq x \leq 0$, with $n = 3$, we have $x_0 = -3$, $x_1 = -2$, $x_2 = -1$, $x_3 = 0$, and $\Delta x = 1$. See Figure 5.39. Thus,

$$\text{Left sum} = f(x_0)\Delta x + f(x_1)\Delta x + f(x_2)\Delta x = -3e^{-(-3)^2} \cdot 1 - 2e^{-(-2)^2} \cdot 1 - 1e^{-(-1)^2} \cdot 1 = -0.4049.$$

(d) No. The rectangles between -3 and 0 are not the same size as those between 0 and 3. See Figure 5.39. There are three rectangles with nonzero height on $[-3, 0]$ and only two on $[0, 3]$.

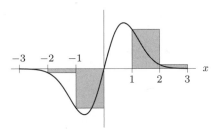

Figure 5.39

33. (a) Yes.
   (b) No, because the sum of the left sums has 20 subdivisions. The result is the left sum approximation with 20 subdivisions to $\int_1^3 f(x)\,dx$.

34. By the Fundamental Theorem,

$$f(1) - f(0) = \int_0^1 f'(x)\,dx,$$

Since $f'(x)$ is negative for $0 \leq x \leq 1$, this integral must be negative and so $f(1) < f(0)$.

35. First rewrite each of the quantities in terms of f', since we have the graph of f'. If A_1 and A_2 are the positive areas shown in Figure 5.40:

$$f(3) - f(2) = \int_2^3 f'(t)\,dt = -A_1$$

$$f(4) - f(3) = \int_3^4 f'(t)\,dt = -A_2$$

$$\frac{f(4) - f(2)}{2} = \frac{1}{2}\int_2^4 f'(t)\,dt = -\frac{A_1 + A_2}{2}$$

Since Area $A_1 >$ Area A_2,

$$A_2 < \frac{A_1 + A_2}{2} < A_1$$

so

$$-A_1 < -\frac{A_1 + A_2}{2} < -A_2$$

and therefore

$$f(3) - f(2) < \frac{f(4) - f(2)}{2} < f(4) - f(3).$$

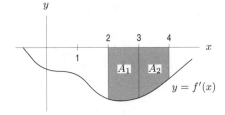

Figure 5.40

36. See Figure 5.41.

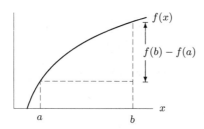

Figure 5.41

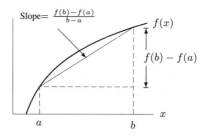

Figure 5.42

37. See Figure 5.42.

38. See Figure 5.43.

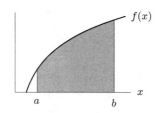

Figure 5.43

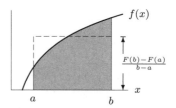

Figure 5.44

39. See Figure 5.44. Note that we are using the interpretation of the definite integral as the length of the interval times the average value of the function on that interval, which we developed in Section 5.3.

40. (a) Splitting the integral in order to make use of the values in the table gives:

$$\frac{1}{\sqrt{2\pi}} \int_1^3 e^{-x^2/2} \, dx = \frac{1}{\sqrt{2\pi}} \int_0^3 e^{-x^2/2} \, dx - \frac{1}{\sqrt{2\pi}} \int_0^1 e^{-x^2/2} \, dx = 0.4987 - 0.3413 = 0.1574.$$

(b) Using the symmetry of $e^{x^2/2}$, we have

$$\frac{1}{\sqrt{2\pi}} \int_{-2}^3 e^{-x^2/2} \, dx = \frac{1}{\sqrt{2\pi}} \int_{-2}^0 e^{-x^2/2} \, dx + \frac{1}{\sqrt{2\pi}} \int_0^3 e^{-x^2/2} \, dx$$

$$= \frac{1}{\sqrt{2\pi}} \int_0^2 e^{-x^2/2} \, dx + \frac{1}{\sqrt{2\pi}} \int_0^3 e^{-x^2/2} \, dx$$

$$= 0.4772 + 0.4987 = 0.9759.$$

41. By the given property, $\int_a^a f(x) \, dx = -\int_a^a f(x) \, dx$, so $2\int_a^a f(x) \, dx = 0$. Thus $\int_a^a f(x) \, dx = 0$.

42. We know that the average value of $v(x) = 4$, so

$$\frac{1}{6-1} \int_1^6 v(x) \, dx = 4, \quad \text{and thus} \quad \int_1^6 v(x) \, dx = 20.$$

Similarly, we are told that

$$\frac{1}{8-6} \int_6^8 v(x) \, dx = 5, \quad \text{so} \quad \int_6^8 v(x) \, dx = 10.$$

The average value for $1 \le x \le 8$ is given by

$$\text{Average value} = \frac{1}{8-1} \int_1^8 v(x) \, dx = \frac{1}{7} \left(\int_1^6 v(x) \, dx + \int_6^8 v(x) \, dx \right) = \frac{20+10}{7} = \frac{30}{7}.$$

Solutions for Chapter 5 Review

Exercises

1. (a) Suppose $f(t)$ is the flowrate in m³/hr at time t. We are only given two values of the flowrate, so in making our estimates of the flow, we use one subinterval, with $\Delta t = 3/1 = 3$:

$$\text{Left estimate} = 3[f(6\text{ am})] = 3 \cdot 100 = 300 \text{ m}^3 \quad \text{(an underestimate)}$$

$$\text{Right estimate} = 3[f(9\text{ am})] = 3 \cdot 280 = 840 \text{ m}^3 \quad \text{(an overestimate)}.$$

The best estimate is the average of these two estimates,

$$\text{Best estimate} = \frac{\text{Left} + \text{Right}}{2} = \frac{300 + 840}{2} = 570 \text{ m}^3.$$

(b) Since the flowrate is increasing throughout, the error, i.e., the difference between over- and under-estimates, is given by

$$\text{Error} \leq \Delta t\,[f(9\text{ am}) - f(6\text{ am})] = \Delta t[280 - 100] = 180\Delta t.$$

We wish to choose Δt so that the the error $180\Delta t \leq 6$, or $\Delta t \leq 6/180 = 1/30$. So the flowrate gauge should be read every $1/30$ of an hour, or every 2 minutes.

2. (a) An upper estimate is $9.81 + 8.03 + 6.53 + 5.38 + 4.41 = 34.16$ m/sec. A lower estimate is $8.03 + 6.53 + 5.38 + 4.41 + 3.61 = 27.96$ m/sec.

(b) The average is $\frac{1}{2}(34.16 + 27.96) = 31.06$ m/sec. Because the graph of acceleration is concave up, this estimate is too high, as can be seen in Figure 5.45. The area of the shaded region is the average of the areas of the rectangles $ABFE$ and $CDFE$.

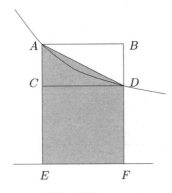

Figure 5.45

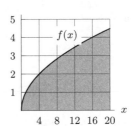

Figure 5.46

3. $\displaystyle\int_0^{20} f(x)\,dx$ is equal to the area shaded in Figure 5.46. We estimate the area by counting boxes. There are about 15 boxes and each box represents 4 square units, so the area shaded is about 60. We have

$$\int_0^{20} f(x)\,dx \approx 60.$$

4. We know that

$$\int_{-3}^{5} f(x)dx = \text{Area above the axis} - \text{Area below the axis}.$$

The area above the axis is about 3 boxes. Since each box has area $(1)(5) = 5$, the area above the axis is about $(3)(5) = 15$. The area below the axis is about 11 boxes, giving an area of about $(11)(5) = 55$. We have

$$\int_{-3}^{5} f(x)dx \approx 15 - 55 = -40.$$

5. We take $\Delta t = 20$. Then:

$$\text{Left-hand sum} = 1.2(20) + 2.8(20) + 4.0(20) + 4.7(20) + 5.1(20)$$
$$= 356.$$
$$\text{Right-hand sum} = 2.8(20) + 4.0(20) + 4.7(20) + 5.1(20) + 5.2(20)$$
$$= 436.$$
$$\int_0^{100} f(t)\, dt \approx \text{Average} = \frac{356 + 436}{2} = 396.$$

6. (a) The total area between $f(x)$ and the x-axis is the sum of the two given areas, so

$$\text{Area} = 7 + 6 = 13.$$

(b) To find the integral, we note that from $x = 3$ to $x = 5$, the function lies below the x-axis, and hence makes a negative contribution to the integral. So

$$\int_0^5 f(x)\, dx = \int_0^3 f(x)dx + \int_3^5 f(x)dx = 7 - 6 = 1.$$

7. The x intercepts of $y = 4 - x^2$ are $x = -2$ and $x = 2$, and the graph is above the x-axis on the interval $[-2, 2]$.

$$\text{Area} = \int_{-2}^2 (4 - x^2)\, dx = 10.667.$$

The integral was evaluated on a calculator.

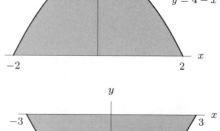

8. The x intercepts of $y = x^2 - 9$ are $x = -3$ and $x = 3$, and since the graph is below the x axis on the interval $[-3, 3]$.

$$\text{Area} = -\int_{-3}^3 (x^2 - 9)\, dx = 36.$$

The integral was evaluated on a calculator.

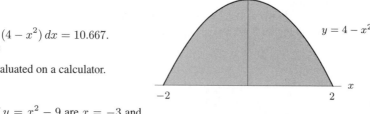

9. Since x intercepts are $x = 0, \pi, 2\pi, \ldots,$

$$\text{Area} = \int_0^\pi \sin x\, dx = 2.$$

The integral was evaluated on a calculator.

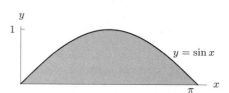

10. Since the θ intercepts of $y = \sin \theta$ are $\theta = 0, \pi, 2\pi, \ldots,$

$$\text{Area} = \int_0^\pi (1 - \sin \theta)\, d\theta = 1.142.$$

The integral was evaluated on a calculator.

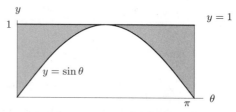

11. The graph of $y = -x^2 + 5x - 4$ is shown in Figure 5.47. We wish to find the area shaded. Since the graph crosses the x-axis at $x = 1$, we must split the integral at $x = 1$. For $x < 1$, the graph is below the x-axis, so the area is the negative of the integral. Thus

$$\text{Area shaded} = -\int_0^1 (-x^2 + 5x - 4)dx + \int_1^3 (-x^2 + 5x - 4)dx.$$

Using a calculator or computer, we find

$$\int_0^1 (-x^2 + 5x - 4)\,dx = -1.8333 \quad \text{and} \quad \int_1^3 (-x^2 + 5x - 4)\,dx = 3.3333.$$

Thus,

$$\text{Area shaded} = 1.8333 + 3.3333 = 5.167.$$

(Notice that $\int_0^3 f(x)\,dx = -1.8333 + 3.333 = 1.5$, but the value of this integral is not the area shaded.)

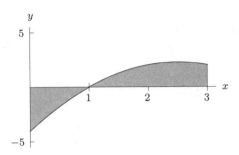

Figure 5.47

12. The graph of $y = \cos x + 7$ is above $y = \ln(x - 3)$ for $5 \le x \le 7$. See Figure 5.48. Therefore

$$\text{Area} = \int_5^7 \cos x + 7 - \ln(x - 3)\,dx = 13.457.$$

The integral was evaluated on a calculator.

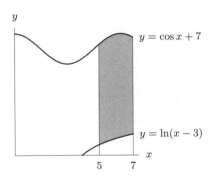

Figure 5.48

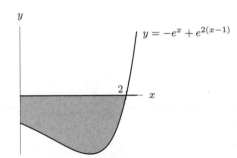

Figure 5.49

13. The graph of $y = -e^x + e^{2(x-1)}$ has intercepts where $e^x = e^{2(x-1)}$, or where $x = 2(x - 1)$, so $x = 2$. See Figure 5.49. Since the region is below the x-axis, the integral is negative, so

$$\text{Area} = -\int_0^2 -e^x + e^{2(x-1)}\,dx = 2.762.$$

The integral was evaluated on a calculator.

14. (a) We calculate the right- and left-hand sums as follows:

$$\text{Left} = 2[80 + 52 + 28 + 10] = 340 \text{ ft.}$$
$$\text{Right} = 2[52 + 28 + 10 + 0] = 180 \text{ ft.}$$

Our best estimate will be the average of these two sums,

$$\text{Best} = \frac{\text{Left} + \text{Right}}{2} = \frac{340 + 180}{2} = 260 \text{ ft.}$$

(b) Since v is decreasing throughout,

$$\text{Left} - \text{Right} = \Delta t \cdot [f(0) - f(8)]$$
$$= 80\Delta t.$$

Since our best estimate is the average of Left and Right, the maximum error is $(80)\Delta t/2$. For $(80)\Delta t/2 \leq 20$, we must have $\Delta t \leq 1/2$. In other words, we must measure the velocity every 0.5 second.

15. By counting squares and fractions of squares, we find that the area under the graph appears to be around 310 (miles/hour) sec, within about 10. So the distance traveled was about $310 \left(\frac{5280}{3600} \right) \approx 455$ feet, within about $10 \left(\frac{5280}{3600} \right) \approx 15$ feet. (Note that 455 feet is about 0.086 miles)

16. Since $v(t) \geq 0$ for $0 \leq t \leq 3$, we can find the total distance traveled by integrating the velocity from $t = 0$ to $t = 3$:

$$\text{Distance} = \int_0^3 \ln(t^2 + 1) \, dt$$
$$= 3.4 \text{ ft, evaluating this integral by calculator.}$$

17. Distance traveled $= \displaystyle\int_0^{1.1} \sin(t^2) \, dt \approx 0.40$ miles.

Problems

18. Using properties of the definite integral, we have:

$$\int_2^5 (2f(x) + 3) \, dx = 17$$

$$2\int_2^5 f(x) \, dx + 3\int_2^5 1 \, dx = 17$$

$$2\int_2^5 f(x) \, dx + 3 \cdot 3 = 17$$

$$2\int_2^5 f(x) \, dx = 8$$

$$\int_2^5 f(x) \, dx = 4.$$

19. We have

$$30 = \int_{-2}^3 f \, dx = \int_{-2}^2 f(x) \, dx + \int_2^3 f(x) \, dx.$$

Since f is odd, $\int_{-2}^2 f(x) \, dx = 0$, so $\int_2^3 f(x) \, dx = 30$.

20. We have

$$8 = \int_{-2}^2 (f(x) - 3) \, dx = \int_{-2}^2 f(x) \, dx - 3\int_{-2}^2 1 \, dx.$$

Thus $\int_{-2}^2 f(x) \, dx = 8 + 3(2 - (-2)) = 20$. Since f is even, $\int_0^2 f(x) \, dx = (1/2)20 = 10$.

21. On the interval $2 \leq x \leq 5$,

$$\begin{array}{c} \text{Average value} \\ \text{of } f \end{array} = \frac{1}{5 - 2} \int_2^5 f(x) \, dx = 4,$$

so

$$\int_2^5 f(x) \, dx = 12.$$

Thus

$$\int_2^5 (3f(x) + 2) \, dx = 3\int_2^5 f(x) \, dx + 2\int_2^5 1 \, dx = 3(12) + 2(5 - 2) = 42.$$

22. This integral represents the area of two triangles, each of base 1 and height 1. See Figure 5.50. Therefore:

$$\int_{-1}^{1} |x|\, dx = \frac{1}{2} \cdot 1 \cdot 1 + \frac{1}{2} \cdot 1 \cdot 1 = 1.$$

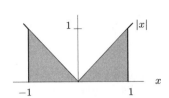

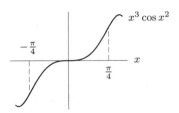

Figure 5.50   **Figure 5.51**

23. This integral is 0 because the function $x^3 \cos(x^2)$ is odd (meaning $f(-x) = -f(x)$), and so the negative contribution to the integral from $-\frac{\pi}{4} < x < 0$ exactly cancels the positive contribution from $0 < x < \frac{\pi}{4}$. See Figure 5.51.

24. (a) Clearly, the points where $x = \sqrt{\pi},\ \sqrt{2\pi},\ \sqrt{3\pi},\ \sqrt{4\pi}$ are where the graph intersects the x-axis because $f(x) = \sin(x^2) = 0$ where x is the square root of some multiple of π.

   (b) Let $f(x) = \sin(x^2)$, and let A, B, C, and D be the areas of the regions indicated in the figure below. Then we see that $A > B > C > D$.

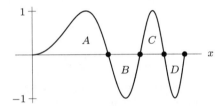

Note that

$$\int_{0}^{\sqrt{\pi}} f(x)\, dx = A, \qquad \int_{0}^{\sqrt{2\pi}} f(x)\, dx = A - B,$$

$$\int_{0}^{\sqrt{3\pi}} f(x)\, dx = A - B + C, \quad \text{and} \quad \int_{0}^{\sqrt{4\pi}} f(x)\, dx = A - B + C - D.$$

It follows that

$$\int_{0}^{\sqrt{\pi}} f(x)\, dx = A > \int_{0}^{\sqrt{3\pi}} f(x)\, dx = A - (B - C) = A - B + C >$$

$$\int_{0}^{\sqrt{4\pi}} f(x)\, dx = A - B + C - D > \int_{0}^{\sqrt{2\pi}} f(x)\, dx = (A - B) > 0.$$

And thus the ordering is $n = 1$, $n = 3$, $n = 4$, and $n = 2$ from largest to smallest. All the numbers are positive.

25. (a) Train A starts earlier than Train B, and stops later. At every moment Train A is going faster than Train B. Both trains increase their speed at a constant rate through the first half of their trip and slow down during the second half. Both trains reach their maximum speed at the same time. The area under the velocity graph for Train A is larger than the area under the velocity graph for Train B, meaning that Train A travels farther—as would be expected, given that its speed is always higher than B's.

   (b) (i) The maximum velocity is read off the vertical axis. The graph for Train A appears to go about twice as high as the graph for Train B; see Figure 5.52. So

$$\frac{\text{Maximum velocity of Train } A}{\text{Maximum velocity of Train } B} = \frac{v_A}{v_B} \approx 2.$$

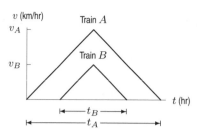

Figure 5.52

(ii) The time of travel is the horizontal distance between the start and stop times (the two t-intercepts). The horizontal distance for Train A appears to be about twice the corresponding distance for Train B; see Figure 5.52. So

$$\frac{\text{Time traveled by Train } A}{\text{Time traveled by Train } B} = \frac{t_A}{t_B} \approx 2.$$

(iii) The distance traveled by each train is given by the area under its graph. Since the area of triangle is $\frac{1}{2} \cdot$ Base $\cdot$ Height, and since the base and height for Train A is approximately twice that for Train B, we have

$$\frac{\text{Distance traveled by Train } A}{\text{Distance traveled by Train } B} = \frac{\frac{1}{2} \cdot v_A \cdot t_A}{\frac{1}{2} \cdot v_B \cdot t_B} \approx 2 \cdot 2 = 4.$$

26. We use left- and right-hand sums to estimate the total amount of coal produced during this period:

$$\text{Left sum} = (10.82)(5) + (13.06)(5) + (14.61)(5) + (14.99)(5) + (18.60)(5) + (19.33)(5) = 457.05.$$

$$\text{Right sum} = (13.06)(5) + (14.61)(5) + (14.99)(5) + (18.60)(5) + (19.33)(5) + (22.46)(5) = 515.25.$$

We see that

$$\text{Total amount of coal produced} \approx \frac{457.05 + 515.25}{2} = 486.15 \text{ quadrillion BTU.}$$

The total amount of coal produced is the definite integral of the rate of coal production $r = f(t)$ given in the table. Since t is in years since 1960, the limits of integration are $t = 0$ and $t = 30$. We have

$$\text{Total amount of coal produced} = \int_0^{30} f(t)dt \text{ quadrillion BTU.}$$

27. (a) Note that the rate $r(t)$ sometimes increases and sometimes decreases in the interval. We can calculate an upper estimate of the volume by choosing $\Delta t = 5$ and then choosing the highest value of $r(t)$ on each interval, and similarly a lower estimate by choosing the lowest value of $r(t)$ on each interval:

$$\text{Upper estimate} = 5[20 + 24 + 24] = 340 \text{ liters.}$$
$$\text{Lower estimate} = 5[12 + 20 + 16] = 240 \text{ liters.}$$

(b) A graph of $r(t)$ along with the areas represented by the choices of $r(t)$ in calculating the lower estimate is shown in Figure 5.53.

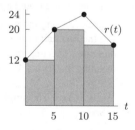

Figure 5.53

28. From $t = 0$ to $t = 3$, you are moving away from home ($v > 0$); thereafter you move back toward home. So you are the farthest from home at $t = 3$. To find how far you are then, we can measure the area under the v curve as about 9 squares, or $9 \cdot 10$ km/hr $\cdot$ 1 hr $= 90$ km. To find how far away from home you are at $t = 5$, we measure the area from $t = 3$ to $t = 5$ as about 25 km, except that this distance is directed toward home, giving a total distance from home during the trip of $90 - 25 = 65$ km.

29. (a) At $t = 20$ minutes, she stops moving toward the lake (with $v > 0$) and starts to move away from the lake (with $v < 0$). So at $t = 20$ minutes the cyclist turns around.

(b) The cyclist is going the fastest when v has the greatest magnitude, either positive or negative. Looking at the graph, we can see that this occurs at $t = 40$ minutes, when $v = -25$ and the cyclist is pedaling at 25 km/hr away from the lake.

(c) From $t = 0$ to $t = 20$ minutes, the cyclist comes closer to the lake, since $v > 0$; thereafter, $v < 0$ so the cyclist moves away from the lake. So at $t = 20$ minutes, the cyclist comes the closest to the lake. To find out how close she is, note that between $t = 0$ and $t = 20$ minutes the distance she has come closer is equal to the area under the graph of v. Each box represents 5/6 of a kilometer, and there are about 2.5 boxes under the graph, giving a distance of about 2 km. Since she was originally 5 km away, she then is about $5 - 2 = 3$ km from the lake.

(d) At $t = 20$ minutes she turns around , since v changes sign then. Since the area below the t-axis is greater than the area above, the farthest she is from the lake is at $t = 60$ minutes. Between $t = 20$ and $t = 60$ minutes, the area under the graph is about 10.8 km. (Since 13 boxes $\cdot 5/6 = 10.8$.) So at $t = 60$ she will be about $3 + 10.8 = 13.8$ km from the lake.

30. Suppose $F(t)$ represents the total quantity of water in the water tower at time t, where t is in days since April 1. Then the graph shown in the problem is a graph of $F'(t)$. By the Fundamental Theorem,

$$F(30) - F(0) = \int_0^{30} F'(t)dt.$$

We can calculate the change in the quantity of water by calculating the area under the curve. If each box represents about 300 liters, there is about one box, or -300 liters, from $t = 0$ to $t = 12$, and 6 boxes, or about $+1800$ liters, from $t = 12$ to $t = 30$. Thus

$$\int_0^{30} F'(t)dt = 1800 - 300 = 1500,$$

so the final amount of water is given by

$$F(30) = F(0) + \int_0^{30} F'(t)dt = 12{,}000 + 1500 = 13{,}500 \text{ liters}.$$

31. (a) At the end of one hour $t = 60$, and $H = 22°$C.

(b)

$$\text{Average temperature} = \frac{1}{60} \int_0^{60} (20 + 980e^{-0.1t})dt$$

$$= \frac{1}{60}(10976) = 183°\text{C}.$$

(c) Average temperature at beginning and end of hour $= (1000 + 22)/2 = 511°$C. The average found in part (b) is smaller than the average of these two temperatures because the bar cools quickly at first and so spends less time at high temperatures. Alternatively, the graph of H against t is concave up.

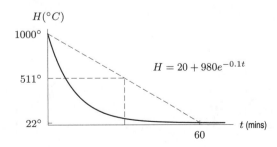

32. If $H(t)$ is the temperature of the coffee at time t, by the Fundamental Theorem of Calculus

$$\text{Change in temperature } = H(10) - H(0) = \int_0^{10} H'(t)\, dt = \int_0^{10} -7e^{-0.1t}\, dt.$$

Therefore,

$$H(10) = H(0) + \int_0^{10} -7(0.9^t)\, dt \approx 90 - 44.2 = 45.8°\text{C}.$$

33. The change in the amount of water is the integral of rate of change, so we have

$$\text{Number of liters pumped out } = \int_0^{60} (5 - 5e^{-0.12t})dt = 258.4 \text{ liters}.$$

Since the tank contained 1000 liters of water initially, we see that

$$\text{Amount in tank after one hour } = 1000 - 258.4 = 741.6 \text{ liters}.$$

34. All the integrals have positive values, since $f \geq 0$. The integral in (ii) is about one-half the integral in (i), due to the apparent symmetry of f. The integral in (iv) will be much larger than the integral in (i), since the two peaks of f^2 rise to 10,000. The integral in (iii) will be smaller than half of the integral in (i), since the peaks in $f^{1/2}$ will only rise to 10. So

$$\int_0^2 (f(x))^{1/2}\, dx < \int_0^1 f(x)\, dx < \int_0^2 f(x)\, dx < \int_0^2 (f(x))^2\, dx.$$

35. In Figure 5.54 the area A_1 is largest, A_2 is next, and A_3 is smallest. We have

$$\text{I} = \int_a^b f(x)\, dx = A_1, \quad \text{II} = \int_a^c f(x)\, dx = A_1 - A_2, \quad \text{III} = \int_a^e f(x)\, dx = A_1 - A_2 + A_3,$$

$$\text{IV} = \int_b^e f(x)\, dx = -A_2 + A_3, \quad \text{V} = \int_b^c f(x)\, dx = -A_2.$$

The relative sizes of A_1, A_2, and A_3 mean that I is positive and largest, III is next largest (since $-A_2 + A_3$ is negative, but less negative than $-A_2$), II is next largest, but still positive (since A_1 is larger than A_2). The integrals IV and V are both negative, but V is more negative. Thus

$$\text{V} < \text{IV} < 0 < \text{II} < \text{III} < \text{I}.$$

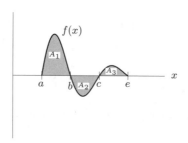

Figure 5.54

36. (a) For $-2 \leq x \leq 2$, f is symmetrical about the y-axis, so $\int_{-2}^0 f(x)\, dx = \int_0^2 f(x)\, dx$ and $\int_{-2}^2 f(x)\, dx = 2\int_0^2 f(x)\, dx$.
(b) For any function f, $\int_0^2 f(x)\, dx = \int_0^5 f(x)\, dx - \int_2^5 f(x)\, dx$.
(c) Note that $\int_{-2}^0 f(x)\, dx = \frac{1}{2}\int_{-2}^2 f(x)\, dx$, so $\int_0^5 f(x)\, dx = \int_{-2}^5 f(x)\, dx - \int_{-2}^0 f(x)\, dx = \int_{-2}^5 f(x)\, dx - \frac{1}{2}\int_{-2}^2 f(x)\, dx.$

37. (a) We know that $\int_2^5 f(x)\,dx = \int_0^5 f(x)\,dx - \int_0^2 f(x)\,dx$. By symmetry, $\int_0^2 f(x)\,dx = \frac{1}{2}\int_{-2}^2 f(x)\,dx$, so $\int_2^5 f(x)\,dx = \int_0^5 f(x)\,dx - \frac{1}{2}\int_{-2}^2 f(x)\,dx$.

(b) $\int_2^5 f(x)\,dx = \int_{-2}^5 f(x)\,dx - \int_{-2}^2 f(x)\,dx = \int_{-2}^5 f(x)\,dx - 2\int_{-2}^0 f(x)\,dx$.

(c) Using symmetry again, $\int_0^2 f(x)\,dx = \frac{1}{2}\left(\int_{-2}^5 f(x)\,dx - \int_2^5 f(x)\,dx\right)$.

38. (a) V, since the slope is constant.

(b) IV, since the net area under this curve is the most negative.

(c) III, since the area under the curve is largest.

(d) II, since the steepest ascent at $t = 0$ occurs on this curve.

(e) III, since average velocity is (total distance)/5, and III moves the largest total distance.

(f) I, since average acceleration is $\dfrac{1}{5}\displaystyle\int_0^5 v'(t)\,dt = \dfrac{1}{5}(v(5) - v(0))$, and in I, the velocity increases the most from start $(t = 0)$ to finish $(t = 5)$.

39. The integrand is a linear function with value b_1 at the left-hand end. At the right-hand end the height is

$$b_1 + \frac{b_2 - b_1}{w}w = b_2.$$

See Figure 5.55. The integral gives the area of the right trapezoid bounded by the x-axis, the lines $x = 0$ and $x = w$, and the integrand. The value of the integral is the area of this trapezoid

$$\int_0^w \left(b_1 + \frac{b_2 - b_1}{w}x\right)dx = \frac{1}{2}w(b_1 + b_2).$$

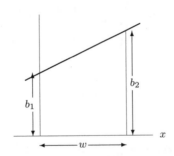

Figure 5.55

40. When the rate at which water is flowing out of the tank is greater than the rate at which it is flowing in, the water level is dropping. When the two rates are equal, which is about 15 minutes from the start, the water level reaches a steady state. The volume of water in the tank at any time t_0 is represented by the difference between the volume of water flowing in and flowing out. The first volume is represented by the area between the horizontal line ("flow in") and the x-axis, and the latter volume is represented by the area between the curve ("flow out") and the x-axis in Figure 5.56. This difference is represented between the two light shaded areas in Figure 5.56. The steady state volume of water in the tank is represented by the difference of the shaded areas in Figure 5.57.

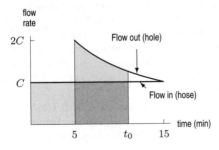

Figure 5.56

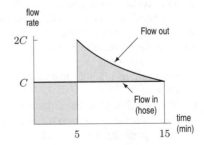

Figure 5.57

41. (a) Looking at the graph, it appears that the graph of B is above $F = 10$ between $t = 2.3$ and $t = 4.2$, or for about 1.9 seconds.

(b) The total impulse of each rocket is represented by the area under its thrust curve. From $t = 0$ to $t = 2$, the graph of A looks like a triangle with base 2 and height 12, for an area of 12. From $t = 2$ to $t = 4$, the graph of A looks a trapezoid with base 2 and heights 13 and 6, for an area of 19. From $t = 4$ to $t = 16$, A is approximately a rectangle with height 5.8 and width 12, for an area of 69.6. Finally, from $t = 16$ to $t = 17$, A looks like a triangle with base 1 and height 5.8, for an area of 2.9. So

$$A's \text{ total impulse } = \text{ Area under } A\text{'s thrust curve } = 12 + 19 + 69.6 + 2.9 = 103.5 \text{ newton-seconds.}$$

(c) Note that when we calculated the impulse in part (b), we multiplied height, measured in newtons, by width, measured in seconds. So the units of impulse are newton-seconds.

(d) The graph of B's thrust looks like a triangle with base 6 and height 22, for a total impulse of about 66 newton-seconds. So rocket A, with total impulse 103.5 newton-seconds, has a larger total impulse than rocket B.

(e) As we can see from the graph, rocket B reaches a maximum thrust of 22, whereas A only reaches a maximum thrust of 13. So rocket B has the largest maximum thrust.

42. (a) About 300 meter^3/sec.

(b) About 250 meter^3/sec.

(c) Looking at the graph, we can see that the 1996 flood reached its maximum just between March and April, for a high of about 1250 meter^3/sec. Similarly, the 1957 flood reached its maximum in mid-June, for a maximum flow rate of 3500 meter^3/sec.

(d) The 1996 flood lasted about 1/3 of a month, or about 10 days. The 1957 flood lasted about 4 months.

(e) The area under the controlled flood graph is about 2/3 box. Each box represents 500 meter^3/sec for one month. Since

$$1 \text{ month } = 30 \frac{\text{days}}{\text{month}} \cdot 24 \frac{\text{hours}}{\text{day}} \cdot 60 \frac{\text{minutes}}{\text{hour}} \cdot 60 \frac{\text{seconds}}{\text{minute}}$$
$$= 2.592 \cdot 10^6 \approx 3 \cdot 10^6 \text{ seconds,}$$

each box represents

$$\text{Flow} \approx (500 \text{ meter}^3/\text{sec}) \cdot (2.6 \cdot 10^6 \text{ sec}) = 13 \cdot 10^8 \text{ meter}^3 \text{ of water.}$$

So, for the artificial flood,

$$\text{Additional flow} \approx \frac{2}{3} \cdot 13 \cdot 10^8 = 9 \cdot 10^8 \text{ meter}^3 \approx 10^9 \text{ meter}^3.$$

(f) The 1957 flood released a volume of water represented by about 12 boxes above the 250 meter/sec baseline. Thus, for the natural flood,

$$\text{Additional flow} \approx 12 \cdot 15 \cdot 10^8 = 1.8 \cdot 10^{10} \approx 2 \cdot 10^{10} \text{ meter}^3.$$

So, the natural flood was nearly 20 times larger than the controlled flood and lasted much longer.

43. (a) The acceleration is positive for $0 \le t < 40$ and for a tiny period before $t = 60$, since the slope is positive over these intervals. Just to the left of $t = 40$, it looks like the acceleration is approaching 0. Between $t = 40$ and a moment just before $t = 60$, the acceleration is negative.

(b) The maximum altitude was about 500 feet, when t was a little greater than 40 (here we are estimating the area under the graph for $0 \le t \le 42$).

(c) The acceleration is greatest when the slope of the velocity is most positive. This happens just before $t = 60$, where the magnitude of the velocity is plunging and the direction of the acceleration is positive, or up.

(d) The deceleration is greatest when the slope of the velocity is most negative. This happens just after $t = 40$.

(e) After the Montgolfier Brothers hit their top climbing speed (at $t = 40$), they suddenly stopped climbing and started to fall. This suggests some kind of catastrophe—the flame going out, the balloon ripping, etc. (In actual fact, in their first flight in 1783, the material covering their balloon, held together by buttons, ripped and the balloon landed in flames.)

(f) The total change in altitude for the Montgolfiers and their balloon is the definite integral of their velocity, or the total area under the given graph (counting the part after $t = 42$ as negative, of course). As mentioned before, the total area of the graph for $0 \le t \le 42$ is about 500. The area for $t > 42$ is about 220. So subtracting, we see that the balloon finished 280 feet or so higher than where it began.

44. (a) The mouse changes direction (when its velocity is zero) at about times 17, 23, and 27.

(b) The mouse is moving most rapidly to the right at time 10 and most rapidly to the left at time 40.

(c) The mouse is farthest to the right when the integral of the velocity, $\int_0^t v(t)\,dt$, is most positive. Since the integral is the sum of the areas above the axis minus the areas below the axis, the integral is largest when the velocity is zero at about 17 seconds. The mouse is farthest to the left of center when the integral is most negative at 40 seconds.

(d) The mouse's speed decreases during seconds 10 to 17, from 20 to 23 seconds, and from 24 seconds to 27 seconds.

(e) The mouse is at the center of the tunnel at any time t for which the integral from 0 to t of the velocity is zero. This is true at time 0 and again somewhere around 35 seconds.

45. (a) When the aircraft is climbing at v ft/min, it takes $1/v$ minutes to climb 1 foot. Therefore

$$\text{Lower estimate} = \left(\frac{1\,\text{min}}{925\,\text{ft}}\right)(1000\,\text{ft}) + \left(\frac{1\,\text{min}}{875\,\text{ft}}\right)(1000\,\text{ft}) + \cdots + \left(\frac{1\,\text{min}}{490\,\text{ft}}\right)(1000\,\text{ft})$$

$$\approx 14.73\,\text{minutes}.$$

$$\text{Upper estimate} = \left(\frac{1\,\text{min}}{875\,\text{ft}}\right)(1000\,\text{ft}) + \left(\frac{1\,\text{min}}{830\,\text{ft}}\right)(1000\,\text{ft}) + \cdots + \left(\frac{1\,\text{min}}{440\,\text{ft}}\right)(1000\,\text{ft})$$

$$\approx 15.93\,\text{minutes}.$$

Note: The Pilot Operating Manual for this aircraft gives 16 minutes as the estimated time required to climb to 10,000 ft.

(b) The difference between upper and lower sums with $\Delta x = 500$ ft would be

$$\text{Difference} = \left(\frac{1\,\text{min}}{440\,\text{ft}} - \frac{1\,\text{min}}{925\,\text{ft}}\right)(500\,\text{ft}) = 0.60\,\text{minutes}.$$

46. The graph of rate against time is the straight line shown in Figure 5.58. Since the shaded area is 270, we have

$$\frac{1}{2}(10 + 50) \cdot t = 270$$

$$t = \frac{270}{60} \cdot 2 = 9\,\text{years}$$

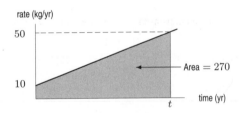

Figure 5.58

47. In (a), $f'(1)$ is the slope of a tangent line at $x = 1$, which is negative. As for (c), the rate of change in $f(x)$ is given by $f'(x)$, and the average value of this over $0 \le x \le a$ is

$$\frac{1}{a-0}\int_0^a f'(x)\,dx = \frac{f(a) - f(0)}{a - 0}.$$

This is the slope of the line through the points $(0, 1)$ and $(a, 0)$, which is less negative that the tangent line at $x = 1$. Therefore, (a) < (c) < 0. The quantity (b) is $\left(\int_0^a f(x)\,dx\right)/a$ and (d) is $\int_0^a f(x)\,dx$, which is the net area under the graph of f (counting the area as negative for f below the x-axis). Since $a > 1$ and $\int_0^a f(x)\,dx > 0$, we have $0 <$(b)$<$(d). Therefore

$$\text{(a)} < \text{(c)} < \text{(b)} < \text{(d)}.$$

48. (a) Divide the interval $0 \le t \le T$ into small subintervals of length Δt on which the temperature is approximately constant. Then if t_i is the ith interval, on that interval

$$\Delta S \approx (H - H_{\min})\Delta t = (f(t_i) - H_{\min})\Delta t.$$

Thus, the total number of degree-days is approximated by

$$S \approx \sum_{i=1}^{n} (f(t_i) - H_{\min}) \Delta t.$$

As $n \to \infty$, we have

$$S = \int_0^T (f(t) - H_{\min}) \, dt.$$

(b) Since $H_{\min} = 15°C$ and $S = 125$ degree-days, the formula in part (a) gives

$$125 = \int_0^T (f(t) - 15) dt.$$

We approximate the definite integral using a Riemann sum:

$$\int_0^T (f(t) - 15) dt = \sum_{i=1}^{n} (f(t_i) - 15) \Delta t.$$

In the table, we have $\Delta t = 1$. We want to find how many terms in the sum are required to (approximately) equal the required number of degree-days, $S = 125$. From the table, we have

$$\sum_{i=1}^{2} (f(t_i) - 15) \Delta t = (20 - 15)1 + (22 - 15)1 = 12,$$

so the sum of degree-days over a two-day period is much smaller than the required sum of 125. Likewise, the sum over a three-day period is only 24:

$$\sum_{i=1}^{3} (f(t_i) - 15) \Delta t = (20 - 15)1 + (22 - 15)1 + (27 - 15)1 = 24.$$

Summing over a ten-day period and an eleven-day period, we find, respectively, that

$$\sum_{i=1}^{10} (f(t_i) - 15) \Delta t = (20 - 15)1 + (22 - 15)1 + (27 - 15)1 + (28 - 15)1 + (27 - 15)1 + (31 - 15)1$$

$$+(29 - 15)1 + (30 - 15)1 + (28 - 15)1 + (25 - 15)1 = 117$$

$$\sum_{i=1}^{11} (f(t_i) - 15) \Delta t = (20 - 15)1 + (22 - 15)1 + (27 - 15)1 + (28 - 15)1 + (27 - 15)1 + (31 - 15)1$$

$$+(29 - 15)1 + (30 - 15)1 + (28 - 15)1 + (25 - 15)1 + (24 - 15)1 = 126.$$

Thus, the sum reaches 125 degree-days somewhere just short of $T = 11$ days.

CAS Challenge Problems

49. (a) We have $\Delta x = (1 - 0)/n = 1/n$ and $x_i = 0 + i \cdot \Delta x = i/n$. So we get

$$\text{Right-hand sum} = \sum_{i=1}^{n} (x_i)^4 \Delta x = \sum_{i=1}^{n} \left(\frac{i}{n}\right)^4 \left(\frac{1}{n}\right) = \sum_{i=1}^{n} \frac{i^4}{n^5}.$$

(b) The CAS gives

$$\text{Right-hand sum} = \sum_{i=1}^{n} \frac{i^4}{n^5} = \frac{6n^4 + 15n^3 + 10n^2 - 1}{30n^4}.$$

(The results may look slightly different depending on the CAS you use.)

(c) Using a CAS or by hand, we get

$$\lim_{n \to \infty} \frac{6n^4 + 15n^3 + 10n^2 - 1}{30n^4} = \lim_{n \to \infty} \frac{6n^4}{30n^4} = \frac{1}{5}.$$

The numerator is dominated by the highest power term, which is $6n^4$, so when n is large, the ratio behaves like $6n^4/30n^4 = 1/5$ as $n \to \infty$. Thus we see that

$$\int_0^1 x^4 dx = \frac{1}{5}.$$

50. (a) A Riemann sum with n subdivisions of $[0, 1]$ has $\Delta x = 1/n$ and $x_i = i/n$. Thus,

$$\text{Right-hand sum} = \sum_{i=1}^{n} \left(\frac{i}{n}\right)^5 \left(\frac{1}{n}\right) = \sum_{i=1}^{n} \frac{i^5}{n^6}.$$

(b) A CAS gives

$$\text{Right-hand sum} = \sum_{i=1}^{n} \frac{i^5}{n^6} = \frac{2n^4 + 6n^3 + 5n^2 - 1}{12n^4}.$$

(c) Taking the limit by hand or using a CAS gives

$$\lim_{n \to \infty} \frac{2n^4 + 6n^3 + 5n^2 - 1}{12n^4} = \lim_{n \to \infty} \frac{2n^4}{12n^4} = \frac{1}{6}.$$

The numerator is dominated by the highest power term, which is $2n^4$, so the ratio behaves like $2n^4/12n^4 = 1/6$, as $n \to \infty$. Thus we see that

$$\int_0^1 x^5 dx = \frac{1}{6}.$$

51. (a) Since the length of the interval of integration is $2 - 1 = 1$, the width of each subdivision is $\Delta t = 1/n$. Thus the endpoints of the subdivision are

$$t_0 = 1, \quad t_1 = 1 + \Delta t = 1 + \frac{1}{n}, \quad t_2 = 1 + 2\Delta t = 1 + \frac{2}{n}, \ldots,$$

$$t_i = 1 + i\Delta t = 1 + \frac{i}{n}, \ldots, \quad t_{n-1} = 1 + (n-1)\Delta t = 1 + \frac{n-1}{n}.$$

Thus, since the integrand is $f(t) = t$,

$$\text{Left-hand sum} = \sum_{i=0}^{n-1} f(t_i)\Delta t = \sum_{i=0}^{n-1} t_i \Delta t = \sum_{i=0}^{n-1} \left(1 + \frac{i}{n}\right) \frac{1}{n} = \sum_{i=0}^{n-1} \frac{n+i}{n^2}.$$

(b) The CAS finds the formula for the Riemann sum

$$\sum_{i=0}^{n-1} \frac{n+i}{n^2} = \frac{\frac{(-1+n)\,n}{2} + n^2}{n^2} = \frac{3}{2} - \frac{1}{2n}.$$

(c) Taking the limit as $n \to \infty$

$$\lim_{n \to \infty} \left(\frac{3}{2} - \frac{1}{2n}\right) = \lim_{n \to \infty} \frac{3}{2} - \lim_{n \to \infty} \frac{1}{2n} = \frac{3}{2} + 0 = \frac{3}{2}.$$

(d) The shape under the graph of $y = t$ between $t = 1$ and $t = 2$ is a trapezoid of width 1, height 1 on the left and 2 on the right. So its area is $1 \cdot (1 + 2)/2 = 3/2$. This is the same answer we got by computing the definite integral.

52. (a) Since the length of the interval of integration is $2 - 1 = 1$, the width of each subdivision is $\Delta t = 1/n$. Thus the endpoints of the subdivision are

$$t_0 = 1, \quad t_1 = 1 + \Delta t = 1 + \frac{1}{n}, \quad t_2 = 1 + 2\Delta t = 1 + \frac{2}{n}, \dots,$$

$$t_i = 1 + i\Delta t = 1 + \frac{i}{n}, \dots, \quad t_{n-1} = 1 + (n-1)\Delta t = 1 + \frac{n-1}{n}.$$

Thus, since the integrand is $f(t) = t^2$,

$$\text{Left-hand sum} = \sum_{i=0}^{n-1} f(t_i)\Delta t = \sum_{i=0}^{n-1} t_i^2 \Delta t = \sum_{i=0}^{n-1} \left(1 + \frac{i}{n}\right)^2 \frac{1}{n} = \sum_{i=0}^{n-1} \frac{(n+i)^2}{n^3}.$$

(b) Using a CAS to find the sum, we get

$$\sum_{i=0}^{n-1} \frac{(n+i)^2}{n^3} = \frac{(-1+2n)\,(-1+7n)}{6n^2} = \frac{7}{3} + \frac{1}{6n^2} - \frac{3}{2n}.$$

(c) Taking the limit as $n \to \infty$

$$\lim_{n\to\infty} \left(\frac{7}{3} + \frac{1}{6n^2} - \frac{3}{2n}\right) = \lim_{n\to\infty} \frac{7}{3} + \lim_{n\to\infty} \frac{1}{6n^2} - \lim_{n\to\infty} \frac{3}{2n} = \frac{7}{3} + 0 + 0 = \frac{7}{3}.$$

(d) We have calculated $\int_1^2 t^2 \, dt$ using Riemann sums. Since t^2 is above the t-axis between $t = 1$ and $t = 2$, this integral is the area; so the area is 7/3.

53. (a) Since the length of the interval of integration is π, the width of each subdivision is $\Delta x = \pi/n$. Thus the endpoints of the subdivision are

$$x_0 = 0, \quad x_1 = 0 + \Delta x = \frac{\pi}{n}, \quad x_2 = 0 + 2\Delta x = \frac{2\pi}{n}, \dots,$$

$$x_i = 0 + i\Delta x = \frac{i\pi}{n}, \quad \dots, \quad x_n = 0 + n\Delta x = \frac{n\pi}{n} = \pi.$$

Thus, since the integrand is $f(x) = \sin x$,

$$\text{Right-hand sum} = \sum_{i=1}^{n} f(x_i)\Delta x = \sum_{i=1}^{n} \sin(x_i)\Delta x = \sum_{i=1}^{n} \sin\left(\frac{i\pi}{n}\right)\frac{\pi}{n}.$$

(b) If the CAS can evaluate this sum, we get

$$\sum_{i=1}^{n} \sin\left(\frac{i\pi}{n}\right)\frac{\pi}{n} = \frac{\pi\cot(\pi/2n)}{n} = \frac{\pi\cos(\pi/2n)}{n\sin(\pi/2n)}.$$

(c) Using the computer algebra system, we find that

$$\lim_{n\to\infty} \frac{\pi\cos(\pi/2n)}{n\sin(\pi/2n)} = 2.$$

(d) The computer algebra system gives

$$\int_0^\pi \sin x \, dx = 2.$$

54. (a) A CAS gives

$$\int_a^b \sin(cx) \, dx = \frac{\cos(ac)}{c} - \frac{\cos(bc)}{c}.$$

(b) If $F(x)$ is an antiderivative of $\sin(cx)$, then the Fundamental Theorem of Calculus says that

$$\int_a^b \sin(cx) \, dx = F(b) - F(a).$$

Comparing this with the answer to part (a), we see that

$$F(b) - F(a) = \frac{\cos(ac)}{c} - \frac{\cos(bc)}{c} = \left(-\frac{\cos(cb)}{c}\right) - \left(-\frac{\cos(ca)}{c}\right).$$

This suggests that

$$F(x) = -\frac{\cos(cx)}{c}.$$

Taking the derivative confirms this:

$$\frac{d}{dx}\left(-\frac{\cos(cx)}{c}\right) = \sin(cx).$$

55. (a) Different systems may give different answers. A typical answer is

$$\int_a^c \frac{x}{1 + bx^2}\,dx = \frac{\ln\left(\frac{\left|c^2b + 1\right|}{\left|a^2b + 1\right|}\right)}{2b}.$$

Some CASs may not have the absolute values in the answer; since $b > 0$, the answer is correct without the absolute values.

(b) Using the properties of logarithms, we can rewrite the answer to part (a) as

$$\int_a^c \frac{x}{1 + bx^2}\,dx = \frac{\ln\left|c^2b + 1\right| - \ln\left|a^2b + 1\right|}{2b} = \frac{\ln\left|c^2b + 1\right|}{2b} - \frac{\ln\left|a^2b + 1\right|}{2b}.$$

If $F(x)$ is an antiderivative of $x/(1 + bx^2)$, then the Fundamental Theorem of Calculus says that

$$\int_a^c \frac{x}{1 + bx^2}\,dx = F(c) - F(a).$$

Thus

$$F(c) - F(a) = \frac{\ln\left|c^2b + 1\right|}{2b} - \frac{\ln\left|a^2b + 1\right|}{2b}.$$

This suggests that

$$F(x) = \frac{\ln\left|1 + bx^2\right|}{2b}.$$

(Since $b > 0$, we know $\left|1 + bx^2\right| = 1 + bx^2$.) Taking the derivative confirms this:

$$\frac{d}{dx}\left(\frac{\ln(1 + bx^2)}{2b}\right) = \frac{x}{1 + bx^2}.$$

CHECK YOUR UNDERSTANDING

1. False. The units of the integral are the product of the units for $f(x)$ times the units for x.

2. True. Since f is increasing, each term in the left-hand sum is less than the corresponding term in the right-hand sum.

3. True. The difference between the left and right sums $= (f(a) - f(b))\Delta t$, where the interval is $a \le t \le b$. Since Δt is halved when the number of subdivisions is doubled, the difference is halved also.

4. False. For example, for a constant function, the difference does not get smaller, since it is always 0. Another example is $f(x) = x^2$ on the interval $-1 \le x \le 1$. By the symmetry of the graph, the difference is always 0.

5. False. The integral is the change in position from $t = q$ to $t = b$. If the velocity changes sign in the interval, the total distance traveled and the change in position will not be the same.

6. True, since $\int_0^2 (f(x) + g(x))dx = \int_0^2 f(x)dx + \int_0^2 g(x)dx$.

7. False. It is possible that $\int_0^2 (f(x) + g(x))dx = 10$ and $\int_0^2 f(x)dx = 4$ and $\int_0^2 g(x)dx = 6$, for instance. For example, if $f(x) = 5x - 3$ and $g(x) = 3$, then $\int_0^2 (f(x) + g(x))\,dx = \int_0^2 5x\,dx = 10$, but $\int_0^2 f(x)\,dx = 4$ and $\int_0^2 g(x)\,dx = 6$.

8. False. We know that $\int_0^4 f(x)dx = \int_0^2 f(x)dx + \int_2^4 f(x)dx$, but it is not true that $\int_2^4 f(x)dx$ must be the same value as $\int_0^2 f(x)dx$. For example, if $f(x) = 3x$, then $\int_0^2 f(x)\,dx = 6$, but $\int_0^4 f(x)\,dx = 24$.

9. True, since $\int_0^2 2f(x)dx = 2\int_0^2 f(x)dx$.

10. False. This would be true if $h(x) = 5f(x)$. However, we cannot assume that $f(5x) = 5f(x)$, so for many functions this statement is false. For example, if f is the constant function $f(x) = 3$, then $h(x) = 3$ as well, so $\int_0^2 f(x)\,dx = \int_0^2 h(x)\,dx = 6$.

11. True. If $a = b$, then $\Delta x = 0$ for any Riemann sum for f on the interval $[a, b]$, so every Riemann sum has value 0. Thus, the limit of the Riemann sums is 0.

12. False. For example, let $a = -1$ and $b = 1$ and $f(x) = x$. Then the areas bounded by the graph of f and the x-axis on the two halves of the interval $[-1, 1]$ cancel with each other and make $\int_{-1}^1 f(x)\,dx = 0$. See Figure 5.59.

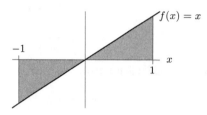

Figure 5.59

13. False. Let $f(x) = 7$ and $g(x) = 9$ for all x.
    Then $\int_1^2 f(x)\,dx + \int_2^3 g(x)\,dx = 7 + 9 = 16$, but $\int_1^3 (f(x) + g(x))\,dx = \int_1^3 16\,dx = 32$.

14. False. If the graph of f is symmetric about the y-axis, this is true, but otherwise it is usually not true. For example, if $f(x) = x + 1$ the area under the graph of f for $-1 \le x \le 0$ is less than the area under the graph of f for $0 \le x \le 1$, so $\int_{-1}^1 f(x)\,dx < 2\int_0^1 f(x)\,dx$. See Figure 5.60.

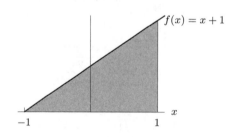

Figure 5.60

15. False. Any function $f(x)$ that is negative between $x = 2$ and $x = 3$ has $\int_2^3 f(x)dx < 0$, so $\int_0^2 f(x)dx > \int_0^3 f(x)dx$.

16. True. Since $\int_0^2 f(x)dx$ is a number, if we use the variable t instead of the variable x in the function f, we get the same number for the definite integral.

17. False. Let $f(x) = x$ and $g(x) = 5$. Then $\int_2^6 f(x)\,dx = 16$ and $\int_2^6 g(x)\,dx = 20$, so $\int_2^6 f(x)\,dx \le \int_2^6 g(x)\,dx$, but $f(x) > g(x)$ for $5 < x < 6$.

18. True, by Theorem 5.4 on Comparison of Definite Integrals:

$$\frac{1}{b-a}\int_a^b f(x)\,dx \le \frac{1}{b-a}\int_a^b g(x)\,dx.$$

19. True. We have

$$\text{Average value of } f \text{ on } [0, 10] = \frac{1}{10 - 0}\int_0^{10} f(x)\,dx$$

$$= \frac{1}{10} \left(\int_0^5 f(x)\, dx + \int_5^{10} f(x)\, dx \right)$$

$$= \frac{1}{2} \left(\frac{1}{5} \int_0^5 f(x)\, dx + \frac{1}{5} \int_5^{10} f(x)\, dx \right)$$

$$= \quad \text{The average of the average value of } f \text{ on } [0, 5] \text{ and the average value of } f \text{ on } [5, 10].$$

20. False. If the values of $f(x)$ on the interval $[c, d]$ are larger than the values of $f(x)$ in the rest of the interval $[a, b]$, then the average value of f on the interval $[c, d]$ is larger than the average value of f on the interval $[a, b]$. For example, suppose

$$f(x) = \begin{cases} 0 & x < 1 \text{ or } x > 2 \\ 1 & 1 \le x \le 2. \end{cases}$$

Then the average value of f on the interval $[1, 2]$ is 1, whereas the average value of f on the interval $[0, 3]$ is $(1/(3 - 0)) \int_0^3 f(x)\,dx = 1/3$.

21. True. We have by the properties of integrals in Theorem 5.3,

$$\int_1^9 f(x)\,dx = \int_1^4 f(x)\,dx + \int_4^9 f(x)\,dx.$$

Since $(1/(4 - 1)) \int_1^4 f(x)\,dx = A$ and $(1/(9 - 4)) \int_4^9 f(x)\,dx = B$, we have

$$\int_1^9 f(x)\,dx = 3A + 5B.$$

Dividing this equation through by 8, we get that the average value of f on the interval $[1, 9]$ is $(3/8)A + (5/8)B$.

22. True. By the properties of integrals in Theorem 5.3, we have:

$$\int_a^b (f(x) + g(x))\,dx = \int_a^b f(x)\,dx + \int_a^b g(x)\,dx.$$

Dividing both sides of this equation through by $b - a$, we get that the average value of $f(x) + g(x)$ is average value of $f(x)$ plus the average value of $g(x)$:

$$\frac{1}{b - a} \int_a^b (f(x) + g(x))\,dx = \frac{1}{b - a} \int_a^b f(x)\,dx + \frac{1}{b - a} \int_a^b g(x)\,dx.$$

23. False. A counterexample is given by

$$f(x) = \begin{cases} 3 & 0 \le x \le 1 \\ 0 & 1 < x \le 2 \end{cases} \quad \text{and} \quad g(x) = \begin{cases} 0 & 0 \le x \le 1 \\ 3 & 1 < x \le 2. \end{cases}$$

Since $f(x)$ is nonzero for $0 \le x < 1$ and $g(x)$ is nonzero for $1 < x \le 2$, the product $f(x)g(x) = 0$ for all x. Thus the average values of $f(x)$ and $g(x)$ are nonzero, but the average of the product is zero.

Specifically, on $[0, 2]$ we have

$$\text{Average}(f) = \frac{1}{2 - 0} \int_0^2 f(x)\, dx = \frac{3}{2}$$

$$\text{Average}(g) = \frac{1}{2 - 0} \int_0^2 g(x)\, dx = \frac{3}{2}$$

$$\text{Average}(f \cdot g) = \frac{1}{2 - 0} \int_0^2 f(x)g(x)\, dx = \frac{1}{2} \int_0^2 0\, dx = 0.$$

but

$$\text{Average}(f) \cdot \text{Average}(g) = \frac{3}{2} \cdot \frac{3}{2} = \frac{9}{4}.$$

24. False. A counterexample is given by $f(x) = 1$ on $[0, 2]$. Then

$$\int_0^2 f(x)\, dx = 2.$$

On the other hand, using $\Delta x = 1/2$ in the 4-term Riemann sum we have

$$\text{Left hand sum} = f(0)\Delta x + f(0.5)\Delta x + f(1)\Delta x + f(1.5)\Delta x$$

$$= 1\left(\frac{1}{2}\right) + 1\left(\frac{1}{2}\right) + 1\left(\frac{1}{2}\right) + 1\left(\frac{1}{2}\right) = 2.$$

25. False. A counterexample is given by the functions f and g in Figure 5.61. The function f is decreasing, g is increasing, and we have

$$\int_1^2 f(x)\, dx = \int_1^2 g(x)\, dx,$$

because both integrals equal $1/2$, the area of of the same sized triangle.

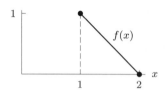

Figure 5.61

26. An example is graphed in Figure 5.62.

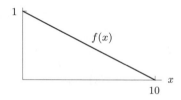

Figure 5.62

Figure 5.63

27. An example is graphed in Figure 5.63.

28. (a) Does not follow; the statement implies that

$$\int_a^b f(x)\, dx + \int_a^b g(x)\, dx = 5 + 7 = 12,$$

but the fact that the two integrals add to 12 does not tell us what the integrals are individually. For example, we could have $\int_a^b f(x)\, dx = 10$ and $\int_a^b g(x)\, dx = 2$.

(b) This follows:

$$\int_a^b (f(x) + g(x))\, dx = \int_a^b f(x)\, dx + \int_a^b g(x)\, dx = 7 + 7 = 14.$$

(c) This follows: rearranging the original statement by subtracting $\int_a^b g(x)\, dx$ from both sides gives

$$\int_a^b (f(x) + g(x))\, dx - \int_a^b g(x)\, dx = \int_a^b f(x)\, dx.$$

Since $f(x) + g(x) = h(x)$, we have $f(x) = h(x) - g(x)$. Substituting for $f(x)$, we get

$$\int_a^b h(x)\, dx - \int_a^b g(x)\, dx = \int_a^b (h(x) - g(x))\, dx.$$

PROJECTS FOR CHAPTER FIVE

1. (a) For Operation 1, we have the following:

(i) A plot of current use versus time is given in Figure 5.64.

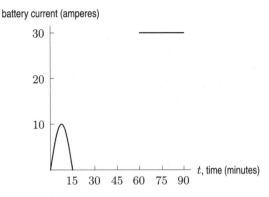

battery current (amperes)

Figure 5.64: Operation 1

The battery current function is given by the formulas

$$D(t) = \begin{cases} 10 \sin \dfrac{2\pi t}{30} & 0 \le t \le 15 \\ 0 & 15 \le t \le 60 \\ 30 & 60 \le t \le 90. \end{cases}$$

(ii) The battery current function gives the rate at which the current is flowing. Thus, the total discharge is given by the integral of the battery current function:

$$\text{Total discharge} = \int_0^{90} D(t)\, dt = \int_0^{15} 10 \sin \frac{2\pi t}{30}\, dt + \int_{15}^{60} 0\, dt + \int_{60}^{90} 30\, dt$$
$$\approx 95.5 + 900$$
$$= 995.5 \text{ ampere-minutes} = 16.6 \text{ ampere-hours}.$$

(iii) The battery can discharge up to 40% of 50 ampere-hours, which is 20 ampere-hours, without damage. Since Operation 1 can be performed with just 16.6 ampere-hours, it is safe.

(b) For Operation 2, we have the following:

(i) The total battery discharge is given by the area under the battery current curve in Figure 5.65. The area under the right-most portion of the curve, (when the satellite is shadowed by the earth), is easily calculated as 30 amps· 30 minutes = 900 ampere-minutes = 15 ampere-hours. For the other part we estimate by trapezoids, which are the average of left and right rectangles on each subinterval. Estimated values of the function are in Table 5.1.

Table 5.1 *Estimated values of the battery current*

Time	0	5	10	15	20	25	30
Current	5	16	18	12	5	12	0

Using $\Delta t = 5$, we see

$$\text{Total discharge} = \frac{1}{2}(5 + 16) \cdot 5 + \frac{1}{2}(16 + 18) \cdot 5 + \frac{1}{2}(18 + 12) \cdot 5$$
$$+ \frac{1}{2}(12 + 5) \cdot 5 + \frac{1}{2}(5 + 12) \cdot 5 + \frac{1}{2}(12 + 0) \cdot 5$$
$$\approx 330 \text{ ampere-minutes} = 5.5 \text{ ampere-hours}.$$

The total estimated discharge is 20.5 ampere-hours.

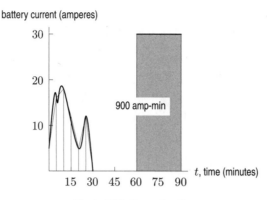

battery current (amperes)

900 amp-min

t, time (minutes)

Figure 5.65: Operation 2

(ii) Since the estimated discharge appears to be an underestimate, Operation 2 probably should not be performed.

2. **(a)** The volume of the cylindrical tank is $\pi \cdot \left(\frac{d}{2}\right)^2 \cdot l$. The volume of the rectangular tank is $w \cdot d \cdot l$. Setting these two volumes equal to each other gives $w = \frac{\pi \cdot d}{4}$.

   If the gas is at a depth of h in the rectangular tank, then the tank is exactly h/d full, since

$$\frac{\text{Volume left in rectangular tank}}{\text{Total volume of rectangular tank}} = \frac{w \cdot h \cdot l}{w \cdot d \cdot l} = \frac{h}{d}.$$

(b) For the same height h in the two tanks, (see Figure 5.66), the error is given by

$$
\begin{aligned}
\text{Error} &= \frac{\text{Fraction of cylindrical}}{\text{tank which is full}} - \frac{h}{d} \\
&= \frac{A_1 l}{\pi(d/2)^2 l} - \frac{h\pi(d/4)l}{d\pi(d/4)l} \\
&= \frac{A_1 l}{\pi(d/2)^2 l} - \frac{A_2 l}{\pi(d^2/4)l} \\
&= \frac{A_1 - A_2}{\pi(d^2/4)}
\end{aligned}
$$

Since the length has canceled out, we can ignore it in calculating the error.

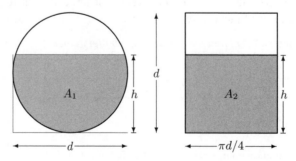

Figure 5.66

(c)

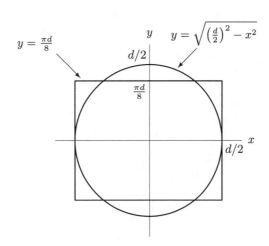

Figure 5.67

(d)

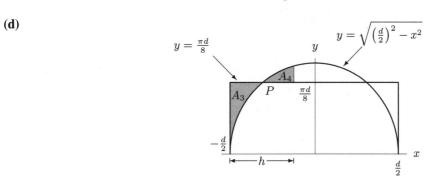

Figure 5.68

For any $0 \leq h \leq d$, Figure 5.68 shows that the error in measuring the fraction of gas remaining, assuming that the tank is rectangular rather than cylindrical, is given by

$$E(h) = 2 \cdot \frac{(A_3 - A_4) \cdot l}{\pi(d^2/4)l} = 2 \cdot \frac{\displaystyle\int_{-(d/2)}^{-(d/2)+h} \left(\frac{\pi d}{8} - \sqrt{\left(\frac{d}{2}\right)^2 - x^2} \right) \, dx}{\pi(d^2/4)}$$

(e) The width of the rectangular tank was chosen so that its volume equals the volume of the cylindrical tank. In addition, the volume of half the rectangular tank equals half the volume of the cylindrical tank. This means that the error $E(h) = 0$ when $h = 0$, $h = d/2$, and $h = d$. Let us consider the value of $E(h)$ as h increases from 0 to $d/2$. When h is slightly above 0, the fact that the line $y = \pi d/8$ is above the circle means that $E(h)$ increases as h increases. After h passes the value corresponding to the point P in Figure 5.68, the error starts to decrease as the circle is above the line.

This means the maximum value of $E(h)$ occurs where the circle and the line cross. This happens when

$$\frac{\pi d}{8} = \sqrt{\left(\frac{d}{2}\right)^2 - x^2}$$

$$x = \pm\sqrt{\frac{d^2}{4} - \frac{\pi^2 d^2}{64}} = \pm\frac{d}{8}\sqrt{16 - \pi^2}$$

Thus,

$$h = \frac{d}{2} + \frac{d}{8}\sqrt{16 - \pi^2} \quad \text{or} \quad h = \frac{d}{2} - \frac{d}{8}\sqrt{16 - \pi^2}.$$

CHAPTER SIX

Solutions for Section 6.1

Exercises

1. See Figure 6.1.

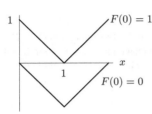

Figure 6.1

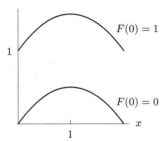

Figure 6.2

2. See Figure 6.2.

3. See Figure 6.3.

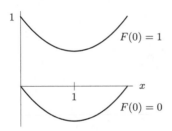

Figure 6.3

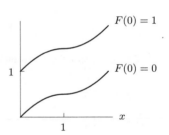

Figure 6.4

4. See Figure 6.4.

5. By the Fundamental Theorem of Calculus, we know that

$$f(2) - f(0) = \int_0^2 f'(x)dx.$$

Using a left-hand sum, we estimate $\int_0^2 f'(x)dx \approx (10)(2) = 20$. Using a right-hand sum, we estimate $\int_0^2 f'(x)dx \approx (18)(2) = 36$. Averaging, we have

$$\int_0^2 f'(x)dx \approx \frac{20 + 36}{2} = 28.$$

We know $f(0) = 100$, so

$$f(2) = f(0) + \int_0^2 f'(x)dx \approx 100 + 28 = 128.$$

Similarly, we estimate

$$\int_2^4 f'(x)dx \approx \frac{(18)(2) + (23)(2)}{2} = 41,$$

so

$$f(4) = f(2) + \int_2^4 f'(x)dx \approx 128 + 41 = 169.$$

Similarly,

$$\int_4^6 f'(x)dx \approx \frac{(23)(2) + (25)(2)}{2} = 48,$$

so

$$f(6) = f(4) + \int_4^6 f'(x)dx \approx 169 + 48 = 217.$$

The values are shown in the table.

x	0	2	4	6
$f(x)$	100	128	169	217

6. The change in $f(x)$ between 0 and 2 is equal to $\int_0^2 f'(x)\,dx$. A left-hand estimate for this integral is $(17)(2) = 34$ and a right hand estimate is $(15)(2) = 30$. Our best estimate is the average, 32. The change in $f(x)$ between 0 and 2 is $+32$. Since $f(0) = 50$, we have $f(2) = 82$. We find the other values similarly. The results are shown in Table 6.1.

Table 6.1

x	0	2	4	6
$f(x)$	50	82	107	119

7. (a) The value of the integral is negative since the area below the x-axis is greater than the area above the x-axis. We count boxes: The area below the x-axis includes approximately 11.5 boxes and each box has area $(2)(1) = 2$, so

$$\int_0^5 f(x)dx \approx -23.$$

The area above the x-axis includes approximately 2 boxes, each of area 2, so

$$\int_5^7 f(x)dx \approx 4.$$

So we have

$$\int_0^7 f(x)dx = \int_0^5 f(x)dx + \int_5^7 f(x)dx \approx -23 + 4 = -19.$$

(b) By the Fundamental Theorem of Calculus, we have

$$F(7) - F(0) = \int_0^7 f(x)dx$$

so,

$$F(7) = F(0) + \int_0^7 f(x)dx = 25 + (-19) = 6.$$

8. Since dP/dt is negative for $t < 3$ and positive for $t > 3$, we know that P is decreasing for $t < 3$ and increasing for $t > 3$. Between each two integer values, the magnitude of the change is equal to the area between the graph dP/dt and the t-axis. For example, between $t = 0$ and $t = 1$, we see that the change in P is -1. Since $P = 2$ at $t = 0$, we must have $P = 1$ at $t = 1$. The other values are found similarly, and are shown in Table 6.2.

Table 6.2

t	1	2	3	4	5
P	1	0	$-1/2$	0	1

Problems

9. (a) Critical points of $F(x)$ are the zeros of f: $x = 1$ and $x = 3$.
   (b) $F(x)$ has a local minimum at $x = 1$ and a local maximum at $x = 3$.
   (c) See Figure 6.5.
   Notice that the graph could also be above or below the x-axis at $x = 3$.

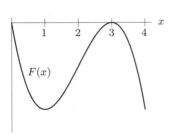

Figure 6.5

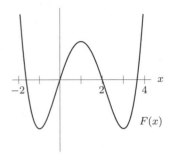

Figure 6.6

10. (a) Critical points of $F(x)$ are $x = -1$, $x = 1$ and $x = 3$.
   (b) $F(x)$ has a local minimum at $x = -1$, a local maximum at $x = 1$, and a local minimum at $x = 3$.
   (c) See Figure 6.6.

11. See Figure 6.7. Note that since $f(x_1) = 0$ and $f'(x_1) < 0$, $F(x_1)$ is a local maximum; since $f(x_3) = 0$ and $f'(x_3) > 0$, $F(x_3)$ is a local minimum. Also, since $f'(x_2) = 0$ and f changes from decreasing to increasing about $x = x_2$, F has an inflection point at $x = x_2$.

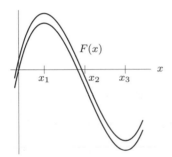

Figure 6.7

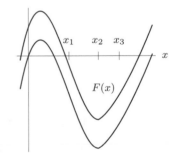

Figure 6.8

12. See Figure 6.8. Note that since $f(x_2) = 0$, $f'(x_2) > 0$, so $F(x_2)$ is a local minimum. Since $f'(x_1) = 0$ and f changes from decreasing to increasing at $x = x_1$, F has an inflection point at $x = x_1$.

13. See Figure 6.9. Note that since $f(x_1) = 0$, $F(x_1)$ is either a local minimum or a point of inflection; it is impossible to tell which from the graph. Since $f'(x_3) = 0$, and f' changes sign around $x = x_3$, $F(x_3)$ is an inflection point. Also, since $f'(x_2) = 0$ and f changes from increasing to decreasing about $x = x_2$, F has another inflection point at $x = x_2$.

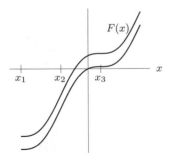

Figure 6.9

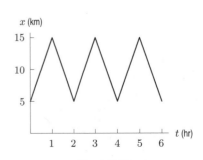

Figure 6.10

14. Between $t = 0$ and $t = 1$, the particle moves at 10 km/hr for 1 hour. Since it starts at $x = 5$, the particle is at $x = 15$ when $t = 1$. See Figure 6.10. The graph of distance is a straight line between $t = 0$ and $t = 1$ because the velocity is constant then.

Between $t = 1$ and $t = 2$, the particle moves 10 km to the left, ending at $x = 5$. Between $t = 2$ and $t = 3$, it moves 10 km to the right again. See Figure 6.10.

As an aside, note that the original velocity graph is not entirely realistic as it suggests the particle reverses direction instantaneously at the end of each hour. In practice this means the reversal of direction occurs over a time interval that is short in comparison to an hour.

15. (a) Starting at $x = 3$, we are given that $f(3) = 0$. Moving to the left on the interval $2 < x < 3$, we have $f'(x) = -1$, so $f(2) = f(3) - (1)(-1) = 1$. On the interval $0 < x < 2$, we have $f'(x) = 1$, so

$$f(0) = f(2) + 1(-2) = -1.$$

Moving to the right from $x = 3$, we know that $f'(x) = 2$ on $3 < x < 4$. So $f(4) = f(3) + 2 = 2$. On the interval $4 < x < 6$, $f'(x) = -2$ so

$$f(6) = f(4) + 2(-2) = -2.$$

On the interval $6 < x < 7$, we have $f'(x) = 1$, so

$$f(7) = f(6) + 1 = -2 + 1 = -1.$$

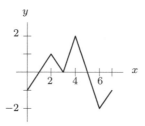

(b) In part (a) we found that $f(0) = -1$ and $f(7) = -1$.

(c) The integral $\int_0^7 f'(x)\, dx$ is given by the sum

$$\int_0^7 f'(x)\, dx = (1)(2) + (-1)(1) + (2)(1) + (-2)(2) + (1)(1) = 0.$$

Alternatively, knowing $f(7)$ and $f(0)$ and using the Fundamental Theorem of Calculus, we have

$$\int_0^7 f'(x)\, dx = f(7) - f(0) = -1 - (-1) = 0.$$

16. We can start by finding four points on the graph of $F(x)$. The first one is given: $F(2) = 3$. By the Fundamental Theorem of Calculus, $F(6) = F(2) + \int_2^6 F'(x)dx$. The value of this integral is -7 (the area is 7, but the graph lies below the x-axis), so $F(6) = 3 - 7 = -4$. Similarly, $F(0) = F(2) - 2 = 1$, and $F(8) = F(6) + 4 = 0$. We sketch a graph of $F(x)$ by connecting these points, as shown in Figure 6.11.

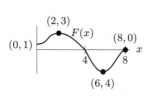

Figure 6.11

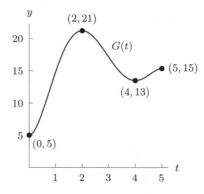

Figure 6.12

17. The critical points are at $(0, 5)$, $(2, 21)$, $(4, 13)$, and $(5, 15)$. A graph is given in Figure 6.12.

18. Looking at the graph of g' in Figure 6.13, we see that the critical points of g occur when $x = 15$ and $x = 40$, since $g'(x) = 0$ at these values. Inflection points of g occur when $x = 10$ and $x = 20$, because $g'(x)$ has a local maximum or minimum at these values. Knowing these four key points, we sketch the graph of $g(x)$ in Figure 6.14.

We start at $x = 0$, where $g(0) = 50$. Since g' is negative on the interval $[0, 10]$, the value of $g(x)$ is decreasing there. At $x = 10$ we have

$$g(10) = g(0) + \int_0^{10} g'(x)\, dx$$
$$= 50 - (\text{area of shaded trapezoid } T_1)$$
$$= 50 - \left(\frac{10 + 20}{2} \cdot 10\right) = -100.$$

Similarly,

$$g(15) = g(10) + \int_{10}^{15} g'(x)\, dx$$
$$= -100 - (\text{area of triangle } T_2)$$
$$= -100 - \frac{1}{2}(5)(20) = -150.$$

Continuing,

$$g(20) = g(15) + \int_{15}^{20} g'(x)\, dx = -150 + \frac{1}{2}(5)(10) = -125,$$

and

$$g(40) = g(20) + \int_{20}^{40} g'(x)\, dx = -125 + \frac{1}{2}(20)(10) = -25.$$

We now find concavity of $g(x)$ in the intervals $[0, 10]$, $[10, 15]$, $[15, 20]$, $[20, 40]$ by checking whether $g'(x)$ increases or decreases in these same intervals. If $g'(x)$ increases, then $g(x)$ is concave up; if $g'(x)$ decreases, then $g(x)$ is concave down. Thus we finally have the graph of $g(x)$ in Figure 6.14.

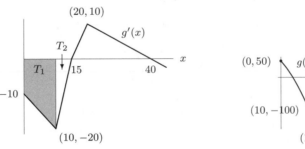

Figure 6.13

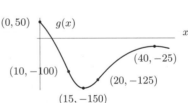

Figure 6.14

19. Between time $t = 0$ and time $t = B$, the velocity of the cork is always positive, which means the cork is moving upward. At time $t = B$, the velocity is zero, and so the cork has stopped moving altogether. Since shortly thereafter the velocity of the cork becomes negative, the cork will next begin to move downward. Thus when $t = B$ the cork has risen as far as it ever will, and is riding on top of the crest of the wave.

From time $t = B$ to time $t = D$, the velocity of the cork is negative, which means it is falling. When $t = D$, the velocity is again zero, and the cork has ceased to fall. Thus when $t = D$ the cork is riding on the bottom of the trough of the wave.

Since the cork is on the crest at time B and in the trough at time D, it is probably midway between crest and trough when the time is midway between B and D. Thus at time $t = C$ the cork is moving through the equilibrium position on its way down. (The equilibrium position is where the cork would be if the water were absolutely calm.) By symmetry, $t = A$ is the time when the cork is moving through the equilibrium position on the way up.

Since acceleration is the derivative of velocity, points where the acceleration is zero would be critical points of the velocity function. Since point A (a maximum) and point C (a minimum) are critical points, the acceleration is zero there.

A possible graph of the height of the cork is shown in Figure 6.15. The horizontal axis represents a height equal to the average depth of the ocean at that point (the equilibrium position of the cork).

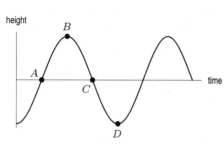

Figure 6.15

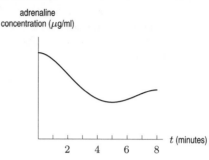

Figure 6.16

20. The rate of change is negative for $t < 5$ and positive for $t > 5$, so the concentration of adrenaline decreases until $t = 5$ and then increases. Since the area under the t-axis is greater than the area over the t-axis, the concentration of adrenaline goes down more than it goes up. Thus, the concentration at $t = 8$ is less than the concentration at $t = 0$. See Figure 6.16.

21. (a) The total volume emptied must increase with time and cannot decrease. The smooth graph (I) that is always increasing is therefore the volume emptied from the bladder. The jagged graph (II) that increases then decreases to zero is the flow rate.

(b) The total change in volume is the integral of the flow rate. Thus, the graph giving total change (I) shows an antiderivative of the rate of change in graph (II).

22. The graph of $f(x) = 2\sin(x^2)$ is shown in Figure 6.17. We see that there are roots at $x = 1.77$ and $x = 2.51$. These are the critical points of $F(x)$. Looking at the graph, it appears that of the three areas marked, A_1 is the largest, A_2 is next, and A_3 is smallest. Thus, as x increases from 0 to 3, the function $F(x)$ increases (by A_1), decreases (by A_2), and then increases again (by A_3). Therefore, the maximum is attained at the critical point $x = 1.77$.

What is the value of the function at this maximum? We know that $F(1) = 5$, so we need to find the change in F between $x = 1$ and $x = 1.77$. We have

$$\text{Change in } F = \int_1^{1.77} 2\sin(x^2)\,dx = 1.17.$$

We see that $F(1.77) = 5 + 1.17 = 6.17$, so the maximum value of F on this interval is 6.17.

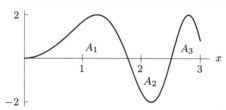

Figure 6.17

23.

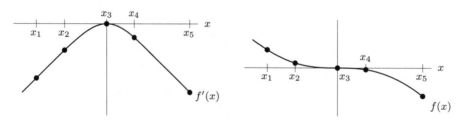

(a) $f(x)$ is greatest at x_1.
(b) $f(x)$ is least at x_5.
(c) $f'(x)$ is greatest at x_3..
(d) $f'(x)$ is least at x_5.
(e) $f''(x)$ is greatest at x_1.
(f) $f''(x)$ is least at x_5.

24. Both $F(x)$ and $G(x)$ have roots at $x = 0$ and $x = 4$. Both have a critical point (which is a local maximum) at $x = 2$. However, since the area under $g(x)$ between $x = 0$ and $x = 2$ is larger than the area under $f(x)$ between $x = 0$ and $x = 2$, the y-coordinate of $G(x)$ at 2 will be larger than the y-coordinate of $F(x)$ at 2. See below.

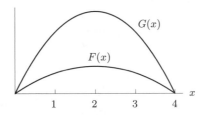

25. (a) Suppose $Q(t)$ is the amount of water in the reservoir at time t. Then

$$Q'(t) = \begin{array}{c} \text{Rate at which water} \\ \text{in reservoir is changing} \end{array} = \begin{array}{c} \text{Inflow} \\ \text{rate} \end{array} - \begin{array}{c} \text{Outflow} \\ \text{rate} \end{array}$$

Thus the amount of water in the reservoir is increasing when the inflow curve is above the outflow, and decreasing when it is below. This means that $Q(t)$ is a maximum where the curves cross in July 1993 (as shown in Figure 6.18), and $Q(t)$ is decreasing fastest when the outflow is farthest above the inflow curve, which occurs about October 1993 (see Figure 6.18).

To estimate values of $Q(t)$, we use the Fundamental Theorem which says that the change in the total quantity of water in the reservoir is given by

$$Q(t) - Q(\text{Jan'93}) = \int_{\text{Jan93}}^{t} (\text{inflow rate} - \text{outflow rate})\, dt$$

$$\text{or} \qquad Q(t) = Q(\text{Jan'93}) + \int_{\text{Jan93}}^{t} (\text{inflow rate} - \text{outflow rate})\, dt.$$

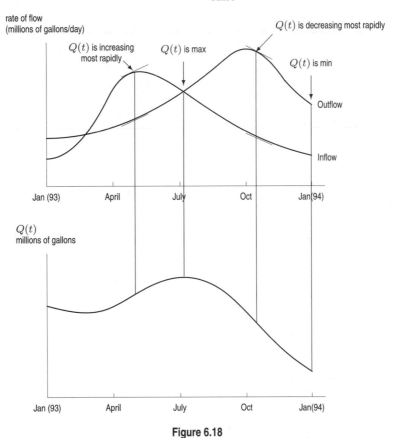

Figure 6.18

(b) See Figure 6.18. Maximum in July 1993. Minimum in Jan 1994.

(c) See Figure 6.18. Increasing fastest in May 1993. Decreasing fastest in Oct 1993.

(d) In order for the water to be the same as Jan '93 the total amount of water which has flowed into the reservoir must be 0. Referring to Figure 6.19, we have

$$\int_{\text{Jan93}}^{\text{July94}} (\text{inflow} - \text{outflow})dt = -A_1 + A_2 - A_3 + A_4 = 0$$

giving $A_1 + A_3 = A_2 + A_4$

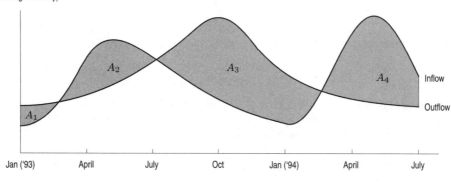

Figure 6.19

Solutions for Section 6.2

Exercises

1. $5x$

2. $\frac{5}{2}x^2$

3. $\frac{1}{3}x^3$

4. $\frac{1}{3}t^3 + \frac{1}{2}t^2$

5. $\sin t$

6. $\frac{2}{3}z^{\frac{3}{2}}$

7. $\ln|z|$

8. $-\dfrac{1}{t}$

9. $-\dfrac{1}{2z^2}$

10. e^z

11. $-\cos t$

12. $\frac{2}{3}t^3 + \frac{3}{4}t^4 + \frac{4}{5}t^5$

13. $\dfrac{t^4}{4} - \dfrac{t^3}{6} - \dfrac{t^2}{2}$

14. $\dfrac{y^5}{5} + \ln|y|$

15. $\sin t + \tan t$

16. $\dfrac{t^2 + 1}{t} = t + \dfrac{1}{t}$, which has antiderivative $\dfrac{t^2}{2} + \ln|t|$

17. $-\cos 2\theta$

18. $e^t + 5\frac{1}{5}e^{5t} = e^t + e^{5t}$

19. $\frac{1}{3}(t+1)^3$

20. $\dfrac{5^x}{\ln 5}$

21. $\dfrac{5}{2}x^2 - \dfrac{2}{3}x^{\frac{3}{2}}$

22. $F(t) = \displaystyle\int 6t\,dt = 3t^2 + C$

23. $H(x) = \displaystyle\int (x^3 - x)\,dx = \dfrac{x^4}{4} - \dfrac{x^2}{2} + C$

24. $F(x) = \displaystyle\int (x^2 - 4x + 7)\,dx = \dfrac{x^3}{3} - 2x^2 + 7x + C$

25. $R(t) = \displaystyle\int (t^3 + 5t - 1)\,dt = \dfrac{t^4}{4} + \dfrac{5}{2}t^2 - t + C$

26. $F(z) = \displaystyle\int (z + e^z)\,dz = \dfrac{z^2}{2} + e^z + C$

27. $G(t) = \displaystyle\int \sqrt{t}\,dt = \dfrac{2}{3}t^{3/2} + C$

28. $G(x) = \displaystyle\int (\sin x + \cos x)\,dx = -\cos x + \sin x + C$

29. $H(x) = \displaystyle\int (4x^3 - 7)\,dx = x^4 - 7x + C$

30. $P(t) = \displaystyle\int (2 + \sin t)\,dt = 2t - \cos t + C$

31. $P(t) = \displaystyle\int \dfrac{1}{\sqrt{t}}\,dt = 2t^{1/2} + C$

32. $G(x) = \displaystyle\int \dfrac{5}{x^3}\,dx = -\dfrac{5}{2x^2} + C$

33. $f(x) = 3$, so $F(x) = 3x + C$. $F(0) = 0$ implies that $3 \cdot 0 + C = 0$, so $C = 0$. Thus $F(x) = 3x$ is the only possibility.

34. $f(x) = 2x$, so $F(x) = x^2 + C$. $F(0) = 0$ implies that $0^2 + C = 0$, so $C = 0$. Thus $F(x) = x^2$ is the only possibility.

35. $f(x) = -7x$, so $F(x) = \dfrac{-7x^2}{2} + C$. $F(0) = 0$ implies that $-\dfrac{7}{2} \cdot 0^2 + C = 0$, so $C = 0$. Thus $F(x) = -7x^2/2$ is the only possibility.

36. $f(x) = \frac{1}{4}x$, so $F(x) = \dfrac{x^2}{8} + C$. $F(0) = 0$ implies that $\frac{1}{8} \cdot 0^2 + C = 0$, so $C = 0$. Thus $F(x) = x^2/8$ is the only possibility.

37. $f(x) = x^2$, so $F(x) = \dfrac{x^3}{3} + C$. $F(0) = 0$ implies that $\dfrac{0^3}{3} + C = 0$, so $C = 0$. Thus $F(x) = \dfrac{x^3}{3}$ is the only possibility.

38. $f(x) = x^{1/2}$, so $F(x) = \frac{2}{3}x^{3/2} + C$. $F(0) = 0$ implies that $\frac{2}{3} \cdot 0^{3/2} + C = 0$, so $C = 0$. Thus $F(x) = \frac{2}{3}x^{3/2}$ is the only possibility.

39. $f(x) = 2 + 4x + 5x^2$, so $F(x) = 2x + 2x^2 + \frac{5}{3}x^3 + C$. $F(0) = 0$ implies that $C = 0$. Thus $F(x) = 2x + 2x^2 + \frac{5}{3}x^3$ is the only possibility.

40. $f(x) = \sin x$, so $F(x) = -\cos x + C$. $F(0) = 0$ implies that $-\cos 0 + C = 0$, so $C = 1$. Thus $F(x) = -\cos x + 1$ is the only possibility.

41. $\displaystyle\int 5x\,dx = \dfrac{5}{2}x^2 + C.$

42. $\displaystyle\int x^3\,dx = \dfrac{x^4}{4} + C$

43. $\displaystyle\int \sin\theta\,d\theta = -\cos\theta + C$

44. $\displaystyle\int (x^3 - 2)\,dx = \dfrac{x^4}{4} - 2x + C$

45. $\int \left(t^2 + \dfrac{1}{t^2} \right) dt = \dfrac{t^3}{3} - \dfrac{1}{t} + C$

46. $\int 4\sqrt{w}\, dw = \dfrac{8}{3} w^{3/2} + C$

47. $\int (x^2 + 5x + 8)\, dx = \dfrac{x^3}{3} + \dfrac{5x^2}{2} + 8x + C$

48. $\int \dfrac{4}{t^2}\, dt = -\dfrac{4}{t} + C$

49. $2t^2 + 7t + C$

50. $\sin\theta + C$

51. $5e^z + C$

52. $\dfrac{x^2}{2} + 2x^{1/2} + C$

53. $-\cos t + C$

54. $\pi x + \dfrac{x^{12}}{12} + C$

55. $\int \left(t^{3/2} + t^{-3/2} \right) dt = \dfrac{2t^{5/2}}{5} - 2t^{-1/2} + C$

56. $\sin(x+1) + C$

57. $\frac{1}{2}e^{2r} + C$

58. $\int \dfrac{1}{e^z}\, dz = \int e^{-z}\, dz = -e^{-z} + C$ $\qquad$ ..

59. $\int \left(y - \dfrac{1}{y} \right)^2 dy = \int \left(y^2 - 2 + \dfrac{1}{y^2} \right) dy = \dfrac{y^3}{3} - 2y - \dfrac{1}{y} + C$

60. $\int_0^3 (x^2 + 4x + 3)\, dx = \left(\dfrac{x^3}{3} + 2x^2 + 3x \right) \Big|_0^3 = (9 + 18 + 9) - 0 = 36$

61. $\int_1^3 \dfrac{1}{t}\, dt = \ln|t| \Big|_1^3 = \ln|3| - \ln|1| = \ln 3 \approx 1.0986.$

62. $\int_0^{\pi/4} \sin x\, dx = -\cos x \Big|_0^{\pi/4} = -\cos\dfrac{\pi}{4} - (-\cos 0) = -\dfrac{\sqrt{2}}{2} + 1 = 0.293.$

63. $\int_0^2 3e^x\, dx = 3e^x \Big|_0^2 = 3e^2 - 3e^0 = 3e^2 - 3 = 19.167.$

64. $\int_2^5 (x^3 - \pi x^2)\, dx = \left(\dfrac{x^4}{4} - \dfrac{\pi x^3}{3} \right) \Big|_2^5 = \dfrac{609}{4} - 39\pi \approx 29.728.$

65. $\int_0^1 \sin\theta\, d\theta = -\cos\theta \Big|_0^1 = 1 - \cos 1 \approx 0.460.$

66. Since $\dfrac{1 + y^2}{y} = \dfrac{1}{y} + y,$

$\int_1^2 \dfrac{1 + y^2}{y}\, dy = \left(\ln|y| + \dfrac{y^2}{2} \right) \Big|_1^2 = \ln 2 + \dfrac{3}{2} \approx 2.193.$

67. $\int_0^2 \left(\dfrac{x^3}{3} + 2x \right) dx = \left(\dfrac{x^4}{12} + x^2 \right) \Big|_0^2 = \dfrac{4}{3} + 4 = 16/3 \approx 5.333.$

68. $\int_0^{\pi/4} (\sin t + \cos t)\, dt = (-\cos t + \sin t) \Big|_0^{\pi/4} = \left(-\dfrac{\sqrt{2}}{2} + \dfrac{\sqrt{2}}{2} \right) - (-1 + 0) = 1.$

69. $\int_0^1 2e^x\, dx = 2e^x \Big|_0^1 = 2e - 2 \approx 3.437.$

70. $\int_{-3}^{-1} \dfrac{2}{r^3}\,dr = -r^{-2}\Big|_{-3}^{-1} = -1 + \dfrac{1}{9} = -8/9 \approx -0.889.$

71. Since $(\tan x)' = \dfrac{1}{\cos^2 x}$, $\int_{0}^{\pi/4} \dfrac{1}{\cos^2 x}\,dx = \tan x\Big|_{0}^{\pi/4} = \tan\dfrac{\pi}{4} - \tan 0 = 1.$

Problems

72. We have
$$\text{Area} = \int_{1}^{4} x^2\,dx = \dfrac{x^3}{3}\Big|_{1}^{4} = \dfrac{4^3}{3} - \dfrac{1^3}{3} = \dfrac{64 - 1}{3} = 21.$$

73. The graph crosses the x-axis where
$$7 - 8x + x^2 = 0$$
$$(x - 7)(x - 1) = 0;$$
so $x = 1$ and $x = 7$. See Figure 6.20. The parabola opens upward and the region is below the x-axis, so
$$\text{Area} = -\int_{1}^{7} (7 - 8x + x^2)\,dx$$
$$= -\left(7x - 4x^2 + \dfrac{x^3}{3}\right)\Big|_{1}^{7} = 36.$$

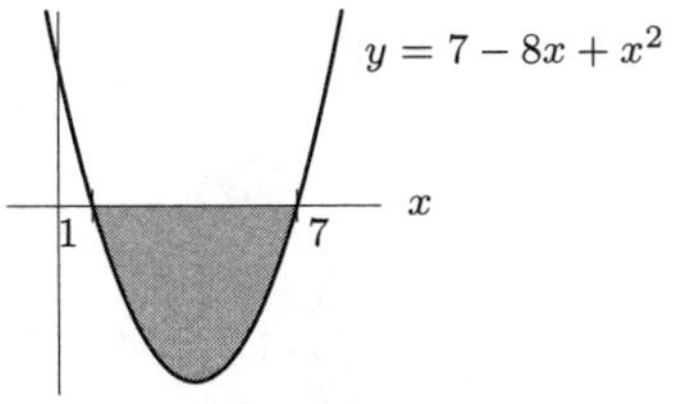

Figure 6.20

74. Since $y = 0$ only when $x = 0$ and $x = 1$, the area lies between these limits and is given by
$$\text{Area} = \int_{0}^{1} x^2(1 - x)^2\,dx = \int_{0}^{1} x^2(1 - 2x + x^2)\,dx = \int_{0}^{1} (x^2 - 2x^3 + x^4)\,dx$$
$$= \dfrac{x^3}{3} - \dfrac{2}{4}x^4 + \dfrac{x^5}{5}\Big|_{0}^{1} = \dfrac{1}{30}.$$

75. Since $y = x^3(1 - x)$ is positive for $0 \le x \le 1$ and $y = 0$, when $x = 0, 1$, the area is given by
$$\text{Area} = \int_{0}^{1} x^3(1 - x)\,dx = \int_{0}^{1} (x^3 - x^4)\,dx = \dfrac{x^4}{4} - \dfrac{x^5}{5}\Big|_{0}^{1} = \dfrac{1}{20}.$$

76. The graph is shown in the figure below. Since $\cos\theta \ge \sin\theta$ for $0 \le \theta \le \pi/4$, we have
$$\text{Area} = \int_{0}^{\pi/4} (\cos\theta - \sin\theta)\,d\theta$$
$$= (\sin\theta + \cos\theta)\Big|_{0}^{\pi/4}$$
$$= \dfrac{1}{\sqrt{2}} + \dfrac{1}{\sqrt{2}} - 1 = \sqrt{2} - 1.$$

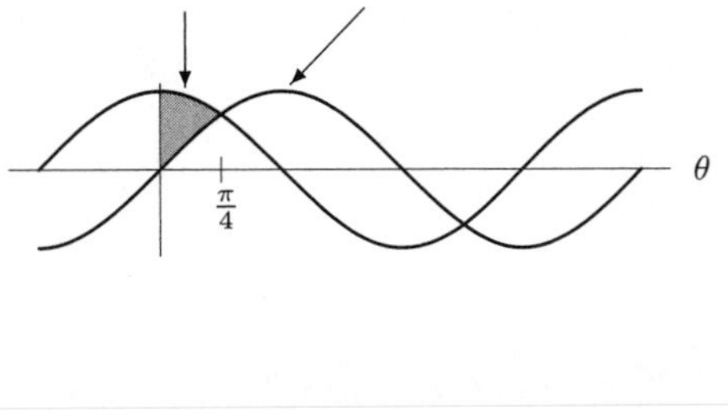

77. Since the graph of $y = e^x$ is above the graph of $y = \cos x$ (see the figure below), we have

$$
\begin{aligned}
\text{Area} &= \int_0^1 (e^x - \cos x)\, dx \\
&= \int_0^1 e^x\, dx - \int_0^1 \cos x\, dx \\
&= e^x \Big|_0^1 - \sin x \Big|_0^1 \\
&= e^1 - e^0 - \sin 1 + \sin 0 \\
&= e - 1 - \sin 1.
\end{aligned}
$$

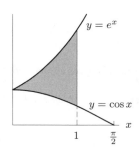

78. The area is given by

$$
\begin{aligned}
A &= \int_{-1}^1 (\cosh x - \sinh x)\, dx = (\sinh x - \cosh x)\Big|_{-1}^1 \\
&= \sinh 1 - \cosh 1 - (\sinh(-1) - \cosh(-1)) \\
&= 2\sinh 1.
\end{aligned}
$$

79. The area under $f(x) = 8x$ between $x = 1$ and $x = b$ is given by $\int_1^b (8x)dx$. Using the Fundamental Theorem to evaluate the integral:

$$
\text{Area} = 4x^2 \Big|_1^b = 4b^2 - 4.
$$

Since the area is 192, we have

$$
\begin{aligned}
4b^2 - 4 &= 192 \\
4b^2 &= 196 \\
b^2 &= 49 \\
b &= \pm 7.
\end{aligned}
$$

Since b is larger than 1, we have $b = 7$.

80. The graph of $y = x^2 - c^2$ has x-intercepts of $x = \pm c$. See Figure 6.21. The shaded area is given by

$$
\begin{aligned}
\text{Area} &= -\int_{-c}^c (x^2 - c^2)\, dx \\
&= -2 \int_0^c (x^2 - c^2)\, dx \\
&= -2 \left(\frac{x^3}{3} - c^2 x \right)\Big|_0^c = -2 \left(\frac{c^3}{3} - c^3 \right) = \frac{4}{3} c^3.
\end{aligned}
$$

We want c to satisfy $(4c^3)/3 = 36$, so $c = 3$.

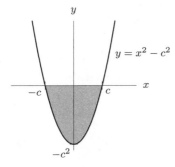

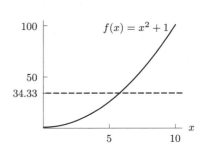

Figure 6.21

Figure 6.22

81. We have

$$\text{Average value} = \frac{1}{10-0}\int_0^{10}(x^2+1)dx = \frac{1}{10}\left(\frac{x^3}{3}+x\right)\Big|_0^{10} = \frac{1}{10}\left(\frac{10^3}{3}+10-0\right) = \frac{103}{3}.$$

We see in Figure 6.22 that the average value of $103/3 \approx 34.33$ for $f(x)$ looks right.

82. The average value of $v(x)$ on the interval $1 \le x \le c$ is

$$\frac{1}{c-1}\int_1^c \frac{6}{x^2}dx = \frac{1}{c-1}\left(-\frac{6}{x}\right)\Big|_1^c = \frac{1}{c-1}\left(\frac{-6}{c}+6\right) = \frac{6}{c}.$$

Since $\dfrac{1}{c-1}\displaystyle\int_1^c \frac{6}{x^2}dx = 1$, we have $\dfrac{6}{c} = 1$, so $c = 6$.

83. (a) The average value of $f(t) = \sin t$ over $0 \le t \le 2\pi$ is given by the formula

$$\text{Average} = \frac{1}{2\pi - 0}\int_0^{2\pi}\sin t\, dt$$

$$= \frac{1}{2\pi}(-\cos t)\Big|_0^{2\pi}$$

$$= \frac{1}{2\pi}(-\cos 2\pi - (-\cos 0)) = 0.$$

We can check this answer by looking at the graph of $\sin t$ below. The area below the curve and above the t-axis over the interval $0 \le t \le \pi$, A_1, is the same as the area above the curve but below the t-axis over the interval $\pi \le t \le 2\pi$, A_2. When we take the integral of $\sin t$ over the entire interval $0 \le t \le 2\pi$, we get $A_1 - A_2 = 0$.

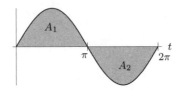

(b) Since

$$\int_0^\pi \sin t\, dt = -\cos t\Big|_0^\pi = -\cos \pi - (-\cos 0) = -(-1) - (-1) = 2,$$

the average value of $\sin t$ on $0 \le t \le \pi$ is given by

$$\text{Average value} = \frac{1}{\pi}\int_0^\pi \sin t\, dt = \frac{2}{\pi}.$$

84. The area beneath the curve in Figure 42.1 is given by

$$\int_0^a y\,dx = \int_0^a (\sqrt{a} - \sqrt{x})^2 dx = \left[ax - \frac{4\sqrt{a}\,x^{3/2}}{3} + \frac{x^2}{2} \right]_0^a = \frac{a^2}{6}.$$

The area of the square is a^2 so the area above the curve is $5a^2/6$. Thus, the ratio of the areas is 5 to 1.

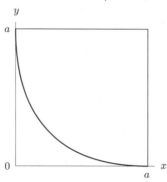

Figure 6.23: The curve
$$\sqrt{x} + \sqrt{y} = \sqrt{a}$$

85. The curves $y = x$ and $y = x^n$ cross at $x = 0$ and $x = 1$. For $0 < x < 1$, the curve $y = x$ is above $y = x^n$. Thus the area is given by

$$A_n = \int_0^1 (x - x^n)\,dx = \left[\frac{x^2}{2} - \frac{x^{n+1}}{n+1} \right]_0^1 = \frac{1}{2} - \frac{1}{n+1} \to \frac{1}{2}.$$

Since $x^n \to 0$ for $0 \le x < 1$, as $n \to \infty$, the area between the curves approaches the area under the line $y = x$ between $x = 0$ and $x = 1$.

86. Since $C'(x) = 4000 + 10x$ we want to evaluate the indefinite integral

$$\int (4000 + 10x)\,dx = 4000x + 5x^2 + K$$

where K is a constant. Thus $C(x) = 5x^2 + 4000x + K$, and the fixed cost of 1,000,000 riyal means that $C(0) = 1{,}000{,}000 = K$. Therefore, the total cost is

$$C(x) = 5x^2 + 4000x + 1{,}000{,}000.$$

Since $C(x)$ depends on x^2, the square of the depth drilled, costs will increase dramatically when x grows large.

87. (a) See Figure 6.24.

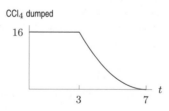

Figure 6.24

(b) 7 years, because $t^2 - 14t + 49 = (t-7)^2$ indicates that the rate of flow was zero after 7 years.

(c)

$$\text{Area under the curve} = 3(16) + \int_3^7 (t^2 - 14t + 49)\,dt$$

$$= 48 + \left(\frac{1}{3}t^3 - 7t^2 + 49t \right) \Big|_3^7$$

$$= 48 + \frac{343}{3} - 343 + 343 - 9 + 63 - 147$$

$$= \frac{208}{3} = 69.333 \text{ cubic yards.}$$

Solutions for Section 6.3

Exercises

1. $y = \displaystyle\int (x^3 + 5)\, dx = \dfrac{x^4}{4} + 5x + C$

2. $y = \displaystyle\int \left(8x + \dfrac{1}{x}\right) dx = 4x^2 + \ln |x| + C$

3. $W = \displaystyle\int 4\sqrt{t}\, dt = \dfrac{8}{3} t^{3/2} + C$

4. $r = \displaystyle\int 3 \sin p\, dp = -3 \cos p + C$

5. Since $y = x + \sin x - \pi$, we differentiate to see that $dy/dx = 1 + \cos x$, so y satisfies the differential equation. To show that it also satisfies the initial condition, we check that $y(\pi) = 0$:

$$y = x + \sin x - \pi$$
$$y(\pi) = \pi + \sin \pi - \pi = 0.$$

6. $y = \displaystyle\int (6x^2 + 4x)\, dx = 2x^3 + 2x^2 + C$. If $y(2) = 10$, then $2(2)^3 + 2(2)^2 + C = 10$ and $C = 10 - 16 - 8 = -14$.
Thus, $y = 2x^3 + 2x^2 - 14$.

7. $P = \displaystyle\int 10e^t\, dt = 10e^t + C$. If $P(0) = 25$, then $10e^0 + C = 25$ so $C = 15$. Thus, $P = 10e^t + 15$.

8. $s = \displaystyle\int (-32t + 100)\, dt = -16t^2 + 100t + C$. If $s = 50$ when $t = 0$, then $-16(0)^2 + 100(0) + C = 50$, so $C = 50$.
Thus $s = -16t^2 + 100t + 50$.

9. Integrating gives

$$\int \frac{dq}{dz}\, dz = \int (2 + \sin z)\, dz = 2z - \cos z + C.$$

If $q = 5$ when $z = 0$, then $2(0) - \cos(0) + C = 5$ so $C = 6$. Thus $q = 2z - \cos z + 6$.

10. We differentiate $y = xe^{-x} + 2$ using the product rule to obtain

$$\frac{dy}{dx} = x\left(e^{-x}(-1)\right) + (1)e^{-x} + 0$$
$$= -xe^{-x} + e^{-x}$$
$$= (1 - x)e^{-x},$$

and so $y = xe^{-x} + 2$ satisfies the differential equation. We now check that $y(0) = 2$:

$$y = xe^{-x} + 2$$
$$y(0) = 0e^0 + 2 = 2.$$

Problems

11. (a) Acceleration $= a(t) = -9.8$ m/sec^2
   Velocity $= v(t) = -9.8t + 40$ m/sec
   Height $= h(t) = -4.9t^2 + 40t + 25$ m

 (b) At the highest point,

$$v(t) = -9.8t + 40 = 0,$$

so

$$t = \frac{40}{9.8} = 4.08 \text{ seconds.}$$

At that time, $h(4.08) = 106.6$ m. We see that the tomato reaches a height of 106.6 m, at 4.08 seconds after it is thrown.

 (c) The tomato lands when $h(t) = 0$, so

$$-4.9t^2 + 40t + 25 = 0.$$

The solutions are $t = -0.58$ and $t = 8.75$ seconds. We see that it lands 8.75 seconds after it is thrown.

12. (a) $y = \int (2x+1)\, dx$, so the solution is $y = x^2 + x + C$.

(b)

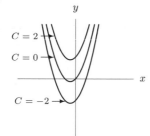

(c) At $y(1) = 5$, we have $1^2 + 1 + C = 5$ and so $C = 3$. Thus we have the solution $y = x^2 + x + 3$.

13.

$$\frac{dy}{dt} = k\sqrt{t} = kt^{1/2}$$

$$y = \frac{2}{3}kt^{3/2} + C.$$

Since $y = 0$ when $t = 0$, we have $C = 0$, so

$$y = \frac{2}{3}kt^{3/2}.$$

14. (a) To find the height of the balloon, we integrate its velocity with respect to time:

$$h(t) = \int v(t)\, dt$$

$$= \int (-32t + 40)\, dt$$

$$= -32\frac{t^2}{2} + 40t + C.$$

Since at $t = 0$, we have $h = 30$, we can solve for C to get $C = 30$, giving us a height of

$$h(t) = -16t^2 + 40t + 30.$$

(b) To find the average velocity between $t = 1.5$ and $t = 3$, we find the total displacement and divide by time.

$$\text{Average velocity} = \frac{h(3) - h(1.5)}{3 - 1.5} = \frac{6 - 54}{1.5} = -32 \text{ ft/sec.}$$

The balloon's average velocity is 32 ft/sec downward.

(c) First, we must find the time when $h(t) = 6$. Solving the equation $-16t^2 + 40t + 30 = 6$, we get

$$6 = -16t^2 + 40t + 30$$
$$0 = -16t^2 + 40t + 24$$
$$0 = 2t^2 - 5t - 3$$
$$0 = (2t+1)(t-3).$$

Thus, $t = -1/2$ or $t = 3$. Since $t = -1/2$ makes no physical sense, we use $t = 3$ to calculate the balloon's velocity. At $t = 3$, we have a velocity of $v(3) = -32(3) + 40 = -56$ ft/sec. So the balloon's velocity is 56 ft/sec downward at the time of impact.

15. Since the car's acceleration is constant, a graph of its velocity against time t is linear, as shown below.

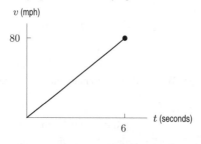

The acceleration is just the slope of this line:

$$\frac{dv}{dt} = \frac{80 - 0 \text{ mph}}{6 \text{ sec}} = \frac{40}{3} = 13.33 \frac{\text{mph}}{\text{sec}}.$$

To convert our units into ft/sec^2,

$$\frac{40}{3} \cdot \frac{\text{mph}}{\text{sec}} \cdot \frac{5280 \text{ ft}}{1 \text{ mile}} \cdot \frac{1 \text{ hour}}{3600 \text{ sec}} = 19.55 \frac{\text{ft}}{\text{sec}^2}$$

16. Since the acceleration $a = dv/dt$, where v is the velocity of the car, we have

$$\frac{dv}{dt} = -0.6t + 4.$$

Integrating gives

$$v = -0.6 \frac{t^2}{2} + 4t + C.$$

The car starts from rest, so $v = 0$ when $t = 0$, and therefore $C = 0$. If x is the distance from the starting point, $v = dx/dt$ and

$$\frac{dx}{dt} = -0.3t^2 + 4t,$$

so

$$x = -\frac{0.3}{3}t^3 + \frac{4}{2}t^2 + C = -0.1t^3 + 2t^2 + C.$$

Since $x = 0$ when $t = 0$, we have $C = 0$, so

$$x = -0.1t^3 + 2t^2.$$

We want to solve for t when $x = 100$:

$$100 = -0.1t^3 + 2t^2.$$

This equation can be rewritten as

$$0.1t^3 - 2t^2 + 100 = 0$$
$$t^3 - 20t^2 + 1000 = 0.$$

The equation can be solved numerically, or by tracing along a graph, or by factoring

$$(t - 10)(t^2 - 10t - 100) = 0.$$

The solutions are $t = 10$ and $t = \frac{10 \pm \sqrt{500}}{2} = -6.18, 16.18$. Since we are told $0 \le t \le 12$, the solution we want is $t = 10$ sec.

17. (a)

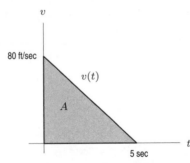

(b) The total distance is represented by the shaded region A, the area under the graph of $v(t)$.

(c) The area A, a triangle, is given by

$$A = \frac{1}{2}(\text{base})(\text{height}) = \frac{1}{2}(5 \text{ sec})(80 \text{ ft/sec}) = 200 \text{ ft}.$$

(d) Using integration and the Fundamental Theorem of Calculus, we have $A = \int_0^5 v(t)\, dt$ or $A = s(5) - s(0)$, where $s(t)$ is an antiderivative of $v(t)$.

We have that $a(t)$, the acceleration, is constant: $a(t) = k$ for some constant k. Therefore $v(t) = kt + C$ for some constant C. We have $80 = v(0) = k(0) + C = C$, so that $v(t) = kt + 80$. Putting in $t = 5, 0 = v(5) = (k)(5) + 80$, or $k = -80/5 = -16$.

Thus $v(t) = -16t + 80$, and an antiderivative for $v(t)$ is $s(t) = -8t^2 + 80t + C$. Since the total distance traveled at $t = 0$ is 0, we have $s(0) = 0$ which means $C = 0$. Finally, $A = \int_0^5 v(t)\, dt = s(5) - s(0) = (-8(5)^2 + (80)(5)) - (-8(0)^2 + (80)(0)) = 200 \text{ ft}$, which agrees with the previous part.

18. Since the acceleration is constant, a graph of the velocity versus time looks like this:

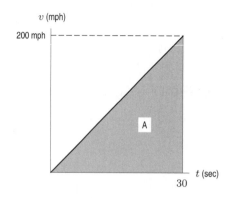

The distance traveled in 30 seconds, which is how long the runway must be, is equal to the area represented by A. We have $A = \frac{1}{2}(\text{base})(\text{height})$. First we convert the required velocity into miles per second.

$$200 \text{ mph} = \frac{200 \text{ miles}}{\text{hour}} \left(\frac{1 \text{ hour}}{60 \text{ minutes}} \right) \left(\frac{1 \text{ minute}}{60 \text{ seconds}} \right)$$
$$= \frac{200}{3600} \frac{\text{miles}}{\text{second}}$$
$$= \frac{1}{18} \text{ miles/second}.$$

Therefore $A = \frac{1}{2}(30 \text{ sec})(200 \text{ mph}) = \frac{1}{2}(30 \text{ sec}) \left(\frac{1}{18} \text{ miles/sec} \right) = \frac{5}{6}$ miles.

19. (a) Since the velocity is constantly decreasing, and $v(6) = 0$, the car stops after 6 seconds.

t (sec)	0	0.5	1	1.5	2	2.5	3	3.5	4	4.5	5	5.5	6
$v(t)$ (ft/sec)	30	27.5	25	22.5	20	17.5	15	12.5	10	7.5	5	2.5	0

(b) Over the interval $a \leq t \leq a + \frac{1}{2}$, the left-hand velocity is $v(a)$, and the right-hand velocity is $v(a + \frac{1}{2})$. Since we are considering half-second intervals, $\Delta t = \frac{1}{2}$, and $n = 12$. The left sum is 97.5 ft., and the right sum is 82.5 ft.

(c) Area A in the figure below represents distance traveled.

$$A = \frac{1}{2}(\text{base})(\text{height}) = \frac{1}{2} \cdot 6 \cdot 30 = 90 \text{ ft.}$$

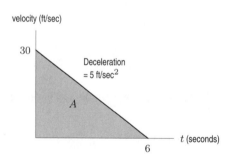

(d) The velocity is constantly decreasing at a rate of 5 ft/sec per second, i.e. after each second the velocity has dropped by 5 units. Therefore $v(t) = 30 - 5t$.

An antiderivative for $v(t)$ is $s(t)$, where $s(t) = 30t - \frac{5}{2}t^2$. Thus by the Fundamental Theorem of Calculus, the distance traveled $= s(6) - s(0) = (30(6) - \frac{5}{2}(6)^2) - (30(0) - \frac{5}{2}(0)^2) = 90$ ft. Since $v(t)$ is decreasing, the left-hand sum in part (b) overestimates the distance traveled, while the right-hand sum underestimates it.

The area A is equal to the average of the left-hand and right-hand sums: 90 ft $= \frac{1}{2}(97.5 \text{ ft} + 82.5 \text{ ft})$. The left-hand sum is an overestimate of A; the right-hand sum is an underestimate.

20. (a)

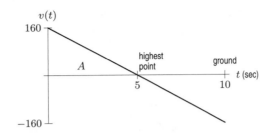

(b) The highest point is at $t = 5$ seconds. The object hits the ground at $t = 10$ seconds, since by symmetry if the object takes 5 seconds to go up, it takes 5 seconds to come back down.

(c) The maximum height is the distance traveled when going up, which is represented by the area A of the triangle above the time axis.

$$\text{Area} = \frac{1}{2}(160 \text{ ft/sec})(5 \text{ sec}) = 400 \text{ feet}.$$

(d) The slope of the line is -32, so $v(t) = -32t + 160$. Antidifferentiating, we get $s(t) = -16t^2 + 160t + s_0$. $s_0 = 0$, so $s(t) = -16t^2 + 160t$. At $t = 5$, $s(t) = -400 + 800 = 400$ ft.

21. The equation of motion is $y = -\frac{gt^2}{2} + v_0 t + y_0 = -16t^2 + 128t + 320$. Taking the first derivative, we get $v = -32t + 128$. The second derivative gives us $a = -32$.

(a) At its highest point, the stone's velocity is zero:
$v = 0 = -32t + 128$, so $t = 4$.

(b) At $t = 4$, the height is $y = -16(4)^2 + 128(4) + 320 = 576$ ft

(c) When the stone hits the beach,

$$y = 0 = -16t^2 + 128t + 320$$
$$0 = -t^2 + 8t + 20 = (10 - t)(2 + t).$$

So $t = 10$ seconds.

(d) Impact is at $t = 10$. The velocity, v, at this time is $v(10) = -32(10) + 128 = -192$ ft/sec. Upon impact, the stone's velocity is 192 ft/sec downward.

22. (a) $a(t) = 1.6$, so $v(t) = 1.6t + v_0 = 1.6t$, since the initial velocity is 0.

(b) $s(t) = 0.8t^2 + s_0$, where s_0 is the rock's initial height.

23. (a) $s = v_0 t - 16t^2$, where $v_0 =$ initial velocity, and $v = s' = v_0 - 32t$. At the maximum height, $v = 0$, so $v_0 = 32t_{max}$. Plugging into the distance equation yields $100 = 32t_{max}^2 - 16t_{max}^2 = 16t_{max}^2$, so $t_{max} = \frac{5}{2}$ seconds, from which we get $v_0 = 32\left(\frac{5}{2}\right) = 80$ ft/sec.

(b) This time $g = 5$ ft/sec^2, so $s = v_0 t - 2.5t^2 = 80t - 2.5t^2$, and $v = s' = 80 - 5t$. At the highest point, $v = 0$, so $t_{max} = \frac{80}{5} = 16$ seconds. Plugging into the distance equation yields $s = 80(16) - 2.5(16)^2 = 640$ ft.

24. The height of an object above the ground which begins at rest and falls for t seconds is

$$s(t) = -16t^2 + K,$$

where K is the initial height. Here the flower pot falls from 200 ft, so $K = 200$. To see when the pot hits the ground, solve $-16t^2 + 200 = 0$. The solution is

$$t = \sqrt{\frac{200}{16}} \approx 3.54 \text{ seconds}.$$

Now, velocity is given by $s'(t) = v(t) = -32t$. So, the velocity when the pot hits the ground is

$$v(3.54) \approx -113.1 \text{ ft/sec},$$

which is approximately 77 mph downward.

25. The first thing we should do is convert our units. We'll bring everything into feet and seconds. Thus, the initial speed of the car is

$$\frac{70 \text{ miles}}{\text{hour}} \left(\frac{1 \text{ hour}}{3600 \text{ sec}}\right) \left(\frac{5280 \text{ feet}}{1 \text{ mile}}\right) \approx 102.7 \text{ ft/sec}.$$

We assume that the acceleration is constant as the car comes to a stop. A graph of its velocity versus time is given in Figure 6.25. We know that the area under the curve represents the distance that the car travels before it comes to a stop, 157 feet. But this area is a triangle, so it is easy to find t_0, the time the car comes to rest. We solve

$$\frac{1}{2}(102.7)t_0 = 157,$$

which gives

$$t_0 \approx 3.06 \text{ sec}.$$

Since acceleration is the rate of change of velocity, the car's acceleration is given by the slope of the line in Figure 6.25. Thus, the acceleration, k, is given by

$$k = \frac{102.7 - 0}{0 - 3.06} \approx -33.56 \text{ ft/sec}^2.$$

Notice that k is negative because the car is slowing down.

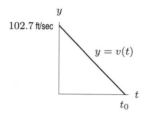

Figure 6.25: Graph of velocity versus time

Solutions for Section 6.4

Exercises

1. By the Fundamental Theorem, $f(x) = F'(x)$. Since f is positive and increasing, F is increasing and concave up. Since $F(0) = \int_0^0 f(t)dt = 0$, the graph of F must start from the origin. See Figure 6.26.

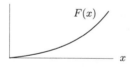

Figure 6.26

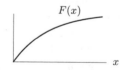

Figure 6.27

2. By the Fundamental Theorem, $f(x) = F'(x)$. Since f is positive and decreasing, F is increasing and concave down. Since $F(0) = \int_0^0 f(t)dt = 0$, the graph of F must start from the origin. See Figure 6.27.

3. Since f is always positive, F is always increasing. F has an inflection point where $f' = 0$. Since $F(0) = \int_0^0 f(t)dt = 0$, F goes through the origin. See Figure 6.28.

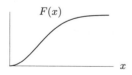

Figure 6.28

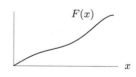

Figure 6.29

4. Since f is always non-negative, F is increasing. F is concave up where f is increasing and concave down where f is decreasing; F has inflection points at the critical points of f. Since $F(0) = \int_0^0 f(t)dt = 0$, the graph of F goes through the origin. See Figure 6.29.

5.

Table 6.3

x	0	0.5	1	1.5	2
$I(x)$	0	0.50	1.09	2.03	3.65

6. Using the Fundamental Theorem, we know that the change in F between $x = 0$ and $x = 0.5$ is given by

$$F(0.5) - F(0) = \int_0^{0.5} \sin t \cos t \, dt \approx 0.115.$$

Since $F(0) = 1.0$, we have $F(0.5) \approx 1.115$. The other values are found similarly, and are given in Table 6.4.

Table 6.4

b	0	0.5	1	1.5	2	2.5	3
$F(b)$	1	1.11492	1.35404	1.4975	1.41341	1.17908	1.00996

7. (a) Again using 0.00001 as the lower limit, because the integral is improper, gives Si(4) = 1.76, Si(5) = 1.55.
  (b) Si(x) decreases when the integrand is negative, which occurs when $\pi < x < 2\pi$.

8. If $f'(x) = \sin(x^2)$, then $f(x)$ is of the form

$$f(x) = C + \int_a^x \sin(t^2) \, dt.$$

Since $f(0) = 7$, we take $a = 0$ and $C = 7$, giving

$$f(x) = 7 + \int_0^x \sin(t^2) \, dt.$$

9. If $f'(x) = \dfrac{\sin x}{x}$, then $f(x)$ is of the form

$$f(x) = C + \int_a^x \frac{\sin t}{t} \, dt.$$

Since $f(1) = 5$, we take $a = 1$ and $C = 5$, giving

$$f(x) = 5 + \int_1^x \frac{\sin t}{t} \, dt.$$

10. If $f'(x) = \text{Si}(x)$, then $f(x)$ is of the form

$$f(x) = C + \int_a^x \text{Si}(t) \, dt.$$

Since $f(0) = 2$, we take $a = 0$ and $C = 2$, giving

$$f(x) = 2 + \int_0^x \text{Si}(t) \, dt.$$

Problems

11. See Figure 6.30.

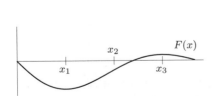

Figure 6.30

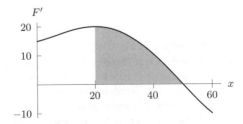

Figure 6.31

12. We know that $F(x)$ increases for $x < 50$ because the derivative of F is positive there. See Figure 6.31. Similarly, $F(x)$ decreases for $x > 50$. Therefore, the graph of F rises until $x = 50$, and then it begins to fall. Thus, the maximum value attained by F is $F(50)$. To evaluate $F(50)$, we use the Fundamental Theorem:

$$F(50) - F(20) = \int_{20}^{50} F'(x)\, dx,$$

which gives

$$F(50) = F(20) + \int_{20}^{50} F'(x)\, dx = 150 + \int_{20}^{50} F'(x)\, dx.$$

The definite integral equals the area of the shaded region under the graph of F', which is roughly 350. Therefore, the greatest value attained by F is $F(50) \approx 150 + 350 = 500$.

13. Since $F'(x) = e^{-x^2}$ and $F(0) = 2$, we have

$$F(x) = F(0) + \int_0^x e^{-t^2}\, dt = 2 + \int_0^x e^{-t^2}\, dt.$$

Substituting $x = 1$ and evaluating the integral numerically gives

$$F(1) = 2 + \int_0^1 e^{-t^2}\, dt = 2.747.$$

14. Since $G'(x) = \cos(x^2)$ and $G(0) = -3$, we have

$$G(x) = G(0) + \int_0^x \cos(t^2)\, dt = -3 + \int_0^x \cos(t^2)\, dt.$$

Substituting $x = -1$ and evaluating the integral numerically gives

$$G(-1) = -3 + \int_0^{-1} \cos(t^2)\, dt = -3.905.$$

15. $\cos(x^2)$.

16. $(1 + x)^{200}$.

17. $\arctan(x^2)$.

18. $\dfrac{d}{dt} \displaystyle\int_t^\pi \cos(z^3)\, dz = \dfrac{d}{dt}\left(-\int_\pi^t \cos(z^3)\, dz\right) = -\cos(t^3).$

19. $\dfrac{d}{dx} \displaystyle\int_x^1 \ln t\, dt = \dfrac{d}{dx}\left(-\int_1^x \ln t\, dt\right) = -\ln x.$

20. Considering $\mathrm{Si}(x^2)$ as the composition of $\mathrm{Si}(u)$ and $u(x) = x^2$, we may apply the chain rule to obtain

$$\begin{aligned}
\frac{d}{dx} &= \frac{d(\mathrm{Si}(u))}{du} \cdot \frac{du}{dx} \\
&= \frac{\sin u}{u} \cdot 2x \\
&= \frac{2\sin(x^2)}{x}.
\end{aligned}$$

21. (a) The definition of g gives $g(0) = \int_0^0 f(t)\, dt = 0$.

(b) The Fundamental Theorem gives $g'(1) = f(1) = -2$.

(c) The function g is concave upward where g'' is positive. Since $g'' = f'$, we see that g is concave up where f is increasing. This occurs on the interval $1 \le x \le 6$.

(d) The function g decreases from $x = 0$ to $x = 3$ and increases for $3 < x \le 8$, and the magnitude of the increase is more than the magnitude of the decrease. Thus g takes its maximum value at $x = 8$.

22. (a) Since $\dfrac{d}{dt}(\cos(2t)) = -2\sin(2t)$, we have $F(\pi) = \displaystyle\int_0^\pi \sin(2t)\, dt = -\dfrac{1}{2}\cos(2t)\Big|_0^\pi = -\dfrac{1}{2}(1-1) = 0.$

(b) $F(\pi) = $ (Area above t-axis) $-$ (Area below t-axis) $= 0$. (The two areas are equal.)

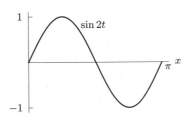

(c) $F(x) \geq 0$ everywhere. $F(x) = 0$ only at integer multiples of π. This can be seen for $x \geq 0$ by noting $F(x) = $ (Area above t-axis) $-$ (Area below t-axis), which is always non-negative and only equals zero when x is an integer multiple of π. For $x > 0$

$$F(-x) = \int_0^{-x} \sin 2t\, dt$$

$$= -\int_{-x}^0 \sin 2t\, dt$$

$$= \int_0^x \sin 2t\, dt = F(x),$$

since the area from $-x$ to 0 is the negative of the area from 0 to x. So we have $F(x) \geq 0$ for all x.

23. (a) $F'(x) = \dfrac{1}{\ln x}$ by the Construction Theorem.

(b) For $x \geq 2$, $F'(x) > 0$, so $F(x)$ is increasing. Since $F''(x) = -\dfrac{1}{x(\ln x)^2} < 0$ for $x \geq 2$, the graph of $F(x)$ is concave down.

(c)

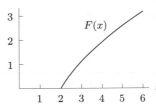

24. If we let $f(x) = \int_2^x \sin(t^2)\, dt$ and $g(x) = x^3$, using the chain rule gives

$$\frac{d}{dx}\int_2^{x^3} \sin(t^2)\, dt = f'(g(x)) \cdot g'(x) = \sin((x^3)^2) \cdot 3x^2 = 3x^2\sin(x^6).$$

25. If we let $f(t) = \int_1^t \cos(x^2)\, dx$ and $g(t) = \sin t$, using the chain rule gives

$$\frac{d}{dt}\int_1^{\sin t} \cos(x^2)\, dx = f'(g(t)) \cdot g'(t) = \cos((\sin t)^2) \cdot \cos t = \cos(\sin^2 t)(\cos t).$$

26. Since $\int_{\cos x}^3 e^{t^2}\, dt = -\int_3^{\cos x} e^{t^2}\, dt$, if we let $f(x) = \int_3^x e^{t^2}\, dt$ and $g(x) = \cos x$, using the chain rule gives

$$\frac{d}{dx}\int_{\cos x}^3 e^{t^2}\, dt = -\frac{d}{dx}\int_3^{\cos x} e^{t^2}\, dt = -f'(g(x)) \cdot g'(x) = -e^{(\cos x)^2}(-\sin x) = \sin x\, e^{\cos^2 x}.$$

27. We split the integral at $x = 1$ (or any other point we choose):

$$\int_{e^t}^{t^3} \sqrt{1 + x^2}\, dx = \int_1^{t^3} \sqrt{1 + x^2}\, dx + \int_{e^t}^1 \sqrt{1 + x^2}\, dx = \int_1^{t^3} \sqrt{1 + x^2}\, dx - \int_1^{e^t} \sqrt{1 + x^2}\, dx.$$

Differentiating each part separately and using the chain rule gives

$$\frac{d}{dt} \int_{e^t}^{t^3} \sqrt{1 + x^2}\, dx = \frac{d}{dt} \int_1^{t^3} \sqrt{1 + x^2}\, dx - \frac{d}{dt} \int_1^{e^t} \sqrt{1 + x^2}\, dx$$

$$= \sqrt{1 + (t^3)^2} \cdot 3t^2 - \sqrt{1 + (e^t)^2} \cdot e^t$$

$$= 3t^2 \sqrt{1 + t^6} - e^t \sqrt{1 + e^{2t}}.$$

28. The indefinite integral of a function is a function whose derivative is the integrand. Thus $s'(t) = v(t - t_0)$.

29. By the Fundamental Construction Theorem, $s'(t) = v(t)$. Hence, by the Fundamental Theorem of Calculus, $\int_a^b v(t)\, dt = s(b) - s(a)$.

30. The derivative of $s(t - t_0)$ is $s'(t - t_0)$, so $s'(t - t_0) = v(t)$. Substituting $w = t - t_0$, so that $t = w + t_0$, we get $s'(w) = v(w + t_0)$. Renaming w to t, we get $s'(t) = v(t + t_0)$.

31. We have $(d/dx)(g(2x)) = f(2x)$. Also, by the chain rule, $(d/dx)(g(2x)) = 2g'(2x)$. So $2g'(2x) = f(2x)$, hence $g'(2x) = (1/2)f(2x)$, and so $g'(x) = (1/2)f(x)$.

32. Since $g(ax)$ is an antiderivative for $af(x)$,

$$\frac{d}{dx} g(ax) = af(x), \quad \text{so, by the chain rule,} \quad ag'(ax) = af(x).$$

Thus $g'(ax) = f(x)$. Putting $w = ax$, so that $x = w/a$, we get $g'(w) = f(w/a)$, or, changing the name of w to x, $g'(x) = f(x/a)$.

33.

$$\frac{d}{dx}[x\,\mathrm{erf}(x)] = \mathrm{erf}(x)\frac{d}{dx}(x) + x\frac{d}{dx}[\mathrm{erf}(x)]$$

$$= \mathrm{erf}(x) + x\frac{d}{dx}\left(\frac{2}{\sqrt{\pi}}\int_0^x e^{-t^2}\, dt\right)$$

$$= \mathrm{erf}(x) + \frac{2}{\sqrt{\pi}}xe^{-x^2}.$$

34. If we let $f(x) = \mathrm{erf}(x)$ and $g(x) = \sqrt{x}$, then we are looking for $\frac{d}{dx}[f(g(x))]$. By the chain rule, this is the same as $g'(x)f'(g(x))$. Since

$$f'(x) = \frac{d}{dx}\left(\frac{2}{\sqrt{\pi}}\int_0^x e^{-t^2}\, dt\right)$$

$$= \frac{2}{\sqrt{\pi}}e^{-x^2}$$

and $g'(x) = \frac{1}{2\sqrt{x}}$, we have

$$f'(g(x)) = \frac{2}{\sqrt{\pi}}e^{-x},$$

and so

$$\frac{d}{dx}[\mathrm{erf}(\sqrt{x})] = \frac{1}{2\sqrt{x}}\frac{2}{\sqrt{\pi}}e^{-x} = \frac{1}{\sqrt{\pi x}}e^{-x}.$$

35. If we let $f(x) = \int_0^x e^{-t^2}\, dt$ and $g(x) = x^3$, then we use the chain rule because we are looking for $\frac{d}{dx}f(g(x)) = f'(g(x)) \cdot g'(x)$. Since $f'(x) = e^{-x^2}$, we have

$$\frac{d}{dx}\left(\int_0^{x^3} e^{-t^2}\, dt\right) = f'(x^3) \cdot 3x^2 = e^{-(x^3)^2} \cdot 3x^2 = 3x^2 e^{-x^6}.$$

36. We split the integral $\int_x^{x^3} e^{-t^2} \, dt$ into two pieces, say at $t = 1$ (though it could be at any other point):

$$\int_x^{x^3} e^{-t^2} \, dt = \int_1^{x^3} e^{-t^2} \, dt + \int_x^1 e^{-t^2} \, dt = \int_1^{x^3} e^{-t^2} \, dt - \int_1^x e^{-t^2} \, dt.$$

We have used the fact that $\int_x^1 e^{-t^2} \, dt = -\int_1^x e^{-t^2} \, dt$. Differentiating gives

$$\frac{d}{dx} \left(\int_x^{x^3} e^{-t^2} \, dt \right) = \frac{d}{dx} \left(\int_1^{x^3} e^{-t^2} \, dt \right) - \frac{d}{dx} \left(\int_1^x e^{-t^2} \, dt \right)$$

For the first integral, we use the chain rule with $g(x) = x^3$ as the inside function, so the final answer is

$$\frac{d}{dx} \left(\int_x^{x^3} e^{-t^2} \, dt \right) = e^{-(x^3)^2} \cdot 3x^2 - e^{-x^2} = 3x^2 e^{-x^6} - e^{-x^2}.$$

Solutions for Section 6.5

Exercises

1. (a) The object is thrown from an initial height of $y = 1.5$ meters.
   (b) The velocity is obtained by differentiating, which gives $v = -9.8t + 7$ m/sec. The initial velocity is $v = 7$ m/sec upward.
   (c) The acceleration due to gravity is obtained by differentiating again, giving $g = -9.8$ m/sec^2, or 9.8 m/sec^2 downward.

2. Since height is measured upward, the initial position of the stone is $h(0) = 250$ meters and the initial velocity is $v = -20$ m/sec. The acceleration due to gravity is $g = -9.8$ m/sec^2. Thus, the height at time t is given by $h(t) = -4.9t^2 - 20t + 250$ meters.

Problems

3. The velocity as a function of time is given by: $v = v_0 + at$. Since the object starts from rest, $v_0 = 0$, and the velocity is just the acceleration times time: $v = -32t$. Integrating this, we get position as a function of time: $y = -16t^2 + y_0$, where the last term, y_0, is the initial position at the top of the tower, so $y_0 = 400$ feet. Thus we have a function giving position as a function of time: $y = -16t^2 + 400$.

  To find at what time the object hits the ground, we find t when $y = 0$. We solve $0 = -16t^2 + 400$ for t, getting $t^2 = 400/16 = 25$, so $t = 5$. Therefore the object hits the ground after 5 seconds. At this time it is moving with a velocity $v = -32(5) = -160$ feet/second.

4. In Problem 3 we used the equation $0 = -16t^2 + 400$ to learn that the object hits the ground after 5 seconds. In a more general form this is the equation $y = -\frac{g}{2}t^2 + v_0 t + y_0$, and we know that $v_0 = 0$, $y_0 = 400$ ft. So the moment the object hits the ground is given by $0 = -\frac{g}{2}t^2 + 400$. In Problem 3 we used $g = 32$ ft/sec^2, but in this case we want to find a g that results in the object hitting the ground after only 5/2 seconds. We put in 5/2 for t and solve for g:

$$0 = -\frac{g}{2}\left(\frac{5}{2}\right)^2 + 400, \text{ so } g = \frac{2(400)}{(5/2)^2} = 128 \text{ ft/sec}^2.$$

5. $a(t) = -32$. Since $v(t)$ is the antiderivative of $a(t)$, $v(t) = -32t + v_0$. But $v_0 = 0$, so $v(t) = -32t$. Since $s(t)$ is the antiderivative of $v(t)$, $s(t) = -16t^2 + s_0$, where s_0 is the height of the building. Since the ball hits the ground in 5 seconds, $s(5) = 0 = -400 + s_0$. Hence $s_0 = 400$ feet, so the window is 400 feet high.

6. Let time $t = 0$ be the moment when the astronaut jumps up. If acceleration due to gravity is 5 ft/sec^2 and initial velocity is 10 ft/sec, then the velocity of the astronaut is described by

$$v(t) = 10 - 5t.$$

Suppose $y(t)$ describes his distance from the surface of the moon. By the Fundamental Theorem,

$$y(t) - y(0) = \int_0^t (10 - 5x) \, dx$$

$$y(t) = 10t - \frac{1}{2} 5t^2.$$

since $y(0) = 0$ (assuming the astronaut jumps off the surface of the moon).

The astronaut reaches the maximum height when his velocity is 0, i.e. when

$$\frac{dy}{dt} = v(t) = 10 - 5t = 0.$$

Solving for t, we get $t = 2$ sec as the time at which he reaches the maximum height from the surface of the moon. At this time his height is

$$y(2) = 10(2) - \frac{1}{2} 5(2)^2 = 10 \text{ ft.}$$

When the astronaut is at height $y = 0$, he either just landed or is about to jump. To find how long it is before he comes back down, we find when he is at height $y = 0$. Set $y(t) = 0$ to get

$$0 = 10t - \frac{1}{2} 5t^2$$
$$0 = 20t - 5t^2$$
$$0 = 4t - t^2$$
$$0 = t(t - 4).$$

So we have $t = 0$ sec (when he jumps off) and $t = 4$ sec (when he lands, which gives the time he spent in the air).

7. Let the acceleration due to gravity equal $-k$ meters/sec^2, for some positive constant k, and suppose the object falls from an initial height of $s(0)$ meters. We have $a(t) = dv/dt = -k$, so that

$$v(t) = -kt + v_0.$$

Since the initial velocity is zero, we have

$$v(0) = -k(0) + v_0 = 0,$$

which means $v_0 = 0$. Our formula becomes

$$v(t) = \frac{ds}{dt} = -kt.$$

This means

$$s(t) = \frac{-kt^2}{2} + s_0.$$

Since

$$s(0) = \frac{-k(0)^2}{2} + s_0,$$

we have $s_0 = s(0)$, and our formula becomes

$$s(t) = \frac{-kt^2}{2} + s(0).$$

Suppose that the object falls for t seconds. Assuming it has not hit the ground, its height is

$$s(t) = \frac{-kt^2}{2} + s(0),$$

so that the distance traveled is

$$s(0) - s(t) = \frac{kt^2}{2} \text{ meters,}$$

which is proportional to t^2.

8. (a) $t = \dfrac{s}{\frac{1}{2}v_{max}}$, where t is the time it takes for an object to travel the distance s, starting from rest with uniform acceleration a. v_{max} is the highest velocity the object reaches. Since its initial velocity is 0, the mean of its highest velocity and initial velocity is $\frac{1}{2}v_{max}$.

(b) By Problem 7, $s = \frac{1}{2}gt^2$, where g is the acceleration due to gravity, so it takes $\sqrt{200/32} = 5/2$ seconds for the body to hit the ground. Since $v = gt$, $v_{max} = 32(\frac{5}{2}) = 80$ ft/sec. Galileo's statement predicts $(100 \text{ ft})/(40 \text{ ft/sec}) = 5/2$ seconds, and so Galileo's result is verified.

(c) If the acceleration is a constant a, then $s = \frac{1}{2}at^2$, and $v_{max} = at$. Thus

$$\frac{s}{\frac{1}{2}v_{max}} = \frac{\frac{1}{2}at^2}{\frac{1}{2}at} = t.$$

9. (a) Since $s(t) = -\frac{1}{2}gt^2$, the distance a body falls in the first second is

$$s(1) = -\frac{1}{2} \cdot g \cdot 1^2 = -\frac{g}{2}.$$

In the second second, the body travels

$$s(2) - s(1) = -\frac{1}{2}\left(g \cdot 2^2 - g \cdot 1^2\right) = -\frac{1}{2}(4g - g) = -\frac{3g}{2}.$$

In the third second, the body travels

$$s(3) - s(2) = -\frac{1}{2}\left(g \cdot 3^2 - g \cdot 2^2\right) = -\frac{1}{2}(9g - 4g) = -\frac{5g}{2},$$

and in the fourth second, the body travels

$$s(4) - s(3) = -\frac{1}{2}\left(g \cdot 4^2 - g \cdot 3^2\right) = -\frac{1}{2}(16g - 9g) = -\frac{7g}{2}.$$

(b) Galileo seems to have been correct. His observation follows from the fact that the differences between consecutive squares are consecutive odd numbers. For, if n is any number, then $n^2 - (n-1)^2 = 2n - 1$, which is the nth odd number (where 1 is the first).

10. If r is the distance from the center of the earth,

$$g = \frac{GM}{r^2},$$

so at 2 meters

$$9.8 = \frac{GM}{(6.4 \times 10^6 + 2)^2}.$$

At 100 meters above the ground,

$$g_{new} = \frac{GM}{(6.4 \times 10^6 + 100)^2}$$

so

$$\frac{g_{new}}{9.8} = \frac{GM}{(6.4 \times 10^6 + 100)^2} \bigg/ \frac{GM}{(6.4 \times 10^6 + 2)^2}$$

$$g_{new} = 9.8\left(\frac{6,400,002}{6,400,100}\right)^2 = 9.79969\ldots \text{ m/sec}^2.$$

Thus, to the first decimal place, the acceleration due to gravity is still 9.8 m/sec^2 at 100 m above the ground. At 100,000 meters above the ground,

$$g_{new} = 9.8\left(\frac{6,400,002}{6,500,000}\right)^2 = 9.5\text{m/sec}^2.$$

Solutions for Chapter 6 Review

Exercises

1. See Figure 6.32

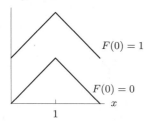

Figure 6.32

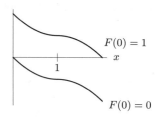

Figure 6.33

2. See Figure 6.33

3. $\frac{5}{2}x^2 + 7x + C$

4. $\displaystyle\int \left(4t + \frac{1}{t}\right) dt = 2t^2 + \ln|t| + C$

5. $\displaystyle\int (2 + \cos t)\, dt = 2t + \sin t + C$

6. $\displaystyle\int 7e^x\, dx = 7e^x + C$

7. $\displaystyle\int (3e^x + 2\sin x)\, dx = 3e^x - 2\cos x + C$

8. $\displaystyle\int (x+3)^2\, dx = \int (x^2 + 6x + 9)\, dx = \frac{x^3}{3} + 3x^2 + 9x + C$

9. $\displaystyle\int \frac{8}{\sqrt{x}}\, dx = 16x^{1/2} + C$

10. $3\ln|t| + \dfrac{2}{t} + C$

11. $e^x + 5x + C$

12. $\frac{2}{5}x^{5/2} - 2\ln|x| + C$

13. $\tan x + C$

14. $\dfrac{1}{\ln 2} 2^x + C$, since $\dfrac{d}{dx}(2^x) = (\ln 2) \cdot 2^x$

15. $\displaystyle\int (x+1)^2\, dx = \frac{(x+1)^3}{3} + C.$

Another way to work the problem is to expand $(x+1)^2$ to $x^2 + 2x + 1$ as follows:

$$\int (x+1)^2\, dx = \int (x^2 + 2x + 1)\, dx = \frac{x^3}{3} + x^2 + x + C.$$

These two answers are the same, since $\dfrac{(x+1)^3}{3} = \dfrac{x^3 + 3x^2 + 3x + 1}{3} = \dfrac{x^3}{3} + x^2 + x + \dfrac{1}{3}$, which is $\dfrac{x^3}{3} + x^2 + x$, plus a constant.

16. $\displaystyle\int (x+1)^3\, dx = \frac{(x+1)^4}{4} + C.$

Another way to work the problem is to expand $(x+1)^3$ to $x^3 + 3x^2 + 3x + 1$:

$$\int (x+1)^3\, dx = \int (x^3 + 3x^2 + 3x + 1)\, dx = \frac{x^4}{4} + x^3 + \frac{3}{2}x^2 + x + C.$$

It can be shown that these answers are the same by expanding $\dfrac{(x+1)^4}{4}$.

17. $\frac{1}{10}(x+1)^{10} + C$

18. Since $f(x) = \dfrac{x+1}{x} = 1 + \dfrac{1}{x}$, the indefinite integral is $x + \ln|x| + C$

19. Since $f(x) = x + 1 + \dfrac{1}{x}$, the indefinite integral is $\dfrac{1}{2}x^2 + x + \ln|x| + C$

20. $3\sin t + 2t^{3/2} + C$

21. $3\sin x + 7\cos x + C$

22. $2\ln|x| - \pi\cos x + C$

23. $2e^x - 8\sin x + C$

24. $P(t) = \displaystyle\int \frac{1}{t}\,dt = \ln|t| + C$

25. $F(x) = \displaystyle\int \frac{1}{x^2}\,dx = -\frac{1}{x} + C$

26. $F(x) = \displaystyle\int \cos x\,dx = \sin x + C$

27. $G(x) = \displaystyle\int \sin x\,dx = -\cos x + C$

28. $F(x) = \displaystyle\int (e^x - 1)\,dx = e^x - x + C$

29. $F(x) = \displaystyle\int 5e^x\,dx = 5e^x + C$

30. $H(t) = \displaystyle\int \frac{5}{t}\,dt = 5\ln|t| + C$

31. $F(t) = \displaystyle\int \left(t + \frac{1}{t}\right)\,dt = \frac{t^2}{2} + \ln|t| + C$

32. $F(x) = \displaystyle\int f(x)\,dx = \int x^2\,dx = \frac{x^3}{3} + C$. If $F(0) = 4$, then $F(0) = 0 + C = 4$ and thus $C = 4$. So $F(x) = \dfrac{x^3}{3} + 4$.

33. We have $F(x) = \dfrac{x^4}{4} + 2x^3 - 4x + C$. Since $F(0) = 4$, we have $4 = 0 + C$, so $C = 4$. So $F(x) = \dfrac{x^4}{4} + 2x^3 - 4x + 4$.

34. $F(x) = \displaystyle\int \sqrt{x}\,dx = \frac{2}{3}x^{3/2} + C$. If $F(0) = 4$, then $F(0) = 0 + C = 4$ and thus $C = 4$. So $F(x) = \dfrac{2}{3}x^{3/2} + 4$.

35. $F(x) = \displaystyle\int e^x\,dx = e^x + C$. If $F(0) = 4$, then $F(0) = 1 + C = 4$ and thus $C = 3$. So $F(x) = e^x + 3$.

36. $F(x) = \displaystyle\int \sin x\,dx = -\cos x + C$. If $F(0) = 4$, then $F(0) = -1 + C = 4$ and thus $C = 5$. So $F(x) = -\cos x + 5$.

37. $F(x) = \displaystyle\int \cos x\,dx = \sin x + C$. If $F(0) = 4$, then $F(0) = 0 + C = 4$ and thus $C = 4$. So $F(x) = \sin x + 4$.

38. We have
$$\int_1^3 (6x^2 + 8x + 5)\,dx = (2x^3 + 4x^2 + 5x)\Big|_1^3 = (54 + 36 + 15) - (2 + 4 + 5) = 94.$$

Problems

39. $\displaystyle\int_0^3 x^2\,dx = \frac{x^3}{3}\bigg|_0^3 = 9 - 0 = 9.$

40. Since $y = x^3 - x = x(x-1)(x+1)$, the graph crosses the axis at the three points shown in Figure 6.34. The two regions have the same area (by symmetry). Since the graph is below the axis for $0 < x < 1$, we have

$$\text{Area} = 2\left(-\int_0^1 \left(x^3 - x\right)\, dx\right)$$

$$= -2\left[\frac{x^4}{4} - \frac{x^2}{2}\right]_0^1 = -2\left(\frac{1}{4} - \frac{1}{2}\right) = \frac{1}{2}.$$

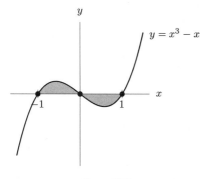

Figure 6.34

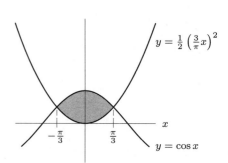

Figure 6.35

41. The area we want (the shaded area in Figure 6.35) is symmetric about the y-axis and so is given by

$$\text{Area} = 2\int_0^{\pi/3} \left(\cos x - \frac{1}{2}\left(\frac{3}{\pi}x\right)^2\right)\, dx$$

$$= 2\int_0^{\pi/3} \cos x\, dx - \int_0^{\pi/3} \frac{9}{\pi^2}x^2\, dx$$

$$= 2\sin x\Big|_0^{\pi/3} - \frac{9}{\pi^2}\cdot\frac{x^3}{3}\Big|_0^{\pi/3}$$

$$= 2\cdot\frac{\sqrt{3}}{2} - \frac{3}{\pi^2}\cdot\frac{\pi^3}{3^3} = \sqrt{3} - \frac{\pi}{9}.$$

42. Since $y < 0$ from $x = 0$ to $x = 1$ and $y > 0$ from $x = 1$ to $x = 3$, we have

$$\text{Area} = -\int_0^1 \left(3x^2 - 3\right)\, dx + \int_1^3 \left(3x^2 - 3\right)\, dx$$

$$= -\left(x^3 - 3x\right)\Big|_0^1 + \left(x^3 - 3x\right)\Big|_1^3$$

$$= -(-2 - 0) + (18 - (-2)) = 2 + 20 = 22.$$

43. (a) See Figure 6.36. Since $f(x) > 0$ for $0 < x < 2$ and $f(x) < 0$ for $2 < x < 5$, we have

$$\text{Area} = \int_0^2 f(x)\, dx - \int_2^5 f(x)\, dx$$

$$= \int_0^2 (x^3 - 7x^2 + 10x)\, dx - \int_2^5 (x^3 - 7x^2 + 10x)\, dx$$

$$= \left(\frac{x^4}{4} - \frac{7x^3}{3} + 5x^2\right)\Big|_0^2 - \left(\frac{x^4}{4} - \frac{7x^3}{3} + 5x^2\right)\Big|_2^5$$

$$= \left[\left(4 - \frac{56}{3} + 20\right) - (0 - 0 + 0)\right] - \left[\left(\frac{625}{4} - \frac{875}{3} + 125\right) - \left(4 - \frac{56}{3} + 20\right)\right]$$

$$= \frac{253}{12}.$$

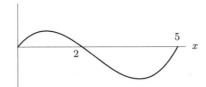

Figure 6.36: Graph of $f(x) = x^3 - 7x^2 + 10x$

(b) Calculating $\int_0^5 f(x)\,dx$ gives

$$\int_0^5 f(x)\,dx = \int_0^5 (x^3 - 7x^2 + 10x)\,dx$$

$$= \left(\frac{x^4}{4} - \frac{7x^3}{3} + 5x^2\right)\Bigg|_0^5$$

$$= \left(\frac{625}{4} - \frac{875}{3} + 125\right) - (0 - 0 + 0)$$

$$= -\frac{125}{12}.$$

This integral measures the difference between the area above the x-axis and the area below the x-axis. Since the definite integral is negative, the graph of $f(x)$ lies more below the x-axis than above it. Since the function crosses the axis at $x = 2$,

$$\int_0^5 f(x)\,dx = \int_0^2 f(x)\,dx + \int_2^5 f(x)\,dx = \frac{16}{3} - \frac{63}{4} = \frac{-125}{12},$$

whereas

$$\text{Area} = \int_0^2 f(x)\,dx - \int_2^5 f(x)\,dx = \frac{16}{3} + \frac{64}{4} = \frac{253}{12}.$$

44. Since the area under the curve is 6, we have

$$\int_1^b \frac{1}{\sqrt{x}}\,dx = 2x^{1/2}\Bigg|_1^b = 2b^{1/2} - 2(1) = 6.$$

Thus $b^{1/2} = 4$ and $b = 16$.

45. The graph of $y = c(1 - x^2)$ has x-intercepts of $x = \pm 1$. See Figure 6.37. Since it is symmetric about the y-axis, we have

$$\text{Area} = \int_{-1}^1 c(1 - x^2)\,dx = 2c \int_0^1 (1 - x^2)\,dx$$

$$= 2c\left(x - \frac{x^3}{3}\right)\Bigg|_0^1 = \frac{4c}{3}.$$

We want the area to be 1, so

$$\frac{4c}{3} = 1, \quad \text{giving} \quad c = \frac{3}{4}.$$

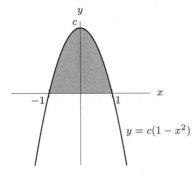

Figure 6.37

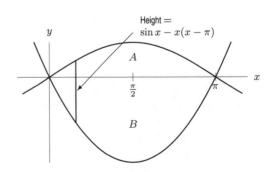

Figure 6.38

46. The curves intersect at $(0, 0)$ and $(\pi, 0)$. At any x-coordinate the "height" between the two curves is $\sin x - x(x - \pi)$. See Figure 6.38.

Thus the total area is

$$\int_0^\pi [\sin x - x(x - \pi)]\, dx = = \int_0^\pi (\sin x - x^2 + \pi x)\, dx$$

$$= \left(-\cos x - \frac{x^3}{3} + \frac{\pi x^2}{2}\right)\Big|_0^\pi$$

$$= \left(1 - \frac{\pi^3}{3} + \frac{\pi^3}{2}\right) - (-1)$$

$$= 2 + \frac{\pi^3}{6}.$$

Another approach is to notice that the area between the two curves is (area A) + (area B).

$$\text{Area B} = -\int_0^\pi x(x - \pi)\, dx \text{ since the function is negative on } 0 \le x \le \pi$$

$$= -\left(\frac{x^3}{3} - \frac{\pi x^2}{2}\right)\Big|_0^\pi = \frac{\pi^3}{2} - \frac{\pi^3}{3} = \frac{\pi^3}{6};$$

$$\text{Area A} = \int_0^\pi \sin x\, dx = -\cos x\Big|_0^\pi = 2.$$

Thus the area is $2 + \frac{\pi^3}{6}$.

47. See Figure 6.39. The average value of $f(x)$ is given by

$$\text{Average} = \frac{1}{9 - 0}\int_0^9 \sqrt{x}\, dx = \frac{1}{9}\left(\frac{2}{3}x^{3/2}\Big|_0^9\right) = \frac{1}{9}\left(\frac{2}{3}9^{3/2} - 0\right) = \frac{1}{9}18 = 2.$$

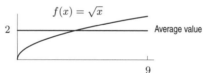

$f(x) = \sqrt{x}$

2 ——————— Average value

9

Figure 6.39

48. The total amount of discharge is the integral of the discharge rate from $t = 0$ to $t = 3$:

$$\text{Total discharge} = \int_0^3 (t^2 - 14t + 49)\, dt$$

$$= \left(\frac{t^3}{3} - 7t^2 + 49t\right)\Big|_0^3$$

$$= (9 - 63 + 147) - 0$$

$$= 93 \text{ cubic meters.}$$

49. (a) Since $f'(t)$ is positive on the interval $0 < t < 2$ and negative on the interval $2 < t < 5$, the function $f(t)$ is increasing on $0 < t < 2$ and decreasing on $2 < t < 5$. Thus $f(t)$ attains its maximum at $t = 2$. Since the area under the t-axis is greater than the area above the t-axis, the function $f(t)$ decreases more than it increases. Thus, the minimum is at $t = 5$.

(b) To estimate the value of f at $t = 2$, we see that the area under $f'(t)$ between $t = 0$ and $t = 2$ is about 1 box, which has area 5. Thus,

$$f(2) = f(0) + \int_0^2 f'(t)dt \approx 50 + 5 = 55.$$

The maximum value attained by the function is $f(2) \approx 55$.

The area between $f'(t)$ and the t-axis between $t = 2$ and $t = 5$ is about 3 boxes, each of which has an area of 5. Thus

$$f(5) = f(2) + \int_2^5 f'(t)dt \approx 55 + (-15) = 40.$$

The minimum value attained by the function is $f(5) = 40$.

(c) Using part (b), we have $f(5) - f(0) = 40 - 50 = -10$. Alternately, we can use the Fundamental Theorem:

$$f(5) - f(0) = \int_0^5 f'(t)dt \approx 5 - 15 = -10.$$

50. (a) We know that $\int_0^3 f'(x)dx = f(3) - f(0)$ from the Fundamental Theorem of Calculus. From the graph of f' we can see that $\int_0^3 f'(x)dx = 2 - 1 = 1$ by subtracting areas between f' and the x-axis. Since $f(0) = 0$, we find that $f(3) = 1$. Similar reasoning gives $f(7) = \int_0^7 f'(x)dx = 2 - 1 + 2 - 4 + 1 = 0$.

(b) We have $f(0) = 0$, $f(2) = 2$, $f(3) = 1$, $f(4) = 3$, $f(6) = -1$, and $f(7) = 0$. So the graph, beginning at $x = 0$, starts at zero, increases to 2 at $x = 2$, decreases to 1 at $x = 3$, increases to 3 at $x = 4$, then passes through a zero as it decreases to -1 at $x = 6$, and finally increases to 0 at 7. Thus, there are three zeroes: $x = 0$, $x = 5.5$, and $x = 7$.

(c)

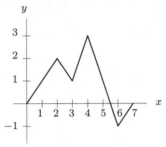

51. See Figure 6.40.

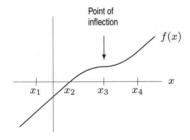

Figure 6.40

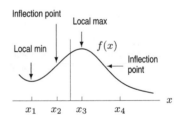

Figure 6.41

52. See Figure 6.41.

53. We have

$$\frac{d}{dx} \int_2^x \arccos(t^7)\, dt = \arccos x^7.$$

54. We have

$$\frac{d}{dt} \int_t^7 \log(x^6)\, dx = -\log t^6.$$

55. If we let $f(x) = \int_5^x \cos(t^3)\, dt$ and $g(x) = e^x$, using the chain rule gives

$$\frac{d}{dx} \int_5^{e^x} \cos(t^3)\, dt = f'(g(x)) \cdot g'(x) = \cos((e^x)^3) \cdot e^x = e^x \cos(e^{3x}).$$

56. Since $\int_{\sin x}^{17} \tan^3 t \, dt = -\int_{17}^{\sin x} \tan^3 t \, dt$, if we let $f(x) = \int_{17}^{x} \tan^3 t \, dt$ and $g(x) = \sin x$, using the chain rule gives

$$\frac{d}{dx} \int_{\sin x}^{17} \tan^3 t \, dt = -\frac{d}{dx} \int_{17}^{\sin x} \tan^3 t \, dt = -f'(g(x)) \cdot g'(x)$$

$$= -\tan^3(\sin x) \cdot \cos x = -(\cos x) \tan^3(\sin x).$$

57. We split the integral at $x = 1$ (or any other point we choose):

$$\int_{t^5}^{\cos t} 4^{7x} \, dx = \int_{1}^{\cos t} 4^{7x} \, dx + \int_{t^5}^{1} 4^{7x} \, dx = \int_{1}^{\cos t} 4^{7x} \, dx - \int_{1}^{t^5} 4^{7x} \, dx.$$

Differentiating each part separately and using the chain rule gives

$$\frac{d}{dt} \int_{t^5}^{\cos t} 4^{7x} \, dx = \frac{d}{dt} \int_{1}^{\cos t} 4^{7x} \, dx - \frac{d}{dt} \int_{1}^{t^5} 4^{7x} \, dx$$

$$= 4^{7\cos t}(-\sin t) - 4^{7t^5}(5t^4)$$

$$= -(\sin t)4^{7\cos t} - 5t^4 4^{7t^5}.$$

58. We split the integral at $x = 1$ (or any other point we choose):

$$\int_{e^t}^{4\sin t} \frac{1+x}{1+x^2} \, dx = \int_{1}^{4\sin t} \frac{1+x}{1+x^2} \, dx + \int_{e^t}^{1} \frac{1+x}{1+x^2} \, dx = \int_{1}^{4\sin t} \frac{1+x}{1+x^2} \, dx - \int_{1}^{e^t} \frac{1+x}{1+x^2} \, dx.$$

Differentiating each part separately and using the chain rule gives

$$\frac{d}{dt} \int_{e^t}^{4\sin t} \frac{1+x}{1+x^2} \, dx = \frac{d}{dt} \int_{1}^{4\sin t} \frac{1+x}{1+x^2} \, dx - \frac{d}{dt} \int_{1}^{e^t} \frac{1+x}{1+x^2} \, dx.$$

$$= \frac{1+4\sin t}{1+(4\sin t)^2} 4\cos t - \frac{1+e^t}{1+(e^t)^2} e^t$$

$$= 4\cos t \frac{1+4\sin t}{1+16\sin^2 t} - e^t \frac{1+e^t}{1+e^{2t}}$$

59. $F(x)$ represents the net area between $(\sin t)/t$ and the t-axis from $t = \frac{\pi}{2}$ to $t = x$, with area counted as negative for $(\sin t)/t$ below the t-axis. As long as the integrand is positive $F(x)$ is increasing. Therefore, the global maximum of $F(x)$ occurs at $x = \pi$ and is given by the area

$$A_1 = \int_{\pi/2}^{\pi} \frac{\sin t}{t} \, dt.$$

At $x = \pi/2$, $F(x) = 0$. Figure 6.42 shows that the area A_1 is larger than the area A_2. Thus $F(x) > 0$ for $\frac{\pi}{2} < x \leq \frac{3\pi}{2}$. Therefore the global minimum is $F(\frac{\pi}{2}) = 0$.

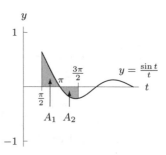

Figure 6.42

60. Since B is the graph of a decreasing function, the graph of its derivative should fall below the x-axis. Thus, f' could be C and f could be B. Since the graph of B is above the x-axis and represents a decreasing function, the function $\int_0^x f(t)\,dt$ should be increasing and concave down. Thus, A could be the graph of $\int_0^x f(t)\,dt$.

61. A function whose derivative is e^{x^2} is of the form

$$f(x) = C + \int_a^x e^{t^2}\,dt \qquad \text{for some value of } C.$$

(a) To ensure that the function goes through the point $(0,3)$, we take $a = 0$ and $C = 3$:

$$f(x) = 3 + \int_0^x e^{t^2}\,dt.$$

(b) To ensure that the function goes through $(-1,5)$, we take $a = -1$ and $C = 5$:

$$f(x) = 5 + \int_{-1}^x e^{t^2}\,dt.$$

62. We know the height is given by

$$s = -25t^2 + 72t + 40,$$

so the velocity is given by

$$v = -50t + 72$$

and the acceleration is given by

$$a = -50.$$

The acceleration due to gravity is -50 ft/sec^2 downward. Since $v(0) = 72$, the object was thrown at 72 ft/sec. Since $s(0) = 40$, the object was thrown from a height of 40 ft.

63. The graph of $h(t)$ must slope downward most steeply when $h'(t)$ has its minimum. The graph of $h(t)$ should have its minimum about two-thirds of the way through the time interval (when the graph of $h'(t)$ intersects the x-axis), and have its final value about half-way between its maximum and minimum values. A possible graph of $h(t)$ is given in Figure 6.43. The placement of the horizontal axis below the graph is arbitrary.

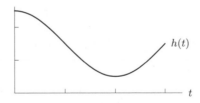

Figure 6.43

64. Let v be the velocity and s be the position of the particle at time t. We know that $a = dv/dt$, so acceleration is the slope of the velocity graph. Similarly, velocity is the slope of the position graph. Graphs of v and s are shown in Figures 6.44 and 6.45, respectively.

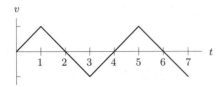

Figure 6.44: Velocity against time

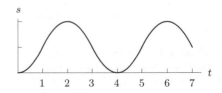

Figure 6.45: Position against time

65. (a) Since 6 sec $= 1/10$ min,

$$\text{Angular acceleration} = \frac{2500 - 1100}{1/10} = 14{,}000 \text{ revs/min}^2.$$

(b) We know angular acceleration is the derivative of angular velocity. Since

$$\text{Angular acceleration} = 14{,}000,$$

we have

$$\text{Angular velocity} = 14{,}000t + C.$$

Measuring time from the moment at which the angular velocity is 1100 revs/min, we have $C = 1100$. Thus,

$$\text{Angular velocity} = 14{,}000t + 1100.$$

Thus the total number of revolutions performed during the period from $t = 0$ to $t = 1/10$ min is given by

$$\begin{array}{l}\text{Number of} \\ \text{revolutions}\end{array} = \int_0^{1/10} (14000t + 1100)dt = 7000t^2 + 1100t \Big|_0^{1/10} = 180 \text{ revolutions.}$$

66. (a) Since the rotor is slowing down at a constant rate,

$$\text{Angular acceleration} = \frac{260 - 350}{1.5} = -60 \text{ revs/min}^2.$$

Units are revolutions per minute per minute, or revs/min^2.

(b) To decrease from 350 to 0 revs/min at a deceleration of 60 revs/min^2,

$$\text{Time needed} = \frac{350}{60} \approx 5.83 \text{ min.}$$

(c) We know angular acceleration is the derivative of angular velocity. Since

$$\text{Angular acceleration} = -60 \text{ revs/min}^2,$$

we have

$$\text{Angular velocity} = -60t + C.$$

Measuring time from the moment when angular velocity is 350 revs/min, we get $C = 350$. Thus

$$\text{Angular velocity} = -60t + 350.$$

So, the total number of revolutions made between the time the angular speed is 350 revs/min and stopping is given by:

$$\text{Number of revolutions} = \int_0^{5.83} (\text{Angular velocity}) \, dt$$

$$= \int_0^{5.83} (-60t + 350)dt = -30t^2 + 350t \Big|_0^{5.83}$$

$$= 1020.83 \text{ revolutions.}$$

67. (a) Using $g = -32$ ft/sec^2, we have

t (sec)	0	1	2	3	4	5
$v(t)$ (ft/sec)	80	48	16	-16	-48	-80

(b) The object reaches its highest point when $v = 0$, which appears to be at $t = 2.5$ seconds. By symmetry, the object should hit the ground again at $t = 5$ seconds.

(c) Left sum $= 80(1) + 48(1) + 16(\frac{1}{2}) = 136$ ft , which is an overestimate.
Right sum $= 48(1) + 16(1) + (-16)(\frac{1}{2}) = 56$ ft , which is an underestimate.
Note that we used a smaller third rectangle of width $1/2$ to end our sum at $t = 2.5$.

(d) We have $v(t) = 80 - 32t$, so antidifferentiation yields $s(t) = 80t - 16t^2 + s_0$.
But $s_0 = 0$, so $s(t) = 80t - 16t^2$.
At $t = 2.5$, $s(t) = 100$ ft., so 100 ft. is the highest point.

68. The velocity of the car decreases at a constant rate, so we can write: $dv/dt = -a$. Integrating this gives $v = -at + C$. The constant of integration C is the velocity when $t = 0$, so $C = 60$ mph $= 88$ ft/sec, and $v = -at + 88$. From this equation we can see the car comes to rest at time $t = 88/a$.

Integrating the expression for velocity we get $s = -\frac{a}{2}t^2 + 88t + C$, where C is the initial position, so $C = 0$. We can use fact that the car comes to rest at time $t = 88/a$ after traveling 200 feet. Start with

$$s = -\frac{a}{2}t^2 + 88t,$$

and substitute $t = 88/a$ and $s = 200$:

$$200 = -\frac{a}{2}\left(\frac{88}{a}\right)^2 + 88\left(\frac{88}{a}\right) = \frac{88^2}{2a}$$

$$a = \frac{88^2}{2(200)} = 19.36 \text{ ft/sec}^2$$

69. (a) In the beginning, both birth and death rates are small; this is consistent with a very small population. Both rates begin climbing, the birth rate faster than the death rate, which is consistent with a growing population. The birth rate is then high, but it begins to decrease as the population increases.

(b)

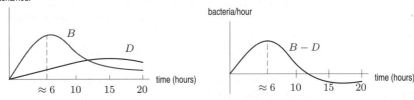

Figure 6.46: Difference between B and D is greatest at $t \approx 6$

The bacteria population is growing most quickly when $B - D$, the rate of change of population, is maximal; that happens when B is farthest above D, which is at a point where the slopes of both graphs are equal. That point is $t \approx 6$ hours.

(c) Total number born by time t is the area under the B graph from $t = 0$ up to time t. See Figure 6.47.

Total number alive at time t is the number born minus the number that have died, which is the area under the B graph minus the area under the D graph, up to time t. See Figure 6.48.

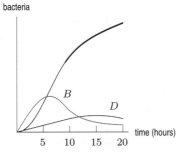

Figure 6.47: Number born by time t is
$\int_0^t B(x)\,dx$

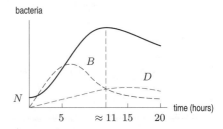

Figure 6.48: Number alive at time t is
$\int_0^t (B(x) - D(x))\,dx$

From Figure 6.48, we see that the population is at a maximum when $B = D$, that is, after about 11 hours. This stands to reason, because $B - D$ is the rate of change of population, so population is maximized when $B - D = 0$, that is, when $B = D$.

70.

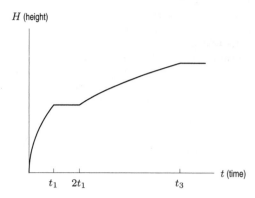

Suppose t_1 is the time to fill the left side to the top of the middle ridge. Since the container gets wider as you go up, the rate dH/dt decreases with time. Therefore, for $0 \leq t \leq t_1$, graph is concave down.

At $t = t_1$, water starts to spill over to right side and so depth of left side does not change. It takes as long for the right side to fill to the ridge as the left side, namely t_1. Thus the graph is horizontal for $t_1 \leq t \leq 2t_1$.

For $t \geq 2t_1$, water level is above the central ridge. The graph is climbing because the depth is increasing, but at a slower rate than for $t \leq t_1$ because the container is wider. The graph is concave down because width is increasing with depth. Time t_3 represents the time when container is full.

71.
- For $[0, t_1]$, the acceleration is constant and positive and the velocity is positive so the displacement is positive. Thus, the work done is positive.
- For $[t_1, t_2]$, the acceleration, and therefore the force, is zero. Therefore, the work done is zero.
- For $[t_2, t_3]$, the acceleration is negative and thus the force is negative. The velocity, and thus the displacement, is positive; therefore the work done is negative.
- For $[t_3, t_4]$, the acceleration (and thus the force) and the velocity (and thus the displacement) are negative. Thus, the work done is positive.
- For $[t_2, t_4]$, the acceleration and thus the force is constant and negative. Velocity both positive and negative; total displacement is 0. Since force is constant, work is 0.

CAS Challenge Problems

72. (a) We have $\Delta x = \dfrac{(b-a)}{n}$ and $x_i = a + i(\Delta x) = a + i\left(\dfrac{b-a}{n}\right)$, so, since $f(x_i) = x_i{}^3$,

$$\text{Riemann sum} = \sum_{i=1}^{n} f(x_i)\Delta x = \sum_{i=1}^{n}\left[a + i\left(\frac{b-a}{n}\right)\right]^3 \left(\frac{b-a}{n}\right).$$

(b) A CAS gives

$$\sum_{i=1}^{n}\left[a + \frac{i(b-a)}{n}\right]^3 \frac{(b-a)}{n} = -\frac{(a-b)(a^3(n-1)^2 + (a^2b + ab^2)(n^2-1) + b^3(n+1)^3)}{4n^2}.$$

Taking the limit as $n \to \infty$ gives

$$\lim_{n \to \infty} \sum_{i=1}^{n}\left[a + i\left(\frac{b-a}{n}\right)\right]^3 \left(\frac{b-a}{n}\right) = -\frac{(a+b)(a-b)(a^2+b^2)}{4}.$$

(c) The answer to part (b) simplifies to $\dfrac{b^4}{4} - \dfrac{a^4}{4}$. Since $\dfrac{d}{dx}\left(\dfrac{x^4}{4}\right) = x^3$, the Fundamental Theorem of Calculus says that

$$\int_a^b x^3\,dx = \frac{x^4}{4}\bigg|_a^b = \frac{b^4}{4} - \frac{a^4}{4}.$$

73. (a) A CAS gives

$$\int e^{2x}\, dx = \frac{1}{2}e^{2x} \qquad \int e^{3x}\, dx = \frac{1}{3}e^{3x} \qquad \int e^{3x+5}\, dx = \frac{1}{3}e^{3x+5}.$$

(b) The three integrals in part (a) obey the rule

$$\int e^{ax+b}\, dx = \frac{1}{a}e^{ax+b}.$$

(c) Checking the formula by calculating the derivative

$$\frac{d}{dx}\left(\frac{1}{a}e^{ax+b}\right) = \frac{1}{a}\frac{d}{dx}e^{ax+b} \qquad \text{by the constant multiple rule}$$

$$= \frac{1}{a}e^{ax+b}\frac{d}{dx}(ax+b) \qquad \text{by the chain rule}$$

$$= \frac{1}{a}e^{ax+b}\cdot a = e^{ax+b}.$$

74. (a) A CAS gives

$$\int \sin(3x)\, dx = -\frac{1}{3}\cos(3x) \qquad \int \sin(4x)\, dx = -\frac{1}{4}\cos(4x) \qquad \int \sin(3x-2)\, dx = -\frac{1}{3}\cos(3x-2).$$

(b) The three integrals in part (a) obey the rule

$$\int \sin(ax+b)\, dx = -\frac{1}{a}\cos(ax+b).$$

(c) Checking the formula by calculating the derivative

$$\frac{d}{dx}\left(-\frac{1}{a}\cos(ax+b)\right) = -\frac{1}{a}\frac{d}{dx}\cos(ax+b) \qquad \text{by the constant multiple rule}$$

$$= -\frac{1}{a}(-\sin(ax+b))\frac{d}{dx}(ax+b) \qquad \text{by the chain rule}$$

$$= -\frac{1}{a}(-\sin(ax+b))\cdot a = \sin(ax+b).$$

75. (a) A CAS gives

$$\int \frac{x-2}{x-1}\, dx = x - \ln|x-1|$$

$$\int \frac{x-3}{x-1}\, dx = x - 2\ln|x-1|$$

$$\int \frac{x-1}{x-2}\, dx = x + \ln|x-2|$$

Although the absolute values are needed in the answer, some CASs may not include them.

(b) The three integrals in part (a) obey the rule

$$\int \frac{x-a}{x-b}\, dx = x + (b-a)\ln|x-b|.$$

(c) Checking the formula by calculating the derivative

$$\frac{d}{dx}\left(x + (b-a)\ln|x-b|\right) = 1 + (b-a)\frac{1}{x-b} \qquad \text{by the sum and constant multiple rules}$$

$$= \frac{(x-b)+(b-a)}{x-b} = \frac{x-a}{x-b}$$

76. (a) A CAS gives

$$\int \frac{1}{(x-1)(x-3)} \, dx = \frac{1}{2}(\ln|x-3| - \ln|x-1|)$$

$$\int \frac{1}{(x-1)(x-4)} \, dx = \frac{1}{3}(\ln|x-4| - \ln|x-1|)$$

$$\int \frac{1}{(x-1)(x+3)} \, dx = \frac{1}{4}(\ln|x+3| - \ln|x-1|).$$

Although the absolute values are needed in the answer, some CASs may not include them.

(b) The three integrals in part (a) obey the rule

$$\int \frac{1}{(x-a)(x-b)} \, dx = \frac{1}{b-a}(\ln|x-b| - \ln|x-a|).$$

(c) Checking the formula by calculating the derivative

$$\begin{aligned}
\frac{d}{dx}\left(\frac{1}{b-a}(\ln|x-b| - \ln|x-a|)\right) &= \frac{1}{b-a}\left(\frac{1}{x-b} - \frac{1}{x-a}\right) \\
&= \frac{1}{b-a}\left(\frac{(x-a)-(x-b)}{(x-a)(x-b)}\right) \\
&= \frac{1}{b-a}\left(\frac{b-a}{(x-a)(x-b)}\right) = \frac{1}{(x-a)(x-b)}.
\end{aligned}$$

CHECK YOUR UNDERSTANDING

1. True. A function can have only one derivative.
2. True. Check by differentiating $\frac{d}{dx}(2(x+1)^{3/2}) = 2 \cdot \frac{3}{2}(x+1)^{1/2} = 3\sqrt{x+1}$.
3. True. Any antiderivative of $3x^2$ is obtained by adding a constant to x^3.
4. True. Any antiderivative of $1/x$ is obtained by adding a constant to $\ln|x|$.
5. False. Differentiating using the product and chain rules gives

$$\frac{d}{dx}\left(\frac{-1}{2x}e^{-x^2}\right) = \frac{1}{2x^2}e^{-x^2} + e^{-x^2}.$$

6. False. It is not true in general that $\int xf(x)dx = x\int f(x)dx$, so this statement is false for many functions $f(x)$. For example, if $f(x) = 1$, then $\int xf(x)\,dx = x^2/2 + C$, but $x\int f(x)\,dx = x(x+C)$.
7. True. Adding a constant to an antiderivative gives another antiderivative.
8. True. If $F(x)$ is an antiderivative of $f(x)$, then $F'(x) = f(x)$, so $dy/dx = f(x)$. Therefore, $y = F(x)$ is a solution to this differential equation.
9. True. If $y = F(x)$ is a solution to the differential equation $dy/dx = f(x)$, then $F'(x) = f(x)$, so $F(x)$ is an antiderivative of $f(x)$.
10. True. If acceleration is $a(t) = k$ for some constant k, $k \neq 0$, then we have

$$\text{Velocity} = v(t) = \int a(t)dt = \int kdt = kt + C_1,$$

for some constant C_1. We integrate again to find position as a function of time:

$$\text{Position} = s(t) = \int v(t)dt = \int (kt+C_1)dt = \frac{kt^2}{2} + C_1 t + C_2,$$

for some constant C_2. Since $k \neq 0$, this is a quadratic polynomial.

11. True. Since $F(x)$ and $G(x)$ are antiderivatives of the same function on an interval, $F(x) - G(x)$ is a constant function. Thus $F(10) - G(10) = F(5) - G(5) > 0$.

12. False. In an initial value problem the value of y is specified at one value of x, but it does not have to be $x = 0$.

13. False. The solution of the initial value problem $dy/dx = 1$ with $y(0) = -5$ is a solution of the differential equation that is not positive at $x = 0$.

14. True. If $dy/dx = f(x) > 0$, then all solutions $y(x)$ have positive derivative and thus are increasing functions.

15. True. Two solutions $y = F(x)$ and $y = G(x)$ of the same differential equation $dy/dx = f(x)$ are both antiderivatives of $f(x)$ and hence they differ by a constant: $F(x) - G(x) = C$ for all x. Since $F(3) \neq G(3)$ we have $C \neq 0$.

16. True. If $y = f(x)$ satisfies the differential equation $dy/dx = \sin x/x$, then $f'(x) = \sin x/x$. Since $(f(x) + 5)' = f'(x) = \sin x/x$, the function $y = f(x) + 5$ is also a solution of the same differential equation.

17. True. All solutions of the differential equation $dy/dt = 3t^2$ are in the family $y(t) = t^3 + C$ of antiderivatives of $3t^2$. The initial condition $y(1) = \pi$ tells us that $y(1) = \pi = 1^3 + C$, so $C = \pi - 1$. Thus $y(t) = t^3 + \pi - 1$ is the only solution of the initial value problem.

18. False. For a counterexample, take $f(x) = g(x) = 1$. Then $F(x) = x$ and $G(x) = x$ are antiderivatives of $f(x)$ and $g(x)$, but $F(x) \cdot G(x) = x^2$ is not an antiderivative of $f(x) \cdot g(x) = 1$.

19. True. The derivative of $F(x) - G(x)$ is $(F(x) - G(x))' = f(x) - f(x) = 0$, so $F(x) - G(x)$ is a constant function.

20. True. The Construction Theorem for Antiderivatives gives a method for building an antiderivative with a definite integral.

21. True. Suppose t is measured in seconds from when the ball was thrown. The acceleration $a = dv/dt$ is -32 ft/sec^2, so the velocity of the ball is $v = -32t + C$ feet/second at time t. At $t = 0$ the velocity is -10, so $v = -32t - 10$. Since $v = ds/dt$, an antiderivative gives the height $s = -16t^2 - 10t + K$ feet of the ball at time t. Since the ball starts at the top of the building, $s = 100$ when $t = 0$. Substituting gives $s = -16t^2 - 10t + 100$. The ball hits the ground when $s = 0$, so we solve $0 = -16t^2 - 10t + 100$. The positive solution $t = 2.2$ tells us that the ball hits the ground after 2.2 seconds.

22. True, by the Second Fundamental Theorem of Calculus.

23. True. We see that
$$F(5) - F(3) = \int_0^5 f(t)dt - \int_0^3 f(t)dt = \int_3^5 f(t)dt.$$

24. False. If f is positive then F is increasing, but if f is negative then F is decreasing.

25. True. Since F and G are both antiderivatives of f, they must differ by a constant. In fact, we can see that the constant C is equal to $\int_0^2 f(t)dt$ since
$$F(x) = \int_0^x f(t)dt = \int_2^x f(t)dt + \int_0^2 f(t)dt = G(x) + C.$$

26. True, since $\int_0^x (f(t) + g(t))dt = \int_0^x f(t)dt + \int_0^x g(t)dt$.

PROJECTS FOR CHAPTER SIX

1. (a) If the poorest $p\%$ of the population has exactly $p\%$ of the goods, then $F(x) = x$.
   (b) Any such F is increasing. For example, the poorest 50% of the population includes the poorest 40%, and so the poorest 50% must own more than the poorest 40%. Thus $F(0.4) \leq F(0.5)$, and so, in general, F is increasing. In addition, it is clear that $F(0) = 0$ and $F(1) = 1$.

   The graph of F is concave up by the following argument. Consider $F(0.05) - F(0.04)$. This is the fraction of resources the fifth poorest percent of the population has. Similarly, $F(0.20) - F(0.19)$ is the fraction of resources that the twentieth poorest percent of the population has. Since the twentieth poorest percent owns more than the fifth poorest percent, we have

$$F(0.05) - F(0.04) \leq F(0.20) - F(0.19).$$

More generally, we can see that

$$F(x_1 + \Delta x) - F(x_1) \leq F(x_2 + \Delta x) - F(x_2)$$

for any x_1 smaller than x_2 and for any increment Δx. Dividing this inequality by Δx and taking the limit as $\Delta x \to 0$, we get

$$F'(x_1) \leq F'(x_2).$$

So, the derivative of F is an increasing function, i.e. F is concave up.

(c) G is twice the shaded area below in the following figure. If the resource is distributed evenly, then G is zero. The larger G is, the more unevenly the resource is distributed. The maximum possible value of G is 1.

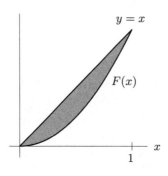

2. (a) In Figure 6.49, the area of the shaded region is $F(M)$. Thus, $F(M) = \int_0^M y(t)\, dt$ and, by the Fundamental Theorem, $F'(M) = y(M)$.

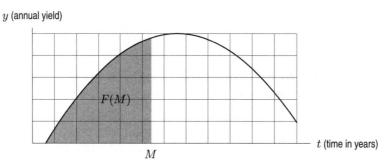

Figure 6.49

(b) Figure 6.50 is a graph of $F(M)$. Note that the graph of y looks like the graph of a quadratic function. Thus, the graph of F looks like a cubic.

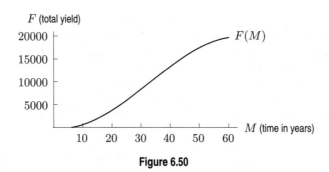

Figure 6.50

(c) We have

$$a(M) = \frac{1}{M}F(M) = \frac{1}{M}\int_0^M y(t)\, dt.$$

(d) If the function $a(M)$ takes on its maximum at some point M, then $a'(M) = 0$. Since

$$a(M) = \frac{1}{M}F(M),$$

differentiating using the quotient rule gives

$$a'(M) = \frac{MF'(M) - F(M)}{M^2} = 0,$$

so $MF'(M) = F(M)$. Since $F'(M) = y(M)$, the condition for a maximum may be written as

$$My(M) = F(M)$$

or as

$$y(M) = a(M).$$

To estimate the value of M which satisfies $My(M) = F(M)$, use the graph of $y(t)$. Notice that $F(M)$ is the area under the curve from 0 to M, and that $My(M)$ is the area of a rectangle of base M and height $y(M)$. Thus, we want the area under the curve to be equal to the area of the rectangle, or $A = B$ in Figure 6.51. This happens when $M \approx 50$ years. In other words, the orchard should be cut down after about 50 years.

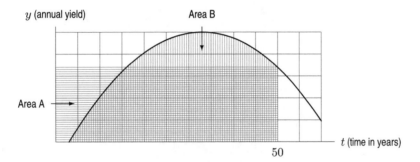

Figure 6.51

CHAPTER SEVEN

Solutions for Section 7.1

Exercises

1. (a) We substitute $w = 1 + x^2$, $dw = 2x\,dx$.

$$\int_{x=0}^{x=1} \frac{x}{1+x^2}\,dx = \frac{1}{2}\int_{w=1}^{w=2} \frac{1}{w}\,dw = \frac{1}{2}\ln|w|\Big|_1^2 = \frac{1}{2}\ln 2.$$

(b) We substitute $w = \cos x$, $dw = -\sin x\,dx$.

$$\int_{x=0}^{x=\frac{\pi}{4}} \frac{\sin x}{\cos x}\,dx = -\int_{w=1}^{w=\sqrt{2}/2} \frac{1}{w}\,dw$$

$$= -\ln|w|\Big|_1^{\sqrt{2}/2} = -\ln\frac{\sqrt{2}}{2} = \frac{1}{2}\ln 2.$$

2. (a) $\frac{d}{dx}\sin(x^2+1) = 2x\cos(x^2+1)$; $\frac{d}{dx}\sin(x^3+1) = 3x^2\cos(x^3+1)$

(b) (i) $\frac{1}{2}\sin(x^2+1) + C$ (ii) $\frac{1}{3}\sin(x^3+1) + C$

(c) (i) $-\frac{1}{2}\cos(x^2+1) + C$ (ii) $-\frac{1}{3}\cos(x^3+1) + C$

3. We use the substitution $w = 3x$, $dw = 3\,dx$.

$$\int e^{3x}\,dx = \frac{1}{3}\int e^w\,dw = \frac{1}{3}e^w + C = \frac{1}{3}e^{3x} + C.$$

Check: $\frac{d}{dx}\left(\frac{1}{3}e^{3x} + C\right) = \frac{1}{3}e^{3x}(3) = e^{3x}$.

4. We use the substitution $w = -x$, $dw = -dx$.

$$\int e^{-x}\,dx = -\int e^w\,dw = -e^w + C = -e^{-x} + C.$$

Check: $\frac{d}{dx}(-e^{-x} + C) = -(-e^{-x}) = e^{-x}$.

5. We use the substitution $w = -0.2t$, $dw = -0.2\,dt$.

$$\int 25e^{-0.2t}\,dt = \frac{25}{-0.2}\int e^w\,dw = -125e^w + C = -125e^{-0.2t} + C.$$

Check: $\frac{d}{dt}(-125e^{-0.2t} + C) = -125e^{-0.2t}(-0.2) = 25e^{-0.2t}$.

6. We use the substitution $w = t^2$, $dw = 2t\,dt$.

$$\int t\cos(t^2)\,dt = \frac{1}{2}\int \cos(w)\,dw = \frac{1}{2}\sin(w) + C = \frac{1}{2}\sin(t^2) + C.$$

Check: $\frac{d}{dt}\left(\frac{1}{2}\sin(t^2) + C\right) = \frac{1}{2}\cos(t^2)(2t) = t\cos(t^2)$.

7. We use the substitution $w = 2x$, $dw = 2\,dx$.

$$\int \sin(2x)\,dx = \frac{1}{2}\int \sin(w)\,dw = -\frac{1}{2}\cos(w) + C = -\frac{1}{2}\cos(2x) + C.$$

Check: $\frac{d}{dx}(-\frac{1}{2}\cos(2x) + C) = \frac{1}{2}\sin(2x)(2) = \sin(2x)$.

8. We use the substitution $w = 3 - t$, $dw = -dt$.

$$\int \sin(3 - t)dt = -\int \sin(w)dw = -(-\cos(w)) + C = \cos(3 - t) + C.$$

Check: $\frac{d}{dt}(\cos(3 - t) + C) = -\sin(3 - t)(-1) = \sin(3 - t)$.

9. We use the substitution $w = -x^2$, $dw = -2x \, dx$.

$$\int xe^{-x^2} \, dx = -\frac{1}{2} \int e^{-x^2}(-2x \, dx) = -\frac{1}{2} \int e^w \, dw$$

$$= -\frac{1}{2}e^w + C = -\frac{1}{2}e^{-x^2} + C.$$

Check: $\frac{d}{dx}(-\frac{1}{2}e^{-x^2} + C) = (-2x)(-\frac{1}{2}e^{-x^2}) = xe^{-x^2}$.

10. We use the substitution $w = y^2 + 5$, $dw = 2y \, dy$.

$$\int y(y^2 + 5)^8 \, dy = \frac{1}{2} \int (y^2 + 5)^8 (2y \, dy)$$

$$= \frac{1}{2} \int w^8 \, dw = \frac{1}{2}\frac{w^9}{9} + C$$

$$= \frac{1}{18}(y^2 + 5)^9 + C.$$

Check: $\frac{d}{dy}(\frac{1}{18}(y^2 + 5)^9 + C) = \frac{1}{18}[9(y^2 + 5)^8(2y)] = y(y^2 + 5)^8$.

11. We use the substitution $w = t^3 - 3$, $dw = 3t^2 \, dt$.

$$\int t^2(t^3 - 3)^{10} \, dt = \frac{1}{3} \int (t^3 - 3)^{10}(3t^2 dt) = \int w^{10}\left(\frac{1}{3} \, dw\right)$$

$$= \frac{1}{3}\frac{w^{11}}{11} + C = \frac{1}{33}(t^3 - 3)^{11} + C.$$

Check: $\frac{d}{dt}[\frac{1}{33}(t^3 - 3)^{11} + C] = \frac{1}{3}(t^3 - 3)^{10}(3t^2) = t^2(t^3 - 3)^{10}$.

12. We use the substitution $w = 1 + 2x^3$, $dw = 6x^2 \, dx$.

$$\int x^2(1 + 2x^3)^2 \, dx = \int w^2(\frac{1}{6} \, dw) = \frac{1}{6}(\frac{w^3}{3}) + C = \frac{1}{18}(1 + 2x^3)^3 + C.$$

Check: $\frac{d}{dx}\left[\frac{1}{18}(1 + 2x^2)^3 + C\right] = \frac{1}{18}[3(1 + 2x^3)^2(6x^2)] = x^2(1 + 2x^3)^2$.

13. We use the substitution $w = x^2 + 3$, $dw = 2x \, dx$.

$$\int x(x^2 + 3)^2 \, dx = \int w^2(\frac{1}{2} \, dw) = \frac{1}{2}\frac{w^3}{3} + C = \frac{1}{6}(x^2 + 3)^3 + C.$$

Check: $\frac{d}{dx}\left[\frac{1}{6}(x^2 + 3)^3 + C\right] = \frac{1}{6}\left[3(x^2 + 3)^2(2x)\right] = x(x^2 + 3)^2$.

14. We use the substitution $w = x^2 - 4$, $dw = 2x \, dx$.

$$\int x(x^2 - 4)^{7/2} \, dx = \frac{1}{2} \int (x^2 - 4)^{7/2}(2xdx) = \frac{1}{2} \int w^{7/2} \, dw$$

$$= \frac{1}{2}\left(\frac{2}{9}w^{9/2}\right) + C = \frac{1}{9}(x^2 - 4)^{9/2} + C.$$

Check: $\frac{d}{dx}\left(\frac{1}{9}(x^2 - 4)^{9/2} + C\right) = \frac{1}{9}\left(\frac{9}{2}(x^2 - 4)^{7/2}\right) 2x = x(x^2 - 4)^{7/2}$.

15. In this case, it seems easier not to substitute.

$$\int y^2(1+y)^2 \, dy = \int y^2(y^2 + 2y + 1) \, dy = \int (y^4 + 2y^3 + y^2) \, dy$$
$$= \frac{y^5}{5} + \frac{y^4}{2} + \frac{y^3}{3} + C.$$

Check: $\dfrac{d}{dy}\left(\dfrac{y^5}{5} + \dfrac{y^4}{2} + \dfrac{y^3}{3} + C\right) = y^4 + 2y^3 + y^2 = y^2(y+1)^2.$

16. We use the substitution $w = 2t - 7$, $dw = 2\, dt$.

$$\int (2t-7)^{73} \, dt = \frac{1}{2}\int w^{73} \, dw = \frac{1}{(2)(74)} w^{74} + C = \frac{1}{148}(2t-7)^{74} + C.$$

Check: $\dfrac{d}{dt}\left[\dfrac{1}{148}(2t-7)^{74} + C\right] = \dfrac{74}{148}(2t-7)^{73}(2) = (2t-7)^{73}.$

17. We use the substitution $w = y + 5$, $dw = dy$, to get

$$\int \frac{dy}{y+5} = \int \frac{dw}{w} = \ln|w| + C = \ln|y+5| + C.$$

Check: $\dfrac{d}{dy}(\ln|y+5| + C) = \dfrac{1}{y+5}.$

18. We use the substitution $w = 4 - x$, $dw = -dx$.

$$\int \frac{1}{\sqrt{4-x}} \, dx = -\int \frac{1}{\sqrt{w}} \, dw = -2\sqrt{w} + C = -2\sqrt{4-x} + C.$$

Check: $\dfrac{d}{dx}(-2\sqrt{4-x} + C) = -2 \cdot \dfrac{1}{2} \cdot \dfrac{1}{\sqrt{4-x}} \cdot -1 = \dfrac{1}{\sqrt{4-x}}.$

19. In this case, it seems easier not to substitute.

$$\int (x^2+3)^2 \, dx = \int (x^4 + 6x^2 + 9) \, dx = \frac{x^5}{5} + 2x^3 + 9x + C.$$

Check: $\dfrac{d}{dx}\left[\dfrac{x^5}{5} + 2x^3 + 9x + C\right] = x^4 + 6x^2 + 9 = (x^2+3)^2.$

20. We use the substitution $w = x^3 + 1$, $dw = 3x^2 \, dx$, to get

$$\int x^2 e^{x^3+1} \, dx = \frac{1}{3}\int e^w \, dw = \frac{1}{3}e^w + C = \frac{1}{3}e^{x^3+1} + C.$$

Check: $\dfrac{d}{dx}\left(\dfrac{1}{3}e^{x^3+1} + C\right) = \dfrac{1}{3}e^{x^3+1} \cdot 3x^2 = x^2 e^{x^3+1}.$

21. We use the substitution $w = \cos\theta + 5$, $dw = -\sin\theta \, d\theta$.

$$\int \sin\theta(\cos\theta + 5)^7 \, d\theta = -\int w^7 \, dw = -\frac{1}{8}w^8 + C$$
$$= -\frac{1}{8}(\cos\theta + 5)^8 + C.$$

Check:

$$\frac{d}{d\theta}\left[-\frac{1}{8}(\cos\theta + 5)^8 + C\right] = -\frac{1}{8} \cdot 8(\cos\theta + 5)^7 \cdot (-\sin\theta)$$
$$= \sin\theta(\cos\theta + 5)^7$$

22. We use the substitution $w = \cos 3t$, $dw = -3\sin 3t\, dt$.

$$\int \sqrt{\cos 3t} \sin 3t\, dt = -\frac{1}{3} \int \sqrt{w}\, dw$$

$$= -\frac{1}{3} \cdot \frac{2}{3} w^{\frac{3}{2}} + C = -\frac{2}{9} (\cos 3t)^{\frac{3}{2}} + C.$$

Check:

$$\frac{d}{dt}\left[-\frac{2}{9}(\cos 3t)^{\frac{3}{2}} + C \right] = -\frac{2}{9} \cdot \frac{3}{2} (\cos 3t)^{\frac{1}{2}} \cdot (-\sin 3t) \cdot 3$$

$$= \sqrt{\cos 3t} \sin 3t.$$

23. We use the substitution $w = \sin\theta$, $dw = \cos\theta\, d\theta$.

$$\int \sin^6 \theta \cos\theta\, d\theta = \int w^6\, dw = \frac{w^7}{7} + C = \frac{\sin^7\theta}{7} + C.$$

Check: $\dfrac{d}{d\theta}\left[\dfrac{\sin^7\theta}{7} + C \right] = \sin^6\theta\cos\theta.$

24. We use the substitution $w = \sin\alpha$, $dw = \cos\alpha\, d\alpha$.

$$\int \sin^3 \alpha \cos\alpha\, d\alpha = \int w^3\, dw = \frac{w^4}{4} + C = \frac{\sin^4\alpha}{4} + C.$$

Check: $\dfrac{d}{d\alpha}\left(\dfrac{\sin^4\alpha}{4} + C \right) = \dfrac{1}{4} \cdot 4\sin^3\alpha \cdot \cos\alpha = \sin^3\alpha\cos\alpha.$

25. We use the substitution $w = \sin 5\theta$, $dw = 5\cos 5\theta\, d\theta$.

$$\int \sin^6 5\theta \cos 5\theta\, d\theta = \frac{1}{5} \int w^6\, dw = \frac{1}{5}\left(\frac{w^7}{7}\right) + C = \frac{1}{35} \sin^7 5\theta + C.$$

Check: $\dfrac{d}{d\theta}(\dfrac{1}{35}\sin^7 5\theta + C) = \dfrac{1}{35}[7\sin^6 5\theta](5\cos 5\theta) = \sin^6 5\theta\cos 5\theta.$

Note that we could also use Problem 23 to solve this problem, substituting $w = 5\theta$ and $dw = 5\, d\theta$ to get:

$$\int \sin^6 5\theta \cos 5\theta\, d\theta = \frac{1}{5} \int \sin^6 w \cos w\, dw$$

$$= \frac{1}{5}\left(\frac{\sin^7 w}{7}\right) + C = \frac{1}{35}\sin^7 5\theta + C.$$

26. We use the substitution $w = \cos 2x$, $dw = -2\sin 2x\, dx$.

$$\int \tan 2x\, dx = \int \frac{\sin 2x}{\cos 2x}\, dx = -\frac{1}{2} \int \frac{dw}{w}$$

$$= -\frac{1}{2} \ln|w| + C = -\frac{1}{2} \ln|\cos 2x| + C.$$

Check:

$$\frac{d}{dx}\left[-\frac{1}{2}\ln|\cos 2x| + C \right] = -\frac{1}{2} \cdot \frac{1}{\cos 2x} \cdot -2\sin 2x$$

$$= \frac{\sin 2x}{\cos 2x} = \tan 2x.$$

27. We use the substitution $w = \ln z$, $dw = \frac{1}{z} \, dz$.

$$\int \frac{(\ln z)^2}{z} \, dz = \int w^2 \, dw = \frac{w^3}{3} + C = \frac{(\ln z)^3}{3} + C.$$

Check: $\frac{d}{dz} \left[\frac{(\ln z)^3}{3} + C \right] = 3 \cdot \frac{1}{3} (\ln z)^2 \cdot \frac{1}{z} = \frac{(\ln z)^2}{z}$.

28. We use the substitution $w = e^t + t$, $dw = (e^t + 1) \, dt$.

$$\int \frac{e^t + 1}{e^t + t} \, dt = \int \frac{1}{w} \, dw = \ln|w| + C = \ln|e^t + t| + C.$$

Check: $\frac{d}{dt} (\ln|e^t + t| + C) = \frac{e^t + 1}{e^t + t}$.

29. We use the substitution $w = y^2 + 4$, $dw = 2y \, dy$.

$$\int \frac{y}{y^2 + 4} \, dy = \frac{1}{2} \int \frac{dw}{w} = \frac{1}{2} \ln|w| + C = \frac{1}{2} \ln(y^2 + 4) + C.$$

(We can drop the absolute value signs since $y^2 + 4 \geq 0$ for all y.)

Check: $\frac{d}{dy} \left[\frac{1}{2} \ln(y^2 + 4) + C \right] = \frac{1}{2} \cdot \frac{1}{y^2 + 4} \cdot 2y = \frac{y}{y^2 + 4}$.

30. We use the substitution $w = \sqrt{x}$, $dw = \frac{1}{2\sqrt{x}} \, dx$.

$$\int \frac{\cos \sqrt{x}}{\sqrt{x}} \, dx = \int \cos w (2 \, dw) = 2 \sin w + C = 2 \sin \sqrt{x} + C.$$

Check: $\frac{d}{dx} (2 \sin \sqrt{x} + C) = 2 \cos \sqrt{x} \left(\frac{1}{2\sqrt{x}} \right) = \frac{\cos \sqrt{x}}{\sqrt{x}}$.

31. We use the substitution $w = \sqrt{y}$, $dw = \frac{1}{2\sqrt{y}} \, dy$.

$$\int \frac{e^{\sqrt{y}}}{\sqrt{y}} \, dy = 2 \int e^w \, dw = 2e^w + C = 2e^{\sqrt{y}} + C.$$

Check: $\frac{d}{dy} (2e^{\sqrt{y}} + C) = 2e^{\sqrt{y}} \cdot \frac{1}{2\sqrt{y}} = \frac{e^{\sqrt{y}}}{\sqrt{y}}$.

32. We use the substitution $w = x + e^x$, $dw = (1 + e^x) \, dx$.

$$\int \frac{1 + e^x}{\sqrt{x + e^x}} \, dx = \int \frac{dw}{\sqrt{w}} = 2\sqrt{w} + C = 2\sqrt{x + e^x} + C.$$

Check: $\frac{d}{dx} (2\sqrt{x + e^x} + C) = 2 \cdot \frac{1}{2} (x + e^x)^{-\frac{1}{2}} \cdot (1 + e^x) = \frac{1 + e^x}{\sqrt{x + e^x}}$.

33. We use the substitution $w = 2 + e^x$, $dw = e^x \, dx$.

$$\int \frac{e^x}{2 + e^x} \, dx = \int \frac{dw}{w} = \ln|w| + C = \ln(2 + e^x) + C.$$

(We can drop the absolute value signs since $2 + e^x \geq 0$ for all x.)

Check: $\frac{d}{dx} [\ln(2 + e^x) + C] = \frac{1}{2 + e^x} \cdot e^x = \frac{e^x}{2 + e^x}$.

34. We use the substitution $w = x^2 + 2x + 19$, $dw = 2(x + 1) dx$.

$$\int \frac{(x + 1)dx}{x^2 + 2x + 19} = \frac{1}{2} \int \frac{dw}{w} = \frac{1}{2} \ln|w| + C = \frac{1}{2} \ln(x^2 + 2x + 19) + C.$$

(We can drop the absolute value signs, since $x^2 + 2x + 19 = (x + 1)^2 + 18 > 0$ for all x.)

Check: $\frac{1}{dx} [\frac{1}{2} \ln(x^2 + 2x + 19)] = \frac{1}{2} \frac{1}{x^2 + 2x + 19} (2x + 2) = \frac{x + 1}{x^2 + 2x + 19}$.

35. We use the substitution $w = 1 + 3t^2$, $dw = 6t\,dt$.

$$\int \frac{t}{1 + 3t^2}\,dt = \int \frac{1}{w}\left(\frac{1}{6}\,dw\right) = \frac{1}{6}\ln|w| + C = \frac{1}{6}\ln(1 + 3t^2) + C.$$

(We can drop the absolute value signs since $1 + 3t^2 > 0$ for all t).

Check: $\dfrac{d}{dt}\left[\dfrac{1}{6}\ln(1 + 3t^2) + C\right] = \dfrac{1}{6}\dfrac{1}{1 + 3t^2}(6t) = \dfrac{t}{1 + 3t^2}.$

36. We use the substitution $w = e^x + e^{-x}$, $dw = (e^x - e^{-x})\,dx$.

$$\int \frac{e^x - e^{-x}}{e^x + e^{-x}}\,dx = \int \frac{dw}{w} = \ln|w| + C = \ln(e^x + e^{-x}) + C.$$

(We can drop the absolute value signs since $e^x + e^{-x} > 0$ for all x).

Check: $\dfrac{d}{dx}[\ln(e^x + e^{-x}) + C] = \dfrac{1}{e^x + e^{-x}}(e^x - e^{-x}).$

37. It seems easier not to substitute.

$$\int \frac{(t + 1)^2}{t^2}\,dt = \int \frac{(t^2 + 2t + 1)}{t^2}\,dt$$

$$= \int \left(1 + \frac{2}{t} + \frac{1}{t^2}\right)\,dt = t + 2\ln|t| - \frac{1}{t} + C.$$

Check: $\dfrac{d}{dt}(t + 2\ln|t| - \dfrac{1}{t} + C) = 1 + \dfrac{2}{t} + \dfrac{1}{t^2} = \dfrac{(t + 1)^2}{t^2}.$

38. We use the substitution $w = \sin(x^2)$, $dw = 2x\cos(x^2)\,dx$.

$$\int \frac{x\cos(x^2)}{\sqrt{\sin(x^2)}}\,dx = \frac{1}{2}\int w^{-\frac{1}{2}}\,dw = \frac{1}{2}(2w^{\frac{1}{2}}) + C = \sqrt{\sin(x^2)} + C.$$

Check: $\dfrac{d}{dx}(\sqrt{\sin(x^2)} + C) = \dfrac{1}{2\sqrt{\sin(x^2)}}[\cos(x^2)]2x = \dfrac{x\cos(x^2)}{\sqrt{\sin(x^2)}}.$

39. Since $d(\sinh x)/dx = \cosh x$, we have

$$\int \cosh x\,dx = \sinh x + C.$$

40. Since $d(\cosh 3t)/dt = 3\sinh 3t$, we have

$$\int \sinh 3t\,dt = \frac{1}{3}\cosh 3t + C.$$

41. Since $d(\cosh z)/dz = \sinh z$, the chain rule shows that

$$\frac{d}{dz}(e^{\cosh z}) = (\sinh z)e^{\cosh z}.$$

Thus,

$$\int (\sinh z)e^{\cosh z}\,dz = e^{\cosh z} + C.$$

42. Since $d(\sinh(2w + 1))/dw = 2\cosh(2w + 1)$, we have

$$\int \cosh(2w + 1)\,dw = \frac{1}{2}\sinh(2w + 1) + C.$$

43. We use the substitution $w = x^2$ and $dw = 2x\,dx$ so

$$\int x\cosh x^2\,dx = \frac{1}{2}\int \cosh w\,dw = \frac{1}{2}\sinh w + C = \frac{1}{2}\sinh x^2 + C.$$

Check this answer by taking the derivative: $\dfrac{d}{dx}\left[\dfrac{1}{2}\sinh x^2 + C\right] = x\cosh x^2.$

44. Use the substitution $w = \cosh x$ and $dw = \sinh x \, dx$ so
$$\int \cosh^2 x \sinh x \, dx = \int w^2 \, dw = \frac{1}{3}w^3 + C = \frac{1}{3}\cosh^3 x + C.$$

Check this answer by taking the derivative: $\frac{d}{dx}\left[\frac{1}{3}\cosh^3 x + C\right] = \cosh^2 x \sinh x.$

45. The general antiderivative is $\int (\pi t^3 + 4t) \, dt = (\pi/4)t^4 + 2t^2 + C.$

46. Make the substitution $w = 3x$, $dw = 3 \, dx$. We have
$$\int \sin 3x \, dx = \frac{1}{3}\int \sin w \, dw = \frac{1}{3}(-\cos w) + C = -\frac{1}{3}\cos 3x + C.$$

47. Make the substitution $w = x^2$, $dw = 2x \, dx$. We have
$$\int 2x \cos(x^2) \, dx = \int \cos w \, dw = \sin w + C = \sin x^2 + C.$$

48. Make the substitution $w = t^3$, $dw = 3t^2 \, dt$. The general antiderivative is $\int 12t^2 \cos(t^3) \, dt = 4\sin(t^3) + C.$

49. Make the substitution $w = 2 - 5x$, then $dw = -5dx$. We have
$$\int \sin(2-5x)dx = \int \sin w \left(-\frac{1}{5}\right) dw = -\frac{1}{5}(-\cos w) + C = \frac{1}{5}\cos(2-5x) + C.$$

50. Make the substitution $w = \sin x$, $dw = \cos x \, dx$. We have
$$\int e^{\sin x}\cos x \, dx = \int e^w \, dw = e^w + C = e^{\sin x} + C.$$

51. Make the substitution $w = x^2 + 1$, $dw = 2x \, dx$. We have
$$\int \frac{x}{x^2+1}dx = \frac{1}{2}\int \frac{dw}{w} = \frac{1}{2}\ln|w| + C = \frac{1}{2}\ln(x^2+1) + C.$$
(Notice that since $x^2 + 1 \geq 0$, $|x^2 + 1| = x^2 + 1$.)

52. Make the substitution $w = 2x$, then $dw = 2dx$. We have
$$\int \frac{1}{3\cos^2 2x} \, dx = \frac{1}{3}\int \frac{1}{\cos^2 w}\left(\frac{1}{2}\right) dw$$
$$= \frac{1}{6}\int \frac{1}{\cos^2 w} \, dw = \frac{1}{6}\tan w + C = \frac{1}{6}\tan 2x + C.$$

53. $\displaystyle\int_0^\pi \cos(x+\pi) \, dx = \sin(x+\pi)\Big|_0^\pi = \sin(2\pi) - \sin(\pi) = 0 - 0 = 0$

54. We substitute $w = \pi x$. Then $dw = \pi \, dx$.
$$\int_{x=0}^{x=\frac{1}{2}} \cos \pi x \, dx = \int_{w=0}^{w=\pi/2} \cos w \left(\frac{1}{\pi} \, dw\right) = \frac{1}{\pi}(\sin w)\Big|_0^{\pi/2} = \frac{1}{\pi}$$

55. $\displaystyle\int_0^{\pi/2} e^{-\cos\theta}\sin\theta \, d\theta = e^{-\cos\theta}\Big|_0^{\pi/2} = e^{-\cos(\pi/2)} - e^{-\cos(0)} = 1 - \frac{1}{e}$

56. $\displaystyle\int_1^2 2xe^{x^2} \, dx = e^{x^2}\Big|_1^2 = e^{2^2} - e^{1^2} = e^4 - e = e(e^3 - 1)$

57. We substitute $w = \sqrt[3]{x} = x^{\frac{1}{3}}$. Then $dw = \frac{1}{3}x^{-\frac{2}{3}} \, dx = \frac{1}{3\sqrt[3]{x^2}} \, dx.$
$$\int_1^8 \frac{e^{\sqrt[3]{x}}}{\sqrt[3]{x^2}}dx = \int_{x=1}^{x=8} e^w (3 \, dw) = 3e^w\Big|_{x=1}^{x=8} = 3e^{\sqrt[3]{x}}\Big|_1^8 = 3(e^2 - e).$$

58. We substitute $w = t + 2$, so $dw = dt$.
$$\int_{t=-1}^{t=e-2} \frac{1}{t+2}dt = \int_{w=1}^{w=e} \frac{dw}{w} = \ln|w|\Big|_1^e = \ln e - \ln 1 = 1.$$

59. We substitute $w = \sqrt{x}$. Then $dw = \frac{1}{2}x^{-1/2}dx$.

$$\int_{x=1}^{x=4} \frac{\cos\sqrt{x}}{\sqrt{x}}\, dx = \int_{w=1}^{w=2} \cos w (2\, dw)$$

$$= 2(\sin w)\Big|_1^2 = 2(\sin 2 - \sin 1).$$

60. We substitute $w = 1 + x^2$. Then $dw = 2x\, dx$.

$$\int_{x=0}^{x=2} \frac{x}{(1+x^2)^2}\, dx = \int_{w=1}^{w=5} \frac{1}{w^2}\left(\frac{1}{2}\, dw\right) = -\frac{1}{2}\left(\frac{1}{w}\right)\Big|_1^5 = \frac{2}{5}.$$

61.

$$\int_{-1}^{3}(x^3 + 5x)\, dx = \frac{x^4}{4}\Big|_{-1}^{3} + \frac{5x^2}{2}\Big|_{-1}^{3} = 40.$$

62. $\int_{-1}^{1} \frac{1}{1+y^2}\, dy = \tan^{-1} y\Big|_{-1}^{1} = \frac{\pi}{2}.$

63. $\int_{1}^{3} \frac{1}{x}\, dx = \ln x\Big|_{1}^{3} = \ln 3.$

64. $\int_{1}^{3} \frac{dt}{(t+7)^2} = \frac{-1}{t+7}\Big|_{1}^{3} = \left(-\frac{1}{10}\right) - \left(-\frac{1}{8}\right) = \frac{1}{40}$

65. $\int_{-1}^{2} \sqrt{x+2}\, dx = \frac{2}{3}(x+2)^{3/2}\Big|_{-1}^{2} = \frac{2}{3}\left[(4)^{3/2} - (1)^{3/2}\right] = \frac{2}{3}(7) = \frac{14}{3}$

66. It turns out that $\frac{\sin x}{x}$ cannot be integrated using elementary methods. However, the function is decreasing on $[1,2]$. One way to see this is to graph the function on a calculator or computer, as has been done below:

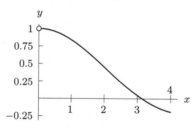

So since our function is monotonic, the error for our left- and right-hand sums is less than or equal to $\left|\frac{\sin 2}{2} - \frac{\sin 1}{1}\right| \Delta t \approx 0.61\Delta t$. So with 13 intervals, our error will be less than 0.05. With $n = 13$, the left sum is about 0.674, and the right sum is about 0.644. For more accurate sums, with $n = 100$ the left sum is about 0.6613 and the right sum is about 0.6574. The actual integral is about 0.6593.

67. Let $w = \sqrt{y+1}$, so $y = w^2 - 1$ and $dy = 2w\, dw$. Thus

$$\int y\sqrt{y+1}\, dy = \int (w^2 - 1)w2w\, dw = 2\int w^4 - w^2\, dw$$

$$= \frac{2}{5}w^5 - \frac{2}{3}w^3 + C = \frac{2}{5}(y+1)^{5/2} - \frac{2}{3}(y+1)^{3/2} + C.$$

68. Let $w = (z+1)^{1/3}$, so $z = w^3 - 1$ and $dz = 3w^2\, dw$. Thus

$$\int z(z+1)^{1/3}\, dz = \int (w^3 - 1)w3w^2\, dw = 3\int w^6 - w^3\, dw$$

$$= \frac{3}{7}w^7 - \frac{3}{4}w^4 + C = \frac{3}{7}(z+1)^{7/3} - \frac{3}{4}(z+1)^{4/3} + C.$$

69. Let $w = \sqrt{t+1}$, so $t = w^2 - 1$ and $dt = 2w\,dw$. Thus

$$\int \frac{t^2 + t}{\sqrt{t+1}}\,dt = \int \frac{(w^2-1)^2 + (w^2-1)}{w} 2w\,dw = 2\int w^4 - w^2\,dw$$

$$= \frac{2}{5}w^5 - \frac{2}{3}w^3 + C = \frac{2}{5}(t+1)^{5/2} - \frac{2}{3}(t+1)^{3/2} + C.$$

70. Let $w = 2 + 2\sqrt{x}$, so $x = ((w-2)/2)^2 = (w/2 - 1)^2$, and $dx = 2(w/2 - 1)(1/2)\,dw = (w/2 - 1)\,dw$. Thus

$$\int \frac{dx}{2 + 2\sqrt{x}} = \int \frac{(w/2 - 1)\,dw}{w} = \int \left(\frac{1}{2} - \frac{1}{w}\right)\,dw$$

$$= \frac{w}{2} - \ln|w| + C = \frac{1}{2}(2 + 2\sqrt{x}) - \ln|2 + 2\sqrt{x}| + C$$

$$= 1 + \sqrt{x} - \ln|2 + 2\sqrt{x}| + C = \sqrt{x} - \ln|2 + 2\sqrt{x}| + C.$$

In the last line, the 1 has been combined with the C.

71. Let $w = \sqrt{x-2}$, so $x = w^2 + 2$ and $dx = 2w\,dw$. Thus

$$\int x^2\sqrt{x-2}\,dx = \int (w^2 + 2)^2 w 2w\,dw = 2\int w^6 + 4w^4 + 4w^2\,dw$$

$$= \frac{2}{7}w^7 + \frac{8}{5}w^5 + \frac{8}{3}w^3 + C$$

$$= \frac{2}{7}(x-2)^{7/2} + \frac{8}{5}(x-2)^{5/2} + \frac{8}{3}(x-2)^{3/2} + C.$$

72. Let $w = \sqrt{1-z}$, so $z = 1 - w^2$ and $dz = -2w\,dw$. Thus

$$\int (z+2)\sqrt{1-z}\,dz = \int (1 - w^2 + 2)w(-2w)\,dw = 2\int w^4 - 3w^2\,dw$$

$$= \frac{2}{5}w^5 - 2w^3 + C = \frac{2}{5}(1-z)^{5/2} - 2(1-z)^{3/2} + C.$$

73. Let $w = \sqrt{t+1}$, so $t = w^2 - 1$ and $dt = 2w\,dw$. Thus

$$\int \frac{t}{\sqrt{t+1}}\,dt = \int \frac{w^2 - 1}{w} 2w\,dw = 2\int w^2 - 1\,dw$$

$$= \frac{2}{3}w^3 - 2w + C = \frac{2}{3}(t+1)^{3/2} - 2(t+1)^{1/2} + C.$$

74. Let $w = \sqrt{2x+1}$, so $x = \frac{1}{2}(w^2 - 1)$ and $dx = w\,dw$. Thus

$$\int \frac{3x-2}{\sqrt{2x+1}}\,dx = \int \frac{3 \cdot \frac{1}{2}(w^2-1) - 2}{w} w\,dw = \int \frac{3}{2}w^2 - \frac{7}{2}\,dw$$

$$= \frac{1}{2}w^3 - \frac{7}{2}w + C = \frac{1}{2}(2x+1)^{3/2} - \frac{7}{2}(2x+1)^{1/2} + C.$$

Problems

75. (a) This integral can be evaluated using integration by substitution. We use $w = x^2$, $dw = 2x\,dx$.

$$\int x\sin x^2\,dx = \frac{1}{2}\int \sin(w)\,dw = -\frac{1}{2}\cos(w) + C = -\frac{1}{2}\cos(x^2) + C.$$

(b) This integral cannot be evaluated using a simple integration by substitution.

(c) This integral cannot be evaluated using a simple integration by substitution.

(d) This integral can be evaluated using integration by substitution. We use $w = 1 + x^2$, $dw = 2x\,dx$.

$$\int \frac{x}{(1+x^2)^2}\,dx = \frac{1}{2}\int \frac{1}{w^2}\,dw = \frac{1}{2}\left(\frac{-1}{w}\right) + C = \frac{-1}{2(1+x^2)} + C.$$

(e) This integral cannot be evaluated using a simple integration by substitution.

(f) This integral can be evaluated using integration by substitution. We use $w = 2 + \cos x$, $dw = -\sin x \, dx$.

$$\int \frac{\sin x}{2 + \cos x} \, dx = -\int \frac{1}{w} \, dw = -\ln|w| + C = -\ln|2 + \cos x| + C.$$

76. (a) If $w = t/2$, then $dw = (1/2)dt$. When $t = 0$, $w = 0$; when $t = 4$, $w = 2$. Thus,

$$\int_0^4 g(t/2) \, dt = \int_0^2 g(w) \, 2dw = 2\int_0^2 g(w) \, dw = 2 \cdot 5 = 10.$$

(b) If $w = 2 - t$, then $dw = -dt$. When $t = 0$, $w = 2$; when $t = 2$, $w = 0$. Thus,

$$\int_0^2 g(2 - t) \, dt = \int_2^0 g(w) \, (-dw) = +\int_0^2 g(w) \, dw = 5.$$

77. (a) If $w = 2t$, then $dw = 2dt$. When $t = 0$, $w = 0$; when $t = 0.5$, $w = 1$. Thus,

$$\int_0^{0.5} f(2t) \, dt = \int_0^1 f(w) \frac{1}{2} dw = \frac{1}{2} \int_0^1 f(w) \, dw = \frac{3}{2}.$$

(b) If $w = 1 - t$, then $dw = -dt$. When $t = 0$, $w = 1$; when $t = 1$, $w = 0$. Thus,

$$\int_0^1 f(1 - t) \, dt = \int_1^0 f(w) \, (-dw) = +\int_0^1 f(w) \, dw = 3.$$

(c) If $w = 3 - 2t$, then $dw = -2dt$. When $t = 1$, $w = 1$; when $t = 1.5$, $w = 0$. Thus,

$$\int_1^{1.5} f(3 - 2t) \, dt = \int_1^0 f(w) \left(-\frac{1}{2} dw\right) = +\frac{1}{2} \int_0^1 f(w) \, dw = \frac{3}{2}.$$

78. (a) The Fundamental Theorem gives

$$\int_{-\pi}^{\pi} \cos^2 \theta \sin \theta \, d\theta = -\frac{\cos^3 \theta}{3} \Big|_{-\pi}^{\pi} = \frac{-(-1)^3}{3} - \frac{-(-1)^3}{3} = 0.$$

This agrees with the fact that the function $f(\theta) = \cos^2 \theta \sin \theta$ is odd and the interval of integration is centered at $x = 0$, thus we must get 0 for the definite integral.

(b) The area is given by

$$\text{Area} = \int_0^{\pi} \cos^2 \theta \sin \theta \, d\theta = -\frac{\cos^3 \theta}{3} \Big|_0^{\pi} = \frac{-(-1)^3}{3} - \frac{-(1)^3}{3} = \frac{2}{3}.$$

79. Since $f(x) = 1/(x + 1)$ is positive on the interval $x = 0$ to $x = 2$, we have

$$\text{Area} = \int_0^2 \frac{1}{x + 1} \, dx = \ln(x + 1) \Big|_0^2 = \ln 3 - \ln 1 = \ln 3.$$

The area is $\ln 3 \approx 1.0986$.

80. To find the area under the graph of $f(x) = xe^{x^2}$, we need to evaluate the definite integral

$$\int_0^2 xe^{x^2} \, dx.$$

This is done in Example 10, Section 7.1, using the substitution $w = x^2$, the result being

$$\int_0^2 xe^{x^2} \, dx = \frac{1}{2}(e^4 - 1).$$

81. See Figure 7.1. The period of $V = V_0 \sin(\omega t)$ is $2\pi/\omega$, so the area under the first arch is given by

$$\text{Area} = \int_0^{\pi/\omega} V_0 \sin(\omega t)\, dt$$

$$= -\frac{V_0}{\omega} \cos(\omega t) \Big|_0^{\pi/\omega}$$

$$= -\frac{V_0}{\omega} \cos(\pi) + \frac{V_0}{\omega} \cos(0)$$

$$= -\frac{V_0}{\omega}(-1) + \frac{V_0}{\omega}(1) = \frac{2V_0}{\omega}.$$

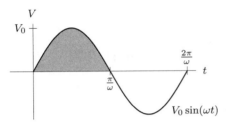

Figure 7.1

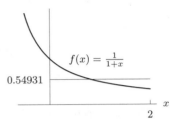

Figure 7.2

82. If $f(x) = \dfrac{1}{x+1}$, the average value of f on the interval $0 \le x \le 2$ is defined to be

$$\frac{1}{2-0} \int_0^2 f(x)\, dx = \frac{1}{2} \int_0^2 \frac{dx}{x+1}.$$

We'll integrate by substitution. We let $w = x + 1$ and $dw = dx$, and we have

$$\int_{x=0}^{x=2} \frac{dx}{x+1} = \int_{w=1}^{w=3} \frac{dw}{w} = \ln w \Big|_1^3 = \ln 3 - \ln 1 = \ln 3.$$

Thus, the average value of $f(x)$ on $0 \le x \le 2$ is $\frac{1}{2} \ln 3 \approx 0.5493$. See Figure 7.2.

83. (a) $\displaystyle\int 4x(x^2 + 1)\, dx = \int (4x^3 + 4x)\, dx = x^4 + 2x^2 + C.$

(b) If $w = x^2 + 1$, then $dw = 2x\, dx$.

$$\int 4x(x^2 + 1)\, dx = \int 2w\, dw = w^2 + C = (x^2 + 1)^2 + C.$$

(c) The expressions from parts (a) and (b) look different, but they are both correct. Note that $(x^2 + 1)^2 + C = x^4 + 2x^2 + 1 + C$. In other words, the expressions from parts (a) and (b) differ only by a constant, so they are both correct antiderivatives.

84. (a) We first try the substitution $w = \sin\theta$, $dw = \cos\theta\, d\theta$. Then

$$\int \sin\theta \cos\theta\, d\theta = \int w\, dw = \frac{w^2}{2} + C = \frac{\sin^2\theta}{2} + C.$$

(b) If we instead try the substitution $w = \cos\theta$, $dw = -\sin\theta\, d\theta$, we get

$$\int \sin\theta \cos\theta\, d\theta = -\int w\, dw = -\frac{w^2}{2} + C = -\frac{\cos^2\theta}{2} + C.$$

(c) Once we note that $\sin 2\theta = 2\sin\theta\cos\theta$, we can also say

$$\int \sin\theta \cos\theta\, d\theta = \frac{1}{2}\int \sin 2\theta\, d\theta.$$

Substituting $w = 2\theta$, $dw = 2\, d\theta$, the above equals

$$\frac{1}{4}\int \sin w\, dw = -\frac{\cos w}{4} + C = -\frac{\cos 2\theta}{4} + C.$$

(d) All these answers are correct. Although they have different forms, they differ from each other only in terms of a constant, and thus they are all acceptable antiderivatives. For example, $1 - \cos^2\theta = \sin^2\theta$, so $\frac{\sin^2\theta}{2} = -\frac{\cos^2\theta}{2} + \frac{1}{2}$. Thus the first two expressions differ only by a constant C.

Similarly, $\cos 2\theta = \cos^2\theta - \sin^2\theta = 2\cos^2\theta - 1$, so $-\frac{\cos 2\theta}{4} = -\frac{\cos^2\theta}{2} + \frac{1}{4}$, and thus the second and third expressions differ only by a constant. Of course, if the first two expressions and the last two expressions differ only in the constant C, then the first and last only differ in the constant as well.

85. We substitute $w = 1 - x$ into $I_{m,n}$. Then $dw = -dx$, and $x = 1 - w$.
When $x = 0$, $w = 1$, and when $x = 1$, $w = 0$, so

$$I_{m,n} = \int_0^1 x^m (1-x)^n dx = \int_1^0 (1-w)^m w^n (-dw)$$

$$= -\int_1^0 w^n (1-w)^m dw = \int_0^1 w^n (1-w)^m dw = I_{n,m}.$$

86. (a) In 1990, we have $P = 5.3e^{0.014(0)} = 5.3$ billion people.
In 2000, we have $P = 5.3e^{0.014(10)} = 6.1$ billion people.

(b) We have

$$\text{Average population} = \frac{1}{10-0} \int_0^{10} 5.3e^{0.014t} dt = \frac{1}{10} \cdot \frac{5.3}{0.014} e^{0.014t} \Big|_0^{10}$$

$$= \frac{1}{10} \left(\frac{5.3}{0.014} (e^{0.14} - e^0) \right) = 5.7.$$

The average population of the world during the 1990s was 5.7 billion people.

87. (a) At time $t = 0$, the rate of oil leakage $= r(0) = 50$ thousand liters/minute.
At $t = 60$, rate $= r(60) = 15.06$ thousand liters/minute.

(b) To find the amount of oil leaked during the first hour, we integrate the rate from $t = 0$ to $t = 60$:

$$\text{Oil leaked} = \int_0^{60} 50e^{-0.02t} dt = \left(-\frac{50}{0.02} e^{-0.02t} \right) \Big|_0^{60}$$

$$= -2500e^{-1.2} + 2500e^0 = 1747 \text{ thousand liters.}$$

88. (a) $E(t) = 1.4e^{0.07t}$

(b)

$$\text{Average Yearly Consumption} = \frac{\text{Total Consumption for the Century}}{100 \text{ years}}$$

$$= \frac{1}{100} \int_0^{100} 1.4e^{0.07t} dt$$

$$= (0.014) \left[\frac{1}{0.07} e^{0.07t} \Big|_0^{100} \right]$$

$$= (0.014) \left[\frac{1}{0.07} (e^7 - e^0) \right]$$

$$= 0.2(e^7 - 1) \approx 219 \text{ million megawatt-hours.}$$

(c) We are looking for t such that $E(t) \approx 219$:

$$1.4e^{0.07t} \approx 219$$

$$e^{0.07t} = 156.4.$$

Taking natural logs,

$$0.07t = \ln 156.4$$

$$t \approx \frac{5.05}{0.07} \approx 72.18.$$

Thus, consumption was closest to the average during 1972.

(d) Between the years 1900 and 2000 the graph of $E(t)$ looks like

From the graph, we can see the t value such that $E(t) = 219$. It lies to the right of $t = 50$, and is thus in the second half of the century.

89. Since $v = \dfrac{dh}{dt}$, it follows that $h(t) = \displaystyle\int v(t)\, dt$ and $h(0) = h_0$. Since

$$v(t) = \frac{mg}{k}\left(1 - e^{-\frac{k}{m}t}\right) = \frac{mg}{k} - \frac{mg}{k}e^{-\frac{k}{m}t},$$

we have

$$h(t) = \int v(t)\, dt = \frac{mg}{k}\int dt - \frac{mg}{k}\int e^{-\frac{k}{m}t}\, dt.$$

The first integral is simply $\dfrac{mg}{k}t + C$. To evaluate the second integral, make the substitution $w = -\dfrac{k}{m}t$. Then

$$dw = -\frac{k}{m}\, dt,$$

so

$$\int e^{-\frac{k}{m}t}\, dt = \int e^{w}\left(-\frac{m}{k}\right)dw = -\frac{m}{k}e^{w} + C = -\frac{m}{k}e^{-\frac{k}{m}t} + C.$$

Thus

$$h(t) = \int v\, dt = \frac{mg}{k}t - \frac{mg}{k}\left(-\frac{m}{k}e^{-\frac{k}{m}t}\right) + C$$

$$= \frac{mg}{k}t + \frac{m^2 g}{k^2}e^{-\frac{k}{m}t} + C.$$

Since $h(0) = h_0$,

$$h_0 = \frac{mg}{k}\cdot 0 + \frac{m^2 g}{k^2}e^{0} + C;$$

$$C = h_0 - \frac{m^2 g}{k^2}.$$

Thus

$$h(t) = \frac{mg}{k}t + \frac{m^2 g}{k^2}e^{-\frac{k}{m}t} - \frac{m^2 g}{k^2} + h_0$$

$$h(t) = \frac{mg}{k}t - \frac{m^2 g}{k^2}\left(1 - e^{-\frac{k}{m}t}\right) + h_0.$$

90. Since v is given as the velocity of a falling body, the height h is decreasing, so $v = -\frac{dh}{dt}$, and it follows that $h(t) = -\displaystyle\int v(t)\, dt$ and $h(0) = h_0$. Let $w = e^{t\sqrt{gk}} + e^{-t\sqrt{gk}}$. Then

$$dw = \sqrt{gk}\left(e^{t\sqrt{gk}} - e^{-t\sqrt{gk}}\right)dt,$$

so $\dfrac{dw}{\sqrt{gk}} = (e^{t\sqrt{gk}} - e^{-t\sqrt{gk}})\, dt$. Therefore,

$$-\int v(t)dt = -\int \sqrt{\frac{g}{k}} \left(\frac{e^{t\sqrt{gk}} - e^{-t\sqrt{gk}}}{e^{t\sqrt{gk}} + e^{-t\sqrt{gk}}} \right) dt$$

$$= -\sqrt{\frac{g}{k}} \int \frac{1}{e^{t\sqrt{gk}} + e^{-t\sqrt{gk}}} \left(e^{t\sqrt{gk}} - e^{-t\sqrt{gk}} \right) dt$$

$$= -\sqrt{\frac{g}{k}} \int \left(\frac{1}{w} \right) \frac{dw}{\sqrt{gk}}$$

$$= -\sqrt{\frac{g}{gk^2}} \ln |w| + C$$

$$= -\frac{1}{k} \ln \left(e^{t\sqrt{gk}} + e^{-t\sqrt{gk}} \right) + C.$$

Since

$$h(0) = -\frac{1}{k} \ln(e^0 + e^0) + C = -\frac{\ln 2}{k} + C = h_0,$$

we have $C = h_0 + \dfrac{\ln 2}{k}$. Thus,

$$h(t) = -\frac{1}{k} \ln \left(e^{t\sqrt{gk}} + e^{-t\sqrt{gk}} \right) + \frac{\ln 2}{k} + h_0 = -\frac{1}{k} \ln \left(\frac{e^{t\sqrt{gk}} + e^{-t\sqrt{gk}}}{2} \right) + h_0.$$

91. (a) In the first case, we are given that $R_0 = 1000$ widgets/year. So we have $R = 1000e^{0.15t}$. To determine the total number sold, we need to integrate this rate over the time period from 0 to 10. So the total number of widgets sold is

$$\int_0^{10} 1000e^{0.15t}\, dt = \frac{1000}{0.15} e^{0.15t} \Big|_0^{10} = 6667(e^{1.5} - 1) \approx 23{,}211 \text{ widgets.}$$

In the second case, the total number of widgets sold is

$$\int_0^{10} 150{,}000{,}000e^{0.15t}\, dt = 1{,}000{,}000{,}000e^{0.15t} \Big|_0^{10} \approx 3.5 \text{ billion widgets.}$$

(b) We want to determine T such that

$$\int_0^T 1000e^{0.15t}\, dt \approx \frac{23{,}211}{2}.$$

Evaluating both sides, we get

$$6667(e^{0.15T} - 1) = 11{,}606$$
$$6667e^{0.15T} = 18273$$
$$e^{0.15T} = 2.740$$
$$0.15T = 1.01, \quad \text{so} \quad T = 6.7 \text{ years.}$$

Similarly, in the second case,

$$\int_0^T 150{,}000{,}000e^{0.15t}\, dt \approx \frac{3{,}500{,}000{,}000}{2}$$

Evaluating both sides, we get

$$(1 \text{ billion})(e^{0.15T} - 1) = 1.75 \text{ billion}$$
$$e^{0.15T} = 2.75$$
$$T \approx 6.7 \text{ years}$$

So the half way mark is reached at the same time regardless of the initial rate.

(c) Since half the widgets are sold in the last $3\frac{1}{2}$ years of the decade, if each widget is expected to last $3\frac{1}{2}$ years, their claim could easily be true.

Solutions for Section 7.2

Exercises

1. Let $u = \arctan x$, $v' = 1$. Then $v = x$ and $u' = \dfrac{1}{1+x^2}$. Integrating by parts, we get:

$$\int 1 \cdot \arctan x\, dx = x \cdot \arctan x - \int x \cdot \frac{1}{1+x^2}\, dx.$$

To compute the second integral use the substitution, $z = 1 + x^2$.

$$\int \frac{x}{1+x^2}\, dx = \frac{1}{2}\int \frac{dz}{z} = \frac{1}{2}\ln|z| + C = \frac{1}{2}\ln(1+x^2) + C.$$

Thus,

$$\int \arctan x\, dx = x \cdot \arctan x - \frac{1}{2}\ln(1+x^2) + C.$$

2. Let $u = t$, $v' = \sin t$. Thus, $v = -\cos t$ and $u' = 1$. With this choice of u and v, integration by parts gives:

$$\int t \sin t\, dt = -t\cos t - \int (-\cos t)\, dt$$
$$= -t\cos t + \sin t + C.$$

3. Let $u = t^2$, $v' = \sin t$ implying $v = -\cos t$ and $u' = 2t$. Integrating by parts, we get:

$$\int t^2 \sin t\, dt = -t^2 \cos t - \int 2t(-\cos t)\, dt.$$

Again, applying integration by parts with $u = t$, $v' = \cos t$, we have:

$$\int t \cos t\, dt = t \sin t + \cos t + C.$$

Thus

$$\int t^2 \sin t\, dt = -t^2 \cos t + 2t \sin t + 2\cos t + C.$$

4. Let $u = t$ and $v' = e^{5t}$, so $u' = 1$ and $v = \frac{1}{5}e^{5t}$.
Then $\int te^{5t}\, dt = \frac{1}{5}te^{5t} - \int \frac{1}{5}e^{5t}\, dt = \frac{1}{5}te^{5t} - \frac{1}{25}e^{5t} + C.$

5. Let $u = t^2$ and $v' = e^{5t}$, so $u' = 2t$ and $v = \frac{1}{5}e^{5t}$.
Then $\int t^2 e^{5t}\, dt = \frac{1}{5}t^2 e^{5t} - \frac{2}{5}\int te^{5t}\, dt.$
Using Problem 4, we have $\int t^2 e^{5t}\, dt = \frac{1}{5}t^2 e^{5t} - \frac{2}{5}(\frac{1}{5}te^{5t} - \frac{1}{25}e^{5t}) + C$
$= \frac{1}{5}t^2 e^{5t} - \frac{2}{25}te^{5t} + \frac{2}{125}e^{5t} + C.$

6. Let $u = p$ and $v' = e^{(-0.1)p}$, $u' = 1$. Thus, $v = \int e^{(-0.1)p}\, dp = -10e^{(-0.1)p}$. With this choice of u and v, integration by parts gives:

$$\int pe^{(-0.1)p}\, dp = p(-10e^{(-0.1)p}) - \int (-10e^{(-0.1)p})\, dp$$
$$= -10pe^{(-0.1)p} + 10 \int e^{(-0.1)p}\, dp$$
$$= -10pe^{(-0.1)p} - 100e^{(-0.1)p} + C.$$

7. Let $u = z + 1$, $v' = e^{2z}$. Thus, $v = \frac{1}{2}e^{2z}$ and $u' = 1$. Integrating by parts, we get:

$$\int (z+1)e^{2z}\, dz = (z+1)\cdot \frac{1}{2}e^{2z} - \int \frac{1}{2}e^{2z}\, dz$$
$$= \frac{1}{2}(z+1)e^{2z} - \frac{1}{4}e^{2z} + C$$
$$= \frac{1}{4}(2z+1)e^{2z} + C.$$

8. Let $u = \ln y$, $v' = y$. Then, $v = \frac{1}{2}y^2$ and $u' = \dfrac{1}{y}$. Integrating by parts, we get:

$$\int y \ln y \, dy = \frac{1}{2}y^2 \ln y - \int \frac{1}{2}y^2 \cdot \frac{1}{y} \, dy$$

$$= \frac{1}{2}y^2 \ln y - \frac{1}{2}\int y \, dy$$

$$= \frac{1}{2}y^2 \ln y - \frac{1}{4}y^2 + C.$$

9. Let $u = \ln x$ and $v' = x^3$, so $u' = \frac{1}{x}$ and $v = \frac{x^4}{4}$.
Then

$$\int x^3 \ln x \, dx = \frac{x^4}{4}\ln x - \int \frac{x^3}{4}\, dx = \frac{x^4}{4}\ln x - \frac{x^4}{16} + C.$$

10. Let $u = \ln 5q$, $v' = q^5$. Then $v = \frac{1}{6}q^6$ and $u' = \dfrac{1}{q}$. Integrating by parts, we get:

$$\int q^5 \ln 5q \, dq = \frac{1}{6}q^6 \ln 5q - \int (5 \cdot \frac{1}{5q}) \cdot \frac{1}{6}q^6 \, dq$$

$$= \frac{1}{6}q^6 \ln 5q - \frac{1}{36}q^6 + C.$$

11. Let $u = \theta^2$ and $v' = \cos 3\theta$, so $u' = 2\theta$ and $v = \frac{1}{3}\sin 3\theta$.
  Then $\int \theta^2 \cos 3\theta \, d\theta = \frac{1}{3}\theta^2 \sin 3\theta - \frac{2}{3}\int \theta \sin 3\theta \, d\theta$. The integral on the right hand side is simpler than our original integral, but to evaluate it we need to again use integration by parts.
  To find $\int \theta \sin 3\theta \, d\theta$, let $u = \theta$ and $v' = \sin 3\theta$, so $u' = 1$ and $v = -\frac{1}{3}\cos 3\theta$.
  This gives

$$\int \theta \sin 3\theta \, d\theta = -\frac{1}{3}\theta \cos 3\theta + \frac{1}{3}\int \cos 3\theta \, d\theta = -\frac{1}{3}\theta \cos 3\theta + \frac{1}{9}\sin 3\theta + C.$$

Thus,

$$\int \theta^2 \cos 3\theta d\theta = \frac{1}{3}\theta^2 \sin 3\theta + \frac{2}{9}\theta \cos 3\theta - \frac{2}{27}\sin 3\theta + C.$$

12. Let $u = \sin \theta$ and $v' = \sin \theta$, so $u' = \cos \theta$ and $v = -\cos \theta$. Then

$$\int \sin^2 \theta \, d\theta = -\sin \theta \cos \theta + \int \cos^2 \theta \, d\theta$$

$$= -\sin \theta \cos \theta + \int (1 - \sin^2 \theta) \, d\theta$$

$$= -\sin \theta \cos \theta + \int 1 \, d\theta - \int \sin^2 \theta \, d\theta.$$

By adding $\int \sin^2 \theta \, d\theta$ to both sides of the above equation, we find that $2\int \sin^2 \theta \, d\theta = -\sin \theta \cos \theta + \theta + C$, so $\int \sin^2 \theta \, d\theta = -\frac{1}{2}\sin \theta \cos \theta + \frac{\theta}{2} + C'$.

13. Let $u = \cos(3\alpha + 1)$ and $v' = \cos(3\alpha + 1)$, so $u' = -3\sin(3\alpha + 1)$, and $v = \frac{1}{3}\sin(3\alpha + 1)$. Then

$$\int \cos^2(3\alpha + 1) \, d\alpha = \int (\cos(3\alpha + 1))\cos(3\alpha + 1) \, d\alpha$$

$$= \frac{1}{3}\cos(3\alpha + 1)\sin(3\alpha + 1) + \int \sin^2(3\alpha + 1) \, d\alpha$$

$$= \frac{1}{3}\cos(3\alpha + 1)\sin(3\alpha + 1) + \int \left(1 - \cos^2(3\alpha + 1)\right) \, d\alpha$$

$$= \frac{1}{3}\cos(3\alpha + 1)\sin(3\alpha + 1) + \alpha - \int \cos^2(3\alpha + 1) \, d\alpha.$$

By adding $\int \cos^2(3\alpha + 1)\, d\alpha$ to both sides of the above equation, we find that

$$2\int \cos^2(3\alpha + 1)\, d\alpha = \frac{1}{3}\cos(3\alpha + 1)\sin(3\alpha + 1) + \alpha + C,$$

which gives

$$\int \cos^2(3\alpha + 1)\, d\alpha = \frac{1}{6}\cos(3\alpha + 1)\sin(3\alpha + 1) + \frac{\alpha}{2} + C.$$

14. Let $u = (\ln t)^2$ and $v' = 1$, so $u' = \dfrac{2\ln t}{t}$ and $v = t$. Then

$$\int (\ln t)^2\, dt = t(\ln t)^2 - 2\int \ln t\, dt = t(\ln t)^2 - 2t\ln t + 2t + C.$$

(We use the fact that $\int \ln x\, dx = x\ln x - x + C$, a result which can be derived using integration by parts.)

15. Let $u = y$ and $v' = (y + 3)^{1/2}$, so $u' = 1$ and $v = \frac{2}{3}(y + 3)^{3/2}$:

$$\int y\sqrt{y + 3}\, dy = \frac{2}{3}y(y + 3)^{3/2} - \int \frac{2}{3}(y + 3)^{3/2}\, dy = \frac{2}{3}y(y + 3)^{3/2} - \frac{4}{15}(y + 3)^{5/2} + C.$$

16. Let $u = t + 2$ and $v' = \sqrt{2 + 3t}$, so $u' = 1$ and $v = \frac{2}{9}(2 + 3t)^{3/2}$. Then

$$\int (t + 2)\sqrt{2 + 3t}\, dt = \frac{2}{9}(t + 2)(2 + 3t)^{3/2} - \frac{2}{9}\int (2 + 3t)^{3/2}\, dt$$

$$= \frac{2}{9}(t + 2)(2 + 3t)^{3/2} - \frac{4}{135}(2 + 3t)^{5/2} + C.$$

17. Let $u = \theta + 1$ and $v' = \sin(\theta + 1)$, so $u' = 1$ and $v = -\cos(\theta + 1)$.

$$\int (\theta + 1)\sin(\theta + 1)\, d\theta = -(\theta + 1)\cos(\theta + 1) + \int \cos(\theta + 1)\, d\theta$$

$$= -(\theta + 1)\cos(\theta + 1) + \sin(\theta + 1) + C.$$

18. Let $u = z$, $v' = e^{-z}$. Thus $v = -e^{-z}$ and $u' = 1$. Integration by parts gives:

$$\int ze^{-z}\, dz = -ze^{-z} - \int (-e^{-z})\, dz$$

$$= -ze^{-z} - e^{-z} + C$$

$$= -(z + 1)e^{-z} + C.$$

19. Let $u = \ln x$, $v' = x^{-2}$. Then $v = -x^{-1}$ and $u' = x^{-1}$. Integrating by parts, we get:

$$\int x^{-2}\ln x\, dx = -x^{-1}\ln x - \int (-x^{-1})\cdot x^{-1}\, dx$$

$$= -x^{-1}\ln x - x^{-1} + C.$$

20. Let $u = y$ and $v' = \dfrac{1}{\sqrt{5 - y}}$, so $u' = 1$ and $v = -2(5 - y)^{1/2}$.

$$\int \frac{y}{\sqrt{5 - y}}\, dy = -2y(5 - y)^{1/2} + 2\int (5 - y)^{1/2}\, dy = -2y(5 - y)^{1/2} - \frac{4}{3}(5 - y)^{3/2} + C.$$

21. $\int \frac{t+7}{\sqrt{5-t}}\,dt = \int \frac{t}{\sqrt{5-t}}\,dt + 7\int (5-t)^{-1/2}\,dt.$

To calculate the first integral, we use integration by parts. Let $u = t$ and $v' = \frac{1}{\sqrt{5-t}}$, so $u' = 1$ and $v = -2(5-t)^{1/2}$. Then

$$\int \frac{t}{\sqrt{5-t}}\,dt = -2t(5-t)^{1/2} + 2\int (5-t)^{1/2}\,dt = -2t(5-t)^{1/2} - \frac{4}{3}(5-t)^{3/2} + C.$$

We can calculate the second integral directly: $7\int (5-t)^{-1/2} = -14(5-t)^{1/2} + C_1$. Thus

$$\int \frac{t+7}{\sqrt{5-t}}\,dt = -2t(5-t)^{1/2} - \frac{4}{3}(5-t)^{3/2} - 14(5-t)^{1/2} + C_2.$$

22. Let $u = (\ln x)^4$ and $v' = x$, so $u' = \frac{4(\ln x)^3}{x}$ and $v = \frac{x^2}{2}$. Then

$$\int x(\ln x)^4\,dx = \frac{x^2(\ln x)^4}{2} - 2\int x(\ln x)^3\,dx.$$

$\int x(\ln x)^3\,dx$ is somewhat less complicated than $\int x(\ln x)^4\,dx$. To calculate it, we again try integration by parts, this time letting $u = (\ln x)^3$ (instead of $(\ln x)^4$) and $v' = x$. We find

$$\int x(\ln x)^3\,dx = \frac{x^2}{2}(\ln x)^3 - \frac{3}{2}\int x(\ln x)^2\,dx.$$

Once again, express the given integral in terms of a less-complicated one. Using integration by parts two more times, we find that

$$\int x(\ln x)^2\,dx = \frac{x^2}{2}(\ln x)^2 - \int x(\ln x)\,dx$$

and that

$$\int x\ln x\,dx = \frac{x^2}{2}\ln x - \frac{x^2}{4} + C.$$

Putting this all together, we have

$$\int x(\ln x)^4\,dx = \frac{x^2}{2}(\ln x)^4 - x^2(\ln x)^3 + \frac{3}{2}x^2(\ln x)^2 - \frac{3}{2}x^2\ln x + \frac{3}{4}x^2 + C.$$

23. Let $u = \arcsin w$ and $v' = 1$, so $u' = \frac{1}{\sqrt{1-w^2}}$ and $v = w$. Then

$$\int \arcsin w\,dw = w\arcsin w - \int \frac{w}{\sqrt{1-w^2}}\,dw = w\arcsin w + \sqrt{1-w^2} + C.$$

24. Let $u = \arctan 7z$ and $v' = 1$, so $u' = \frac{7}{1+49z^2}$ and $v = z$. Now $\int \frac{7z\,dz}{1+49z^2}$ can be evaluated by the substitution $w = 1 + 49z^2$, $dw = 98z\,dz$, so

$$\int \frac{7z\,dz}{1+49z^2} = 7\int \frac{\frac{1}{98}\,dw}{w} = \frac{1}{14}\int \frac{dw}{w} = \frac{1}{14}\ln|w| + C = \frac{1}{14}\ln(1+49z^2) + C$$

So

$$\int \arctan 7z\,dz = z\arctan 7z - \frac{1}{14}\ln(1+49z^2) + C.$$

25. This integral can first be simplified by making the substitution $w = x^2$, $dw = 2x\,dx$. Then

$$\int x\arctan x^2\,dx = \frac{1}{2}\int \arctan w\,dw.$$

To evaluate $\int \arctan w\,dw$, we'll use integration by parts. Let $u = \arctan w$ and $v' = 1$, so $u' = \frac{1}{1+w^2}$ and $v = w$. Then

$$\int \arctan w\,dw = w\arctan w - \int \frac{w}{1+w^2}\,dw = w\arctan w - \frac{1}{2}\ln|1+w^2| + C.$$

Since $1 + w^2$ is never negative, we can drop the absolute value signs. Thus, we have

$$\int x \arctan x^2 \, dx = \frac{1}{2} \left(x^2 \arctan x^2 - \frac{1}{2} \ln(1 + (x^2)^2) + C \right)$$

$$= \frac{1}{2} x^2 \arctan x^2 - \frac{1}{4} \ln(1 + x^4) + C.$$

26. Let $u = x^2$ and $v' = xe^{x^2}$, so $u' = 2x$ and $v = \frac{1}{2} e^{x^2}$. Then

$$\int x^3 e^{x^2} \, dx = \frac{1}{2} x^2 e^{x^2} - \int xe^{x^2} \, dx = \frac{1}{2} x^2 e^{x^2} - \frac{1}{2} e^{x^2} + C.$$

Note that we can also do this problem by substitution and integration by parts. If we let $w = x^2$, so $dw = 2x \, dx$, then $\int x^3 e^{x^2} \, dx = \frac{1}{2} \int we^w \, dw$. We could then perform integration by parts on this integral to get the same result.

27. To simplify matters, let us try the substitution $w = x^3$, $dw = 3x^2 \, dx$. Then

$$\int x^5 \cos x^3 \, dx = \frac{1}{3} \int w \cos w \, dw.$$

Now we integrate by parts. Let $u = w$ and $v' = \cos w$, so $u' = 1$ and $v = \sin w$. Then

$$\frac{1}{3} \int w \cos w \, dw = \frac{1}{3} [w \sin w - \int \sin w \, dw]$$

$$= \frac{1}{3} [w \sin w + \cos w] + C$$

$$= \frac{1}{3} x^3 \sin x^3 + \frac{1}{3} \cos x^3 + C$$

28. Let $u = x, u' = 1$ and $v' = \sinh x, v = \cosh x$. Integrating by parts, we get

$$\int x \sinh x \, dx = x \cosh x - \int \cosh x \, dx$$

$$= x \cosh x - \sinh x + C.$$

29. Let $u = x - 1, u' = 1$ and $v' = \cosh x, v = \sinh x$. Integrating by parts, we get

$$\int (x - 1) \cosh x \, dx = (x - 1) \sinh x - \int \sinh x \, dx$$

$$= (x - 1) \sinh x - \cosh x + C.$$

30. $\displaystyle\int_1^5 \ln t \, dt = (t \ln t - t) \Big|_1^5 = 5 \ln 5 - 4 \approx 4.047$

31. $\displaystyle\int_3^5 x \cos x \, dx = (\cos x + x \sin x) \Big|_3^5 = \cos 5 + 5 \sin 5 - \cos 3 - 3 \sin 3 \approx -3.944.$

32. We use integration by parts. Let $u = z$ and $v' = e^{-z}$, so $u' = 1$ and $v = -e^{-z}$.

$$\text{Then } \int_0^{10} ze^{-z} \, dz = -ze^{-z} \Big|_0^{10} + \int_0^{10} e^{-z} \, dz$$

$$= -10e^{-10} + (-e^{-z}) \Big|_0^{10}$$

$$= -11e^{-10} + 1$$

$$\approx 0.9995.$$

33. $\displaystyle\int_1^3 t \ln t \, dt = \left(\frac{1}{2} t^2 \ln t - \frac{1}{2} t \right) \Big|_1^3 = \frac{9}{2} \ln 3 - 2 \approx 2.944.$

34. We use integration by parts. Let $u = \arctan y$ and $v' = 1$, so $u' = \frac{1}{1+y^2}$ and $v = y$. Thus

$$
\int_0^1 \arctan y \, dy = (\arctan y)y \Big|_0^1 - \int_0^1 \frac{y}{1+y^2} \, dy
$$
$$
= \frac{\pi}{4} - \frac{1}{2}\ln|1+y^2| \Big|_0^1
$$
$$
= \frac{\pi}{4} - \frac{1}{2}\ln 2 \approx 0.439.
$$

35. $\int_0^5 \ln(1+t) \, dt = ((1+t)\ln(1+t) - (1+t)) \Big|_0^5 = 6\ln 6 - 5 \approx 5.751.$

36. We use integration by parts. Let $u = \arcsin z$ and $v' = 1$, so $u' = \dfrac{1}{\sqrt{1-z^2}}$ and $v = z$. Then

$$
\int_0^1 \arcsin z \, dz = z \arcsin z \Big|_0^1 - \int_0^1 \frac{z}{\sqrt{1-z^2}} \, dz = \frac{\pi}{2} - \int_0^1 \frac{z}{\sqrt{1-z^2}} \, dz.
$$

To find $\displaystyle\int_0^1 \frac{z}{\sqrt{1-z^2}} \, dz$, we substitute $w = 1 - z^2$, so $dw = -2z \, dz$.
Then

$$
\int_{z=0}^{z=1} \frac{z}{\sqrt{1-z^2}} \, dz = -\frac{1}{2}\int_{w=1}^{w=0} w^{-\frac{1}{2}} \, dw = \frac{1}{2}\int_{w=0}^{w=1} w^{-\frac{1}{2}} \, dw = w^{\frac{1}{2}}\Big|_0^1 = 1.
$$

Thus our final answer is $\frac{\pi}{2} - 1 \approx 0.571.$

37. To simplify the integral, we first make the substitution $z = u^2$, so $dz = 2u \, du$. Then

$$
\int_{u=0}^{u=1} u \arcsin u^2 \, du = \frac{1}{2}\int_{z=0}^{z=1} \arcsin z \, dz.
$$

From Problem 36, we know that $\int_0^1 \arcsin z \, dz = \frac{\pi}{2} - 1$. Thus,

$$
\int_0^1 u \arcsin u^2 \, du = \frac{1}{2}\left(\frac{\pi}{2} - 1\right) \approx 0.285.
$$

Problems

38. (a) This integral can be evaluated using integration by parts with $u = x$, $v' = \sin x$.
(b) We evaluate this integral using the substitution $w = 1 + x^3$.
(c) We evaluate this integral using the substitution $w = x^2$.
(d) We evaluate this integral using the substitution $w = x^3$.
(e) We evaluate this integral using the substitution $w = 3x + 1$.
(f) This integral can be evaluated using integration by parts with $u = x^2$, $v' = \sin x$.
(g) This integral can be evaluated using integration by parts with $u = \ln x$, $v' = 1$.

39.

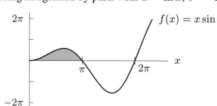

The graph of $f(x) = x \sin x$ is shown above. The first positive zero is at $x = \pi$, so, using integration by parts,

$$
\begin{aligned}
\text{Area} &= \int_0^\pi x \sin x \, dx \\
&= -x \cos x \Big|_0^\pi + \int_0^\pi \cos x \, dx \\
&= -x \cos x \Big|_0^\pi + \sin x \Big|_0^\pi \\
&= -\pi \cos \pi - (-0 \cos 0) + \sin \pi - \sin 0 = \pi.
\end{aligned}
$$

40. From integration by parts in Problem 12, we obtain

$$
\int \sin^2 \theta \, d\theta = -\frac{1}{2} \sin \theta \cos \theta + \frac{1}{2} \theta + C.
$$

Using the identity given in the book, we have

$$
\int \sin^2 \theta \, d\theta = \int \frac{1 - \cos 2\theta}{2} \, d\theta = \frac{1}{2}\theta - \frac{1}{4} \sin 2\theta + C.
$$

Although the answers differ in form, they are really the same, since (by one of the standard double angle formulas) $-\frac{1}{4} \sin 2\theta = -\frac{1}{4}(2 \sin \theta \cos \theta) = -\frac{1}{2} \sin \theta \cos \theta$.

41. Integration by parts: let $u = \cos \theta$ and $v' = \cos \theta$, so $u' = -\sin \theta$ and $v = \sin \theta$.

$$
\begin{aligned}
\int \cos^2 \theta \, d\theta &= \sin \theta \cos \theta - \int (-\sin \theta)(\sin \theta) \, d\theta \\
&= \sin \theta \cos \theta + \int \sin^2 \theta \, d\theta.
\end{aligned}
$$

Now use $\sin^2 \theta = 1 - \cos^2 \theta$.

$$
\begin{aligned}
\int \cos^2 \theta \, d\theta &= \sin \theta \cos \theta + \int (1 - \cos^2 \theta) \, d\theta \\
&= \sin \theta \cos \theta + \int d\theta - \int \cos^2 \theta \, d\theta.
\end{aligned}
$$

Adding $\int \cos^2 \theta \, d\theta$ to both sides, we have

$$
2 \int \cos^2 \theta \, d\theta = \sin \theta \cos \theta + \theta + C
$$

$$
\int \cos^2 \theta \, d\theta = \frac{1}{2} \sin \theta \cos \theta + \frac{1}{2}\theta + C'.
$$

Use the identity $\cos^2 \theta = \frac{1 + \cos 2\theta}{2}$.

$$
\int \cos^2 \theta \, d\theta = \int \frac{1 + \cos 2\theta}{2} \, d\theta = \frac{1}{2}\theta + \frac{1}{4} \sin 2\theta + C.
$$

The only difference is in the two terms $\frac{1}{2} \sin \theta \cos \theta$ and $\frac{1}{4} \sin 2\theta$, but since $\sin 2\theta = 2 \sin \theta \cos \theta$, we have $\frac{1}{4} \sin 2\theta = \frac{1}{4}(2 \sin \theta \cos \theta) = \frac{1}{2} \sin \theta \cos \theta$, so there is no real difference between the formulas.

42. First, let $u = e^x$ and $v' = \sin x$, so $u' = e^x$ and $v = -\cos x$.

Thus $\int e^x \sin x \, dx = -e^x \cos x + \int e^x \cos x \, dx$. To calculate $\int e^x \cos x \, dx$, we again need to use integration by parts. Let $u = e^x$ and $v' = \cos x$, so $u' = e^x$ and $v = \sin x$.

Thus

$$
\int e^x \cos x \, dx = e^x \sin x - \int e^x \sin x \, dx.
$$

This gives

$$\int e^x \sin x \, dx = e^x \sin x - e^x \cos x - \int e^x \sin x \, dx.$$

By adding $\int e^x \sin x \, dx$ to both sides, we obtain

$$2 \int e^x \sin x \, dx = e^x (\sin x - \cos x) + C.$$

$$\text{Thus} \int e^x \sin x \, dx = \frac{1}{2} e^x (\sin x - \cos x) + C.$$

This problem could also be done in other ways; for example, we could have started with $u = \sin x$ and $v' = e^x$ as well.

43. Let $u = e^\theta$ and $v' = \cos \theta$, so $u' = e^\theta$ and $v = \sin \theta$. Then $\int e^\theta \cos \theta \, d\theta = e^\theta \sin \theta - \int e^\theta \sin \theta \, d\theta$.

In Problem 42 we found that $\int e^x \sin x \, dx = \frac{1}{2} e^x (\sin x - \cos x) + C.$

$$\int e^\theta \cos \theta \, d\theta = e^\theta \sin \theta - \left[\frac{1}{2} e^\theta (\sin \theta - \cos \theta) \right] + C$$

$$= \frac{1}{2} e^\theta (\sin \theta + \cos \theta) + C.$$

44. We integrate by parts. Since in Problem 42 we found that $\int e^x \sin x \, dx = \frac{1}{2} e^x (\sin x - \cos x)$, we let $u = x$ and $v' = e^x \sin x$, so $u' = 1$ and $v = \frac{1}{2} e^x (\sin x - \cos x)$.

$$\text{Then} \int x e^x \sin x \, dx = \frac{1}{2} x e^x (\sin x - \cos x) - \frac{1}{2} \int e^x (\sin x - \cos x) \, dx$$

$$= \frac{1}{2} x e^x (\sin x - \cos x) - \frac{1}{2} \int e^x \sin x \, dx + \frac{1}{2} \int e^x \cos x \, dx.$$

Using Problems 42 and 43, we see that this equals

$$\frac{1}{2} x e^x (\sin x - \cos x) - \frac{1}{4} e^x (\sin x - \cos x) + \frac{1}{4} e^x (\sin x + \cos x) + C$$

$$= \frac{1}{2} x e^x (\sin x - \cos x) + \frac{1}{2} e^x \cos x + C.$$

45. Again we use Problems 42 and 43. Integrate by parts, letting $u = \theta$ and $v' = e^\theta \cos \theta$, so $u' = 1$ and $v = \frac{1}{2} e^\theta (\sin \theta + \cos \theta)$. Then

$$\int \theta e^\theta \cos \theta \, d\theta = \frac{1}{2} \theta e^\theta (\sin \theta + \cos \theta) - \frac{1}{2} \int e^\theta (\sin \theta + \cos \theta) \, d\theta$$

$$= \frac{1}{2} \theta e^\theta (\sin \theta + \cos \theta) - \frac{1}{2} \int e^\theta \sin \theta \, d\theta - \frac{1}{2} \int e^\theta \cos \theta \, d\theta$$

$$= \frac{1}{2} \theta e^\theta (\sin \theta + \cos \theta) - \frac{1}{4} e^\theta (\sin \theta - \cos \theta) - \frac{1}{4} (\sin \theta + \cos \theta) + C$$

$$= \frac{1}{2} \theta e^\theta (\sin \theta + \cos \theta) - \frac{1}{2} e^\theta \sin \theta + C.$$

46. We integrate by parts. Since we know what the answer is supposed to be, it's easier to choose u and v'. Let $u = x^n$ and $v' = e^x$, so $u' = n x^{n-1}$ and $v = e^x$. Then

$$\int x^n e^x \, dx = x^n e^x - n \int x^{n-1} e^x \, dx.$$

47. We integrate by parts. Let $u = x^n$ and $v' = \cos ax$, so $u' = nx^{n-1}$ and $v = \frac{1}{a}\sin ax$. Then

$$\int x^n \cos ax\, dx = \frac{1}{a}x^n \sin ax - \int (nx^{n-1})(\frac{1}{a}\sin ax)\, dx$$

$$= \frac{1}{a}x^n \sin ax - \frac{n}{a}\int x^{n-1}\sin ax\, dx.$$

48. We integrate by parts. Let $u = x^n$ and $v' = \sin ax$, so $u' = nx^{n-1}$ and $v = -\frac{1}{a}\cos ax$.

Then $\displaystyle\int x^n \sin ax\, dx = -\frac{1}{a}x^n \cos ax - \int (nx^{n-1})(-\frac{1}{a}\cos ax)\, dx$

$$= -\frac{1}{a}x^n \cos ax + \frac{n}{a}\int x^{n-1}\cos ax\, dx.$$

49. We integrate by parts. Since we know what the answer is supposed to be, it's easier to choose u and v'. Let $u = \cos^{n-1} x$ and $v' = \cos x$, so $u' = (n-1)\cos^{n-2} x(-\sin x)$ and $v = \sin x$.
Then

$$\int \cos^n x\, dx = \cos^{n-1} x \sin x + (n-1)\int \cos^{n-2} x \sin^2 x\, dx$$

$$= \cos^{n-1} x \sin x + (n-1)\int \cos^{n-2} x(1 - \cos^2 x)\, dx$$

$$= \cos^{n-1} x \sin x - (n-1)\int \cos^n x\, dx + (n-1)\int \cos^{n-2} x\, dx.$$

Thus, by adding $(n-1)\int \cos^n x\, dx$ to both sides of the equation, we find

$$n\int \cos^n x\, dx = \cos^{n-1} x \sin x + (n-1)\int \cos^{n-2} x\, dx,$$

so $\displaystyle\int \cos^n dx = \frac{1}{n}\cos^{n-1} x \sin x + \frac{n-1}{n}\int \cos^{n-2} x\, dx.$

50. (a) One way to avoid integrating by parts is to take the derivative of the right hand side instead. Since $\int e^{ax}\sin bx\, dx$ is the antiderivative of $e^{ax}\sin bx$,

$$e^{ax}\sin bx = \frac{d}{dx}[e^{ax}(A\sin bx + B\cos bx) + C]$$

$$= ae^{ax}(A\sin bx + B\cos bx) + e^{ax}(Ab\cos bx - Bb\sin bx)$$

$$= e^{ax}[(aA - bB)\sin bx + (aB + bA)\cos bx].$$

Thus $aA - bB = 1$ and $aB + bA = 0$. Solving for A and B in terms of a and b, we get

$$A = \frac{a}{a^2 + b^2}, \quad B = -\frac{b}{a^2 + b^2}.$$

Thus

$$\int e^{ax}\sin bx = e^{ax}\left(\frac{a}{a^2 + b^2}\sin bx - \frac{b}{a^2 + b^2}\cos bx\right) + C.$$

(b) If we go through the same process, we find

$$ae^{ax}[(aA - bB)\sin bx + (aB + bA)\cos bx] = e^{ax}\cos bx.$$

Thus $aA - bB = 0$, and $aB + bA = 1$. In this case, solving for A and B yields

$$A = \frac{b}{a^2 + b^2}, \ B = \frac{a}{a^2 + b^2}.$$

Thus $\int e^{ax} \cos bx = e^{ax} \left(\frac{b}{a^2+b^2} \sin bx + \frac{a}{a^2+b^2} \cos bx \right) + C$.

51. Since $f'(x) = 2x$, integration by parts tells us that

$$\int_0^{10} f(x)g'(x)\, dx = f(x)g(x) \Big|_0^{10} - \int_0^{10} f'(x)g(x)\, dx$$

$$= f(10)g(10) - f(0)g(0) - 2\int_0^{10} xg(x)\, dx.$$

We can use left and right Riemann Sums with $\Delta x = 2$ to approximate $\int_0^{10} xg(x)\, dx$:

Left sum $\approx 0 \cdot g(0)\Delta x + 2 \cdot g(2)\Delta x + 4 \cdot g(4)\Delta x + 6 \cdot g(6)\Delta x + 8 \cdot g(8)\Delta x$
$$= (0(2.3) + 2(3.1) + 4(4.1) + 6(5.5) + 8(5.9))\, 2 = 205.6.$$

Right sum $\approx 2 \cdot g(2)\Delta x + 4 \cdot g(4)\Delta x + 6 \cdot g(6)\Delta x + 8 \cdot g(8)\Delta x + 10 \cdot g(10)\Delta x$
$$= (2(3.1) + 4(4.1) + 6(5.5) + 8(5.9) + 10(6.1))\, 2 = 327.6.$$

A good estimate for the integral is the average of the left and right sums, so

$$\int_0^{10} xg(x)\, dx \approx \frac{205.6 + 327.6}{2} = 266.6.$$

Substituting values for f and g, we have

$$\int_0^{10} f(x)g'(x)\, dx = f(10)g(10) - f(0)g(0) - 2\int_0^{10} xg(x)\, dx$$

$$\approx 10^2(6.1) - 0^2(2.3) - 2(266.6) = 76.8 \approx 77.$$

52. Using integration by parts we have

$$\int_0^1 xf''(x)dx = xf'(x) \Big|_0^1 - \int_0^1 f'(x)dx$$

$$= 1 \cdot f'(1) - 0 \cdot f'(0) - [f(1) - f(0)]$$

$$= 2 - 0 - 5 + 6 = 3.$$

53. (a) We have

$$F(a) = \int_0^a x^2 e^{-x}\, dx$$

$$= -x^2 e^{-x} \Big|_0^a + \int_0^a 2xe^{-x}\, dx$$

$$= (-x^2 e^{-x} - 2xe^{-x}) \Big|_0^a + 2\int_0^a e^{-x}\, dx$$

$$= (-x^2 e^{-x} - 2xe^{-x} - 2e^{-x}) \Big|_0^a$$

$$= -a^2 e^{-a} - 2ae^{-a} - 2e^{-a} + 2.$$

(b) $F(a)$ is increasing because $x^2 e^{-x}$ is positive, so as a increases, the area under the curve from 0 to a also increases and thus the integral increases.

(c) We have $F'(a) = a^2 e^{-a}$, so

$$F''(a) = 2ae^{-a} - a^2 e^{-a} = a(2 - a)e^{-a}.$$

We see that $F''(a) > 0$ for $0 < a < 2$, so F is concave up on this interval.

54. We have

$$\text{Bioavailability} = \int_0^3 15te^{-0.2t}\,dt.$$

We first use integration by parts to evaluate the indefinite integral of this function. Let $u = 15t$ and $v' = e^{-0.2t}\,dt$, so $u' = 15\,dt$ and $v = -5e^{-0.2t}$. Then,

$$\int 15te^{-0.2t}\,dt = (15t)(-5e^{-0.2t}) - \int (-5e^{-0.2t})(15\,dt)$$

$$= -75te^{-0.2t} + 75\int e^{-0.2t}\,dt = -75te^{-0.2} - 375e^{-0.2t} + C.$$

Thus,

$$\int_0^3 15te^{-0.2t}\,dt = \left. (-75te^{-0.2t} - 375e^{-0.2t}) \right|_0^3 = -329.29 + 375 = 45.71.$$

The bioavailability of the drug over this time interval is 45.71 (ng/ml)-hours.

55. (a) Increasing V_0 increases the maximum value of V, since this maximum is V_0. Increasing ω or ϕ does not affect the maximum of V.

(b) Since

$$\frac{dV}{dt} = -\omega V_0 \sin(\omega t + \phi),$$

the maximum of dV/dt is ωV_0. Thus, the maximum of dV/dt is increased if V_0 or ω is increased, and is unaffected if ϕ is increased.

(c) The period of $V = V_0 \cos(\omega t + \phi)$ is $2\pi/\omega$, so

$$\text{Average value} = \frac{1}{2\pi/\omega} \int_0^{2\pi/\omega} (V_0 \cos(\omega t + \phi))^2\,dt.$$

Substituting $x = \omega t + \phi$, we have $dx = \omega\,dt$. When $t = 0$, $x = \phi$, and when $t = 2\pi/\omega$, $x = 2\pi + \phi$. Thus,

$$\text{Average value} = \frac{\omega}{2\pi} \int_\phi^{2\pi+\phi} V_0^2 (\cos x)^2 \frac{1}{\omega}\,dx$$

$$= \frac{V_0^2}{2\pi} \int_\phi^{2\pi+\phi} (\cos x)^2\,dx.$$

Using integration by parts and the fact that $\sin^2 x = 1 - \cos^2 x$, we see that

$$\text{Average value} = \frac{V_0^2}{2\pi} \left[\frac{1}{2}(\cos x \sin x + x) \right]_\phi^{2\pi+\phi}$$

$$= \frac{V_0^2}{4\pi} [\cos(2\pi + \phi)\sin(2\pi + \phi) + (2\pi + \phi) - \cos\phi\sin\phi - \phi]$$

$$= \frac{V_0^2}{4\pi} \cdot 2\pi = \frac{V_0^2}{2}.$$

Thus, increasing V_0 increases the average value; increasing ω or ϕ has no effect.

However, it is not in fact necessary to compute the integral to see that ω does not affect the average value, since all ω's dropped out of the average value expression when we made the substitution $x = \omega t + \phi$.

56. (a) We know that $\dfrac{dE}{dt} = r$, so the total energy E used in the first T hours is given by $E = \displaystyle\int_0^T te^{-at}\,dt$. We use integration by parts. Let $u = t$, $v' = e^{-at}$. Then $u' = 1$, $v = -\frac{1}{a}e^{-at}$.

$$E = \int_0^T te^{-at}\,dt$$

$$= \left. -\frac{t}{a}e^{-at} \right|_0^T - \int_0^T \left(-\frac{1}{a}e^{-at} \right) dt$$

$$= -\frac{1}{a}Te^{-aT} + \frac{1}{a}\int_0^T e^{-at}\,dt$$

$$= -\frac{1}{a}Te^{-aT} + \frac{1}{a^2}(1 - e^{-aT}).$$

(b)

$$\lim_{T \to \infty} E = -\frac{1}{a} \lim_{T \to \infty} \left(\frac{T}{e^{aT}} \right) + \frac{1}{a^2} \left(1 - \lim_{T \to \infty} \frac{1}{e^{aT}} \right).$$

Since $a > 0$, the second limit on the right hand side in the above expression is 0. In the first limit, although both the numerator and the denominator go to infinity, the denominator e^{aT} goes to infinity more quickly than T does. So in the end the denominator e^{aT} is much greater than the numerator T. Hence $\lim_{T \to \infty} \dfrac{T}{e^{aT}} = 0$. (You can check this by graphing $y = \dfrac{T}{e^{aT}}$ on a calculator or computer for some values of a.) Thus $\lim_{T \to \infty} E = \dfrac{1}{a^2}$.

57. (a) We want to compute C_1, with $C_1 > 0$, such that

$$\int_0^1 (\Psi_1(x))^2 \, dx = \int_0^1 (C_1 \sin(\pi x))^2 \, dx = C_1^2 \int_0^1 \sin^2(\pi x) \, dx = 1.$$

We use integration by parts with $u = v' = \sin(\pi x)$.
So $u' = \pi \cos(\pi x)$ and $v = -\frac{1}{\pi} \cos(\pi x)$. Thus

$$\int_0^1 \sin^2(\pi x) \, dx = -\frac{1}{\pi} \sin(\pi x) \cos(\pi x) \Big|_0^1 + \int_0^1 \cos^2(\pi x) \, dx$$

$$= -\frac{1}{\pi} \sin(\pi x) \cos(\pi x) \Big|_0^1 + \int_0^1 (1 - \sin^2(\pi x)) \, dx.$$

Moving $\int_0^1 \sin^2(\pi x) \, dx$ from the right side to the left side of the equation and solving, we get

$$2 \int_0^1 \sin^2(\pi x) \, dx = -\frac{1}{\pi} \sin(\pi x) \cos(\pi x) \Big|_0^1 + \int_0^1 1 \, dx = 0 + 1 = 1,$$

so

$$\int_0^1 \sin^2(\pi x) \, dx = \frac{1}{2}.$$

Thus, we have

$$\int_0^1 (\Psi_1(x))^2 \, dx = C_1^2 \int_0^1 \sin^2(\pi x) \, dx = \frac{C_1^2}{2}.$$

So, to normalize Ψ_1, we take $C_1 > 0$ such that

$$\frac{C_1^2}{2} = 1 \quad \text{so} \quad C_1 = \sqrt{2}.$$

(b) To normalize Ψ_n, we want to compute C_n, with $C_n > 0$, such that

$$\int_0^1 (\Psi_n(x))^2 \, dx = C_n^2 \int_0^1 \sin^2(n\pi x) \, dx = 1.$$

The solution to part (a) shows us that

$$\int \sin^2(\pi t) \, dt = -\frac{1}{2\pi} \sin(\pi t) \cos(\pi t) + \frac{1}{2} \int 1 \, dt.$$

In the integral for Ψ_n, we make the substitution $t = nx$, so $dx = \frac{1}{n} dt$. Since $t = 0$ when $x = 0$ and $t = n$ when $x = 1$, we have

$$\int_0^1 \sin^2(n\pi x) \, dx = \frac{1}{n} \int_0^n \sin^2(\pi t) \, dt$$

$$= \frac{1}{n} \left(-\frac{1}{2\pi} \sin(\pi t) \cos(\pi t) \Big|_0^n + \frac{1}{2} \int_0^n 1 \, dt \right)$$

$$= \frac{1}{n} \left(0 + \frac{n}{2} \right) = \frac{1}{2}.$$

Thus, we have

$$\int_0^1 (\Psi_n(x))^2 \, dx = C_n^2 \int_0^1 \sin^2(n\pi x) \, dx = \frac{C_n^2}{2}.$$

So to normalize Ψ_n, we take C_n such that

$$\frac{C_n^2}{2} = 1 \quad \text{so} \quad C_n = \sqrt{2}.$$

Solutions for Section 7.3

Exercises

1. $\dfrac{1}{10} e^{(-3\theta)} (-3\cos\theta + \sin\theta) + C.$
(Let $a = -3, b = 1$ in II-9.)

2. $\dfrac{1}{6} x^6 \ln x - \dfrac{1}{36} x^6 + C.$ (Let $n = 5$ in III-13.)

3. The integrand, a polynomial, x^3, multiplied by $\sin 5x$, is in the form of III-15. There are only three successive derivatives of x^3 before 0 is reached (namely, $3x^2$, $6x$, and 6), so there will be four terms. The signs in the terms will be $-++-$, as given in III-15, so we get

$$\int x^3 \sin 5x \, dx = -\frac{1}{5} x^3 \cos 5x + \frac{1}{25} \cdot 3x^2 \sin 5x + \frac{1}{125} \cdot 6x \cos 5x - \frac{1}{625} \cdot 6 \sin 5x + C.$$

4. Formula III-13 applies only to functions of the form $x^n \ln x$, so we'll have to multiply out and separate into two integrals.

$$\int (x^2 + 3) \ln x \, dx = \int x^2 \ln x \, dx + 3 \int \ln x \, dx.$$

Now we can use formula III-13 on each integral separately, to get

$$\int (x^2 + 3) \ln x \, dx = \frac{x^3}{3} \ln x - \frac{x^3}{9} + 3(x \ln x - x) + C.$$

5. Note that you can't use substitution here: letting $w = x^3 + 5$ does not work, since there is no $dw = 3x^2 \, dx$ in the integrand. What will work is simply multiplying out the square: $(x^3 + 5)^2 = x^6 + 10x^3 + 25$. Then use I-1:

$$\int (x^3 + 5)^2 \, dx = \int x^6 \, dx + 10 \int x^3 \, dx + 25 \int 1 \, dx = \frac{1}{7} x^7 + 10 \cdot \frac{1}{4} x^4 + 25x + C.$$

6. $-\dfrac{1}{5} \cos^5 w + C$
(Let $x = \cos w$, as suggested in IV-23. Then $-\sin w \, dw = dx$, and $\int \sin w \cos^4 w \, dw = -\int x^4 \, dx$.)

7. $-\dfrac{1}{4} \sin^3 x \cos x - \dfrac{3}{8} \sin x \cos x + \dfrac{3}{8} x + C.$
(Use IV-17.)

8. $\dfrac{1}{\sqrt{3}} \arctan \dfrac{y}{\sqrt{3}} + C.$
(Let $a = \sqrt{3}$ in V-24).

9. $\left(\dfrac{1}{2} x^3 - \dfrac{3}{4} x^2 + \dfrac{3}{4} x - \dfrac{3}{8} \right) e^{2x} + C.$
(Let $a = 2, p(x) = x^3$ in III-14.)

10. We first factor out the 9 and then use formula V-24:

$$\int \frac{dx}{9x^2 + 16} = \int \frac{dx}{9(x^2 + 16/9)} = \frac{1}{9} \cdot \frac{1}{4/3} \arctan \left(\frac{x}{4/3} \right) + C$$
$$= \frac{1}{12} \arctan \left(\frac{3x}{4} \right) + C.$$

11. We first factor out the 16 and then use formula V-28 to get

$$\int \frac{dx}{\sqrt{25 - 16x^2}} = \int \frac{dx}{\sqrt{16(25/16 - x^2)}} = \frac{1}{4} \int \frac{dx}{\sqrt{(5/4)^2 - x^2}}$$
$$= \frac{1}{4} \arcsin \left(\frac{x}{5/4} \right) + C$$
$$= \frac{1}{4} \arcsin \left(\frac{4x}{5} \right) + C.$$

12. The integral suggests formula VI-29, but is not a perfect match because of the coefficient of 9. One way to deal with the 9 is to factor it out, so that, using formula IV-29,

$$\int \frac{dx}{\sqrt{9x^2 + 25}} = \int \frac{dx}{\sqrt{9(x^2 + 25/9)}} = \frac{1}{3} \int \frac{dx}{\sqrt{x^2 + (5/3)^2}} = \frac{1}{3} \ln \left| x + \sqrt{x^2 + \left(\frac{5}{3}\right)^2} \right| + C.$$

Alternatively, we can write

$$\int \frac{dx}{\sqrt{9x^2 + 25}} = \int \frac{dx}{\sqrt{(3x)^2 + 25}}.$$

We now use the substitution $w = 3x$, so that $dw = 3dx$, and the integral becomes

$$\int \frac{\frac{1}{3} dw}{\sqrt{w^2 + 25}} = \frac{1}{3} \ln \left| w + \sqrt{w^2 + 25} \right| + C = \frac{1}{3} \ln \left| 3x + \sqrt{9x^2 + 25} \right| + C.$$

13. $\dfrac{5}{16} \sin 3\theta \sin 5\theta + \dfrac{3}{16} \cos 3\theta \cos 5\theta + C.$
(Let $a = 3, b = 5$ in II-12.)

14. $\dfrac{3}{16} \cos 3\theta \sin 5\theta - \dfrac{5}{16} \sin 3\theta \cos 5\theta + C.$
(Let $a = 3, b = 5$ in II-10.)

15. $\left(\dfrac{1}{3} x^2 - \dfrac{2}{9} x + \dfrac{2}{27} \right) e^{3x} + C.$
(Let $a = 3, p(x) = x^2$ in III-14.)

16. $\dfrac{1}{3} e^{x^3} + C.$
(Substitute $w = x^3$, $dw = 3x^2 \, dx$. It is not necessary to use the table.)

17. $\left(\dfrac{1}{3} x^4 - \dfrac{4}{9} x^3 + \dfrac{4}{9} x^2 - \dfrac{8}{27} x + \dfrac{8}{81} \right) e^{3x} + C.$
(Let $a = 3, p(x) = x^4$ in III-14.)

18. Substitute $w = 5u$, $dw = 5 \, du$. Then

$$\int u^5 \ln(5u) \, du = \frac{1}{5^6} \int w^5 \ln w \, dw$$

$$= \frac{1}{5^6} \left(\frac{1}{6} w^6 \ln w - \frac{1}{36} w^6 + C \right)$$

$$= \frac{1}{6} u^6 \ln 5u - \frac{1}{36} u^6 + C.$$

Or use $\ln 5u = \ln 5 + \ln u$.

$$\int u^5 \ln 5u \, du = \ln 5 \int u^5 \, du + \int u^5 \ln u \, du$$

$$= \frac{u^6}{6} \ln 5 + \frac{1}{6} u^6 \ln u - \frac{1}{36} u^6 + C \quad \text{(using III-13)}$$

$$= \frac{u^6}{6} \ln 5u - \frac{1}{36} u^6 + C.$$

19. Let $m = 3$ in IV-21.

$$\int \frac{1}{\cos^3 x} \, dx = \frac{1}{2} \frac{\sin x}{\cos^2 x} + \frac{1}{2} \int \frac{1}{\cos x} \, dx$$

$$= \frac{1}{2} \frac{\sin x}{\cos^2 x} + \frac{1}{4} \ln \left| \frac{\sin x + 1}{\sin x - 1} \right| + C \text{ by IV-22.}$$

20. Use long division to reorganize the integral:

$$\int \frac{t^2 + 1}{t^2 - 1}\, dt = \int \left(1 + \frac{2}{t^2 - 1}\right)\, dt = \int dt + \int \frac{2}{(t-1)(t+1)}\, dt.$$

To get this second integral, let $a = 1, b = -1$ in V-26, so

$$\int \frac{t^2 + 1}{t^2 - 1}\, dt = t + \ln|t - 1| - \ln|t + 1| + C.$$

21. Substitute $w = x^2$, $dw = 2x\, dx$. Then $\int x^3 \sin x^2\, dx = \frac{1}{2}\int w \sin w\, dw$. By III-15, we have

$$\int w \sin w\, dw = -\frac{1}{2}w \cos w + \frac{1}{2}\sin w + C = -\frac{1}{2}x^2 \cos x^2 + \frac{1}{2}\sin x^2 + C.$$

22. $\frac{1}{45}(7 \cos 2y \sin 7y - 2 \sin 2y \cos 7y) + C.$
(Let $a = 2, b = 7$ in II-11.)

23.

$$\int y^2 \sin 2y\, dy = -\frac{1}{2}y^2 \cos 2y + \frac{1}{4}(2y)\sin 2y + \frac{1}{8}(2)\cos 2y + C$$

$$= -\frac{1}{2}y^2 \cos 2y + \frac{1}{2}y \sin 2y + \frac{1}{4}\cos 2y + C.$$

(Use $a = 2, p(y) = y^2$ in III-15.)

24. $\frac{1}{34}e^{5x}(5 \sin 3x - 3 \cos 3x) + C.$
(Let $a = 5, b = 3$ in II-8.)

25. Use IV-21 twice to get the exponent down to 1:

$$\int \frac{1}{\cos^5 x}\, dx = \frac{1}{4}\frac{\sin x}{\cos^4 x} + \frac{3}{4}\int \frac{1}{\cos^3 x}\, dx$$

$$\int \frac{1}{\cos^3 x}\, dx = \frac{1}{2}\frac{\sin x}{\cos^2 x} + \frac{1}{2}\int \frac{1}{\cos x}\, dx.$$

Now use IV-22 to get

$$\int \frac{1}{\cos x}\, dx = \frac{1}{2}\ln\left|\frac{(\sin x) + 1}{(\sin x) - 1}\right| + C.$$

Putting this all together gives

$$\int \frac{1}{\cos^5 x}\, dx = \frac{1}{4}\frac{\sin x}{\cos^4 x} + \frac{3}{8}\frac{\sin x}{\cos^2 x} + \frac{3}{16}\ln\left|\frac{(\sin x) + 1}{(\sin x) - 1}\right| + C.$$

26. Substitute $w = 2\theta$, $dw = 2\, d\theta$. Then use IV-19, letting $m = 2$.

$$\int \frac{1}{\sin^2 2\theta}\, d\theta = \frac{1}{2}\int \frac{1}{\sin^2 w}\, dw = \frac{1}{2}(-\frac{\cos w}{\sin w}) + C = -\frac{1}{2\tan w} + C = -\frac{1}{2\tan 2\theta} + C.$$

27. Substitute $w = 3\theta$, $dw = 3\, d\theta$. Then use IV-19, letting $m = 3$.

$$\int \frac{1}{\sin^3 3\theta}\, d\theta = \frac{1}{3}\int \frac{1}{\sin^3 w}\, dw = \frac{1}{3}\left[-\frac{1}{2}\frac{\cos w}{\sin^2 w} + \frac{1}{2}\int \frac{1}{\sin w}\, dw\right]$$

$$= -\frac{1}{6}\frac{\cos w}{\sin^2 w} + \frac{1}{6}\left[\frac{1}{2}\ln\left|\frac{\cos(w) - 1}{\cos(w) + 1}\right| + C\right] \text{ by IV-20}$$

$$= -\frac{1}{6}\frac{\cos 3\theta}{\sin^2 3\theta} + \frac{1}{12}\ln\left|\frac{\cos(3\theta) - 1}{\cos(3\theta) + 1}\right| + C.$$

28. Substitute $w = 7x$, $dw = 7\,dx$. Then use IV-21.

$$
\int \frac{1}{\cos^4 7x}\,dx = \frac{1}{7}\int \frac{1}{\cos^4 w}\,dw = \frac{1}{7}\left[\frac{1}{3}\frac{\sin w}{\cos^3 w} + \frac{2}{3}\int \frac{1}{\cos^2 w}\,dw\right]
$$
$$
= \frac{1}{21}\frac{\sin w}{\cos^3 w} + \frac{2}{21}\left[\frac{\sin w}{\cos w} + C\right]
$$
$$
= \frac{1}{21}\frac{\tan w}{\cos^2 w} + \frac{2}{21}\tan w + C
$$
$$
= \frac{1}{21}\frac{\tan 7x}{\cos^2 7x} + \frac{2}{21}\tan 7x + C.
$$

29.

$$
\int \frac{1}{x^2 + 4x + 3}\,dx = \int \frac{1}{(x+1)(x+3)}\,dx = \frac{1}{2}(\ln|x+1| - \ln|x+3|) + C.
$$

(Let $a = -1$ and $b = -3$ in V-26).

30. Using the advice in IV-23, since both m and n are even and since n is negative, we convert everything to cosines, since $\cos x$ is in the denominator.

$$
\int \tan^4 x\,dx = \int \frac{\sin^4 x}{\cos^4 x}\,dx
$$
$$
= \int \frac{(1 - \cos^2 x)^2}{\cos^4 x}\,dx
$$
$$
= \int \frac{1}{\cos^4 x}\,dx - 2\int \frac{1}{\cos^2 x}\,dx + \int 1\,dx.
$$

By IV-21

$$
\int \frac{1}{\cos^4 x}\,dx = \frac{1}{3}\frac{\sin x}{\cos^3 x} + \frac{2}{3}\int \frac{1}{\cos^2 x}\,dx,
$$
$$
\int \frac{1}{\cos^2 x}\,dx = \frac{\sin x}{\cos x} + C.
$$

Substituting back in, we get

$$
\int \tan^4 x\,dx = \frac{1}{3}\frac{\sin x}{\cos^3 x} - \frac{4}{3}\frac{\sin x}{\cos x} + x + C.
$$

31.

$$
\int \frac{dz}{z(z-3)} = -\frac{1}{3}(\ln|z| - \ln|z-3|) + C.
$$

(Let $a = 0, b = 3$ in V-26.)

32.

$$
\int \frac{dy}{4 - y^2} = -\int \frac{dy}{(y+2)(y-2)} = -\frac{1}{4}(\ln|y-2| - \ln|y+2|) + C.
$$

(Let $a = 2, b = -2$ in V-26.)

33. $\arctan(z + 2) + C.$
(Substitute $w = z + 2$ and use V-24, letting $a = 1$.)

34.

$$
\int \frac{1}{y^2 + 4y + 5}\,dy = \int \frac{1}{1 + (y+2)^2}\,dy = \arctan(y + 2) + C.
$$

(Substitute $w = y + 2$, and let $a = 1$ in V-24).

35.

$$
\int \frac{1}{x^2 + 4x + 4}\,dx = \int \frac{1}{(x+2)^2}\,dx = -\frac{1}{x+2} + C.
$$

You need not use the table.

36. We use the method of IV-23 in the table. Using the Pythagorean Identity, we rewrite the integrand:

$$\sin^3 x = \left(\sin^2 x\right) \sin x = \left(1 - \cos^2 x\right) \sin x = \sin x - \cos^2 x \sin x.$$

Thus, we have

$$\int \sin^3 x \, dx = \int \left(\sin x - \cos^2 x \sin x\right) dx$$

$$= \int \sin x \, dx - \int \cos^2 x \sin x \, dx.$$

The first of these new integrals can be easily found. The second can be found using the substitution $w = \cos x$ so $dw = -\sin x \, dx$. The second integral becomes

$$\int \cos^2 x \sin x \, dx = -\int w^2 dw$$

$$= -\frac{1}{3}w^3 + C$$

$$= -\frac{1}{3}\cos^3 x + C,$$

so the final answer is

$$\int \sin^3 x \, dx = \int \sin x \, dx - \int \cos^2 x \sin x \, dx$$

$$= -\cos x + (1/3)\cos^3 x + C.$$

37.

$$\int \sin^3 3\theta \cos^2 3\theta \, d\theta = \int (\sin 3\theta)(\cos^2 3\theta)(1 - \cos^2 3\theta) \, d\theta$$

$$= \int \sin 3\theta (\cos^2 3\theta - \cos^4 3\theta) \, d\theta.$$

Using an extension of the tip given in rule IV-23, we let $w = \cos 3\theta$, $dw = -3\sin 3\theta \, d\theta$.

$$\int \sin 3\theta (\cos^2 3\theta - \cos^4 3\theta) \, d\theta = -\frac{1}{3}\int (w^2 - w^4) \, dw$$

$$= -\frac{1}{3}\left(\frac{w^3}{3} - \frac{w^5}{5}\right) + C$$

$$= -\frac{1}{9}(\cos^3 3\theta) + \frac{1}{15}(\cos^5 3\theta) + C.$$

38. If we make the substitution $w = 2z^2$ then $dw = 4z \, dz$, and the integral becomes:

$$\int ze^{2z^2} \cos(2z^2) \, dz = \frac{1}{4}\int e^w \cos w \, dw$$

Now we can use Formula 9 from the table of integrals to get:

$$\frac{1}{4}\int e^w \cos w \, dw = \frac{1}{4}\left[\frac{1}{2}e^w(\cos w + \sin w) + C\right]$$

$$= \frac{1}{8}e^w(\cos w + \sin w) + C$$

$$= \frac{1}{8}e^{2z^2}(\cos 2z^2 + \sin 2z^2) + C.$$

39. Since $\cosh^2 x - \sinh^2 x = 1$ we rewrite $\sinh^3 x$ as $\sinh x \sinh^2 x = \sinh x(\cosh^2 x - 1)$. Then

$$\int \sinh^3 x \cosh^2 x \, dx = \int \sinh x(\cosh^2 x - 1)\cosh^2 x \, dx$$

$$= \int (\cosh^4 x - \cosh^2 x)\sinh x \, dx.$$

Now use the substitution $w = \cosh x$, $dw = \sinh x \, dx$ to find

$$\int (w^4 - w^2) \, dw = \frac{1}{5}w^5 - \frac{1}{3}w^3 + C = \frac{1}{5}\cosh^5 x - \frac{1}{3}\cosh^3 x + C.$$

40. Since $\cosh^2 x - \sinh^2 x = 1$ we rewrite $\cosh^3 x$ as $\cosh x \cosh^2 x = \cosh x(1 + \sinh^2 x)$. This gives

$$\int \sinh^2 x \cosh^3 x \, dx = \int \sinh^2 x(\sinh^2 x + 1)\cosh x \, dx$$

$$= \int (\sinh^4 x + \sinh^2 x)\cosh x \, dx.$$

Now use the substitution $w = \sinh x$, $dw = \cosh x \, dx$ to find

$$\int (w^4 - w^2) \, dw = \frac{1}{5}w^5 - \frac{1}{3}w^3 + C = \frac{1}{5}\sinh^5 x + \frac{1}{3}\sinh^3 x + C.$$

41. Substitute $w = 3\alpha$, $dw = 3\,d\alpha$. Then $d\alpha = \frac{1}{3}\,dw$. We have

$$\int_{\alpha=0}^{\alpha=\frac{\pi}{12}} \sin 3\alpha \, d\alpha = \frac{1}{3}\int_{w=0}^{w=\frac{\pi}{4}} \sin w \, dw$$

$$= -\frac{1}{3}\cos w \Big|_0^{\frac{\pi}{4}}$$

$$= -\frac{1}{3}\left(\frac{\sqrt{2}}{2} - 1\right) = \frac{1}{3}\left(1 - \frac{\sqrt{2}}{2}\right).$$

42. $\displaystyle\int_0^1 \frac{1}{x^2 + 2x + 1} \, dx = \int_0^1 \frac{1}{(x+1)^2} \, dx.$

We substitute $w = x + 1$, so $dw = dx$. Note that when $x = 1$, we have $w = 2$, and when $x = 0$, we have $w = 1$.

$$\int_{x=0}^{x=1} \frac{1}{(x+1)^2} \, dx = \int_{w=1}^{w=2} \frac{1}{w^2} \, dw = -\frac{1}{w}\Big|_{w=1}^{w=2} = -\frac{1}{2} + 1 = \frac{1}{2}.$$

43. Let $w = x + 2$, giving $dw = dx$. When $x = 0$, $w = 2$, and when $x = 1$, $w = 3$. Thus,

$$\int_0^1 \frac{(x+2)}{(x+2)^2 + 1} dx = \int_2^3 \frac{w}{w^2 + 1} \, dw.$$

For the last integral, we make the substitution $u = w^2 + 1$, $du = 2w \, dw$. Then, we have

$$\int_2^3 \frac{w}{w^2 + 1} \, dw = \frac{1}{2}\ln|w^2 + 1|\Big|_2^3$$

$$= \frac{1}{2}(\ln|10| - \ln|5|)$$

$$= \frac{1}{2}\ln\left(\frac{10}{5}\right) = \frac{1}{2}\ln(2)$$

44. Let $w = x^2$, $dw = 2x \, dx$. When $x = 0$, $w = 0$, and when $x = \frac{1}{\sqrt{2}}$, $w = \frac{1}{2}$. Then

$$\int_0^{\frac{1}{\sqrt{2}}} \frac{x \, dx}{\sqrt{1 - x^4}} = \int_0^{\frac{1}{2}} \frac{\frac{1}{2} \, dw}{\sqrt{1 - w^2}} = \frac{1}{2}\arcsin w \Big|_0^{\frac{1}{2}} = \frac{1}{2}\left(\arcsin\frac{1}{2} - \arcsin 0\right) = \frac{\pi}{12}.$$

Problems

45. Using II-10 in the integral table, if $m \neq \pm n$, then

$$\int_{-\pi}^{\pi} \sin m\theta \sin n\theta \, d\theta = \frac{1}{n^2 - m^2} [m \cos m\theta \sin n\theta - n \sin m\theta \cos n\theta] \Big|_{-\pi}^{\pi}$$

$$= \frac{1}{n^2 - m^2} [(m \cos m\pi \sin n\pi - n \sin m\pi \cos n\pi) - (m \cos(-m\pi) \sin(-n\pi) - n \sin(-m\pi) \cos(-n\pi))]$$

But $\sin k\pi = 0$ for all integers k, so each term reduces to 0, making the whole integral reduce to 0.

46. Using formula II-11, if $m \neq \pm n$, then

$$\int_{-\pi}^{\pi} \cos m\theta \cos n\theta \, d\theta = \frac{1}{n^2 - m^2} (n \cos m\theta \sin n\theta - m \sin m\theta \cos n\theta) \Big|_{-\pi}^{\pi}.$$

We see that in the evaluation, each term will have a $\sin k\pi$ term, so the expression reduces to 0.

47. (a)

$$\frac{1}{1-0} \int_0^1 V_0 \cos(120\pi t) dt = \frac{V_0}{120\pi} \sin(120\pi t) \Big|_0^1$$

$$= \frac{V_0}{120\pi} [\sin(120\pi) - \sin(0)]$$

$$= \frac{V_0}{120\pi} [0 - 0] = 0.$$

(b) Let's find the average of V^2 first.

$$\overline{V^2} = \text{Average of } V^2 = \frac{1}{1-0} \int_0^1 V^2 dt$$

$$= \frac{1}{1-0} \int_0^1 (V_0 \cos(120\pi t))^2 dt$$

$$= V_0^2 \int_0^1 \cos^2(120\pi t) dt$$

Now, let $120\pi t = x$, and $dt = \frac{dx}{120\pi}$. So

$$\overline{V^2} = \frac{V_0^2}{120\pi} \int_0^{120\pi} \cos^2 x \, dx.$$

$$= \frac{V_0^2}{120\pi} \left(\frac{1}{2} \cos x \sin x + \frac{1}{2} x \right) \Big|_0^{120\pi} \qquad \text{II-18}$$

$$= \frac{V_0^2}{120\pi} 60\pi = \frac{V_0^2}{2}.$$

So, the average of V^2 is $\frac{V_0^2}{2}$ and $\overline{V} = \sqrt{\text{average of } V^2} = \frac{V_0}{\sqrt{2}}$.

(c) $V_0 = \sqrt{2} \cdot \overline{V} = 110\sqrt{2} \approx 156$ volts.

48. (a) Since $R(T)$ is the rate or production, we find the total production by integrating:

$$\int_0^N R(t) \, dt = \int_0^N (A + Be^{-t} \sin(2\pi t)) \, dt$$

$$= NA + B \int_0^N e^{-t} \sin(2\pi t) \, dt.$$

Let $a = -1$ and $b = 2\pi$ in II-8.

$$= NA + \frac{B}{1 + 4\pi^2} e^{-t}(-\sin(2\pi t) - 2\pi \cos(2\pi t))\Big|_0^N.$$

Since N is an integer (so $\sin 2\pi N = 0$ and $\cos 2\pi N = 1$),

$$\int_0^N R(t)\, dt = NA + B\frac{2\pi}{1 + 4\pi^2}(1 - e^{-N}).$$

Thus the total production is $NA + \frac{2\pi B}{1+4\pi^2}(1 - e^{-N})$ over the first N years.

(b) The average production over the first N years is

$$\int_0^N \frac{R(t)\, dt}{N} = A + \frac{2\pi B}{1 + 4\pi^2}\left(\frac{1 - e^{-N}}{N}\right).$$

(c) As $N \to \infty$, $A + \frac{2\pi B}{1+4\pi^2}\frac{1-e^{-N}}{N} \to A$, since the second term in the sum goes to 0. This is why A is called the average!

(d) When t gets large, the term $Be^{-t}\sin(2\pi t)$ gets very small. Thus, $R(t) \approx A$ for most t, so it makes sense that the average of $\int_0^N R(t)\, dt$ is A as $N \to \infty$.

(e) This model is not reasonable for long periods of time, since an oil well has finite capacity and will eventually "run dry." Thus, we cannot expect average production to be close to constant over a long period of time.

49. We want to calculate

$$\int_0^1 C_n \sin(n\pi x) \cdot C_m \sin(m\pi x)\, dx.$$

We use II-11 from the table of integrals with $a = n\pi$, $b = m\pi$. Since $n \neq m$, we see that

$$\int_0^1 \Psi_n(x) \cdot \Psi_m(x)\, dx = C_n C_m \int_0^1 \sin(n\pi x)\sin(m\pi x)\, dx$$

$$= \frac{C_n C_m}{m^2\pi^2 - n^2\pi^2}\left(n\pi \cos(n\pi x)\sin(m\pi x) - m\pi \sin(n\pi x)\cos(m\pi x)\right)\Big|_0^1$$

$$= \frac{C_n C_m}{(m^2 - n^2)\pi^2}\left(n\pi \cos(n\pi)\sin(m\pi) - m\pi \sin(n\pi)\cos(m\pi)\right.$$

$$\left. -n\pi \cos(0)\sin(0) + m\pi \sin(0)\cos(0)\right)$$

$$= 0$$

since $\sin(0) = \sin(n\pi) = \sin(m\pi) = 0$.

Solutions for Section 7.4

Exercises

1. Since $25 - x^2 = (5 - x)(5 + x)$, we take

$$\frac{20}{25 - x^2} = \frac{A}{5 - x} + \frac{B}{5 + x}.$$

So,

$$20 = A(5 + x) + B(5 - x)$$
$$20 = (A - B)x + 5A + 5B,$$

giving

$$A - B = 0$$
$$5A + 5B = 20.$$

Thus $A = B = 2$ and

$$\frac{20}{25 - x^2} = \frac{2}{5 - x} + \frac{2}{5 + x}.$$

2. Since $6x + x^2 = x(6 + x)$, we take

$$\frac{x + 1}{6x + x^2} = \frac{A}{x} + \frac{B}{6 + x}.$$

So,

$$x + 1 = A(6 + x) + Bx$$
$$x + 1 = (A + B)x + 6A,$$

giving

$$A + B = 1$$
$$6A = 1.$$

Thus $A = 1/6$, and $B = 5/6$ so

$$\frac{x + 1}{6x + x^2} = \frac{1/6}{x} + \frac{5/6}{6 + x}.$$

3. Since $y^3 - 4y = y(y - 2)(y + 2)$, we take

$$\frac{8}{y^3 - 4y} = \frac{A}{y} + \frac{B}{y - 2} + \frac{C}{y + 2}.$$

So,

$$8 = A(y - 2)(y + 2) + By(y + 2) + Cy(y - 2)$$
$$8 = (A + B + C)y^2 + (2B - 2C)y - 4A,$$

giving

$$A + B + C = 0$$
$$2B - 2C = 0$$
$$-4A = 8.$$

Thus $A = -2$, $B = C = 1$ so

$$\frac{8}{y^3 - 4y} = \frac{-2}{y} + \frac{1}{y - 2} + \frac{1}{y + 2}.$$

4. Since $s^2 + 3s + 2 = (s + 2)(s + 1)$, we have

$$\frac{2(1 + s)}{s(s^2 + 3s + 2)} = \frac{2(1 + s)}{s(s + 2)(s + 1)} = \frac{2}{s(s + 2)},$$

so we take

$$\frac{2}{s(s + 2)} = \frac{A}{s} + \frac{B}{s + 2}.$$

Thus,

$$2 = A(s + 2) + Bs$$
$$2 = (A + B)s + 2A,$$

giving

$$A + B = 0$$
$$2A = 2.$$

Thus $A = 1$ and $B = -1$ and

$$\frac{2(1 + s)}{s(s^2 + 3s + 2)} = \frac{1}{s} - \frac{1}{s + 2}.$$

5. Since $s^4 - 1 = (s^2 - 1)(s^2 + 1) = (s - 1)(s + 1)(s^2 + 1)$, we have

$$\frac{2}{s^4 - 1} = \frac{A}{s - 1} + \frac{B}{s + 1} + \frac{Cs + D}{s^2 + 1}.$$

Thus,

$$2 = A(s + 1)(s^2 + 1) + B(s - 1)(s^2 + 1) + (Cs + D)(s - 1)(s + 1)$$
$$2 = (A + B + C)s^3 + (A - B + D)s^2 + (A + B - C)s + (A - B - D),$$

giving

$$A + B + C = 0$$
$$A - B + D = 0$$
$$A + B - C = 0$$
$$A - B - D = 2.$$

From the first and third equations we find $A + B = 0$ and $C = 0$. From the second and fourth we find $A - B = 1$ and $D = -1$. Thus $A = 1/2$ and $B = -1/2$ and

$$\frac{2}{s^4 - 1} = \frac{1}{2(s - 1)} - \frac{1}{2(s + 1)} - \frac{1}{s^2 + 1}.$$

6. Since $y^3 - y^2 + y - 1 = (y - 1)(y^2 + 1)$, we take

$$\frac{2y}{y^3 - y^2 + y - 1} = \frac{A}{y - 1} + \frac{By + C}{y^2 + 1}$$

So,

$$2y = A(y^2 + 1) + (By + C)(y - 1)$$
$$2y = (A + B)y^2 + (C - B)y + A - C,$$

giving

$$A + B = 0$$
$$-B + C = 2$$
$$A - C = 0.$$

Thus $A = C = 1$, $B = -1$ so

$$\frac{2y}{y^3 - y^2 + y - 1} = \frac{1}{y - 1} + \frac{1 - y}{y^2 + 1}.$$

7. Since $w^4 - w^3 = w^3(w - 1)$, we have

$$\frac{1}{w^4 - w^3} = \frac{A}{w - 1} + \frac{B}{w} + \frac{C}{w^2} + \frac{D}{w^3}.$$

Thus,

$$1 = Aw^3 + B(w - 1)w^2 + C(w - 1)w + D(w - 1)$$
$$1 = (A + B)w^3 + (-B + C)w^2 + (-C + D)w + (-D),$$

giving

$$A + B = 0$$
$$-B + C = 0$$
$$-C + D = 0$$
$$-D = 1.$$

Thus $A = 1$, $B = -1$, $C = -1$ and $D = -1$ so

$$\frac{1}{w^4 - w^3} = \frac{1}{w - 1} - \frac{1}{w} - \frac{1}{w^2} - \frac{1}{w^3}.$$

8. Using the result of Problem 1, we have

$$\int \frac{20}{25 - x^2}\, dx = \int \frac{2}{5 - x}\, dx + \int \frac{2}{5 + x}\, dx = -2\ln|5 - x| + 2\ln|5 + x| + C.$$

9. Using the result of Problem 2, we have

$$\int \frac{x + 1}{6x + x^2}\, dx = \int \frac{1/6}{x}\, dx + \int \frac{5/6}{6 + x}\, dx = \frac{1}{6}\left(\ln|x| + 5\ln|6 + x|\right) + C.$$

10. Using the result of Problem 3, we have

$$\int \frac{8}{y^3 - 4y}\, dy = \int \frac{-2}{y}\, dy + \int \frac{1}{y - 2}\, dy + \int \frac{1}{y + 2}\, dy = -2\ln|y| + \ln|y - 2| + \ln|y + 2| + C.$$

11. Using the result of Exercise 4, we have

$$\int \frac{2(1 + s)}{s(s^2 + 3s + 2)}\, ds = \int \left(\frac{1}{s} - \frac{1}{s + 2}\right) ds = \ln|s| - \ln|s + 2| + C.$$

12. Using the result of Exercise 5, we have

$$\int \frac{2}{s^4 - 1}\, ds = \int \left(\frac{1}{2(s - 1)} - \frac{1}{2(s + 1)} - \frac{1}{s^2 + 1}\right) ds = \frac{1}{2}\ln|s - 1| - \frac{1}{2}\ln|s + 1| - \arctan s + C.$$

13. Using the result of Problem 6, we have

$$\int \frac{2y}{y^3 - y^2 + y - 1}\, dy = \int \frac{1}{y - 1}\, dy + \int \frac{1 - y}{y^2 + 1}\, dy = \ln|y - 1| + \arctan y - \frac{1}{2}\ln\left|y^2 + 1\right| + C.$$

14. Using the result of Exercise 7, we have

$$\int \frac{1}{w^4 - w^3}\, dw = \int \left(\frac{1}{w - 1} - \frac{1}{w} - \frac{1}{w^2} - \frac{1}{w^3}\right) dw = \ln|w - 1| - \ln|w| + \frac{1}{w} + \frac{1}{2w^2} + C.$$

15. We let

$$\frac{3x^2 - 8x + 1}{x^3 - 4x^2 + x + 6} = \frac{A}{x - 2} + \frac{B}{x + 1} + \frac{C}{x - 3}$$

giving

$$3x^2 - 8x + 1 = A(x + 1)(x - 3) + B(x - 2)(x - 3) + C(x - 2)(x + 1)$$
$$3x^2 - 8x + 1 = (A + B + C)x^2 - (2A + 5B + C)x - 3A + 6B - 2C$$

so

$$A + B + C = 3$$
$$-2A - 5B - C = -8$$
$$-3A + 6B - 2C = 1.$$

Thus, $A = B = C = 1$, so

$$\int \frac{3x^2 - 8x + 1}{x^3 - 4x^2 + x + 6}\, dx = \int \frac{dx}{x - 2} + \int \frac{dx}{x + 1} + \int \frac{dx}{x - 3} = \ln|x - 2| + \ln|x + 1| + \ln|x - 3| + K.$$

16. We let

$$\frac{1}{x^3 - x^2} = \frac{1}{x^2(x-1)} = \frac{A}{x} + \frac{B}{x^2} + \frac{C}{x-1}$$

giving

$$1 = Ax(x-1) + B(x-1) + Cx^2$$
$$1 = (A+C)x^2 + (B-A)x - B$$

so

$$A + C = 0$$
$$B - A = 0$$
$$-B = 1.$$

Thus, $A = B = -1, C = 1$, so

$$\int \frac{dx}{x^3 - x^2} = -\int \frac{dx}{x} - \int \frac{dx}{x^2} + \int \frac{dx}{x-1} = -\ln|x| + x^{-1} + \ln|x-1| + K.$$

17. We let

$$\frac{10x+2}{x^3 - 5x^2 + x - 5} = \frac{10x+2}{(x-5)(x^2+1)} = \frac{A}{x-5} + \frac{Bx+C}{x^2+1}$$

giving

$$10x + 2 = A(x^2+1) + (Bx+C)(x-5)$$
$$10x + 2 = (A+B)x^2 + (C-5B)x + A - 5C$$

so

$$A + B = 0$$
$$C - 5B = 10$$
$$A - 5C = 2.$$

Thus, $A = 2, B = -2, C = 0$, so

$$\int \frac{10x+2}{x^3 - 5x^2 + x - 5} \, dx = \int \frac{2}{x-5} \, dx - \int \frac{2x}{x^2+1} \, dx = 2\ln|x-5| - \ln\left|x^2+1\right| + K.$$

18. Division gives

$$\frac{x^4 + 12x^3 + 15x^2 + 25x + 11}{x^3 + 12x^2 + 11x} = x + \frac{4x^2 + 25x + 11}{x^3 + 12x^2 + 11x}.$$

Since $x^3 + 12x^2 + 11x = x(x+1)(x+11)$, we write

$$\frac{4x^2 + 25x + 11}{x^3 + 12x^2 + 11x} = \frac{A}{x} + \frac{B}{x+1} + \frac{C}{x+11}$$

giving

$$4x^2 + 25x + 11 = A(x+1)(x+11) + Bx(x+11) + Cx(x+1)$$
$$4x^2 + 25x + 11 = (A+B+C)x^2 + (12A+11B+C)x + 11A$$

so

$$A + B + C = 4$$
$$12A + 11B + C = 25$$
$$11A = 11.$$

Thus, $A = B = 1, C = 2$ so

$$\int \frac{x^4 + 12x^3 + 15x^2 + 25x + 11}{x^3 + 12x^2 + 11x} \, dx = \int x \, dx + \int \frac{dx}{x} + \int \frac{dx}{x+1} + \int \frac{2dx}{x+11}$$
$$= \frac{x^2}{2} + \ln|x| + \ln|x+1| + 2\ln|x+11| + K.$$

19. Division gives

$$\frac{x^4 + 3x^3 + 2x^2 + 1}{x^2 + 3x + 2} = x^2 + \frac{1}{x^2 + 3x + 2}.$$

Since $x^2 + 3x + 2 = (x+1)(x+2)$, we write

$$\frac{1}{x^2 + 3x + 2} = \frac{1}{(x+1)(x+2)} = \frac{A}{x+1} + \frac{B}{x+2},$$

giving

$$1 = A(x+2) + B(x+1)$$
$$1 = (A+B)x + 2A + B$$

so

$$A + B = 0$$
$$2A + B = 1.$$

Thus, $A = 1$, $B = -1$ so

$$\int \frac{x^4 + 3x^3 + 2x^2 + 1}{x^2 + 3x + 2}\, dx = \int x^2\, dx + \int \frac{dx}{x+1} - \int \frac{dx}{x+2}$$

$$= \frac{x^3}{3} + \ln|x+1| - \ln|x+2| + C.$$

20. Since $x = (3/2)\sin t$, we have $dx = (3/2)\cos t\, dt$. Substituting into the integral gives

$$\int \frac{1}{\sqrt{9 - 4x^2}} = \int \frac{1}{\sqrt{9 - 9\sin^2 t}}\left(\frac{3}{2}\cos t\right) dt = \int \frac{1}{2}dt = \frac{1}{2}t + C = \frac{1}{2}\arcsin\left(\frac{2x}{3}\right) + C.$$

21. Completing the square gives $x^2 + 4x + 5 = 1 + (x+2)^2$. Since $x + 2 = \tan t$ and $dx = (1/\cos^2 t)dt$, we have

$$\int \frac{1}{x^2 + 4x + 5}\, dx = \int \frac{1}{1 + \tan^2 t} \cdot \frac{1}{\cos^2 t}dt = \int dt = t + C = \arctan(x+2) + C.$$

22. Since $x = \sin t + 2$, we have

$$4x - 3 - x^2 = 4(\sin t + 2) - 3 - (\sin t + 2)^2 = 1 - \sin^2 t = \cos^2 t$$

and $dx = \cos t\, dt$, so substitution gives

$$\int \frac{1}{\sqrt{4x - 3 - x^2}} = \int \frac{1}{\sqrt{\cos^2 t}}\cos t\, dt = \int dt = t + C = \arcsin(x-2) + C.$$

23. (a) Substitute $w = x^2 + 10$, so $dw = 2x\, dx$.

(b) Substitute $x = \sqrt{10}\tan\theta$.

Problems

24. Since $x^2 + 2x + 2 = (x+1)^2 + 1$, we have

$$\int \frac{1}{x^2 + 2x + 2}\, dx = \int \frac{1}{(x+1)^2 + 1}dx.$$

Substitute $x + 1 = \tan\theta$, so $x = (\tan\theta) - 1$.

25. Since $x^2 + 6x + 9$ is a perfect square, we write

$$\int \frac{1}{x^2 + 6x + 25}\, dx = \int \frac{1}{(x^2 + 6x + 9) + 16}dx = \int \frac{1}{(x+3)^2 + 16}dx.$$

We use the trigonometric substitution $x + 3 = 4\tan\theta$, so $x = 4\tan\theta - 3$.

26. Since $y^2 + 3y + 3 = (y + 3/2)^2 + (3 - 9/4) = (y + 3/2)^2 + 3/4$, we have

$$\int \frac{dy}{y^2 + 3y + 3} = \int \frac{dy}{(y + 3/2)^2 + 3/4}.$$

Substitute $y + 3/2 = \tan\theta$, so $y = (\tan\theta) - 3/2$.

27. Since $x^2 + 2x + 2 = (x + 1)^2 + 1$, we have

$$\int \frac{x + 1}{x^2 + 2x + 2}\, dx = \int \frac{x + 1}{(x + 1)^2 + 1}\, dx.$$

Substitute $w = (x + 1)^2$, so $dw = 2(x + 1)\, dx$.

This integral can also be calculated without completing the square, by substituting $w = x^2 + 2x + 2$, so $dw = 2(x + 1)\, dx$.

28. Since $2z - z^2 = 1 - (z - 1)^2$, we have

$$\int \frac{4}{\sqrt{2z - z^2}}\, dz = 4 \int \frac{1}{\sqrt{1 - (z - 1)^2}}\, dz.$$

Substitute $z - 1 = \sin\theta$, so $z = (\sin\theta) + 1$.

29. Since $2z - z^2 = 1 - (z - 1)^2$, we have

$$\int \frac{z - 1}{\sqrt{2z - z^2}}\, dz = \int \frac{z - 1}{\sqrt{1 - (z - 1)^2}}\, dz.$$

Substitute $w = 1 - (z - 1)^2$, so $dw = -2(z - 1)\, dz$.

30. Since $t^2 + 4t + 7 = (t + 2)^2 + 3$, we have

$$\int (t + 2)\sin(t^2 + 4t + 7)\, dt = \int (t + 2)\sin((t + 2)^2 + 3)\, dt.$$

Substitute $w = (t + 2)^2 + 3$, so $dw = 2(t + 2)\, dt$.

This integral can also be computed without completing the square, by substituting $w = t^2 + 4t + 7$, so $dw = (2t + 4)\, dt$.

31. Since $\theta^2 - 4\theta = (\theta - 2)^2 - 4$, we have

$$\int (2 - \theta)\cos(\theta^2 - 4\theta)\, d\theta = \int -(\theta - 2)\cos((\theta - 2)^2 - 4)\, d\theta.$$

Substitute $w = (\theta - 2)^2 - 4$, so $dw = 2(\theta - 2)\, d\theta$.

This integral can also be computed without completing the square, by substituting $w = \theta^2 - 4\theta$, so $dw = (2\theta - 4)\, d\theta$.

32. We write

$$\frac{1}{(x - 5)(x - 3)} = \frac{A}{x - 5} + \frac{B}{x - 3},$$

giving

$$1 = A(x - 3) + B(x - 5)$$
$$1 = (A + B)x - (3A + 5B)$$

so

$$A + B = 0$$
$$-3A - 5B = 1.$$

Thus, $A = 1/2$, $B = -1/2$, so

$$\int \frac{1}{(x - 5)(x - 3)}\, dx = \int \frac{1/2}{x - 5}\, dx - \int \frac{1/2}{x - 3}\, dx = \frac{1}{2} \ln|x - 5| - \frac{1}{2} \ln|x - 3| + C.$$

33. We write

$$\frac{1}{(x+2)(x+3)} = \frac{A}{x+2} + \frac{B}{x+3},$$

giving

$$1 = A(x+3) + B(x+2)$$
$$1 = (A+B)x + (3A+2B)$$

so

$$A + B = 0$$
$$3A + 2B = 1.$$

Thus, $A = 1$, $B = -1$, so

$$\int \frac{1}{(x+2)(x+3)} \, dx = \int \frac{1}{x+2} \, dx - \int \frac{1}{x+3} \, dx = \ln|x+2| - \ln|x+3| + C.$$

34. We write

$$\frac{1}{(x+7)(x-2)} = \frac{A}{x+7} + \frac{B}{x-2},$$

giving

$$1 = A(x-2) + B(x+7)$$
$$1 = (A+B)x + (-2A+7B)$$

so

$$A + B = 0$$
$$-2A + 7B = 1.$$

Thus, $A = -1/9$, $B = 1/9$, so

$$\int \frac{1}{(x+7)(x-2)} \, dx = -\int \frac{1/9}{x+7} \, dx + \int \frac{1/9}{x-2} \, dx = -\frac{1}{9}\ln|x+7| + \frac{1}{9}\ln|x-2| + C.$$

35. The denominator $x^2 - 3x + 2$ can be factored as $(x-1)(x-2)$. Splitting the integrand into partial fractions with denominators $(x-1)$ and $(x-2)$, we have

$$\frac{x}{x^2 - 3x + 2} = \frac{x}{(x-1)(x-2)} = \frac{A}{x-1} + \frac{B}{x-2}.$$

Multiplying by $(x-1)(x-2)$ gives the identity

$$x = A(x-2) + B(x-1)$$

so

$$x = (A+B)x - 2A - B.$$

Since this equation holds for all x, the constant terms on both sides must be equal. Similarly, the coefficient of x on both sides must be equal. So

$$-2A - B = 0$$
$$A + B = 1.$$

Solving these equations gives $A = -1$, $B = 2$ and the integral becomes

$$\int \frac{x}{x^2 - 3x + 2} \, dx = -\int \frac{1}{x-1} \, dx + 2\int \frac{1}{x-2} \, dx = -\ln|x-1| + 2\ln|x-2| + C.$$

36. This can be done by formula V–26 in the integral table or by partial fractions

$$\int \frac{dz}{z^2 + z} = \int \frac{dz}{z(z+1)} = \int \left(\frac{1}{z} - \frac{1}{z+1}\right) dz = \ln|z| - \ln|z+1| + C.$$

Check:

$$\frac{d}{dz}\left(\ln|z| - \ln|z+1| + C\right) = \frac{1}{z} - \frac{1}{z+1} = \frac{1}{z^2 + z}.$$

37. We know $x^2 + 5x + 4 = (x+1)(x+4)$, so we can use V-26 of the integral table with $a = -1$ and $b = -4$ to write

$$\int \frac{dx}{x^2 + 5x + 4} = \frac{1}{3}\left(\ln|x+1| - \ln|x+4|\right) + C.$$

38. We use partial fractions and write

$$\frac{1}{3P - 3P^2} = \frac{A}{3P} + \frac{B}{1-P},$$

multiply through by $3P(1-P)$, and then solve for A and B, getting $A = 1$ and $B = 1/3$. So

$$\int \frac{dP}{3P - 3P^2} = \int \left(\frac{1}{3P} + \frac{1}{3(1-P)}\right) dP = \frac{1}{3}\int \frac{dP}{P} + \frac{1}{3}\int \frac{dP}{1-P}$$

$$= \frac{1}{3}\ln|P| - \frac{1}{3}\ln|1-P| + C = \frac{1}{3}\ln\left|\frac{P}{1-P}\right| + C.$$

39. Using partial fractions, we have:

$$\frac{3x+1}{x^2 - 3x + 2} = \frac{3x+1}{(x-1)(x-2)} = \frac{A}{x-1} + \frac{B}{x-2}.$$

Multiplying by $(x-1)$ and $(x-2)$, this becomes

$$3x + 1 = A(x-2) + B(x-1)$$
$$= (A+B)x - 2A - B$$

which produces the system of equations

$$\begin{cases} A + B = 3 \\ -2A - B = 1. \end{cases}$$

Solving this system yields $A = -4$ and $B = 7$. So,

$$\int \frac{3x+1}{x^2 - 3x + 2} dx = \int \left(-\frac{4}{x-1} + \frac{7}{x-2}\right) dx$$

$$= -4\int \frac{dx}{x-1} + 7\int \frac{dx}{x-2}$$

$$= -4\ln|x-1| + 7\ln|x-2| + C.$$

40. Since $2y^2 + 3y + 1 = (2y+1)(y+1)$, we write

$$\frac{y+2}{2y^2 + 3y + 1} = \frac{A}{2y+1} + \frac{B}{y+1},$$

giving

$$y + 2 = A(y+1) + B(2y+1)$$
$$y + 2 = (A + 2B)y + A + B$$

so

$$A + 2B = 1$$
$$A + B = 2.$$

Thus, $A = 3$, $B = -1$, so

$$\int \frac{y+2}{2y^2 + 3y + 1} dy = \int \frac{3}{2y+1} dy - \int \frac{1}{y+1} dy = \frac{3}{2}\ln|2y+1| - \ln|y+1| + C.$$

41. Since $x^3 + x = x(x^2 + 1)$ cannot be factored further, we write

$$\frac{x+1}{x^3+x} = \frac{A}{x} + \frac{Bx+C}{x^2+1}.$$

Multiplying by $x(x^2 + 1)$ gives

$$x + 1 = A(x^2 + 1) + (Bx + C)x$$
$$x + 1 = (A + B)x^2 + Cx + A,$$

so

$$A + B = 0$$
$$C = 1$$
$$A = 1.$$

Thus, $A = C = 1$, $B = -1$, and we have

$$\int \frac{x+1}{x^3+x}\,dx = \int \left(\frac{1}{x} + \frac{-x+1}{x^2+1}\right) = \int \frac{dx}{x} - \int \frac{x\,dx}{x^2+1} + \int \frac{dx}{x^2+1}$$
$$= \ln|x| - \frac{1}{2}\ln\left|x^2+1\right| + \arctan x + K.$$

42. Since $x^2 + x^4 = x^2(1 + x^2)$ cannot be factored further, we write

$$\frac{x-2}{x^2+x^4} = \frac{A}{x} + \frac{B}{x^2} + \frac{Cx+D}{1+x^2}.$$

Multiplying by $x^2(1 + x^2)$ gives

$$x - 2 = Ax(1 + x^2) + B(1 + x^2) + (Cx + D)x^2$$
$$x - 2 = (A + C)x^3 + (B + D)x^2 + Ax + B,$$

so

$$A + C = 0$$
$$B + D = 0$$
$$A = 1$$
$$B = -2.$$

Thus, $A = 1$, $B = -2$, $C = -1$, $D = 2$, and we have

$$\int \frac{x-2}{x^2+x^4}\,dx = \int \left(\frac{1}{x} - \frac{2}{x^2} + \frac{-x+2}{1+x^2}\right)\,dx = \int \frac{dx}{x} - 2\int \frac{dx}{x^2} - \int \frac{x\,dx}{1+x^2} + 2\int \frac{dx}{1+x^2}$$
$$= \ln|x| + \frac{2}{x} - \frac{1}{2}\ln\left|1+x^2\right| + 2\arctan x + K.$$

43. Let $x = 3\sin\theta$ so $dx = 3\cos\theta\,d\theta$, giving

$$\int \frac{x^2}{\sqrt{9-x^2}}\,dx = \int \frac{9\sin^2\theta}{\sqrt{9-9\sin^2\theta}}\,3\cos\theta\,d\theta = \int \frac{(9\sin^2\theta)(3\cos\theta)}{3\cos\theta}\,d\theta = 9\int \sin^2\theta\,d\theta.$$

Integrating by parts and using the identity $\cos^2\theta + \sin^2\theta = 1$ gives

$$\int \sin^2\theta\,d\theta = -\sin\theta\cos\theta + \int \cos^2\theta\,d\theta = -\sin\theta\cos\theta + \int (1 - \sin^2\theta)\,d\theta$$

$$\int \sin^2\theta\,d\theta = -\frac{1}{2}\sin\theta\cos\theta + \frac{\theta}{2} + C.$$

Since $\sin\theta = x/3$ and $\cos\theta = \sqrt{1 - x^2/9} = \sqrt{9 - x^2}/3$, and $\theta = \arcsin(x/3)$, we have

$$\int \frac{x^2}{\sqrt{9 - x^2}}\, dx = 9 \int \sin^2\theta\, d\theta = -\frac{9}{2}\sin\theta\cos\theta + \frac{9}{2}\theta + C$$

$$= -\frac{9}{2}\cdot\frac{x}{3}\frac{\sqrt{9 - x^2}}{3} + \frac{9}{2}\arcsin\left(\frac{x}{3}\right) + C = -\frac{x}{2}\sqrt{9 - x^2} + \frac{9}{2}\arcsin\left(\frac{x}{3}\right) + C$$

44. Let $y = 5\tan\theta$ so $dy = (5/\cos^2\theta)\, d\theta$. Since $1 + \tan^2\theta = 1/\cos^2\theta$, we have

$$\int \frac{y^2}{25 + y^2}\, dy = \int \frac{25\tan^2\theta}{25(1 + \tan^2\theta)}\cdot\frac{5}{\cos^2\theta}\, d\theta = 5\int \tan^2\theta\, d\theta.$$

Using $1 + \tan^2\theta = 1/\cos^2\theta$ again gives

$$\int \frac{y^2}{25 + y^2}\, dy = 5\int \tan^2\theta\, d\theta = 5\int \left(\frac{1}{\cos^2\theta} - 1\right) d\theta = 5\tan\theta - 5\theta + C.$$

In addition, since $\theta = \arctan(y/5)$, we get

$$\int \frac{y^2}{25 + y^2}\, dy = y - 5\arctan\left(\frac{y}{5}\right) + C.$$

45. Let $t = \tan\theta$ so $dt = (1/\cos^2\theta)d\theta$. Since $\sqrt{1 + \tan^2\theta} = 1/\cos\theta$, we have

$$\int \frac{dt}{t^2\sqrt{1 + t^2}} = \int \frac{1/\cos^2\theta}{\tan^2\theta\sqrt{1 + \tan^2\theta}}\, d\theta = \int \frac{\cos\theta}{\tan^2\theta\cos^2\theta}\, d\theta = \int \frac{\cos\theta}{\sin^2\theta}\, d\theta.$$

The last integral can be evaluated by guess-and-check or by substituting $w = \sin\theta$. The result is

$$\int \frac{dt}{t^2\sqrt{1 + t^2}} = \int \frac{\cos\theta}{\sin^2\theta}\, d\theta = -\frac{1}{\sin\theta} + C.$$

Since $t = \tan\theta$ and $1/\cos^2\theta = 1 + \tan^2\theta$, we have

$$\cos\theta = \frac{1}{\sqrt{1 + \tan^2\theta}} = \frac{1}{\sqrt{1 + t^2}}.$$

In addition, $\tan\theta = \sin\theta/\cos\theta$ so

$$\sin\theta = \tan\theta\cos\theta = \frac{t}{\sqrt{1 + t^2}}.$$

Thus

$$\int \frac{dt}{t^2\sqrt{1 + t^2}} = -\frac{\sqrt{1 + t^2}}{t} + C.$$

46. Since $(4 - z^2)^{3/2} = (\sqrt{4 - z^2})^3$, we substitute $z = 2\sin\theta$, so $dz = 2\cos\theta\, d\theta$. We get

$$\int \frac{dz}{(4 - z^2)^{3/2}} = \int \frac{2\cos\theta\, d\theta}{(4 - 4\sin^2\theta)^{3/2}} = \int \frac{2\cos\theta\, d\theta}{8\cos^3\theta} = \frac{1}{4}\int \frac{d\theta}{\cos^2\theta} = \frac{1}{4}\tan\theta + C$$

Since $\sin\theta = z/2$, we have $\cos\theta = \sqrt{1 - (z/2)^2} = (\sqrt{4 - z^2})/2$, so

$$\int \frac{dz}{(4 - z^2)^{3/2}} = \frac{1}{4}\tan\theta + C = \frac{1}{4}\frac{\sin\theta}{\cos\theta} + C = \frac{1}{4}\frac{z/2}{(\sqrt{4 - z^2})/2} + C = \frac{z}{4\sqrt{4 - z^2}} + C$$

47. We have

$$\frac{10}{(s + 2)(s^2 + 1)} = \frac{A}{s + 2} + \frac{Bs + C}{s^2 + 1}.$$

Thus,

$$10 = A(s^2 + 1) + (Bs + C)(s + 2)$$
$$10 = (A + B)s^2 + (2B + C)s + (A + 2C),$$

giving

$$A + B = 0$$
$$2B + C = 0$$
$$A + 2C = 10.$$

Thus, from the first two equations we have $C = -2B = 2A$, which, when used in the third, gives $5A = 10$, so that $A = 2$, $B = -2$, and $C = 4$. We now have

$$\frac{10}{(s+2)(s^2+1)} = \frac{2}{s+2} + \frac{-2s+4}{s^2+1} = \frac{2}{s+2} - \frac{2s}{s^2+1} + \frac{4}{s^2+1},$$

so

$$\int \frac{10}{(s+2)(s^2+1)}\, ds = \int \left(\frac{2}{s+2} - \frac{2s}{s^2+1} + \frac{4}{s^2+1}\right)\, ds = 2\ln|s+2| - \ln\left|s^2+1\right| + 4\arctan s + C.$$

48. Completing the square, we get

$$x^2 + 4x + 13 = (x+2)^2 + 9.$$

We use the substitution $x + 2 = 3\tan t$, then $dx = (3/\cos^2 t)\, dt$. Since $\tan^2 t + 1 = 1/\cos^2 t$, the integral becomes

$$\int \frac{1}{(x+2)^2+9}\, dx = \int \frac{1}{9\tan^2 t + 9}\cdot\frac{3}{\cos^2 t}\, dt = \int \frac{1}{3}\, dt = \frac{1}{3}\arctan\left(\frac{x+2}{3}\right) + C.$$

49. Using the substitution $w = e^x$, we get $dw = e^x dx$, so we have

$$\int \frac{e^x}{(e^x - 1)(e^x + 2)}\, dx = \int \frac{dw}{(w-1)(w+2)}.$$

But

$$\frac{1}{(w-1)(w+2)} = \frac{1}{3}\left(\frac{1}{w-1} - \frac{1}{w+2}\right),$$

so

$$\int \frac{e^x}{(e^x - 1)(e^x + 2)}\, dx = \int \frac{1}{3}\left(\frac{1}{w-1} - \frac{1}{w+2}\right)\, dw$$
$$= \frac{1}{3}(\ln|w-1| - \ln|w+2|) + C$$
$$= \frac{1}{3}(\ln|e^x - 1| - \ln|e^x + 2|) + C.$$

50. Notice that because $\frac{3x}{(x-1)(x-4)}$ is negative for $2 \le x \le 3$,

$$\text{Area} = -\int_2^3 \frac{3x}{(x-1)(x-4)}\, dx.$$

Using partial fractions gives

$$\frac{3x}{(x-1)(x-4)} = \frac{A}{x-1} + \frac{B}{x-4} = \frac{(A+B)x - B - 4A}{(x-1)(x-4)}.$$

Multiplying through by $(x-1)(x-4)$ gives

$$3x = (A+B)x - B - 4A$$

so $A = -1$ and $B = 4$. Thus

$$-\int_2^3 \frac{3x}{(x-1)(x-4)}\, dx = -\int_2^3 \left(\frac{-1}{x-1} + \frac{4}{x-4}\right)\, dx = \left.(\ln|x-1| - 4\ln|x-4|)\right|_2^3 = 5\ln 2.$$

51. We have

$$\text{Area} = \int_0^1 \frac{3x^2 + x}{(x^2 + 1)(x + 1)}\,dx.$$

Using partial fractions gives

$$\frac{3x^2 + x}{(x^2 + 1)(x + 1)} = \frac{Ax + B}{x^2 + 1} + \frac{C}{x + 1}$$

$$= \frac{(Ax + B)(x + 1) + C(x^2 + 1)}{(x^2 + 1)(x + 1)}$$

$$= \frac{(A + C)x^2 + (A + B)x + B + C}{(x^2 + 1)(x + 1)}.$$

Thus

$$3x^2 + x = (A + C)x^2 + (A + B)x + B + C,$$

giving

$$3 = A + C, \quad 1 = A + B, \quad \text{and} \quad 0 = B + C,$$

with solution

$$A = 2, B = -1, C = 1.$$

Thus

$$\text{Area} = \int_0^1 \frac{3x^2 + x}{(x^2 + 1)(x + 1)}\,dx$$

$$= \int_0^1 \left(\frac{2x}{x^2 + 1} - \frac{1}{x^2 + 1} + \frac{1}{x + 1} \right)\,dx$$

$$= \ln(x^2 + 1) - \arctan x + \ln|x + 1| \Big|_0^1$$

$$= 2\ln 2 - \pi/4.$$

52. We have

$$\text{Area} = \int_0^{1/2} \frac{x^2}{\sqrt{1 - x^2}}\,dx.$$

Let $x = \sin\theta$ so $dx = \cos\theta\,d\theta$ and $\sqrt{1 - x^2} = \sqrt{1 - \sin^2\theta} = \cos\theta$. When $x = 0, \theta = 0$. When $x = 1/2, \theta = \pi/6$.

$$\int_0^{1/2} \frac{x^2}{\sqrt{1 - x^2}}\,dx = \int_0^{\pi/6} \frac{\sin^2\theta}{\sqrt{1 - \sin^2\theta}} \cos\theta\,d\theta = \int_0^{\pi/6} \sin^2\theta\,d\theta$$

$$= \left(\frac{\theta}{2} - \frac{\sin\theta\cos\theta}{2} \right) \Big|_0^{\pi/6} = \frac{\pi}{12} - \frac{\sqrt{3}}{8}.$$

The integral $\int \sin^2\theta\,d\theta$ is done using parts and the identity $\cos^2\theta + \sin^2\theta = 1$.

53. We have

$$\text{Area} = \int_0^{\sqrt{2}} \frac{x^3}{\sqrt{4 - x^2}}\,dx.$$

Let $x = 2\sin\theta$ so $dx = 2\cos\theta\,d\theta$ and $\sqrt{4 - x^2} = \sqrt{4 - 4\sin^2\theta} = 2\cos\theta$. When $x = 0, \theta = 0$ and when $x = \sqrt{2}, \theta = \pi/4$.

$$\int_0^{\sqrt{2}} \frac{x^3}{\sqrt{4 - x^2}}\,dx = \int_0^{\pi/4} \frac{(2\sin\theta)^3}{\sqrt{4 - (2\sin\theta)^2}} 2\cos\theta\,d\theta$$

$$= 8\int_0^{\pi/4} \sin^3\theta\,d\theta = 8\int_0^{\pi/4} (\sin\theta - \sin\theta\cos^2\theta)\,d\theta$$

$$= 8\left(-\cos\theta + \frac{\cos^3\theta}{3} \right) \Big|_0^{\pi/4} = 8\left(\frac{2}{3} - \frac{5}{6\sqrt{2}} \right).$$

54. We have

$$\text{Area} = \int_0^3 \frac{1}{\sqrt{x^2+9}} \, dx.$$

Let $x = 3\tan\theta$ so $dx = (3/\cos^2\theta)d\theta$ and

$$\sqrt{x^2+9} = \sqrt{\frac{9\sin^2\theta}{\cos^2\theta}+9} = \frac{3}{\cos\theta}.$$

When $x = 0, \theta = 0$ and when $x = 3, \theta = \pi/4$. Thus

$$\int_0^3 \frac{1}{\sqrt{x^2+9}}\,dx = \int_0^{\pi/4} \frac{1}{\sqrt{9\tan^2\theta+9}} \frac{3}{\cos^2\theta}\,d\theta = \int_0^{\pi/4} \frac{1}{3/\cos\theta} \cdot \frac{3}{\cos^2\theta}\,d\theta = \int_0^{\pi/4} \frac{1}{\cos\theta}\,d\theta$$

$$= \frac{1}{2}\ln\left|\frac{\sin\theta+1}{\sin\theta-1}\right|\Bigg|_0^{\pi/4} = \frac{1}{2}\ln\left|\frac{1/\sqrt{2}+1}{1/\sqrt{2}-1}\right| = \frac{1}{2}\ln\left(\frac{1+\sqrt{2}}{\sqrt{2}-1}\right).$$

This answer can be simplified to $\ln(1+\sqrt{2})$ by multiplying the numerator and denominator of the fraction by $(\sqrt{2}+1)$ and using the properties of logarithms. The integral $\int(1/\cos\theta)d\theta$ is done using the Table of Integrals.

55. We have

$$\text{Area} = \int_{\sqrt{3}}^3 \frac{1}{x\sqrt{x^2+9}} \, dx.$$

Let $x = 3\tan\theta$ so $dx = (3/\cos^2\theta)d\theta$ and

$$x\sqrt{x^2+9} = 3\frac{\sin\theta}{\cos\theta}\sqrt{\frac{9\sin^2\theta}{\cos^2\theta}+9} = \frac{9\sin\theta}{\cos^2\theta}.$$

When $x = \sqrt{3}, \theta = \pi/6$ and when $x = 3, \theta = \pi/4$. Thus

$$\int_{\sqrt{3}}^3 \frac{1}{x\sqrt{x^2+9}}\,dx = \int_{\pi/6}^{\pi/4} \frac{1}{9\sin\theta/\cos^2\theta} \cdot \frac{3}{\cos^2\theta}\,d\theta = \frac{1}{3}\int_{\pi/6}^{\pi/4} \frac{1}{\sin\theta}\,d\theta$$

$$= \frac{1}{3}\cdot\frac{1}{2}\ln\left|\frac{\cos\theta-1}{\cos\theta+1}\right|\Bigg|_{\pi/6}^{\pi/4} = \frac{1}{6}\left(\ln\left|\frac{1/\sqrt{2}-1}{1/\sqrt{2}+1}\right| - \ln\left|\frac{\sqrt{3}/2-1}{\sqrt{3}/2+1}\right|\right)$$

$$= \frac{1}{6}\left(\ln\left|\frac{1-\sqrt{2}}{1+\sqrt{2}}\right| + \ln\left|\frac{\sqrt{3}+2}{\sqrt{3}-2}\right|\right).$$

This answer can be simplified by multiplying the first fraction by $(1-\sqrt{2})$ in numerator and denominator and the second one by $(\sqrt{3}+2)$. This gives

$$\text{Area} = \frac{1}{6}\left(\ln(3-2\sqrt{2}) + \ln(7+4\sqrt{3})\right) = \frac{1}{6}\ln((3-2\sqrt{2})(7+4\sqrt{3})).$$

The integral $\int(1/\sin\theta)d\theta$ is done using the Table of Integrals.

56. Using partial fractions, we write

$$\frac{1}{1-x^2} = \frac{A}{1+x} + \frac{B}{1-x}$$
$$1 = A(1-x) + B(1+x) = (B-A)x + A + B.$$

So, $B - A = 0$ and $A + B = 1$, giving $A = B = 1/2$. Thus

$$\int \frac{dx}{1-x^2} = \frac{1}{2}\int\left(\frac{1}{1+x} + \frac{1}{1-x}\right)\,dx = \frac{1}{2}\left(\ln|1+x| - \ln|1-x|\right) + C.$$

Using the substitution $x = \sin\theta$, we get $dx = \cos\theta\,d\theta$, we have

$$\int \frac{dx}{1-x^2} = \int \frac{\cos\theta}{1-\sin^2\theta}\,d\theta = \int \frac{\cos\theta}{\cos^2\theta}\,d\theta = \int \frac{1}{\cos\theta}\,d\theta.$$

The Table of Integrals Formula IV-22 gives

$$\int \frac{dx}{1 - x^2} = \int \frac{1}{\cos \theta} \, d\theta = \frac{1}{2} \ln \left| \frac{(\sin \theta) + 1}{(\sin \theta) - 1} \right| + C = \frac{1}{2} \ln \left| \frac{x + 1}{x - 1} \right| + C.$$

The properties of logarithms and the fact that $|x - 1| = |1 - x|$ show that the two results are the same:

$$\frac{1}{2} \ln \left| \frac{x + 1}{x - 1} \right| = \frac{1}{2} \left(\ln |1 + x| - \ln |1 - x| \right).$$

57. Using partial fractions, we write

$$\frac{2x}{x^2 - 1} = \frac{A}{x + 1} + \frac{B}{x - 1}$$
$$2x = A(x - 1) + B(x + 1) = (A + B)x - A + B.$$

So, $A + B = 2$ and $-A + B = 0$, giving $A = B = 1$. Thus

$$\int \frac{2x}{x^2 - 1} \, dx = \int \left(\frac{1}{x + 1} + \frac{1}{x - 1} \right) \, dx = \ln |x + 1| + \ln |x - 1| + C.$$

Using the substitution $w = x^2 - 1$, we get $dw = 2x \, dx$, so we have

$$\int \frac{2x}{x^2 - 1} \, dx = \int \frac{dw}{w} = \ln |w| + C = \ln \left| x^2 - 1 \right| + C.$$

The properties of logarithms show that the two results are the same:

$$\ln |x + 1| + \ln |x - 1| = \ln |(x + 1)(x - 1)| = \ln \left| x^2 - 1 \right|.$$

58. Using partial fractions, we write

$$\frac{3x^2 + 1}{x^3 + x} = \frac{3x^2 + 1}{x(x^2 + 1)} = \frac{A}{x} + \frac{Bx + C}{x^2 + 1}$$
$$3x^2 + 1 = A(x^2 + 1) + (Bx + C)x = (A + B)x^2 + Cx + A.$$

So, $A + B = 3$, $C = 0$ and $A = 1$, giving $B = 2$. Thus

$$\int \frac{3x^2 + 1}{x^3 + x} \, dx = \int \left(\frac{1}{x} + \frac{2x}{x^2 + 1} \right) \, dx = \ln |x| + \ln \left| x^2 + 1 \right| + C.$$

Using the substitution $w = x^3 + x$, we get $dw = (3x^2 + 1)dx$, so we have

$$\int \frac{3x^2 + 1}{x^3 + x} \, dx = \int \frac{dw}{w} = \ln |w| + C = \ln \left| x^3 + x \right| + C.$$

The properties of logarithms show that the two results are the same:

$$\ln |x| + \ln \left| x^2 + 1 \right| + C = \ln \left| x(x^2 + 1) \right| + C = \ln \left| x^3 + x \right| + C.$$

59. (a) We differentiate:

$$\frac{d}{d\theta} \left(-\frac{1}{\tan \theta} \right) = \frac{1}{\tan^2 \theta} \cdot \frac{1}{\cos^2 \theta} = \frac{1}{\frac{\sin^2 \theta}{\cos^2 \theta}} \cdot \frac{1}{\cos^2 \theta} = \frac{1}{\sin^2 \theta}.$$

Thus,

$$\int \frac{1}{\sin^2 \theta} \, d\theta = -\frac{1}{\tan \theta} + C.$$

(b) Let $y = \sqrt{5} \sin \theta$ so $dy = \sqrt{5} \cos \theta \, d\theta$ giving

$$\int \frac{dy}{y^2 \sqrt{5 - y^2}} = \int \frac{\sqrt{5} \cos \theta}{5 \sin^2 \theta \sqrt{5 - 5 \sin^2 \theta}} \, d\theta = \frac{1}{5} \int \frac{\sqrt{5} \cos \theta}{\sin^2 \theta \sqrt{5} \cos \theta} \, d\theta$$

$$= \frac{1}{5} \int \frac{1}{\sin^2 \theta} \, d\theta = -\frac{1}{5 \tan \theta} + C.$$

Since $\sin \theta = y/\sqrt{5}$, we have $\cos \theta = \sqrt{1 - (y/\sqrt{5})^2} = \sqrt{5 - y^2}/\sqrt{5}$. Thus,

$$\int \frac{dy}{y^2 \sqrt{5 - y^2}} = -\frac{1}{5 \tan \theta} + C = -\frac{\sqrt{5 - y^2}/\sqrt{5}}{5(y/\sqrt{5})} + C = -\frac{\sqrt{5 - y^2}}{5y} + C.$$

60. (a) If $a \neq b$, we have

$$\int \frac{1}{(x-a)(x-b)} \, dx = \int \frac{1}{a-b} \left(\frac{1}{x-a} - \frac{1}{x-b} \right) dx = \frac{1}{a-b} (\ln|x-a| - \ln|x-b|) + C.$$

(b) If $a = b$, we have

$$\int \frac{1}{(x-a)(x-a)} \, dx = \int \frac{1}{(x-a)^2} \, dx = -\frac{1}{x-a} + C.$$

61. (a) If $a \neq b$, we have

$$\int \frac{x}{(x-a)(x-b)} \, dx = \int \frac{1}{a-b} \left(\frac{a}{x-a} - \frac{b}{x-b} \right) dx = \frac{1}{a-b} (a \ln|x-a| - b \ln|x-b|) + C.$$

(b) If $a = b$, we have

$$\int \frac{x}{(x-a)^2} \, dx = \int \left(\frac{1}{x-a} + \frac{a}{(x-a)^2} \right) dx = \ln|x-a| - \frac{a}{x-a} + C.$$

62. (a) If $a > 0$, then

$$x^2 - a = (x - \sqrt{a})(x + \sqrt{a}).$$

This means that we can use partial fractions:

$$\frac{1}{x^2 - a} = \frac{A}{x - \sqrt{a}} + \frac{B}{x + \sqrt{a}},$$

giving

$$1 = A(x + \sqrt{a}) + B(x - \sqrt{a}),$$

so $A + B = 0$ and $(A - B)\sqrt{a} = 1$. Thus, $A = -B = 1/(2\sqrt{a})$.

So

$$\int \frac{1}{x^2 - a} \, dx = \int \frac{1}{2\sqrt{a}} \left(\frac{1}{x - \sqrt{a}} - \frac{1}{x + \sqrt{a}} \right) dx = \frac{1}{2\sqrt{a}} (\ln|x - \sqrt{a}| - \ln|x + \sqrt{a}|) + C.$$

(b) If $a = 0$, we have

$$\int \frac{1}{x^2} \, dx = -\frac{1}{x} + C.$$

(c) If $a < 0$, then $-a > 0$ so $x^2 - a = x^2 + (-a)$ cannot be factored. Thus

$$\int \frac{1}{x^2 - a} \, dx = \int \frac{1}{x^2 + (-a)} \, dx = \frac{1}{\sqrt{-a}} \arctan \left(\frac{x}{\sqrt{-a}} \right) + C.$$

63. (a) We integrate to find

$$\int \frac{b}{x(1-x)} \, dx = b \int \left(\frac{1}{x} + \frac{1}{1-x} \right) dx = b(\ln|x| - \ln|1-x|) + C = b \ln \left| \frac{x}{1-x} \right| + C,$$

so

$$t(p) = \int_a^p \frac{b}{x(1-x)} \, dx = b \ln \left(\frac{p}{1-p} \right) - b \ln \left(\frac{a}{1-a} \right) = b \ln \left(\frac{p(1-a)}{a(1-p)} \right).$$

(b) We know that $t(0.01) = 0$ so

$$0 = b \ln \left(\frac{0.01(1-a)}{0.99a} \right).$$

But $b > 0$ and $\ln x = 0$ means $x = 1$, so

$$\frac{0.01(1-a)}{0.99a} = 1$$
$$0.01(1-a) = 0.99a$$
$$0.01 - 0.01a = 0.99a$$
$$a = 0.01.$$

(c) We know that $t(0.5) = 1$ so

$$1 = b \ln \left(\frac{0.5 \cdot 0.99}{0.5 \cdot 0.01} \right) = b \ln 99, b = \frac{1}{\ln 99} = 0.218.$$

(d) We have

$$t(0.9) = \int_{0.01}^{0.9} \frac{0.218}{x(1-x)} \, dx = \frac{1}{\ln 99} \ln \left(\frac{0.9(1 - 0.01)}{0.01(1 - 0.9)} \right) = 1.478.$$

64. (a) We want to evaluate the integral

$$T = \int_0^{a/2} \frac{k \, dx}{(a - x)(b - x)}.$$

Using partial fractions, we have

$$\frac{k}{(a - x)(b - x)} = \frac{C}{a - x} + \frac{D}{b - x}$$

$$k = C(b - x) + D(a - x)$$

$$k = -(C + D)x + Cb + Da$$

so

$$0 = -(C + D)$$

$$k = Cb + Da,$$

giving

$$C = -D = \frac{k}{b - a}.$$

Thus, the time is given by

$$T = \int_0^{a/2} \frac{k \, dx}{(a - x)(b - x)} = \frac{k}{b - a} \int_0^{a/2} \left(\frac{1}{a - x} - \frac{1}{b - x} \right) dx$$

$$= \frac{k}{b - a} \left(-\ln|a - x| + \ln|b - x| \right) \Big|_0^{a/2}$$

$$= \frac{k}{b - a} \ln \left| \frac{b - x}{a - x} \right| \Big|_0^{a/2}$$

$$= \frac{k}{b - a} \left(\ln \left(\frac{2b - a}{a} \right) - \ln \left(\frac{b}{a} \right) \right)$$

$$= \frac{k}{b - a} \ln \left(\frac{2b - a}{b} \right).$$

(b) A similar calculation with x_0 instead of $a/2$ leads to the following expression for the time

$$T = \int_0^{x_0} \frac{k \, dx}{(a - x)(b - x)} = \frac{k}{b - a} \ln \left| \frac{b - x}{a - x} \right| \Big|_0^{x_0}$$

$$= \frac{k}{b - a} \left(\ln \left| \frac{b - x_0}{a - x_0} \right| - \ln \left(\frac{b}{a} \right) \right).$$

As $x_0 \to a$, the value of $|a - x_0| \to 0$, so $|b - x_0|/|a - x_0| \to \infty$. Thus, $T \to \infty$ as $x_0 \to a$. In other words, the time taken tends to infinity.

Solutions for Section 7.5

Exercises

1. (a) The approximation LEFT(2) uses two rectangles, with the height of each rectangle determined by the left-hand endpoint. See Figure 7.3. We see that this approximation is an underestimate.

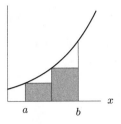

Figure 7.3

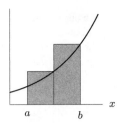

Figure 7.4

(b) The approximation RIGHT(2) uses two rectangles, with the height of each rectangle determined by the right-hand endpoint. See Figure 7.4. We see that this approximation is an overestimate.

(c) The approximation TRAP(2) uses two trapezoids, with the height of each trapezoid given by the secant line connecting the two endpoints. See Figure 7.5. We see that this approximation is an overestimate.

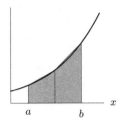

Figure 7.5

(d) The approximation MID(2) uses two rectangles, with the height of each rectangle determined by the height at the midpoint. Alternately, we can view MID(2) as a trapezoid rule where the height is given by the tangent line at the midpoint. Both interpretations are shown in Figure 7.6. We see from the tangent line interpretation that this approximation is an underestimate

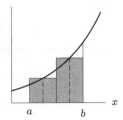

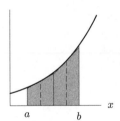

Figure 7.6

2. (a) The approximation LEFT(2) uses two rectangles, with the height of each rectangle determined by the left-hand endpoint. See Figure 7.7. We see that this approximation is an overestimate.

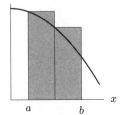

Figure 7.7

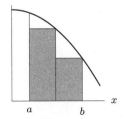

Figure 7.8

(b) The approximation RIGHT(2) uses two rectangles, with the height of each rectangle determined by the right-hand endpoint. See Figure 7.8. We see that this approximation is an underestimate.

(c) The approximation TRAP(2) uses two trapezoids, with the height of each trapezoid given by the secant line connecting the two endpoints. See Figure 7.9. We see that this approximation is an underestimate.

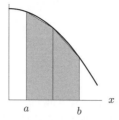

Figure 7.9

(d) The approximation MID(2) uses two rectangles, with the height of each rectangle determined by the height at the midpoint. Alternately, we can view MID(2) as a trapezoid rule where the height is given by the tangent line at the midpoint. Both interpretations are shown in Figure 7.10. We see from the tangent line interpretation that this approximation is an overestimate.

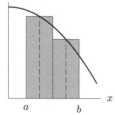   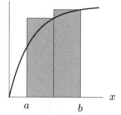

Figure 7.10

3. (a) The approximation LEFT(2) uses two rectangles, with the height of each rectangle determined by the left-hand endpoint. See Figure 7.11. We see that this approximation is an underestimate.

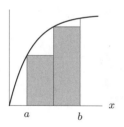

Figure 7.11   **Figure 7.12**

(b) The approximation RIGHT(2) uses two rectangles, with the height of each rectangle determined by the right-hand endpoint. See Figure 7.12. We see that this approximation is an overestimate.

(c) The approximation TRAP(2) uses two trapezoids, with the height of each trapezoid given by the secant line connecting the two endpoints. See Figure 7.13. We see that this approximation is an underestimate.

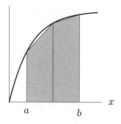

Figure 7.13

(d) The approximation MID(2) uses two rectangles, with the height of each rectangle determined by the height at the midpoint. Alternately, we can view MID(2) as a trapezoid rule where the height is given by the tangent line at the midpoint. Both interpretations are shown in Figure 7.14. We see from the tangent line interpretation that this approximation is an overestimate.

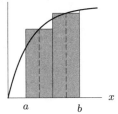 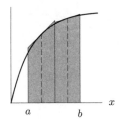

Figure 7.14

4. (a) The approximation LEFT(2) uses two rectangles, with the height of each rectangle determined by the left-hand endpoint. See Figure 7.15. We see that this approximation is an overestimate.

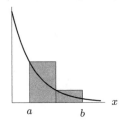 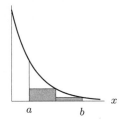

Figure 7.15   **Figure 7.16**

(b) The approximation RIGHT(2) uses two rectangles, with the height of each rectangle determined by the right-hand endpoint. See Figure 7.16. We see that this approximation is an underestimate.

(c) The approximation TRAP(2) uses two trapezoids, with the height of each trapezoid given by the secant line connecting the two endpoints. See Figure 7.17. We see that this approximation is an overestimate.

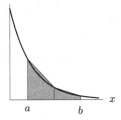

Figure 7.17

(d) The approximation MID(2) uses two rectangles, with the height of each rectangle determined by the height at the midpoint. Alternately, we can view MID(2) as a trapezoid rule where the height is given by the tangent line at the midpoint. Both interpretations are shown in Figure 7.18. We see from the tangent line interpretation that this approximation is an underestimate.

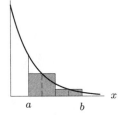 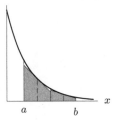

Figure 7.18

5. (a) The approximation LEFT(2) uses two rectangles, with the height of each rectangle determined by the left-hand endpoint. See Figure 7.19. We see that this approximation is an underestimate (that is, it is more negative).

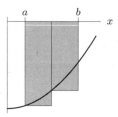

Figure 7.19

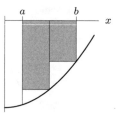

Figure 7.20

(b) The approximation RIGHT(2) uses two rectangles, with the height of each rectangle determined by the right-hand endpoint. See Figure 7.20. We see that this approximation is an overestimate (that is, it is less negative).

(c) The approximation TRAP(2) uses two trapezoids, with the height of each trapezoid given by the secant line connecting the two endpoints. See Figure 7.21. We see that this approximation is an overestimate (that is, it is less negative).

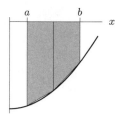

Figure 7.21

(d) The approximation MID(2) uses two rectangles, with the height of each rectangle determined by the height at the midpoint. Alternately, we can view MID(2) as a trapezoid rule where the height is given by the tangent line at the midpoint. Both interpretations are shown in Figure 7.22. We see from the tangent line interpretation that this approximation is an underestimate (that is, it is more negative).

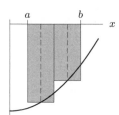

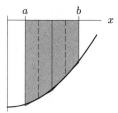

Figure 7.22

6. (a) The approximation LEFT(2) uses two rectangles, with the height of each rectangle determined by the left-hand endpoint. See Figure 7.23. We see that this approximation is an overestimate (that is, it is less negative).

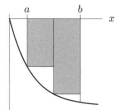

Figure 7.23

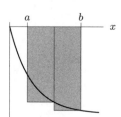

Figure 7.24

(b) The approximation RIGHT(2) uses two rectangles, with the height of each rectangle determined by the right-hand endpoint. See Figure 7.24. We see that this approximation is an underestimate (that is, it is more negative).

(c) The approximation TRAP(2) uses two trapezoids, with the height of each trapezoid given by the secant line connecting the two endpoints. See Figure 7.25. We see that this approximation is an overestimate (that is, it is less negative).

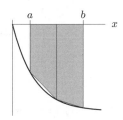

Figure 7.25

(d) The approximation MID(2) uses two rectangles, with the height of each rectangle determined by the height at the midpoint. Alternately, we can view MID(2) as a trapezoid rule where the height is given by the tangent line at the midpoint. Both interpretations are shown in Figure 7.26. We see from the tangent line interpretation that this approximation is an underestimate (that is, the approximation is more negative).

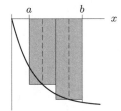   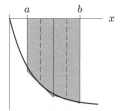

Figure 7.26

7. (a) Since two rectangles are being used, the width of each rectangle is 3. The height is given by the left-hand endpoint so we have

$$\text{LEFT}(2) = f(0) \cdot 3 + f(3) \cdot 3 = 0^2 \cdot 3 + 3^2 \cdot 3 = 27.$$

(b) Since two rectangles are being used, the width of each rectangle is 3. The height is given by the right-hand endpoint so we have

$$\text{RIGHT}(2) = f(3) \cdot 3 + f(6) \cdot 3 = 3^2 \cdot 3 + 6^2 \cdot 3 = 135.$$

(c) We know that TRAP is the average of LEFT and RIGHT and so

$$\text{TRAP}(2) = \frac{27 + 135}{2} = 81.$$

(d) Since two rectangles are being used, the width of each rectangle is 3. The height is given by the height at the midpoint so we have

$$\text{MID}(2) = f(1.5) \cdot 3 + f(4.5) \cdot 3 = (1.5)^2 \cdot 3 + (4.5)^2 \cdot 3 = 67.5.$$

8. (a)

$$
\begin{aligned}
\text{LEFT}(2) &= 2 \cdot f(0) + 2 \cdot f(2) \\
&= 2 \cdot 1 + 2 \cdot 5 \\
&= 12 \\
\text{RIGHT}(2) &= 2 \cdot f(2) + 2 \cdot f(4) \\
&= 2 \cdot 5 + 2 \cdot 17 \\
&= 44
\end{aligned}
$$

(b)

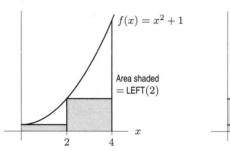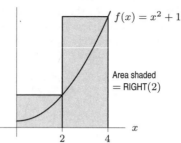

LEFT(2) is an underestimate, while RIGHT(2) is an overestimate.

9. (a)

$$MID(2) = 2 \cdot f(1) + 2 \cdot f(3)$$
$$= 2 \cdot 2 + 2 \cdot 10$$
$$= 24$$
$$TRAP(2) = \frac{LEFT(2) + RIGHT(2)}{2}$$
$$= \frac{12 + 44}{2} \quad \text{(see Problem 8)}$$
$$= 28$$

(b)

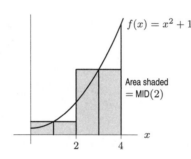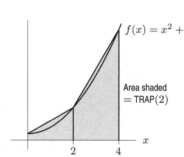

MID(2) is an underestimate, since $f(x) = x^2 + 1$ is concave up and a tangent line will be below the curve. TRAP(2) is an overestimate, since a secant line lies above the curve.

10. (a) Since two rectangles are being used, the width of each rectangle is $\pi/2$. The height is given by the left-hand endpoint so we have

$$LEFT(2) = f(0) \cdot \frac{pi}{2} + f(\pi/2) \cdot \frac{pi}{2} = \sin 0 \cdot \frac{pi}{2} + \sin(\pi/2) \cdot \frac{pi}{2} = \frac{pi}{2}.$$

(b) Since two rectangles are being used, the width of each rectangle is $\pi/2$. The height is given by the right-hand endpoint so we have

$$RIGHT(2) = f(\pi/2) \cdot \frac{pi}{2} + f(\pi) \cdot \frac{pi}{2} = \sin(\pi/2) \cdot \frac{pi}{2} + \sin(\pi) \cdot \frac{pi}{2} = \frac{pi}{2}.$$

(c) We know that TRAP is the average of LEFT and RIGHT and so

$$TRAP(2) = \frac{\frac{pi}{2} + \frac{pi}{2}}{2} = \frac{pi}{2}.$$

(d) Since two rectangles are being used, the width of each rectangle is $\pi/2$. The height is given by the height at the midpoint so we have

$$MID(2) = f(\pi/4) \cdot \frac{pi}{2} + f(3\pi/4) \cdot \frac{pi}{2} = \sin(\pi/4) \cdot \frac{pi}{2} + \sin(3\pi/4) \cdot \frac{pi}{2} = \frac{\sqrt{2}\pi}{2}.$$

Problems

11. (a) (i) Let $f(x) = \frac{1}{1+x^2}$. The left-hand Riemann sum is

$$\frac{1}{8}\left(f(0) + f\left(\frac{1}{8}\right) + f\left(\frac{2}{8}\right) + \cdots + f\left(\frac{7}{8}\right)\right)$$
$$= \frac{1}{8}\left(\frac{64}{64} + \frac{64}{65} + \frac{64}{68} + \frac{64}{73} + \frac{64}{80} + \frac{64}{89} + \frac{64}{100} + \frac{64}{113}\right)$$
$$\approx 8(0.1020) = 0.8160.$$

(ii) Let $f(x) = \frac{1}{1+x^2}$. The right-hand Riemann sum is

$$\frac{1}{8}\left(f\left(\frac{1}{8}\right) + f\left(\frac{2}{8}\right) + f\left(\frac{3}{8}\right) + \cdots + f(1)\right)$$
$$= \frac{1}{8}\left(\frac{64}{65} + \frac{64}{68} + \frac{64}{73} + \frac{64}{80} + \frac{64}{89} + \frac{64}{100} + \frac{64}{113} + \frac{64}{128}\right)$$
$$\approx 0.8160 - \frac{1}{16} = 0.7535.$$

(iii) The trapezoid rule gives us that

$$\text{TRAP}(8) = \frac{\text{LEFT}(8) + \text{RIGHT}(8)}{2} \approx 0.7847.$$

(b) Since $1 + x^2$ is increasing for $x > 0$, so $\frac{1}{1+x^2}$ is decreasing over the interval. Thus

$$\text{RIGHT}(8) < \int_0^1 \frac{1}{1+x^2}\, dx < \text{LEFT}(8)$$

$$0.7535 < \frac{\pi}{4} < 0.8160$$

$$3.014 < \pi < 3.264.$$

12. Let $s(t)$ be the distance traveled at time t and $v(t)$ be the velocity at time t. Then the distance traveled during the interval $0 \leq t \leq 6$ is

$$s(6) - s(0) = s(t)\Big|_0^6$$
$$= \int_0^6 s'(t)\, dt \quad \text{(by the Fundamental Theorem)}$$
$$= \int_0^6 v(t)\, dt.$$

We estimate the distance by estimating this integral.

From the table, we find: $\text{LEFT}(6) = 31$, $\text{RIGHT}(6) = 39$, $\text{TRAP}(6) = 35$.

13. Since the function is decreasing, LEFT is an overestimate and RIGHT is an underestimate. Since the graph is concave down, secant lines lie below the graph so TRAP is an underestimate and tangent lines lie above the graph so MID is an overestimate. We can see that MID and TRAP are closer to the exact value than LEFT and RIGHT. In order smallest to largest, we have:

$\text{RIGHT}(n) < \text{TRAP}(n) < \text{Exact value} < \text{MID}(n) < \text{LEFT}(n)$.

14. For a decreasing function whose graph is concave up, the diagrams below show that RIGHT < MID < TRAP < LEFT. Thus,

(a) $0.664 = \text{LEFT}, 0.633 = \text{TRAP}, 0.632 = \text{MID}$, and $0.601 = \text{RIGHT}$.

(b) $0.632 < \text{true value} < 0.633$.

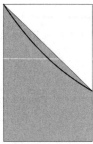
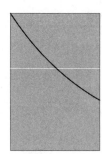

| RIGHT = 0.601 | MID = 0.632 | TRAP = 0.633 | LEFT = 0.664 |

15. $f(x)$ is increasing, so RIGHT gives an overestimate and LEFT gives an underestimate.

16. $f(x)$ is concave down, so MID gives an overestimate and TRAP gives an underestimate.

17. $f(x)$ is decreasing and concave up, so LEFT and TRAP give overestimates and RIGHT and MID give underestimates.

18. $f(x)$ is concave up, so TRAP gives an overestimate and MID gives an underestimate.

19. (a) Since $f(x)$ is closer to horizontal (that is, $|f'| < |g'|$), LEFT and RIGHT will be more accurate with $f(x)$.

(b) Since $g(x)$ has more curvature, MID and TRAP will be more accurate with $f(x)$.

20. (a) TRAP(4) gives probably the best estimate of the integral. We cannot calculate MID(4).

$$\text{LEFT}(4) = 3 \cdot 100 + 3 \cdot 97 + 3 \cdot 90 + 3 \cdot 78 = 1095$$
$$\text{RIGHT}(4) = 3 \cdot 97 + 3 \cdot 90 + 3 \cdot 78 + 3 \cdot 55 = 960$$
$$\text{TRAP}(4) = \frac{1095 + 960}{2} = 1027.5.$$

(b) Because there are no points of inflection, the graph is either concave down or concave up. By plotting points, we see that it is concave down. So TRAP(4) is an underestimate.

21. (a) $\displaystyle\int_0^{2\pi} \sin\theta\, d\theta = -\cos\theta \Big|_0^{2\pi} = 0.$

(b) MID(1) is 0 since the midpoint of 0 and 2π is π, and $\sin\pi = 0$. Thus MID(1) $= 2\pi(\sin\pi) = 0$. The midpoints we use for MID(2) are $\pi/2$ and $3\pi/2$, and $\sin(\pi/2) = -\sin(3\pi/2)$. Thus MID(2) $= \pi\sin(\pi/2) + \pi\sin(3\pi/2) = 0$.

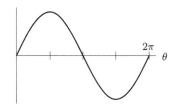

(c) MID(3) = 0.

In general, MID(n) = 0 for all n, even though your calculator (because of round-off error) might not return it as such. The reason is that $\sin(x) = -\sin(2\pi - x)$. If we use MID($n$), we will always take sums where we are adding pairs of the form $\sin(x)$ and $\sin(2\pi - x)$, so the sum will cancel to 0. (If n is odd, we will get a $\sin\pi$ in the sum which does not pair up with anything — but $\sin\pi$ is already 0.)

22. (a)

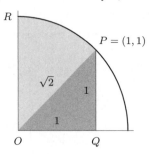

The graph of $y = \sqrt{2-x^2}$ is the upper half of a circle of radius $\sqrt{2}$ centered at the origin. The integral represents the area under this curve between the lines $x = 0$ and $x = 1$. From the picture, we see that this area can be split into 2 parts, A_1 and A_2. Notice since $OQ = QP = 1$, $\triangle OQP$ is isosceles. Thus $\angle POQ = \angle ROP = \frac{\pi}{4}$, and A_1 is exactly $\frac{1}{8}$ of the entire circle. Thus the total area is

$$\text{Area} = A_1 + A_2 = \frac{1}{8}\pi(\sqrt{2})^2 + \frac{1 \cdot 1}{2} = \frac{\pi}{4} + \frac{1}{2}.$$

(b) LEFT(5) ≈ 1.32350,   RIGHT(5) $\approx 1.24066, T$
 TRAP(5) ≈ 1.28208,   MID(5) ≈ 1.28705

Exact value ≈ 1.285398163

Left-hand error ≈ -0.03810,   Right-hand error ≈ 0.04474,
Trapezoidal error ≈ 0.00332,   Midpoint error ≈ -0.001656

Thus right-hand error > trapezoidal error > 0 > midpoint error > left-hand error, and |midpt error| < |trap error| < |left-error| < |right-error|.

23. We approximate the area of the playing field by using Riemann sums. From the data provided,

$$\text{LEFT}(10) = \text{RIGHT}(10) = \text{TRAP}(10) = 89{,}000 \text{ square feet.}$$

Thus approximately

$$\frac{89{,}000 \text{ sq. ft.}}{200 \text{ sq. ft./lb.}} = 445 \text{ lbs. of fertilizer}$$

should be necessary.

24.

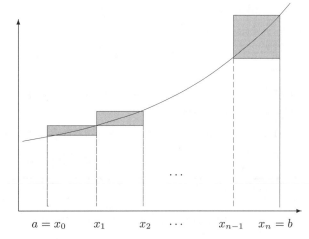

From the diagram, the difference between RIGHT(n) and LEFT(n) is the area of the shaded rectangles.
$$\text{RIGHT}(n) = f(x_1)\Delta x + f(x_2)\Delta x + \cdots + f(x_n)\Delta x$$
$$\text{LEFT}(n) = f(x_0)\Delta x + f(x_1)\Delta x + \cdots + f(x_{n-1})\Delta x$$
Notice that the terms in these two sums are the same, except that RIGHT(n) contains $f(x_n)\Delta x$ ($= f(b)\Delta x$), and LEFT(n) contains $f(x_0)\Delta x$ ($= f(a)\Delta x$). Thus

$$\text{RIGHT}(n) = \text{LEFT}(n) + f(x_n)\Delta x - f(x_0)\Delta x$$
$$= \text{LEFT}(n) + f(b)\Delta x - f(a)\Delta x$$

25.

$$\text{TRAP}(n) = \frac{\text{LEFT}(n) + \text{RIGHT}(n)}{2}$$
$$= \frac{\text{LEFT}(n) + \text{LEFT}(n) + f(b)\Delta x - f(a)\Delta x}{2}$$
$$= \text{LEFT}(n) + \frac{1}{2}(f(b) - f(a))\Delta x$$

26.

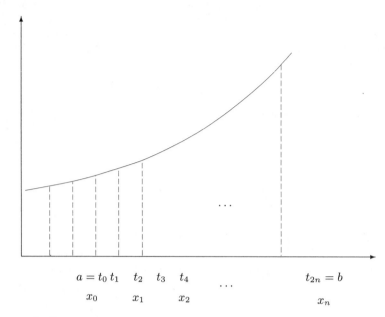

$$a = t_0 \ t_1 \quad t_2 \quad t_3 \quad t_4 \qquad \cdots \qquad t_{2n} = b$$
$$x_0 \qquad x_1 \qquad x_2 \qquad\qquad\qquad x_n$$

Divide the interval $[a, b]$ into n pieces, by $x_0, x_1, x_2, \ldots, x_n$, and also into $2n$ pieces, by $t_0, t_1, t_2, \ldots, t_{2n}$. Then the x's coincide with the even t's, so $x_0 = t_0$, $x_1 = t_2$, $x_2 = t_4$, $\ldots$, $x_n = t_{2n}$ and $\Delta t = \frac{1}{2}\Delta x$.

$$\text{LEFT}(n) = f(x_0)\Delta x + f(x_1)\Delta x + \cdots + f(x_{n-1})\Delta x$$

Since $\text{MID}(n)$ is obtained by evaluating f at the midpoints $t_1, t_3, t_5, \ldots$ of the x intervals, we get

$$\text{MID}(n) = f(t_1)\Delta x + f(t_3)\Delta x + \cdots + f(t_{2n-1})\Delta x$$

Now

$$\text{LEFT}(2n) = f(t_0)\Delta t + f(t_1)\Delta t + f(t_2)\Delta t + \cdots + f(t_{2n-1})\Delta t.$$

Regroup terms, putting all the even t's first, the odd t's last:

$$\text{LEFT}(2n) = f(t_0)\Delta t + f(t_2)\Delta t + \cdots + f(t_{2n-2})\Delta t + f(t_1)\Delta t + f(t_3)\Delta t + \cdots + f(t_{2n-1})\Delta t$$

$$= \underbrace{f(x_0)\frac{\Delta x}{2} + f(x_1)\frac{\Delta x}{2} + \cdots + f(x_{n-1})\frac{\Delta x}{2}}_{\text{LEFT}(n)/2} + \underbrace{f(t_1)\frac{\Delta x}{2} + f(t_3)\frac{\Delta x}{2} + \cdots + f(t_{2n-1})\frac{\Delta x}{2}}_{\text{MID}(n)/2}$$

So

$$\text{LEFT}(2n) = \frac{1}{2}(\text{LEFT}(n) + \text{MID}(n))$$

27. When $n = 10$, we have $a = 1; b = 2; \Delta x = \frac{1}{10}; f(a) = 1; f(b) = \frac{1}{2}$.
$\text{LEFT}(10) \approx 0.71877, \text{RIGHT}(10) \approx 0.66877, \text{TRAP}(10) \approx 0.69377$
We have
$\text{RIGHT}(10) = \text{LEFT}(10) + f(b)\Delta x - f(a)\Delta x = 0.71877 + \frac{1}{10}(\frac{1}{2}) - \frac{1}{10}(1) = 0.66877$, and $\text{TRAP}(10) = \text{LEFT}(10) + \frac{\Delta x}{2}(f(b) - f(a)) = 0.71877 + \frac{1}{10}\frac{1}{2}(\frac{1}{2} - 1) = 0.69377$,
so the equations are verified.

28. First, we compute:

$$(f(b) - f(a))\Delta x = (f(b) - f(a))\left(\frac{b-a}{n}\right)$$

$$= (f(5) - f(2))\left(\frac{3}{n}\right)$$

$$= (21 - 13)\left(\frac{3}{n}\right)$$

$$= \frac{24}{n}$$

RIGHT(10) = LEFT(10) + 24 = 3.156 + 2.4 = 5.556.
TRAP(10) = LEFT(10) + $\frac{1}{2}$(2.4) = 3.156 + 1.2 = 4.356.
LEFT(20) = $\frac{1}{2}$(LEFT(10) + MID(10)) = $\frac{1}{2}$(3.156 + 3.242) = 3.199.
RIGHT(20) = LEFT(20) + 2.4 = 3.199 + 1.2 = 4.399.
TRAP(20) = LEFT(20) + $\frac{1}{2}$(1.2) = 3.199 + 0.6 = 3.799.

Solutions for Section 7.6

Exercises

1. We saw in Problem 7 in Section 7.5 that, for this definite integral, we have LEFT(2) = 27, RIGHT(2) = 135, TRAP(2) = 81, and MID(2) = 67.5. Thus,

$$\text{SIMP}(2) = \frac{2\text{MID}(2) + \text{TRAP}(2)}{3} = \frac{2(67.5) + 81}{3} = 72.$$

   Notice that

$$\int_0^6 x^2 \, dx = \frac{x^3}{3}\bigg|_0^6 = \frac{6^3}{3} - \frac{0^3}{3} = 72,$$

   and so SIMP(2) gives the exact value of the integral in this case.

2. (a) From Problem 9 on page 462, for $\int_0^4 (x^2 + 1)\, dx$, we have MID(2)= 24 and TRAP(2)= 28. Thus,

$$\begin{aligned}
\text{SIMP}(2) &= \frac{2\text{MID}(2) + \text{TRAP}(2)}{3} \\
&= \frac{2(24) + 28}{3} \\
&= \frac{76}{3}.
\end{aligned}$$

   (b)

$$\int_0^4 (x^2 + 1)\, dx = \left(\frac{x^3}{3} + x\right)\bigg|_0^4 = \left(\frac{64}{3} + 4\right) - (0 + 0) = \frac{76}{3}$$

   (c) Error= 0. Simpson's Rule gives the exact answer.

Problems

3. (a)

Table 7.1 *Errors for the left and right rule approximations to $\int_1^2 \frac{1}{x}\, dx = 0.6931471806\ldots$*

n	LEFT(n)	Left error	RIGHT(n)	Right error
2	0.833333	−0.14019	0.583333	0.10981
4	0.759524	−0.06638	0.634524	0.05862
8	0.725372	−0.03222	0.662872	0.03028
16	0.709016	−0.01587	0.677766	0.01538
32	0.701021	−0.00787	0.685396	0.00775
64	0.697069	−0.00392	0.689256	0.00389
128	0.695104	−0.00196	0.691198	0.00195

   (b) The left errors are negative and the right errors are positive. This occurs because $f(x) = 1/x$ is decreasing, meaning that the left sums are overestimates and the right sums are underestimates. Doubling n approximately halves the error.

(c)

Table 7.2 *Errors for the trapezoid and midpoint rule approximations to $\int_1^2 \frac{1}{x}\,dx = 0.6931471806\ldots$*

n	TRAP(n)	Trap error	MID(n)	Mid error
2	0.708333	−0.01518	0.685714	0.00743
4	0.697024	−0.00387	0.691220	0.00193
8	0.694122	−0.00097	0.692661	0.00049
16	0.6933912	−0.000244	0.6930252	0.000122
32	0.6932082	−0.000061	0.6931166	0.000031
64	0.6931624	−0.000015	0.6931396	0.000008
128	0.6931510	−0.000004	0.6931453	0.000002

(d) The trapezoid errors are negative because $f(x) = 1/x$ is concave up, and thus, the trapezoids overestimate. The midpoint errors are positive. Doubling n approximately quarters the error.

(e)

Table 7.3 *Errors for Simpson's rule for $\int_1^2 \frac{1}{x}\,dx = 0.6931471806\ldots$*

n	SIMP(n)	error
2	0.69325396825	−0.000106788
4	0.69315453065	−0.000007350
8	0.69314765282	−0.000000472
16	0.69314721029	−0.000000030
32	0.69314718242	−0.000000002

The error is multiplied by approximately $1/16$ when n is doubled.

4. (a) $\displaystyle\int_0^2 (x^3 + 3x^2)\,dx = \left(\frac{x^4}{4} + x^3\right)\Bigg|_0^2 = 12.$

(b) SIMP$(2) = 12$.
SIMP$(4) = 12$.
SIMP$(100) = 12$.
SIMP$(n) = 12$ for all n. Simpson's rule always gives the exact answer if the integrand is a polynomial of degree less than 4.

5. (a) $\displaystyle\int_0^4 e^x\,dx = e^x\Big|_0^4 = e^4 - e^0 \approx 53.598\ldots.$

(b) Computing the sums directly, since $\Delta x = 2$, we have
LEFT$(2) = 2 \cdot e^0 + 2 \cdot e^2 \approx 2(1) + 2(7.389) = 16.778;$ error $= 36.820$.
RIGHT$(2) = 2 \cdot e^2 + 2 \cdot e^4 \approx 2(7.389) + 2(54.598) = 123.974;$ error $= -70.376$.
TRAP$(2) = \dfrac{16.778 + 123.974}{2} = 70.376;$ error $= 16.778$.
MID$(2) = 2 \cdot e^1 + 2 \cdot e^3 \approx 2(2.718) + 2(20.086) = 45.608;$ error $= 7.990$.
SIMP$(2) = \dfrac{2(45.608) + 70.376}{3} = 53.864;$ error $= -0.266$.

(c) Similarly, since $\Delta x = 1$, we have LEFT$(4) = 31.193;$ error $= 22.405$
RIGHT$(4) = 84.791;$ error $= -31.193$
TRAP$(4) = 57.992;$ error $= -4.394$
MID$(4) = 51.428;$ error $= 2.170$
SIMP$(4) = 53.616;$ error $= -0.018$

(d) For LEFT and RIGHT, we expect the error to go down by $1/2$, and this is very roughly what we see. For MID and TRAP, we expect the error to go down by $1/4$, and this is approximately what we see. For SIMP, we expect the error to go down by $1/2^4 = 1/16$, and this is approximately what we see.

6. Here, the error in the approximation using $n = 10$ is $4 - 2.346 = 1.654$.

(a) Since the error in the LEFT approximation is proportional to $1/n$, when we triple n from 10 to 30 the error is divided by 3, so the error here is $1.654/3 = 0.551333$, giving LEFT$(30) = 4 - 0.551333 \approx 3.449$.

(b) The procedure here is identical to part (a), except that the TRAP error is proportional to $1/n^2$, so the error in TRAP(30) will be $1.654/3^2 = 0.183778$, giving TRAP(30) $= 4 - 0.183778 \approx 3.816$.

(c) For SIMP, the error will be $1.654/3^4 = 0.0204198$, giving SIMP(30) $= 4 - 0.0204198 \approx 3.980$.

7. (a) For the left-hand rule, error is approximately proportional to $\frac{1}{n}$. If we let n_p be the number of subdivisions needed for accuracy to p places, then there is a constant k such that

$$5 \times 10^{-5} = \frac{1}{2} \times 10^{-4} \approx \frac{k}{n_4}$$

$$5 \times 10^{-9} = \frac{1}{2} \times 10^{-8} \approx \frac{k}{n_8}$$

$$5 \times 10^{-13} = \frac{1}{2} \times 10^{-12} \approx \frac{k}{n_{12}}$$

$$5 \times 10^{-21} = \frac{1}{2} \times 10^{-20} \approx \frac{k}{n_{20}}$$

Thus the ratios $n_4 : n_8 : n_{12} : n_{20} \approx 1 : 10^4 : 10^8 : 10^{16}$, and assuming the computer time necessary is proportional to n_p, the computer times are approximately

4 places:	2 seconds	
8 places:	2×10^4 seconds	$\approx$ 6 hours
12 places:	2×10^8 seconds	$\approx$ 6 years
20 places:	2×10^{16} seconds	$\approx$ 600 million years

(b) For the trapezoidal rule, error is approximately proportional to $\frac{1}{n^2}$. If we let N_p be the number of subdivisions needed for accuracy to p places, then there is a constant C such that

$$5 \times 10^{-5} = \frac{1}{2} \times 10^{-4} \approx \frac{C}{N_4{}^2}$$

$$5 \times 10^{-9} = \frac{1}{2} \times 10^{-8} \approx \frac{C}{N_8{}^2}$$

$$5 \times 10^{-13} = \frac{1}{2} \times 10^{-12} \approx \frac{C}{N_{12}{}^2}$$

$$5 \times 10^{-21} = \frac{1}{2} \times 10^{-20} \approx \frac{C}{N_{20}{}^2}$$

Thus the ratios $N_4{}^2 : N_8{}^2 : N_{12}{}^2 : N_{20}{}^2 \approx 1 : 10^4 : 10^8 : 10^{16}$, and the ratios $N_4 : N_8 : N_{12} : N_{20} \approx 1 : 10^2 : 10^4 : 10^8$. So the computer times are approximately

4 places:	2 seconds	
8 places:	2×10^2 seconds	$\approx$ 3 minutes
12 places:	2×10^4 seconds	$\approx$ 6 hours
20 places:	2×10^8 seconds	$\approx$ 6 years

8. (a) If $f(x) = 1$, then

$$\int_a^b f(x)\, dx = (b - a).$$

Also,

$$\frac{h}{3}\left(\frac{f(a)}{2} + 2f(m) + \frac{f(b)}{2}\right) = \frac{b-a}{3}\left(\frac{1}{2} + 2 + \frac{1}{2}\right) = (b - a).$$

So the equation holds for $f(x) = 1$.

If $f(x) = x$, then

$$\int_a^b f(x)\,dx = \frac{x^2}{2}\bigg|_a^b = \frac{b^2 - a^2}{2}.$$

Also,

$$\frac{h}{3}\left(\frac{f(a)}{2} + 2f(m) + \frac{f(b)}{2}\right) = \frac{b-a}{3}\left(\frac{a}{2} + 2\frac{a+b}{2} + \frac{b}{2}\right)$$

$$= \frac{b-a}{3}\left(\frac{a}{2} + a + b + \frac{b}{2}\right)$$

$$= \frac{b-a}{3}\left(\frac{3}{2}b + \frac{3}{2}a\right)$$

$$= \frac{(b-a)(b+a)}{2}$$

$$= \frac{b^2 - a^2}{2}.$$

So the equation holds for $f(x) = x$.

If $f(x) = x^2$, then $\int_a^b f(x)\,dx = \frac{x^3}{3}\bigg|_a^b = \frac{b^3 - a^3}{3}$. Also,

$$\frac{h}{3}\left(\frac{f(a)}{2} + 2f(m) + \frac{f(b)}{2}\right) = \frac{b-a}{3}\left(\frac{a^2}{2} + 2\left(\frac{a+b}{2}\right)^2 + \frac{b^2}{2}\right)$$

$$= \frac{b-a}{3}\left(\frac{a^2}{2} + \frac{a^2 + 2ab + b^2}{2} + \frac{b^2}{2}\right)$$

$$= \frac{b-a}{3}\left(\frac{2a^2 + 2ab + 2b^2}{2}\right)$$

$$= \frac{b-a}{3}\left(a^2 + ab + b^2\right)$$

$$= \frac{b^3 - a^3}{3}.$$

So the equation holds for $f(x) = x^2$.

(b) For any quadratic function, $f(x) = Ax^2 + Bx + C$, the "Facts about Sums and Constant Multiples of Integrands" give us:

$$\int_a^b f(x)\,dx = \int_a^b (Ax^2 + Bx + C)\,dx = A\int_a^b x^2\,dx + B\int_a^b x\,dx + C\int_a^b 1\,dx.$$

Now we use the results of part (a) to get:

$$\int_a^b f(x)\,dx = A\frac{h}{3}\left(\frac{a^2}{2} + 2m^2 + \frac{b^2}{2}\right) + B\frac{h}{3}\left(\frac{a}{2} + 2m + \frac{b}{2}\right) + C\frac{h}{3}\left(\frac{1}{2} + 2\cdot 1 + \frac{1}{2}\right)$$

$$= \frac{h}{3}\left(\frac{Aa^2 + Ba + C}{2} + 2(Am^2 + Bm + C) + \frac{Ab^2 + Bb + C}{2}\right)$$

$$= \frac{h}{3}\left(\frac{f(a)}{2} + 2f(m) + \frac{f(b)}{2}\right)$$

9. (a) Suppose $q_i(x)$ is the quadratic function approximating $f(x)$ on the subinterval $[x_i, x_{i+1}]$, and m_i is the midpoint of the interval, $m_i = (x_i + x_{i+1})/2$. Then, using the equation in Problem 8, with $a = x_i$ and $b = x_{i+1}$ and $h = \Delta x = x_{i+1} - x_i$:

$$\int_{x_i}^{x_{i+1}} f(x)\,dx \approx \int_{x_i}^{x_{i+1}} q_i(x)\,dx = \frac{\Delta x}{3}\left(\frac{q_i(x_i)}{2} + 2q_i(m_i) + \frac{q_i(x_{i+1})}{2}\right).$$

(b) Summing over all subintervals gives

$$\int_a^b f(x)\,dx \approx \sum_{i=0}^{n-1} \int_{x_i}^{x_{i+1}} q_i(x)\,dx = \sum_{i=0}^{n-1} \frac{\Delta x}{3}\left(\frac{q_i(x_i)}{2} + 2q_i(m_i) + \frac{q_i(x_{i+1})}{2}\right).$$

Splitting the sum into two parts:

$$= \frac{2}{3} \sum_{i=0}^{n-1} q_i(m_i)\Delta x + \frac{1}{3} \sum_{i=0}^{n-1} \frac{q_i(x_i) + q_i(x_{i+1})}{2} \Delta x$$

$$= \frac{2}{3} \text{MID}(n) + \frac{1}{3} \text{TRAP}(n)$$

$$= \text{SIMP}(n).$$

Solutions for Section 7.7

Exercises

1. (a) See Figure 7.27. The area extends out infinitely far along the positive x-axis.

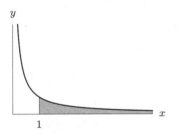

Figure 7.27

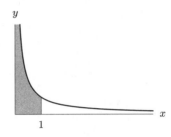

Figure 7.28

(b) See Figure 7.28. The area extends up infinitely far along the positive y-axis.

2. We have

$$\int_0^\infty e^{-0.4x} dx = \lim_{b \to \infty} \int_0^b e^{-0.4x} dx = \lim_{b \to \infty} (-2.5e^{-0.4x})|_0^b = \lim_{b \to \infty} (-2.5e^{-0.4b} + 2.5).$$

As $b \to \infty$, we know $e^{-0.4b} \to 0$ and so we see that the integral converges to 2.5. See Figure 7.29. The area continues indefinitely out to the right.

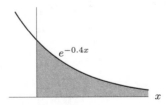

Figure 7.29

3. (a) We use a calculator or computer to evaluate the integrals.
When $b = 5$, we have $\int_0^5 xe^{-x} dx = 0.9596$.
When $b = 10$, we have $\int_0^{10} xe^{-x} dx = 0.9995$.
When $b = 20$, we have $\int_0^{20} xe^{-x} dx = 0.99999996$.
(b) It appears from the answers to part (a) that $\int_0^\infty xe^{-x} dx = 1.0$.

4. (a) See Figure 7.30. The total area under the curve is shaded.

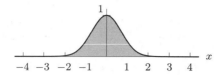

Figure 7.30

(b) When $a = 1$, we use a calculator or computer to see that $\int_{-1}^{1} e^{-x^2} dx = 1.49365$.
Similarly, we have:
When $a = 2$, the value of the integral is 1.76416.
When $a = 3$, the value of the integral is 1.77241.
When $a = 4$, the value of the integral is 1.77245.
When $a = 5$, the value of the integral is 1.77245.

(c) It appears that the integral $\int_{-\infty}^{\infty} e^{-x^2} dx$ converges to approximately 1.77245.

5. We have

$$\int_{1}^{\infty} \frac{1}{5x+2} dx = \lim_{b\to\infty} \int_{1}^{b} \frac{1}{5x+2} dx = \lim_{b\to\infty} \left(\frac{1}{5} \ln(5x+2) \right)\Big|_{1}^{b} = \lim_{b\to\infty} \left(\frac{1}{5} \ln(5b+2) - \frac{1}{5} \ln(7) \right).$$

As $b \leftarrow \infty$, we know that $\ln(5b+2) \to \infty$, and so this integral diverges.

6. We have

$$\int_{1}^{\infty} \frac{1}{(x+2)^2} dx = \lim_{b\to\infty} \int_{1}^{b} \frac{1}{(x+2)^2} dx = \lim_{b\to\infty} \left(\frac{-1}{x+2} \right)\Big|_{1}^{b} = \lim_{b\to\infty} \left(\frac{-1}{b+2} - \frac{-1}{3} \right) = 0 + \frac{1}{3} = \frac{1}{3}.$$

This integral converges to $1/3$.

7. We have

$$\int_{0}^{\infty} xe^{-x^2} dx = \lim_{b\to\infty} \int_{0}^{b} xe^{-x^2} dx = \lim_{b\to\infty} \left(\frac{-1}{2} e^{-x^2} \right)\Big|_{0}^{b} = \lim_{b\to\infty} \left(\frac{-1}{2} e^{-b^2} - \frac{-1}{2} \right) = 0 + \frac{1}{2} = \frac{1}{2}.$$

This integral converges to $1/2$.

8.

$$\int_{1}^{\infty} e^{-2x} dx = \lim_{b\to\infty} \int_{1}^{b} e^{-2x} dx = \lim_{b\to\infty} -\frac{e^{-2x}}{2}\Big|_{1}^{b}$$
$$= \lim_{b\to\infty} (-e^{-2b}/2 + e^{-2}/2) = 0 + e^{-2}/2 = e^{-2}/2,$$

where the first limit is 0 because $\lim_{x\to\infty} e^{-x} = 0$.

9. Using integration by parts with $u = x$ and $v' = e^{-x}$, we find that

$$\int xe^{-x} dx = -xe^{-x} - \int -e^{-x} dx = -(1+x)e^{-x}$$

so

$$\int_{0}^{\infty} \frac{x}{e^x} dx = \lim_{b\to\infty} \int_{0}^{b} \frac{x}{e^x} dx$$
$$= \lim_{b\to\infty} -1(1+x)e^{-x}\Big|_{0}^{b}$$
$$= \lim_{b\to\infty} \left[1 - (1+b)e^{-b} \right]$$
$$= 1.$$

10.

$$\int_{1}^{\infty} \frac{x}{4+x^2} = \lim_{b\to\infty} \int_{1}^{b} \frac{x}{4+x^2} dx = \lim_{b\to\infty} \frac{1}{2} \ln|4+x^2|\Big|_{1}^{b} = \lim_{b\to\infty} \frac{1}{2} \ln|4+b^2| - \frac{1}{2} \ln 5.$$

As $b \to \infty$, $\ln|4+b^2| \to \infty$, so the limit diverges.

11.

$$\int_{-\infty}^{0} \frac{e^x}{1+e^x}\, dx = \lim_{b\to-\infty} \int_{b}^{0} \frac{e^x}{1+e^x}\, dx$$

$$= \lim_{b\to-\infty} \ln|1+e^x|\Big|_{b}^{0}$$

$$= \lim_{b\to-\infty} [\ln|1+e^0| - \ln|1+e^b|]$$

$$= \ln(1+1) - \ln(1+0) = \ln 2.$$

12. First, we note that $1/(z^2+25)$ is an even function. Therefore,

$$\int_{-\infty}^{\infty} \frac{dz}{z^2+25} = \int_{-\infty}^{0} \frac{dz}{z^2+25} + \int_{0}^{\infty} \frac{dz}{z^2+25} = 2\int_{0}^{\infty} \frac{dz}{z^2+25}.$$

We'll now evaluate this improper integral by using a limit:

$$\int_{0}^{\infty} \frac{dz}{z^2+25} = \lim_{b\to\infty} \left(\frac{1}{5}\arctan(b/5) - \frac{1}{5}\arctan(0)\right) = \frac{1}{5}\cdot\frac{\pi}{2} = \frac{\pi}{10}.$$

So the original integral is twice that, namely $\pi/5$.

13. This is an improper integral because $\sqrt{16-x^2} = 0$ at $x = 4$. So

$$\int_{0}^{4} \frac{dx}{\sqrt{16-x^2}} = \lim_{b\to 4^-} \int_{0}^{b} \frac{dx}{\sqrt{16-x^2}}$$

$$= \lim_{b\to 4^-} (\arcsin x/4)\Big|_{0}^{b}$$

$$= \lim_{b\to 4^-} [\arcsin(b/4) - \arcsin(0)] = \pi/2 - 0 = \pi/2.$$

14.

$$\int_{\pi/4}^{\pi/2} \frac{\sin x}{\sqrt{\cos x}}\, dx = \lim_{b\to\pi/2^-} \int_{\pi/4}^{b} \frac{\sin x}{\sqrt{\cos x}}\, dx$$

$$= \lim_{b\to\pi/2^-} -\int_{\pi/4}^{b} (\cos x)^{-1/2}(-\sin x)\, dx$$

$$= \lim_{b\to\pi/2^-} -2(\cos x)^{1/2}\Big|_{\pi/4}^{b}$$

$$= \lim_{b\to\pi/2^-} [-2(\cos b)^{1/2} + 2(\cos \pi/4)^{1/2}]$$

$$= 2\left(\frac{\sqrt{2}}{2}\right)^{\frac{1}{2}} = 2^{\frac{3}{4}}.$$

15. This integral is improper because $1/v$ is undefined at $v = 0$. To evaluate it, we must split the region of integration up into two pieces, from 0 to 1 and from -1 to 0. But notice,

$$\int_{0}^{1} \frac{1}{v}\, dv = \lim_{b\to 0^+} \int_{b}^{1} \frac{1}{v}\, dv = \lim_{b\to 0^+} \left(\ln v\Big|_{b}^{1}\right) = -\ln b.$$

As $b \to 0^+$, this goes to infinity and the integral diverges, so our original integral also diverges.

16.

$$\lim_{a\to 0^+} \int_{a}^{1} \frac{x^4+1}{x}\, dx = \lim_{a\to 0^+} \left(\frac{x^4}{4} + \ln x\right)\Big|_{a}^{1} = \lim_{a\to 0^+} [1/4 - (a^4/4 + \ln a)],$$

which diverges as $a \to 0$, since $\ln a \to -\infty$.

17.

$$\int_1^\infty \frac{1}{x^2+1}\,dx = \lim_{b\to\infty} \int_1^b \frac{1}{x^2+1}\,dx$$

$$= \lim_{b\to\infty} \arctan(x)\Big|_1^b$$

$$= \lim_{b\to\infty} [\arctan(b) - \arctan(1)]$$

$$= \pi/2 - \pi/4 = \pi/4.$$

18.

$$\int_1^\infty \frac{1}{\sqrt{x^2+1}}\,dx = \lim_{b\to\infty} \int_1^b \frac{1}{\sqrt{x^2+1}}\,dx$$

$$= \lim_{b\to\infty} \ln\left|x + \sqrt{x^2+1}\right|\Big|_1^b$$

$$= \lim_{b\to\infty} \ln(b + \sqrt{b^2+1}) - \ln(1+\sqrt{2}).$$

As $b \to \infty$, this limit does not exist, so the integral diverges.

19. We use V-26 with $a = 4$ and $b = -4$:

$$\int_0^4 \frac{1}{u^2 - 16}\,du = \lim_{b\to 4^-} \int_0^b \frac{1}{u^2 - 16}\,du$$

$$= \lim_{b\to 4^-} \int_0^b \frac{1}{(u-4)(u+4)}\,du$$

$$= \lim_{b\to 4^-} \frac{(\ln|u-4| - \ln|u+4|)}{8}\Big|_0^b$$

$$= \lim_{b\to 4^-} \frac{1}{8}\left(\ln|b-4| + \ln 4 - \ln|b+4| - \ln 4\right).$$

As $b \to 4^-$, $\ln|b-4| \to -\infty$, so the limit does not exist and the integral diverges.

20.

$$\int_1^\infty \frac{y}{y^4+1}\,dy = \lim_{b\to\infty} \frac{1}{2} \int_1^b \frac{2y}{(y^2)^2+1}\,dy$$

$$= \lim_{b\to\infty} \frac{1}{2}\arctan(y^2)\Big|_1^b$$

$$= \lim_{b\to\infty} \frac{1}{2}[\arctan(b^2) - \arctan 1]$$

$$= (1/2)[\pi/2 - \pi/4] = \pi/8.$$

21. With the substitution $w = \ln x$, $dw = \frac{1}{x}dx$,

$$\int \frac{dx}{x\ln x} = \int \frac{1}{w}\,dw = \ln|w| + C = \ln|\ln x| + C$$

so

$$\int_2^\infty \frac{dx}{x\ln x} = \lim_{b\to\infty} \int_2^b \frac{dx}{x\ln x}$$

$$= \lim_{b\to\infty} \ln|\ln x|\Big|_2^b$$

$$= \lim_{b\to\infty} [\ln|\ln b| - \ln|\ln 2|].$$

As $b \to \infty$, the limit goes to ∞ and hence the integral diverges.

22. With the substitution $w = \ln x$, $dw = \frac{1}{x}dx$,

$$\int \frac{\ln x}{x}\,dx = \int w\,dw = \frac{1}{2}w^2 + C = \frac{1}{2}(\ln x)^2 + C$$

so

$$\int_0^1 \frac{\ln x}{x}\,dx = \lim_{a\to 0^+}\int_a^1 \frac{\ln x}{x}\,dx = \lim_{a\to 0^+}\frac{1}{2}[\ln(x)]^2\Big|_a^1 = \lim_{a\to 0^+} -\frac{1}{2}[\ln(a)]^2.$$

As $a \to 0^+$, $\ln a \to -\infty$, so the integral diverges.

23. This is a proper integral; use V-26 in the integral table with $a = 4$ and $b = -4$.

$$\int_{16}^{20}\frac{1}{y^2 - 16}\,dy = \int_{16}^{20}\frac{1}{(y-4)(y+4)}\,dy$$

$$= \frac{\ln|y-4| - \ln|y+4|}{8}\Big|_{16}^{20}$$

$$= \frac{\ln 16 - \ln 24 - (\ln 12 - \ln 20)}{8}$$

$$= \frac{\ln 320 - \ln 288}{8} = \frac{1}{8}\ln(10/9) = 0.01317.$$

24. As in Problem 21, $\int \frac{dx}{x\ln x} = \ln|\ln x| + C$, so

$$\int_1^2 \frac{dx}{x\ln x} = \lim_{b\to 1^+}\int_b^2 \frac{dx}{x\ln x}$$

$$= \lim_{b\to 1^+}\ln|\ln x|\Big|_b^2$$

$$= \lim_{b\to 1^+}\ln(\ln 2) - \ln(\ln b).$$

As $b \to 1^+$, $\ln(\ln b) \to -\infty$, so the integral diverges.

25. Using the substitution $w = -x^{\frac{1}{2}}$, $-2dw = x^{-\frac{1}{2}}\,dx$,

$$\int e^{-x^{\frac{1}{2}}}x^{-\frac{1}{2}}\,dx = -2\int e^w\,dw = -2e^{-x^{\frac{1}{2}}} + C.$$

So

$$\int_0^\pi \frac{1}{\sqrt{x}}e^{-\sqrt{x}}\,dx = \lim_{b\to 0^+}\int_b^\pi \frac{1}{\sqrt{x}}e^{-\sqrt{x}}\,dx$$

$$= \lim_{b\to 0^+}-2e^{-\sqrt{x}}\Big|_b^\pi$$

$$= 2 - 2e^{-\sqrt{\pi}}.$$

26. Letting $w = \ln x$, $dw = \frac{1}{x}dx$,

$$\int \frac{dx}{x(\ln x)^2} = \int w^{-2}\,dw = -w^{-1} + C = -\frac{1}{\ln x} + C,$$

so

$$\int_3^\infty \frac{dx}{x(\ln x)^2} = \lim_{b\to\infty}\int_3^b \frac{dx}{x(\ln x)^2}$$

$$= \lim_{b\to\infty}\left(-\frac{1}{\ln b} + \frac{1}{\ln 3}\right)$$

$$= \frac{1}{\ln 3}.$$

27.

$$\int_0^2 \frac{1}{\sqrt{4-x^2}}\,dx = \lim_{b\to 2^-}\int_0^b \frac{1}{\sqrt{4-x^2}}\,dx$$

$$= \lim_{b\to 2^-}\arcsin\frac{x}{2}\bigg|_0^b$$

$$= \lim_{b\to 2^-}\arcsin\frac{b}{2} = \arcsin 1 = \frac{\pi}{2}.$$

28. $\displaystyle\int_4^\infty \frac{dx}{(x-1)^2} = \lim_{b\to\infty}\int_4^b \frac{dx}{(x-1)^2} = \lim_{b\to\infty} -\frac{1}{(x-1)}\bigg|_4^b = \lim_{b\to\infty}\left[-\frac{1}{b-1}+\frac{1}{3}\right] = \frac{1}{3}.$

29. $\displaystyle\int \frac{dx}{x^2-1} = \int \frac{dx}{(x-1)(x+1)} = \frac{1}{2}(\ln|x-1| - \ln|x+1|) + C = \frac{1}{2}\left(\ln\frac{|x-1|}{|x+1|}\right) + C,$ so

$$\int_4^\infty \frac{dx}{x^2-1} = \lim_{b\to\infty}\int_4^b \frac{dx}{x^2-1}$$

$$= \lim_{b\to\infty}\frac{1}{2}\left(\ln\frac{|x-1|}{|x+1|}\right)\bigg|_4^b$$

$$= \lim_{b\to\infty}\left[\frac{1}{2}\ln\left(\frac{b-1}{b+1}\right) - \frac{1}{2}\ln\frac{3}{5}\right]$$

$$= -\frac{1}{2}\ln\frac{3}{5} = \frac{1}{2}\ln\frac{5}{3}.$$

30.

$$\int_7^\infty \frac{dy}{\sqrt{y-5}} = \lim_{b\to\infty}\int_7^b \frac{dy}{\sqrt{y-5}}$$

$$= \lim_{b\to\infty}2\sqrt{y-5}\bigg|_7^b$$

$$= \lim_{b\to\infty}(2\sqrt{b-5} - 2\sqrt{2}).$$

As $b\to\infty$, this limit goes to ∞, so the integral diverges.

31. The integrand is undefined at $y = -3$ and $y = 3$. To consider the limits one at a time, divide the integral at $y = 0$;

$$\int_0^3 \frac{y\,dy}{\sqrt{9-y^2}} = \lim_{b\to 3^-}\int_0^b \frac{y}{\sqrt{9-y^2}}\,dy = \lim_{b\to 3^-}\left(-(9-y^2)^{1/2}\right)\bigg|_0^b$$

$$= \lim_{b\to 3^-}\left(3 - (9-b^2)^{1/2}\right) = 3.$$

A similar argument shows that

$$\int_{-3}^0 \frac{y\,dy}{\sqrt{9-y^2}} = \lim_{b\to -3^+}\int_b^0 \frac{y}{\sqrt{9-y^2}}\,dy = \lim_{b\to -3^+}\left(-(9-y^2)^{1/2}\right)\bigg|_b^0$$

$$= \lim_{b\to -3^+}\left(-3 + (9-b^2)^{1/2}\right) = -3.$$

Thus the original integral converges to a value of 0:

$$\int_{-3}^3 \frac{y\,dy}{\sqrt{9-y^2}} = \int_{-3}^0 \frac{y\,dy}{\sqrt{9-y^2}} + \int_0^3 \frac{y\,dy}{\sqrt{9-y^2}} = -3 + 3 = 0.$$

32. The integrand is undefined at $\theta = 4$, so we must split the integral there.

$$\int_4^6 \frac{d\theta}{(4-\theta)^2} = \lim_{a \to 4^+} \int_a^6 \frac{d\theta}{(4-\theta)^2} = \lim_{a \to 4^+} (4-\theta)^{-1} \Big|_a^6 = \lim_{a \to 4^+} \left(\frac{1}{-2} - \frac{1}{4-a} \right).$$

Since $1/(4-a) \to -\infty$ as $a \to 4$ from the right, the integral does not converge. It is not necessary to check the convergence of $\int_3^4 \frac{d\theta}{(4-\theta)^2}$. However, we could have started with $\int_3^4 \frac{d\theta}{(4-\theta)^2}$, instead of $\int_4^6 \frac{d\theta}{(4-\theta)^2}$, and arrived at the same conclusion.

Problems

33. Since the graph is above the x-axis for $x \geq 0$, we have

$$\text{Area} = \int_0^\infty x e^{-x} \, dx = \lim_{b \to \infty} \int_0^b x e^{-x} \, dx$$

$$= \lim_{b \to \infty} \left(-x e^{-x} \Big|_0^b + \int_0^b e^{-x} \, dx \right)$$

$$= \lim_{b \to \infty} \left(-b e^{-b} - e^{-x} \Big|_0^b \right)$$

$$= \lim_{b \to \infty} (-b e^{-b} - e^{-b} + e^0) = 1.$$

34. The curve has an asymptote at $t = \frac{\pi}{2}$, and so the area integral is improper there.

$$\text{Area} = \int_0^{\frac{\pi}{2}} \frac{dt}{\cos^2 t} = \lim_{b \to \frac{\pi}{2}} \int_0^b \frac{dt}{\cos^2 t} = \lim_{b \to \frac{\pi}{2}} \tan t \Big|_0^b,$$

which diverges. Therefore the area is infinite.

35. The factor $\ln x$ grows slowly enough not to change the convergence or divergence of the integral, although it will change what it converges or diverges to.

Integrating by parts or using the table of integrals, we get

$$\int_e^\infty x^p \ln x \, dx = \lim_{b \to \infty} \int_e^b x^p \ln x \, dx$$

$$= \lim_{b \to \infty} \left[\frac{1}{p+1} x^{p+1} \ln x - \frac{1}{(p+1)^2} x^{p+1} \right] \Big|_e^b$$

$$= \lim_{b \to \infty} \left[\left(\frac{1}{p+1} b^{p+1} \ln b - \frac{1}{(p+1)^2} b^{p+1} \right) \right.$$

$$\left. - \left(\frac{1}{p+1} e^{p+1} - \frac{1}{(p+1)^2} e^{p+1} \right) \right].$$

If $p > -1$, then $(p+1)$ is positive and the limit does not exist since b^{p+1} and $\ln b$ both approach ∞ as b does.

If $p < -1$, then $(p+1)$ is negative and both b^{p+1} and $b^{p+1} \ln b$ approach 0 as $b \to \infty$. (This follows by looking at graphs of $x^{p+1} \ln x$ (for different values of p), or by noting that $\ln x$ grows more slowly than x^{p+1} tends to 0.) So the value of the integral is $-p e^{p+1}/(p+1)^2$.

The case $p = -1$ has to be handled separately. For $p = -1$,

$$\int_e^\infty \frac{\ln x}{x} \, dx = \lim_{b \to \infty} \int_e^b \frac{\ln x}{x} \, dx = \lim_{b \to \infty} \frac{(\ln x)^2}{2} \Big|_e^b = \lim_{b \to \infty} \left(\frac{(\ln b)^2 - 1}{2} \right).$$

As $b \to \infty$, this limit does not exist, so the integral diverges if $p = -1$.

To summarize, $\int_e^\infty x^p \ln x \, dx$ converges for $p < -1$ to the value $-p e^{p+1}/(p+1)^2$.

36. The factor $\ln x$ grows slowly enough (as $x \to 0^+$) not to change the convergence or divergence of the integral, although it will change what it converges or diverges to.

   The integral is always improper, because $\ln x$ is not defined for $x = 0$. Integrating by parts (or, alternatively, the integral table) yields

$$\int_0^e x^p \ln x \, dx = \lim_{a \to 0^+} \int_a^e x^p \ln x \, dx$$

$$= \lim_{a \to 0^+} \left(\frac{1}{p+1} x^{p+1} \ln x - \frac{1}{(p+1)^2} x^{p+1} \right) \Bigg|_a^e$$

$$= \lim_{a \to 0^+} \left[\left(\frac{1}{p+1} e^{p+1} - \frac{1}{(p+1)^2} e^{p+1} \right) \right.$$

$$\left. - \left(\frac{1}{p+1} a^{p+1} \ln a - \frac{1}{(p+1)^2} a^{p+1} \right) \right].$$

If $p < -1$, then $(p+1)$ is negative, so as $a \to 0^+$, $a^{p+1} \to \infty$ and $\ln a \to -\infty$, and therefore the limit does not exist.

   If $p > -1$, then $(p+1)$ is positive and it's easy to see that $a^{p+1} \to 0$ as $a \to 0$. Looking at graphs of $x^{p+1} \ln x$ (for different values of p) shows that $a^{p+1} \ln a \to 0$ as $a \to 0$. This is not so easy to see analytically. It's true because if we let $t = \frac{1}{a}$ then

$$\lim_{a \to 0^+} a^{p+1} \ln a = \lim_{t \to \infty} \left(\frac{1}{t} \right)^{p+1} \ln \left(\frac{1}{t} \right) = \lim_{t \to \infty} -\frac{\ln t}{t^{p+1}}.$$

This last limit is zero because $\ln t$ grows very slowly, much more slowly than t^{p+1}. So if $p > -1$, the integral converges and equals $e^{p+1}[1/(p+1) - 1/(p+1)^2] = pe^{p+1}/(p+1)^2$.

   What happens if $p = -1$? Then we get

$$\int_0^e \frac{\ln x}{x} \, dx = \lim_{a \to 0^+} \int_a^e \frac{\ln x}{x} \, dx$$

$$= \lim_{a \to 0^+} \frac{(\ln x)^2}{2} \Bigg|_a^e$$

$$= \lim_{a \to 0^+} \left(\frac{1 - (\ln a)^2}{2} \right).$$

Since $\ln a \to -\infty$ as $a \to 0^+$, this limit does not exist.

   To summarize, $\int_0^e x^p \ln x$ converges for $p > -1$ to the value $pe^{p+1}/(p+1)^2$.

37. (a) We have

$$\int_0^\infty \frac{e^{-y/\alpha}}{\alpha} \, dy = \lim_{b \to \infty} -e^{-y/\alpha} \Bigg|_0^b = \lim_{b \to \infty} (1 - e^{-b/\alpha}) = 1.$$

(b) Using integration by parts with $u = y$ and $v' = (1/\alpha)e^{-y/\alpha}$, so $u' = 1$, $v = -e^{-y/\alpha}$, we have

$$\int_0^\infty \frac{ye^{-y/\alpha}}{\alpha} \, dy = \lim_{b \to \infty} \int_0^b \frac{ye^{-y/\alpha}}{\alpha} \, dy$$

$$= \lim_{b \to \infty} \left(-ye^{-y/\alpha} \Bigg|_0^b + \int_0^b e^{-y/\alpha} \, dy \right)$$

$$= \lim_{b \to \infty} \left(-be^{-b/\alpha} - \alpha e^{-y/\alpha} \Bigg|_0^b \right)$$

$$= \lim_{b \to \infty} (-be^{-b/\alpha} - \alpha e^{-b/\alpha} + \alpha)$$

Since $\lim_{b \to \infty} -be^{-b/\alpha} = \lim_{b \to \infty} e^{-b/\alpha} = 0$, we have

$$\int \frac{ye^{-y/\alpha}}{\alpha} \, dy = \alpha.$$

(c) Using integration by parts, this time with $u = y^2$, $v' = (1/\alpha)e^{-y/\alpha}$, so $u' = 2y$, $v = -e^{-y/\alpha}$, we have

$$\int_0^\infty \frac{y^2 e^{-y/\alpha}}{\alpha}\, dy = \lim_{b \to \infty} \int_0^b \frac{y^2 e^{-y/\alpha}}{\alpha}\, dy$$

$$= \lim_{b \to \infty} \left(-y^2 e^{-y/\alpha} \Big|_0^b + 2 \int_0^b y e^{-y/\alpha}\, dy \right)$$

$$= \lim_{b \to \infty} -b^2 e^{-b/\alpha} + 2 \int_0^\infty y e^{-y/\alpha}\, dy$$

Now $\lim_{b \to \infty} -b^2 e^{-b/\alpha} = 0$ and in part (b) we found

$$\int_0^\infty \frac{y e^{-y/\alpha}}{\alpha}\, dy = \alpha,$$

so

$$\int_0^\infty y e^{-y/\alpha}\, dy = \alpha^2.$$

Thus,

$$\int_0^\infty \frac{y^2 e^{-y/\alpha}}{\alpha}\, dy = 2 \int_0^\infty y e^{-y/\alpha}\, dy = 2\alpha^2.$$

38. We let $t = (x - a)/\sqrt{b}$. This means that $dt = dx/\sqrt{b}$, and that $t = \pm\infty$ when $x = \pm\infty$. We have

$$\int_{-\infty}^\infty e^{-(x-a)^2/b}\, dx = \int_{-\infty}^\infty e^{-t^2} \left(\sqrt{b}\, dt \right) = \sqrt{b} \int_{-\infty}^\infty e^{-t^2}\, dt = \sqrt{b}\sqrt{\pi} = \sqrt{b\pi}.$$

39. We calculate

$$m_1 = \frac{1}{\sqrt{2\pi}} \int_{-\infty}^\infty x e^{-x^2/2}\, dx.$$

Since the integrand is odd, for any b, the integral

$$\int_{-b}^b x e^{-x^2/2}\, dx = 0.$$

Thus,

$$m_1 = \frac{1}{\sqrt{2\pi}} \int_{-\infty}^\infty x e^{-x^2/2}\, dx = \frac{1}{\sqrt{2\pi}} \lim_{b \to \infty} \int_{-b}^b x e^{-x^2/2}\, dx = 0.$$

40. We calculate

$$m_2 = \frac{1}{\sqrt{2\pi}} \int_{-\infty}^\infty x^2 e^{-x^2/2}\, dx.$$

We integrate by parts with $u = x$, $v' = x e^{-x^2/2}$, so $u' = 1$, $v = -e^{-x^2/2}$, so

$$\int_{-b}^b x^2 e^{-x^2/2}\, dx = -x e^{-x^2/2} \Big|_{-b}^b + \int_{-b}^b e^{-x^2/2}\, dx = -2b e^{-b^2/2} + \int_{-b}^b e^{-x^2/2}\, dx.$$

Now $2b e^{-b^2/2} \to 0$ as $b \to \infty$, so

$$m_2 = \frac{1}{\sqrt{2\pi}} \int_{-\infty}^\infty x^2 e^{-x^2/2}\, dx = \frac{1}{\sqrt{2\pi}} \int_{-\infty}^\infty e^{-x^2/2}\, dx = \frac{1}{\sqrt{2\pi}} \cdot \sqrt{2\pi} = 1.$$

41. We calculate

$$m_3 = \frac{1}{\sqrt{2\pi}} \int_{-\infty}^{\infty} x^3 e^{-x^2/2} \, dx.$$

Since the integrand is odd, for any b, the integral

$$\int_{-b}^{b} x^3 e^{-x^2/2} \, dx = 0.$$

Thus,

$$m_3 = \frac{1}{\sqrt{2\pi}} \int_{-\infty}^{\infty} x^3 e^{-x^2/2} \, dx = \frac{1}{\sqrt{2\pi}} \lim_{b \to \infty} \int_{-b}^{b} x^3 e^{-x^2/2} \, dx = 0.$$

42. We calculate

$$m_4 = \frac{1}{\sqrt{2\pi}} \int_{-\infty}^{\infty} x^4 e^{-x^2/2} \, dx.$$

We integrate by parts with $u = x^3$, $v' = xe^{-x^2/2}$, so $u' = 3x^2$, $v = -e^{-x^2/2}$, so

$$\int_{-b}^{b} x^4 e^{-x^2/2} \, dx = -x^3 e^{-x^2/2} \Big|_{-b}^{b} + \int_{-b}^{b} 3x^2 e^{-x^2/2} \, dx = -2b^3 e^{-b^2/2} + \int_{-b}^{b} 3x^2 e^{-x^2/2} \, dx.$$

Integrating by parts again, this time with $u = 3x$ and $v' = xe^{-x^2/2}$, so $u' = 3$, $v = -e^{-x^2/2}$ gives

$$\int_{-b}^{b} x^4 e^{-x^2/2} \, dx = -2b^3 e^{-b^2/2} - 3xe^{-x^2/2} \Big|_{-b}^{b} + \int_{-b}^{b} 3e^{-x^2/2} \, dx$$

$$= -2b^3 e^{-b^2/2} - 6be^{-b^2/2} + 3 \int_{-b}^{b} e^{-x^2/2} \, dx.$$

Now $b^3 e^{-b^2/2} \to 0$ and $be^{-b^2/2} \to 0$ as $b \to \infty$, so

$$m_4 = \frac{1}{\sqrt{2\pi}} \int_{-\infty}^{\infty} x^4 e^{-x^2/2} \, dx = \frac{3}{\sqrt{2\pi}} \int_{-\infty}^{\infty} e^{-x^2/2} \, dx = \frac{3}{\sqrt{2\pi}} \cdot \sqrt{2\pi} = 3.$$

43. (a)

$$\Gamma(1) = \int_0^{\infty} e^{-t} \, dt$$

$$= \lim_{b \to \infty} \int_0^{b} e^{-t} \, dt$$

$$= \lim_{b \to \infty} -e^{-t} \Big|_0^{b}$$

$$= \lim_{b \to \infty} [1 - e^{-b}] = 1.$$

Using Problem 9,

$$\Gamma(2) = \int_0^{\infty} te^{-t} \, dt = 1.$$

(b) We integrate by parts. Let $u = t^n$, $v' = e^{-t}$. Then $u' = nt^{n-1}$ and $v = -e^{-t}$, so

$$\int t^n e^{-t} \, dt = -t^n e^{-t} + n \int t^{n-1} e^{-t} \, dt.$$

So

$$\Gamma(n+1) = \int_0^{\infty} t^n e^{-t} \, dt$$

$$= \lim_{b \to \infty} \int_0^b t^n e^{-t}\, dt$$

$$= \lim_{b \to \infty} \left[-t^n e^{-t} \Big|_0^b + n \int_0^b t^{n-1} e^{-t}\, dt \right]$$

$$= \lim_{b \to \infty} -b^n e^{-b} + \lim_{b \to \infty} n \int_0^b t^{n-1} e^{-t}\, dt$$

$$= 0 + n \int_0^\infty t^{n-1} e^{-t}\, dt$$

$$= n\Gamma(n).$$

(c) We already have $\Gamma(1) = 1$ and $\Gamma(2) = 1$. Using $\Gamma(n+1) = n\Gamma(n)$ we can get

$$\Gamma(3) = 2\Gamma(2) = 2$$
$$\Gamma(4) = 3\Gamma(3) = 3 \cdot 2$$
$$\Gamma(5) = 4\Gamma(4) = 4 \cdot 3 \cdot 2.$$

So it appears that $\Gamma(n)$ is just the first $n-1$ numbers multiplied together, so $\Gamma(n) = (n-1)!$.

44. (a) Using a calculator or a computer, the graph is:

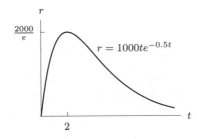

(b) People are getting sick fastest when the rate of infection is highest, i.e. when r is at its maximum. Since

$$r' = 1000e^{-0.5t} - 1000(0.5)te^{-0.5t}$$
$$= 500e^{-0.5t}(2 - t)$$

this must occur at $t = 2$.

(c) The total number of sick people $= \displaystyle\int_0^\infty 1000te^{-0.5t}\, dt.$

Using integration by parts, with $u = t$, $v' = e^{-0.5t}$:

$$\text{Total} = \lim_{b \to \infty} 1000 \left(\frac{-t}{0.5} e^{-0.5t} \Big|_0^b - \int_0^b \frac{-1}{0.5} e^{-0.5t}\, dt \right)$$

$$= \lim_{b \to \infty} 1000 \left(-2be^{-0.5b} - \frac{2}{0.5} e^{-0.5b} \right) \Big|_0^b$$

$$= \lim_{b \to \infty} 1000 \left(-2be^{-0.5b} - 4e^{-0.5b} + 4 \right)$$

$$= 4000 \text{ people.}$$

45. The energy required is

$$E = \int_1^\infty \frac{kq_1 q_2}{r^2}\, dr = kq_1 q_2 \lim_{b \to \infty} -\frac{1}{r} \Big|_1^b$$
$$= (9 \times 10^9)(1)(1)(1) = 9 \times 10^9 \text{ joules}$$

Solutions for Section 7.8

Exercises

1. For large x, the integrand behaves like $1/x^2$ because

$$\frac{x^2}{x^4 + 1} \approx \frac{x^2}{x^4} = \frac{1}{x^2}.$$

Since $\int_1^\infty \frac{dx}{x^2}$ converges, we expect our integral to converge. More precisely, since $x^4 + 1 > x^4$, we have

$$\frac{x^2}{x^4 + 1} < \frac{x^2}{x^4} = \frac{1}{x^2}.$$

Since $\int_1^\infty \frac{dx}{x^2}$ is convergent, the comparison test tells us that $\int_1^\infty \frac{x^2}{x^4 + 1}\, dx$ converges also.

2. For large x, the integrand behaves like $1/x$ because

$$\frac{x^3}{x^4 - 1} \approx \frac{x^3}{x^4} = \frac{1}{x}.$$

Since $\int_2^\infty \frac{1}{x}\, dx$ does not converge, we expect our integral not to converge. More precisely, since $x^4 - 1 < x^4$, we have

$$\frac{x^3}{x^4 - 1} > \frac{x^3}{x^4} = \frac{1}{x}.$$

Since $\int_2^\infty \frac{1}{x}\, dx$ does not converge, the comparison test tells us that $\int_2^\infty \frac{x^3}{x^4 - 1}\, dx$ does not converge either.

3. The integrand is continuous for all $x \geq 1$, so whether the integral converges or diverges depends only on the behavior of the function as $x \to \infty$. As $x \to \infty$, polynomials behave like the highest powered term. Thus, as $x \to \infty$, the integrand $\frac{x^2 + 1}{x^3 + 3x + 2}$ behaves like $\frac{x^2}{x^3}$ or $\frac{1}{x}$. Since $\int_1^\infty \frac{1}{x}\, dx$ diverges, we predict that the given integral will diverge.

4. The integrand is continuous for all $x \geq 1$, so whether the integral converges or diverges depends only on the behavior of the function as $x \to \infty$. As $x \to \infty$, polynomials behave like the highest powered term. Thus, as $x \to \infty$, the integrand $\frac{1}{x^2 + 5x + 1}$ behaves like $\frac{1}{x^2}$. Since $\int_1^\infty \frac{1}{x^2}\, dx$ converges, we predict that the given integral will converge.

5. The integrand is continuous for all $x \geq 1$, so whether the integral converges or diverges depends only on the behavior of the function as $x \to \infty$. As $x \to \infty$, polynomials behave like the highest powered term. Thus, as $x \to \infty$, the integrand $\frac{x}{x^2 + 2x + 4}$ behaves like $\frac{x}{x^2}$ or $\frac{1}{x}$. Since $\int_1^\infty \frac{1}{x}\, dx$ diverges, we predict that the given integral will diverge.

6. The integrand is continuous for all $x \geq 1$, so whether the integral converges or diverges depends only on the behavior of the function as $x \to \infty$. As $x \to \infty$, polynomials behave like the highest powered term. Thus, as $x \to \infty$, the integrand $\frac{x^2 - 6x + 1}{x^2 + 4}$ behaves like $\frac{x^2}{x^2}$ or 1. Since $\int_1^\infty 1\, dx$ diverges, we predict that the given integral will diverge.

7. The integrand is continuous for all $x \geq 1$, so whether the integral converges or diverges depends only on the behavior of the function as $x \to \infty$. As $x \to \infty$, polynomials behave like the highest powered term. Thus, as $x \to \infty$, the integrand $\frac{5x + 2}{x^4 + 8x^2 + 4}$ behaves like $\frac{5x}{x^4}$ or $\frac{5}{x^3}$. Since $\int_1^\infty \frac{5}{x^3}\, dx$ converges, we predict that the given integral will converge.

8. For large t, the 2 is negligible in comparison to e^{5t}, so the integrand behaves like e^{-5t}. Thus

$$\frac{1}{e^{5t} + 2} \approx \frac{1}{e^{5t}} = e^{-5t}.$$

More precisely, since $e^{5t} + 2 > e^{5t}$, we have

$$\frac{1}{e^{5t} + 2} < \frac{1}{e^{5t}} = e^{-5t}.$$

Since $\int_1^\infty e^{-5t}\, dt$ converges, by the Comparison Theorem $\int_1^\infty \frac{1}{e^{5t} + 2}\, dt$ converges also.

9. The integrand is continuous for all $x \geq 1$, so whether the integral converges or diverges depends only on the behavior of the function as $x \to \infty$. As $x \to \infty$, polynomials behave like the highest powered term. Thus, as $x \to \infty$, the integrand $\dfrac{x^2 + 4}{x^4 + 3x^2 + 11}$ behaves like $\dfrac{x^2}{x^4}$ or $\dfrac{1}{x^2}$. Since $\displaystyle\int_1^\infty \dfrac{1}{x^2}\, dx$ converges, we predict that the given integral will converge.

10. It converges:
$$\int_{50}^\infty \frac{dz}{z^3} = \lim_{b \to \infty} \int_{50}^b \frac{dz}{z^3} = \lim_{b \to \infty} \left(-\frac{1}{2} z^{-2} \Big|_{50}^b \right) = \frac{1}{2} \lim_{b \to \infty} \left(\frac{1}{50^2} - \frac{1}{b^2} \right) = \frac{1}{5000}$$

11. Since $\dfrac{1}{1 + x} \geq \dfrac{1}{2x}$ and $\dfrac{1}{2} \displaystyle\int_0^\infty \dfrac{1}{x}\, dx$ diverges, we have that $\displaystyle\int_1^\infty \dfrac{dx}{1 + x}$ diverges.

12. If $x \geq 1$, we know that $\dfrac{1}{x^3 + 1} \leq \dfrac{1}{x^3}$, and since $\displaystyle\int_1^\infty \dfrac{dx}{x^3}$ converges, the improper integral $\displaystyle\int_1^\infty \dfrac{dx}{x^3 + 1}$ converges.

13. The integrand is unbounded as $t \to 5$. We substitute $w = t - 5$, so $dw = dt$. When $t = 5$, $w = 0$ and when $t = 8$, $w = 3$.
$$\int_5^8 \frac{6}{\sqrt{t - 5}}\, dt = \int_0^3 \frac{6}{\sqrt{w}}\, dw.$$

Since
$$\int_0^3 \frac{6}{\sqrt{w}}\, dw = \lim_{a \to 0^+} 6 \int_a^3 \frac{1}{\sqrt{w}}\, dw = 6 \lim_{a \to 0^+} 2w^{1/2} \Big|_a^3 = 12 \lim_{a \to 0^+} \left(\sqrt{3} - \sqrt{a} \right) = 12\sqrt{3},$$
our integral converges.

14. The integral converges.
$$\int_0^1 \frac{1}{x^{19/20}}\, dx = \lim_{a \to 0} \int_a^1 \frac{1}{x^{19/20}}\, dx = \lim_{a \to 0} 20 x^{1/20} \Big|_a^1 = \lim_{a \to 0} 20 \left(1 - a^{1/20} \right) = 20.$$

15. This integral diverges. To see this, substitute $t + 1 = w$, $dt = dw$. So,
$$\int_{t=-1}^{t=5} \frac{dt}{(t + 1)^2} = \int_{w=0}^{w=6} \frac{dw}{w^2},$$
which diverges.

16. Since we know the antiderivative of $\dfrac{1}{1 + u^2}$, we can use the Fundamental Theorem of Calculus to evaluate the integral. Since the integrand is even, we write
$$\int_{-\infty}^\infty \frac{du}{1 + u^2} = 2 \int_0^\infty \frac{du}{1 + u^2} = 2 \lim_{b \to \infty} \int_0^b \frac{du}{1 + u^2}$$
$$= 2 \lim_{b \to \infty} \arctan b = 2 \left(\frac{\pi}{2} \right) = \pi.$$

Thus, the integral converges to π.

17. Since $\dfrac{1}{u + u^2} < \dfrac{1}{u^2}$ for $u \geq 1$, and since $\displaystyle\int_1^\infty \dfrac{du}{u^2}$ converges, $\displaystyle\int_1^\infty \dfrac{du}{u + u^2}$ converges.

18. This improper integral diverges. We expect this because, for large θ, $\dfrac{1}{\sqrt{\theta^2 + 1}} \approx \dfrac{1}{\sqrt{\theta^2}} = \dfrac{1}{\theta}$ and $\displaystyle\int_1^\infty \dfrac{d\theta}{\theta}$ diverges. More precisely, for $\theta \geq 1$
$$\frac{1}{\sqrt{\theta^2 + 1}} \geq \frac{1}{\sqrt{\theta^2 + \theta^2}} = \frac{1}{\sqrt{2}\sqrt{\theta^2}} = \frac{1}{\sqrt{2}} \cdot \frac{1}{\theta}$$
and $\displaystyle\int_1^\infty \dfrac{d\theta}{\theta}$ diverges. (The factor $\dfrac{1}{\sqrt{2}}$ does not affect the divergence.)

19. For $\theta \geq 2$, we have $\dfrac{1}{\sqrt{\theta^3 + 1}} \leq \dfrac{1}{\sqrt{\theta^3}} = \dfrac{1}{\theta^{\frac{3}{2}}}$, and $\displaystyle\int_2^\infty \dfrac{d\theta}{\theta^{3/2}}$ converges (check by integration), so $\displaystyle\int_2^\infty \dfrac{d\theta}{\sqrt{\theta^3 + 1}}$ converges.

20. This integral is improper at $\theta = 0$. For $0 \leq \theta \leq 1$, we have $\dfrac{1}{\sqrt{\theta^3 + \theta}} \leq \dfrac{1}{\sqrt{\theta}}$, and since $\displaystyle\int_0^1 \dfrac{1}{\sqrt{\theta}}\, d\theta$ converges, $\displaystyle\int_0^1 \dfrac{d\theta}{\sqrt{\theta^3 + \theta}}$ converges.

21. Since $\dfrac{1}{1 + e^y} \leq \dfrac{1}{e^y} = e^{-y}$ and $\displaystyle\int_0^\infty e^{-y}\, dy$ converges, the integral $\displaystyle\int_0^\infty \dfrac{dy}{1 + e^y}$ converges.

22. This integral is convergent because, for $\phi \geq 1$,

$$\frac{2 + \cos\phi}{\phi^2} \leq \frac{3}{\phi^2},$$

and $\displaystyle\int_1^\infty \dfrac{3}{\phi^2}\, d\phi = 3\int_1^\infty \dfrac{1}{\phi^2}\, d\phi$ converges.

23. Since $\dfrac{1}{e^z + 2^z} < \dfrac{1}{e^z} = e^{-z}$ for $z \geq 0$, and $\displaystyle\int_0^\infty e^{-z}\, dz$ converges, $\displaystyle\int_0^\infty \dfrac{dz}{e^z + 2^z}$ converges.

24. Since $\dfrac{1}{\phi^2} \leq \dfrac{2 - \sin\phi}{\phi^2}$ for $0 < \phi \leq \pi$, and since $\displaystyle\int_0^\pi \dfrac{1}{\phi^2}\, d\phi$ diverges, $\displaystyle\int_0^\pi \dfrac{2 - \sin\phi}{\phi^2}\, d\phi$ must diverge.

25. Since $\dfrac{3 + \sin\alpha}{\alpha} \geq \dfrac{2}{\alpha}$ for $\alpha \geq 4$, and since $\displaystyle\int_4^\infty \dfrac{2}{\alpha}\, d\alpha$ diverges, then $\displaystyle\int_4^\infty \dfrac{3 + \sin\alpha}{\alpha}\, d\alpha$ diverges.

26. If we integrate e^{-x^2} from 1 to 10, we get 0.139. This answer does not change noticeably if you extend the region of integration to from 1 to 11, say, or even up to 1000. There's a reason for this; and the reason is that the tail, $\int_{10}^\infty e^{-x^2}\, dx$, is very small indeed. In fact

$$\int_{10}^\infty e^{-x^2}\, dx \leq \int_{10}^\infty e^{-x}\, dx = e^{-10},$$

which is very small. (In fact, the tail integral is less than $e^{-100}/10$. Can you prove that? [Hint: $e^{-x^2} \leq e^{-10x}$ for $x \geq 10$.])

27. Approximating the integral by $\int_0^{10} e^{-x^2} \cos^2 x\, dx$ yields 0.606 to two decimal places. This is a good approximation to the improper integral because the "tail" is small:

$$\int_{10}^\infty e^{-x^2} \cos^2 x\, dx \leq \int_{10}^\infty e^{-x}\, dx = e^{-10},$$

which is very small.

Problems

28. (a) The area is infinite. The area under $1/x$ is infinite and the area under $1/x^2$ is 1. So the area between the two has to be infinite also.

(b) Since $f(x)$ is bounded between 0 and $1/x^2$, and the area under $1/x^2$ is finite, $f(x)$ will have finite area by the comparison test. Similarly, $h(x)$ lies above $1/x$, whose area is infinite, so $h(x)$ must have infinite area as well. We can tell nothing about the area of $g(x)$, because the comparison test tells us nothing about a function larger than a function with finite area but smaller than one with infinite area. Finally, $k(x)$ will certainly have infinite area, because it has a lower bound m, for some $m > 0$. Thus, $\int_0^a k(x)\, dx \geq ma$, and since the latter does not converge as $a \to \infty$, neither can the former.

29. The convergence or divergence of an improper integral depends on the long-term behavior of the integrand, not on its short-term behavior. Figure 7.31 suggests that $g(x) \leq f(x)$ for all values of x beyond $x = k$. Since $\int_k^\infty f(x)\, dx$ converges, we expect $\int_k^\infty g(x)\, dx$ converges also.

However we are interested in $\int_a^\infty g(x)\, dx$. Breaking the integral into two parts enables us to use the fact that $\int_k^\infty g(x)\, dx$ is finite:

$$\int_a^\infty g(x)\, dx = \int_a^k g(x)\, dx + \int_k^\infty g(x)\, dx.$$

The first integral is also finite because the interval from a to k is finite. Therefore, we expect $\int_a^\infty g(x)\, dx$ converges.

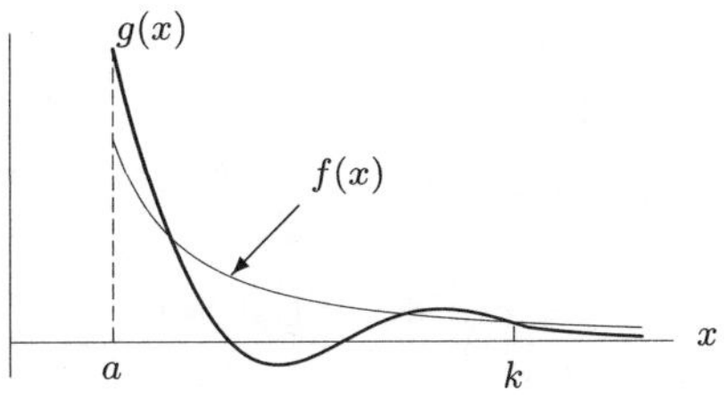

Figure 7.31

30. First let's calculate the indefinite integral $\displaystyle\int \frac{dx}{x(\ln x)^p}$. Let $\ln x = w$, then $\dfrac{dx}{x} = dw$. So

$$\int \frac{dx}{x(\ln x)^p} = \int \frac{dw}{w^p}$$
$$= \begin{cases} \ln|w| + C, & \text{if } p = 1 \\ \frac{1}{1-p} w^{1-p} + C, & \text{if } p \neq 1 \end{cases}$$
$$= \begin{cases} \ln|\ln x| + C, & \text{if } p = 1 \\ \frac{1}{1-p}(\ln x)^{1-p} + C, & \text{if } p \neq 1. \end{cases}$$

Notice that $\lim\limits_{x \to \infty} \ln x = +\infty$.

(a) $p = 1$:

$$\int_2^\infty \frac{dx}{x \ln x} = \lim_{b \to \infty} \left(\ln|\ln b| - \ln|\ln 2| \right) = +\infty.$$

(b) $p < 1$:

$$\int_2^\infty \frac{dx}{x(\ln x)^p} = \frac{1}{1-p} \left(\lim_{b \to \infty} (\ln b)^{1-p} - (\ln 2)^{1-p} \right) = +\infty.$$

(c) $p > 1$:

$$\int_2^\infty \frac{dx}{x(\ln x)^p} = \frac{1}{1-p} \left(\lim_{b \to \infty} (\ln b)^{1-p} - (\ln 2)^{1-p} \right)$$
$$= \frac{1}{1-p} \left(\lim_{b \to \infty} \frac{1}{(\ln b)^{p-1}} - (\ln 2)^{1-p} \right)$$
$$= -\frac{1}{1-p}(\ln 2)^{1-p}.$$

Thus, $\displaystyle\int_2^\infty \frac{dx}{x(\ln x)^p}$ is convergent for $p > 1$, divergent for $p \leq 1$.

31. The indefinite integral $\displaystyle\int \frac{dx}{x(\ln x)^p}$ is computed in Problem 30. Let $\ln x = w$, then $\dfrac{dx}{x} = dw$. Notice that $\lim\limits_{x \to 1} \ln x = 0$, and $\lim\limits_{x \to 0^+} \ln x = -\infty$.

For this integral notice that $\ln 1 = 0$, so the integrand blows up at $x = 1$.

(a) $p = 1$:

$$\int_1^2 \frac{dx}{x \ln x} = \lim_{a \to 1^+} \left(\ln|\ln 2| - \ln|\ln a| \right)$$

Since $\ln a \to 0$ as $a \to 1$, $\ln|\ln a| \to -\infty$ as $b \to 1$. So the integral is divergent.

(b) $p < 1$:

$$\int_1^2 \frac{dx}{x(\ln x)^p} = \frac{1}{1-p} \lim_{a \to 1^+} \left((\ln 2)^{1-p} - (\ln a)^{1-p} \right)$$
$$= \frac{1}{1-p}(\ln 2)^{1-p}.$$

(c) $p > 1$:

$$\int_1^2 \frac{dx}{x(\ln x)^p} = \frac{1}{1-p} \lim_{a \to 1+} \left((\ln 2)^{1-p} - (\ln a)^{1-p} \right)$$

As $\lim_{a \to 1+} (\ln a)^{1-p} = \lim_{a \to 1+} \frac{1}{(\ln a)^{p-1}} = +\infty$, the integral diverges.

Thus, $\int_1^2 \frac{dx}{x(\ln x)^p}$ is convergent for $p < 1$, divergent for $p \geq 1$.

32. To find a, we first calculate $\int_0^{10} e^{-\frac{x^2}{2}} \, dx$. Since $\frac{x^2}{2} \geq x$ for $x \geq 10$, this will differ from $\int_0^\infty e^{-\frac{x^2}{2}} \, dx$ by at most

$$\int_{10}^\infty e^{-\frac{x^2}{2}} \, dx \leq \int_{10}^\infty e^{-x} \, dx = e^{-10},$$

which is very small. Using Simpson's rule with 100 intervals (well more than necessary), we find $\int_0^{10} e^{-\frac{x^2}{2}} \, dx \approx$ 1.253314137. Thus, since $e^{-\frac{x^2}{2}}$ is even, $\int_{-10}^{10} e^{-\frac{x^2}{2}} \, dx \approx 2.506628274$, and this is extremely close to $\int_{-\infty}^\infty e^{-\frac{x^2}{2}} \, dx$. To find a, we need $\int_{-\infty}^\infty ae^{-\frac{x^2}{2}} \, dx = 1$.

$$a = \frac{1}{\int_{-\infty}^\infty e^{-\frac{x^2}{2}} \, dx} \approx 0.399 \text{ to three decimal places.}$$

33. (a) If we substitute $w = x - k$ and $dw = dx$, we find

$$\int_{-\infty}^\infty ae^{-\frac{(x-k)^2}{2}} \, dx = \int_{-\infty}^\infty ae^{-\frac{w^2}{2}} \, dw.$$

This integral is the same as the integral in Problem 32, so the value of a will be the same, namely 0.399.

(b) The answer is the same because $g(x)$ is the same as $f(x)$ in Problem 32 except that it is shifted by k to the right. Since we are integrating from $-\infty$ to ∞, however, this shift does not mean anything for the integral.

34. (a) Since $e^{-x^2} \leq e^{-3x}$ for $x \geq 3$,

$$\int_3^\infty e^{-x^2} \, dx \leq \int_3^\infty e^{-3x} \, dx$$

Now

$$\int_3^\infty e^{-3x} \, dx = \lim_{b \to \infty} \int_3^b e^{-3x} \, dx = \lim_{b \to \infty} -\frac{1}{3} e^{-3x} \Big|_3^b$$

$$= \lim_{b \to \infty} \frac{e^{-9}}{3} - \frac{e^{-3b}}{3} = \frac{e^{-9}}{3}.$$

Thus

$$\int_3^\infty e^{-x^2} \, dx \leq \frac{e^{-9}}{3}.$$

(b) By reasoning similar to part (a),

$$\int_n^\infty e^{-x^2} \, dx \leq \int_n^\infty e^{-nx} \, dx,$$

and

$$\int_n^\infty e^{-nx} \, dx = \frac{1}{n} e^{-n^2},$$

so

$$\int_n^\infty e^{-x^2} \, dx \leq \frac{1}{n} e^{-n^2}.$$

35. (a) The tangent line to e^t has slope $(e^t)' = e^t$. Thus at $t = 0$, the slope is $e^0 = 1$. The line passes through $(0, e^0) = (0, 1)$. Thus the equation of the tangent line is $y = 1 + t$. Since e^t is everywhere concave up, its graph is always above the graph of any of its tangent lines; in particular, e^t is always above the line $y = 1 + t$. This is tantamount to saying

$$1 + t \le e^t,$$

with equality holding only at the point of tangency, $t = 0$.

(b) If $t = \dfrac{1}{x}$, then the above inequality becomes

$$1 + \frac{1}{x} \le e^{1/x}, \text{ or } e^{1/x} - 1 \ge \frac{1}{x}.$$

Since $t = \dfrac{1}{x}$, t is never zero. Therefore, the inequality is strict, and we write

$$e^{1/x} - 1 > \frac{1}{x}.$$

(c) Since $e^{1/x} - 1 > \dfrac{1}{x}$,

$$\frac{1}{x^5 \left(e^{1/x} - 1\right)} < \frac{1}{x^5 \left(\frac{1}{x}\right)} = \frac{1}{x^4}.$$

Since $\displaystyle\int_1^\infty \frac{dx}{x^4}$ converges, $\displaystyle\int_1^\infty \frac{dx}{x^5 \left(e^{1/x} - 1\right)}$ converges.

Solutions for Chapter 7 Review

Exercises

1. Since $\dfrac{d}{dt} \cos t = -\sin t$, we have

$$\int \sin t \, dt = -\cos t + C, \text{ where } C \text{ is a constant.}$$

2. Let $2t = w$, then $2dt = dw$, so $dt = \frac{1}{2} dw$, so

$$\int \cos 2t \, dt = \int \frac{1}{2} \cos w \, dw = \frac{1}{2} \sin w + C = \frac{1}{2} \sin 2t + C,$$

where C is a constant.

3. Let $5z = w$, then $5dz = dw$, which means $dz = \frac{1}{5} dw$, so

$$\int e^{5z} \, dz = \int e^w \cdot \frac{1}{5} dw = \frac{1}{5} \int e^w \, dw = \frac{1}{5} e^w + C = \frac{1}{5} e^{5z} + C,$$

where C is a constant.

4. Using the power rule gives $\dfrac{3}{2} w^2 + 7w + C$.

5. Since $\displaystyle\int \sin w \, d\theta = -\cos w + C$, the substitution $w = 2\theta$, $dw = 2 \, d\theta$ gives $\displaystyle\int \sin 2\theta \, d\theta = -\frac{1}{2} \cos 2\theta + C$.

6. Let $w = x^3 - 1$, then $dw = 3x^2 dx$ so that

$$\int (x^3 - 1)^4 x^2 \, dx = \frac{1}{3} \int w^4 \, dw = \frac{1}{15} w^5 + C = \frac{1}{15} (x^3 - 1)^5 + C.$$

7. The power rule gives $\dfrac{2}{5}x^{5/2} + \dfrac{3}{5}x^{5/3} + C$

8. From the rule for antidifferentiation of exponentials, we get

$$\int (e^x + 3^x)\, dx = e^x + \frac{1}{\ln 3} \cdot 3^x + C.$$

9. Either expand $(r+1)^3$ or use the substitution $w = r+1$. If $w = r+1$, then $dw = dr$ and

$$\int (r+1)^3\, dr = \int w^3\, dw = \frac{1}{4}w^4 + C = \frac{1}{4}(r+1)^4 + C.$$

10. Rewrite the integrand as

$$\int \left(\frac{4}{x^2} - \frac{3}{x^3}\right) dx = 4\int x^{-2}\, dx - 3\int x^{-3}\, dx = -4x^{-1} + \frac{3}{2}x^{-2} + C.$$

11. Dividing by x^2 gives

$$\int \left(\frac{x^3 + x + 1}{x^2}\right) dx = \int \left(x + \frac{1}{x} + \frac{1}{x^2}\right) dx = \frac{1}{2}x^2 + \ln|x| - \frac{1}{x} + C.$$

12. Let $w = 1 + \ln x$, then $dw = dx/x$ so that

$$\int \frac{(1 + \ln x)^2}{x}\, dx = \int w^2 dw = \frac{1}{3}w^3 + C = \frac{1}{3}(1 + \ln x)^3 + C.$$

13. Substitute $w = t^2$, so $dw = 2t\, dt$.

$$\int te^{t^2}\, dt = \frac{1}{2}\int e^{t^2} 2t\, dt = \frac{1}{2}\int e^w\, dw = \frac{1}{2}e^w + C = \frac{1}{2}e^{t^2} + C.$$

Check:

$$\frac{d}{dt}\left(\frac{1}{2}e^{t^2} + C\right) = 2t\left(\frac{1}{2}e^{t^2}\right) = te^{t^2}.$$

14. Integration by parts with $u = x$, $v' = \cos x$ gives

$$\int x\cos x\, dx = x\sin x - \int \sin x\, dx + C = x\sin x + \cos x + C.$$

Or use III-16 with $p(x) = x$ and $a = 1$ in the integral table.

15. Integration by parts twice gives

$$\int x^2 e^{2x}\, dx = \frac{x^2 e^{2x}}{2} - \int 2xe^{2x}\, dx = \frac{x^2}{2}e^{2x} - \frac{x}{2}e^{2x} + \frac{1}{4}e^{2x} + C$$

$$= (\frac{1}{2}x^2 - \frac{1}{2}x + \frac{1}{4})e^{2x} + C.$$

Or use the integral table, III-14 with $p(x) = x^2$ and $a = 1$.

16. Using substitution with $w = 1 - x$ and $dw = -dx$, we get

$$\int x\sqrt{1-x}\, dx = -\int (1-w)\sqrt{w}\, dw = \frac{2}{5}w^{5/2} - \frac{2}{3}w^{3/2} + C = \frac{2}{5}(1-x)^{5/2} - \frac{2}{3}(1-x)^{3/2} + C.$$

17. Integration by parts with $u = \ln x$, $v' = x$ gives

$$\int x\ln x\, dx = \frac{x^2}{2}\ln x - \int \frac{1}{2}x\, dx = \frac{1}{2}x^2\ln x - \frac{1}{4}x^2 + C.$$

Or use the integral table, III-13, with $n = 1$.

18. We integrate by parts, with $u = y$, $v' = \sin y$. We have $u' = 1$, $v = -\cos y$, and

$$\int y \sin y \, dy = -y \cos y - \int (-\cos y) \, dy = -y \cos y + \sin y + C.$$

Check:

$$\frac{d}{dy}(-y \cos y + \sin y + C) = -\cos y + y \sin y + \cos y = y \sin y.$$

19. We integrate by parts, using $u = (\ln x)^2$ and $v' = 1$. Then $u' = 2\frac{\ln x}{x}$ and $v = x$, so

$$\int (\ln x)^2 \, dx = x(\ln x)^2 - 2 \int \ln x \, dx.$$

But, integrating by parts or using the integral table, $\int \ln x \, dx = x \ln x - x + C$. Therefore,

$$\int (\ln x)^2 \, dx = x(\ln x)^2 - 2x \ln x + 2x + C.$$

Check:

$$\frac{d}{dx} \left[x(\ln x)^2 - 2x \ln x + 2x + C \right] = (\ln x)^2 + x\frac{2 \ln x}{x} - 2 \ln x - 2x\frac{1}{x} + 2 = (\ln x)^2.$$

20. Remember that $\ln(x^2) = 2 \ln x$. Therefore,

$$\int \ln(x^2) \, dx = 2 \int \ln x \, dx = 2x \ln x - 2x + C.$$

Check:

$$\frac{d}{dx}(2x \ln x - 2x + C) = 2 \ln x + \frac{2x}{x} - 2 = 2 \ln x = \ln(x^2).$$

21. Using the exponent rules and the chain rule, we have

$$\int e^{0.5-0.3t} \, dt = e^{0.5} \int e^{-0.3t} \, dt = -\frac{e^{0.5}}{0.3} e^{-0.3t} + C = -\frac{e^{0.5-0.3t}}{0.3} + C.$$

22. Let $\sin \theta = w$, then $\cos \theta \, d\theta = dw$, so

$$\int \sin^2 \theta \cos \theta \, d\theta = \int w^2 \, dw = \frac{1}{3}w^3 + C = \frac{1}{3} \sin^3 \theta + C,$$

where C is a constant.

23. Substitute $w = 4 - x^2$, $dw = -2x \, dx$:

$$\int x\sqrt{4 - x^2} \, dx = -\frac{1}{2} \int \sqrt{w} \, dw = -\frac{1}{3}w^{3/2} + C = -\frac{1}{3}(4 - x^2)^{3/2} + C.$$

Check

$$\frac{d}{dx} \left[-\frac{1}{3}(4 - x^2)^{3/2} + C \right] = -\frac{1}{3} \left[\frac{3}{2}(4 - x^2)^{1/2}(-2x) \right] = x\sqrt{4 - x^2}.$$

24. Expanding the numerator and dividing, we have

$$\int \frac{(u + 1)^3}{u^2} \, du = \int \frac{(u^3 + 3u^2 + 3u + 1)}{u^2} \, du = \int \left(u + 3 + \frac{3}{u} + \frac{1}{u^2} \right) du$$

$$= \frac{u^2}{2} + 3u + 3 \ln |u| - \frac{1}{u} + C.$$

Check:

$$\frac{d}{du} \left(\frac{u^2}{2} + 3u + 3 \ln |u| - \frac{1}{u} + C \right) = u + 3 + 3/u + 1/u^2 = \frac{(u + 1)^3}{u^2}.$$

25. Substitute $w = \sqrt{y}$, $dw = 1/(2\sqrt{y})\,dy$. Then

$$\int \frac{\cos\sqrt{y}}{\sqrt{y}}\,dy = 2\int \cos w\,dw = 2\sin w + C = 2\sin\sqrt{y} + C.$$

Check:

$$\frac{d}{dy} 2\sin\sqrt{y} + C = \frac{2\cos\sqrt{y}}{2\sqrt{y}} = \frac{\cos\sqrt{y}}{\sqrt{y}}.$$

26. Since $\dfrac{d}{dz}(\tan z) = \dfrac{1}{\cos^2 z}$, we have

$$\int \frac{1}{\cos^2 z}\,dz = \tan z + C.$$

Check:

$$\frac{d}{dz}(\tan z + C) = \frac{d}{dz}\frac{\sin z}{\cos z} = \frac{(\cos z)(\cos z) - (\sin z)(-\sin z)}{\cos^2 z} = \frac{1}{\cos^2 z}.$$

27. Denote $\displaystyle\int \cos^2\theta\,d\theta$ by A. Let $u = \cos\theta$, $v' = \cos\theta$. Then, $v = \sin\theta$ and $u' = -\sin\theta$. Integrating by parts, we get:

$$A = \cos\theta\sin\theta - \int (-\sin\theta)\sin\theta\,d\theta.$$

Employing the identity $\sin^2\theta = 1 - \cos^2\theta$, the equation above becomes:

$$A = \cos\theta\sin\theta + \int d\theta - \int \cos^2\theta\,d\theta$$
$$= \cos\theta\sin\theta + \theta - A + C.$$

Solving this equation for A, and using the identity $\sin 2\theta = 2\cos\theta\sin\theta$ we get:

$$A = \int \cos^2\theta\,d\theta = \frac{1}{4}\sin 2\theta + \frac{1}{2}\theta + C.$$

[Note: An alternate solution would have been to use the identity $\cos^2\theta = \frac{1}{2}\cos 2\theta + \frac{1}{2}$.]

28. Multiplying out and integrating term by term:

$$\int t^{10}(t - 10)\,dt = \int (t^{11} - 10t^{10})\,dt = \int t^{11}\,dt - 10\int t^{10}\,dt = \frac{1}{12}t^{12} - \frac{10}{11}t^{11} + C.$$

29. Substitute $w = 2x - 6$. Then $dw = 2\,dx$ and

$$\int \tan(2x - 6)\,dx = \frac{1}{2}\int \tan w\,dw = \frac{1}{2}\int \frac{\sin w}{\cos w}\,dw$$
$$= -\frac{1}{2}\ln|\cos w| + C \text{ by substitution or by I-7 of the integral table.}$$
$$= -\frac{1}{2}\ln|\cos(2x - 6)| + C.$$

30. Let $\ln x = w$, then $\frac{1}{x}\,dx = dw$, so

$$\int \frac{(\ln x)^2}{x}\,dx = \int w^2\,dw = \frac{1}{3}w^3 + C = \frac{1}{3}(\ln x)^3 + C, \text{ where } C \text{ is a constant.}$$

31. Multiplying out, dividing, and then integrating yields

$$\int \frac{(t + 2)^2}{t^3}\,dt = \int \frac{t^2 + 4t + 4}{t^3}\,dt = \int \frac{1}{t}\,dt + \int \frac{4}{t^2}\,dt + \int \frac{4}{t^3}\,dt = \ln|t| - \frac{4}{t} - \frac{2}{t^2} + C,$$

where C is a constant.

32. Integrating term by term:

$$\int \left(x^2 + 2x + \frac{1}{x}\right) dx = \frac{1}{3}x^3 + x^2 + \ln|x| + C,$$

where C is a constant.

33. Dividing and then integrating, we obtain

$$\int \frac{t+1}{t^2} dt = \int \frac{1}{t} dt + \int \frac{1}{t^2} dt = \ln|t| - \frac{1}{t} + C, \text{ where } C \text{ is a constant.}$$

34. Let $t^2 + 1 = w$, then $2t\,dt = dw$, $t\,dt = \frac{1}{2}dw$, so

$$\int te^{t^2+1}\,dt = \int e^w \cdot \frac{1}{2}\,dw = \frac{1}{2}\int e^w\,dw = \frac{1}{2}e^w + C = \frac{1}{2}e^{t^2+1} + C,$$

where C is a constant.

35. Let $\cos\theta = w$, then $-\sin\theta\,d\theta = dw$, so

$$\int \tan\theta\,d\theta = \int \frac{\sin\theta}{\cos\theta}\,d\theta = \int \frac{-1}{w}\,dw$$
$$= -\ln|w| + C = -\ln|\cos\theta| + C,$$

where C is a constant.

36. If $u = \sin(5\theta)$, $du = \cos(5\theta) \cdot 5\,d\theta$, so

$$\int \sin(5\theta)\cos(5\theta)d\theta = \frac{1}{5}\int \sin(5\theta) \cdot 5\cos(5\theta)d\theta = \frac{1}{5}\int u\,du$$
$$= \frac{1}{5}\left(\frac{u^2}{2}\right) + C = \frac{1}{10}\sin^2(5\theta) + C$$

or

$$\int \sin(5\theta)\cos(5\theta)d\theta = \frac{1}{2}\int 2\sin(5\theta)\cos(5\theta)d\theta = \frac{1}{2}\int \sin(10\theta)d\theta \quad \text{(using } \sin(2x) = 2\sin x \cos x\text{)}$$
$$= \frac{-1}{20}\cos(10\theta) + C.$$

37. Using substitution,

$$\int \frac{x}{x^2+1}\,dx = \int \frac{1/2}{w}\,dw \qquad (x^2+1 = w, 2x\,dx = dw, x\,dx = \frac{1}{2}\,dw)$$
$$= \frac{1}{2}\int \frac{1}{w}\,dw = \frac{1}{2}\ln|w| + C = \frac{1}{2}\ln|x^2+1| + C,$$

where C is a constant.

38. Since $\frac{d}{dz}(\arctan z) = \frac{1}{1+z^2}$, we have

$$\int \frac{dz}{1+z^2} = \arctan z + C, \text{ where } C \text{ is a constant.}$$

39. Let $w = 2z$, so $dw = 2dz$. Then, since $\frac{d}{dw}\arctan w = \frac{1}{1+w^2}$, we have

$$\int \frac{dz}{1+4z^2} = \int \frac{\frac{1}{2}dw}{1+w^2} = \frac{1}{2}\arctan w + C = \frac{1}{2}\arctan 2z + C.$$

40. Let $w = \cos 2\theta$. Then $dw = -2 \sin 2\theta \, d\theta$, hence

$$\int \cos^3 2\theta \sin 2\theta \, d\theta = -\frac{1}{2} \int w^3 \, dw = -\frac{w^4}{8} + C = -\frac{\cos^4 2\theta}{8} + C.$$

Check:

$$\frac{d}{d\theta}\left(-\frac{\cos^4 2\theta}{8}\right) = -\frac{(4 \cos^3 2\theta)(-\sin 2\theta)(2)}{8} = \cos^3 2\theta \sin 2\theta.$$

41. Let $\cos 5\theta = w$, then $-5 \sin 5\theta \, d\theta = dw$, $\sin 5\theta \, d\theta = -\frac{1}{5} dw$. So

$$\int \sin 5\theta \cos^3 5\theta \, d\theta = \int w^3 \cdot \left(-\frac{1}{5}\right) dw = -\frac{1}{5} \int w^3 \, dw = -\frac{1}{20} w^4 + C$$

$$= -\frac{1}{20} \cos^4 5\theta + C,$$

where C is a constant.

42.

$$\int \sin^3 z \cos^3 z \, dz = \int \sin z (1 - \cos^2 z) \cos^3 z \, dz$$

$$= \int \sin z \cos^3 z \, dz - \int \sin z \cos^5 z \, dz$$

$$= \int w^3 (-dw) - \int w^5 (-dw) \quad (\text{let } \cos z = w, \text{ so } -\sin z \, dz = dw)$$

$$= -\int w^3 \, dw + \int w^5 \, dw$$

$$= -\frac{1}{4} w^4 + \frac{1}{6} w^6 + C$$

$$= -\frac{1}{4} \cos^4 z + \frac{1}{6} \cos^6 z + C,$$

where C is a constant.

43. If $u = t - 10$, $t = u + 10$ and $dt = 1 \, du$, so substituting we get

$$\int (u + 10) u^{10} du = \int (u^{11} + 10 u^{10}) \, du = \frac{1}{12} u^{12} + \frac{10}{11} u^{11} + C$$

$$= \frac{1}{12} (t - 10)^{12} + \frac{10}{11} (t - 10)^{11} + C.$$

44. Let $\sin \theta = w$, then $\cos \theta \, d\theta = dw$, so

$$\int \cos \theta \sqrt{1 + \sin \theta} \, d\theta = \int \sqrt{1 + w} \, dw$$

$$= \frac{(1 + w)^{3/2}}{3/2} + C = \frac{2}{3} (1 + \sin \theta)^{3/2} + C,$$

where C is a constant.

45.

$$\int x e^x \, dx = x e^x - \int e^x \, dx \qquad (\text{let } x = u, e^x = v', e^x = v)$$

$$= x e^x - e^x + C,$$

where C is a constant.

46.

$$\int t^3 e^t \, dt = t^3 e^t - \int 3t^2 e^t \, dt \qquad (\text{let } t^3 = u, e^t = v', 3t^2 = u', e^t = v)$$

$$= t^3 e^t - 3 \int t^2 e^t \, dt \qquad (\text{let } t^2 = u, e^t = v')$$

$$= t^3 e^t - 3(t^2 e^t - \int 2t e^t \, dt)$$

$$= t^3 e^t - 3t^2 e^t + 6 \int t e^t \, dt \qquad (\text{let } t = u, e^t = v')$$

$$= t^3 e^t - 3t^2 e^t + 6(t e^t - \int e^t \, dt)$$

$$= t^3 e^t - 3t^2 e^t + 6t e^t - 6e^t + C,$$

where C is a constant.

47. Let $x^2 = w$, then $2x \, dx = dw$, $x = 1 \Rightarrow w = 1$, $x = 3 \Rightarrow w = 9$. Thus,

$$\int_1^3 x(x^2 + 1)^{70} \, dx = \int_1^9 (w + 1)^{70} \frac{1}{2} \, dw$$

$$= \frac{1}{2} \cdot \frac{1}{71}(w + 1)^{71} \Big|_1^9$$

$$= \frac{1}{142}(10^{71} - 2^{71}).$$

48. Let $w = 3z + 5$ and $dw = 3 \, dz$. Then

$$\int (3z + 5)^3 \, dz = \frac{1}{3} \int w^3 \, dw = \frac{1}{12} w^4 + C = \frac{1}{12}(3z + 5)^4 + C.$$

49. Rewrite $9 + u^2$ as $9[1 + (u/3)^2]$ and let $w = u/3$, then $dw = du/3$ so that

$$\int \frac{du}{9 + u^2} = \frac{1}{3} \int \frac{dw}{1 + w^2} = \frac{1}{3} \arctan w + C = \frac{1}{3} \arctan \left(\frac{u}{3} \right) + C.$$

50. Let $u = \sin w$, then $du = \cos w \, dw$ so that

$$\int \frac{\cos w}{1 + \sin^2 w} \, dw = \int \frac{du}{1 + u^2} = \arctan u + C = \arctan(\sin w) + C.$$

51. Let $w = \ln x$, then $dw = (1/x) dx$ which gives

$$\int \frac{1}{x} \tan(\ln x) \, dx = \int \tan w \, dw = \int \frac{\sin w}{\cos w} \, dw = -\ln(|\cos w|) + C = -\ln(|\cos(\ln x)|) + C.$$

52. Let $w = \ln x$, then $dw = (1/x) dx$ so that

$$\int \frac{1}{x} \sin(\ln x) \, dx = \int \sin w \, dw = -\cos w + C = -\cos(\ln x) + C.$$

53. Let $u = 2x$, then $du = 2 \, dx$ so that

$$\int \frac{dx}{\sqrt{1 - 4x^2}} = \frac{1}{2} \int \frac{du}{\sqrt{1 - u^2}} = \frac{1}{2} \arcsin u + C = \frac{1}{2} \arcsin(2x) + C.$$

54. Let $u = 16 - w^2$, then $du = -2w\,dw$ so that

$$\int \frac{w\,dw}{\sqrt{16 - w^2}} = -\frac{1}{2} \int \frac{du}{\sqrt{u}} = -\sqrt{u} + C = -\sqrt{16 - w^2} + C.$$

55. Dividing and then integrating term by term, we get

$$\int \frac{e^{2y} + 1}{e^{2y}} \, dy = \int \left(\frac{e^{2y}}{e^{2y}} + \frac{1}{e^{2y}} \right) dy = \int (1 + e^{-2y}) \, dy = \int dy + \left(-\frac{1}{2} \right) \int e^{-2y} (-2) \, dy$$

$$= y - \frac{1}{2} e^{-2y} + C.$$

56. Let $u = 1 - \cos w$, then $du = \sin w\,dw$ which gives

$$\int \frac{\sin w\,dw}{\sqrt{1 - \cos w}} = \int \frac{du}{\sqrt{u}} = 2\sqrt{u} + C = 2\sqrt{1 - \cos w} + C.$$

57. Let $w = \ln x$. Then $dw = (1/x)dx$ which gives

$$\int \frac{dx}{x \ln x} = \int \frac{dw}{w} = \ln |w| + C = \ln |\ln x| + C.$$

58. Let $w = 3u + 8$, then $dw = 3du$ and

$$\int \frac{du}{3u + 8} = \int \frac{dw}{3w} = \frac{1}{3} \ln |3u + 8| + C.$$

59. Let $w = \sqrt{x^2 + 1}$, then $dw = \dfrac{x\,dx}{\sqrt{x^2 + 1}}$ so that

$$\int \frac{x}{\sqrt{x^2 + 1}} \cos \sqrt{x^2 + 1} \, dx = \int \cos w\,dw = \sin w + C = \sin \sqrt{x^2 + 1} + C.$$

60. Integrating by parts using $u = t^2$ and $dv = \dfrac{t\,dt}{\sqrt{1+t^2}}$ gives $du = 2t\,dt$ and $v = \sqrt{1 + t^2}$. Now

$$\int \frac{t^3}{\sqrt{1 + t^2}} \, dt = t^2 \sqrt{1 + t^2} - \int 2t \sqrt{1 + t^2} \, dt$$

$$= t^2 \sqrt{1 + t^2} - \frac{2}{3}(1 + t^2)^{3/2} + C$$

$$= \sqrt{1 + t^2}(t^2 - \frac{2}{3}(1 + t^2)) + C$$

$$= \sqrt{1 + t^2} \frac{(t^2 - 2)}{3} + C.$$

61. Using integration by parts, let $r = u$ and $dt = e^{ku}du$, so $dr = du$ and $t = (1/k)e^{ku}$. Thus

$$\int u e^{ku} \, du = \frac{u}{k} e^{ku} - \frac{1}{k} \int e^{ku} \, du = \frac{u}{k} e^{ku} - \frac{1}{k^2} e^{ku} + C.$$

62. Let $u = w + 5$, then $du = dw$ and noting that $w = u - 5$ we obtain

$$\int (w + 5)^4 w \, dw = \int u^4 (u - 5) \, du$$

$$= \int \left(u^5 - 5u^4 \right) du$$

$$= \frac{1}{6} u^6 - u^5 + C$$

$$= \frac{1}{6} (w + 5)^6 - (w + 5)^5 + C.$$

63. $\int e^{\sqrt{2x+3}}\,dx = \dfrac{1}{\sqrt{2}}\int e^{\sqrt{2x+3}}\sqrt{2}\,dx.$ If $u = \sqrt{2}x + 3$, $du = \sqrt{2}\,dx$, so

$$\frac{1}{\sqrt{2}}\int e^u\,du = \frac{1}{\sqrt{2}}e^u + C = \frac{1}{\sqrt{2}}e^{\sqrt{2x+3}} + C.$$

64. Integrate by parts letting $u = (\ln r)^2$ and $dv = r\,dr$, then $du = (2/r)\ln r\,dr$ and $v = r^2/2$. We get

$$\int r(\ln r)^2\,dr = \frac{1}{2}r^2(\ln r)^2 - \int r\ln r\,dr.$$

Then using integration by parts again with $u = \ln r$ and $dv = r\,dr$, so $du = dr/r$ and $v = r^2/2$, we get

$$\int r\ln^2 r\,dr = \frac{1}{2}r^2(\ln r)^2 - \left[\frac{1}{2}r^2\ln r - \frac{1}{2}\int r\,dr\right] = \frac{1}{2}r^2(\ln r)^2 - \frac{1}{2}r^2\ln r + \frac{1}{4}r^2 + C.$$

65. $\int (e^x + x)^2\,dx = \int (e^{2x} + 2xe^x + x^2)\,dy.$ Separating into three integrals, we have

$$\int e^{2x}\,dx = \frac{1}{2}\int e^{2x}2\,dx = \frac{1}{2}e^{2x} + C_1,$$

$$\int 2xe^x\,dx = 2\int xe^x\,dx = 2xe^x - 2e^x + C_2$$

from Formula II-13 of the integral table or integration by parts, and

$$\int x^2\,dx = \frac{x^3}{3} + C_3.$$

Combining the results and writing $C = C_1 + C_2 + C_3$, we get

$$\frac{1}{2}e^{2x} + 2xe^x - 2e^x + \frac{x^3}{3} + C.$$

66. Integrate by parts, $r = \ln u$ and $dt = u^2\,du$, so $dr = (1/u)\,du$ and $t = (1/3)u^3$. We have

$$\int u^2\ln u\,du = \frac{1}{3}u^3\ln u - \frac{1}{3}\int u^2\,du = \frac{1}{3}u^3\ln u - \frac{1}{9}u^3 + C.$$

67. The integral table yields

$$\int \frac{5x+6}{x^2+4}\,dx = \frac{5}{2}\ln|x^2+4| + \frac{6}{2}\arctan\frac{x}{2} + C$$
$$= \frac{5}{2}\ln|x^2+4| + 3\arctan\frac{x}{2} + C.$$

Check:

$$\frac{d}{dx}\left(\frac{5}{2}\ln|x^2+4| + \frac{6}{2}\arctan\frac{x}{2} + C\right) = \frac{5}{2}\left(\frac{1}{x^2+4}(2x) + 3\frac{1}{1+(x/2)^2}\frac{1}{2}\right)$$
$$= \frac{5x}{x^2+4} + \frac{6}{x^2+4} = \frac{5x+6}{x^2+4}.$$

68. Using Table IV-19, let $m = 3$, $w = 2x$, and $dw = 2dx$. Then

$$\int \frac{1}{\sin^3(2x)}\,dx = \frac{1}{2}\int \frac{1}{\sin^3 w}\,dw$$
$$= \frac{1}{2}\left[\frac{-1}{(3-1)}\frac{\cos w}{\sin^2 w}\right] + \frac{1}{4}\int \frac{1}{\sin w}\,dw,$$

and using Table IV-20, we have

$$\int \frac{1}{\sin w}\, dw = \frac{1}{2} \ln \left| \frac{\cos w - 1}{\cos w + 1} \right| + C.$$

Thus,

$$\int \frac{1}{\sin^3(2x)}\, dx = -\frac{\cos 2x}{4 \sin^2 2x} + \frac{1}{8} \ln \left| \frac{\cos 2x - 1}{\cos 2x + 1} \right| + C.$$

69. We can factor $r^2 - 100 = (r - 10)(r + 10)$ so we can use Table V-26 (with $a = 10$ and $b = -10$) to get

$$\int \frac{dr}{r^2 - 100} = \frac{1}{20} \left[\ln |r - 10| + \ln |r + 10| \right] + C.$$

70. Integration by parts will be used twice here. First let $u = y^2$ and $dv = \sin(cy)\, dy$, then $du = 2y\, dy$ and $v = -(1/c)\cos(cy)$. Thus

$$\int y^2 \sin(cy)\, dy = -\frac{y^2}{c} \cos(cy) + \frac{2}{c} \int y \cos(cy)\, dy.$$

Now use integration by parts to evaluate the integral in the right hand expression. Here let $u = y$ and $dv = \cos(cy)dy$ which gives $du = dy$ and $v = (1/c)\sin(cy)$. Then we have

$$\int y^2 \sin(cy)\, dy = -\frac{y^2}{c} \cos(cy) + \frac{2}{c} \left(\frac{y}{c} \sin(cy) - \frac{1}{c} \int \sin(cy)\, dy \right)$$

$$= -\frac{y^2}{c} \cos(cy) + \frac{2y}{c^2} \sin(cy) + \frac{2}{c^3} \cos(cy) + C.$$

71. Integration by parts will be used twice. First let $u = e^{-ct}$ and $dv = \sin(kt)dt$, then $du = -ce^{-ct}dt$ and $v = (-1/k)\cos kt$. Then

$$\int e^{-ct} \sin kt\, dt = -\frac{1}{k} e^{-ct} \cos kt - \frac{c}{k} \int e^{-ct} \cos kt\, dt$$

$$= -\frac{1}{k} e^{-ct} \cos kt - \frac{c}{k} \left(\frac{1}{k} e^{-ct} \sin kt + \frac{c}{k} \int e^{-ct} \sin kt\, dt \right)$$

$$= -\frac{1}{k} e^{-ct} \cos kt - \frac{c}{k^2} e^{-ct} \sin kt - \frac{c^2}{k^2} \int e^{-ct} \sin kt\, dt$$

Solving for $\int e^{-ct} \sin kt\, dt$ gives

$$\frac{k^2 + c^2}{k^2} \int e^{-ct} \sin kt\, dt = -\frac{e^{-ct}}{k^2} \left(k \cos kt + c \sin kt \right),$$

so

$$\int e^{-ct} \sin kt\, dt = -\frac{e^{-ct}}{k^2 + c^2} \left(k \cos kt + c \sin kt \right) + C.$$

72. Using II-9 from the integral table, with $a = 5$ and $b = 3$, we have

$$\int e^{5x} \cos(3x)\, dx = \frac{1}{25 + 9} e^{5x} \left[5 \cos(3x) + 3 \sin(3x) \right] + C$$

$$= \frac{1}{34} e^{5x} \left[5 \cos(3x) + 3 \sin(3x) \right] + C.$$

73. Since $\int (x^{\sqrt{k}} + (\sqrt{k})^x)dx = \int x^{\sqrt{k}} dx + \int (\sqrt{k})^x\, dx$, for the first integral, use Formula I-1 with $n = \sqrt{k}$. For the second integral, use Formula I-3 with $a = \sqrt{k}$. The result is

$$\int (x^{\sqrt{x}} + (\sqrt{k})^x)\, dx = \frac{x^{(\sqrt{k})+1}}{(\sqrt{k}) + 1} + \frac{(\sqrt{k})^x}{\ln \sqrt{k}} + C.$$

74. Factor $\sqrt{3}$ out of the integrand and use VI-30 of the integral table with $u = 2x$ and $du = 2dx$ to get

$$\int \sqrt{3 + 12x^2}\, dx = \int \sqrt{3}\sqrt{1 + 4x^2}\, dx$$

$$= \frac{\sqrt{3}}{2} \int \sqrt{1 + u^2}\, du$$

$$= \frac{\sqrt{3}}{4} \left(u\sqrt{1 + u^2} + \int \frac{1}{\sqrt{1 + u^2}}\, du \right).$$

Then from VI-29, simplify the integral on the right to get

$$\int \sqrt{3 + 12x^2}\, dx = \frac{\sqrt{3}}{4} \left(u\sqrt{1 + u^2} + \ln |u + \sqrt{1 + u^2}| \right) + C$$

$$= \frac{\sqrt{3}}{4} \left(2x\sqrt{1 + (2x)^2} + \ln |2x + \sqrt{1 + (2x)^2}| \right) + C.$$

75. By completing the square, we get

$$x^2 - 3x + 2 = (x^2 - 3x + (-\frac{3}{2})^2) + 2 - \frac{9}{4} = (x - \frac{3}{2})^2 - \frac{1}{4}.$$

Then

$$\int \frac{1}{\sqrt{x^2 - 3x + 2}}\, dx = \int \frac{1}{\sqrt{(x - \frac{3}{2})^2 - \frac{1}{4}}}\, dx.$$

Let $w = (x - (3/2))$, then $dw = dx$ and $a^2 = 1/4$. Then we have

$$\int \frac{1}{\sqrt{x^2 - 3x + 2}}\, dx = \int \frac{1}{\sqrt{w^2 - a^2}}\, dw$$

and from VI-29 of the integral table we have

$$\int \frac{1}{\sqrt{w^2 - a^2}}\, dw = \ln \left| w + \sqrt{w^2 - a^2} \right| + C$$

$$= \ln \left| \left(x - \frac{3}{2}\right) + \sqrt{\left(x - \frac{3}{2}\right)^2 - \frac{1}{4}} \right| + C$$

$$= \ln \left| \left(x - \frac{3}{2}\right) + \sqrt{x^2 - 3x + 2} \right| + C.$$

76. First divide $x^2 + 3x + 2$ into x^3 to obtain

$$\frac{x^3}{x^2 + 3x + 2} = x - 3 + \frac{7x + 6}{x^2 + 3x + 2}.$$

Since $x^2 + 3x + 2 = (x + 1)(x + 2)$, we can use V-27 of the integral table (with $c = 7$, $d = 6$, $a = -1$, and $b = -2$) to get

$$\int \frac{7x + 6}{x^2 + 3x + 2}\, dx = -\ln |x + 1| + 8 \ln |x + 2| + C.$$

Including the terms $x - 3$ from the long division and integrating them gives

$$\int \frac{x^3}{x^2 + 3x + 2}\, dx = \int \left(x - 3 + \frac{7x + 6}{x^2 + 3x + 6} \right) dx = \frac{1}{2}x^2 - 3x - \ln |x + 1| + 8 \ln |x + 2| + C.$$

77. First divide $x^2 + 1$ by $x^2 - 3x + 2$ to obtain

$$\frac{x^2 + 1}{x^2 - 3x + 2} = 1 + \frac{3x - 1}{x^2 - 3x + 2}.$$

Factoring $x^2 - 3x + 2 = (x - 2)(x - 1)$ we can use V-27 (with $c = 3$, $d = -1$, $a = 2$ and $b = 1$) to write

$$\int \frac{3x - 1}{x^2 - 3x + 2}\, dx = 5 \ln|x - 2| - 2 \ln|x - 1| + C.$$

Remembering to include the extra term of $+1$ we got when dividing, we get

$$\int \frac{x^2 + 1}{x^2 - 3x + 2}\, dx = \int \left(1 + \frac{3x - 1}{x^2 - 3x + 2}\right)\, dx = x + 5 \ln|x - 2| - 2 \ln|x - 1| + C.$$

78. We can factor the denominator into $ax(x + \frac{b}{a})$, so

$$\int \frac{dx}{ax^2 + bx} = \frac{1}{a} \int \frac{1}{x(x + \frac{b}{a})}$$

Now we can use V-26 (with $A = 0$ and $B = -\frac{b}{a}$ to give

$$\frac{1}{a} \int \frac{1}{x(x + \frac{b}{a})} = \frac{1}{a} \cdot \frac{a}{b} \left(\ln|x| - \ln\left|x + \frac{b}{a}\right|\right) + C = \frac{1}{b} \left(\ln|x| - \ln\left|x + \frac{b}{a}\right|\right) + C.$$

79. Let $w = ax^2 + 2bx + c$, then $dw = (2ax + 2b)dx$ so that

$$\int \frac{ax + b}{ax^2 + 2bx + c}\, dx = \frac{1}{2} \int \frac{dw}{w} = \frac{1}{2} \ln|w| + C = \frac{1}{2} \ln|ax^2 + 2bx + c| + C.$$

80. Multiplying out and integrating term by term,

$$\int \left(\frac{x}{3} + \frac{3}{x}\right)^2 dx = \int \left(\frac{x^2}{9} + 2 + \frac{9}{x^2}\right)\, dx = \frac{1}{9}\left(\frac{x^3}{3}\right) + 2x + 9\left(\frac{x^{-1}}{-1}\right) + C = \frac{x^3}{27} + 2x - \frac{9}{x} + C.$$

81. If $u = 2^t + 1$, $du = 2^t(\ln 2)\, dt$, so

$$\int \frac{2^t}{2^t + 1}\, dt = \frac{1}{\ln 2} \int \frac{2^t \ln 2}{2^t + 1}\, dt = \frac{1}{\ln 2} \int \frac{1}{u} = \frac{1}{\ln 2} \ln|u| + C = \frac{1}{\ln 2} \ln|2^t + 1| + C.$$

82. If $u = 1 - x$, $du = -1\, dx$, so

$$\int 10^{1-x} dx = -1 \int 10^{1-x}(-1\, dx) = -1 \int 10^u\, du = -1 \frac{10^u}{\ln 10} + C = -\frac{1}{\ln 10} 10^{1-x} + C.$$

83. Multiplying out and integrating term by term gives

$$\int (x^2 + 5)^3 dx = \int (x^6 + 15x^4 + 75x^2 + 125)dx = \frac{1}{7}x^7 + 15\frac{x^5}{5} + 75\frac{x^3}{3} + 125x + C$$
$$= \frac{1}{7}x^7 + 3x^5 + 25x^3 + 125x + C.$$

84. Integrate by parts letting $r = v$ and $dt = \arcsin v\, dv$ then $dr = dv$ and to find t we integrate $\arcsin v\, dv$ by parts letting $x = \arcsin v$ and $dy = dv$. This gives

$$t = v \arcsin v - \int (1/\sqrt{1 - v^2})v\, dv = v \arcsin v + \sqrt{1 - v^2}.$$

Now, back to the original integration by parts, and we have

$$\int v \arcsin v \, dv = v^2 \arcsin v + v\sqrt{1 - v^2} - \int \left[v \arcsin v + \sqrt{1 - v^2} \right] \, dv.$$

Adding $\int v \arcsin v \, dv$ to both sides of the above line we obtain

$$2 \int v \arcsin v \, dv = v^2 \arcsin v + v\sqrt{1 - v^2} - \int \sqrt{1 - v^2} \, dv$$

$$= v^2 \arcsin v + v\sqrt{1 - v^2} - \frac{1}{2}v\sqrt{1 - v^2} - \frac{1}{2}\arcsin v + C.$$

Dividing by 2 gives

$$\int v \arcsin v \, dv = \left(\frac{v^2}{2} - \frac{1}{4} \right) \arcsin v + \frac{1}{4}v\sqrt{1 - v^2} + K,$$

where $K = C/2$.

85. By VI-30 in the table of integrals, we have

$$\int \sqrt{4 - x^2} \, dx = \frac{x\sqrt{4 - x^2}}{2} + 2 \int \frac{1}{\sqrt{4 - x^2}} \, dx.$$

The same table informs us in formula VI-28 that

$$\int \frac{1}{\sqrt{4 - x^2}} \, dx = \arcsin \frac{x}{2} + C.$$

Thus

$$\int \sqrt{4 - x^2} \, dx = \frac{x\sqrt{4 - x^2}}{2} + 2 \arcsin \frac{x}{2} + C.$$

86. By long division, $\dfrac{z^3}{z - 5} = z^2 + 5z + 25 + \dfrac{125}{z - 5}$, so

$$\int \frac{z^3}{z - 5} dz = \int \left(z^2 + 5z + 25 + \frac{125}{z - 5} \right) dz = \frac{z^3}{3} + \frac{5z^2}{2} + 25z + 125 \int \frac{1}{z - 5} dz$$

$$= \frac{z^3}{3} + \frac{5}{2}z^2 + 25z + 125 \ln |z - 5| + C.$$

87. If $u = 1 + \cos^2 w$, $du = 2(\cos w)^1(- \sin w) \, dw$, so

$$\int \frac{\sin w \cos w}{1 + \cos^2 w} \, dw = -\frac{1}{2} \int \frac{-2 \sin w \cos w}{1 + \cos^2 w} \, dw = -\frac{1}{2} \int \frac{1}{u} \, du = -\frac{1}{2} \ln |u| + C$$

$$= -\frac{1}{2} \ln |1 + \cos^2 w| + C.$$

88. $\displaystyle\int \frac{1}{\tan(3\theta)} d\theta = \int \frac{1}{\left(\frac{\sin(3\theta)}{\cos(3\theta)} \right)} d\theta = \int \frac{\cos(3\theta)}{\sin(3\theta)} d\theta.$ If $u = \sin(3\theta)$, $du = \cos(3\theta) \cdot 3d\theta$, so

$$\int \frac{\cos(3\theta)}{\sin(3\theta)} d\theta = \frac{1}{3} \int \frac{3 \cos(3\theta)}{\sin(3\theta)} d\theta = \frac{1}{3} \int \frac{1}{u} du = \frac{1}{3} \ln |u| + C = \frac{1}{3} \ln |\sin(3\theta)| + C.$$

89. $\displaystyle\int \frac{x}{\cos^2 x} dx = \int x \frac{1}{\cos^2 x} dx.$ Using integration by parts with $u = x$, $du = dx$ and $dv = \dfrac{1}{\cos^2 x} dx$, $v = \tan x$, we have

$$\int x \left(\frac{1}{\cos^2 x} dx \right) = x \tan x - \int \tan x \, dx.$$

Formula I-7 gives the final result of $x \tan x - (-\ln |\cos x|) + C = x \tan x + \ln |\cos x| + C.$

90. Dividing and integrating term by term gives

$$\int \frac{x+1}{\sqrt{x}}\,dx = \int \left(\frac{x}{\sqrt{x}} + \frac{1}{\sqrt{x}}\right)\,dx = \int (x^{1/2} + x^{-1/2})\,dx = \frac{x^{3/2}}{\frac{3}{2}} + \frac{x^{1/2}}{\frac{1}{2}} + C = \frac{2}{3}x^{3/2} + 2\sqrt{x} + C.$$

91. If $u = \sqrt{x+1}$, $u^2 = x + 1$ with $x = u^2 - 1$ and $dx = 2u\,du$. Substituting, we get

$$\int \frac{x}{\sqrt{x+1}}\,dx = \int \frac{(u^2 - 1)2u\,du}{u} = \int (u^2 - 1)2\,du = 2\int (u^2 - 1)\,du$$

$$= \frac{2u^3}{3} - 2u + C = \frac{2(\sqrt{x+1})^3}{3} - 2\sqrt{x+1} + C.$$

92. $\int \frac{\sqrt{\sqrt{x}+1}}{\sqrt{x}} = \int (\sqrt{x}+1)^{1/2}\frac{1}{\sqrt{x}}\,dx$; if $u = \sqrt{x} + 1$, $du = \frac{1}{2\sqrt{x}}\,dx$, so we have

$$2\int (\sqrt{x}+1)^{1/2}\frac{1}{2\sqrt{x}}\,dx = 2\int u^{1/2}\,du = 2\left(\frac{u^{3/2}}{\frac{3}{2}}\right) + C = \frac{4}{3}u^{3/2} + C = \frac{4}{3}(\sqrt{x}+1)^{3/2} + C.$$

93. If $u = e^{2y} + 1$, then $du = e^{2y}2\,dy$, so

$$\int \frac{e^{2y}}{e^{2y}+1}\,dy = \frac{1}{2}\int \frac{2e^{2y}}{e^{2y}+1}\,dy = \frac{1}{2}\int \frac{1}{u}\,du = \frac{1}{2}\ln|u| + C = \frac{1}{2}\ln|e^{2y}+1| + C.$$

94. If $u = z^2 - 5$, $du = 2z\,dz$, then

$$\int \frac{z}{(z^2-5)^3}\,dz = \int (z^2-5)^{-3}z\,dz = \frac{1}{2}\int (z^2-5)^{-3}2z\,dz = \frac{1}{2}\int u^{-3}\,du = \frac{1}{2}\left(\frac{u^{-2}}{-2}\right) + C$$

$$= \frac{1}{-4(z^2-5)^2} + C.$$

95. Letting $u = z - 5$, $z = u + 5$, $dz = du$, and substituting, we have

$$\int \frac{z}{(z-5)^3}\,dz = \int \frac{u+5}{u^3}\,du = \int (u^{-2} + 5u^{-3})\,du = \frac{u^{-1}}{-1} + 5\left(\frac{u^{-2}}{-2}\right) + C$$

$$= \frac{-1}{(z-5)} + \frac{-5}{2(z-5)^2} + C.$$

96. If $u = 1 + \tan x$ then $du = \frac{1}{\cos^2 x}\,dx$, and so

$$\int \frac{(1+\tan x)^3}{\cos^2 x}\,dx = \int (1+\tan x)^3\frac{1}{\cos^2 x}\,dx = \int u^3\,du = \frac{u^4}{4} + C = \frac{(1+\tan x)^4}{4} + C.$$

97. $\int \frac{(2x-1)e^{x^2}}{e^x}\,dx = \int e^{x^2-x}(2x-1)dx.$ If $u = x^2 - x$, $du = (2x-1)dx$, so

$$\int e^{x^2-x}(2x-1)dx = \int e^u\,du$$

$$= e^u + c$$

$$= e^{x^2-x} + C.$$

98. We use the substitution $w = x^2 + x$, $dw = (2x + 1)\,dx$.

$$\int (2x + 1)e^{x^2} e^x \, dx = \int (2x + 1)e^{x^2 + x} \, dx = \int e^w \, dw$$
$$= e^w + C = e^{x^2 + x} + C.$$

Check: $\dfrac{d}{dx}(e^{x^2 + x} + C) = e^{x^2 + x} \cdot (2x + 1) = (2x + 1)e^{x^2} e^x.$

99. Let $w = 2 + 3\cos x$, so $dw = -3\sin x \, dx$, giving $-\dfrac{1}{3}\,dw = \sin x \, dx$. Then

$$\int \sin x \left(\sqrt{2 + 3\cos x}\right) dx = \int \sqrt{w}\left(-\frac{1}{3}\right) dw = -\frac{1}{3}\int \sqrt{w}\,dw$$
$$= \left(-\frac{1}{3}\right)\frac{w^{\frac{3}{2}}}{\frac{3}{2}} + C = -\frac{2}{9}(2 + 3\cos x)^{\frac{3}{2}} + C.$$

100. Using Table III-14, with $a = -4$ we have

$$\int (x^2 - 3x + 2)e^{-4x} \, dx = -\frac{1}{4}(x^2 - 3x + 2)e^{-4x}$$
$$-\frac{1}{16}(2x - 3)e^{-4x} - \frac{1}{64}(2)e^{-4x} + C.$$
$$= \frac{1}{32}e^{-4x}(-11 + 20x - 8x^2) + C.$$

101. Let $x = 2\theta$, then $dx = 2d\theta$. Thus

$$\int \sin^2(2\theta)\cos^3(2\theta)\,d\theta = \frac{1}{2}\int \sin^2 x \cos^3 x \, dx.$$

We let $w = \sin x$ and $dw = \cos x \, dx$. Then

$$\frac{1}{2}\int \sin^2 x \cos^3 x \, dx = \frac{1}{2}\int \sin^2 x \cos^2 x \cos x \, dx$$
$$= \frac{1}{2}\int \sin^2 x(1 - \sin^2 x)\cos x \, dx$$
$$= \frac{1}{2}\int w^2(1 - w^2)\,dw = \frac{1}{2}\int (w^2 - w^4)\,dw$$
$$= \frac{1}{2}\left(\frac{w^3}{3} - \frac{w^5}{5}\right) + C = \frac{1}{6}\sin^3 x - \frac{1}{10}\sin^5 x + C$$
$$= \frac{1}{6}\sin^3(2\theta) - \frac{1}{10}\sin^5(2\theta) + C.$$

102. If $u = 2\sin x$, then $du = 2\cos x \, dx$, so

$$\int \cos(2\sin x)\cos x \, dx = \frac{1}{2}\int \cos(2\sin x)2\cos x \, dx = \frac{1}{2}\int \cos u \, du$$
$$= \frac{1}{2}\sin u + C = \frac{1}{2}\sin(2\sin x) + C.$$

103. Let $w = x + \sin x$, then $dw = (1 + \cos x)\,dx$ which gives

$$\int (x + \sin x)^3(1 + \cos x)\,dx = \int w^3 \, dw = \frac{1}{4}w^4 + C = \frac{1}{4}(x + \sin x)^4 + C.$$

104. Using Table III-16,

$$
\int \left(2x^3 + 3x + 4\right) \cos(2x)\, dx = \frac{1}{2}(2x^3 + 3x + 4) \sin(2x)
$$

$$
+ \frac{1}{4}(6x^2 + 3) \cos(2x)
$$

$$
- \frac{1}{8}(12x) \sin(2x) - \frac{3}{4} \cos(2x) + C.
$$

$$
= 2\sin(2x) + x^3 \sin(2x) + \frac{3x^2}{2} \cos(2x) + C.
$$

105. Use the substitution $w = \sinh x$ and $dw = \cosh x\, dx$ so

$$
\int \sinh^2 x \cosh x\, dx = \int w^2\, dw = \frac{w^3}{3} + C = \frac{1}{3} \sinh^3 x + C.
$$

Check this answer by taking the derivative: $\dfrac{d}{dx} \left[\dfrac{1}{3} \sinh^3 x + C \right] = \sinh^2 x \cosh x.$

106. We use the substitution $w = x^2 + 2x$ and $dw = (2x + 2)\, dx$ so

$$
\int (x+1) \sinh(x^2 + 2x)\, dx = \frac{1}{2} \int \sinh w\, dw = \frac{1}{2} \cosh w + C = \frac{1}{2} \cosh(x^2 + 2x) + C.
$$

Check this answer by taking the derivative: $\dfrac{d}{dx} \left[\dfrac{1}{2} \cosh(x^2 + 2x) + C \right] = \dfrac{1}{2}(2x+2) \sinh(x^2+2x) = (x+1) \sinh(x^2 + 2x).$

107. Substitute $w = 1 + x^2$, $dw = 2x\, dx$. Then $x\, dx = \dfrac{1}{2} dw$, and

$$
\int_{x=0}^{x=1} x(1 + x^2)^{20}\, dx = \frac{1}{2} \int_{w=1}^{w=2} w^{20}\, dw = \left. \frac{w^{21}}{42} \right|_{1}^{2} = \frac{299593}{6} = 49932\frac{1}{6}.
$$

108. Substitute $w = x^2 + 4$, $dw = 2x\, dx$. Then,

$$
\int_{x=4}^{x=1} x\sqrt{x^2 + 4}\, dx = \frac{1}{2} \int_{w=20}^{w=5} w^{\frac{1}{2}}\, dw = \left. \frac{1}{3} w^{\frac{3}{2}} \right|_{20}^{5}
$$

$$
= \frac{1}{3}\left(5^{\frac{3}{2}} - 8 \cdot 5^{\frac{3}{2}}\right) = -\frac{7}{3} \cdot 5^{3/2} = -\frac{35}{3}\sqrt{5}
$$

109. We substitute $w = \cos\theta + 5$, $dw = -\sin\theta\, d\theta$. Then

$$
\int_{\theta=0}^{\theta=\pi} \sin\theta\, d\theta (\cos\theta + 5)^7 = -\int_{w=6}^{w=4} w^7 dw = \int_{w=4}^{w=6} w^7 dw = \left. \frac{w^8}{8} \right|_{4}^{6} = 201{,}760.
$$

110. Let $w = 1 + 5x^2$. We have $dw = 10x\, dx$, so $\dfrac{dw}{10} = x\, dx$. When $x = 0$, $w = 1$. When $x = 1$, $w = 6$.

$$
\frac{x\, dx}{1 + 5x^2} = \int_{1}^{6} \frac{\frac{1}{10} dw}{w} = \frac{1}{10} \int_{1}^{6} \frac{dw}{w} = \left. \frac{1}{10} \ln|w| \right|_{1}^{6}
$$

$$
= \frac{1}{10}(\ln 6 - \ln 1) = \frac{\ln 6}{10}
$$

111.

$$
\int_{1}^{2} \frac{x^2 + 1}{x}\, dx = \int_{1}^{2} \left(x + \frac{1}{x}\right) dx = \left. \left(\frac{x^2}{2} + \ln|x|\right) \right|_{1}^{2} = \frac{3}{2} + \ln 2.
$$

112. Using integration by parts, we have

$$\int_1^3 \ln(x^3)\,dx = 3\int_1^3 \ln x\,dx = 3(x\ln x - x)\Big|_1^3 = 9\ln 3 - 6 \approx 3.8875.$$

This matches the approximation given by Simpson's rule with 10 intervals.

113. In Problem 19, we found that

$$\int (\ln x)^2\,dx = x(\ln x)^2 - 2x\ln x + 2x + C.$$

Thus

$$\int_1^e (\ln x)^2\,dx = [x(\ln x)^2 - 2x\ln x + 2x]\Big|_1^e = e - 2 \approx 0.71828.$$

This matches the approximation given by Simpson's rule with 10 intervals.

114. Integrating by parts, we take $u = e^{2x}$, $u' = 2e^{2x}$, $v' = \sin 2x$, and $v = -\frac{1}{2}\cos 2x$, so

$$\int e^{2x}\sin 2x\,dx = -\frac{e^{2x}}{2}\cos 2x + \int e^{2x}\cos 2x\,dx.$$

Integrating by parts again, with $u = e^{2x}$, $u' = 2e^{2x}$, $v' = \cos 2x$, and $v = \frac{1}{2}\sin 2x$, we get

$$\int e^{2x}\cos 2x\,dx = \frac{e^{2x}}{2}\sin 2x - \int e^{2x}\sin 2x\,dx.$$

Substituting into the previous equation, we obtain

$$\int e^{2x}\sin 2x\,dx = -\frac{e^{2x}}{2}\cos 2x + \frac{e^{2x}}{2}\sin 2x - \int e^{2x}\sin 2x\,dx.$$

Solving for $\int e^{2x}\sin 2x\,dx$ gives

$$\int e^{2x}\sin 2x\,dx = \frac{1}{4}e^{2x}(\sin 2x - \cos 2x) + C.$$

This result can also be obtained using II-8 in the integral table. Thus

$$\int_{-\pi}^{\pi} e^{2x}\sin 2x = [\frac{1}{4}e^{2x}(\sin 2x - \cos 2x)]\Big|_{-\pi}^{\pi} = \frac{1}{4}(e^{-2\pi} - e^{2\pi}) \approx -133.8724.$$

We get -133.37 using Simpson's rule with 10 intervals. With 100 intervals, we get -133.8724. Thus our answer matches the approximation of Simpson's rule.

115.

$$\int_0^{10} ze^{-z}\,dz = [-ze^{-z}]\Big|_0^{10} - \int_0^{10} -e^{-z}\,dz \qquad (\text{let } z = u, e^{-z} = v', -e^{-z} = v)$$

$$= -10e^{-10} - [e^{-z}]\Big|_0^{10}$$

$$= -10e^{-10} - e^{-10} + 1$$

$$= -11e^{-10} + 1.$$

116. Let $\sin\theta = w$, $\cos\theta\,d\theta = dw$. So, if $\theta = -\frac{\pi}{3}$, then $w = -\frac{\sqrt{3}}{2}$, and if $\theta = \frac{\pi}{4}$, then $w = \frac{\sqrt{2}}{2}$. So we have

$$\int_{-\pi/3}^{\pi/4} \sin^3\theta\cos\theta\,d\theta = \int_{-\sqrt{3}/2}^{\sqrt{2}/2} w^3\,dw = \frac{1}{4}w^4\Big|_{-\sqrt{3}/2}^{\sqrt{2}/2} = \frac{1}{4}\left[\left(\frac{\sqrt{2}}{2}\right)^4 - \left(\frac{-\sqrt{3}}{2}\right)^4\right] = -\frac{5}{64}.$$

117. Let $\sqrt{x} = w$, $\frac{1}{2}x^{-\frac{1}{2}}\,dx = dw$, $\frac{dx}{\sqrt{x}} = 2\,dw$. If $x = 1$ then $w = 1$, and if $x = 4$ so $w = 2$. So we have

$$\int_1^4 \frac{e^{\sqrt{x}}}{\sqrt{x}}\,dx = \int_1^2 e^w \cdot 2\,dw = 2e^w \Big|_1^2 = 2(e^2 - e) \approx 9.34.$$

118.

$$\int_0^1 \frac{dx}{x^2 + 1} = \tan^{-1} x \Big|_0^1 = \tan^{-1} 1 - \tan^{-1} 0 = \frac{\pi}{4} - 0 = \frac{\pi}{4}.$$

119. We put the integral in a convenient form for a substitution by using the fact that $\sin^2\theta = 1 - \cos^2\theta$. Thus: $\displaystyle\int_{-\frac{\pi}{4}}^{\frac{\pi}{4}} \cos^2\theta \sin^5\theta\,d\theta =$

$$\int_{-\frac{\pi}{4}}^{\frac{\pi}{4}} \cos^2\theta (1 - \cos^2\theta)^2 \sin\theta\,d\theta.$$

Now, we can make a substitution which helps. We let $w = \cos\theta$, so $dw = -\sin\theta\,d\theta$.
Note that $w = \dfrac{\sqrt{2}}{2}$ when $\theta = -\dfrac{\pi}{4}$ and when $\theta = \dfrac{\pi}{4}$. Thus after our substitution, we get

$$-\int_{w=\frac{\pi}{4}}^{w=\frac{\pi}{4}} w^2 (1 - w^2)^2 \, dw.$$

Since the upper and lower limits of integration are the same, this definite integral must equal 0. Notice that we could have deduced this fact immediately, since $\cos^5\theta$ is even and $\sin^5\theta$ is odd, so $\cos^2\theta\sin^5\theta$ is odd.
Thus $\displaystyle\int_{-\frac{\pi}{4}}^{0} \cos^2\theta\sin^5\theta\,d\theta = -\int_{0}^{\frac{\pi}{4}} \cos^2\theta\sin^5\theta\,d\theta$, and the given integral must evaluate to 0.

120. We substitute $w = x^2 + 4x + 5$, so $dw = (2x + 4)\,dx$. Notice that when $x = -2$, $w = 1$, and when $x = 0$, $w = 5$.

$$\int_{x=-2}^{x=0} \frac{2x + 4}{x^2 + 4x + 5}\,dx = \int_{w=1}^{w=5} \frac{1}{w}\,dw = \ln|w|\Big|_{w=1}^{w=5} = \ln 5.$$

121. Splitting the integrand into partial fractions with denominators $(x - 2)$ and $(x + 2)$, we have

$$\frac{1}{(x - 2)(x + 2)} = \frac{A}{x - 2} + \frac{B}{x + 2}.$$

Multiplying by $(x - 2)(x + 2)$ gives the identity

$$1 = A(x + 2) + B(x - 2)$$

so

$$1 = (A + B)x + 2A - 2B.$$

Since this equation holds for all x, the constant terms on both sides must be equal. Similarly, the coefficient of x on both sides must be equal. So

$$2A - 2B = 1$$
$$A + B = 0.$$

Solving these equations gives $A = 1/4$, $B = -1/4$ and the integral becomes

$$\int \frac{1}{(x - 2)(x + 2)}\,dx = \frac{1}{4}\int \frac{1}{x - 2}\,dx - \frac{1}{4}\int \frac{1}{x + 2}\,dx = \frac{1}{4}\left(\ln|x - 2| - \ln|x + 2|\right) + C.$$

122. Let $x = 5\sin t$. Then $dx = 5\cos t\,dt$, so substitution gives

$$\int \frac{1}{\sqrt{25 - x^2}} = \int \frac{5\cos t}{\sqrt{25 - 25\sin^2 t}}\,dt = \int dt = t + C = \arcsin\left(\frac{x}{5}\right) + C.$$

123. Splitting the integrand into partial fractions with denominators x and $(x+5)$, we have

$$\frac{1}{x(x+5)} = \frac{A}{x} + \frac{B}{x+5}.$$

Multiplying by $x(x+5)$ gives the identity

$$1 = A(x+5) + Bx$$

so

$$1 = (A+B)x + 5A.$$

Since this equation holds for all x, the constant terms on both sides must be equal. Similarly, the coefficient of x on both sides must be equal. So

$$5A = 1$$
$$A + B = 0.$$

Solving these equations gives $A = 1/5$, $B = -1/5$ and the integral becomes

$$\int \frac{1}{x(x+5)}\,dx = \frac{1}{5}\int \frac{1}{x}\,dx - \frac{1}{5}\int \frac{1}{x+5}\,dx = \frac{1}{5}\left(\ln|x| - \ln|x+5|\right) + C.$$

124. We use the trigonometric substitution $3x = \sin\theta$. Then $dx = \frac{1}{3}\cos\theta\,d\theta$ and substitution gives

$$\int \frac{1}{\sqrt{1-9x^2}}\,dx = \int \frac{1}{\sqrt{1-\sin^2\theta}} \cdot \frac{1}{3}\cos\theta\,d\theta = \frac{1}{3}\int \frac{\cos\theta}{\sqrt{\cos^2\theta}}\,d\theta$$

$$= \frac{1}{3}\int 1\,d\theta = \frac{1}{3}\theta + C = \frac{1}{3}\arcsin(3x) + C.$$

125. Splitting the integrand into partial fractions with denominators x, $(x+2)$ and $(x-1)$, we have

$$\frac{2x+3}{x(x+2)(x-1)} = \frac{A}{x} + \frac{B}{x+2} + \frac{C}{x-1}.$$

Multiplying by $x(x+2)(x-1)$ gives the identity

$$2x + 3 = A(x+2)(x-1) + Bx(x-1) + Cx(x+2)$$

so

$$2x + 3 = (A+B+C)x^2 + (A-B+2C)x - 2A.$$

Since this equation holds for all x, the constant terms on both sides must be equal. Similarly, the coefficient of x on both sides must be equal. So

$$-2A = 3$$
$$A - B + 2C = 2$$
$$A + B + C = 0.$$

Solving these equations gives $A = -3/2$, $B = -1/6$ and $C = 5/3$. The integral becomes

$$\int \frac{2x+3}{x(x+2)(x-1)}\,dx = -\frac{3}{2}\int \frac{1}{x}\,dx - \frac{1}{6}\int \frac{1}{x+2} + \frac{5}{3}\int \frac{1}{x-1}\,dx$$

$$= -\frac{3}{2}\ln|x| - \frac{1}{6}\ln|x+2| + \frac{5}{3}\ln|x-1| + C.$$

126. The denominator can be factored to give $x(x-1)(x+1)$. Splitting the integrand into partial fractions with denominators x, $x-1$, and $x+1$, we have

$$\frac{3x+1}{x(x-1)(x+1)} = \frac{A}{x-1} + \frac{B}{x+1} + \frac{C}{x}.$$

Multiplying by $x(x-1)(x+1)$ gives the identity

$$3x+1 = Ax(x+1) + Bx(x-1) + C(x-1)(x+1)$$

so

$$3x+1 = (A+B+C)x^2 + (A-B)x - C.$$

Since this equation holds for all x, the constant terms on both sides must be equal. Similarly, the coefficient of x and x^2 on both sides must be equal. So

$$-C = 1$$
$$A - B = 3$$
$$A + B + C = 0.$$

Solving these equations gives $A = 2$, $B = -1$ and $C = -1$. The integral becomes

$$\int \frac{3x+1}{x(x+1)(x-1)} dx = \int \frac{2}{x-1} dx - \int \frac{1}{x+1} dx - \int \frac{1}{x} dx$$
$$= 2\ln|x-1| - \ln|x+1| - \ln|x| + C.$$

127. Splitting the integrand into partial fractions with denominators $(1+x)$, $(1+x)^2$ and x, we have

$$\frac{1+x^2}{x(1+x)^2} = \frac{A}{1+x} + \frac{B}{(1+x)^2} + \frac{C}{x}.$$

Multiplying by $x(1+x)^2$ gives the identity

$$1+x^2 = Ax(1+x) + Bx + C(1+x)^2$$

so

$$1+x^2 = (A+C)x^2 + (A+B+2C)x + C.$$

Since this equation holds for all x, the constant terms on both sides must be equal. Similarly, the coefficient of x and x^2 on both sides must be equal. So

$$C = 1$$
$$A + B + 2C = 0$$
$$A + C = 1.$$

Solving these equations gives $A = 0$, $B = -2$ and $C = 1$. The integral becomes

$$\int \frac{1+x^2}{(1+x)^2 x} dx = -2 \int \frac{1}{(1+x)^2} dx + \int \frac{1}{x} dx = \frac{2}{1+x} + \ln|x| + C.$$

128. Completing the square, we get

$$x^2 + 2x + 2 = (x+1)^2 + 1.$$

We use the substitution $x+1 = \tan t$, so $dx = (1/\cos^2 t)dt$. Since $\tan^2 t + 1 = 1/\cos^2 t$, the integral becomes

$$\int \frac{1}{(x+1)^2+1} dx = \int \frac{1}{\tan^2 t + 1} \cdot \frac{1}{\cos^2 t} dt = \int dt = t + C = \arctan(x+1) + C.$$

129. Completing the square in the denominator gives

$$\int \frac{dx}{x^2 + 4x + 5} = \int \frac{dx}{(x+2)^2 + 1}.$$

We make the substitution $\tan \theta = x + 2$. Then $dx = \frac{1}{\cos^2 \theta} d\theta$.

$$\int \frac{dx}{(x+2)^2 + 1} = \int \frac{d\theta}{\cos^2 \theta (\tan^2 \theta + 1)}$$

$$= \int \frac{d\theta}{\cos^2 \theta (\frac{\sin^2 \theta}{\cos^2 \theta} + 1)}$$

$$= \int \frac{d\theta}{\sin^2 \theta + \cos^2 \theta}$$

$$= \int d\theta = \theta + C$$

But since $\tan \theta = x + 2$, $\theta = \arctan(x + 2)$, and so $\theta + C = \arctan(x + 2) + C$.

130. We use the trigonometric substitution $bx = a \sin \theta$. Then $dx = \frac{a}{b} \cos \theta \, d\theta$, and we have

$$\int \frac{1}{\sqrt{a^2 - (bx)^2}} \, dx = \int \frac{1}{\sqrt{a^2 - (a\sin\theta)^2}} \cdot \frac{a}{b} \cos \theta \, d\theta = \int \frac{1}{a\sqrt{1 - \sin^2 \theta}} \cdot \frac{a}{b} \cos \theta \, d\theta$$

$$= \frac{1}{b} \int \frac{\cos \theta}{\sqrt{\cos^2 \theta}} \, d\theta = \frac{1}{b} \int 1 \, d\theta = \frac{1}{b} \theta + C = \frac{1}{b} \arcsin\left(\frac{bx}{a}\right) + C.$$

131. Using the substitution $w = \sin x$, we get $dw = \cos x \, dx$, so we have

$$\int \frac{\cos x}{\sin^3 x + \sin x} \, dx = \int \frac{dw}{w^3 + w}.$$

But

$$\frac{1}{w^3 + w} = \frac{1}{w(w^2 + 1)} = \frac{1}{w} - \frac{w}{w^2 + 1},$$

so

$$\int \frac{\cos x}{\sin^3 x + \sin x} \, dx = \int \left(\frac{1}{w} - \frac{w}{w^2 + 1}\right) dw$$

$$= \ln |w| - \frac{1}{2} \ln |w^2 + 1| + C$$

$$= \ln |\sin x| - \frac{1}{2} \ln |\sin^2 x + 1| + C.$$

132. Using the substitution $w = e^x$, we get $dw = e^x dx$, so we have

$$\int \frac{e^x}{e^{2x} - 1} \, dx = \int \frac{dw}{w^2 - 1}.$$

But

$$\frac{1}{w^2 - 1} = \frac{1}{(w-1)(w+1)} = \frac{1}{2}\left(\frac{1}{w-1} - \frac{1}{w+1}\right),$$

so

$$\int \frac{e^x}{e^{2x} - 1} \, dx = \int \frac{1}{2}\left(\frac{1}{w-1} - \frac{1}{w+1}\right) dw$$

$$= \frac{1}{2}(\ln|w - 1| - \ln|w + 1|) + C$$

$$= \frac{1}{2}(\ln|e^x - 1| - \ln|e^x + 1|) + C.$$

133. $\int_{4}^{\infty} \dfrac{dt}{t^{3/2}}$ should converge, since $\int_{1}^{\infty} \dfrac{dt}{t^{n}}$ converges for $n > 1$.
We calculate its value.

$$\int_{4}^{\infty} \frac{dt}{t^{3/2}} = \lim_{b \to \infty} \int_{4}^{b} t^{-3/2}\, dt = \lim_{b \to \infty} -2t^{-1/2}\Big|_{4}^{b} = \lim_{b \to \infty} \left(1 - \frac{2}{\sqrt{b}}\right) = 1.$$

134. $\int \dfrac{dx}{x \ln x} = \ln|\ln x| + C$. (Substitute $w = \ln x$, $dw = \frac{1}{x}\, dx$).
Thus

$$\int_{10}^{\infty} \frac{dx}{x \ln x} = \lim_{b \to \infty} \int_{10}^{b} \frac{dx}{x \ln x} = \lim_{b \to \infty} \ln|\ln x|\Big|_{10}^{b} = \lim_{b \to \infty} \ln(\ln b) - \ln(\ln 10).$$

As $b \to \infty$, $\ln(\ln b) \to \infty$, so this diverges.

135. To find $\int we^{-w}\, dw$, integrate by parts, with $u = w$ and $v' = e^{-w}$. Then $u' = 1$ and $v = -e^{-w}$.
Then

$$\int we^{-w}\, dw = -we^{-w} + \int e^{-w}\, dw = -we^{-w} - e^{-w} + C.$$

Thus

$$\int_{0}^{\infty} we^{-w}\, dw = \lim_{b \to \infty} \int_{0}^{b} we^{-w}\, dw = \lim_{b \to \infty} \left(-we^{-w} - e^{-w}\right)\Big|_{0}^{b} = 1.$$

136. The trouble spot is at $x = 0$, so we write

$$\int_{-1}^{1} \frac{1}{x^4}\, dx = \int_{-1}^{0} \frac{1}{x^4}\, dx + \int_{0}^{1} \frac{1}{x^4}\, dx.$$

However, both these integrals diverge. For example,

$$\int_{0}^{1} \frac{1}{x^4}\, dx = \lim_{a \to 0^+} \int_{a}^{1} \frac{1}{x^4}\, dx = \lim_{a \to 0^+} -\frac{x^{-3}}{3}\Big|_{a}^{1} = \lim_{a \to 0^+} \left(\frac{1}{3a^3} - \frac{1}{3}\right).$$

Since this limit does not exist, $\int_{0}^{1} \dfrac{1}{x^4}\, dx$ diverges and so the original integral diverges.

137. Since the value of $\tan\theta$ is between -1 and 1 on the interval $-\pi/4 \le \theta \le \pi/4$, our integral is not improper and so converges. Moreover, since $\tan\theta$ is an odd function, we have

$$\int_{-\frac{\pi}{4}}^{\frac{\pi}{4}} \tan\theta\, d\theta = \int_{-\frac{\pi}{4}}^{0} \tan\theta\, d\theta + \int_{0}^{\frac{\pi}{4}} \tan\theta\, d\theta$$

$$= -\int_{-\frac{\pi}{4}}^{0} \tan(-\theta)\, d\theta + \int_{0}^{\frac{\pi}{4}} \tan\theta\, d\theta$$

$$= -\int_{0}^{\frac{\pi}{4}} \tan\theta\, d\theta + \int_{0}^{\frac{\pi}{4}} \tan\theta\, d\theta = 0.$$

138. It is easy to see that this integral converges:

$$\frac{1}{4 + z^2} < \frac{1}{z^2}, \quad \text{and so} \quad \int_{2}^{\infty} \frac{1}{4 + z^2}\, dz < \int_{2}^{\infty} \frac{1}{z^2}\, dz = \frac{1}{2}.$$

We can also find its exact value.

$$\int_{2}^{\infty} \frac{1}{4 + z^2}\, dz = \lim_{b \to \infty} \int_{2}^{b} \cdot \frac{1}{4 + z^2}\, dz$$

$$= \lim_{b \to \infty} \left(\frac{1}{2} \arctan \frac{z}{2}\Big|_{2}^{b}\right)$$

$$= \lim_{b \to \infty} \left(\frac{1}{2} \arctan \frac{b}{2} - \frac{1}{2} \arctan 1\right)$$

$$= \frac{1}{2}\frac{\pi}{2} - \frac{1}{2}\frac{\pi}{4} = \frac{\pi}{8}.$$

Note that $\frac{\pi}{8} < \frac{1}{2}$.

139. We find the exact value:

$$
\begin{aligned}
\int_{10}^{\infty} \frac{1}{z^2 - 4}\, dz &= \int_{10}^{\infty} \frac{1}{(z+2)(z-2)}\, dz \\
&= \lim_{b \to \infty} \int_{10}^{b} \frac{1}{(z+2)(z-2)}\, dz \\
&= \lim_{b \to \infty} \frac{1}{4}\left(\ln|z-2| - \ln|z+2|\right)\Big|_{10}^{b} \\
&= \frac{1}{4} \lim_{b \to \infty}\left[(\ln|b-2| - \ln|b+2|) - (\ln 8 - \ln 12)\right] \\
&= \frac{1}{4} \lim_{b \to \infty}\left[\left(\ln\frac{b-2}{b+2}\right) + \ln\frac{3}{2}\right] \\
&= \frac{1}{4}(\ln 1 + \ln 3/2) = \frac{\ln 3/2}{4}.
\end{aligned}
$$

140. Substituting $w = t + 5$, we see that our integral is just $\int_{0}^{15} \frac{dw}{\sqrt{w}}$. This will converge, since $\int_{0}^{b} \frac{dw}{w^p}$ converges for $0 < p < 1$. We find its exact value:

$$
\int_{0}^{15} \frac{dw}{\sqrt{w}} = \lim_{a \to 0^+} \int_{a}^{15} \frac{dw}{\sqrt{w}} = \lim_{a \to 0^+} 2w^{\frac{1}{2}}\Big|_{a}^{15} = 2\sqrt{15}.
$$

141. Since $\sin\phi < \phi$ for $\phi > 0$,

$$
\int_{0}^{\frac{\pi}{2}} \frac{1}{\sin\phi}\, d\phi > \int_{0}^{\frac{\pi}{2}} \frac{1}{\phi}\, d\phi,
$$

The integral on the right diverges, so the integral on the left must also. Alternatively, we use IV-20 in the integral table to get

$$
\begin{aligned}
\int_{0}^{\frac{\pi}{2}} \frac{1}{\sin\phi}\, d\phi &= \lim_{b \to 0^+} \int_{b}^{\frac{\pi}{2}} \frac{1}{\sin\phi}\, d\phi \\
&= \lim_{b \to 0^+} \frac{1}{2} \ln\left|\frac{\cos\phi - 1}{\cos\phi + 1}\right|\,\Big|_{b}^{\frac{\pi}{2}} \\
&= -\frac{1}{2} \lim_{b \to 0^+} \ln\left|\frac{\cos b - 1}{\cos b + 1}\right|.
\end{aligned}
$$

As $b \to 0^+$, $\cos b - 1 \to 0$ and $\cos b + 1 \to 2$, so $\ln\left|\frac{\cos b - 1}{\cos b + 1}\right| \to -\infty$. Thus the integral diverges.

142. Let $\phi = 2\theta$. Then $d\phi = 2\, d\theta$, and

$$
\begin{aligned}
\int_{0}^{\pi/4} \tan 2\theta\, d\theta &= \int_{0}^{\pi/2} \frac{1}{2} \tan\phi\, d\phi = \int_{0}^{\pi/2} \frac{1}{2} \frac{\sin\phi}{\cos\phi}\, d\phi \\
&= \lim_{b \to (\pi/2)^-} \int_{0}^{b} \frac{1}{2} \frac{\sin\phi}{\cos\phi}\, d\phi = \lim_{b \to (\pi/2)^-} -\frac{1}{2} \ln|\cos\phi|\,\Big|_{0}^{b}.
\end{aligned}
$$

As $b \to \pi/2$, $\cos\phi \to 0$, so $\ln|\cos\phi| \to -\infty$. Thus the integral diverges.

One could also see this by noting that $\cos x \approx \pi/2 - x$ and $\sin x \approx 1$ for x close to $\pi/2$: therefore, $\tan x \approx 1/(\frac{\pi}{2} - x)$, the integral of which diverges.

143. The integrand $\frac{x}{x+1} \to 1$ as $x \to \infty$, so there's no way $\int_{1}^{\infty} \frac{x}{x+1}\, dx$ can converge.

144. This function is difficult to integrate, so instead we try to compare it with some other function. Since $\frac{\sin^2 \theta}{\theta^2 + 1} \geq 0$, we see that $\int_0^\infty \frac{\sin^2 \theta}{\theta^2 + 1} \, d\theta \geq 0$. Also, since $\sin^2 \theta \leq 1$,

$$\int_0^\infty \frac{\sin^2 \theta}{\theta^2 + 1} \, d\theta \leq \int_0^\infty \frac{1}{\theta^2 + 1} \, d\theta = \lim_{b \to \infty} \arctan \theta \Big|_0^b = \frac{\pi}{2}.$$

Thus $\int_0^\infty \frac{\sin^2 \theta}{\theta^2 + 1} \, d\theta$ converges, and its value is between 0 and $\frac{\pi}{2}$.

145. $\int_0^\pi \tan^2 \theta d\theta = \tan \theta - \theta + C$, by formula IV-23. The integrand blows up at $\theta = \frac{\pi}{2}$, so

$$\int_0^\pi \tan^2 \theta d\theta = \int_0^{\frac{\pi}{2}} \tan^2 \theta d\theta + \int_{\frac{\pi}{2}}^\pi \tan^2 \theta d\theta = \lim_{b \to \frac{\pi}{2}} [\tan \theta - \theta]_0^b + \lim_{a \to \frac{\pi}{2}} [\tan \theta - \theta]_a^\pi$$

which is undefined.

146. Since $0 \leq \sin x < 1$ for $0 \leq x \leq 1$, we have

$$(\sin x)^{\frac{3}{2}} < (\sin x)$$

$$\text{so} \quad \frac{1}{(\sin x)^{\frac{3}{2}}} > \frac{1}{(\sin x)}$$

$$\text{or} \quad (\sin x)^{-\frac{3}{2}} > (\sin x)^{-1}$$

Thus $\int_0^1 (\sin x)^{-1} dx = \lim_{a \to 0} \ln \left| \frac{1}{\sin x} - \frac{1}{\tan x} \right|_a^1$, which is infinite.

Hence, $\int_0^1 (\sin x)^{-\frac{3}{2}} dx$ is infinite.

Problems

147. Since the definition of f is different on $0 \leq t \leq 1$ than it is on $1 \leq t \leq 2$, break the definite integral at $t = 1$.

$$\int_0^2 f(t) \, dt = \int_0^1 f(t) \, dt + \int_1^2 f(t) \, dt$$

$$= \int_0^1 t^2 \, dt + \int_1^2 (2 - t) \, dt$$

$$= \frac{t^3}{3} \Big|_0^1 + \left(2t - \frac{t^2}{2} \right) \Big|_1^2$$

$$= 1/3 + 1/2 = 5/6 \approx 0.833$$

148. (a) (i) Multiplying out gives

$$\int (x^2 + 10x + 25) \, dx = \frac{x^3}{3} + 5x^2 + 25x + C.$$

(ii) Substituting $w = x + 5$, so $dw = dx$, gives

$$\int (x + 5)^2 \, dx = \int w^2 \, dw = \frac{w^3}{3} + C = \frac{(x + 5)^3}{3} + C.$$

(b) The results of the two calculations are not the same since

$$\frac{(x + 5)^3}{3} + C = \frac{x^3}{3} + \frac{15x^2}{3} + \frac{75x}{3} + \frac{125}{3} + C.$$

However they differ only by a constant, $125/3$, as guaranteed by the Fundamental Theorem of Calculus.

149. (a) Since $h(z)$ is even, we know that $\int_0^1 h(z)\,dz = \int_{-1}^0 h(z)\,dz$. Since $\int_{-1}^1 h(z)\,dz = \int_{-1}^0 h(z)\,dz + \int_0^1 h(z)\,dz$, we

see that $\int_{-1}^1 h(z)\,dz = 2\int_0^1 h(z)\,dz = 7$. Thus $\int_0^1 h(z)\,dz = 3.5$

(b) If $w = z + 3$, then $dw = dz$. When $z = -4$, $w = -1$; when $z = -2$, $w = 1$. Thus,

$$\int_{-4}^{-2} 5h(z+3)\,dt = 5\int_{-1}^1 h(w)\,(dw) = 5 \cdot 7 = 35.$$

150.

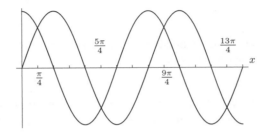

As is evident from the accompanying figure of the graphs of $y = \sin x$ and $y = \cos x$, the crossings occur at $x = \frac{\pi}{4}, \frac{5\pi}{4}, \frac{9\pi}{4}, \ldots$, and the regions bounded by any two consecutive crossings have the same area. So picking two consecutive crossings, we get an area of

$$\text{Area} = \int_{\frac{\pi}{4}}^{\frac{5\pi}{4}} (\sin x - \cos x)\,dx$$
$$= 2\sqrt{2}.$$

(Note that we integrated $\sin x - \cos x$ here because for $\frac{\pi}{4} \le x \le \frac{5\pi}{4}$, $\sin x \ge \cos x$.)

151. The point of intersection of the two curves $y = x^2$ and $y = 6 - x$ is at (2,4). The average height of the shaded area is the average value of the difference between the functions:

$$\frac{1}{(2-0)} \int_0^2 ((6-x) - x^2)\,dx = \left(3x - \frac{x^2}{4} - \frac{x^3}{6} \right)\Big|_0^2 = \frac{11}{3}.$$

152. The average width of the shaded area in the figure below is the average value of the horizontal distance between the two functions. If we call this horizontal distance $h(y)$, then the average width is

$$\frac{1}{(6-0)} \int_0^6 h(y)\,dy.$$

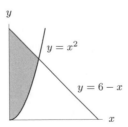

We could compute this integral if we wanted to, but we don't need to. We can simply note that the integral (without the $\frac{1}{6}$ term) is just the area of the shaded region; similarly, the integral in Problem 151 is *also* just the area of the shaded region. So they are the same. Now we know that our average width is just $\frac{1}{3}$ as much as the average height, since we divide by 6 instead of 2. So the answer is $\frac{11}{9}$.

153. (a) i. 0   ii. $\frac{2}{\pi}$ iii. $\frac{1}{2}$

(b) Average value of $f(t) <$ Average value of $k(t) <$ Average value of $g(t)$

We can look at the three functions in the range $-\frac{\pi}{2} \le x \le \frac{3\pi}{2}$, since they all have periods of 2π ($|\cos t|$ and $(\cos t)^2$ also have a period of π, but that does not hurt our calculation). It is clear from the graphs of the three functions below that the average value for $\cos t$ is 0 (since the area above the x-axis is equal to the area below it), while the average values for the other two are positive (since they are everywhere positive, except where they are 0).

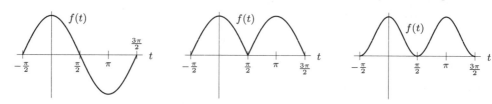

It is also fairly clear from the graphs that the average value of $g(t)$ is greater than the average value of $k(t)$; it is also possible to see this algebraically, since

$$(\cos t)^2 = |\cos t|^2 \le |\cos t|$$

because $|\cos t| \le 1$ (and both of these $\le$'s are $<$'s at all the points where the functions are not 0 or 1).

154. This calculation cannot be correct because the integrand is positive everywhere, yet the value given for the integral is negative.

The calculation is incorrect because the integral is improper but has not been treated as such. The integral is improper because the integrand $1/x^2$ is undefined at $x = 0$. To determine whether the integral converges we split the integral into two improper integrals:

$$\int_{-2}^{2} \frac{1}{x^2}\, dx = \int_{-2}^{0} \frac{1}{x^2}\, dx + \int_{0}^{2} \frac{1}{x^2}\, dx.$$

To decide whether the second integral converges, we compute

$$\int_{0}^{2} \frac{1}{x^2}\, dx = \lim_{a \to 0^+} \int_{a}^{2} \frac{1}{x^2}\, dx = \lim_{a \to 0^+} \left(-\frac{1}{2} + \frac{1}{a} \right).$$

The limit does not exist, and $\int_{0}^{2}(1/x^2)\, dx$ diverges, so the original the integral $\int_{-2}^{2} 1/x^2\, dx$ diverges.

155. (a) We have

$$E(x) + F(x) = \int \frac{e^x}{e^x + e^{-x}}\, dx + \int \frac{e^{-x}}{e^x + e^{-x}}\, dx = \int \frac{e^x + e^{-x}}{e^x + e^{-x}}\, dx = \int 1\, dx = x + C_1.$$

(b) We have

$$E(x) - F(x) = \int \frac{e^x}{e^x + e^{-x}}\, dx - \int \frac{e^{-x}}{e^x + e^{-x}}\, dx = \int \frac{e^x - e^{-x}}{e^x + e^{-x}}\, dx = \ln \left| e^x + e^{-x} \right| + C_2,$$

by using the substitution $w = e^x + e^{-x}$ in the final integral.

(c) We have

$$E(x) + F(x) = x + C_1$$
$$E(x) - F(x) = \ln \left| e^x + e^{-x} \right| + C_2.$$

Adding and subtracting we find

$$E(x) = \frac{x}{2} + \frac{1}{2} \ln \left| e^x + e^{-x} \right| + C,$$

where the arbitrary constant $C = (C_1 + C_2)/2$, and

$$F(x) = \frac{x}{2} - \frac{1}{2} \ln \left| e^x + e^{-x} \right| + C,$$

where $C = (C_1 - C_2)/2$.

156. Since $f(x)$ is decreasing on $[a, b]$, the left-hand Riemann sums are all overestimates and the right-hand sums are all underestimates. Because increasing the number of subintervals generally brings an approximation closer to the actual value, LEFT(10) is closer to the actual value (i.e., smaller, since the left sums are overestimates) than LEFT(5), and analogously for RIGHT(10) and RIGHT(5). Since the graph of $f(x)$ is concave down, a secant line lies below the curve and a tangent line lies above the curve. Therefore, TRAP is an underestimate and MID is an overestimate. Putting these observations together, we have

$$\text{RIGHT}(5) < \text{RIGHT}(10) < \text{TRAP}(10) < \text{Exact value} < \text{MID}(10) < \text{LEFT}(10) < \text{LEFT}(5).$$

157. Use integration by parts, with $u = x$ and $dv = xe^{-x^2}$. Then $v = -(1/2)e^{-x^2}$, and

$$\int_0^b x^2 e^{-x^2}\, dx = -\frac{1}{2}xe^{-x^2}\Big|_0^b + \int_0^b \frac{1}{2}e^{-x^2}\, dx$$

$$= -\frac{1}{2}be^{-b^2} + \frac{1}{2}\int_0^b e^{-x^2}\, dx.$$

Since the exponential grows faster than any power,

$$\lim_{b\to\infty} be^{-b^2} = \lim_{b\to\infty}\frac{b}{e^{b^2}} = 0.$$

So

$$\int_0^b x^2 e^{-x^2}\, dx = 0 + \frac{1}{2}\int_0^\infty e^{-x^2}\, dx = \frac{1}{2}\cdot\frac{\sqrt{\pi}}{2} = \frac{\sqrt{\pi}}{4}.$$

158. We complete the square in the exponent so that we can make a substitution:

$$m(t) = \frac{1}{\sqrt{2\pi}}\int_{-\infty}^\infty e^{tx}e^{-x^2/2}\, dx$$

$$= \frac{1}{\sqrt{2\pi}}\int_{-\infty}^\infty e^{-(x^2-2tx)/2}\, dx$$

$$= \frac{1}{\sqrt{2\pi}}\int_{-\infty}^\infty e^{-((x^2-2tx+t^2)-t^2)/2}\, dx$$

$$= \frac{1}{\sqrt{2\pi}}\int_{-\infty}^\infty e^{-(x-t)^2/2}\cdot e^{t^2/2}\, dx$$

$$= \frac{e^{t^2/2}}{\sqrt{2\pi}}\int_{-\infty}^\infty e^{-(x-t)^2/2}\, dx.$$

Substitute $w = x - t$, then $dw = dx$ and $w = \infty$ when $x = \infty$, and $w = -\infty$ when $x = -\infty$. Thus

$$m(t) = \frac{e^{t^2/2}}{\sqrt{2\pi}}\int_{-\infty}^\infty e^{-w^2/2}\, dw = \frac{e^{t^2/2}}{\sqrt{2\pi}}\cdot\sqrt{2\pi}$$

$$m(t) = e^{t^2/2}.$$

159. (a) We calculate the integral using partial fractions with denominators P and $L - P$:

$$\frac{k}{P(L-P)} = \frac{A}{P} + \frac{B}{L-P}$$

$$k = A(L-P) + BP$$

$$k = (B-A)P + AL.$$

Thus,

$$B - A = 0$$

$$AL = k,$$

so $A = B = k/L$, and the time is given by

$$T = \int_{L/4}^{L/2}\frac{k\, dP}{P(L-P)} = \frac{k}{L}\int_{L/4}^{L/2}\left(\frac{1}{P} + \frac{1}{L-P}\right)dP = \frac{k}{L}(\ln|P| - \ln|L-P|)\Big|_{L/4}^{L/2}$$

$$= \frac{k}{L}\left(\ln\left(\frac{L}{2}\right) - \ln\left(\frac{L}{2}\right) - \ln\left(\frac{L}{4}\right) + \ln\left(\frac{3L}{4}\right)\right)$$

$$= \frac{k}{L}\ln\left(\frac{3L/4}{L/4}\right) = \frac{k}{L}\ln(3).$$

(b) A similar calculation gives the following expression for the time:

$$T = \frac{k}{L}(\ln|P| - \ln|L - P|)\Big|_{P_1}^{P_2} = \frac{k}{L}\left(\ln|P_2| - \ln|L - P_2| - \ln|P_1| + \ln|L - P_1|\right).$$

If $P_2 \to L$, then $L - P_2 \to 0$, so $\ln P_2 \to \ln L$, and $\ln(L - P_2) \to -\infty$. Thus the time tends to infinity.

160. If $I(t)$ is average per capita income t years after 1987, then $I'(t) = r(t)$.

(a) Since $t = 8$ in 1995, by the Fundamental Theorem,

$$I(8) - I(0) = \int_0^8 r(t)\,dt = \int_0^8 480(1.024)^t\,dt$$

$$= \frac{480(1.024)^t}{\ln(1.024)}\Big|_0^8 = 4228$$

so $I(8) = 26{,}000 + 4228 = 30{,}228$.

(b)

$$I(t) - I(0) = \int_0^t r(t)\,dt = \int_0^t 480(1.024)^t\,dt$$

$$= \frac{480(1.024)^t}{\ln(1.024)}\Big|_0^t$$

$$= \frac{480}{\ln(1.024)}\left((1.024)^t - 1\right)$$

$$= 20{,}239\left((1.024)^t - 1\right)$$

Thus, since $I(0) = 26{,}000$,

$$I(t) = 26{,}000 + 20{,}239(1.024^t - 1) = 20{,}239(1.024)^t + 5761.$$

161. (a) Since the rate is given by $r(t) = 2te^{-2t}$ ml/sec, by the Fundamental Theorem of Calculus, the total quantity is given by the definite integral:

$$\text{Total quantity} \approx \int_0^\infty 2te^{-2t}\,dt = 2\lim_{b\to\infty}\int_0^b te^{-2t}\,dt.$$

Integration by parts with $u = t$, $v' = e^{-2t}$ gives

$$\text{Total quantity} \approx 2\lim_{b\to\infty}\left(-\frac{t}{2}e^{-2t} - \frac{1}{4}e^{-2t}\right)\Big|_0^b$$

$$= 2\lim_{b\to\infty}\left(\frac{1}{4} - \left(\frac{b}{2} + \frac{1}{4}\right)e^{-2b}\right) = 2\cdot\frac{1}{4} = 0.5 \text{ ml}.$$

(b) At the end of 5 seconds,

$$\text{Quantity received} = \int_0^5 2te^{-2t}\,dt \approx 0.49975 \text{ ml}.$$

Since $0.49975/0.5 = 0.9995 = 99.95\%$, the patient has received 99.95% of the dose in the first 5 seconds.

162. The rate at which petroleum is being used t years after 1990 is given by

$$r(t) = 1.4 \cdot 10^{20}(1.02)^t \text{ joules/year}.$$

Between 1990 and M years later

$$\text{Total quantity of petroleum used} = \int_0^M 1.4 \cdot 10^{20}(1.02)^t\,dt = 1.4 \cdot 10^{20}\frac{(1.02)^t}{\ln(1.02)}\Big|_0^M$$

$$= \frac{1.4 \cdot 10^{20}}{\ln(1.02)}\left((1.02)^M - 1\right) \text{ joules}.$$

Setting the total quantity used equal to 10^{22} gives

$$\frac{1.4 \cdot 10^{20}}{\ln(1.02)} \left((1.02)^M - 1\right) = 10^{22}$$

$$(1.02)^M = \frac{100\ln(1.02)}{1.4} + 1 = 2.41$$

$$M = \frac{\ln(2.41)}{\ln(1.02)} \approx 45 \text{ years.}$$

So we will run out of petroleum in 2035.

163. (a) We have

$$S = \int_0^{18} (30 - 10)dt = 20 \int_0^{18} dt = 20(18 - 0) = 360.$$

The units of S are degree-days, because the integrand $f(t) - 10$ has units of $°C$, and dt has units of days.

(b) In Figure 7.32, $f(t)$ and H_{min} are represented by the horizontal lines at $H = 30$ and $H = 10$, and T is represented by a vertical line at $t = 18$. The value of S, given by the definite integral, is represented by the area of the rectangle bounded by the vertical lines $t = 0$ (the H-axis) and $t = 18$, and the horizontal lines $H = 10$ and $H = 30$.

(c) The temperature cycles from a high of $30°C$ to a low of $10°C$ once every 6 days. During the 18-day period the temperature completes 3 complete cycles. The area between this curve and the horizontal line $H = H_{min} = 10$ gives the value of the definite integral. See Figure 7.33. In order to get the same area as before, (namely $S = 360$), we see that T_2 must be larger than $T = 18$. Thus we want T_2 to satisfy:

$$S = \int_0^{T_2} (g(t) - 10)dt = \int_0^{T_2} \left(10\cos\left(\frac{2\pi t}{6}\right) + 10\right) dt = 360.$$

Notice that, by symmetry, the area on the interval $0 \le t \le 18$ is half the area shown in Figure 7.32. Thus, we expect that $T_2 = 2T = 36$. We can check this by calculation, using a substitution to evaluate the integral:

$$S = \int_0^{36} \left(10\cos\left(\frac{2\pi t}{6}\right) + 10\right) dt = \left(10 \cdot \frac{6}{2\pi}\sin\left(\frac{2\pi t}{6}\right) + 10t\right)\Bigg|_0^{T_2} = 360.$$

Thus, if $T_2 = 36$, the integral evaluates to $S = 360$, as required. Thus, 36 days are required for development for with these temperatures.

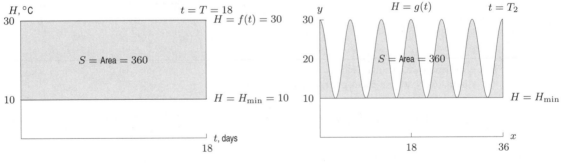

Figure 7.32   Figure 7.33

CAS Challenge Problems

164. (a) A CAS gives

$$\int \frac{\ln x}{x} dx = \frac{(\ln x)^2}{2}$$

$$\int \frac{(\ln x)^2}{x} dx = \frac{(\ln x)^3}{3}$$

$$\int \frac{(\ln x)^3}{x} dx = \frac{(\ln x)^4}{4}$$

(b) Looking at the answers to part (a),

$$\int \frac{(\ln x)^n}{x}\, dx = \frac{(\ln x)^{n+1}}{n+1} + C.$$

(c) Let $w = \ln x$. Then $dw = (1/x)dx$, and

$$\int \frac{(\ln x)^n}{x}\, dx = \int w^n\, dw = \frac{w^{n+1}}{n+1} + C = \frac{(\ln x)^{n+1}}{n} + C.$$

165. (a) A CAS gives

$$\int \ln x\, dx = -x + x\ln x$$

$$\int (\ln x)^2\, dx = 2x - 2x\ln x + x(\ln x)^2$$

$$\int (\ln x)^3\, dx = -6x + 6x\ln x - 3x(\ln x)^2 + x(\ln x)^3$$

$$\int (\ln x)^4\, dx = 24x - 24x\ln x + 12x(\ln x)^2 - 4x(\ln x)^3 + x(\ln x)^4$$

(b) In each of the cases in part (a), the expression for the integral $\int (\ln x)^n\, dx$ has two parts. The first part is simply a multiple of the expression for $\int (\ln x)^{n-1}\, dx$. For example, $\int (\ln x)^2\, dx$ starts out with $2x - 2x\ln x = -2\int \ln x\, dx$. Similarly, $\int (\ln x)^3\, dx$ starts out with $-6x + 6x\ln x - 3(\ln x)^2 = -3\int (\ln x)^2\, dx$, and $\int (\ln x)^4\, dx$ starts out with $-4\int (\ln x)^3\, dx$. The remaining part of each antiderivative is a single term: it's $x(\ln x)^2$ in the case $n = 2$, it's $x(\ln x)^3$ for $n = 3$, and it's $x(\ln x)^4$ for $n = 4$. The general pattern is

$$\int (\ln x)^n\, dx = -n \int (\ln x)^{n-1}\, dx + x(\ln x)^n.$$

To check this formula, we use integration by parts. Let $u = (\ln x)^n$ so $u' = n(\ln x)^{n-1}/x$ and $v' = 1$ so $v = x$. Then

$$\int (\ln x)^n\, dx = x(\ln x)^n - \int n\frac{(\ln x)^{n-1}}{x} \cdot x\, dx$$

$$\int (\ln x)^n\, dx = x(\ln x)^n - n \int (\ln x)^{n-1}\, dx.$$

This is the result we obtained before.

Alternatively, we can check our result by differentiation:

$$\frac{d}{dx}\left(-n \int (\ln x)^{n-1}\, dx + x(\ln x)^n\right) = -n(\ln x)^{n-1} + \frac{d}{dx}(x(\ln x)^n)$$

$$= -n(\ln x)^{n-1} + (\ln x)^n + x \cdot n(\ln x)^{n-1}\frac{1}{x}$$

$$= -n(\ln x)^{n-1} + (\ln x)^n + n(\ln x)^{n-1} = (\ln x)^n.$$

Therefore,

$$\int (\ln x)^n\, dx = -n \int (\ln x)^{n-1}\, dx + x(\ln x)^n.$$

166. (a) A possible answer from the CAS is

$$\int \sin^3 x\, dx = \frac{-9\cos(x) + \cos(3x)}{12}.$$

(b) Differentiating

$$\frac{d}{dx}\left(\frac{-9\cos(x) + \cos(3x)}{12}\right) = \frac{9\sin(x) - 3\sin(3x)}{12} = \frac{3\sin x - \sin(3x)}{4}.$$

(c) Using the identities, we get

$$\sin(3x) = \sin(x + 2x) = \sin x \cos 2x + \cos x \sin 2x$$
$$= \sin x(1 - 2\sin^2 x) + \cos x(2\sin x \cos x)$$
$$= \sin x - 2\sin^3 x + 2\sin x(1 - \sin^2 x)$$
$$= 3\sin x - 4\sin^3 x.$$

Thus,

$$3\sin x - \sin(3x) = 3\sin x - (3\sin x - 4\sin^3 x) = 4\sin^3 x,$$

so

$$\frac{3\sin x - \sin(3x)}{4} = \sin^3 x.$$

167. (a) A possible answer is

$$\int \sin x \cos x \cos(2x)\, dx = -\frac{\cos(4x)}{16}.$$

Different systems may give the answer in a different form.

(b)

$$\frac{d}{dx}\left(-\frac{\cos(4x)}{16}\right) = \frac{\sin(4x)}{4}.$$

(c) Using the double angle formula $\sin 2A = 2\sin A \cos A$ twice, we get

$$\frac{\sin(4x)}{4} = \frac{2\sin(2x)\cos(2x)}{4} = \frac{2 \cdot 2\sin x \cos x \cos(2x)}{4} = \sin x \cos x \cos(2x).$$

168. (a) A possible answer from the CAS is

$$\int \frac{x^4}{(1+x^2)^2}\, dx = x + \frac{x}{2\,(1+x^2)} - \frac{3}{2}\arctan(x).$$

Different systems may give the answer in different form.

(b) Differentiating gives

$$\frac{d}{dx}\left(x + \frac{x}{2\,(1+x^2)} - \frac{3}{2}\arctan(x)\right) = 1 - \frac{x^2}{(1+x^2)^2} - \frac{1}{1+x^2}.$$

(c) Putting the result of part (b) over a common denominator, we get

$$1 - \frac{x^2}{(1+x^2)^2} - \frac{1}{1+x^2} = \frac{\left(1+x^2\right)^2 - x^2 - (1+x^2)}{(1+x^2)^2}$$
$$= \frac{1 + 2x^2 + x^4 - x^2 - 1 - x^2}{(1+x^2)^2} = \frac{x^4}{(1+x^2)^2}.$$

CHECK YOUR UNDERSTANDING

1. False. The subdivision size $\Delta x = (1/10)(6 - 2) = 4/10$.

2. True, since $\Delta x = (6 - 2)/n = 4/n$.

3. False. If f is decreasing, then on each subinterval the value of $f(x)$ at the left endpoint is larger than the value at the right endpoint, which means that LEFT(n) >RIGHT(n) for any n.

4. False. As n approaches infinity, LEFT(n) approaches the value of the integral $\int_2^6 f(x)dx$, which is generally not 0.

5. True. We have

$$\text{LEFT}(n) - \text{RIGHT}(n) = (f(x_0) + f(x_1) + \cdots + f(x_{n-1}))\Delta x - (f(x_1) + f(x_2) + \cdots + f(x_n))\Delta x.$$

On the right side of the equation, all terms cancel except the first and last, so:

$$\text{LEFT}(n) - \text{RIGHT}(n) = (f(x_0) - f(x_n))\Delta x = (f(2) - f(6))\Delta x.$$

This is also discussed in Section 5.1.

6. True. This follows from the fact that $\Delta x = (6 - 2)/n = 4/n$.

7. False. Since $\text{LEFT}(n) - \text{RIGHT}(n) = (f(2) - f(6))\Delta x$, we have $\text{LEFT}(n) = \text{RIGHT}(n)$ for any function such that $f(2) = f(6)$. Such a function, for example $f(x) = (x - 4)^2$, need not be a constant function.

8. False. Although $\text{TRAP}(n)$ is usually a better estimate, it is not always better. If $f(2) = f(6)$, then $\text{LEFT}(n) = \text{RIGHT}(n)$ and hence $\text{TRAP}(n) = \text{LEFT}(n) = \text{RIGHT}(n)$, so in this case $\text{TRAP}(n)$ is no better.

9. False. This is true if f is an increasing function or if f is a decreasing function, but it is not true in general. For example, suppose that $f(2) = f(6)$. Then $\text{LEFT}(n) = \text{RIGHT}(n)$ for all n, which means that if $\int_2^6 f(x)dx$ lies between $\text{LEFT}(n)$ and $\text{RIGHT}(n)$, then it must equal $\text{LEFT}(n)$, which is not always the case.

   For example, if $f(x) = (x - 4)^2$ and $n = 1$, then $f(2) = f(6) = 4$, so

   $$\text{LEFT}(1) = \text{RIGHT}(1) = 4 \cdot (6 - 2) = 16.$$

   However

   $$\int_2^6 (x - 4)^2 dx = \frac{(x - 4)^3}{3}\bigg|_2^6 = \frac{2^3}{3} - \left(-\frac{2^3}{3}\right) = \frac{16}{3}.$$

   In this example, since $\text{LEFT}(n) = \text{RIGHT}(n)$, we have $\text{TRAP}(n) = \text{LEFT}(n)$. However trapezoids overestimate the area, since the graph of f is concave up. This is also discussed in Section 7.5.

10. True. Let $w = f(x)$, so $dw = f'(x)\,dx$, then

    $$\int f'(x)\cos(f(x))\,dx = \int \cos w\,dw = \sin w + C = \sin(f(x)) + C.$$

11. False. Differentiating gives

    $$\frac{d}{dx}\ln|f(x)| = \frac{1}{f(x)} \cdot f'(x),$$

    so, in general

    $$\int \frac{1}{f(x)}\,dx \neq \ln|f(x)| + C.$$

12. True. Let $w = 5 - t^2$, then $dw = -2t\,dt$.

13. True. Rewrite $\sin^7 \theta = \sin \theta \sin^6 \theta = \sin \theta (1 - \cos^2 \theta)^3$. Expanding, substituting $w = \cos \theta, dw = -\sin \theta\,d\theta$, and integrating gives a polynomial in w, which is a polynomial in $\cos \theta$.

14. False. Completing the square gives

    $$\int \frac{dx}{x^2 + 4x + 5} = \int \frac{dx}{(x + 2)^2 + 1} = \arctan(x + 2) + C.$$

15. False. Factoring gives

    $$\int \frac{dx}{x^2 + 4x - 5} = \int \frac{dx}{(x + 5)(x - 1)} = \frac{1}{6}\int\left(\frac{1}{x - 1} - \frac{1}{x + 5}\right)dx = \frac{1}{6}(\ln|x - 1| - \ln|x + 5|) + C.$$

16. True. Let $w = \ln x, dw = x^{-1}\,dx$. Then

    $$\int x^{-1}((\ln x)^2 + (\ln x)^3)\,dx = \int (w^2 + w^3)\,dw = \frac{w^3}{3} + \frac{w^4}{4} + C = \frac{(\ln x)^3}{3} + \frac{(\ln x)^4}{4} + C.$$

17. True. Let $u = t, v' = \sin(5 - t)$, so $u' = 1, v = \cos(5 - t)$. Then the integral $\int 1 \cdot \cos(5 - t)\,dt$ can be done by guess-and-check or by substituting $w = 5 - t$.

18. True. Since

    $$\lim_{b \to \infty}\int_0^b f(x)dx = \int_0^a f(x)dx + \lim_{b \to \infty}\int_a^b f(x)dx,$$

    the limit on the left side of the equation is finite exactly when the limit on the right side is finite. Thus, if $\int_0^\infty f(x)dx$ converges, then so does $\int_a^\infty f(x)dx$.

19. diverges.

True. Suppose that f has period p. Then $\int_0^p f(x)dx$, $\int_p^{2p} f(x)dx$, $\int_{2p}^{3p} f(x)dx,\ldots$ are all equal. If we let $k = \int_0^p f(x)dx$, then $\int_0^{np} f(x)dx = nk$, for any positive integer n. Since $f(x)$ is positive, so is k. Thus as n approaches ∞, the value of $\int_0^{np} f(x)dx = nk$ approaches ∞. That means that $\lim_{b\to\infty} \int_0^b f(x)dx$ is not finite; that is, the integral diverges.

20. False. Let $f(x) = 1/(x+1)$. Then

$$\int_0^\infty \frac{1}{x+1}dx = \lim_{b\to\infty} \ln|x+1|\Big|_0^b = \lim_{b\to\infty} \ln(b+1),$$

but $\lim_{b\to\infty} \ln(b+1)$ does not exist.

21. False. Let $f(x) = x + 1$. Then

$$\int_0^\infty \frac{1}{x+1}dx = \lim_{b\to\infty} \ln|x+1|\Big|_0^b = \lim_{b\to\infty} \ln(b+1),$$

but $\lim_{b\to\infty} \ln(b+1)$ does not exist.

22. True. By properties of integrals and limits,

$$\lim_{b\to\infty} \int_0^b (f(x) + g(x))dx = \lim_{b\to\infty} \int_0^b f(x)dx + \lim_{b\to\infty} \int_0^b g(x)dx.$$

Since the two limits on the right side of the equation are finite, the limit on the left side is also finite, that is, $\int_0^\infty (f(x) + g(x))dx$ converges.

23. False. For example, let $f(x) = x$ and $g(x) = -x$. Then $f(x) + g(x) = 0$, so $\int_0^\infty (f(x) + g(x))\,dx$ converges, even though $\int_0^\infty f(x)\,dx$ and $\int_0^\infty g(x)\,dx$ diverge.

24. True. By properties of integrals and limits,

$$\lim_{b\to\infty} \int_0^b af(x)\,dx = a \lim_{b\to\infty} \int_0^b f(x)\,dx.$$

Thus, the limit on the left of the equation is finite exactly when the limit on the right side of the equation is finite. Thus $\int_0^\infty af(x)\,dx$ converges if $\int_0^\infty f(x)\,dx$ converges.

25. True. Make the substitution $w = ax$. Then $dw = a\,dx$, so

$$\int_0^b f(ax)\,dx = \frac{1}{a} \int_0^c f(w)\,dw,$$

where $c = ab$. As b approaches infinity, so does c, since a is constant. Thus the limit of the left side of the equation as b approaches infinity is finite exactly when the limit of the right side of the equation as c approaches infinity is finite. That is, $\int_0^\infty f(ax)\,dx$ converges exactly when $\int_0^\infty f(x)\,dx$ converges.

26. True. Make the substitution $w = a + x$, so $dw = dx$. Then $w = a$ when $x = 0$, and $w = a + b$ when $x = b$, so

$$\int_0^b f(a + x)\,dx = \int_a^{b+a} f(w)\,dw = \int_a^c f(w)\,dw$$

where $c = b+a$. As b approaches infinity, so does c, since a is constant. Thus the limit of the left side of the equation as b approaches infinity is finite exactly when the limit of the right side of the equation as c approaches infinity is finite. Since $\int_0^\infty f(x)\,dx$ converges, we know that $\lim_{c\to\infty} \int_0^c f(w)\,dw$ is finite, so $\lim_{c\to\infty} \int_a^c f(w)\,dw$ is finite for any positive a. Thus, $\int_0^\infty f(a + x)\,dx$ converges.

27. False. We have

$$\int_0^b (a + f(x))\,dx = \int_0^b a\,dx + \int_0^b f(x)\,dx.$$

Since $\int_0^\infty f(x)\,dx$ converges, the second integral on the right side of the equation has a finite limit as b approaches infinity. But the first integral on the right side has an infinite limit as b approaches infinity, since $a \neq 0$. Thus the right side all together has an infinite limit, which means that $\int_0^\infty (a + f(x))\,dx$ diverges.

PROJECTS FOR CHAPTER SEVEN

1. (a) If $e^t \geq 1 + t$, then

$$e^x = 1 + \int_0^x e^t \, dt$$

$$\geq 1 + \int_0^x (1 + t) \, dt = 1 + x + \frac{1}{2}x^2.$$

We can keep going with this idea. Since $e^t \geq 1 + t + \frac{1}{2}t^2$,

$$e^x = 1 + \int_0^x e^t \, dt$$

$$\geq 1 + \int_0^x \left(1 + t + \frac{1}{2}t^2\right) dt = 1 + x + \frac{1}{2}x^2 + \frac{1}{6}x^3.$$

We notice that each term in our summation is of the form $\frac{x^n}{n!}$. Furthermore, we see that if we have a sum $1 + x + \frac{x^2}{2} + \cdots + \frac{x^n}{n!}$ such that

$$e^x \geq 1 + x + \frac{x^2}{2} + \cdots + \frac{x^n}{n!},$$

then

$$e^x = 1 + \int_0^x e^t \, dt$$

$$\geq 1 + \int_0^x \left(1 + t + \frac{t^2}{2} + \cdots + \frac{t^n}{n!}\right) dt$$

$$= 1 + x + \frac{x^2}{2} + \frac{x^3}{6} + \cdots + \frac{x^{n+1}}{(n+1)!}.$$

Thus we can continue this process as far as we want, so

$$e^x \geq 1 + x + \frac{1}{2}x^2 + \cdots + \frac{1}{n!}x^n = \sum_{j=0}^{n} \frac{x^j}{j!} \text{ for any } n.$$

(In fact, it turns out that if you let n get larger and larger and keep adding up terms, your values approach exactly e^x.)

(b) We note that $\sin x = \int_0^x \cos t \, dt$ and $\cos x = 1 - \int_0^x \sin t \, dt$. Thus, since $\cos t \leq 1$, we have

$$\sin x \leq \int_0^x 1 \, dt = x.$$

Now using $\sin t \leq t$, we have

$$\cos x \leq 1 - \int_0^x t \, dt = 1 - \frac{1}{2}x^2.$$

Then we just keep going:

$$\sin x \leq \int_0^x \left(1 - \frac{1}{2}t^2\right) dt = x - \frac{1}{6}x^3.$$

Therefore

$$\cos x \leq 1 - \int_0^x \left(t - \frac{1}{6}t^3\right) dt = 1 - \frac{1}{2}x^2 + \frac{1}{24}x^4.$$

2. (a) (i)

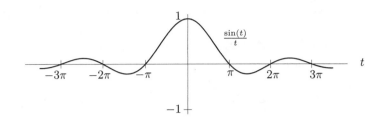

(ii) $\text{Si}(x)$ neither always decreases nor always increases, since its derivative, $x^{-1}\sin x$, has both positive and negative values for $x > 0$. For positive x, $\text{Si}(x)$ is the area under the curve $\frac{\sin t}{t}$ and above the t-axis from $t = 0$ to $t = x$, minus the area above the curve and below the t-axis. Looking at the graph above, one can see that this difference of areas is going to always be positive.

(iii)

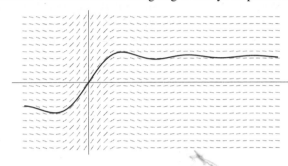

It seems that the limit exists: the curve drawn in the slope field,

$$y = Si(x) = \int_0^x \frac{\sin t}{t}\, dt,$$

seems to approach some limiting height as $x \to \infty$. (In fact, the limiting height is $\pi/2$.)

(b) (i)

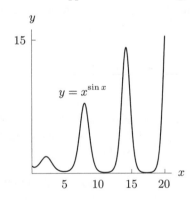

(ii)

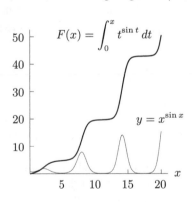

(iii)

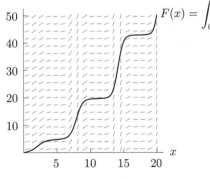

(c) (i) The most obvious feature of the graph of $y = \sin(x^2)$ is its symmetry about the y-axis. This means the function $g(x) = \sin(x^2)$ is an even function, i.e. for all x, we have $g(x) = g(-x)$. Since $\sin(x^2)$ is even, its antiderivative F must be odd, that is $F(-x) = -F(-x)$. To see this, set $F(t) = \int_0^t \sin(x^2)\, dx$, then

$$F(-t) = \int_0^{-t} \sin(x^2)\, dx = -\int_{-t}^0 \sin(x^2)\, dx = -\int_0^t \sin(x^2)\, dx = -F(t),$$

since the area from $-t$ to 0 is the same as the area from 0 to t. Thus $F(t) = -F(-t)$ and F is odd.

The second obvious feature of the graph of $y = \sin(x^2)$ is that it oscillates between -1 and 1 with a "period" which goes to zero as $|x|$ increases. This implies that $F'(x)$ alternates between intervals where it is positive or negative, and increasing or decreasing, with frequency growing arbitrarily large as $|x|$ increases. Thus $F(x)$ itself similarly alternates between intervals where it is increasing or decreasing, and concave up or concave down.

Finally, since $y = \sin(x^2) = F'(x)$ passes through $(0,0)$, and $F(0) = 0$, F is tangent to the x-axis at the origin.

(ii)

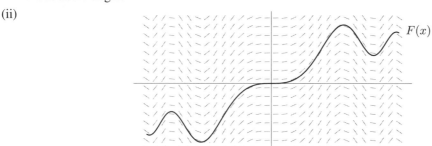

Figure 7.34

F never crosses the x-axis in the region $x > 0$, and $\lim\limits_{x \to \infty} F(x)$ exists. One way to see these facts is to note that by the Construction Theorem,

$$F(x) = F(x) - F(0) = \int_0^x F'(t)\, dt.$$

So $F(x)$ is just the area between the curve $y = \sin(t^2)$ and the t-axis for $0 \le t \le x$ (with area above the t-axis counting positively, and area below the t-axis counting negatively). Now looking at the graph of curve, we see that this area will include alternating pieces above and below the t-axis. We can also see that the area of these pieces is approaching 0 as we go further out. So we add a piece, take a piece away, add another piece, take another piece away, and so on.

It turns out that this means that the sums of the pieces converge. To see this, think of walking from point A to point B. If you walk almost to B, then go a smaller distance toward A, then a yet smaller distance back toward B, and so on, you will eventually approach some point between A and B. So we can see that $\lim\limits_{x \to \infty} F(x)$ exists. Also, since we always subtract a smaller piece than we just added, and the first piece is added instead of subtracted, we see that we never get a negative sum; thus $F(x)$ is never negative in the region $x > 0$, so $F(x)$ never crosses the x-axis there.

CHAPTER EIGHT

Solutions for Section 8.1

Exercises

1. Each strip is a rectangle of length 3 and width Δx, so

$$\text{Area of strip } = 3\Delta x, \quad \text{so}$$

$$\text{Area of region } = \int_0^5 3 \, dx = 3x \Big|_0^5 = 15.$$

Check: This area can also be computed using Length $\times$ Width $= 5 \cdot 3 = 15$.

2. Using similar triangles, the height, y, of the strip is given by

$$\frac{y}{3} = \frac{x}{6} \quad \text{so} \quad y = \frac{x}{2}.$$

Thus,

$$\text{Area of strip } \approx y\Delta x = \frac{x}{2}\Delta x,$$

so

$$\text{Area of region } = \int_0^6 \frac{x}{2} \, dx = \frac{x^2}{4} \Big|_0^6 = 9.$$

Check: This area can also be computed using the formula $\frac{1}{2}$ Base $\cdot$ Height $= \frac{1}{2} \cdot 6 \cdot 3 = 9$.

3. By similar triangles, if w is the length of the strip at height h, we have

$$\frac{w}{3} = \frac{5-h}{5} \quad \text{so} \quad w = 3\left(1 - \frac{h}{5}\right).$$

Thus,

$$\text{Area of strip } \approx w\Delta h = 3\left(1 - \frac{h}{5}\right)\Delta h.$$

$$\text{Area of region } = \int_0^5 3\left(1 - \frac{h}{5}\right) dh = \left(3h - \frac{3h^2}{10}\right)\Big|_0^5 = \frac{15}{2}.$$

Check: This area can also be computed using the formula $\frac{1}{2}$ Base $\cdot$ Height $= \frac{1}{2} \cdot 3 \cdot 5 = \frac{15}{2}$.

4. Suppose the length of the strip shown is w. Then the Pythagorean theorem gives

$$h^2 + \left(\frac{w}{2}\right)^2 = 3^2 \quad \text{so} \quad w = 2\sqrt{3^2 - h^2}.$$

Thus

$$\text{Area of strip } \approx w\Delta h = 2\sqrt{3^2 - h^2}\Delta h,$$

$$\text{Area of region } = \int_{-3}^3 2\sqrt{3^2 - h^2} \, dh.$$

Using VI-30 in the Table of Integrals, we have

$$\text{Area } = \left(h\sqrt{3^2 - h^2} + 3^2 \arcsin\left(\frac{h}{3}\right)\right)\Big|_{-3}^3 = 9(\arcsin 1 - \arcsin(-1)) = 9\pi.$$

Check: This area can also be computed using the formula $\pi r^2 = 9\pi$.

5. The strip has width Δy, so the variable of integration is y. The length of the strip is x. Since $x^2 + y^2 = 10$ and the region is in the first quadrant, solving for x gives $x = \sqrt{10 - y^2}$. Thus

$$\text{Area of strip} \approx x \Delta y = \sqrt{10 - y^2}\, dy.$$

The region stretches from $y = 0$ to $y = \sqrt{10}$, so

$$\text{Area of region} = \int_0^{\sqrt{10}} \sqrt{10 - y^2}\, dy.$$

Evaluating using VI-30 from the Table of Integrals, we have

$$\text{Area} = \frac{1}{2}\left(y\sqrt{10 - y^2} + 10 \arcsin\left(\frac{y}{\sqrt{10}}\right)\right)\Bigg|_0^{\sqrt{10}} = 5(\arcsin 1 - \arcsin 0) = \frac{5}{2}\pi.$$

Check: This area can also be computed using the formula $\frac{1}{4}\pi r^2 = \frac{1}{4}\pi(\sqrt{10})^2 = \frac{5}{2}\pi$.

6. The strip has width Δy, so the variable of integration is y. The length of the strip is $2x$ for $x \geq 0$. For positive x, we have $x = y$. Thus,

$$\text{Area of strip} \approx 2x \Delta y = 2y \Delta y.$$

Since the region extends from $y = 0$ to $y = 4$,

$$\text{Area of region} = \int_0^4 2y\, dy = y^2 \Big|_0^4 = 16.$$

Check: The area of the region can be computed by $\frac{1}{2}$ Base $\cdot$ Height $= \frac{1}{2} \cdot 8 \cdot 4 = 16$.

7. The width of the strip is Δy, so the variable of integration is y. Since the graphs are $x = y$ and $x = y^2$, the length of the strip is $y - y^2$, and

$$\text{Area of strip} \approx (y - y^2)\Delta y.$$

The curves cross at the points $(0, 0)$ and $(1, 1)$, so

$$\text{Area of region} = \int_0^1 (y - y^2)\, dy = \frac{y^2}{2} - \frac{y^3}{3}\Bigg|_0^1 = \frac{1}{6}.$$

8. The width of the strip is Δx, so the variable of integration is x. The line has equation $y = 6 - 3x$. The length of the strip is $6 - 3x - (x^2 - 4) = 10 - 3x - x^2$. (Since $x^2 - 4$ is negative where the graph is below the x-axis, subtracting $x^2 - 4$ there adds the length below the x-axis.) Thus

$$\text{Area of strip} \approx (10 - 3x - x^2)\Delta x.$$

Both graphs cross the x-axis where $x = 2$, so

$$\text{Area of region} = \int_0^2 (10 - 3x - x^2)\, dx = 10x - \frac{3}{2}x^2 - \frac{x^3}{3}\Bigg|_0^2 = \frac{34}{3}.$$

9. Each slice is a circular disk with radius $r = 2$ cm.

$$\text{Volume of disk} = \pi r^2 \Delta x = 4\pi \Delta x \text{ cm}^3.$$

Summing over all disks, we have

$$\text{Total volume} \approx \sum 4\pi \Delta x \text{ cm}^3.$$

Taking a limit as $\Delta x \to 0$, we get

$$\text{Total volume} = \lim_{\Delta x \to 0} \sum 4\pi \Delta x = \int_0^9 4\pi\, dx \text{ cm}^3.$$

Evaluating gives

$$\text{Total volume} = 4\pi x \Big|_0^9 = 36\pi \text{ cm}^3.$$

Check: The volume of the cylinder can also be calculated using the formula $V = \pi r^2 h = \pi 2^2 \cdot 9 = 36\pi \text{ cm}^3$.

10. Each slice is a circular disk. Since the radius of the cone is 2 cm and the length is 6 cm, the radius is one-third of the distance from the vertex. Thus, the radius at x is $r = x/3$ cm. See Figure 8.1.

$$\text{Volume of slice} \approx \pi r^2 \Delta x = \frac{\pi x^2}{9} \Delta x \text{ cm}^3.$$

Summing over all disks, we have

$$\text{Total volume} \approx \sum \pi \frac{x^2}{9} \Delta x \text{ cm}^3.$$

Taking a limit as $\Delta x \to 0$, we get

$$\text{Total volume} = \lim_{\Delta x \to 0} \sum \pi \frac{x^2}{9} \Delta x = \int_0^6 \pi \frac{x^2}{9} \, dx \text{ cm}^3.$$

Evaluating, we get

$$\text{Total volume} = \frac{\pi}{9} \frac{x^3}{3} \Big|_0^6 = \frac{\pi}{9} \cdot \frac{6^3}{3} = 8\pi \text{ cm}^3.$$

Check: The volume of the cone can also be calculated using the formula $V = \frac{1}{3}\pi r^2 h = \frac{1}{3}\pi 2^2 \cdot 6 = 8\pi \text{ cm}^3$.

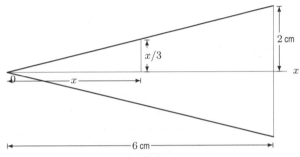

Figure 8.1

11. Each slice is a circular disk. From Figure 8.2, we see that the radius at height y is $r = \frac{2}{5}y$ cm. Thus

$$\text{Volume of disk} \approx \pi r^2 \Delta y = \pi \left(\frac{2}{5}y\right)^2 \Delta y = \frac{4}{25}\pi y^2 \Delta y \text{ cm}^3.$$

Summing over all disks, we have

$$\text{Total volume} \approx \sum \frac{4\pi}{25} y^2 \Delta y \text{ cm}^3.$$

Taking the limit as $\Delta y \to 0$, we get

$$\text{Total volume} = \lim_{\Delta y \to 0} \sum \frac{4\pi}{25} y^2 \Delta y = \int_0^5 \frac{4\pi}{25} y^2 \, dy \text{ cm}^3.$$

Evaluating gives

$$\text{Total volume} = \frac{4\pi}{25} \frac{y^3}{3} \Big|_0^5 = \frac{20}{3}\pi \text{ cm}^3.$$

Check: The volume of the cone can also be calculated using the formula $V = \frac{1}{3}\pi r^2 h = \frac{\pi}{3}2^2 \cdot 5 = \frac{20}{3}\pi \text{ cm}^3$.

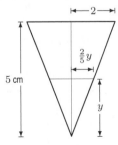

Figure 8.2

12. Each slice is a rectangular slab of length 10 m and width that decreases with height. See Figure 8.3. At height y, the length x is given by the Pythagorean Theorem

$$y^2 + x^2 = 7^2.$$

Solving gives $x = \sqrt{7^2 - y^2}$ m. Thus the width of the slab is $2x = 2\sqrt{7^2 - y^2}$ and

$$\text{Volume of slab} = \text{Length} \cdot \text{Width} \cdot \text{Height} = 10 \cdot 2\sqrt{7^2 - y^2} \cdot \Delta y = 20\sqrt{7^2 - y^2}\Delta y \text{ m}^3.$$

Summing over all slabs, we have

$$\text{Total volume} \approx \sum 20\sqrt{7^2 - y^2}\Delta y \text{ m}^3.$$

Taking a limit as $\Delta y \to 0$, we get

$$\text{Total volume} = \lim_{\Delta y \to 0} \sum 20\sqrt{7^2 - y^2}\Delta y = \int_0^7 20\sqrt{7^2 - y^2}\, dy \text{ m}^3.$$

To evaluate, we use the table of integrals or the fact that $\int_0^7 \sqrt{7^2 - y^2}\, dy$ represents the area of a quarter circle of radius 7, so

$$\text{Total volume} = \int_0^7 20\sqrt{7^2 - y^2}\, dy = 20 \cdot \frac{1}{4}\pi 7^2 = 245\pi \text{ m}^3.$$

Check: the volume of a half cylinder can also be calculated using the formula $V = \frac{1}{2}\pi r^2 h = \frac{1}{2}\pi 7^2 \cdot 10 = 245\pi \text{ m}^3$.

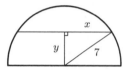

Figure 8.3

13. Each slice is a circular disk. See Figure 8.4. The radius of the sphere is 5 mm, and the radius r at height y is given by the Pythagorean Theorem

$$y^2 + r^2 = 5^2.$$

Solving gives $r = \sqrt{5^2 - y^2}$ mm. Thus,

$$\text{Volume of disk} \approx \pi r^2 \Delta y = \pi(5^2 - y^2)\Delta y \text{ mm}^3.$$

Summing over all disks, we have

$$\text{Total volume} \approx \sum \pi(5^2 - y^2)\Delta y \text{ mm}^3.$$

Taking the limit as $\Delta y \to 0$, we get

$$\text{Total volume} = \lim_{\Delta y \to 0} \sum \pi(5^2 - y^2)\Delta y = \int_0^5 \pi(5^2 - y^2)\, dy \text{ mm}^3.$$

Evaluating gives

$$\text{Total volume} = \pi\left(25y - \frac{y^3}{3}\right)\Bigg|_0^5 = \frac{250}{3}\pi \text{ mm}^3.$$

Check: The volume of a hemisphere can be calculated using the formula $V = \frac{2}{3}\pi r^3 = \frac{2}{3}\pi 5^3 = \frac{250}{3}\pi \text{ mm}^3$.

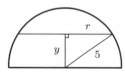

Figure 8.4

14. Each slice is a square; the side length decreases as we go up the pyramid. See Figure 8.5. Since the base of the pyramid is equal to its vertical height, the slice at distance y from the base, or $(2-y)$ from the top, has side $(2-y)$. Thus

$$\text{Volume of slice } \approx (2-y)^2 \Delta y \text{ m}^3.$$

Summing over all slices, we get

$$\text{Total volume } \approx \sum (2-y)^2 \Delta y \text{ m}^3.$$

$$\text{Total volume } = \lim_{\Delta y \to 0} \sum (2-y)^2 \Delta y = \int_0^2 (2-y)^2 \, dy \text{ m}^3.$$

Evaluating, we find

$$\text{Total volume } = \int_0^2 (4 - 4y + y^2) \, dy = \left(4y - 2y^2 + \frac{y^3}{3} \right) \Bigg|_0^2 = \frac{8}{3} \text{ m}^3.$$

Check: The volume of the pyramid can also be calculated using the formula $V = \frac{1}{3}b^2h = \frac{1}{3}2^2 \cdot 2 = \frac{8}{3}$ m^3.

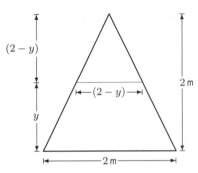

Figure 8.5

Problems

15. Triangle of base and height 1 and 3. See Figure 8.6. (Either 1 or 3 can be the base. A non-right triangle is also possible.)

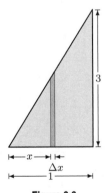

Figure 8.6

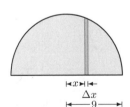

Figure 8.7

16. Semicircle of radius $r = 9$. See Figure 8.7.

17. Quarter circle of radius $r = \sqrt{15}$. See Figure 8.8.

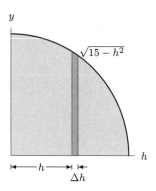

Figure 8.8

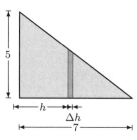

Figure 8.9

18. Triangle of base and height 7 and 5. See Figure 8.9. (Either 7 or 5 can be the base. A non-right triangle is also possible.)

19. Hemisphere with radius 12. See Figure 8.10.

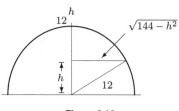

Figure 8.10

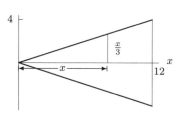

Figure 8.11

20. Cone with height 12 and radius $12/3 = 4$. See Figure 8.11.

21. Cone with height 6 and radius 3. See Figure 8.12.

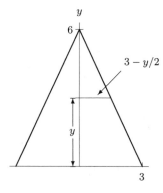

Figure 8.12

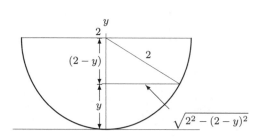

Figure 8.13

22. Hemisphere with radius 2. See Figure 8.13.

23.

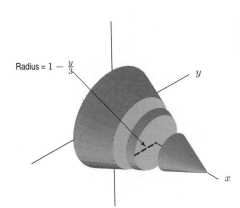

Figure 8.14

Slice parallel to the base of the cone, or, equivalently, rotate the line $x = (3 - y)/3$ about the y–axis. (One can also slice the other way.) See Figure 8.14. The volume V is given by

$$V = \int_{y=0}^{y=3} \pi x^2 \, dy = \int_0^3 \pi \left(\frac{3-y}{3} \right)^2 dy$$

$$= \pi \int_0^3 \left(1 - \frac{2y}{3} + \frac{y^2}{9} \right) dy$$

$$= \pi \left(y - \frac{y^2}{3} + \frac{y^3}{27} \right) \bigg|_0^3 = \pi.$$

24.

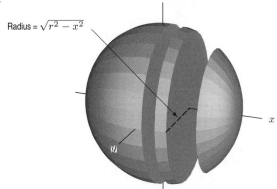

We slice up the sphere in planes perpendicular to the x-axis. Each slice is a circle, with radius $y = \sqrt{r^2 - x^2}$; that's the radius because $x^2 + y^2 = r^2$ when $z = 0$. Then the volume is

$$V \approx \sum \pi (y^2) \, \Delta x = \sum \pi (r^2 - x^2) \, \Delta x.$$

Therefore, as Δx tends to zero, we get

$$V = \int_{x=-r}^{x=r} \pi (r^2 - x^2) \, dx$$

$$= 2 \int_{x=0}^{x=r} \pi (r^2 - x^2) \, dx$$

$$= 2 \left(\pi r^2 x - \frac{\pi x^3}{3} \right) \bigg|_0^r$$

$$= \frac{4 \pi r^3}{3}.$$

25.

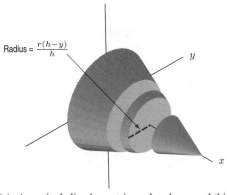

This cone is what you get when you rotate the line $x = r(h - y)/h$ about the y–axis. So slicing perpendicular to the y–axis yields

$$V = \int_{y=0}^{y=h} \pi x^2 \, dy = \pi \int_0^h \left(\frac{(h-y)r}{h} \right)^2 dy$$

$$= \pi \frac{r^2}{h^2} \int_0^h (h^2 - 2hy + y^2) \, dy$$

$$= \frac{\pi r^2}{h^2} \left[h^2 y - hy^2 + \frac{y^3}{3} \right] \bigg|_0^h = \frac{\pi r^2 h}{3}.$$

26. (a) A vertical slice has a triangular shape and thickness Δx. See Figure 8.15.

$$\text{Volume of slice } = \text{ Area of triangle } \cdot \Delta x = \frac{1}{2} \text{ Base } \cdot \text{ Height } \cdot \Delta x = \frac{1}{2} \cdot 2 \cdot 3 \Delta x = 3 \Delta x \text{ cm}^3.$$

Thus,

$$\text{Total volume } = \lim_{\Delta x \to 0} \sum 3 \Delta x = \int_0^4 3 \, dx = 3x \bigg|_0^4 = 12 \text{ cm}^3.$$

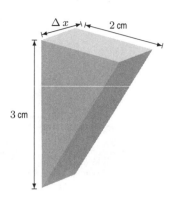

Figure 8.15

(b) A horizontal slice has a rectangular shape and thickness Δh. See Figure 8.16. Using similar triangles, we see that

$$\frac{w}{2} = \frac{3-h}{3},$$

so

$$w = \frac{2}{3}(3-h) = 2 - \frac{2}{3}h.$$

Thus

$$\text{Volume of slice} \approx 4w\Delta h = 4\left(2 - \frac{2}{3}h\right)\Delta h = \left(8 - \frac{8}{3}h\right)\Delta h.$$

So,

$$\text{Total volume} = \lim_{\Delta h \to 0}\sum\left(8 - \frac{8}{3}h\right)\Delta h = \int_0^3\left(8 - \frac{8}{3}h\right)dh = \left(8h - \frac{4h^2}{3}\right)\Big|_0^3 = 12 \text{ cm}^3.$$

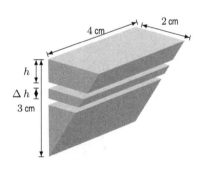

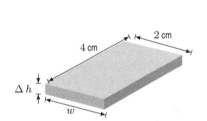

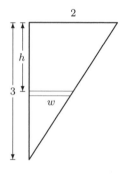

Figure 8.16

27. We slice the water into horizontal slices, each of which is a rectangle. See Figure 8.17.

$$\text{Volume of slice} \approx 150w\Delta h \text{ km}^3.$$

To find w in terms of h, we use the similar triangles in Figure 8.18:

$$\frac{w}{3} = \frac{h}{0.2} \quad \text{so} \quad w = 15h.$$

So

$$\text{Volume of slice} \approx 150 \cdot 15h\Delta h = 2250h\Delta h \text{ km}^3.$$

Summing over all slices and letting $\Delta h \to 0$ gives

$$\text{Total volume} = \lim_{\Delta h \to 0}\sum 2250h\Delta h = \int_0^{0.2} 2250h \, dh \text{ km}^3.$$

Evaluating the integral gives

$$\text{Total volume} = 2250\frac{h^2}{2}\Big|_0^{0.2} = 45 \text{ km}^3.$$

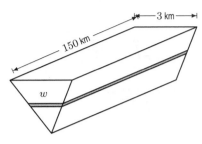

Figure 8.17

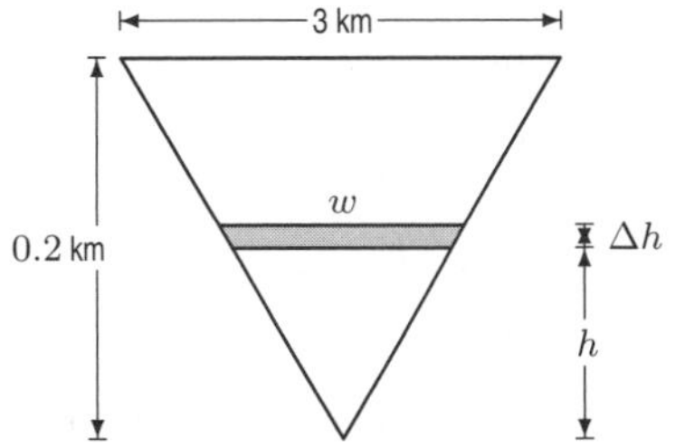

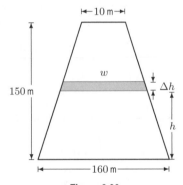

Figure 8.18

28. To calculate the volume of material, we slice the dam horizontally. See Figure 8.19. The slices are rectangular, so

$$\text{Volume of slice} \approx 1400w\Delta h \text{ m}^3.$$

Since w is a linear function of h, and $w = 160$ when $h = 0$, and $w = 10$ when $h = 150$, this function has slope $= (10 - 160)/150 = -1$. Thus

$$w = 160 - h \text{ meters},$$

so

$$\text{Volume of slice} \approx 1400(160 - h)\Delta h \text{ m}^3.$$

Summing over all slices and taking the limit as $\Delta h \to 0$ gives

$$\text{Total volume} = \lim_{\Delta h \to 0} \sum 1400(160 - h)\Delta h = \int_0^{150} 1400(160 - h) \, dh \text{ m}^3.$$

Evaluating the integral gives

$$\text{Total volume} = 1400\left(160h - \frac{h^2}{2}\right)\Big|_0^{150} = 1.785 \cdot 10^7 \text{ m}^3.$$

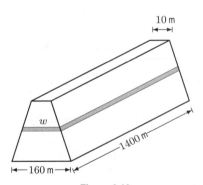

Figure 8.19

Figure 8.20

Solutions for Section 8.2

Exercises

1. The volume is given by

$$V = \int_0^1 \pi y^2 \, dx = \int_0^1 \pi x^4 \, dx = \pi \frac{x^5}{5}\Big|_0^1 = \frac{\pi}{5}.$$

2. The volume is given by

$$V = \int_1^2 \pi y^2 \, dx = \int_1^2 \pi(x+1)^4 \, dx = \left. \frac{\pi(x+1)^5}{5} \right|_1^2 = \frac{211\pi}{5}.$$

3. The volume is given by

$$V = \int_{-2}^0 \pi(4 - x^2)^2 \, dx = \pi \int_{-2}^0 (16 - 8x^2 + x^4) \, dx = \pi \left(16x - \frac{8x^3}{3} + \frac{x^5}{5} \right) \bigg|_{-2}^0 = \frac{256\pi}{15}.$$

4. The volume is given by

$$V = \int_{-1}^1 \pi(\sqrt{x+1})^2 \, dx = \pi \int_{-1}^1 (x+1) \, dx = \pi \left(\frac{x^2}{2} + x \right) \bigg|_{-1}^1 = 2\pi.$$

5. The volume is given by

$$V = \int_{-1}^1 \pi y^2 \, dx = \int_{-1}^1 \pi(e^x)^2 \, dx = \int_{-1}^1 \pi e^{2x} \, dx = \left. \frac{\pi}{2} e^{2x} \right|_{-1}^1 = \frac{\pi}{2}(e^2 - e^{-2}).$$

6. The volume is given by

$$V = \int_0^{\pi/2} \pi y^2 \, dx = \int_0^{\pi/2} \pi \cos^2 x \, dx.$$

Integration by parts gives

$$V = \frac{\pi}{2}(\cos x \sin x + x) \bigg|_0^{\pi/2} = \frac{\pi^2}{4}.$$

7. The volume is given by

$$V = \int_0^1 \pi \left(\frac{1}{x+1} \right)^2 \, dx = \pi \int_0^1 \frac{dx}{(x+1)^2} = -\pi(x+1)^{-1} \bigg|_0^1 = \pi \left(1 - \frac{1}{2} \right) = \frac{\pi}{2}.$$

8. The volume is given by

$$V = \pi \int_0^1 (\sqrt{\cosh 2x})^2 \, dx = \pi \int_0^1 \cosh 2x \, dx = \left. \frac{\pi}{2} \sinh 2x \right|_0^1 = \frac{\pi}{2} \sinh 2.$$

9. Since the graph of $y = x^2$ is below the graph of $y = x$ for $0 \leq x \leq 1$, the volume is given by

$$V = \int_0^1 \pi x^2 \, dx - \int_0^1 \pi(x^2)^2 \, dx = \pi \int_0^1 (x^2 - x^4) \, dx = \pi \left(\frac{x^3}{3} - \frac{x^5}{5} \right) \bigg|_0^1 = \frac{2\pi}{15}.$$

10. Since the graph of $y = e^{3x}$ is above the graph of $y = e^x$ for $0 \leq x \leq 1$, the volume is given by

$$V = \int_0^1 \pi(e^{3x})^2 \, dx - \int_0^1 \pi(e^x)^2 \, dx = \int_0^1 \pi(e^{6x} - e^{2x}) \, dx = \pi \left(\frac{e^{6x}}{6} - \frac{e^{2x}}{2} \right) \bigg|_0^1 = \pi \left(\frac{e^6}{6} - \frac{e^2}{2} + \frac{1}{3} \right).$$

11. Note that this function is actually $x^{3/2}$ in disguise. So

$$L = \int_0^2 \sqrt{1 + \left[\frac{3}{2} x^{\frac{1}{2}} \right]^2} \, dx = \int_{x=0}^{x=2} \sqrt{1 + \frac{9}{4} x} \, dx$$

$$= \frac{4}{9} \int_{w=1}^{w=\frac{11}{2}} w^{\frac{1}{2}} \, dw$$

$$= \frac{8}{27} w^{\frac{3}{2}} \bigg|_1^{\frac{11}{2}} = \frac{8}{27} \left(\left(\frac{11}{2} \right)^{\frac{3}{2}} - 1 \right) \approx 3.526,$$

where we set $w = 1 + \frac{9}{4}x$, so $dx = \frac{4}{9}dw$.

12. This is a one-quarter of the circumference of a circle of radius 2. That circumference is $2 \cdot 2\pi = 4\pi$, so the length is $\frac{4\pi}{4} = \pi$.

13. Since $f'(x) = \sinh x$, the arc length is given by

$$L = \int_0^2 \sqrt{1 + \sinh^2 x}\, dx = \int_0^2 \sqrt{\cosh^2 x}\, dx = \int_0^2 \cosh x\, dx = \sinh x \Big|_0^2 = \sinh 2.$$

14. The length is

$$\int_1^2 \sqrt{(x'(t))^2 + (y'(t))^2 + (z'(t))^2}\, dt = \int_1^2 \sqrt{5^2 + 4^2 + (-1)^2}\, dt = \sqrt{42}.$$

This is the length of a straight line from the point $(8, 5, 2)$ to $(13, 9, 1)$.

15. We have

$$D = \int_0^1 \sqrt{(-e^t \sin(e^t))^2 + (e^t \cos(e^t))^2}\, dt$$
$$= \int_0^1 \sqrt{e^{2t}}\, dt = \int_0^1 e^t\, dt$$
$$= e - 1.$$

This is the length of the arc of a unit circle from the point $(\cos 1, \sin 1)$ to $(\cos e, \sin e)$—in other words between the angles $\theta = 1$ and $\theta = e$. The length of this arc is $(e - 1)$.

16. We have

$$D = \int_0^{2\pi} \sqrt{(-3 \sin 3t)^2 + (5 \cos 5t)^2}\, dt.$$

We cannot find this integral symbolically, but numerical methods show $D \approx 24.6$.

Problems

17. (a) Slicing the region perpendicular to the x-axis gives disks of radius y. See Figure 8.21.

$$\text{Volume of slice} \approx \pi y^2 \Delta x = \pi(x^2 - 1)\Delta x.$$

Thus,

$$\text{Total volume} = \lim_{\Delta x \to 0} \sum \pi(x^2 - 1)\Delta x = \int_2^3 \pi(x^2 - 1)\, dx = \pi\left(\frac{x^3}{3} - x\right)\Big|_2^3$$
$$= \pi\left(9 - 3 - \left(\frac{8}{3} - 2\right)\right) = \frac{16\pi}{3}.$$

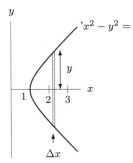

Figure 8.21

(b) The arc length, L, of the curve $y = f(x)$ is given by $L = \int_a^b \sqrt{1 + (f'(x))^2}\, dx$. In this problem y is an implicit function of x. Solving for y gives $y = \sqrt{x^2 - 1}$ as the equation of the top half of the hyperbola. Differentiating gives

$$\frac{dy}{dx} = \frac{1}{2}(x^2 - 1)^{-1/2}(2x) = \frac{x}{\sqrt{x^2 - 1}}.$$

Thus

$$\text{Arc length} = \int_2^3 \sqrt{1 + \left(\frac{x}{\sqrt{x^2 - 1}}\right)^2}\, dx = \int_2^3 \sqrt{1 + \frac{x^2}{x^2 - 1}}\, dx = \int_2^3 \sqrt{\frac{2x^2 - 1}{x^2 - 1}}\, dx = 1.48.$$

18.

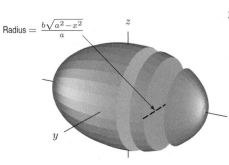

Radius $= \dfrac{b\sqrt{a^2 - x^2}}{a}$

$$y^2 = b^2\left(1 - \frac{x^2}{a^2}\right).$$

$$\begin{aligned}
V &= \int_{-a}^{a} \pi y^2\, dx = \pi \int_{-a}^{a} b^2\left(1 - \frac{x^2}{a^2}\right) dx \\
&= 2\pi b^2 \int_0^a \left(1 - \frac{x^2}{a^2}\right) dx = 2\pi b^2 \left[x - \frac{x^3}{3a^2}\right]_0^a \\
&= 2\pi b^2 \left(a - \frac{a^3}{3a^2}\right) = 2\pi b^2\left(a - \frac{1}{3}a\right) \\
&= \frac{4}{3}\pi a b^2.
\end{aligned}$$

19.

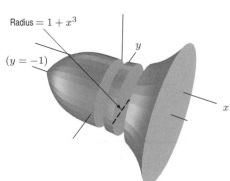

Radius $= 1 + x^3$

$(y = -1)$

We slice the region perpendicular to the x–axis. The Riemann sum we get is $\sum \pi(x^3 + 1)^2 \Delta x$. So the volume V is the integral

$$\begin{aligned}
V &= \int_{-1}^{1} \pi(x^3 + 1)^2\, dx \\
&= \pi \int_{-1}^{1} (x^6 + 2x^3 + 1)\, dx \\
&= \pi \left(\frac{x^7}{7} + \frac{x^4}{2} + x\right)\Bigg|_{-1}^{1} \\
&= (16/7)\pi \approx 7.18.
\end{aligned}$$

20.

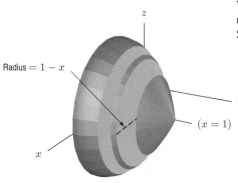

Radius $= 1 - x$

$(x = 1)$

We slice the region perpendicular to the y–axis. The Riemann sum we get is $\sum \pi(1 - x)^2 \Delta y = \sum \pi(1 - y^2)^2 \Delta y$. So the volume V is the integral

$$\begin{aligned}
V &= \int_0^1 \pi(1 - y^2)^2\, dy \\
&= \pi \int_0^1 (1 - 2y^2 + y^4)\, dy \\
&= \pi \left(y - \frac{2y^3}{3} + \frac{y^5}{5}\right)\Bigg|_0^1 \\
&= (8/15)\pi \approx 1.68.
\end{aligned}$$

21.

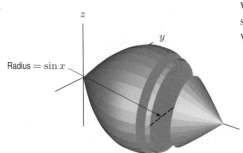

Radius $= \sin x$

We take slices perpendicular to the x–axis. The Riemann sum for approximating the volume is $\sum \pi \sin^2 x \Delta x$. The volume is the integral corresponding to that sum, namely

$$\begin{aligned}
V &= \int_0^\pi \pi \sin^2 x\, dx \\
&= \pi \left[-\frac{1}{2}\sin x \cos x + \frac{1}{2}x\right]\Bigg|_0^\pi = \frac{\pi^2}{2} \approx 4.935.
\end{aligned}$$

22. Slice the object into disks horizontally, as in Figure 8.22. A typical disk has thickness Δy and radius $x = \sqrt{y}$. Thus

$$\text{Volume of slice } \approx \pi x^2 \Delta y = \pi y \, \Delta y.$$

$$\text{Volume of solid } = \lim_{\Delta y \to 0} \sum \pi y \, \Delta y = \int_0^1 \pi y \, dy = \pi \frac{y^2}{2} \bigg|_0^1 = \frac{\pi}{2}.$$

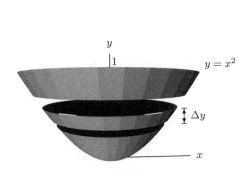

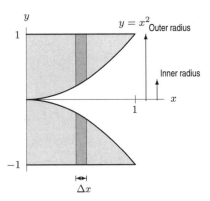

Figure 8.22   **Figure 8.23**: Cross-section of solid

23. Slice the object into rings vertically, as is Figure 8.23. A typical ring has thickness Δx and outer radius $y = 1$ and inner radius $y = x^2$.

$$\text{Volume of slice } \approx \pi 1^2 \Delta x - \pi y^2 \Delta x = \pi(1 - x^4) \, \Delta x.$$

$$\text{Volume of solid } = \lim_{\Delta x \to 0} \sum \pi(1 - x^4) \, \Delta x = \int_0^1 \pi(1 - x^4) \, dx = \pi \left(x - \frac{x^5}{5} \right) \bigg|_0^1 = \frac{4}{5}\pi.$$

24. The region is cylindrical with a hole around the axis of rotation, $y = -2$. Slice it into rings vertically, as in Figure 8.24. A typical ring has thickness Δx and outer radius $1 + 2 = 3$ and inner radius $y + 2 = x^2 + 2$. Thus

$$\text{Volume of slice } \approx \pi 3^2 \Delta x - \pi(x^2 + 2)^2 \Delta x = \pi(5 - x^4 - 4x^2) \, \Delta x.$$

$$\text{Volume of solid } = \int_0^1 \pi(5 - x^4 - 4x^2) \, \Delta x = \pi \left(5x - \frac{x^5}{5} - \frac{4}{3}x^3 \right) \bigg|_0^1 = \frac{52\pi}{15}.$$

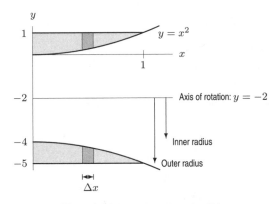

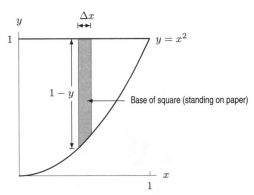

Figure 8.24: Cross-section of solid   **Figure 8.25**: Base of solid

25. Slicing perpendicularly to the x-axis gives squares whose thickness is Δx and whose side is $1 - y = 1 - x^2$. See Figure 8.25. Thus

$$\text{Volume of square slice } \approx (1 - x^2)^2 \Delta x = (1 - 2x^2 + x^4)\,\Delta x.$$

$$\text{Volume of solid } = \int_0^1 (1 - 2x^2 + x^4)\,dx = x - \frac{2}{3}x^3 + \frac{x^5}{5}\bigg|_0^1 = \frac{8}{15}.$$

26. Slicing perpendicularly to the x-axis gives semicircles whose thickness is Δx and whose diameter is $1 - y = 1 - x^2$. See Figure 8.26. Thus

$$\text{Volume of semicircular slice } \approx \pi \left(\frac{1 - x^2}{2} \right)^2 \Delta x = \frac{\pi}{4}(1 - 2x^2 + x^4)\,\Delta x.$$

$$\text{Volume of solid } = \int_0^1 \frac{\pi}{4}(1 - 2x^2 + x^4)\,dx = \frac{\pi}{4}\left(x - \frac{2}{3}x^3 + \frac{x^5}{5} \right)\bigg|_0^1 = \frac{\pi}{4} \cdot \frac{8}{15} = \frac{2\pi}{15}.$$

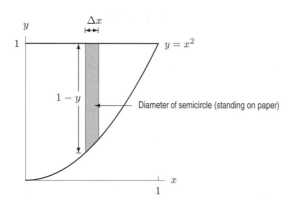

Figure 8.26: Base of solid

Figure 8.27: Base of solid

27. An equilateral triangle of side s has height $\sqrt{3}s/2$ and

$$\text{Area } = \frac{1}{2} \cdot s \cdot \frac{\sqrt{3}s}{2} = \frac{\sqrt{3}}{4}s^2.$$

Slicing perpendicularly to the y-axis gives equilateral triangles whose thickness is Δy and whose side is $x = \sqrt{y}$. See Figure 8.27. Thus

$$\text{Volume of triangular slice } \approx \frac{\sqrt{3}}{4}(\sqrt{y})^2 \Delta y = \frac{\sqrt{3}}{4}y\,\Delta y.$$

$$\text{Volume of solid } = \int_0^1 \frac{\sqrt{3}}{4}y\,dy = \frac{\sqrt{3}}{4}\frac{y^2}{2}\bigg|_0^1 = \frac{\sqrt{3}}{8}.$$

28.

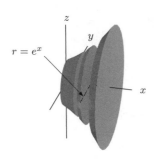

This is the volume of revolution gotten from the rotating the curve $y = e^x$. Take slices perpendicular to the x-axis. They will be circles with radius e^x, so

$$V = \int_{x=0}^{x=1} \pi y^2\,dx = \pi \int_0^1 e^{2x}\,dx$$

$$= \frac{\pi e^{2x}}{2}\bigg|_0^1 = \frac{\pi(e^2 - 1)}{2} \approx 10.036.$$

29.

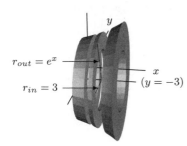

We slice the volume with planes perpendicular to the line $y = -3$. This divides the curve into thin washers, as in Example 3 on page 376 of the text, whose volumes are

$$\pi r_{out}^2 dx - \pi r_{in}^2 dx = \pi(3 + y)^2 dx - \pi 3^2 dx.$$

So the integral we get from adding all these washers up is

$$V = \int_{x=0}^{x=1} [\pi(3 + y)^2 - \pi 3^2] \, dx$$

$$= \pi \int_0^1 [(3 + e^x)^2 - 9] \, dx$$

$$= \pi \int_0^1 [e^{2x} + 6e^x] \, dx = \pi \left[\frac{e^{2x}}{2} + 6e^x\right]\Big|_0^1$$

$$= \pi[(e^2/2 + 6e) - (1/2 + 6)] \approx 42.42.$$

30.

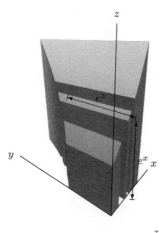

This problem can be done by slicing the volume into washers with planes perpendicular to the axis of rotation, $y = 7$, just like in Example 3. This time the outside radius of a washer is 7, and the inside radius is $7 - e^x$. Therefore, the volume V is

$$V = \int_{x=0}^{x=1} [\pi 7^2 - \pi(7 - e^x)^2] \, dx = \pi \int_0^1 (14e^x - e^{2x}) \, dx$$

$$= \pi \left[14e^x - \frac{1}{2}e^{2x}\right]\Big|_0^1 = \pi \left[14e - \frac{1}{2}e^2 - \left(14 - \frac{1}{2}\right)\right]$$

$$\approx 65.54.$$

31.

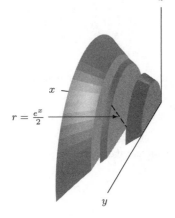

We now slice perpendicular to the x-axis. As stated in the problem, the cross-sections obtained thereby will be squares, with base length e^x. The volume of one square slice is $(e^x)^2 \, dx$. (Look at the picture.) Adding up the volumes of the slices yields

$$\text{Volume} = \int_{x=0}^{x=1} y^2 \, dx = \int_0^1 e^{2x} \, dx$$

$$= \frac{e^{2x}}{2}\Big|_0^1 = \frac{e^2 - 1}{2} \approx 3.195.$$

32.

We slice perpendicular to the x-axis. As stated in the problem, the cross-sections obtained thereby will be semicircles, with radius $\frac{e^x}{2}$. The volume of one semicircular slice is $\frac{1}{2}\pi \left(\frac{e^x}{2}\right)^2 dx$. (Look at the picture.) Adding up the volumes of the slices yields

$$\text{Volume} = \int_{x=0}^{x=1} \pi \frac{y^2}{2} \, dx = \frac{\pi}{8} \int_0^1 e^{2x} \, dx$$

$$= \frac{\pi e^{2x}}{16}\Big|_0^1 = \frac{\pi(e^2 - 1)}{16} \approx 1.25.$$

33. (a) We can begin by slicing the pie into horizontal slabs of thickness Δh located at height h. To find the radius of each slice, we note that radius increases linearly with height. Since $r = 4.5$ when $h = 3$ and $r = 3.5$ when $h = 0$, we should have $r = 3.5 + h/3$. Then the volume of each slab will be $\pi r^2 \, \Delta h = \pi(3.5 + h/3)^2 \, \Delta h$. To find the total volume of the pie, we integrate this from $h = 0$ to $h = 3$:

$$
\begin{aligned}
V &= \pi \int_0^3 \left(3.5 + \frac{h}{3} \right)^2 \, dh \\
&= \pi \left[\frac{h^3}{27} + \frac{7h^2}{6} + \frac{49h}{4} \right] \Bigg|_0^3 \\
&= \pi \left[\frac{3^3}{27} + \frac{7(3^2)}{6} + \frac{49(3)}{4} \right] \approx 152 \text{ in}^3.
\end{aligned}
$$

(b) We use 1.5 in as a rough estimate of the radius of an apple. This gives us a volume of $(4/3)\pi(1.5)^3 \approx 10 \text{ in}^3$. Since $152/10 \approx 15$, we would need about 15 apples to make a pie.

34. (a) The volume can be computed by several methods, not all of them requiring integration. We will slice horizontally, forming rectangular slabs of length 100 cm, height Δy, width w and integrate. See Figure 8.28.

Figure 8.28

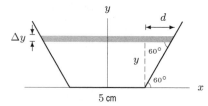

Figure 8.29

From the right triangle, we see

$$
\frac{y}{d} = \tan 60° = \sqrt{3}
$$

so

$$
d = \frac{y}{\sqrt{3}}.
$$

Thus

$$
w = 5 + 2d = 5 + \frac{2y}{\sqrt{3}}.
$$

The volume of the slab is

$$
\Delta V \approx 100 w \Delta y = 100 \left(5 + \frac{2y}{\sqrt{3}} \right) \Delta y,
$$

so the total volume is given by

$$
\begin{aligned}
\text{Volume} &= \lim_{\Delta y \to 0} \sum \Delta V = \lim_{\Delta y \to 0} \sum 100 \left(5 + \frac{2y}{\sqrt{3}} \right) \Delta y \\
&= \int_0^h 100 \left(5 + \frac{2y}{\sqrt{3}} \right) dy = 100 \left(5y + \frac{y^2}{\sqrt{3}} \right) \Bigg|_0^h = 100 \left(5h + \frac{h^2}{\sqrt{3}} \right) \text{ cm}^3.
\end{aligned}
$$

(b) The maximum value of h is $h = 5 \sin 60° = 5\sqrt{3}/2$ cm ≈ 4.33 cm.

(c) The maximum volume of water that the gutter can hold is given by substituting $h = 5\sqrt{3}/2$ into the volume:

$$
\text{Maximum volume} = 100 \left(5 \cdot \frac{5\sqrt{3}}{2} + \left(\frac{5\sqrt{3}}{2} \right)^2 \Big/ \sqrt{3} \right) = \frac{2500}{4}(2\sqrt{3} + \sqrt{3}) = 1875\sqrt{3} \approx 3247.6 \text{ cm}^3.
$$

(d) Because the gutter is narrower at the bottom than the top, if it is filled with half the maximum possible volume of water, the gutter will be filled to a depth of more than half of 4.33 cm.

(e) We want to solve for the value of h such that

$$\text{Volume} = 100\left(5h + \frac{h^2}{\sqrt{3}}\right) = \frac{1}{2} \cdot 1875\sqrt{3} = \frac{1}{2}V_{\text{max}}$$

$$5h + \frac{h^2}{\sqrt{3}} = 16.238.$$

Solving gives $h = 2.52$ and $h = -11.18$. Since only positive values of h are meaningful, $h = 2.52$ cm.

35.

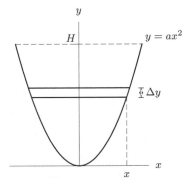

We divide the interior of the boat into flat slabs of thickness Δy and width $2x = 2\sqrt{y/a}$. (See above.) We have

$$\text{Volume of slab} \approx 2xL\Delta y = 2L\sqrt{\frac{y}{a}}\Delta y.$$

We are interested in the total volume of the region $0 \le y \le H$, so

$$\text{Total volume} = \lim_{\Delta y \to 0}\sum 2L\left(\frac{y}{a}\right)^{(1/2)}\Delta y = \int_0^H 2L\left(\frac{y}{a}\right)^{(1/2)} dy$$

$$= \frac{2L}{\sqrt{a}}\int_0^H y^{(1/2)} dy = \frac{4LH^{(3/2)}}{3\sqrt{a}}.$$

If L and H are in meters,

$$\text{Buoyancy force} = \frac{40,000LH^{(3/2)}}{3\sqrt{a}} \text{ newtons.}$$

36. We can find the volume of the tree by slicing it into a series of thin horizontal cylinders of height dh and circumference C. The volume of each cylindrical disk will then be

$$V = \pi r^2\, dh = \pi\left(\frac{C}{2\pi}\right)^2 dh = \frac{C^2\, dh}{4\pi}.$$

Summing all such cylinders, we have the total volume of the tree as

$$\text{Total volume} = \frac{1}{4\pi}\int_0^{120} C^2\, dh.$$

We can estimate this volume using a trapezoidal approximation to the integral with $\Delta h = 20$:

$$\text{LEFT estimate} = \frac{1}{4\pi}[20(31^2 + 28^2 + 21^2 + 17^2 + 12^2 + 8^2)] = \frac{1}{4\pi}(53660).$$

$$\text{RIGHT estimate} = \frac{1}{4\pi}[20(28^2 + 21^2 + 17^2 + 12^2 + 8^2 + 2^2)] = \frac{1}{4\pi}(34520).$$

$$\text{TRAP} = \frac{1}{4\pi}(44090) \approx 3509 \text{ cubic inches.}$$

37. (a) The volume, V, contained in the bowl when the surface has height h is

$$V = \int_0^h \pi x^2 \, dy.$$

However, since $y = x^4$, we have $x^2 = \sqrt{y}$ so that

$$V = \int_0^h \pi \sqrt{y} \, dy = \frac{2}{3} \pi h^{3/2}.$$

Differentiating gives $dV/dh = \pi h^{1/2} = \pi \sqrt{h}$. We are given that $dV/dt = -6\sqrt{h}$, where the negative sign reflects the fact that V is decreasing. Using the chain rule we have

$$\frac{dh}{dt} = \frac{dh}{dV} \cdot \frac{dV}{dt} = \frac{1}{dV/dh} \cdot \frac{dV}{dt} = \frac{1}{\pi \sqrt{h}} \cdot (-6\sqrt{h}) = -\frac{6}{\pi}.$$

Thus, $dh/dt = -6/\pi$, a constant.

(b) Since $dh/dt = -6/\pi$ we know that $h = -6t/\pi + C$. However, when $t = 0$, $h = 1$, therefore $h = 1 - 6t/\pi$. The bowl is empty when $h = 0$, that is when $t = \pi/6$ units.

38. The problem appears complicated, because we are now working in three dimensions. However, if we take one dimension at a time, we will see that the solution is not too difficult. For example, let's just work at a constant depth, say 0. We apply the trapezoid rule to find the approximate area along the length of the boat. For example, by the trapezoid rule the approximate area at depth 0 from the front of the boat to 10 feet toward the back is $\frac{(2+8)\cdot 10}{2} = 50$. Overall, at depth 0 we have that the area for each length span is as follows:

Table 8.1

length span:	0–10	10–20	20–30	30–40	40–50	50–60
depth 0	50	105	145	165	165	130

We can fill in the whole chart the same way:

Table 8.2

length span:		0–10	10–20	20–30	30–40	40–50	50–60
	0	50	105	145	165	165	130
	2	25	60	90	105	105	90
depth	4	15	35	50	65	65	50
	6	5	15	25	35	35	25
	8	0	5	10	10	10	10

Now, to find the volume, we just apply the trapezoid rule to the depths and areas. For example, according to the trapezoid rule the approximate volume as the depth goes from 0 to 2 and the length goes from 0 to 10 is $\frac{(50+25)\cdot 2}{2} = 75$. Again, we fill in a chart:

Table 8.3

length span:		0–10	10–20	20–30	30–40	40–50	50–60
	0–2	75	165	235	270	270	220
depth	2–4	40	95	140	170	170	140
span	4–6	20	50	75	100	100	75
	6–8	5	20	35	45	45	35

Adding all this up, we find the volume is approximately 2595 cubic feet.

You might wonder what would have happened if we had done our trapezoids along the depth axis first instead of along the length axis. If you try this, you'd find that you come up with the same answers in the volume chart! For the trapezoid rule, it does not matter which axis you choose first.

39. (a) The equation of a circle of radius r around the origin is $x^2 + y^2 = r^2$. This means that $y^2 = r^2 - x^2$, so $2y(dy/dx) = -2x$, and $dy/dx = -x/y$. Since the circle is symmetric about both axes, its arc length is 4 times the arc length in the first quadrant, namely

$$4 \int_0^r \sqrt{1 + \left(\frac{dy}{dx}\right)^2}\, dx = 4 \int_0^r \sqrt{1 + \left(-\frac{x}{y}\right)^2}\, dx.$$

(b) Evaluating this integral yields

$$4 \int_0^r \sqrt{1 + \left(-\frac{x}{y}\right)^2}\, dx = 4 \int_0^r \sqrt{1 + \frac{x^2}{r^2 - x^2}}\, dx = 4 \int_0^r \sqrt{\frac{r^2}{r^2 - x^2}}\, dx$$

$$= 4r \int_0^r \sqrt{\frac{1}{r^2 - x^2}}\, dx = 4r(\arcsin(x/r)) \Big|_0^r = 2\pi r.$$

This is the expected answer.

40. As can be seen in Figure 8.30, the region has three straight sides and one curved one. The lengths of the straight sides are 1, 1, and e. The curved side is given by the equation $y = f(x) = e^x$. We can find its length by the formula

$$\int_0^1 \sqrt{1 + f'(x)^2}\, dx = \int_0^1 \sqrt{1 + (e^x)^2}\, dx = \int_0^1 \sqrt{1 + e^{2x}}\, dx.$$

Evaluating the integral numerically gives 2.0035. The total length, therefore, is about $1 + 1 + e + 2.0035 \approx 6.722$.

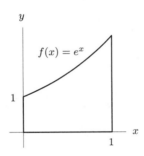

Figure 8.30

41. Since $y = (e^x + e^{-x})/2$, $y' = (e^x - e^{-x})/2$. The length of the catenary is

$$\int_{-1}^1 \sqrt{1 + (y')^2}\, dx = \int_{-1}^1 \sqrt{1 + \left[\frac{e^x - e^{-x}}{2}\right]^2}\, dx = \int_{-1}^1 \sqrt{1 + \frac{e^{2x}}{4} - \frac{1}{2} + \frac{e^{-2x}}{4}}\, dx$$

$$= \int_{-1}^1 \sqrt{\left[\frac{e^x + e^{-x}}{2}\right]^2}\, dx = \int_{-1}^1 \frac{e^x + e^{-x}}{2}\, dx$$

$$= \left[\frac{e^x - e^{-x}}{2}\right] \Big|_{-1}^1 = e - e^{-1}.$$

42. Since the ellipse is symmetric about its axes, we can just find its arc length in the first quadrant and multiply that by 4. To determine the arc length of this section, we first solve for y in terms of x: since $x^2/4 + y^2 = 1$ is the equation for the ellipse, we have $y^2 = 1 - x^2/4$, so $y = \sqrt{1 - x^2/4}$. We also need to find dy/dx; we can do this by differentiating $y^2 = 1 - x^2/4$ implicitly, obtaining $2y\,dy/dx = -x/2$, whence $dy/dx = -x/(4y)$. We now set up the integral:

$$\begin{aligned}\text{Circumference of ellipse} \atop \text{in first quadrant} \quad &= \int_0^2 \sqrt{1 + \left(-\frac{x}{4y}\right)^2}\, dx = \int_0^2 \sqrt{1 + \frac{x^2}{16y^2}}\, dx\\[2mm] &= \int_0^2 \sqrt{1 + \frac{x^2}{16 - 4x^2}}\, dx = \int_0^2 \sqrt{\frac{16 - 3x^2}{16 - 4x^2}}\, dx.\end{aligned}$$

This is an improper integral, since $16 - 4x^2 = 0$ for $x = 2$. Hence, integrating it numerically is somewhat tricky. However, we can integrate numerically from 0 to 1.999, and then use a vertical line to approximate the last section. The upper point of the line is $(1.999, 0.016)$; the lower point is $(2, 0)$. The length of the line connecting these two points is $\sqrt{(2 - 1.999)^2 + (0 - 0.016)^2} \approx 0.016$. Approximating the integral from 0 to 1.999 gives 2.391; hence the total arc length of the first quadrant is approximately $2.391 + 0.016 = 2.407$. So the arc length of the whole ellipse is about $4 \cdot 2.407 \approx 9.63$.

43. Here are many functions which "work."

- Any linear function $y = mx + b$ "works." This follows because $\frac{dy}{dx} = m$ is constant for such functions. So

$$\int_a^b \sqrt{1 + \left(\frac{dy}{dx}\right)^2} \, dx = \int_a^b \sqrt{1 + m^2} \, dx = (b - a)\sqrt{1 + m^2}.$$

- The function $y = \frac{x^4}{8} + \frac{1}{4x^2}$ "works": $\frac{dy}{dx} = \frac{1}{2}(x^3 - 1/x^3)$, and

$$\int \sqrt{1 + \left(\frac{dy}{dx}\right)^2} \, dx = \int \sqrt{1 + \frac{\left(x^3 - \frac{1}{x^3}\right)^2}{4}} \, dx = \int \sqrt{1 + \frac{x^6}{4} - \frac{1}{2} + \frac{1}{4x^6}} \, dx$$

$$= \int \sqrt{\frac{1}{4}\left(x^3 + \frac{1}{x^3}\right)^2} \, dx = \int \frac{1}{2}\left(x^3 + \frac{1}{x^3}\right) \, dx$$

$$= \left[\frac{x^4}{8} - \frac{1}{4x^2}\right] + C.$$

- One more function that "works" is $y = \ln(\cos x)$; we have $\frac{dy}{dx} = -\sin x / \cos x$. Hence

$$\int \sqrt{1 + \left(\frac{dy}{dx}\right)^2} \, dx. = \int \sqrt{1 + \left(\frac{-\sin x}{\cos x}\right)^2} \, dx = \int \sqrt{1 + \frac{\sin^2 x}{\cos^2 x}} \, dx$$

$$= \int \sqrt{\frac{\sin^2 x + \cos^2 x}{\cos^2 x}} \, dx = \int \sqrt{\frac{1}{\cos^2 x}} \, dx$$

$$= \int \frac{1}{\cos x} \, dx = \frac{1}{2} \ln \left|\frac{\sin x + 1}{\sin x - 1}\right| + C,$$

where the last integral comes from IV-22 of the integral tables.

44. (a) If $f(x) = \int_0^x \sqrt{g'(t)^2 - 1} \, dt$, then, by the Fundamental Theorem of Calculus, $f'(x) = \sqrt{g'(x)^2 - 1}$. So the arc length of f from 0 to x is

$$\int_0^x \sqrt{1 + (f'(t))^2} \, dt = \int_0^x \sqrt{1 + (\sqrt{g'(t)^2 - 1})^2} \, dt$$

$$= \int_0^x \sqrt{1 + g'(t)^2 - 1} \, dt$$

$$= \int_0^x g'(t) \, dt = g(x) - g(0) = g(x).$$

(b) If g is the arc length of any function f, then by the Fundamental Theorem of Calculus, $g'(x) = \sqrt{1 + f'(x)^2} \geq 1$. So if $g'(x) < 1$, g cannot be the arc length of a function.

(c) We find a function f whose arc length from 0 to x is $g(x) = 2x$. Using part (a), we see that

$$f(x) = \int_0^x \sqrt{(g'(t))^2 - 1} \, dt = \int_0^x \sqrt{2^2 - 1} \, dt = \sqrt{3}x.$$

This is the equation of a line. Does it make sense to you that the arc length of a line segment depends linearly on its right endpoint?

Solutions for Section 8.3

Exercises

1. With $r = 1$ and $\theta = 2\pi/3$, we find $x = r\cos\theta = 1 \cdot \cos(2\pi/3) = -1/2$ and $y = r\sin\theta = 1 \cdot \sin(2\pi/3) = \sqrt{3}/2$.
The rectangular coordinates are $(-1/2, \sqrt{3}/2)$.

2. With $r = \sqrt{3}$ and $\theta = -3\pi/4$, we find $x = r\cos\theta = \sqrt{3}\cos(-3\pi/4) = \sqrt{3}(-\sqrt{2}/2) = -\sqrt{6}/2$ and $y = r\sin\theta = \sqrt{3}\sin(-3\pi/4) = \sqrt{3}(-\sqrt{2}/2) = -\sqrt{6}/2$.
The rectangular coordinates are $(-\sqrt{6}/2, -\sqrt{6}/2)$.

3. With $r = 2\sqrt{3}$ and $\theta = -\pi/6$, we find $x = r\cos\theta = 2\sqrt{3}\cos(-\pi/6) = 2\sqrt{3} \cdot \sqrt{3}/2 = 3$ and $y = r\sin\theta = 2\sqrt{3}\sin(-\pi/6) = 2\sqrt{3}(-1/2) = -\sqrt{3}$.
The rectangular coordinates are $(3, -\sqrt{3})$.

4. With $r = 2$ and $\theta = 5\pi/6$, we find $x = r\cos\theta = 2\cos(5\pi/6) = 2(-\sqrt{3}/2) = -\sqrt{3}$ and $y = r\sin\theta = 2\sin(5\pi/6) = 2(1/2) = 1$.
The rectangular coordinates are $(-\sqrt{3}, 1)$.

5. With $x = 1$ and $y = 1$, find r from $r = \sqrt{x^2 + y^2} = \sqrt{1^2 + 1^2} = \sqrt{2}$. Find θ from $\tan\theta = y/x = 1/1 = 1$. Thus, $\theta = \tan^{-1}(1) = \pi/4$. Since $(1, 1)$ is in the first quadrant this is a correct θ. The polar coordinates are $(\sqrt{2}, \pi/4)$.

6. With $x = -1$ and $y = 0$, find $r = \sqrt{x^2 + y^2} = \sqrt{(-1)^2 + 0^2} = 1$. Find θ from $\tan\theta = y/x = 0/(-1) = 0$. Thus, $\theta = \tan^{-1}(0) = 0$. Since $(-1, 0)$ is on the x-axis between the second and third quadrant, $\theta = \pi$. The polar coordinates are $(1, \pi)$.

7. With $x = \sqrt{6}$ and $y = -\sqrt{2}$, find $r = \sqrt{(\sqrt{6})^2 + (-\sqrt{2})^2} = \sqrt{8} = 2\sqrt{2}$. Find θ from $\tan\theta = y/x = -\sqrt{2}/\sqrt{6} = -1/\sqrt{3}$. Thus, $\theta = \tan^{-1}(-1/\sqrt{3}) = -\pi/6$. Since $(\sqrt{6}, -\sqrt{2})$ is in the fourth quadrant, this is the correct θ. The polar coordinates are $(2\sqrt{2}, -\pi/6)$.

8. With $x = -\sqrt{3}$ and $y = 1$, find $r = \sqrt{(-\sqrt{3})^2 + 1^2} = \sqrt{4} = 2$. Find θ from $\tan\theta = y/x = 1/(-\sqrt{3})$. Thus, $\theta = \tan^{-1}(-1/\sqrt{3}) = -\pi/6$. Since $(-\sqrt{3}, 1)$ is in the second quadrant, $\theta = -\pi/6 + \pi = 5\pi/6$. The polar coordinates are $(2, 5\pi/6)$.

9. (a) Table 8.4 contains values of $r = 1 - \sin\theta$, both exact and rounded to one decimal.

Table 8.4

θ	0	$\pi/3$	$\pi/2$	$2\pi/3$	π	$4\pi/3$	$3\pi/2$	$5\pi/3$	2π	$7\pi/3$	$5\pi/2$	$8\pi/3$
r	1	$1-\sqrt{3}/2$	0	$1-\sqrt{3}/2$	1	$1+\sqrt{3}/2$	2	$1+\sqrt{3}/2$	1	$1-\sqrt{3}/2$	0	$1-\sqrt{3}/2$
r	1	0.134	0	0.134	1	1.866	2	1.866	1	0.134	0	0.134

(b) See Figure 8.31.

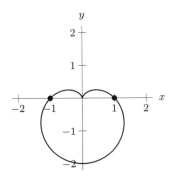

Figure 8.31

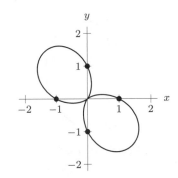

Figure 8.32

(c) The circle has equation $r = 1/2$. The cardioid is $r = 1 - \sin\theta$. Solving these two simultaneously gives

$$1/2 = 1 - \sin\theta,$$

or

$$\sin \theta = 1/2.$$

Thus, $\theta = \pi/6$ or $5\pi/6$. This gives the points $(x, y) = ((1/2) \cos \pi/6, (1/2) \sin \pi/6) = (\sqrt{3}/4, 1/4)$ and $(x, y) = ((1/2) \cos 5\pi/6, (1/2) \sin 5\pi/6) = (-\sqrt{3}/4, 1/4)$ as the location of intersection.

(d) The curve $r = 1 - \sin 2\theta$, pictured in Figure 8.32, has two regions instead of the one region that $r = 1 - \sin \theta$ has. This is because $1 - \sin 2\theta$ will be 0 twice for every 2π cycle in θ, as opposed to once for every 2π cycle in θ for $1 - \sin \theta$.

10. There will be n loops. See Figures 8.33-8.36.

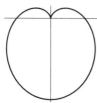
Figure 8.33: $n = 1$

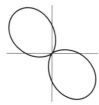
Figure 8.34: $n = 2$

Figure 8.35: $n = 3$

Figure 8.36: $n = 4$

11. The graph will begin to draw over itself for any $\theta \geq 2\pi$ so the graph will look the same in all three cases. See Figure 8.37.

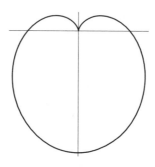
Figure 8.37

12. The curve will be a smaller loop inside a larger loop with an intersection point at the origin. Larger n values increase the size of the loops. See Figures 8.38-8.40.

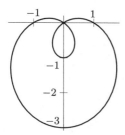
Figure 8.38: $n = 2$

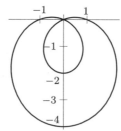
Figure 8.39: $n = 3$

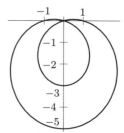
Figure 8.40: $n = 4$

13. See Figures 8.41 and 8.42. The first curve will be similar to the second curve, except the cardioid (heart) will be rotated clockwise by $90°$ ($\pi/2$ radians). This makes sense because of the identity $\sin \theta = \cos(\theta - \pi/2)$.

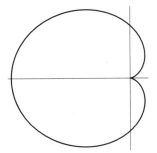

Figure 8.41: $r = 1 - \cos\theta$

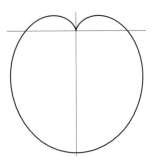

Figure 8.42: $r = 1 - \sin\theta$

14. Let $0 \le \theta \le 2\pi$ and $3/16 \le r \le 1/2$.

15. A loop starts and ends at the origin, that is, when $r = 0$. This happens first when $\theta = \pi/4$ and next when $\theta = 5\pi/4$. This can also be seen by using a trace mode on a calculator. Thus restricting θ so that $\pi/4 \le \theta \le 5\pi/4$ will graph the upper loop only. See Figure 8.43. To show only the other loop use $0 \le \theta \le \pi/4$ and $5\pi/4 \le \theta \le 2\pi$. See Figure 8.44.

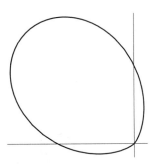

Figure 8.43: $\pi/4 \le \theta \le 5\pi/4$

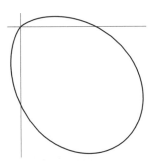

Figure 8.44: $0 \le \theta \le \pi/4$ and
$5\pi/4 \le \theta \le 2\pi$

16. (a) Let $0 \le \theta \le \pi/4$ and $0 \le r \le 1$.
   (b) Break the region into two pieces: one with $0 \le x \le \sqrt{2}/2$ and $0 \le y \le x$, the other with $\sqrt{2}/2 \le x \le 1$ and $0 \le y \le \sqrt{1 - x^2}$.

17. The region is given by $\sqrt{8} \le r \le \sqrt{18}$ and $\pi/4 \le \theta \le \pi/2$.

18. The region is given by $0 \le r \le 2$ and $-\pi/6 \le \theta \le \pi/6$.

19. The circular arc has equation $r = 1$, for $0 \le \theta \le \pi/2$. the vertical line $x = 2$ has polar equation $r\cos\theta = 2$, or $r = 2/\cos\theta$. So the region is described by $0 \le \theta \le \pi/2$ and $1 \le r \le 2/\cos\theta$.

Problems

20. The formula for area is

$$A = \frac{1}{2}\int_\alpha^\beta r^2\,d\theta$$

Therefore, since

$$A = \frac{1}{2}\int_0^{\pi/3} \sin^2(3\theta)\,d\theta = \frac{1}{2}\int_0^{\pi/3} (\sin 3\theta)^2\,d\theta,$$

we have $r = \sin 3\theta$. The integral represents the shaded area inside one petal of the three-petaled rose curve, $r = \sin 3\theta$, in Figure 8.45.

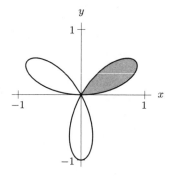

Figure 8.45: Graph of $r = \sin 3\theta$

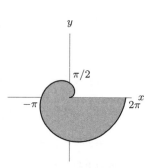

Figure 8.46: Spiral $r = \theta$

21. The spiral is shown in Figure 8.46.

$$\text{Area} = \frac{1}{2} \int_0^{2\pi} \theta^2 \, d\theta = \frac{1}{6} \theta^3 \Big|_0^{2\pi} = \frac{8\pi^3}{6}.$$

22. The region between the spirals is shaded in Figure 8.47.

$$\text{Area} = \frac{1}{2} \int_0^{2\pi} \left((2\theta)^2 - \theta^2 \right) d\theta = \frac{1}{2} \int_0^{2\pi} 3\theta^2 \, d\theta = \frac{1}{2} \theta^3 \Big|_0^{2\pi} = 4\pi^3.$$

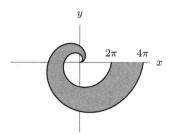

Figure 8.47: Region between the inner spiral, $r = \theta$, and the outer spiral, $r = 2\theta$

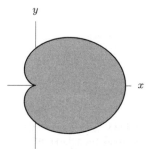

Figure 8.48: Cardioid $r = 1 + \cos\theta$

23. The cardioid is shown in Figure 8.48. The following integral can be evaluated using a calculator or by parts or using the table of integrals.

$$\text{Area} = \frac{1}{2} \int_0^{2\pi} (1 + \cos\theta)^2 \, d\theta = \frac{1}{2} \int_0^{2\pi} \left(1 + 2\cos\theta + \cos^2\theta \right) d\theta$$

$$= \frac{1}{2} \left(\theta + 2\sin\theta + \frac{1}{2}\cos\theta\sin\theta + \frac{1}{2}\theta \right) \Big|_0^{2\pi} = \frac{1}{2} (2\pi + 0 + 0 + \pi) = \frac{3\pi}{2}.$$

24. (a) See Figure 8.49. In polar coordinates, the line $x = 1$ is $r\cos\theta = 1$, so its equation is

$$r = \frac{1}{\cos\theta}.$$

The circle of radius 2 centered at the origin has equation

$$r = 2.$$

(b) The line and circle intersect where

$$\frac{1}{\cos\theta} = 2$$

$$\cos\theta = \frac{1}{2}$$

$$\theta = -\frac{\pi}{3}, \frac{\pi}{3}.$$

Thus,

$$\text{Area} = \frac{1}{2}\int_{-\pi/3}^{\pi/3}\left(2^2 - \left(\frac{1}{\cos\theta}\right)^2\right)d\theta.$$

(c) Evaluating gives

$$\text{Area} = \frac{1}{2}\int_{-\pi/3}^{\pi/3}\left(4 - \frac{1}{\cos^2\theta}\right)d\theta = \frac{1}{2}(4\theta - \tan\theta)\Big|_{-\pi/3}^{\pi/3} = \frac{4\pi}{3} - \sqrt{3}.$$

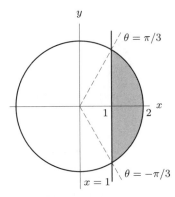

Figure 8.49

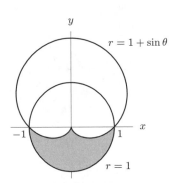

Figure 8.50

25. See Figure 8.50. Notice that the curves intersect at $(1,0)$, where $\theta = 0, 2\pi$, and at $(-1,0)$, where $\theta = \pi$, so

$$\text{Area} = \frac{1}{2}\int_{\pi}^{2\pi}(1^2 - (1+\sin\theta)^2)\,d\theta = \frac{1}{2}\int_{\pi}^{2\pi}(-2\sin\theta - \sin^2\theta)\,d\theta.$$

Using a calculator, integration by parts, or formula IV-17 in the integral table, we have

$$\text{Area} = \frac{1}{2}\left(2\cos\theta + \frac{1}{2}\sin\theta\cos\theta - \frac{1}{2}\theta\right)\Big|_{\pi}^{2\pi} = \frac{1}{2}\left(2\cdot2 + 0 - \frac{1}{2}\pi\right) = 2 - \frac{\pi}{4}.$$

26. The two curves intersect where

$$1 - \sin\theta = \frac{1}{2}$$

$$\sin\theta = \frac{1}{2}$$

$$\theta = \frac{\pi}{6}, \frac{5\pi}{6}.$$

See Figure 8.51. We find the area of the right half and multiply that answer by 2 to get the entire area. The integrals can be computed numerically with a calculator or, as we show, using integration by parts or formula IV-17 in the integral tables.

$$\text{Area of right half} = \frac{1}{2}\int_{-\pi/2}^{\pi/6}\left((1-\sin\theta)^2 - \left(\frac{1}{2}\right)^2\right)d\theta$$

$$= \frac{1}{2}\int_{-\pi/2}^{\pi/6}\left(1 - 2\sin\theta + \sin^2\theta - \frac{1}{4}\right)d\theta$$

$$= \frac{1}{2} \int_{-\pi/2}^{\pi/6} \left(\frac{3}{4} - 2 \sin \theta + \sin^2 \theta \right) d\theta$$

$$= \frac{1}{2} \left(\frac{3}{4} \theta + 2 \cos \theta - \frac{1}{2} \sin \theta \cos \theta + \frac{1}{2} \theta \right) \Big|_{-\pi/2}^{\pi/6}$$

$$= \frac{1}{2} \left(\frac{5\pi}{6} + \frac{7\sqrt{3}}{8} \right).$$

Thus,

$$\text{Total area} = \frac{5\pi}{6} + \frac{7\sqrt{3}}{8}.$$

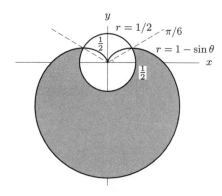

Figure 8.51

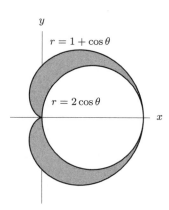

Figure 8.52

27. Figure 8.52 shows the curves which touch at $(2, 0)$ and the origin. However, the circle lies entirely inside the cardioid, so we find the area by subtracting the area of the circle from that of the cardioid. To find the areas, we take the integrals.

The cardioid, $r = 1 + \cos \theta$, starts at $(2, 0)$ when $\theta = 0$ and traces the top half, reaching the origin when $\theta = \pi$. Thus

$$\text{Area of cardioid} = 2 \cdot \frac{1}{2} \int_0^\pi (1 + \cos \theta)^2 \, d\theta.$$

The circle starts at $(2, 0)$ when $\theta = 0$ and traces the top half, reaching the origin when $\theta = \pi/2$. Thus

$$\text{Area of circle} = 2 \cdot \frac{1}{2} \int_0^{\pi/2} (2 \cos \theta)^2 \, d\theta.$$

The area, A, we want is therefore

$$\text{Area} = 2 \cdot \frac{1}{2} \int_0^\pi (1 + \cos \theta)^2 \, d\theta - 2 \cdot \frac{1}{2} \int_0^{\pi/2} (2 \cos \theta)^2 \, d\theta$$

$$= \int_0^\pi (1 + 2 \cos \theta + \cos^2 \theta) \, d\theta - \int_0^{\pi/2} 4 \cos^2 \theta \, d\theta$$

$$= \left(\theta + 2 \sin \theta + \frac{1}{2} (\sin \theta \cos \theta + \theta) \right) \Big|_0^\pi - \frac{4}{2} (\sin \theta \cos \theta + \theta) \Big|_0^{\pi/2}$$

$$= \frac{3}{2} \pi - 2 \cdot \frac{\pi}{2} = \frac{\pi}{2}.$$

Alternatively, we could compute the area of the cardioid and subtract the area of the circle of radius 1 from it.

The integrals can be computed numerically using a calculator, or, as we show, using integration by parts or formula IV-18 from the integral tables.

28. (a) The graph of $r = 2\cos\theta$ is a circle of radius 1 centered at $(1, 0)$; the graph of $r = 2\sin\theta$ is a circle of radius 1 centered at $(0, 1)$. See Figure 8.53.

(b) The Cartesian coordinates of the points of intersection are at $(0, 0)$ and $(1, 1)$.

The origin corresponds to $\theta = \pi/2$ on $r = 2\cos\theta$ and to $\theta = 0$ on $r = 2\sin\theta$. The point $(1, 1)$ has polar coordinates $r = \sqrt{2}, \theta = \pi/4$.

We find the area below the line $\theta = \pi/4$ and above $r = 2\sin\theta$ and double it:

$$\text{Area} = 2 \cdot \frac{1}{2} \int_0^{\pi/4} (2\sin\theta)^2 \, d\theta = 4 \int_0^{\pi/4} \sin^2\theta \, d\theta.$$

Using a calculator, integration by parts or formula IV-17 from the integral tables,

$$\text{Area} = 4 \left(-\frac{1}{2}\sin\theta\cos\theta + \frac{\theta}{2} \right)\Bigg|_0^{\pi/4} = -2 \cdot \frac{1}{2} + 2\frac{\pi}{4} = \frac{\pi}{2} - 1.$$

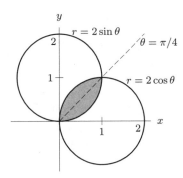

Figure 8.53

29. The area is

$$A = \frac{1}{2}\int_0^a r^2 \, d\theta = \frac{1}{2}\int_0^a \theta^2 \, d\theta = 1$$

$$\frac{1}{2}\left(\frac{\theta^3}{3}\right)\Bigg|_0^a = 1$$

$$\frac{a^3}{6} = 1$$

$$a^3 = 6$$

$$a = \sqrt[3]{6}.$$

30. (a) See Figure 8.54.

(b) The curves intersect when $r^2 = 2$

$$4\cos 2\theta = 2$$

$$\cos 2\theta = \frac{1}{2}.$$

In the first quadrant:

$$2\theta = \frac{\pi}{3} \quad \text{so} \quad \theta = \frac{\pi}{6}.$$

Using symmetry, the area in the first quadrant can be multiplied by 4 to find the area of the total bounded region.

$$\text{Area} = 4\left(\frac{1}{2}\right)\int_0^{\pi/6} (4\cos 2\theta - 2) \, d\theta$$

$$= 2\left(\frac{4\sin 2\theta}{2} - 2\theta\right)\Bigg|_0^{\pi/6}$$

$$= 4\sin\frac{\pi}{3} - \frac{2}{3}\pi$$

$$= 4\frac{\sqrt{3}}{2} - \frac{2}{3}\pi$$

$$= 2\sqrt{3} - \frac{2}{3}\pi = 1.370.$$

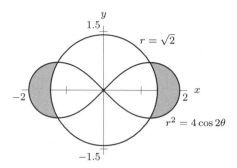

Figure 8.54

31. The slope of the tangent line at $\theta = \pi/3$ is $dy/dx = \sqrt{3}/5$. Since $x = 3\sin(2\theta)\cos\theta$ and $y = 3\sin(2\theta)\sin\theta$, when $\theta = \pi/3$, we have $x = 3\sqrt{3}/4$ and $y = 9/4$. Thus, the equation of the tangent line is

$$y - \frac{9}{4} = \frac{\sqrt{3}}{5}\left(x - \frac{3\sqrt{3}}{4}\right)$$

$$y = \frac{\sqrt{3}}{5}x - \frac{9}{20} + \frac{9}{4}$$

$$y = \frac{\sqrt{3}}{5}x + \frac{9}{5}.$$

32. We first find the points with horizontal and vertical tangents in the first quadrant and then use symmetry to obtain the points in other quadrants.

The slope of the tangent line is

$$\frac{dy}{dx} = \frac{6\cos(2\theta)\sin\theta + 3\sin(2\theta)\cos\theta}{6\cos(2\theta)\cos\theta - 3\sin(2\theta)\sin\theta}.$$

The curve has a horizontal tangent where

$$6\cos(2\theta)\sin\theta + 3\sin(2\theta)\cos\theta = 0.$$

Solving this equation numerically for $0 < \theta < \pi/2$, we have $\theta = 0.9553$; in addition $\theta = 0$ is a solution. Thus, there are horizontal tangents where $x = 1.633$ and $y = 2.309$ and where $x = 0$, $y = 0$. Thus, the five points with horizontal tangents are

$$(1.633, 2.309);\quad (-1.633, 2.309);\quad (-1.633, -2.309);\quad (1.633, -2.309);\quad (0, 0).$$

The curve has vertical tangents where

$$6\cos(2\theta)\cos\theta - 3\sin(2\theta)\sin\theta = 0.$$

Solving this equation numerically for $0 < \theta < \pi/2$, we have $\theta = 0.6155$; in addition $\theta = \pi/2$ is a solution. Thus, there are vertical tangents where $x = 2.309$, $y = 1.633$, and where $x = 0, y = 0$. Thus, there are five points with vertical tangents:

$$(2.309, 1.633);\quad (-2.309, 1.633);\quad (-2.309, -1.633);\quad (2.309, -1.633);\quad (0, 0).$$

33. We can express x and y in terms of θ as a parameter. Since $r = \theta$, we have

$$x = r\cos\theta = \theta\cos\theta \quad \text{and} \quad y = r\sin\theta = \theta\sin\theta.$$

Calculating the slope using the parametric formula,

$$\frac{dy}{dx} = \frac{dy/d\theta}{dx/d\theta},$$

we have

$$\frac{dy}{dx} = \frac{\sin\theta + \theta\cos\theta}{\cos\theta - \theta\sin\theta}.$$

Horizontal tangents occur where $dy/dx = 0$, so

$$\sin\theta + \theta\cos\theta = 0$$
$$\theta = -\tan\theta.$$

Solving this equation numerically gives

$$\theta = 0, 2.029, 4.913.$$

Vertical tangents occur where dy/dx is undefined, so

$$\cos\theta - \theta\sin\theta = 0$$
$$\theta = \frac{1}{\tan\theta} = \cot\theta.$$

Solving this equation numerically gives

$$\theta = 0.860, 3.426.$$

34. (a) Expressing x and y parametrically in terms of θ, we have

$$x = r\cos\theta = \frac{\cos\theta}{\theta} \quad \text{and} \quad y = r\sin\theta = \frac{\sin\theta}{\theta}.$$

The slope of the tangent line is given by

$$\frac{dy}{dx} = \frac{dy/d\theta}{dx/d\theta} = \left(\frac{\theta\cos\theta - \sin\theta}{\theta^2}\right) \Big/ \left(\frac{-\theta\sin\theta - \cos\theta}{\theta^2}\right) = \frac{\sin\theta - \theta\cos\theta}{\cos\theta + \theta\sin\theta}.$$

At $\theta = \pi/2$, we have

$$\frac{dy}{dx}\Big|_{\theta=\pi/2} = \frac{1 - (\pi/2)0}{0 + (\pi/2)1} = \frac{2}{\pi}.$$

At $\theta = \pi/2$, we have $x = 0$, $y = 2/\pi$, so the equation of the tangent line is

$$y = \frac{2}{\pi}x + \frac{2}{\pi}.$$

(b) As $\theta \to 0$,

$$x = \frac{\cos\theta}{\theta} \to \infty \quad \text{and} \quad y = \frac{\sin\theta}{\theta} \to 1.$$

Thus, $y = 1$ is a horizontal asymptote. See Figure 8.55.

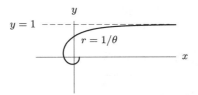

Figure 8.55

35. The limaçon is given by $r = 1 + 2\cos\theta$; see Figure 8.56. At $\theta = 0$, the graph is at $(3, 0)$; as θ increases, the graph sweeps out the top arc (on which the maximum value of y occurs), reaching the origin when

$$1 + 2\cos\theta = 0$$
$$\cos\theta = -\frac{1}{2}$$
$$\theta = \frac{2\pi}{3}.$$

Thus, we want to find the maximum value of y on the interval $0 \le \theta \le 2\pi/3$. Since $y = r\sin\theta$, we want to find the maximum value of

$$y = (1 + 2\cos\theta)\sin\theta = \sin\theta + 2\cos\theta\sin\theta.$$

At a critical point

$$\frac{dy}{d\theta} = \cos\theta - 2\sin^2\theta + 2\cos^2\theta = 0$$
$$\cos\theta - 2(1 - \cos^2\theta) + 2\cos^2\theta = 0$$
$$4\cos^2\theta + \cos\theta - 2 = 0$$
$$\cos\theta = \frac{-1 \pm \sqrt{33}}{8} = 0.593, -0.843.$$

Thus, $\theta = \cos^{-1}(0.593) = 0.936$ and $\theta = \cos^{-1}(-0.843) = 2.574$ are the critical values. Since 2.574 is outside the interval $0 \le \theta \le 2\pi/3$, there is one critical point $\theta = 0.963$.

At the endpoints of the interval, $y = 0$. At $\theta = 0.936$, we have $y = 1.760$, which is the maximum value.

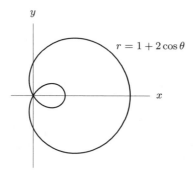

Figure 8.56: The inner loop has $r < 0$

36. Since $x = \theta\cos\theta$ and $y = \theta\sin\theta$, we have

$$\text{Arc length } = \int_0^{2\pi} \sqrt{(\cos\theta - \theta\sin\theta)^2 + (\sin\theta + \theta\cos\theta)^2}\, d\theta = \int_0^{2\pi} \sqrt{1 + \theta^2}\, d\theta = 21.256.$$

37. Since $x = \cos\theta/\theta$ and $y = \sin\theta/\theta$, we have

$$\text{Arc length } = \int_\pi^{2\pi} \sqrt{\left(\frac{-\theta\sin\theta - \cos\theta}{\theta^2}\right)^2 + \left(\frac{\theta\cos\theta - \sin\theta}{\theta^2}\right)^2}\, d\theta$$
$$= \int_\pi^{2\pi} \sqrt{\frac{\theta^2 + 1}{\theta^4}}\, d\theta = 0.712.$$

38. Parameterized by θ, the curve $r = f(\theta)$ is given by $x = f(\theta)\cos\theta$ and $y = f(\theta)\sin\theta$. Then

$$\text{Arc length } = \int_\alpha^\beta \sqrt{\left(\frac{dx}{d\theta}\right)^2 + \left(\frac{dy}{d\theta}\right)^2}\, d\theta$$
$$= \int_\alpha^\beta \sqrt{(f'(\theta)\cos\theta - f(\theta)\sin\theta)^2 + (f'(\theta)\sin\theta + f(\theta)\cos\theta)^2}\, d\theta$$

$$= \int_{\alpha}^{\beta} \sqrt{(f'(\theta))^2 \cos^2 \theta - 2f'(\theta)f(\theta)\cos\theta\sin\theta + (f(\theta))^2 \sin^2\theta}$$

$$\overline{+(f'(\theta))^2 \sin^2\theta + 2f'(\theta)f(\theta)\sin\theta\cos\theta + (f(\theta))^2 \cos^2\theta}\, d\theta$$

$$= \int_{\alpha}^{\beta} \sqrt{(f'(\theta))^2(\cos^2\theta + \sin^2\theta) + (f(\theta))^2(\sin^2\theta + \cos^2\theta)}\, d\theta$$

$$= \int_{\alpha}^{\beta} \sqrt{(f'(\theta))^2 + (f(\theta))^2}\, d\theta.$$

Solutions for Section 8.4

Exercises

1. Since density is e^{-x} gm/cm,

$$\text{Mass} = \int_0^{10} e^{-x}\, dx = -e^{-x}\Big|_0^{10} = 1 - e^{-10} \text{ gm.}$$

2. Strips perpendicular to the x-axis have length 3, area $3\Delta x$, and mass $5 \cdot 3\Delta x$ gm. Thus

$$\text{Mass} = \int_0^2 5 \cdot 3\, dx = \int_0^2 15\, dx.$$

Strips perpendicular to the y-axis have length 2, area $2\Delta y$, and mass $5 \cdot 2\Delta y$ gm. Thus

$$\text{Mass} = \int_0^3 5 \cdot 2\, dy = \int_0^3 10\, dy.$$

3. (a) Suppose we choose an x, $0 \le x \le 2$. If Δx is a small fraction of a meter, then the density of the rod is approximately $\delta(x)$ anywhere from x to $x + \Delta x$ meters from the left end of the rod (see below). The mass of the rod from x to $x + \Delta x$ meters is therefore approximately $\delta(x)\Delta x = (2 + 6x)\Delta x$. If we slice the rod into N pieces, then a Riemann sum is $\sum_{i=1}^{N}(2 + 6xi)\Delta x$.

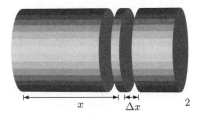

(b) The definite integral is

$$M = \int_0^2 \delta(x)\, dx = \int_0^2 (2 + 6x)\, dx = (2x + 3x^2)\Big|_0^2 = 16 \text{ grams.}$$

4. We have

$$\text{Moment} = \int_0^2 x\delta(x)\, dx = \int_0^2 x(2 + 6x)\, dx$$

$$= \int_0^2 (6x^2 + 2x)\, dx = (2x^3 + x^2)\Big|_0^2 = 20 \text{ gram-meters.}$$

Now, using this and Problem 3 (b), we have

$$\text{Center of mass} = \frac{\text{Moment}}{\text{Mass}} = \frac{20 \text{ gram-meters}}{16 \text{ grams}} = \frac{5}{4} \text{ meters (from its left end).}$$

5. (a) Figure 8.57 shows a graph of the density function.

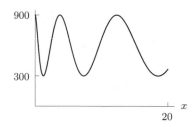

Figure 8.57

(b) Suppose we choose an x, $0 \leq x \leq 20$. We approximate the density of the number of the cars between x and $x + \Delta x$ miles as $\delta(x)$ cars per mile. Therefore, the number of cars between x and $x + \Delta x$ is approximately $\delta(x)\Delta x$. If we slice the 20 mile strip into N slices, we get that the total number of cars is

$$C \approx \sum_{i=1}^{N} \delta(x_i)\Delta x = \sum_{i=1}^{N} \left[600 + 300\sin(4\sqrt{x_i + 0.15})\right]\Delta x,$$

where $\Delta x = 20/N$. (This is a right-hand approximation; the corresponding left-hand approximation is $\sum_{i=0}^{N-1} \delta(x_i)\Delta x$.)

(c) As $N \to \infty$, the Riemann sum above approaches the integral

$$C = \int_0^{20} (600 + 300\sin 4\sqrt{x + 0.15})\, dx.$$

If we calculate the integral numerically, we find $C \approx 11513$. We can also find the integral exactly as follows:

$$C = \int_0^{20} (600 + 300\sin 4\sqrt{x + 0.15})\, dx$$

$$= \int_0^{20} 600\, dx + \int_0^{20} 300\sin 4\sqrt{x + 0.15}\, dx$$

$$= 12000 + 300\int_0^{20} \sin 4\sqrt{x + 0.15}\, dx.$$

Let $w = \sqrt{x + 0.15}$, so $x = w^2 - 0.15$ and $dx = 2w\, dw$. Then

$$\int_{x=0}^{x=20} \sin 4\sqrt{x + 0.15}\, dx = 2\int_{w=\sqrt{0.15}}^{w=\sqrt{20.15}} w\sin 4w\, dw, \text{ (using integral table III-15)}$$

$$= 2\left[-\frac{1}{4}w\cos 4w + \frac{1}{16}\sin 4w\right]\Bigg|_{\sqrt{0.15}}^{\sqrt{20.15}}$$

$$\approx -1.624.$$

Using this, we have $C \approx 12000 + 300(-1.624) \approx 11513$, which matches our numerical approximation.

6. (a) Orient the rectangle in the coordinate plane in such a way that the side referred to in the problem—call it S—lies on the y-axis from $y = 0$ to $y = 5$, as shown in Figure 8.58. We may subdivide the rectangle into strips of width Δx and length 5. If the left side of a given strip is a distance x away from S (i.e., the y-axis), its density 2 is $1/(1 + x^4)$. If Δx is small enough, the density of the strip is approximately constant—i.e., the density of the whole strip is about $1/(1 + x^4)$. The mass of the strip is just its density times its area, or $5\Delta x/(1 + x^4)$. Thus the mass of the whole rectangle is approximated by the Riemann sum

$$\sum \frac{5\Delta x}{1 + x^4},$$

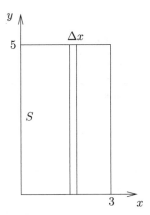

Figure 8.58

(b) The exact mass of the rectangle is obtained by letting $\Delta x \to 0$ in the Riemann sums above, giving us the integral

$$\int_0^3 \frac{5\,dx}{1+x^4}.$$

Since it is not easy to find an antiderivative of $5/(1+x^4)$, we evaluate this integral numerically, getting 5.5.

7. The total mass is 7 grams. The center of mass is given by

$$\overline{x} = \frac{2(-3)+5(4)}{7} = 2 \text{ cm to right of origin.}$$

8. The total mass is 9 gm, and so the center of mass is located at $\overline{x} = \frac{1}{9}(-10 \cdot 5 + 1 \cdot 3 + 2 \cdot 1) = -5$.

Problems

9. Since the density varies with x, the region must be sliced perpendicular to the x-axis. This has the effect of making the density approximately constant on each strip. See Figure 8.59. Since a strip is of height y, its area is approximately $y\Delta x$. The density on the strip is $\delta(x) = 1 + x$ gm/cm^2. Thus

$$\text{Mass of strip} \approx \text{Density} \cdot \text{Area} \approx (1+x)y\Delta x \text{ gm.}$$

Because the tops of the strips end on two different lines, one for $x \geq 0$ and the other for $x < 0$, the mass is calculated as the sum of two integrals. See Figure 8.59. For the left part of the region, $y = x + 1$, so

$$\text{Mass of left part} = \lim_{\Delta x \to 0} \sum (1+x)y\Delta x = \int_{-1}^0 (1+x)(x+1)\,dx$$

$$= \int_{-1}^0 (1+x)^2\,dx = \left.\frac{(x+1)^3}{3}\right|_{-1}^0 = \frac{1}{3} \text{ gm.}$$

From Figure 8.59, we see that for the right part of the region, $y = -x + 1$, so

$$\text{Mass of right part} = \lim_{\Delta x \to 0} \sum (1+x)y\Delta x = \int_0^1 (1+x)(-x+1)\,dx$$

$$= \int_0^1 (1-x^2)\,dx = \left.x - \frac{x^3}{3}\right|_0^1 = \frac{2}{3} \text{ gm.}$$

$$\text{Total mass} = \frac{1}{3} + \frac{2}{3} = 1 \text{ gm.}$$

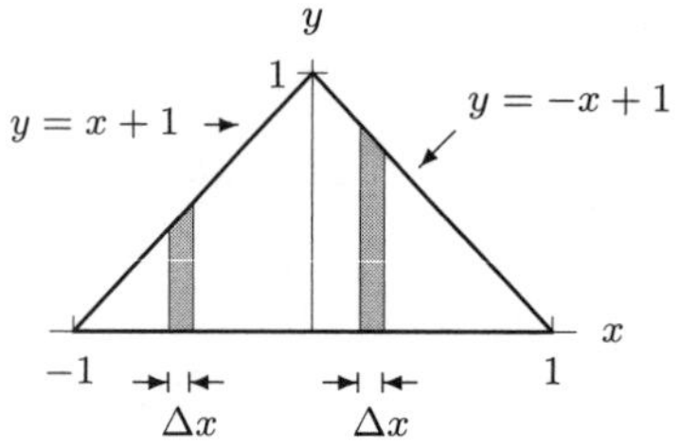

Figure 8.59

10. (a) Partition $[0, 10{,}000]$ into N subintervals of width Δr. The area in the ith subinterval is $\approx 2\pi r_i \Delta r$. So the total mass in the slick $= M \approx \sum_{i=1}^{N} 2\pi r_i \left(\frac{50}{1+r_i}\right) \Delta r$.

(b) $M = \displaystyle\int_0^{10{,}000} 100\pi \frac{r}{1+r} \, dr$. We may rewrite $\frac{r}{1+r}$ as $\frac{1+r}{1+r} - \frac{1}{1+r} = 1 - \frac{1}{1+r}$, so that

$$M = \int_0^{10{,}000} 100\pi(1 - \frac{1}{1+r}) \, dr = 100\pi \left(r - \ln|1+r| \Big|_0^{10{,}000} \right)$$

$$= 100\pi(10{,}000 - \ln(10{,}001)) \approx 3.14 \times 10^6 \text{ kg}.$$

(c) We wish to find an R such that

$$\int_0^R 100\pi \frac{r}{1+r} \, dr = \frac{1}{2} \int_0^{10{,}000} 100\pi \frac{r}{1+r} \, dr \approx 1.57 \times 10^6.$$

So $100\pi(R - \ln|R+1|) \approx 1.57 \times 10^6$; $R - \ln|R+1| \approx 5000$. By trial and error, we find $R \approx 5009$ meters.

11. (a) We form a Riemann sum by slicing the region into concentric rings of radius r and width Δr. Then the volume deposited on one ring will be the height $H(r)$ multiplied by the area of the ring. A ring of width Δr will have an area given by

$$\text{Area} = \pi(r + \Delta r)^2 - \pi(r^2)$$
$$= \pi(r^2 + 2r\Delta r + (\Delta r)^2 - r^2)$$
$$= \pi(2r\Delta r + (\Delta r)^2).$$

Since Δr is approaching zero, we can approximate

$$\text{Area of ring} \approx \pi(2r\Delta r + 0) = 2\pi r \Delta r.$$

From this, we have

$$\Delta V \approx H(r) \cdot 2\pi r \Delta r.$$

Thus, summing the contributions from all rings we have

$$V \approx \sum H(r) \cdot 2\pi r \Delta r.$$

Taking the limit as $\Delta r \to 0$, we get

$$V = \int_0^5 2\pi r \left(0.115 e^{-2r}\right) dr.$$

(b) We use integration by parts:

$$V = 0.23\pi \int_0^5 \left(r e^{-2r}\right) dr$$

$$= 0.23\pi \left(\frac{r e^{-2r}}{-2} - \frac{e^{-2r}}{4} \right) \Bigg|_0^5$$

$$\approx 0.181 (\text{millimeters}) \cdot (\text{kilometers})^2 = 0.181 \cdot 10^{-3} \cdot 10^6 \text{ meters}^3 = 181 \text{ cubic meters}.$$

12. Partition $a \leq x \leq b$ into N subintervals of width $\Delta x = \dfrac{(b-a)}{N}$; $a = x_0 < x_1 < \cdots < x_N = b$. The mass of the strip on the ith subinterval is approximately $m_i = \delta(x_i)[f(x_i) - g(x_i)]\Delta x$. If we use a right-hand Riemann sum, the approximation for the total mass is

$$\sum_{i=1}^{N} \delta(x_i)[f(x_i) - g(x_i)]\Delta x, \text{ and the exact mass is } M = \int_a^b \delta(x)[f(x) - g(x)]dx.$$

13. (a) Use the formula for the volume of a cylinder:

$$\text{Volume} = \pi r^2 l.$$

Since it is only a half cylinder

$$\text{Volume of shed} = \frac{1}{2}\pi r^2 l.$$

(b) Set up the axes as shown in Figure 8.60. The density can be defined as

$$\text{Density} = ky.$$

Now slice the sawdust horizontally into slabs of thickness Δy as shown in Figure 8.61, and calculate

$$\text{Volume of slab} \approx 2xl\Delta y = 2l(\sqrt{r^2 - y^2})\Delta y.$$

$$\text{Mass of slab} = \text{Density} \cdot \text{Volume} \approx 2kly\sqrt{r^2 - y^2}\Delta y.$$

Finally, we compute the total mass of sawdust:

$$\text{Total mass of sawdust} = \int_0^r 2kly\sqrt{r^2 - y^2}\, dy = -\frac{2}{3}kl(r^2 - y^2)^{3/2}\Big|_0^r = \frac{2klr^3}{3}.$$

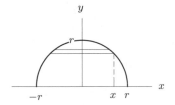

Figure 8.60

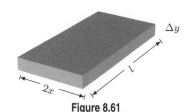

Figure 8.61

14. First we rewrite the chart, listing the density with the corresponding distance from the center of the earth (x km below the surface is equivalent to $6370 - x$ km from the center):

This gives us spherical shells whose volumes are $\frac{4}{3}\pi(r_i^3 - r_{i+1}^3)$ for any two consecutive distances from the origin. We will assume that the density of the earth is increasing with depth. Therefore, the average density of the ith shell is between D_i and D_{i+1}, the densities at top and bottom of shell i. So $\frac{4}{3}\pi D_{i+1}(r_i^3 - r_{i+1}^3)$ and $\frac{4}{3}\pi D_i(r_i^3 - r_{i+1}^3)$ are upper and lower bounds for the mass of the shell.

Table 8.5

i	x_i	$r_i = 6370 - x_i$	D_i
0	0	6370	3.3
1	1000	5370	4.5
2	2000	4370	5.1
3	2900	3470	5.6
4	3000	3370	10.1
5	4000	2370	11.4
6	5000	1370	12.6
7	6000	370	13.0
8	6370	0	13.0

To get a rough approximation of the mass of the earth, we don't need to use all the data. Let's just use the densities at $x = 0, 2900, 5000$ and 6370 km. Calculating an upper bound on the mass,

$$M_U = \frac{4}{3}\pi[13.0(1370^3 - 0^3) + 12.6(3470^3 - 1370^3) + 5.6(6370^3 - 3470^3)] \cdot 10^{15} \approx 7.29 \times 10^{27} \text{ g}.$$

The factor of 10^{15} may appear unusual. Remember the radius is given in kilometers and the density is given in g/cm^3, so we must convert kilometers to centimeters: $1 \text{ km } = 10^5 \text{ cm}$, so $1 \text{ km}^3 = 10^{15} \text{ cm}^3$.

The lower bound is

$$M_L = \frac{4}{3}\pi[12.6(1370^3 - 0^3) + 5.6(3470^3 - 1370^3) + 3.3(6370^3 - 3470^3)] \cdot 10^{15} \approx 4.05 \times 10^{27} \text{ g}.$$

Here, our upper bound is just under 2 times our lower bound.

Using all our data, we can find a more accurate estimate. The upper and lower bounds are

$$M_U = \frac{4}{3}\pi \sum_{i=0}^{7} D_{i+1}(r_i^3 - r_{i+1}^3) \cdot 10^{15} \text{ g}$$

and

$$M_L = \frac{4}{3}\pi \sum_{i=0}^{7} D_i(r_i^3 - r_{i+1}^3) \cdot 10^{15} \text{ g}.$$

We have

$$\begin{aligned}
M_U = \frac{4}{3}\pi[&4.5(6370^3 - 5370^3) + 5.1(5370^3 - 4370^3) + 5.6(4370^3 - 3470^3) \\
&+ 10.1(3470^3 - 3370^3) + 11.4(3370^3 - 2370^3) + 12.6(2370^3 - 1370^3) \\
&+ 13.0(1370^3 - 370^3) + 13.0(370^3 - 0^3)] \cdot 10^{15} \text{ g} \\
\approx\; & 6.50 \times 10^{27} \text{ g}
\end{aligned}$$

and

$$\begin{aligned}
M_L = \frac{4}{3}\pi[&3.3(6370^3 - 5370^3) + 4.5(5370^3 - 4370^3) + 5.1(4370^3 - 3470^3) \\
&+ 5.6(3470^3 - 3370^3) + 10.1(3370^3 - 2370^3) + 11.4(2370^3 - 1370^3) \\
&+ 12.6(1370^3 - 370^3) + 13.0(370^3 - 0^3)] \cdot 10^{15} \text{ g} \\
\approx\; & 5.46 \times 10^{27} \text{ g}.
\end{aligned}$$

15. We slice time into small intervals. Since t is given in seconds, we convert the minute to 60 seconds. We consider water loss over the time interval $0 \leq t \leq 60$. We also need to convert inches into feet since the velocity is given in ft/sec. Since 1 inch $= 1/12$ foot, the square hole has area $1/144$ square feet. For water flowing through a hole with constant velocity v, the amount of water which has passed through in some time, Δt, can be pictured as the rectangular solid in Figure 8.62, which has volume

$$\text{Area} \cdot \text{Height} = \text{Area} \cdot \text{Velocity} \cdot \text{Time}.$$

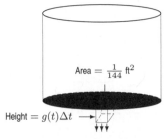

Figure 8.62: Volume of water passing
through hole

Over a small time interval of length Δt, starting at time t, water flows with a nearly constant velocity $v = g(t)$ through a hole $1/144$ square feet in area. In Δt seconds, we know that

$$\text{Water lost} \approx \left(\frac{1}{144}\ \text{ft}^2\right)(g(t)\ \text{ft/sec})(\Delta t\ \text{sec}) = \left(\frac{1}{144}\right)g(t)\,\Delta t\ \text{ft}^3.$$

Adding the water from all subintervals gives

$$\text{Total water lost} \approx \sum \frac{1}{144}g(t)\,\Delta t\ \text{ft}^3.$$

As $\Delta t \to 0$, the sum tends to the definite integral:

$$\text{Total water lost} = \int_0^{60} \frac{1}{144}g(t)\,dt\ \text{ft}^3.$$

16. (a) Divide the atmosphere into spherical shells of thickness Δh. See Figure 8.63. The density on a typical shell, $\rho(h)$, is approximately constant. The volume of the shell is approximately the surface area of a sphere of radius $r_e + h$ meters times Δh, where $r_e = 6.4 \cdot 10^6$ meters is the radius of the earth,

$$\text{Volume of Shell} \approx 4\pi(r_e + h_i)^2\Delta h.$$

A Riemann sum for the total mass is

$$\text{Mass} \approx \sum 4\pi(r_e + h)^2 \times 1.28e^{-0.000124h_i}\,\Delta h\ \text{kg}.$$

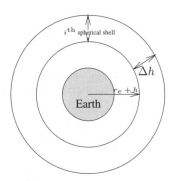

Figure 8.63

(b) This Riemann sum becomes the integral

$$\text{Mass} = 4\pi \int_0^{100} (r_e + h)^2 \cdot 1.28e^{-0.000124h}\,dh$$

$$= 4\pi \int_0^{100} (6.4 \cdot 10^6 + h)^2 \cdot 1.28e^{-0.000124h}\,dh.$$

Evaluating the integral using numerical methods gives $M = 6.5 \cdot 10^{16}$ kg.

17. We need the numerator of $\bar{x}$, to be zero, i.e. $\sum x_i m_i = 0$. Since all of the masses are the same, we can factor them out and write $4\sum x_i = 0$. Thus the fourth mass needs to be placed so that all of the positions sum to zero. The first three positions sum to $(-6 + 1 + 3) = -2$, so the fourth mass needs to be placed at $x = 2$.

18. We have

$$\text{Total mass of the rod} = \int_0^3 (1 + x^2)\,dx = \left[x + \frac{x^3}{3}\right]\Bigg|_0^3 = 12 \text{ grams}.$$

In addition,

$$\text{Moment} = \int_0^3 x(1 + x^2)\,dx = \left[\frac{x^2}{2} + \frac{x^4}{4}\right]\Bigg|_0^3 = \frac{99}{4} \text{ gram-meters}.$$

Thus, the center of mass is at the position $\bar{x} = \frac{99/4}{12} = 2.06$ meters.

19. The center of mass is

$$\bar{x} = \frac{\int_0^\pi x(2 + \sin x)\, dx}{\int_0^\pi (2 + \sin x)\, dx}.$$

The numerator is $\int_0^\pi (2x + x\sin x)\, dx = (x^2 - x\cos x + \sin x)\Big|_0^\pi = \pi^2 + \pi$.

The denominator is $\int_0^\pi (2 + \sin x)\, dx = (2x - \cos x)\Big|_0^\pi = 2\pi + 2$. So the center of mass is at

$$\bar{x} = \frac{\pi^2 + \pi}{2\pi + 2} = \frac{\pi(\pi + 1)}{2(\pi + 1)} = \frac{\pi}{2}.$$

20. (a) We find that

$$\text{Moment} = \int_0^1 x(1 + kx^2)\, dx = \left(\frac{x^2}{2} + \frac{kx^4}{4}\right)\Big|_0^1 = \frac{1}{2} + \frac{k}{4} \text{ gram-meters,}$$

and that

$$\text{Total mass} = \int_0^1 (1 + kx^2)\, dx = \left(x + \frac{kx^3}{3}\right)\Big|_0^1 = 1 + \frac{k}{3} \text{ grams.}$$

Thus, the center of mass is

$$\bar{x} = \frac{\frac{1}{2} + \frac{k}{4}}{1 + \frac{k}{3}} = \frac{3}{4}\left(\frac{2 + k}{3 + k}\right) \text{ meters.}$$

(b) Let $f(k) = \frac{3}{4}\left(\frac{2+k}{3+k}\right)$. Then $f'(k) = \frac{3}{4}\left(\frac{1}{(3+k)^2}\right)$, which is always positive, so f is an increasing function of k. Since $f(0) = 0.5$, this is the smallest value of f. As $k \to \infty$, $f(k) \to 3/4 = 0.75$. So $f(k)$ is always between 0.5 and 0.75.

21. (a) The density is minimum at $x = -1$ and increases as x increases, so more of the mass of the rod is in the right half of the rod. We thus expect the balancing point to be to the right of the origin.

(b) We need to compute

$$\int_{-1}^1 x(3 - e^{-x})\, dx = \left(\frac{3}{2}x^2 + xe^{-x} + e^{-x}\right)\Big|_{-1}^1 \quad \text{(using integration by parts)}$$

$$= \frac{3}{2} + e^{-1} + e^{-1} - \left(\frac{3}{2} - e^1 + e^1\right) = \frac{2}{e}.$$

We must divide this result by the total mass, which is given by

$$\int_{-1}^1 (3 - e^{-x})\, dx = (3x + e^{-x})\Big|_{-1}^1 = 6 - e + \frac{1}{e}.$$

We therefore have

$$\bar{x} = \frac{2/e}{6 - e + (1/e)} = \frac{2}{1 + 6e - e^2} \approx 0.2.$$

22. Since the region is symmetric about the x-axis, $\bar{y} = 0$.

To find $\bar{x}$, we first find the density. The area of the disk is $\pi/2$ m^2, so it has density $3/(\pi/2) = 6/\pi$ kg/m^2. We find the mass of the small strip of width Δx in Figure 8.64. The height of the strip is $\sqrt{1 - x^2}$, so

$$\text{Area of the small strip} \approx A_x(x)\Delta x = 2 \cdot \sqrt{1 - x^2}\,\Delta x \text{ m}^2.$$

When multiplied by the density $6/\pi$, we get

$$\text{Mass of the strip} \approx \frac{12}{\pi} \cdot \sqrt{1 - x^2}\,\Delta x \text{ kg.}$$

We then sum the product of these masses with x, and take the limit as $\Delta x \to 0$ to get

$$\text{Moment} = \int_0^1 \frac{12}{\pi}x\sqrt{1 - x^2}\, dx = -\frac{4}{\pi}(1 - x^2)^{3/2}\Big|_0^1 = \frac{4}{\pi} \text{ meter.}$$

Finally, we divide by the total mass 3 kg to get the result $\bar{x} = 4/(3\pi)$ meters.

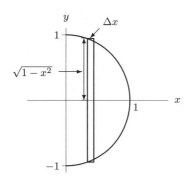

Figure 8.64: Area of a small strip

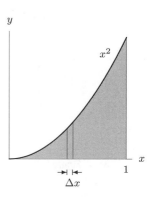

Figure 8.65

23. (a) Since the density is constant, the mass is the product of the area of the plate and its density.

$$\text{Area of the plate } = \int_0^1 x^2 \, dx = \frac{1}{3}x^3 \Big|_0^1 = \frac{1}{3} \text{ cm}^2.$$

Thus the mass of the plate is $2 \cdot 1/3 = 2/3$ gm.

(b) See Figure 8.65. Since the region is "fatter" closer to $x = 1$, $\bar{x}$ is greater than $1/2$.

(c) To find the center of mass along the x-axis, we slice the region into vertical strips of width Δx. See Figure 8.65. Then

$$\text{Area of strip } = A_x(x)\Delta x \approx x^2 \Delta x$$

Then, since the density is 2 gm/cm^2, we have

$$\bar{x} = \frac{\int_0^1 2x^3 \, dx}{2/3} = \frac{3}{2} \cdot \frac{2x^4}{4} \Big|_0^1 = 3\left(\frac{1}{4}\right) = \frac{3}{4}\text{cm}.$$

This is greater than $1/2$, as predicted in part (b).

24. (a) Since the density is constant, the mass is the product of the area of the plate and its density.

$$\text{Area of the plate } = \int_0^1 \sqrt{x} \, dx = \frac{2}{3}x^{3/2} \Big|_0^1 = \frac{2}{3} \text{ cm}^2.$$

Thus the mass of the plate is $5 \cdot 2/3 = 10/3$ gm.

(b) To find $\bar{x}$, we slice the region into vertical strips of width Δx. See Figure 8.66. Then

$$\text{Area of strip } = A_x(x)\Delta x \approx \sqrt{x}\Delta x \text{ cm}^2.$$

Then, since the density is 5 gm/cm^2, we have

$$\bar{x} = \frac{\int x\delta A_x(x) \, dx}{\text{Mass}} = \frac{\int_0^1 5x^{3/2} \, dx}{10/3} = \frac{3}{10} \cdot 2x^{5/2} \Big|_0^1 = \frac{3}{5} \text{ cm}.$$

To find $\bar{y}$, we slice the region into horizontal strips of width Δy

$$\text{Area of horizontal strip } = A_y(y)\Delta y \approx (1 - x)\Delta y = (1 - y^2)\Delta y \text{ cm}^2.$$

Then, since the density is 5 gm/cm^2, we have

$$\bar{y} = \frac{\int y\delta A_y(y) \, dy}{\text{Mass}} = \frac{\int_0^1 5(y - y^3) \, dy}{10/3} = \frac{3}{10} \cdot 5\left(\frac{y^2}{2} - \frac{y^4}{4}\right)\Big|_0^1 = \frac{3}{10} \cdot \frac{5}{4} = \frac{3}{8} \text{ cm}.$$

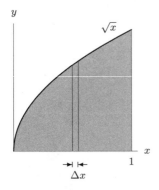

Figure 8.66

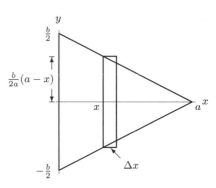

Figure 8.67

25. The triangle is symmetric about the x axis, so $\bar{y} = 0$.

To find $\bar{x}$, we first calculate the density. The area of the triangle is $ab/2$, so it has density $2m/(ab)$ where m is the total mass of the triangle. We need to find the mass of a small strip of width Δx located at x_i (see Figure 8.67).

$$\text{Area of the small strip} \approx A_x(x)\Delta x = 2 \cdot \frac{b(a - x)}{2a}\Delta x.$$

Multiplying by the density $2m/(ab)$ gives

$$\text{Mass of the strip} \approx 2m\frac{(a - x)}{a^2}\Delta x.$$

We then sum the product of these masses with x_i, and take the limit as $\Delta x \to 0$ to get

$$\text{Moment} = \int_0^a \frac{2mx(a - x)}{a^2}\,dx = \frac{2m}{a^2}\left(\frac{ax^2}{2} - \frac{x^3}{3}\right)\Big|_0^a = \frac{2m}{a^2}\left(\frac{a^3}{2} - \frac{a^3}{3}\right) = \frac{ma}{3}.$$

Finally, we divide by the total mass m to get the desired result $\bar{x} = a/3$, which is independent of the length of the base b.

26. Stand the cone with the base horizontal, with center at the origin. Symmetry gives us that $\bar{x} = \bar{y} = 0$. Since the cone is fatter near its base we expect the center of mass to be nearer to the base.

Slice the cone into disks parallel to the xy-plane.

As we saw in Example 2 on page 369, a disk of thickness Δz at height z above the base has

$$\text{Volume of disk} = A_z(z)\Delta z \approx \pi(5 - z)^2\Delta z \text{ cm}^3.$$

Thus, since the density is δ,

$$\bar{z} = \frac{\int z\delta A_z(z)\,dz}{\text{Mass}} = \frac{\int_0^5 z \cdot \delta\pi(5 - z)^2\,dz}{\text{Mass}} \text{ cm}.$$

To evaluate the integral in the numerator, we factor out the constant density δ and π to get

$$\int_0^5 z \cdot \delta\pi(5 - z)^2\,dz = \delta\pi\int_0^5 z(25 - 10z + z^2)\,dz = \delta\pi\left(\frac{25z^2}{2} - \frac{10z^3}{3} + \frac{z^4}{4}\right)\Big|_0^5 = \frac{625}{12}\delta\pi.$$

We divide this result by the total mass of the cone, which is $\left(\frac{1}{3}\pi 5^2 \cdot 5\right)\delta$:

$$\bar{z} = \frac{\frac{625}{12}\delta\pi}{\frac{1}{3}\pi 5^3\delta} = \frac{5}{4} = 1.25 \text{ cm}.$$

As predicted, the center of mass is closer to the base of the cone than its top.

27. Since the density is constant, the total mass of the solid is the product of the volume of the solid and its density: $\delta\pi(1 - e^{-2})/2$. By symmetry, $\bar{y} = 0$. To find $\bar{x}$, we slice the solid into disks of width Δx, perpendicular to the x-axis. See Figure 8.68. A disk at x has radius $y = e^{-x}$, so

$$\text{Volume of disk} = A_x(x)\Delta x = \pi y^2\Delta x = \pi e^{-2x}\Delta x.$$

Since the density is δ, we have

$$\overline{x} = \frac{\int_0^1 x \cdot \delta\pi e^{-2x}\,dx}{\text{Total mass}} = \frac{\delta\pi \int_0^1 xe^{-2x}\,dx}{\delta\pi(1 - e^{-2})/2} = \frac{2}{1 - e^{-2}} \int_0^1 xe^{-2x}\,dx.$$

The integral $\int xe^{-2x}\,dx$ can be done by parts: let $u = x$ and $v' = e^{-2x}$. Then $u' = 1$ and $v = e^{-2x}/(-2)$. So

$$\int xe^{-2x}\,dx = \frac{xe^{-2x}}{-2} - \int \frac{e^{-2x}}{-2}\,dx = \frac{xe^{-2x}}{-2} - \frac{e^{-2x}}{4}.$$

and then

$$\int_0^1 xe^{-2x}\,dx = \left(\frac{xe^{-2x}}{-2} - \frac{e^{-2x}}{4} \right) \Bigg|_0^1 = \left(\frac{e^{-2}}{-2} - \frac{e^{-2}}{4} \right) - \left(0 - \frac{1}{4} \right) = \frac{1 - 3e^{-2}}{4}.$$

The final result is:

$$\overline{x} = \frac{2}{1 - e^{-2}} \cdot \frac{1 - 3e^{-2}}{4} = \frac{1 - 3e^{-2}}{2 - 2e^{-2}} \approx 0.343.$$

Notice that $\overline{x}$ is less that $1/2$, as we would expect from the fact that the solid is wider near the origin.

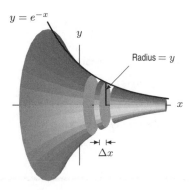

Figure 8.68

28. (a) Position the pyramid so that the center of its base lies at the origin on the xy-plane. Slice the pyramid into square slabs parallel to its base. We compute the mass of the pyramid by adding the masses of the slabs.

   The mass of a slab is its volume multiplied by the density δ. To compute the volume of a slab, we need to get an expression for the side s of the slab in terms of its height z. Using the similar triangles in Figure 8.69, we see that

$$\frac{s}{40} = \frac{(10 - z)}{10}.$$

Thus $s = 4(10 - z)$. Since the area of the square slab's face is s^2,

$$\text{Volume of the slab} \approx A_z(z)\Delta z = s^2 \Delta z = 16(10 - z)^2 \Delta z.$$

$$\text{Mass of slab} = 16\delta(10 - z)^2 \Delta z.$$

The mass of the pyramid can be found by summing all of the masses of the slabs, and letting the thickness Δz approach zero:

$$\text{Total mass} = \lim_{\Delta z \to 0} \sum 16\delta(10 - z)^2 \Delta z = \int_0^{10} 16\delta(10 - z)^2\,dz = \frac{-16\delta(10 - z)^3}{3} \Bigg|_0^{10} = \frac{16000\delta}{3}\,\text{gm}.$$

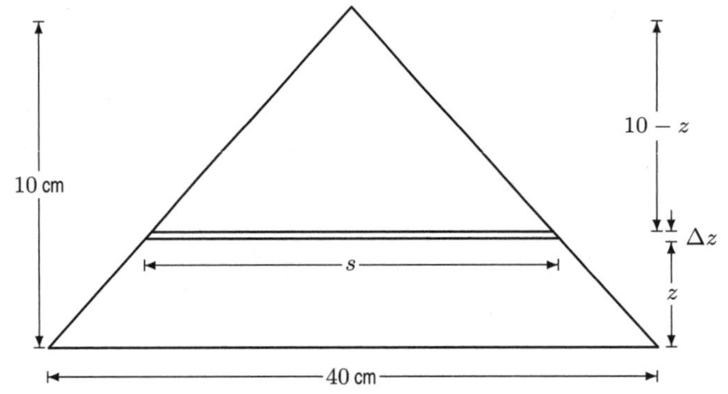

Figure 8.69

(b) From symmetry, we have $\bar{x} = \bar{y} = 0$. Since the pyramid is fatter near its base we expect the center of mass to be nearer to the base. Since

$$\text{Volume of slab} = A_z(z)\Delta z = 16(10 - z)^2\Delta z,$$

$$\bar{z} = \frac{\int_0^{10} z \cdot 16\delta(10 - z)^2\, dz}{\text{Total mass}}.$$

To evaluate the integral in the numerator, we factor out the constant 16δ and expand the integrand to get

$$16\delta \int_0^{10} (100z - 20z^2 + z^3)\, dz = 16\delta \left(50z^2 + \frac{-20z^3}{3} + \frac{z^4}{4} \right)\Bigg|_0^{10} = \frac{40000\delta}{3}.$$

We divide this result by the total mass $16000\delta/3$ of the pyramid

$$\bar{z} = \frac{40000\delta/3}{16000\delta/3} = \frac{40000}{16000} = 2.5\,\text{cm}.$$

As predicted, the center of mass is closer to the base of the pyramid than its top.

Solutions for Section 8.5

Exercises

1. The work done is given by

$$W = \int_1^2 3x\, dx = \frac{3}{2}x^2 \Bigg|_1^2 = \frac{9}{2} \text{ joules.}$$

2. The work done is given by

$$W = \int_0^3 3x\, dx = \frac{3}{2}x^2 \Bigg|_0^3 = \frac{27}{2} \text{ joules.}$$

3. (a) For compression from $x = 0$ to $x = 1$,

$$\text{Work } = \int_0^1 3x\, dx = \frac{3}{2}x^2 \Bigg|_0^1 = \frac{3}{2} = 1.5 \text{ joules.}$$

For compression from $x = 4$ to $x = 5$,

$$\text{Work } = \int_4^5 3x\, dx = \frac{3}{2}x^2 \Bigg|_4^5 = \frac{3}{2}(25 - 16) = \frac{27}{2} = 13.5 \text{ joules.}$$

(b) The second answer is larger. Since the force increases with x, for a given displacement, the work done is larger for larger x values. Thus, we expect more work to be done in moving from $x = 4$ to $x = 5$ than from $x = 0$ to $x = 1$.

4. Since the gravitational force is

$$F = \frac{4 \cdot 10^{14}}{r^2} \text{ newtons}$$

and r varies between $6.4 \cdot 10^6$ and $7.4 \cdot 10^6$ meters,

$$\text{Work done } = \int_{6.4 \cdot 10^6}^{7.4 \cdot 10^6} \frac{4 \cdot 10^{14}}{r^2} \, dr = -4.10^{14} \frac{1}{r} \Big|_{6.4 \cdot 10^6}^{7.4 \cdot 10^6}$$

$$= 4 \cdot 10^{14} \left(\frac{1}{6.4 \cdot 10^6} - \frac{1}{7.4 \cdot 10^6} \right) = 8.4 \cdot 10^6 \text{ joules.}$$

5. The force exerted on the satellite by the earth (and vice versa!) is GMm/r^2, where r is the distance from the center of the earth to the center of the satellite, m is the mass of the satellite, M is the mass of the earth, and G is the gravitational constant. So the total work done is

$$\int_{6.4 \cdot 10^6}^{8.4 \cdot 10^6} F \, dr = \int_{6.4 \cdot 10^6}^{8.4 \cdot 10^6} \frac{GMm}{r^2} \, dr = \left(\frac{-GMm}{r} \right) \Big|_{6.4 \cdot 10^6}^{8.4 \cdot 10^6} \approx 1.489 \cdot 10^{10} \text{ joules.}$$

Problems

6. Let x be the distance from ground to the bucket of cement. At height x, if the bucket is lifted by Δx, the work done is $500\Delta x + 0.5(75 - x)\Delta x$. See Figure 8.70. The $500\Delta x$ term is due to the bucket of cement; the $0.5(75 - x)\Delta x$ term is due to the remaining cable. So the total work, W, required to lift the bucket is

$$W = \int_0^{30} 500dx + \int_0^{30} 0.5(75 - x)dx$$

$$= 500 \cdot 30 + 0.5(75 \cdot 30 - \frac{1}{2}30^2)$$

$$= 15,900 \text{ ft-lb.}$$

Figure 8.70

7. When the anchor has been lifted through h feet, the length of chain in the water is $25 - h$ feet, so the total weight of the anchor and chain in the water is $50 + 3(25 - h)$ lb. Then

$$\text{Work to lift the anchor and chain } \Delta h \text{ higher} = \text{Weight} \cdot \text{Distance lifted}$$
$$= (100 + 3(25 - h))\Delta h.$$

To find the total work, we integrate from $h = 0$ to $h = 25$:

$$W = \int_0^{25} (100 + 3(25 - h))dh = \int_0^{25} (175 - 3h)dh = \left(175h - \frac{3h^2}{2} \right) \Big|_0^{25} = 3437.5 \text{ft-lbs.}$$

8. To lift the weight an additional height Δh off the ground from a height of h, we must do work on the weight and the amount of rope not yet pulled onto the roof. Since the roof is 30 ft off the ground, there will be $30 - h$ feet remaining of rope, for a weight of $4(30 - h)$. So the work required to raise the weight and the rope a height Δh will be $\Delta h(1000 + 4(30 - h))$. To find the total work, we integrate this quantity from $h = 0$ to $h = 10$:

$$\text{Work} = \int_0^{10} (1000 + 4(30 - h)) \, dh$$

$$= \int_0^{10} (1120 - 4h) \, dh$$

$$= (1120h - 2h^2)\Big|_0^{10}$$

$$= 11,200 - 200$$

$$= 11,000 \text{ ft-lbs.}$$

9. The bucket moves upward at $40/10 = 4$ meters/minute. If time is in minutes, at time t the bucket is at a height of $x = 4t$ meters above the ground. See Figure 8.71.

The water drips out at a rate of $5/10 = 0.5$ kg/minute. Initially there is 20 kg of water in the bucket, so at time t minutes, the mass of water remaining is

$$m = 20 - 0.5t \text{ kg.}$$

Consider the time interval between t and $t + \Delta t$. During this time the bucket moves a distance $\Delta x = 4\Delta t$ meters. So, during this interval,

$$\text{Work done} \approx mg\Delta x = (20 - 0.5t)g4\Delta t \text{ joules.}$$

$$\text{Total work done} = \lim_{\Delta t \to 0} \sum (20 - 0.5t)g4\Delta t = 4g \int_0^{10} (20 - 0.5t)\, dt$$

$$= 4g(20t - 0.25t^2)\Big|_0^{10} = 700g = 700(9.8) = 6860 \text{ joules.}$$

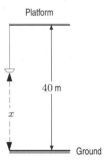

Platform

40 m

x

Ground

Figure 8.71

10. Consider lifting a rectangular slab of water h feet from the top up to the top. See Figure 8.72. The area of such a slab is $(10)(20) = 200$ square feet; if the thickness is dh, then the volume of such a slab is $200\, dh$ cubic feet. This much water weighs 62.4 pounds per ft^3, so the weight of such a slab is $(200\, dh)(62.4) = 12480\, dh$ pounds. To lift that much water h feet requires $12480h\, dh$ foot-pounds of work. To lift the whole tank, we lift one plate at a time; integrating over the slabs yields

$$\int_0^{15} 12480h\, dh = \frac{12480h^2}{2}\Big|_0^{15} = \frac{12480 \cdot 15^2}{2} = 1,404,000 \text{ foot-pounds.}$$

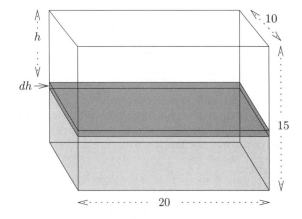

h

$dh \rightarrow$

10

15

20

Figure 8.72

11. We slice the water horizontally and find the work required to pump each horizontal slice of water over the top. See Figure 8.73. At a distance h ft above the bottom, a slice of thickness Δh has

$$\text{Volume} \approx 50 \cdot 20 \Delta h \text{ ft}^3.$$

Since the density of water is ρ lb/ft^3,

$$\text{Weight of the slice} \approx \rho(50 \cdot 20 \cdot \Delta h) \text{ lbs.}$$

The distance to lift the slice of water at height h ft is $10 - h$ ft, so

$$\begin{aligned}
\text{Work to move one slice} &= \rho \cdot \text{Volume} \cdot \text{Distance lifted} \\
&\approx \rho(50 \cdot 20 \cdot \Delta h)(10 - h) \\
&= 100\rho(10 - h)\Delta h \text{ ft-lb.}
\end{aligned}$$

The work done, W, to pump all the water is the sum of the work done on the pieces:

$$W \approx \sum 100\rho(10 - h)\Delta h.$$

As $\Delta h \to 0$, we obtain a definite integral. Since h varies from $h = 0$ to $h = 9$ and $\rho = 62.4$ lb/ft^3, the total work is:

$$W = \int_0^9 100\rho(10 - h)dh = 62400 \left(10h - \frac{h^2}{2} \right) \Big|_0^9 = 62400(49.5) = 3,088,800.$$

The work to pump all the water out is 3,088,800 ft-lbs.

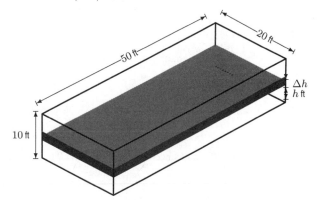

Figure 8.73

12. Let x be the distance measured from the bottom the tank. See Figure 8.74. To pump a layer of water of thickness Δx at x feet from the bottom, the work needed is

$$(62.4)\pi 6^2(20 - x)\Delta x.$$

Therefore, the total work is

$$\begin{aligned}
W &= \int_0^{10} 36 \cdot (62.4)\pi(20 - x)dx \\
&= 36 \cdot (62.4)\pi \left(20x - \frac{1}{2}x^2 \right) \Big|_0^{10} \\
&= 36 \cdot (62.4)\pi(200 - 50) \\
&\approx 1,058,591.1 \text{ ft-lb.}
\end{aligned}$$

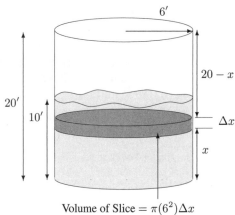

Volume of Slice $= \pi(6^2)\Delta x$

Figure 8.74

13. Let x be the distance from the bottom of the tank. See Figure 8.75. To pump a layer of water of thickness Δx at x feet from the bottom to 10 feet above the tank, the work done is $(62.4)\pi 6^2(30-x)\Delta x$. Thus the total work is

$$\int_0^{20} 36 \cdot (62.4)\pi(30-x)dx$$

$$= 36 \cdot (62.4)\pi\left(30x - \frac{1}{2}x^2\right)\bigg|_0^{20}$$

$$= 36 \cdot (62.4)\pi\left(30(20) - \frac{1}{2}20^2\right)$$

$$\approx 2{,}822{,}909.50 \text{ ft-lb.}$$

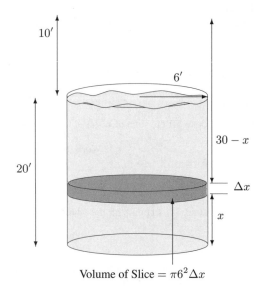

Volume of Slice $= \pi 6^2 \Delta x$

Figure 8.75

14. (a) We slice the water horizontally. Each slice is a cylindrical slab of radius 4 and thickness Δh, so

$$\text{Volume of each slab} \approx \pi 4^2 \Delta h \text{ ft}^3.$$

See Figure 8.76. The density of water is δ lb/ft^3, so

$$\text{Weight of slab} \approx \delta\pi 4^2 \Delta h \text{ lb.}$$

Water at a height of h ft must be lifted a distance of $10 - h$ ft.

$$\text{Work to move one slice} = \delta \cdot \text{Volume} \cdot \text{Distance lifted}$$

$$\approx \delta(\pi(4)^2\Delta h)(10-h) \text{ ft-lb.}$$

Since the density of water is $\delta = 62.4$ lb/ft^3 and since h varies from $h = 0$ to $h = 10$, the total work, W, is:

$$W = \int_0^{10} \delta(\pi 4^2)(10-h)dh = 16\delta\pi\int_0^{10}(10-h)dh = 998.4\pi\left(10h - \frac{h^2}{2}\right)\bigg|_0^{10} = 156{,}828 \text{ ft-lb.}$$

The total work required is 156,828 ft-lbs.

(b) This is the same as part (a) except the water must be lifted a distance of $15 - h$ ft. The total work is:

$$W = \int_0^{10} \delta(\pi 4^2)(15-h)dh = 16\delta\pi\int_0^{10}(15-h)dh = 998.4\pi\left(15h - \frac{h^2}{2}\right)\bigg|_0^{10} = 313{,}656 \text{ ft-lb.}$$

The total work required is 313,656 ft-lbs.

(c) This is the same as part (a) except that h varies from $h = 0$ to $h = 8$. The total work is:

$$W = \int_0^{8} \delta(\pi 4^2)(10-h)dh = 16\delta\pi\int_0^{8}(10-h)dh = 998.4\pi\left(10h - \frac{h^2}{2}\right)\bigg|_0^{8} = 150{,}555.$$

The total work required is 150,555 ft-lbs.

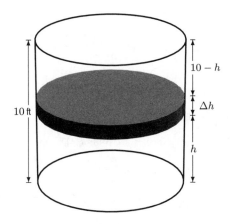

Figure 8.76

15. We begin by slicing the oil into slabs at a distance h below the surface with thickness Δh. We can then calculate the volume of the slab and the work needed to raise this slab to the surface, a distance of h.

$$\text{Volume of } \Delta h \text{ disk} = \pi r^2 \Delta h = 25\pi \Delta h$$
$$\text{Weight of } \Delta h \text{ disk} = (25\pi)(50)\Delta h$$
$$\text{Distance to raise} = h$$
$$\text{Work to raise} = (25\pi)(50)(h)\Delta h.$$

Integrating the work over all such slabs, we have

$$\begin{aligned}
\text{Work} &= \int_{19}^{25} (50)(25\pi)(h)\, dh \\
&= 625\pi h^2 \Big|_{19}^{25} \\
&= 390{,}625\pi - 225{,}625\pi \\
&\approx 518{,}363 \text{ ft-lbs.}
\end{aligned}$$

A diagram of this tank is shown in Figure 8.77.

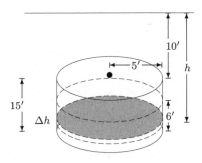

Figure 8.77

16. We slice the water horizontally as in Figure 8.78. We use similar triangles to find the radius r of the slice at height h in terms of h:

$$\frac{r}{h} = \frac{4}{12} \quad \text{so} \quad r = \frac{1}{3}h.$$

At height h,

$$\text{Volume of slice} \approx \pi r^2 \Delta h = \pi \left(\frac{1}{3}h\right)^2 \Delta h \text{ ft}^3.$$

The density of water is δ lb/ft^3, so

$$\text{Weight of slice} \approx \delta\pi \left(\frac{1}{3}h\right)^3 \Delta h \text{ lb}.$$

The water at height h must be lifted a distance of $12 - h$ ft, so

$$\text{Work to move slice} = \delta \cdot \text{Volume} \cdot \text{Distance lifted}$$

$$\approx \delta \left(\pi \left(\frac{1}{3}h\right)^2 \Delta h\right)(12 - h) \text{ ft-lb}.$$

The work done, W, to lift all the water is the sum of the work done on the pieces:

$$W \approx \sum \delta\pi(\frac{1}{3}h)^2\Delta h(12 - h) \text{ ft-lb}.$$

As $\Delta h \to 0$, we obtain a definite integral. Since h varies from $h = 0$ to $h = 9$, and $\delta = 62.4$, we have:

$$W = \int_0^9 \delta\pi(\frac{1}{3}h)^2(12 - h)dh = \frac{62.4\pi}{9}\int_0^9 (12h^2 - h^3)dh = \frac{62.4\pi}{9}\left(4h^3 - \frac{h^4}{4}\right)\Big|_0^9 = 27{,}788 \text{ ft-lb}.$$

The work to pump all the water out is $27{,}788$ ft-lbs.

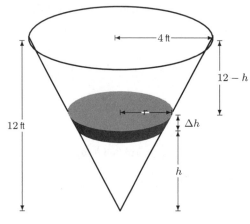

Figure 8.78

17. Let h represent distance below the surface in feet. We slice the tank up into horizontal slabs of thickness Δh. From looking at Figure 8.79, we can see that the slabs will be rectangular. The length of any slab is 12 feet. The width w of a slab h units below the ground will equal $2x$, where $(14 - h)^2 + x^2 = 16$, so $w = 2\sqrt{4^2 - (14 - h)^2}$. The volume of such a slab is therefore $12w\,\Delta h = 24\sqrt{16 - (14 - h)^2}\,\Delta h$ cubic feet; the slab weighs $42 \cdot 24\sqrt{16 - (14 - h)^2}\,\Delta h = 1008\sqrt{16 - (14 - h)^2}\,\Delta h$ pounds. So the total work done in pumping out all the gasoline is

$$\int_{10}^{18} 1008h\sqrt{16 - (14 - h)^2}\,dh = 1008\int_{10}^{18} h\sqrt{16 - (14 - h)^2}\,dh.$$

Substitute $s = 14 - h$, $ds = -dh$. We get

$$1008\int_{10}^{18} h\sqrt{16 - (14 - h)^2}\,dh = -1008\int_4^{-4} (14 - s)\sqrt{16 - s^2}\,ds$$

$$= 1008 \cdot 14\int_{-4}^4 \sqrt{16 - s^2}\,ds - 1008\int_{-4}^4 s\sqrt{16 - s^2}\,ds.$$

The first integral represents the area of a semicircle of radius 4, which is 8π. The second is the integral of an odd function, over the interval $-4 \le s \le 4$, and is therefore 0. Hence, the total work is $1008 \cdot 14 \cdot 8\pi \approx 354{,}673$ foot-pounds.

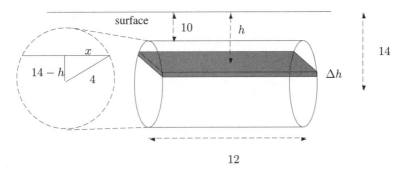

Figure 8.79

18. Divide the muddy water into horizontal slabs of thickness Δh. See Figure 8.80. Then for a typical slab

$$\text{Volume of slab} = \pi(0.5)^2 \Delta h \text{ m}^3$$
$$\text{Mass of slab} \approx \delta(h)\pi(0.5)^2 \Delta h = 0.25\pi(1 + kh)\Delta h \text{ kg}$$

The water in this slab is moved a distance of $h + 0.3$ meters to the rim of the barrel. Now

$$\text{Work done} = \text{Mass} \cdot g \cdot \text{Distance moved},$$

and work is measured in newtons if mass is in kilograms and distance is in meters, so

$$\text{Work done in moving slab} \approx 0.25\pi(1 + kh)g(h + 0.3)\Delta h \text{ joules.}$$

Since the slices run from $h = 0$ to $h = 1.5$, we have

$$\text{Total work done} = \int_0^{1.5} 0.25\pi(1 + kh)g(h + 0.3)\, dh$$
$$= 0.366(k + 1.077)g\pi \text{ joules}$$

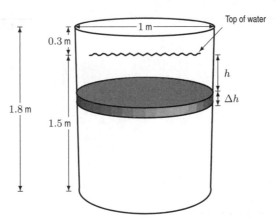

Figure 8.80

19. (a) We divide the triangular end into horizontal strips of thickness Δh. The length of a strip, s, depends on its height h from the bottom. See Figure 8.81. We use similar triangles to see that

$$\frac{s}{h} = \frac{2}{3} \quad \text{so} \quad s = \frac{2}{3}h.$$

Since each strip is approximately a rectangle, at height h,

$$\text{Area of strip} \approx \frac{2}{3}h\Delta h \text{ ft}^2.$$

Since the depth at height h is $3 - h$, writing δ for the density of water, we have:

$$\text{Force on one strip} = \delta \cdot \text{Depth} \cdot \text{Area}$$

$$\approx \delta(3 - h)\left(\frac{2}{3}h\Delta h\right) \text{ lb.}$$

To find the total force, F, we integrate the force on a strip from $h = 0$ to $h = 3$, using $\delta = 62.4$ lb/ft^3:

$$F = \int_0^3 \delta(3 - h)\frac{2}{3}h\,dh = \frac{2}{3}\delta\int_0^3 (3h - h^2)dh = \frac{2}{3}62.4\left(\frac{3h^2}{2} - \frac{h^3}{3}\right)\Bigg|_0^3 = 187.2 \text{ lbs.}$$

(b) To find the work, we slice the water horizontally. Each slice is a rectangular slab with thickness Δh, length 15 ft, and width s as in Figure 8.82. As we saw in part (a), at a height of h we have $s = \frac{2}{3}h$. At height h,

$$\text{Volume of slab} \approx 15\left(\frac{2}{3}h\right)\Delta h \text{ ft}^3.$$

The distance to lift the slice at height h is $3 - h$, so if δ is the density of water, we have:

$$\text{Work to lift one slice} = \delta \cdot \text{Volume} \cdot \text{Distance lifted}$$

$$\approx \delta(15(\frac{2}{3}h)\Delta h)(3 - h) \text{ ft-lb.}$$

To find the total work, W, we integrate the work to lift a slice from $h = 0$ to $h = 3$, using $\delta = 62.4$ lb/ft^3.

$$W = \int_0^3 \delta 15\left(\frac{2}{3}h\right)(3 - h)\,dh = 10\delta\int_0^3 (3h - h^2)dh = 10\cdot 62.4\left(\frac{3h^2}{2} - \frac{h^3}{3}\right)\Bigg|_0^3 = 10\delta(4.5) = 2808 \text{ ft-lbs.}$$

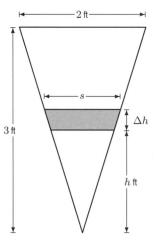

Figure 8.81

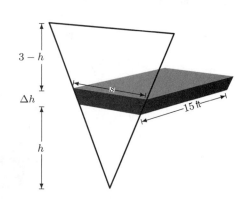

Figure 8.82

20. (a) Divide the wall into N horizontal strips, each of which is of height Δh. See Figure 8.83. The area of each strip is $1000\Delta h$, and the pressure at depth h_i is $62.4h_i$, so we approximate the force on the strip as $1000(62.4h_i)\Delta h$.

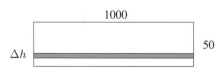

Figure 8.83

Therefore,

$$\text{Force on the Dam} \approx \sum_{i=0}^{N-1} 1000(62.4h_i)\Delta h.$$

(b) As $N \to \infty$, the Riemann sum becomes the integral, so the force on the dam is

$$\int_0^{50} (1000)(62.4h) \, dh = 62400 \frac{h^2}{2} \bigg|_0^{50} = 78{,}000{,}000 \text{ pounds.}$$

21. See Figure 8.84.

For the bottom: The bottom of the tank is at constant depth 15 feet, and therefore is under constant pressure, $15 \cdot 62.4 = 936 \text{ lb/ft}^2$. The area of the base is 200 ft^2, so

$$\text{Total force on bottom } = 200 \text{ ft}^2 \cdot 936 \text{ lb/ft}^2 = 187200 \text{ lb.}$$

For the 15×10 side: The area of a horizontal strip of width dh is $10 \, dh$ square feet, and the pressure at height h is $62.4h$ pounds per square foot. Therefore, the force on such a strip is $62.4h(10 \, dh)$ pounds. Hence,

$$\text{Total force on the } 15 \times 10 \text{ side } = \int_0^{15} (62.4h)(10) \, dh = 624 \frac{h^2}{2} \bigg|_0^{15} = 70200 \text{ lbs.}$$

For the 15×20 side: Similarly,

$$\text{Total force on the } 15 \times 20 \text{ side } = \int_0^{15} (62.4h)(20) \, dh = 1248 \frac{h^2}{2} \bigg|_0^{15} = 140400 \text{ lbs.}$$

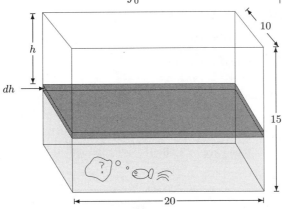

Figure 8.84

22. We divide the water against the dam into horizontal strips, each of thickness Δh and length 100.

$$\text{Area of each strip } \approx 100 \Delta h \text{ ft}^2.$$

See Figure 8.85. The strip at height h ft from the bottom is at a water depth of $40 - h$, so, if δ lb/ft^3 is the density of water, we have:

$$\text{Force of one strip} = \delta \cdot \text{Depth} \cdot \text{Area}$$
$$\approx \delta(40 - h)(100\Delta h) \text{ lb.}$$

To find the total force, F, we integrate the force on a strip from $h = 0$ to $h = 40$, using $\delta = 62.4$ lb/ft^3:

$$F = \int_0^{40} \delta(40 - h)100 \, dh = 100 \cdot 62.4 \left(40h - \frac{h^2}{2}\right) \bigg|_0^{40} = 6240(800) = 4{,}992{,}000 \text{ft-lbs.}$$

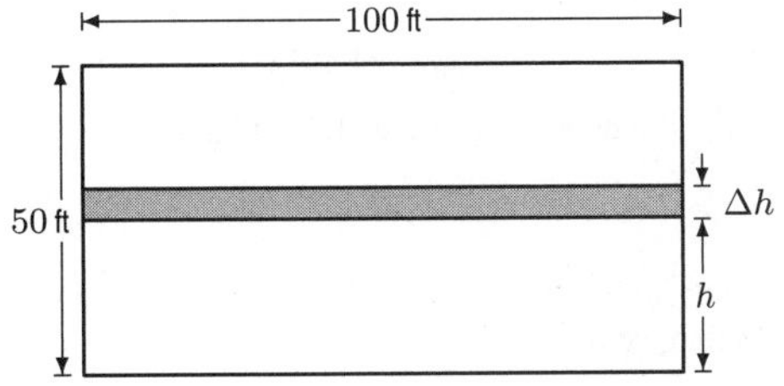

Figure 8.85

23. Bottom:
$$\text{Water force } = 62.4(2)(12) = 1497.6 \text{ lbs.}$$

Front and back:
$$\text{Water force } = (62.4)(4) \int_0^2 (2 - x)\, dx = (62.4)(4)(2x - \frac{1}{2}x^2)\Big|_0^2$$
$$= (62.4)(4)(2) = 499.2 \text{ lbs.}$$

Both sides:
$$\text{Water force } = (62.4)(3) \int_0^2 (2 - x)\, dx = (62.4)(3)(2) = 374.4 \text{ lbs.}$$

24. (a) Since the density of water is $\delta = 1000$ kg/m^3, at the base of the dam, water pressure $\delta g h = 1000 \cdot 9.8 \cdot 180 = 1.76 \cdot 10^6$ nt/m^2.

(b) To set up a definite integral giving the force, we divide the dam into horizontal strips. We use horizontal strips because the pressure along each strip is approximately constant, since each part is at approximately the same depth. See Figure 8.86.
$$\text{Area of strip } = 2000\Delta h \text{ m}^2.$$

Pressure at depth of h meters $= \delta g h = 9800h$ nt/m^2. Thus,
$$\text{Force on strip } \approx \text{ Pressure } \times \text{ Area } = 9800h \cdot 2000\Delta h = 1.96 \cdot 10^7 h\Delta h \text{ nt.}$$

Summing over all strips and letting $\Delta h \to 0$ gives:
$$\text{Total force } = \lim_{\Delta h \to 0} \sum 1.96 \cdot 10^7 h\Delta h = 1.96 \cdot 10^7 \int_0^{180} h\, dh \text{ newtons.}$$

Evaluating gives
$$\text{Total force } = 1.96 \cdot 10^7 \frac{h^2}{2}\Big|_0^{180} = 3.2 \cdot 10^{11} \text{ newtons.}$$

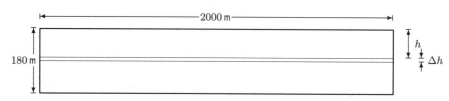

Figure 8.86

25. (a) At a depth of 350 feet,
$$\text{Pressure } = 62.4 \cdot 350 = 21{,}840 \text{ lb/ft}^2.$$

To imagine this pressure, we convert to pounds per square inch, giving a pressure of $21{,}840/144 = 151.7$ lb/in^2.

(b) (i) When the square is held horizontally, the pressure is constant at 21,840 lbs/ft^2, so
$$\text{Force } = \text{ Pressure } \cdot \text{ Area } = 21{,}840 \cdot 5^2 = 546{,}000 \text{ pounds.}$$

(ii) When the square is held vertically, only the bottom is at 350 feet. Dividing into horizontal strips, as in Figure 8.87, we have
$$\text{Area of strip } = 5\Delta h \text{ ft}^2.$$

Since the pressure on a strip at a depth of h feet is $62.4h$ lb/ft^2,
$$\text{Force on strip } \approx 62.4h \cdot 5\Delta h = 312h\Delta h \text{ pounds.}$$

Summing over all strips and taking the limit as $\Delta h \to 0$ gives a definite integral. The strips vary between a depth of 350 feet and 345 feet, so
$$\text{Total force } = \lim_{\Delta h \to 0} \sum 312h\Delta h = \int_{345}^{350} 312h\, dh \text{ pounds.}$$

Evaluating gives

$$\text{Total force} = 312\frac{h^2}{2}\bigg|_{345}^{350} = 156(350^2 - 345^2) = 542{,}100 \text{ pounds.}$$

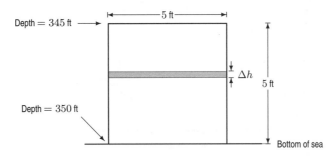

Figure 8.87

26. (a) Since water has density 62.4 lb/ft^3, at a depth of $12{,}500$ feet,

$$\text{Pressure} = \text{Density} \times \text{Depth} = 62.4 \cdot 12{,}500 = 780{,}000 \text{ lb/square foot.}$$

To imagine this pressure, observe that it is equivalent to $780{,}000/144 \approx 5400$ pounds per square inch.

(b) To calculate the pressure on the porthole (window), we slice it into horizontal strips, as the pressure remains approximately constant along each one. See Figure 8.88. Since each strip is approximately rectangular

$$\text{Area of strip} \approx 2r\Delta h \text{ ft}^2.$$

To calculate r in terms of h, we use the Pythagorean Theorem:

$$r^2 + h^2 = 9$$
$$r = \sqrt{9 - h^2},$$

so

$$\text{Area of strip} \approx 2\sqrt{9 - h^2}\Delta h \text{ ft}^2.$$

The center of the porthole is at a depth of $12{,}500$ feet below the surface, so the strip shown in Figure 8.88 is at a depth of $(12{,}500 - h)$ feet. Thus, pressure on the strip is $62.4(12{,}500 - h)$ lb/ft^2, so

$$\text{Force on strip} = \text{Pressure} \times \text{Area} \approx 62.4(12{,}500 - h)2\sqrt{9 - h^2}\Delta h \text{ lb}$$
$$= 124.8(12{,}500 - h)\sqrt{9 - h^2}\Delta h \text{ lb.}$$

To get the total force, we sum over all strips and take the limit as $\Delta h \to 0$. Since h ranges from -3 to 3, we get the integral

$$\text{Total force} = \lim_{\Delta h \to 0} \sum 124.8(12{,}500 - h)\sqrt{9 - h^2}\Delta h$$
$$= 124.8 \int_{-3}^{3} (12{,}500 - h)\sqrt{9 - h^2} \, dh \text{ lb.}$$

Evaluating the integral numerically, we obtain a total force of $2.2 \cdot 10^7$ pounds.

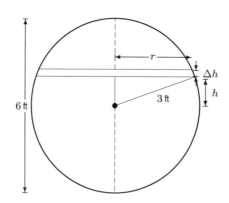

Figure 8.88: Center of circle is 12,500 ft below
the surface of ocean

27. We divide the dam into horizontal strips since the pressure is then approximately constant on each one. See Figure 8.89.

$$\text{Area of strip } \approx w\Delta h \text{ m}^2.$$

Since w is a linear function of h, and $w = 3600$ when $h = 0$, and $w = 3000$ when $h = 100$, the function has slope $(3000 - 3600)/100 = -6$. Thus,

$$w = 3600 - 6h,$$

so

$$\text{Area of strip } \approx (3600 - 6h)\Delta h \text{ m}^2.$$

The density of water is $\delta = 1000 \text{ kg/m}^3$, so the pressure at depth h meters $= \delta g h = 1000 \cdot 9.8h = 9800h$ nt/m². Thus,

$$\text{Total force } = \lim_{\Delta h \to 0} \sum 9800h(3600 - 6h)\Delta h = 9800 \int_0^{100} h(3600 - 6h) \, dh \text{ newtons.}$$

Evaluating the integral gives

$$\text{Total force } = 9800(1800h^2 - 2h^3)\Big|_0^{100} = 1.6 \cdot 10^{11} \text{ newtons.}$$

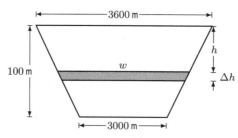

Figure 8.89

28. We need to divide the disk up into circular rings of charge and integrate their contributions to the potential (at P) from 0 to a. These rings, however, are not uniformly distant from the point P. A ring of radius z is $\sqrt{R^2 + z^2}$ away from point P (see Figure 8.90).

The ring has area $2\pi z \, \Delta z$, and charge $2\pi z \sigma \, \Delta z$. The potential of the ring is then $\dfrac{2\pi z \sigma \, \Delta z}{\sqrt{R^2 + z^2}}$ and the total potential at point P is

$$\int_0^a \frac{2\pi z \sigma \, dz}{\sqrt{R^2 + z^2}} = \pi \sigma \int_0^a \frac{2z \, dz}{\sqrt{R^2 + z^2}}.$$

We make the substitution $u = z^2$. Then $du = 2z\,dz$. We obtain

$$\pi\sigma \int_0^a \frac{2z\,dz}{\sqrt{R^2 + z^2}} = \pi\sigma \int_0^{a^2} \frac{du}{\sqrt{R^2 + u}} = \pi\sigma(2\sqrt{R^2 + u})\Big|_0^{a^2}$$

$$= \pi\sigma(2\sqrt{R^2 + z^2})\Big|_0^a = 2\pi\sigma(\sqrt{R^2 + a^2} - R).$$

(The substitution $u = R^2 + z^2$ or $\sqrt{R^2 + z^2}$ works also.)

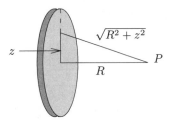
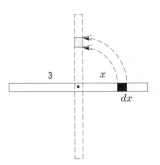

Figure 8.90

29. The density of the rod is $10\,\text{kg}/6\,\text{m} = \frac{5}{3}\frac{\text{kg}}{\text{m}}$. A little piece, dx m, of the rod thus has mass $5/3\,dx$ kg. If this piece has an angular velocity of 2 rad/sec, then its actual velocity is $2|x|$ m/sec. This is because a radian angle sweeps out an arc length equal to the radius of the circle, and in this case the little piece moves in circles about the origin of radius $|x|$. See Figure 8.91. The kinetic energy of the little piece is $mv^2/2 = (5/3\,dx)(2|x|)^2/2 = \frac{10}{3}x^2\,dx$.

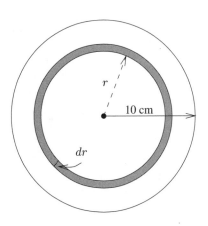

Figure 8.91

Therefore,

$$\text{Total Kinetic Energy} = \int_{-3}^3 \frac{10x^2}{3}\,dx = \frac{20}{3}\left[\frac{x^3}{3}\right]\Big|_0^3 = 60\,\text{kg}\cdot\text{m}^2/\text{sec}^2 = 60\,\text{joules}.$$

30. We slice the record into rings in such a way that every point has approximately the same speed: use concentric circles around the hole. See Figure 8.92. We assume the record is a flat disk of uniform density: since its mass is 50 grams and its area is $\pi(10\text{cm})^2 = 100\pi\,\text{cm}^2$, the record has density $\frac{50}{100\pi} = \frac{1}{2\pi}\frac{\text{gram}}{\text{cm}^2}$. So a ring of width dr, having area about $2\pi r\,dr\,\text{cm}^2$, has mass approximately $(2\pi r\,dr)(1/2\pi) = r\,dr$ gm. At radius r, the velocity of the ring is

$$33\tfrac{1}{3}\frac{\text{rev}}{\text{min}}\cdot\frac{1\,\text{min}}{60\,\text{sec}}\cdot\frac{2\pi r\,\text{cm}}{1\,\text{rev}} = \frac{10\pi r}{9}\frac{\text{cm}}{\text{sec}}.$$

Figure 8.92

The kinetic energy of the ring is

$$\frac{1}{2}mv^2 = \frac{1}{2}(r\,dr\text{ grams})\left(\frac{10\pi r}{9}\,\frac{\text{cm}}{\text{sec}}\right)^2 = \frac{50\pi^2 r^3\,dr}{81}\,\frac{\text{gram}\cdot\text{cm}^2}{\text{sec}^2}.$$

So the kinetic energy of the record, summing the energies of all these rings, is

$$\int_0^{10}\frac{50\pi^2 r^3\,dr}{81} = \frac{25\pi^2 r^4}{162}\bigg|_0^{10} \approx 15231\,\frac{\text{gram}\cdot\text{cm}^2}{\text{sec}^2} = 15231\text{ ergs}.$$

31. The density of the rod, in mass per unit length, is M/l (see Figure 8.93). So a slice of size dr has mass $\frac{M\,dr}{l}$. It pulls the small mass m with force $Gm\frac{M\,dr}{l}/r^2 = \frac{GmM\,dr}{lr^2}$. So the total gravitational attraction between the rod and point is

$$\int_a^{a+l}\frac{GmM\,dr}{lr^2} = \frac{GmM}{l}\left(-\frac{1}{r}\right)\bigg|_a^{a+l}$$

$$= \frac{GmM}{l}\left(\frac{1}{a}-\frac{1}{a+l}\right)$$

$$= \frac{GmM}{l}\frac{l}{a(a+l)} = \frac{GmM}{a(a+l)}.$$

Figure 8.93

32. This time, let's split the second rod into small slices of length dr. See Figure 8.94. Each slice is of mass $\frac{M_2}{l_2}\,dr$, since the density of the second rod is $\frac{M_2}{l_2}$. Since the slice is small, we can treat it as a particle at distance r away from the end of the first rod, as in Problem 31. By that problem, the force of attraction between the first rod and particle is

$$\frac{GM_1\frac{M_2}{l_2}\,dr}{(r)(r+l_1)}.$$

So the total force of attraction between the rods is

$$\int_a^{a+l_2}\frac{GM_1\frac{M_2}{l_2}\,dr}{(r)(r+l_1)} = \frac{GM_1M_2}{l_2}\int_a^{a+l_2}\frac{dr}{(r)(r+l_1)}$$

$$= \frac{GM_1M_2}{l_2}\int_a^{a+l_2}\frac{1}{l_1}\left(\frac{1}{r}-\frac{1}{r+l_1}\right)\,dr.$$

$$= \frac{GM_1M_2}{l_1l_2}\left(\ln|r|-\ln|r+l_1|\right)\bigg|_a^{a+l_2}$$

$$= \frac{GM_1M_2}{l_1l_2}\left[\ln|a+l_2|-\ln|a+l_1+l_2|-\ln|a|+\ln|a+l_1|\right]$$

$$= \frac{GM_1M_2}{l_1l_2}\ln\left[\frac{(a+l_1)(a+l_2)}{a(a+l_1+l_2)}\right].$$

This result is symmetric: if you switch l_1 and l_2 or M_1 and M_2, you get the same answer. That means it's not important which rod is "first," and which is "second."

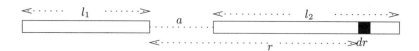

Figure 8.94

33. In Figure 8.95, consider a small piece of the ring of length Δl and mass

$$\Delta M = \frac{\Delta l M}{2\pi a}.$$

The gravitational force exerted by the small piece of the ring is along the line QP. As we sum over all pieces of the ring, the components perpendicular to the line OP cancel. The components of the force toward the point O are all in the same direction, so the net force is in this direction. The small piece of length Δl and mass $\Delta l M/2\pi a$ is at a distance of $\sqrt{a^2 + y^2}$ from P, so

$$\text{Gravitational force from small piece} = \Delta F = \frac{G \frac{\Delta l M}{2\pi a} m}{(\sqrt{a^2 + y^2})^2} = \frac{GMm\Delta l}{2\pi a(a^2 + y^2)}.$$

Thus the force toward O exerted by the small piece is given by

$$\Delta F \cos\theta = \Delta F \frac{y}{\sqrt{a^2 + y^2}} = \frac{GMm\Delta l}{2\pi a(a^2 + y^2)} \frac{y}{\sqrt{a^2 + y^2}} = \frac{GMmy\Delta l}{2\pi a(a^2 + y^2)^{3/2}}.$$

The total force toward O is given by $F \approx \sum \Delta F \cos\theta$, so

$$F = \frac{GMmy \cdot \text{Total length}}{2\pi a(a^2 + y^2)^{3/2}} = \frac{GMmy2\pi a}{2\pi a(a^2 + y^2)^{3/2}} = \frac{GMmy}{(a^2 + y^2)^{3/2}}.$$

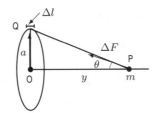

Figure 8.95

34. Divide the disk into rings of radius r, width Δr, as shown in Figure 8.96.
Then

$$\text{Area of ring} \approx 2\pi r\Delta r.$$

Since total area of disk is πa^2,

$$\text{Mass of ring} \approx \frac{2\pi r\Delta r}{\pi a^2} M = \frac{2r M}{a^2}\Delta r.$$

Thus, calculating the gravitational force due to the ring, we have

$$\text{Gravitational force on } m \text{ due to ring} = G\left(\frac{2r M}{a^2}\Delta r\right) \frac{my}{(r^2 + y^2)^{3/2}} = \frac{2GMmyr}{a^2(r^2 + y^2)^{3/2}}\Delta r.$$

Summing over all rings, we get

$$\text{Total gravitational force on } m \text{ due to disk} \approx \sum \frac{2GMmyr}{a^2(r^2 + y^2)^{3/2}}\Delta r.$$

As $\Delta r \to 0$, we get

$$\text{Gravitational force on } m \text{ due to disk} = \int_0^a \frac{2GMmyr}{a^2(r^2 + y^2)^{3/2}} dr = \frac{2GMmy}{a^2} \cdot \frac{-1}{(r^2 + y^2)^{1/2}}\bigg|_0^a$$

$$= \frac{2GMmy}{a^2}\left(\frac{1}{y} - \frac{1}{(a^2 + y^2)^{1/2}}\right).$$

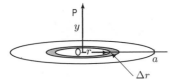

Figure 8.96

Solutions for Section 8.6

Exercises

1. At any time t, in a time interval Δt, an amount of $1000\Delta t$ is deposited into the account. This amount earns interest for $(10 - t)$ years giving a future value of $1000e^{(0.08)(10-t)}$. Summing all such deposits, we have

$$\text{Future value} = \int_0^{10} 1000e^{0.08(10-t)} \, dt = \$15{,}319.30.$$

2.

$$\text{Future Value} = \int_0^{15} 3000e^{0.06(15-t)} \, dt = 3000e^{0.9} \int_0^{15} e^{-0.06t} \, dt$$

$$= 3000e^{0.9} \left(\frac{1}{-0.06} e^{-0.06t} \right) \Big|_0^{15} = 3000e^{0.9} \left(\frac{1}{-0.06} e^{-0.9} + \frac{1}{0.06} e^0 \right)$$

$$\approx \$72{,}980.16$$

$$\text{Present Value} = \int_0^{15} 3000e^{-0.06t} \, dt = 3000 \left(-\frac{1}{0.06} \right) e^{-0.06t} \Big|_0^{15}$$

$$\approx \$29{,}671.52.$$

There's a quicker way to calculate the present value of the income stream, since the future value of the income stream is (as we've shown) $\$72{,}980.16$, the present value of the income stream must be the present value of $\$72{,}980.16$. Thus,

$$\text{Present Value} = \$72{,}980.16(e^{-.06 \cdot 15})$$

$$\approx \$29{,}671.52,$$

which is what we got before.

3. We compute the future value first: we have

$$\text{Future value} = \int_0^5 2000e^{0.08(5-t)} \, dt = \$12{,}295.62.$$

We can compute the present value using an integral and the income stream or using the future value. We compute the present value, P, from the future value:

$$12295.62 = Pe^{0.08(5)} \quad \text{so} \quad P = 8242.00.$$

The future value of this income stream is $\$12{,}295.62$ and the present value of this income stream is $\$8{,}242.00$.

4. (a) We compute the future value of this income stream:

$$\text{Future value} = \int_0^{20} 1000e^{0.07(20-t)} \, dt = \$43{,}645.71.$$

After 20 years, the account will contain $\$43{,}645.71$.

(b) The person has deposited $\$1000$ every year for 20 years, for a total of $\$20{,}000$.

(c) The total interest earned is $\$43{,}645.71 - \$20{,}000 = \$23{,}645.71$.

Problems

5.

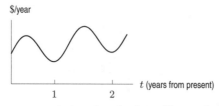

The graph reaches a peak each summer, and a trough each winter. The graph shows sunscreen sales increasing from cycle to cycle. This gradual increase may be due in part to inflation and to population growth.

6. (a) The lump sum payment has a present value of 104 million dollars . We compute the present value of the other option in each case. An award of \$197 million paid out continuously over 26 years works out to an income stream of 7.576923 million dollars per year.

If the interest rate is 6%, compounded continuously, we have

$$\text{Present value at 6\%} = \int_0^{26} 7.576923e^{-0.06t}\,dt = 99.75.$$

The present value of this option is about 99.75 million dollars. Since this is less than the lump sum payment of 104 million dollars, the lump sum payment is preferable if the interest rate is 6%.

If the interest rate is 5%, we have

$$\text{Present value at 5\%} = \int_0^{26} 7.576923e^{-0.05t}\,dt = 110.24.$$

The present value of this option is about 110.24 million dollars. Since this is greater than the lump sum payment of 104 million dollars, taking payments continuously over 26 years is the better option if the interest rate is 5%.

(b) Since the winner chose the lump sum option, she was assuming that interest rates would be high (above about 5.5%).

7. (a) Solve for $P(t) = P$.

$$100000 = \int_0^{10} Pe^{0.10(10-t)}\,dt = Pe\int_0^{10} e^{-0.10t}\,dt$$

$$= \frac{Pe}{-0.10}e^{-0.10t}\Big|_0^{10} = Pe(-3.678 + 10)$$

$$= P \cdot 17.183.$$

So, $P \approx \$5820$ per year.

(b) To answer this, we'll calculate the present value of \$100,000:

$$100000 = Pe^{0.10(10)}$$

$$P \approx \$36,787.94.$$

8. (a) Let L be the number of years for the balance to reach \$10,000. Since our income stream is \$1000 per year, the future value of this income stream should equal (in L years) \$10,000. Thus

$$10000 = \int_0^L 1000e^{0.05(L-t)}\,dt = 1000e^{0.05L}\int_0^L e^{-0.05t}\,dt$$

$$= 1000e^{0.05L}\left(-\frac{1}{0.05}\right)e^{-0.05t}\Big|_0^L = 20000e^{0.05L}\left(1 - e^{-0.05L}\right)$$

$$= 20000e^{0.05L} - 20000$$

so $\quad e^{0.05L} = \frac{3}{2}$

$$L = 20\ln\left(\frac{3}{2}\right) \approx 8.11 \text{ years.}$$

(b) We want

$$10000 = 2000e^{0.05L} + \int_0^L 1000e^{0.05(L-t)}\,dt.$$

The first term on the right hand side is the future value of our initial balance. The second term is the future value of our income stream. We want this sum to equal \$10,000 in L years. We solve for L:

$$10000 = 2000e^{0.05L} + 1000e^{0.05L}\int_0^L e^{-0.05t}\,dt$$

$$= 2000e^{0.05L} + 1000e^{0.05L}\left(\frac{1}{-0.05}\right)e^{-0.05t}\Big|_0^L$$

$$= 2000e^{0.05L} + 20000e^{0.05L}\left(1 - e^{-0.05L}\right)$$

$$= 2000e^{0.05L} + 20000e^{0.05L} - 20000.$$

So,

$$22000e^{0.05L} = 30000$$

$$e^{0.05L} = \frac{30000}{22000}$$

$$L = 20\ln\frac{15}{11} \approx 6.203 \text{ years.}$$

9. You should choose the payment which gives you the highest present value. The immediate lump-sum payment of $2800 obviously has a present value of exactly $2800, since you are getting it now. We can calculate the present value of the installment plan as:

$$PV = 1000e^{-0.06(0)} + 1000e^{-0.06(1)} + 1000e^{-0.06(2)}$$

$$\approx \$2828.68.$$

Since the installment payments offer a (slightly) higher present value, you should accept this option.

10. (a) We calculate the future values of the two options:

$$FV_1 = 6e^{0.1(3)} + 2e^{0.1(2)} + 2e^{0.1(1)} + 2e^{0.1(0)}$$

$$\approx 8.099 + 2.443 + 2.210 + 2$$

$$= \$14.752 \text{ million.}$$

$$FV_2 = e^{0.1(3)} + 2e^{0.1(2)} + 4e^{0.1(1)} + 6e^{0.1(0)}$$

$$\approx 1.350 + 2.443 + 4.421 + 6$$

$$= \$14.214 \text{ million.}$$

As we can see, the first option gives a higher future value, so he should choose Option 1.

(b) From the future value we can easily derive the present value using the formula $PV = FVe^{-rt}$. So the present value is

$$\text{Option 1: } PV = 14.752e^{0.1(-3)} \approx \$10.929 \text{ million.}$$

$$\text{Option 2: } PV = 14.214e^{0.1(-3)} \approx \$10.530 \text{ million.}$$

11. At any time t, the company receives income of $s(t)$ per year. It will then invest this money for a length of $2 - t$ years at 6% interest, giving it future value of $s(t)e^{(0.06)(2-t)}$ from this income. If we sum all such incomes over the two-year period, we can find the total value of the sales:

$$\text{Value} = \int_0^2 s(t)e^{(0.06)(2-t)}\,dt = \int_0^2 \left[50e^{-t}e^{(0.06)(2-t)}\right]\,dt$$

$$= \int_0^2 \left[50e^{0.12-1.06t}\right]\,dt = \left(\frac{-53.1838}{e^{1.06t}}\right)\Bigg|_0^2 = \$46,800.$$

12. Price in future $= P(1 + 20\sqrt{t})$.

The present value V of price satisfies $V = P(1 + 20\sqrt{t})e^{-0.05t}$.

We want to maximize V. To do so, we find the critical points of $V(t)$ for $t \geq 0$. (Recall that $\sqrt{t}$ is nondifferentiable at $t = 0$.)

$$\frac{dV}{dt} = P\left[\frac{20}{2\sqrt{t}}e^{-0.05t} + (1 + 20\sqrt{t})(-0.05e^{-0.05t})\right]$$

$$= Pe^{-0.05t}\left[\frac{10}{\sqrt{t}} - 0.05 - \sqrt{t}\right].$$

Setting $\frac{dV}{dt} = 0$ gives $\frac{10}{\sqrt{t}} - 0.05 - \sqrt{t} = 0$. Using a calculator, we find $t \approx 10$ years. Since $V'(t) > 0$ for $0 < t < 10$ and $V'(t) < 0$ for $t > 10$, we confirm that this is a maximum. Thus, the best time to sell the wine is in 10 years.

13. (a) Suppose the oil extracted over the time period $[0, M]$ is S. (See Figure 8.97.) Since $q(t)$ is the rate of oil extraction, we have:

$$S = \int_0^M q(t)dt = \int_0^M (a - bt)dt = \int_0^M (10 - 0.1t)\, dt.$$

To calculate the time at which the oil is exhausted, set $S = 100$ and try different values of M. We find $M = 10.6$ gives

$$\int_0^{10.6} (10 - 0.1t)\, dt = 100,$$

so the oil is exhausted in 10.6 years.

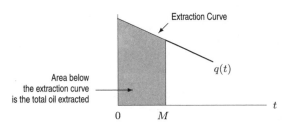

Figure 8.97

(b) Suppose p is the oil price, C is the extraction cost per barrel, and r is the interest rate. We have the present value of the profit as

$$\text{Present value of profit} = \int_0^M (p - C)q(t)e^{-rt}dt$$

$$= \int_0^{10.6} (20 - 10)(10 - 0.1t)e^{-0.1t}\, dt$$

$$= 624.9 \text{ million dollars.}$$

14. One good way to approach the problem is in terms of present values. In 1980, the present value of Germany's loan was 20 billion DM. Now let's figure out the rate that the Soviet Union would have to give money to Germany to pay off 10% interest on the loan by using the formula for the present value of a continuous stream. Since the Soviet Union sends gas at a constant rate, the rate of deposit, $P(t)$, is a constant c. Since they don't start sending the gas until after 5 years have passed, the present value of the loan is given by:

$$\text{Present Value} = \int_5^\infty P(t)e^{-rt}\, dt.$$

We want to find c so that

$$20,000,000,000 = \int_5^\infty ce^{-rt}\, dt = c\int_5^\infty e^{-rt}\, dt$$

$$= c\lim_{b \to \infty} \left. (-10e^{-0.10t}) \right|_5^b = ce^{-0.10(5)}$$

$$\approx 6.065c.$$

Dividing, we see that c should be about 3.3 billion DM per year. At 0.10 DM per m^3 of natural gas, the Soviet Union must deliver gas at the constant, continuous rate of about 33 billion m^3 per year.

15. Measuring money in thousands of dollars, the equation of the line representing the demand curve passes through (50, 980) and (350, 560). Its slope is $(560 - 980)/(350 - 50) = -420/300$. See Figure 8.98. So the equation is $y - 560 = -\frac{420}{300}(x - 350)$, i.e. $y - 560 = -\frac{7}{5}x + 490$. Thus

$$\text{Consumer surplus} = \int_0^{350} \left(-\frac{7}{5}x + 1050\right)\, dx - 350 \cdot 560 = \left. -\frac{7}{10}x^2 + 1050x \right|_0^{350} - 196000$$

$$= 85,750.$$

(Note that $85{,}750 = \frac{1}{2} \cdot 490 \cdot 350$, the area of the triangle in Figure 8.98. We could have used this instead of the integral to find the consumer surplus.)

Recalling that our unit measure for the price axis is $1000/car, the consumer surplus is $85,750,000.

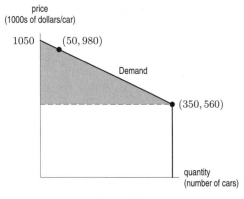

Figure 8.98

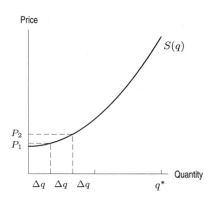

Figure 8.99

16. The supply curve, $S(q)$, represents the minimum price p per unit that the suppliers will be willing to supply some quantity q of the good for. See Figure 8.99. If the suppliers have q^* of the good and q^* is divided into subintervals of size Δq, then if the consumers could offer the suppliers for each Δq a price increase just sufficient to induce the suppliers to sell an additional Δq of the good, the consumers' total expenditure on q^* goods would be

$$p_1 \Delta q + p_2 \Delta q + \cdots = \sum p_i \Delta q.$$

As $\Delta q \to 0$ the Riemann sum becomes the integral $\displaystyle\int_0^{q^*} S(q)\, dq$. Thus $\displaystyle\int_0^{q^*} S(q)\, dq$ is the amount the consumers would pay if suppliers could be forced to sell at the lowest price they would be willing to accept.

17.

$$\int_0^{q^*} (p^* - S(q))\, dq = \int_0^{q^*} p^*\, dq - \int_0^{q^*} S(q)\, dq$$

$$= p^* q^* - \int_0^{q^*} S(q)\, dq.$$

Using Problem 16, this integral is the extra amount consumers pay (i.e., suppliers earn over and above the minimum they would be willing to accept for supplying the good). It results from charging the equilibrium price.

18. (a) $p^* q^*$ = the total amount paid for q^* of the good at equilibrium. See Figure 8.100.

(b) $\int_0^{q^*} D(q)\, dq$ = the maximum consumers would be willing to pay if they had to pay the highest price acceptable to them for each additional unit of the good. See Figure 8.101.

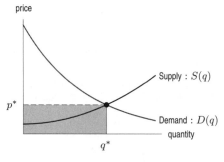

Figure 8.100

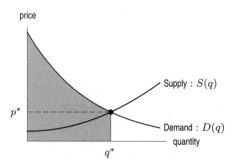

Figure 8.101

(c) $\int_0^{q^*} S(q)\,dq$ = the minimum suppliers would be willing to accept if they were paid the minimum price acceptable to them for each additional unit of the good. See Figure 8.102.

(d) $\int_0^{q^*} D(q)\,dq - p^*q^*$ = consumer surplus. See Figure 8.103.

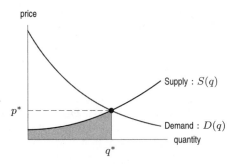

Figure 8.102

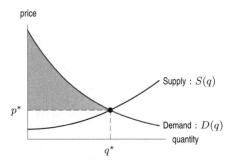

Figure 8.103

(e) $p^*q^* - \int_0^{q^*} S(q)\,dq$ = producer surplus. See Figure 8.104.

(f) $\int_0^{q^*} (D(q) - S(q))\,dq$ = producer surplus and consumer surplus. See Figure 8.105.

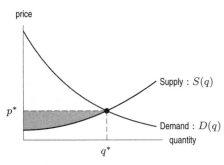

Figure 8.104

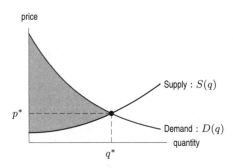

Figure 8.105

19.

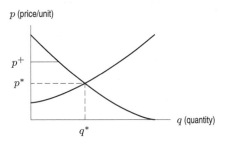

Figure 8.106: What effect does the artificially high price, p^+, have?

(a) A graph of possible demand and supply curves for the milk industry is given in Figure 8.106, with the equilibrium price and quantity labeled p^* and q^* respectively. Suppose that the price is fixed at the artificially high price labeled p^+ in Figure 8.106. Recall that the consumer surplus is the difference between the amount the consumers did pay (p^+) and the amount they would have been willing to pay (given on the demand curve). This is the area shaded in Figure 8.107(i). Notice that this consumer surplus is clearly less than the consumer surplus at the equilibrium price, shown in Figure 8.107(ii).

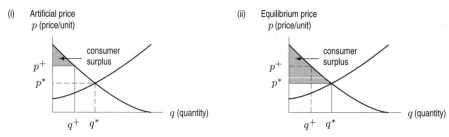

Figure 8.107: Consumer surplus for the milk industry

(b) At a price of p^+, the quantity sold, q^+, is less than it would have been at the equilibrium price. The producer surplus is the area between p^+ and the supply curve *at this reduced demand*. This area is shaded in Figure 8.108(i). Compare this producer surplus (at the artificially high price) to the producer surplus in Figure 8.108(ii) (at the equilibrium price). It appears that in this case, producer surplus is greater at the artificial price than at the equilibrium price. (Different supply and demand curves might have led to a different answer.)

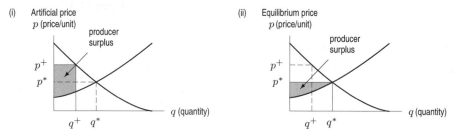

Figure 8.108: Producer surplus for the milk industry

(c) The total gains from trade (Consumer surplus + Producer surplus) at the artificially high price of p^+ is the area shaded in Figure 8.109(i). The total gains from trade at the equilibrium price of p^* is the area shaded in Figure 8.109(ii). It is clear that, under artificial price conditions, total gains from trade go down. The total financial effect of the artificially high price on all producers and consumers combined is a negative one.

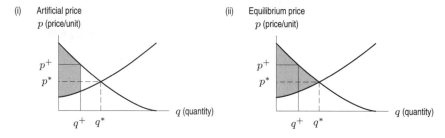

Figure 8.109: Total gains from trade

20.

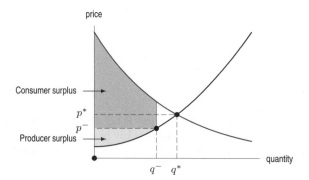

(a) The producer surplus is the area on the graph between p^- and the supply function. Lowering the price also lowers the producer surplus.

(b) Note that the consumer surplus—the area between the line p^- and the supply curve—increases or decreases depending on the functions describing the supply and demand and on the lowered price. (For example, the consumer surplus seems to be increased in the graph above, but if the price were brought down to \$0 then the consumer surplus would be zero, and hence clearly less than the consumer surplus at equilibrium.)

(c) The graph above shows that the total gains from the trade are decreased.

Solutions for Section 8.7

Exercises

1.

% of population
per dollar of income
income

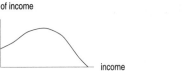

Figure 8.110: Density function

% of population having
at least this income
income

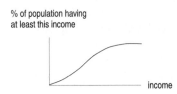

Figure 8.111: Cumulative distribution function

2.

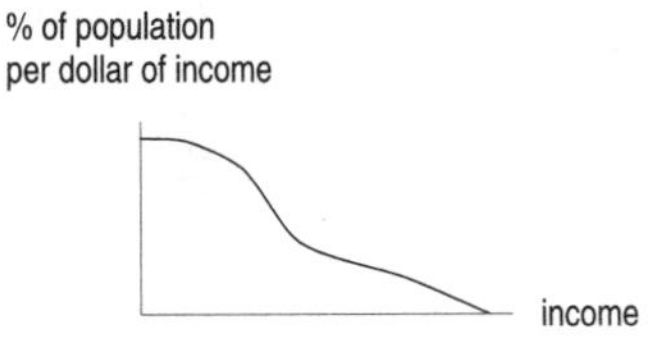

% of population
per dollar of income
income

Figure 8.112: Density function

% of population having
at least this income
income

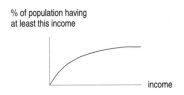

Figure 8.113: Cumulative distribution function

3.

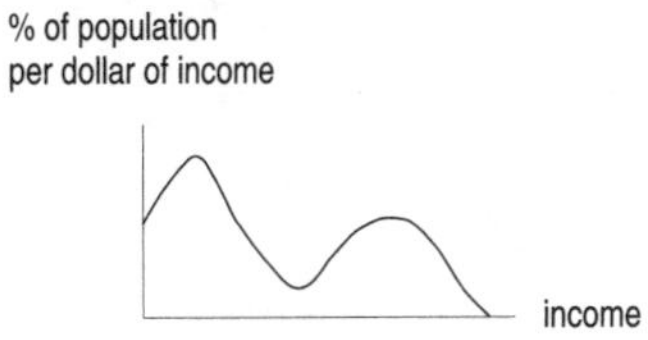

% of population
per dollar of income
income

Figure 8.114: Density function

% of population having
at least this income
income

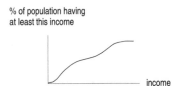

Figure 8.115: Cumulative distribution function

4. Since the function takes on the value of 4, it cannot be a cdf (whose maximum value is 1). In addition, the function decreases for $x > c$, which means that it is not a cdf. Thus, this function is a pdf. The area under a pdf is 1, so $4c = 1$ giving $c = \frac{1}{4}$. The pdf is $p(x) = 4$ for $0 \le x \le \frac{1}{4}$, so the cdf is given in Figure 8.116 by

$$P(x) = \begin{cases} 0 & \text{for} \quad x < 0 \\ 4x & \text{for} \quad 0 \le x \le \dfrac{1}{4} \\ 1 & \text{for} \quad x > \dfrac{1}{4} \end{cases}$$

P(x)
1
1/4
x

Figure 8.116

P(x)
1
4
x

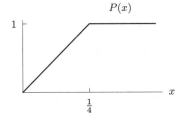

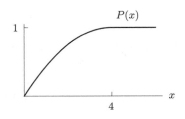

Figure 8.117

5. Since the function is decreasing, it cannot be a cdf (whose values never decrease). Thus, the function is a pdf.
The area under a pdf is 1, so, using the formula for the area of a triangle, we have

$$\frac{1}{2}4c = 1, \quad \text{giving} \quad c = \frac{1}{2}.$$

The pdf is

$$p(x) = \frac{1}{2} - \frac{1}{8}x \quad \text{for} \quad 0 \le x \le 4,$$

so the cdf is given in Figure 8.117 by

$$P(x) = \begin{cases} 0 & \text{for} \quad x < 0 \\ \dfrac{x}{2} - \dfrac{x^2}{16} & \text{for} \quad 0 \le x \le 4 \\ 1 & \text{for} \quad x > 4. \end{cases}$$

6. Since the function levels off at the value of c, the area under the graph is not finite, so it is not 1. Thus, this function cannot be a pdf.
It is a cdf and $c = 1$. The cdf is given by

$$P(x) = \begin{cases} 0 & \text{for} \quad x < 0 \\ \dfrac{x}{5} & \text{for} \quad 0 \le x \le 5 \\ 1 & \text{for} \quad x > 5. \end{cases}$$

The pdf in Figure 8.118 is given by

$$p(x) = \begin{cases} 0 & \text{for} \quad x < 0 \\ 1/5 & \text{for} \quad 0 \le x \le 5 \\ 0 & \text{for} \quad x > 5. \end{cases}$$

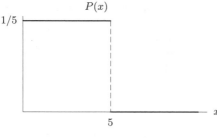

Figure 8.118

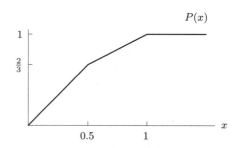

Figure 8.119

7. This function decreases, so it cannot be a cdf. Since the graph must represent a pdf, the area under it is 1. The region consists of two rectangles, each of base 0.5, and one of height $2c$ and one of height c, so

$$\text{Area} = 2c(0.5) + c(0.5) = 1$$

$$c = \frac{1}{1.5} = \frac{2}{3}$$

The pdf is therefore

$$p(x) = \begin{cases} 0 & \text{for} \quad x < 0 \\ 4/3 & \text{for} \quad 0 \le x \le 0.5 \\ 2/3 & \text{for} \quad 0.5 < x \le 1 \\ 0 & \text{for} \quad x > 1. \end{cases}$$

The cdf $P(x)$ is the antiderivative of this function with $P(0) = 0$. See Figure 8.119. The formula for $P(x)$ is

$$P(x) = \begin{cases} 0 & \text{for} \quad x < 0 \\ 4x/3 & \text{for} \quad 0 \le x \le 0.5 \\ 2/3 + (2/3)(x - 0.5) & \text{for} \quad 0.5 < x \le 1 \\ 1 & \text{for} \quad x > 1. \end{cases}$$

8. This function increases and levels off to c. The area under the curve is not finite, so it is not 1. Thus, the function must be a cdf, not a pdf, and $3c = 1$, so $c = 1/3$.

The pdf, $p(x)$ is the derivative, or slope, of the function shown, so, using $c = 1/3$,

$$p(x) = \begin{cases} 0 & \text{for} \quad x < 0 \\ (1/3 - 0)/(2 - 0) = 1/6 & \text{for} \quad 0 \le x \le 2 \\ (1 - 1/3)/(4 - 2) = 1/3 & \text{for} \quad 2 < x \le 4 \\ 0 & \text{for} \quad x > 4. \end{cases}$$

See Figure 8.120.

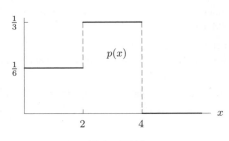

Figure 8.120

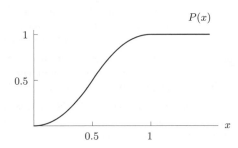

Figure 8.121

9. This function does not level off to 1, and it is not always increasing. Thus, the function is a pdf. Since the area under the curve must be 1, using the formula for the area of a triangle,

$$\frac{1}{2} \cdot c \cdot 1 = 1 \quad \text{so} \quad c = 2.$$

Thus, the pdf is given by

$$p(x) = \begin{cases} 0 & \text{for} \quad x < 0 \\ 4x & \text{for} \quad 0 \le x \le 0.5 \\ 2 - 4(x - 0.5) = 4 - 4x & \text{for} \quad 0.5 < x \le 1 \\ 0 & \text{for} \quad x > 0. \end{cases}$$

To find the cdf, we integrate each part of the function separately, making sure that the constants of integration are arranged so that the cdf is continuous.

Since $\int 4x\,dx = 2x^2 + C$ and $P(0) = 0$, we have $2(0)^2 + C = 0$ so $C = 0$. Thus $P(x) = 2x^2$ on $0 \le x \le 0.5$. At $x = 0.5$, the cdf has value $P(0.5) = 2(0.5)^2 = 0.5$. Thus, we arrange that the integral of $4 - 4x$ goes through the point $(0.5, 0.5)$. Since $\int (4 - 4x)\,dx = 4x - 2x^2 + C$, we have

$$4(0.5) - 2(0.5)^2 + C = 0.5 \quad \text{giving} \quad C = -1.$$

Thus

$$P(x) = \begin{cases} 0 & \text{for} \quad x < 0 \\ 2x^2 & \text{for} \quad 0 \le x \le 0.5 \\ 4x - 2x^2 - 1 & \text{for} \quad 0.5 < x \le 1 \\ 1 & \text{for} \quad x > 1. \end{cases}$$

See Figure 8.121.

Problems

10. No. Though the density function has its maximum value at 50, this does not mean that a large fraction of the population receives scores near 50. The value $p(50)$ can not be interpreted as a probability. Probability corresponds to *area* under the graph of a density function. Most of the area in this case is in the broad hump covering the range $0 \le x \le 40$, very little in the peak around $x = 50$. Most people score in the range $0 \le x \le 40$.

11. (a) Let $P(x)$ be the cumulative distribution function of the heights of the unfertilized plants. As do all cumulative distribution functions, $P(x)$ rises from 0 to 1 as x increases. The greatest number of plants will have heights in the range where $P(x)$ rises the most. The steepest rise appears to occur at about $x = 1$ m. Reading from the graph we see that $P(0.9) \approx 0.2$ and $P(1.1) \approx 0.8$, so that approximately $P(1.1) - P(0.9) = 0.8 - 0.2 = 0.6 = 60\%$ of the unfertilized plants grow to heights between 0.9 m and 1.1 m. Most of the plants grow to heights in the range 0.9 m to 1.1 m.

   (b) Let $P_A(x)$ be the cumulative distribution function of the plants that were fertilized with A. Since $P_A(x)$ rises the most in the range 0.7 m $\leq x \leq$ 0.9 m, many of the plants fertilized with A will have heights in the range 0.7 m to 0.9 m. Reading from the graph of P_A, we find that $P_A(0.7) \approx 0.2$ and $P_A(0.9) \approx 0.8$, so $P_A(0.9) - P_A(0.7) \approx 0.8 - 0.2 = 0.6 = 60\%$ of the plants fertilized with A have heights between 0.7 m and 0.9 m. Fertilizer A had the effect of stunting the growth of the plants.

   On the other hand, the cumulative distribution function $P_B(x)$ of the heights of the plants fertilized with B rises the most in the range 1.1 m $\leq x \leq$ 1.3 m, so most of these plants have heights in the range 1.1 m to 1.3 m. Fertilizer B caused the plants to grow about 0.2 m taller than they would have with no fertilizer.

12. (a) $F(7) = 0.6$ tells us that 60% of the trees in the forest have height 7 meters or less.

   (b) $F(7) > F(6)$. There are more trees of height less than 7 meters than trees of height less than 6 meters because every tree of height ≤ 6 meters also has height ≤ 7 meters.

13. For a small interval Δx around 68, the fraction of the population of American men with heights in this interval is about $(0.2)\Delta x$. For example, taking $\Delta x = 0.1$, we can say that approximately $(0.2)(0.1) = 0.02 = 2\%$ of American men have heights between 68 and 68.1 inches.

14. We want to find the cumulative distribution function for the age density function. We see that $P(10)$ is equal to 0.15 since the table shows that 15% of the population is between 0 and 10 years of age. Also,

$$P(20) = \frac{\text{Fraction of the population}}{\text{between 0 and 20 years old}} = 0.15 + 0.14 = 0.29$$

and

$$P(30) = 0.15 + 0.14 + 0.14 = 0.43.$$

Continuing in this way, we obtain the values for $P(t)$ shown in Table 8.6.

Table 8.6 *Cumulative distribution function of ages in the US*

t	0	10	20	30	40	50	60	70	80	90	100
$P(t)$	0	0.15	0.29	0.43	0.60	0.74	0.84	0.92	0.97	0.99	1.00

15. (a) The two functions are shown below. The choice is based on the fact that the cumulative distribution does not decrease.

   (b) The cumulative distribution levels off to 1, so the top mark on the vertical scale must be 1.

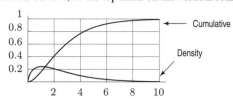

The total area under the density function must be 1. Since the area under the density function is about 2.5 boxes, each box must have area $1/2.5 = 0.4$. Since each box has a height of 0.2, the base must be 2.

16. (a) The area under the graph of the height density function $p(x)$ is concentrated in two humps centered at 0.5 m and 1.1 m. The plants can therefore be separated into two groups, those with heights in the range 0.3 m to 0.7 m, corresponding to the first hump, and those with heights in the range 0.9 m to 1.3 m, corresponding to the second hump. This grouping of the grasses according to height is probably close to the species grouping. Since the second hump contains more area than the first, there are more plants of the tall grass species in the meadow.

   (b) As do all cumulative distribution functions, the cumulative distribution function $P(x)$ of grass heights rises from 0 to 1 as x increases. Most of this rise is achieved in two spurts, the first as x goes from 0.3 m to 0.7 m, and the second as x goes from 0.9 m to 1.3 m. The plants can therefore be separated into two groups, those with heights in the range 0.3 m to 0.7 m, corresponding to the first spurt, and those with heights in the range 0.9 m to 1.3 m, corresponding to the second spurt. This grouping of the grasses according to height is the same as the grouping we made in part (a), and is probably close to the species grouping.

   (c) The fraction of grasses with height less than 0.7 m equals $P(0.7) = 0.25 = 25\%$. The remaining 75% are the tall grasses.

17. (a) The percentage of calls lasting from 1 to 2 minutes is given by the integral

$$\int_1^2 p(x)\,dx \int_1^2 0.4e^{-0.4x}\,dx = e^{-0.4} - e^{-0.8} \approx 22.1\%.$$

(b) A similar calculation (changing the limits of integration) gives the percentage of calls lasting 1 minute or less as

$$\int_0^1 p(x)\,dx = \int_0^1 0.4e^{-0.4x}\,dx = 1 - e^{-0.4} \approx 33.0\%.$$

(c) The percentage of calls lasting 3 minutes or more is given by the improper integral

$$\int_3^\infty p(x)\,dx = \lim_{b\to\infty} \int_3^b 0.4e^{-0.4x}\,dx = \lim_{b\to\infty}\left(e^{-1.2} - e^{-0.4b}\right) = e^{-1.2} \approx 30.1\%.$$

(d) The cumulative distribution function is the integral of the probability density; thus,

$$C(h) = \int_0^h p(x)\,dx = \int_0^h 0.4e^{-0.4x}\,dx = 1 - e^{-0.4h}.$$

18. (a) The fraction of students passing is given by the area under the curve from 2 to 4 divided by the total area under the curve. This appears to be about $\frac{2}{3}$.

(b) The fraction with honor grades corresponds to the area under the curve from 3 to 4 divided by the total area. This is about $\frac{1}{3}$.

(c) The peak around 2 probably exists because many students work to get just a passing grade.

(d)

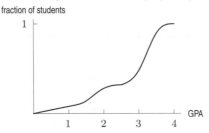

19. (a) Most of the earth's surface is below sea level. Much of the earth's surface is either around 3 miles below sea level or exactly at sea level. It appears that essentially all of the surface is between 4 miles below sea level and 2 miles above sea level. Very little of the surface is around 1 mile below sea level.

(b) The fraction below sea level corresponds to the area under the curve from -4 to 0 divided by the total area under the curve. This appears to be about $\frac{3}{4}$.

20. (a) We must have $\int_0^\infty f(t)\,dt = 1$, for even though it is possible that any given person survives the disease, everyone eventually dies. Therefore,

$$\int_0^\infty cte^{-kt}\,dt = 1.$$

Integrating by parts gives

$$\int_0^b cte^{-kt}\,dt = -\frac{c}{k}te^{-kt}\Big|_0^b + \int_0^b \frac{c}{k}e^{-kt}\,dt$$

$$= \left(-\frac{c}{k}te^{-kt} - \frac{c}{k^2}e^{-kt}\right)\Big|_0^b$$

$$= \frac{c}{k^2} - \frac{c}{k}be^{-kb} - \frac{c}{k^2}e^{-kb}.$$

As $b \to \infty$, we see

$$\int_0^\infty cte^{-kt}\,dt = \frac{c}{k^2} = 1 \quad \text{so} \quad c = k^2.$$

(b) We are told that $\int_0^5 f(t)dt = 0.4$, so using the fact that $c = k^2$ and the antiderivatives from part (a), we have

$$\int_0^5 k^2 te^{-kt}dt = \left(-\frac{k^2}{k}te^{-kt} - \frac{k^2}{k^2}e^{-kt}\right)\Bigg|_0^5$$
$$= 1 - 5ke^{-5k} - e^{-5k} = 0.4$$

so

$$5ke^{-5k} + e^{-5k} = 0.6.$$

Since this equation cannot be solved exactly, we use a calculator or computer to find $k = 0.275$. Since $c = k^2$, we have $c = (0.275)^2 = 0.076$.

(c) The cumulative death distribution function, $C(t)$, represents the fraction of the population that have died up to time t. Thus,

$$C(t) = \int_0^t k^2 xe^{-kx}dx = \left(-kxe^{-kx} - e^{-kx}\right)\Big|_0^t$$
$$= 1 - kte^{-kt} - e^{-kt}.$$

Solutions for Section 8.8

Exercises

1.

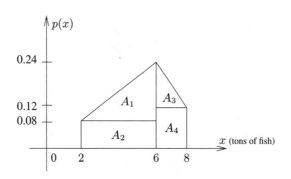

Splitting the figure into four pieces, we see that

$$\text{Area under the curve} = A_1 + A_2 + A_3 + A_4$$
$$= \frac{1}{2}(0.16)4 + 4(0.08) + \frac{1}{2}(0.12)2 + 2(0.12)$$
$$= 1.$$

We expect the area to be 1, since $\int_{-\infty}^{\infty} p(x)\,dx = 1$ for any probability density function, and $p(x)$ is 0 except when $2 \le x \le 8$.

2. Recall that the mean is $\int_{-\infty}^{\infty} xp(x)\,dx$. In the fishing example, $p(x) = 0$ except when $2 \le x \le 8$, so the mean is

$$\int_2^8 xp(x)\,dx.$$

Using the equation for $p(x)$ from the graph,

$$\int_2^8 xp(x)\,dx = \int_2^6 xp(x)\,dx + \int_6^8 xp(x)\,dx$$

$$= \int_2^6 x(0.04x)\,dx + \int_6^8 x(-0.06x + 0.6)\,dx$$

$$= \left.\frac{0.04x^3}{3}\right|_2^6 + \left.\left(-0.02x^3 + 0.3x^2\right)\right|_6^8$$

$$\approx 5.253 \text{ tons.}$$

3. (a)

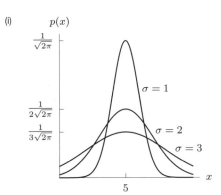

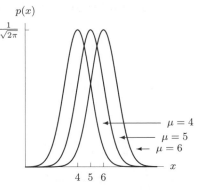

(b) Recall that the mean is the "balancing point." In other words, if the area under the curve was made of cardboard, we'd expect it to balance at the mean. All of the graphs are symmetric across the line $x = \mu$, so μ is the "balancing point" and hence the mean.

As the graphs also show, increasing σ flattens out the graph, in effect lessening the concentration of the data near the mean. Thus, the smaller the σ value, the more data is clustered around the mean.

Problems

4. (a) Since $d(e^{-ct})/dt = ce^{-ct}$, we have

$$c\int_0^6 e^{-ct}\,dt = -e^{-ct}\Big|_0^6 = 1 - e^{-6c} = 0.1,$$

so

$$c = -\frac{1}{6}\ln 0.9 \approx 0.0176.$$

(b) Similarly, with $c = 0.0176$, we have

$$c\int_6^{12} e^{-ct}\,dt = -e^{-ct}\Big|_6^{12}$$

$$= e^{-6c} - e^{-12c} = 0.9 - 0.81 = 0.09,$$

so the probability is 9%.

5. (a) We can find the proportion of students by integrating the density $p(x)$ between $x = 1.5$ and $x = 2$:

$$P(2) - P(1.5) = \int_{1.5}^2 \frac{x^3}{4}\,dx$$

$$= \left.\frac{x^4}{16}\right|_{1.5}^2$$

$$= \frac{(2)^4}{16} - \frac{(1.5)^4}{16} = 0.684,$$

so that the proportion is 0.684 : 1 or 68.4%.

(b) We find the mean by integrating x times the density over the relevant range:

$$\text{Mean} = \int_0^2 x \left(\frac{x^3}{4} \right) dx$$

$$= \int_0^2 \frac{x^4}{4} \, dx$$

$$= \left. \frac{x^5}{20} \right|_0^2$$

$$= \frac{2^5}{20} = 1.6 \text{ hours.}$$

(c) The median will be the time T such that exactly half of the students are finished by time T, or in other words

$$\frac{1}{2} = \int_0^T \frac{x^3}{4} \, dx$$

$$\frac{1}{2} = \left. \frac{x^4}{16} \right|_0^T$$

$$\frac{1}{2} = \frac{T^4}{16}$$

$$T = \sqrt[4]{8} = 1.682 \text{ hours.}$$

6. (a) Since $\displaystyle\int_0^\infty p(x) \, dx = 1$, we have

$$1 = \int_0^\infty a e^{-0.122x} \, dx$$

$$= \left. \frac{a}{-0.122} e^{-0.122x} \right|_0^\infty = \frac{a}{0.122}.$$

So $a = 0.122$.

(b)

$$P(x) = \int_0^x p(t) \, dt$$

$$= \int_0^x 0.122 e^{-0.122t} \, dt$$

$$= \left. -e^{0.122t} \right|_0^x = 1 - e^{-0.122x}.$$

(c) Median is the x such that

$$P(x) = 1 - e^{-0.122x} = 0.5.$$

So $e^{-0.122x} = 0.5$. Thus,

$$x = -\frac{\ln 0.5}{0.122} \approx 5.68 \text{ seconds}$$

and

$$\text{Mean} = \int_0^\infty x(0.122) e^{-0.122x} \, dx = -\int_0^\infty x \left(-0.122 e^{-0.122x} \right) dx.$$

We now use integration by parts. Let $u = -x$ and $v' = -0.122 e^{-0.122x}$. Then $u' = -1$, and $v = e^{-0.122x}$. Therefore,

$$\text{Mean} = \left. -x e^{-0.122x} \right|_0^\infty + \int_0^\infty e^{-0.122x} \, dx = \frac{1}{0.122} \approx 8.20 \text{ seconds.}$$

(d)

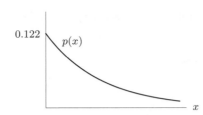

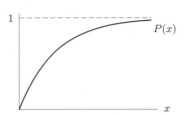

7. (a) The cumulative distribution function

$$P(t) = \int_0^t p(x)dx = \text{Area under graph of density function } p(x) \text{ for } 0 \le x \le t$$

$$= \text{Fraction of population who survive } t \text{ years or less after treatment}$$

$$= \text{Fraction of population who survive up to } t \text{ years after treatment.}$$

(b) The probability that a randomly selected person survives for at least t years is the probability that he lives t years or longer, so

$$S(t) = \int_t^\infty p(x)\,dx = \lim_{b \to \infty} \int_t^b Ce^{-Ct}\,dx$$

$$= \lim_{b \to \infty} -e^{-Ct}\Big|_t^b = \lim_{b \to \infty} -e^{-Cb} - (-e^{-Ct}) = e^{-Ct},$$

or equivalently,

$$S(t) = 1 - \int_0^t p(x)\,dx = 1 - \int_0^t Ce^{-Ct}\,dx = 1 + e^{-Ct}\Big|_0^t = 1 + (e^{-Ct} - 1) = e^{-Ct}.$$

(c) The probability of surviving at least two years is

$$S(2) = e^{-C(2)} = 0.70$$

so

$$\ln e^{-C(2)} = \ln 0.70$$
$$-2C = \ln 0.7$$
$$C = -\frac{1}{2}\ln 0.7 \approx 0.178.$$

8. (a) The probability you dropped the glove within a kilometer of home is given by

$$\int_0^1 2e^{-2x}dx = -e^{-2x}\Big|_0^1 = -e^{-2} + 1 \approx 0.865.$$

(b) Since the probability that the glove was dropped within y km $= \int_0^y p(x)dx = 1 - e^{-2y}$, we solve

$$1 - e^{-2y} = 0.95$$
$$e^{-2y} = 0.05$$
$$y = \frac{\ln 0.05}{-2} \approx 1.5 \text{ km.}$$

9. (a) Since $\mu = 100$ and $\sigma = 15$:

$$p(x) = \frac{1}{15\sqrt{2\pi}}e^{-\frac{1}{2}\left(\frac{x-100}{15}\right)^2}.$$

(b) The fraction of the population with IQ scores between 115 and 120 is (integrating numerically)

$$\int_{115}^{120} p(x)\,dx = \int_{115}^{120} \frac{1}{15\sqrt{2\pi}}e^{-\frac{(x-100)^2}{450}}\,dx$$

$$= \frac{1}{15\sqrt{2\pi}}\int_{115}^{120} e^{-\frac{(x-100)^2}{450}}\,dx$$

$$\approx 0.067 = 6.7\% \text{ of the population.}$$

10. (a) The normal distribution of car speeds with $\mu = 58$ and $\sigma = 4$ is shown in Figure 8.122.

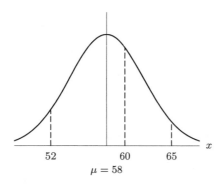

$\mu = 58$

Figure 8.122

The probability that a randomly selected car is going between 60 and 65 is equal to the area under the curve from $x = 60$ to $x = 65$,

$$\text{Probability} = \frac{1}{4\sqrt{2\pi}} \int_{60}^{65} e^{-(x-58)^2/(2 \cdot 4^2)} \, dx \approx 0.2685.$$

We obtain the value 0.2685 using a calculator or computer.

(b) To find the fraction of cars going under 52 km/hr, we evaluate the integral

$$\text{Fraction} = \frac{1}{4\sqrt{2\pi}} \int_0^{52} e^{-(x-58)^2/32} \, dx \approx 0.067.$$

Thus, approximately 6.7% of the cars are going less than 52 km/hr.

11. (a) First, we find the critical points of $p(x)$:

$$\frac{d}{dx}p(x) = \frac{1}{\sigma\sqrt{2\pi}} \left[\frac{-2(x-\mu)}{2\sigma^2}\right] e^{-\frac{(x-\mu)^2}{2\sigma^2}}$$

$$= -\frac{(x-\mu)}{\sigma^3\sqrt{2\pi}} e^{-\frac{(x-\mu)^2}{2\sigma^2}}.$$

This implies $x = \mu$ is the only critical point of $p(x)$.

To confirm that $p(x)$ is maximized at $x = \mu$, we rely on the first derivative test. As $-\frac{1}{\sigma^3\sqrt{2\pi}}e^{-\frac{(x-\mu)^2}{2\sigma^2}}$ is always negative, the sign of $p'(x)$ is the opposite of the sign of $(x-\mu)$; thus $p'(x) > 0$ when $x < \mu$, and $p'(x) < 0$ when $x > \mu$.

(b) To find the inflection points, we need to find where $p''(x)$ changes sign; that will happen only when $p''(x) = 0$. As

$$\frac{d^2}{dx^2}p(x) = -\frac{1}{\sigma^3\sqrt{2\pi}}e^{-\frac{(x-\mu)^2}{2\sigma^2}} \left[-\frac{(x-\mu)^2}{\sigma^2} + 1\right],$$

$p''(x)$ changes sign when $\left[-\frac{(x-\mu)^2}{\sigma^2} + 1\right]$ does, since the sign of the other factor is always negative. This occurs when

$$-\frac{(x-\mu)^2}{\sigma^2} + 1 = 0,$$

$$-(x-\mu)^2 = -\sigma^2,$$

$$x - \mu = \pm\sigma.$$

Thus, $x = \mu + \sigma$ or $x = \mu - \sigma$. Since $p''(x) > 0$ for $x < \mu - \sigma$ and $x > \mu + \sigma$ and $p''(x) < 0$ for $\mu - \sigma \le x \le \mu + \sigma$, these are in fact points of inflection.

(c) μ represents the mean of the distribution, while σ is the standard deviation. In other words, σ gives a measure of the "spread" of the distribution, i.e., how tightly the observations are clustered about the mean. A small σ tells us that most of the data are close to the mean; a large σ tells us that the data is spread out.

12. The fraction of the population within one standard deviation of the mean is given by

$$\text{Fraction within } \sigma \text{ of mean} = \int_{-\sigma}^{\sigma} \frac{1}{\sqrt{2\pi}\sigma} e^{-x^2/(2\sigma^2)}\, dx.$$

Let us substitute $w = \dfrac{x}{\sigma}$ so that $dw = \dfrac{1}{\sigma}dx$, and when $x = \pm\sigma$, $w = \pm 1$. Then we have

$$\text{Fraction} = \int_{-\sigma}^{\sigma} \frac{1}{\sqrt{2\pi}\sigma} e^{-x^2/(2\sigma^2)}\, dx = \int_{-1}^{1} \frac{1}{\sqrt{2\pi}\sigma} e^{-w^2/2} \cdot \sigma\, dw = \int_{-1}^{1} \frac{1}{\sqrt{2\pi}} e^{-w^2/2}\, dw.$$

This integral is independent of σ. Evaluating the integral numerically gives 0.68, showing that about 68% of the population lies within one standard deviation of the mean.

13. It is not (a) since a probability density must be a non-negative function; not (c) since the total integral of a probability density must be 1; (b) and (d) are probability density functions, but (d) is not a good model. According to (d), the probability that the next customer comes after 4 minutes is 0. In real life there should be a positive probability of not having a customer in the next 4 minutes. So (b) is the best answer.

14. (a) P is the cumulative distribution function, so the percentage of the population that made between \$20,000 and \$50,000 is
$$P(50) - P(20) = 99\% - 75\% = 24\%.$$
Therefore $\frac{6}{25}$ of the population made between \$20,000 and \$50,000.

(b) The median income is the income such that half the people made less than this amount. Looking at the chart, we see that $P(12.6) = 50\%$, so the median must be \$12,600.

(c) The cumulative distribution function looks something like Figure 8.123. The density function is the derivative of the cumulative distribution. Qualitatively it looks like Figure 8.124.

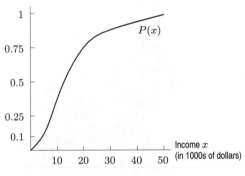

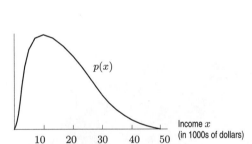

Figure 8.123: Cumulative distribution   **Figure 8.124**: Density function

The density function has a maximum at about \$8000. This means that more people have incomes around \$8000 than around any other amount. On the density function, this is the highest point. On the cumulative distribution, this is the point of steepest slope (because $P' = p$), which is also the point of inflection.

15. (a) Let the $p(r)$ be the density function. Then $P(r) = \int_0^r p(x)\, dx$, and from the Fundamental Theorem of Calculus, $p(r) = \frac{d}{dr}P(r) = \frac{d}{dr}\left(1 - (2r^2 + 2r + 1)e^{-2r}\right) = -(4r + 2)e^{-2r} + 2(2r^2 + 2r + 1)e^{-2r}$, or $p(r) = 4r^2 e^{-2r}$.

We have that $p'(r) = 8r(e^{-2r}) - 8r^2 e^{-2r} = e^{-2r} \cdot 8r(1 - r)$, which is zero when $r = 0$ or $r = 1$, negative when $r > 1$, and positive when $r < 1$. Thus $p(1) = 4e^{-2} \approx 0.54$ is a relative maximum.

Here are sketches of $p(r)$ and the cumulative position $P(r)$:

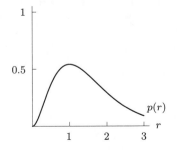

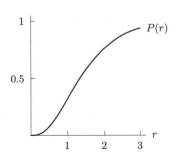

(b) The median distance is the distance r such that $P(r) = 1 - (2r^2 + 2r + 1)e^{-2r} = 0.5$, or equivalently, $(2r^2 + 2r + 1)e^{-2r} = 0.5$.

By experimentation with a calculator, we find that $r \approx 1.33$ Bohr radii is the median distance.

The mean distance is equal to the value of the integral $\int_0^\infty rp(r)\,dr = \lim_{x \to \infty} \int_0^x rp(r)\,dr$. We have that $\int_0^x rp(r)\,dr = \int_0^x 4r^3 e^{-2r}\,dr$. Using the integral table, we get

$$\int_0^x 4r^3 e^{-2r}\,dr = \left[\left(-\frac{1}{2}\right)4r^3 - \frac{1}{4}(12r^2) - \frac{1}{8}(24r) - \frac{1}{16}(24)\right]e^{-2x}\Bigg|_0^x$$
$$= \frac{3}{2} - \left[2x^3 + 3x^2 + 3x + \frac{3}{2}\right]e^{-2x}.$$

Taking the limit of this expression as $x \to \infty$, we see that all terms involving (powers of x or constants) $\cdot\, e^{-2x}$ have limit 0, and thus the mean distance is 1.5 Bohr radii.

The most likely distance is obtained by maximizing $p(r) = 4r^2 e^{-2r}$; as we have already seen this corresponds to $r = 1$ Bohr unit.

(c) Because it is the most likely distance of the electron from the nucleus.

Solutions for Chapter 8 Review

Exercises

1. Vertical slices are circular. Horizontal slices would be similar to ellipses in cross-section, or at least ovals (a word derived from *ovum*, the Latin word for egg).

 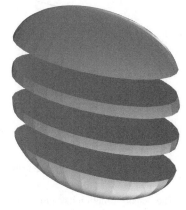

Figure 8.125

2. The limits of integration are 0 and b, and the rectangle represents the region under the curve $f(x) = h$ between these limits. Thus,

$$\text{Area of rectangle} = \int_0^b h\,dx = hx\Big|_0^b = hb.$$

3. The circle $x^2 + y^2 = r^2$ cannot be expressed as a function $y = f(x)$, since for every x with $-r < x < r$, there are two corresponding y values on the circle. However, if we consider the top half of the circle only, as shown below, we have $x^2 + y^2 = r^2$, or $y^2 = r^2 - x^2$, and taking the positive square root, we have that $y = \sqrt{r^2 - x^2}$ is the equation of the top semicircle.

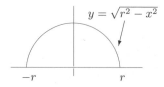

Then
$$\text{Area of Circle} = 2(\text{Area of semicircle}) = 2\int_{-r}^{r}\sqrt{r^2 - x^2}\, dx$$

We evaluate this using integral table formula 30.

$$2\int_{x=-r}^{x=r}\sqrt{r^2 - x^2}\, dx = 2\left[\frac{1}{2}\left(x\sqrt{r^2 - x^2} + r^2\arcsin\frac{x}{r}\right)\right]\Bigg|_{-r}^{r}$$
$$= r^2(\arcsin 1 - \arcsin(-1))$$
$$= r^2\left(\frac{\pi}{2} - \left(-\frac{\pi}{2}\right)\right) = \pi r^2.$$

4. Name the slanted line $y = f(x)$. Then the triangle is the region under the line $y = f(x)$ and between the lines $y = 0$ and $x = b$. Thus,
$$\text{Area of triangle} = \int_{0}^{b} f(x)\, dx.$$

Since $f(x)$ is a line of slope h/b which passes through the origin, its equation is $f(x) = hx/b$. Thus,
$$\text{Area of triangle} = \int_{0}^{b}\frac{hx}{b}\, dx = \frac{hx^2}{2b}\Bigg|_{0}^{b} = \frac{hb^2}{2b} = \frac{hb}{2}.$$

5. We slice the region vertically. Each rotated slice is approximately a cylinder with radius $y = x^2 + 1$ and thickness Δx. See Figure 8.126. The volume of a typical slice is $\pi(x^2 + 1)^2\Delta x$. The volume, V, of the object is the sum of the volumes of the slices:
$$V \approx \sum \pi(x^2 + 1)^2\Delta x.$$

As $\Delta x \to 0$ we obtain an integral.

$$V = \int_{0}^{4}\pi(x^2 + 1)^2 dx = \pi\int_{0}^{4}(x^4 + 2x^2 + 1)dx = \pi\left(\frac{x^5}{5} + \frac{2x^3}{3} + x\right)\Bigg|_{0}^{4} = \frac{3772\pi}{15} = 790.006.$$

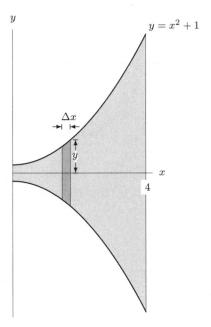

Figure 8.126

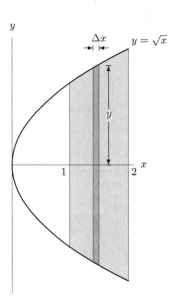

Figure 8.127

6. We slice the region vertically. Each rotated slice is approximately a cylinder with radius $y = \sqrt{x}$ and thickness Δx. See Figure 8.127. The volume of a typical slice is $\pi(\sqrt{x})^2\Delta x$. The volume, V, of the object is the sum of the volumes of the slices:

$$V \approx \sum \pi(\sqrt{x})^2\Delta x.$$

As $\Delta x \to 0$ we obtain an integral.

$$V = \int_1^2 \pi(\sqrt{x})^2\,dx = \pi\int_1^2 x\,dx = \pi\left(\frac{x^2}{2}\right)\Big|_1^2 = \frac{3\pi}{2} = 4.712.$$

7. We slice the region vertically. Each rotated slice is approximately a cylinder with radius $y = e^{-2x}$ and thickness Δx. See Figure 8.128. The volume of a typical slice is $\pi(e^{-2x})^2\Delta x$. The volume, V, of the object is the sum of the volumes of the slices:

$$V \approx \sum \pi(e^{-2x})^2\Delta x.$$

As $\Delta x \to 0$ we obtain an integral.

$$V = \int_0^1 \pi(e^{-2x})^2\,dx = \pi\int_0^1 e^{-4x}\,dx = \pi\left(-\frac{1}{4}\right)(e^{-4x})\Big|_0^1 = -\frac{\pi}{4}(e^{-4}-1) = 0.771.$$

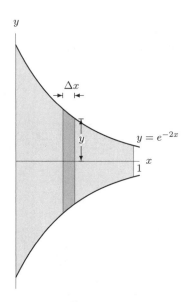

Figure 8.128

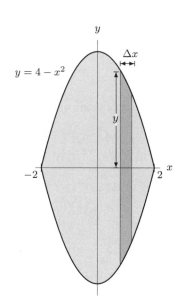

Figure 8.129

8. We slice the region vertically. Each rotated slice is approximately a cylinder with radius $y = 4 - x^2$ and thickness Δx. See Figure 8.129. The volume, V, of a typical slice is $\pi(4-x^2)^2\Delta x$. The volume of the object is the sum of the volumes of the slices:

$$V \approx \sum \pi(4-x^2)^2\Delta x.$$

As $\Delta x \to 0$ we obtain an integral. Since the region lies between $x = -2$ and $x = 2$, we have:

$$V = \int_{-2}^2 \pi(4-x^2)^2\,dx = \pi\int_{-2}^2 (16 - 8x^2 + x^4)\,dx = \pi\left(16x - \frac{8x^3}{3} + \frac{x^5}{5}\right)\Big|_{-2}^2 = \frac{512\pi}{15} = 107.233.$$

9. We divide the region into vertical strips of thickness Δx. As a slice is rotated about the x-axis, it creates a disk of radius r_{out} from which has been removed a smaller circular disk of inside radius r_{in}. We see in Figure 8.130 that $r_{\text{out}} = 2x$ and $r_{\text{in}} = x$. Thus,

$$\text{Volume of a slice} \approx \pi(r_{\text{out}})^2\Delta x - \pi(r_{\text{in}})^2\Delta x = \pi(2x)^2\Delta x - \pi(x)^2\Delta x.$$

To find the total volume, V, we integrate this quantity between $x = 0$ and $x = 3$:

$$V = \int_0^3 (\pi(2x)^2 - \pi(x)^2)dx = \pi \int_0^3 (4x^2 - x^2)\, dx = \pi \int_0^3 3x^2\, dx = \pi x^3 \Big|_0^3 = 27\pi = 84.823.$$

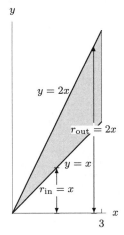

Figure 8.130

10. Each slice is a circular disk. The radius, r, of the disk increases with h and is given in the problem by $r = \sqrt{h}$. Thus

$$\text{Volume of slice} \approx \pi r^2 \Delta h = \pi h \Delta h.$$

Summing over all slices, we have

$$\text{Total volume} \approx \sum \pi h \Delta h.$$

Taking a limit as $\Delta h \to 0$, we get

$$\text{Total volume} = \lim_{\Delta h \to 0} \sum \pi h \Delta h = \int_0^{12} \pi h\, dh.$$

Evaluating gives

$$\text{Total volume} = \pi \frac{h^2}{2} \Big|_0^{12} = 72\pi.$$

11. We slice the cone horizontally into cylindrical disks with radius r and thickness Δh. See Figure 8.131. The volume of each disk is $\pi r^2 \Delta h$. We use the similar triangles in Figure 8.132 to write r as a function of h:

$$\frac{r}{h} = \frac{3}{12} \quad \text{so} \quad r = \frac{1}{4}h.$$

The volume of the disk at height h is $\pi(\frac{1}{4}h)^2 \Delta h$. To find the total volume, we integrate this quantity from $h = 0$ to $h = 12$.

$$V = \int_0^{12} \pi \left(\frac{1}{4}h\right)^2 dh = \frac{\pi}{16} \frac{h^3}{3} \Big|_0^{12} = 36\pi = 113.097\ \text{m}^3.$$

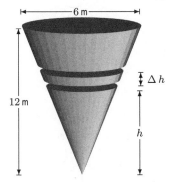

Figure 8.131

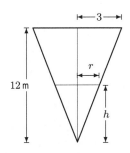

Figure 8.132

12. (a) We slice the pyramid horizontally. See Figure 8.133. Each slice is a square slab of thickness Δh, so the volume of a slice at height h is $s^2 \Delta h$, where s is the length of a side. We use the similar triangles in Figure 8.134 to write s as a function of h:

$$\frac{s}{10 - h} = \frac{8}{10} \quad \text{so} \quad s = 0.8(10 - h).$$

The volume of the slice at height h is $(0.8(10 - h))^2 \Delta h$. To find the total volume, we integrate this quantity from $h = 0$ to $h = 10$.

$$V = \int_0^{10} (0.8(10 - h))^2 \, dh = 0.64 \int_0^{10} (h - 10)^2 \, dh = \frac{16}{75} (h - 10)^3 \Big|_0^{10} = \frac{640}{3} = 213.333 \text{ m}^3.$$

(b) As in part (a),

$$\text{Volume of a slice at height } h \approx s^2 \Delta h = (0.8(10 - h))^2 \Delta h.$$

The height h ranges from $h = 0$ to $h = 6$. We have

$$V = \int_0^6 (0.8(10 - h))^2 \, dh = 0.64 \int_0^6 (h - 10)^2 \, dh = \frac{16}{75} (h - 10)^3 \Big|_0^6 = \frac{4992}{25} = 199.680 \text{ m}^3.$$

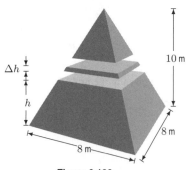

Figure 8.133

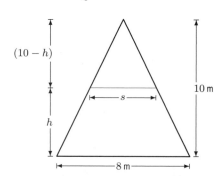

Figure 8.134

13. We slice the tank horizontally. There is an outside radius r_{out} and an inside radius r_{in} and, at height h,

$$\text{Volume of a slice} \approx \pi (r_{\text{out}})^2 \Delta h - \pi (r_{\text{in}})^2 \Delta h.$$

See Figure 8.135. We see that $r_{\text{out}} = 3$ for every slice. We use similar triangles to find r_{in} in terms of the height h:

$$\frac{r_{\text{in}}}{h} = \frac{3}{6} \quad \text{so} \quad r_{\text{in}} = \frac{1}{2} h.$$

At height h,

$$\text{Volume of slice} \approx \pi (3)^2 \Delta h - \pi \left(\frac{1}{2} h\right)^2 \Delta h.$$

To find the total volume, we integrate this quantity from $h = 0$ to $h = 6$.

$$V = \int_0^6 \left(\pi (3)^2 - \pi \left(\frac{1}{2} h\right)^2\right) dh = \pi \int_0^6 \left(9 - \frac{1}{4} h^2\right) dh = \pi \left(9h - \frac{h^3}{12}\right) \Big|_0^6 = 36\pi = 113.097 \text{ m}^3.$$

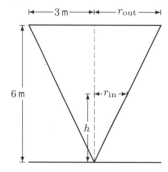

Figure 8.135

14. Since $f(x) = \sin x$, $f'(x) = \cos(x)$, so

$$\text{Arc Length} = \int_0^\pi \sqrt{1 + \cos^2 x}\, dx.$$

15. We'll find the arc length of the top half of the ellipse, and multiply that by 2. In the top half of the ellipse, the equation $(x^2/a^2) + (y^2/b^2) = 1$ implies

$$y = +b\sqrt{1 - \frac{x^2}{a^2}}.$$

Differentiating $(x^2/a^2) + (y^2/b^2) = 1$ implicitly with respect to x gives us

$$\frac{2x}{a^2} + \frac{2y}{b^2}\frac{dy}{dx} = 0,$$

so

$$\frac{dy}{dx} = \frac{\frac{-2x}{a^2}}{\frac{2y}{b^2}} = -\frac{b^2 x}{a^2 y}.$$

Substituting this into the arc length formula, we get

$$\begin{aligned}
\text{Arc Length} &= \int_{-a}^{a} \sqrt{1 + \left(-\frac{b^2 x}{a^2 y}\right)^2}\, dx \\
&= \int_{-a}^{a} \sqrt{1 + \left(\frac{b^4 x^2}{a^4 (b^2)(1 - \frac{x^2}{a^2})}\right)}\, dx \\
&= \int_{-a}^{a} \sqrt{1 + \left(\frac{b^2 x^2}{a^2(a^2 - x^2)}\right)}\, dx.
\end{aligned}$$

Hence the arc length of the entire ellipse is

$$2\int_{-a}^{a} \sqrt{1 + \left(\frac{b^2 x^2}{a^2(a^2 - x^2)}\right)}\, dx.$$

16. Since $f'(x) = \cos x$, we have

$$L = \int_0^3 \sqrt{1 + (f'(x))^2}\, dx = \int_0^3 \sqrt{1 + \cos^2 x}\, dx = 3.621.$$

We see in Figure 8.136 that the length of the curve is slightly longer than the length of the x-axis from $x = 0$ to $x = 3$, so the answer of 3.621 makes sense.

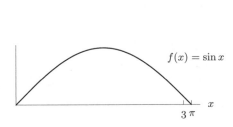

Figure 8.136

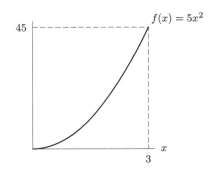

Figure 8.137

17. Since $f'(x) = 10x$, we have

$$L = \int_0^3 \sqrt{1 + (f'(x))^2}\, dx = \int_0^3 \sqrt{1 + (10x)^2}\, dx = \int_0^3 \sqrt{1 + 100x^2}\, dx = 45.230.$$

We see in Figure 8.137 that the length of the curve is definitely longer than 45 and slightly longer than $\sqrt{45^2 + 3^2} = 45.10$, so the answer of 45.230 is reasonable.

Problems

18. (a) The points of intersection are $x = 0$ to $x = 2$, so we have

$$\text{Area} = \int_0^2 (2x - x^2)dx = x^2 - \frac{x^3}{3}\bigg|_0^2 = \frac{4}{3} = 1.333.$$

(b) The outside radius is $2x$ and the inside radius is x^2, so we have

$$\text{Volume} = \int_0^2 (\pi(2x)^2 - \pi(x^2)^2)dx = \pi \int_0^2 (4x^2 - x^4)dx = \frac{\pi}{15}(20x^3 - 3x^5)\bigg|_0^2 = \frac{64\pi}{15} = 13.404.$$

(c) The length of the perimeter is equal to the length of the top plus the length of the bottom. Using the arclength formula, and the fact that the derivative of $2x$ is 2 and the derivative of x^2 is $2x$, we have

$$L = \int_0^2 \sqrt{1 + 2^2}\, dx + \int_0^2 \sqrt{1 + (2x)^2}\, dx = 4.4721 + 4.6468 = 9.119.$$

19. (a) See Figure 8.138

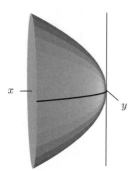

Figure 8.138: Rotated Region

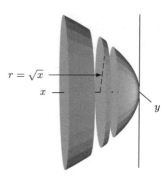

Figure 8.139: Cutaway View

(b) Divide [0,1] into N subintervals of width $\Delta x = \frac{1}{N}$. The volume of the ith disc is $\pi(\sqrt{x_i})^2 \Delta x = \pi x_i \Delta x$. So, $V \approx \sum_{i=1}^{N} \pi x_i \Delta x$. See Figure 8.139

(c)

$$\text{Volume} = \int_0^1 \pi x\, dx = \frac{\pi}{2}x^2\bigg|_0^1 = \frac{\pi}{2} \approx 1.57.$$

20. (a) See Figure 8.140.

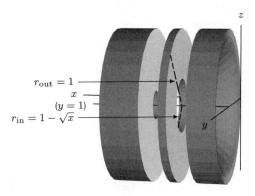

$r_{\text{out}} = 1$

x

$(y = 1)$

$r_{\text{in}} = 1 - \sqrt{x}$

y

Figure 8.140

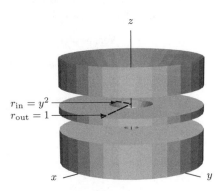

$r_{\text{in}} = y^2$

$r_{\text{out}} = 1$

x y

Figure 8.141

Slice the figure perpendicular to the x–axis. One gets washers of inner radius $1 - \sqrt{x}$ and outer radius 1. Therefore,

$$V = \int_0^1 \left(\pi 1^2 - \pi(1 - \sqrt{x})^2\right)\,dx$$

$$= \pi \int_0^1 \left(1 - [1 - 2\sqrt{x} + x]\right) dx$$

$$= \pi \left[\frac{4}{3}x^{\frac{3}{2}} - \frac{1}{2}x^2\right]_0^1 = \frac{5\pi}{6} \approx 2.62.$$

(b) See Figure 8.141. Note that $x = y^2$. We now integrate over y instead of x, slicing perpendicular to the y–axis. This gives us washers of inner radius x and outer radius 1. So

$$V = \int_{y=0}^{y=1} \left(\pi 1^2 - \pi x^2\right) dy$$

$$= \int_0^1 \pi(1 - y^4) dy$$

$$= \left(\pi y - \frac{\pi}{5}y^5\right)\bigg|_0^1 = \pi - \frac{\pi}{5} = \frac{4\pi}{5} \approx 2.51.$$

21. (a) Since $y = ax^2$ is non-negative, we integrate to find the area:

$$\text{Area} = \int_0^2 (ax^2) dx = a\frac{x^3}{3}\bigg|_0^2 = \frac{8a}{3}.$$

(b) Each slice of the object is approximately a cylinder with radius ax^2 and thickness Δx. We have

$$\text{Volume} = \int_0^2 \pi(ax^2)^2 dx = \pi a^2 \frac{x^5}{5}\bigg|_0^2 = \frac{32}{5}a^2\pi.$$

22. (a) Since $y = e^{-bx}$ is non-negative, we integrate to find the area:

$$\text{Area} = \int_0^1 (e^{-bx}) dx = \frac{-1}{b}e^{-bx}\bigg|_0^1 = \frac{1}{b}(1 - e^{-b}).$$

(b) Each slice of the object is approximately a cylinder with radius e^{-bx} and thickness Δx. We have

$$\text{Volume} = \int_0^1 \pi(e^{-bx})^2 dx = \pi \int_0^1 e^{-2bx} dx = \frac{-\pi}{2b}e^{-2bx}\bigg|_0^1 = \frac{\pi}{2b}(1 - e^{-2b}).$$

23. (a) We divide the region into vertical strips of thickness Δx. As a slice is rotated about the x-axis, it creates a disk of radius r_{out} from which has been removed a smaller circular disk of radius r_{in}. We see in Figure 8.142 that $r_{\text{out}} = \sin x$ and $r_{\text{in}} = 0.5x$. Thus,

$$\text{Volume of a slice} \approx \pi(r_{\text{out}})^2 \Delta x - \pi(r_{\text{in}})^2 \Delta x = \pi(\sin x)^2 \Delta x - \pi(0.5x)^2 \Delta x.$$

To find the total volume, we integrate this quantity between the points of intersection $x = 0$ and $x = 1.9$:

$$V = \int_0^{1.9} (\pi(\sin x)^2 - \pi(0.5x)^2)dx = \pi \left(-\frac{\sin x \cos x}{2} - \frac{x^3}{12} + x \right) \Bigg|_0^{1.9} = 1.669.$$

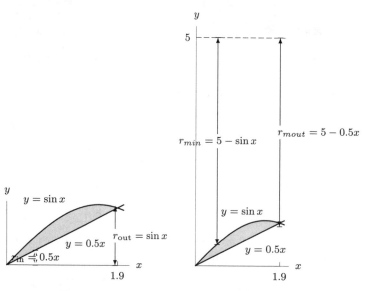

Figure 8.142   **Figure 8.143**

(b) We see in Figure 8.143 that $r_{\text{out}} = 5 - 0.5x$ and $r_{\text{in}} = 5 - \sin x$. Thus,

$$\text{Volume of a slice} \approx \pi(r_{\text{out}})^2 \Delta x - \pi(r_{\text{in}})^2 \Delta x = \pi(5 - 0.5x)^2 \Delta x - \pi(5 - \sin x)^2 \Delta x.$$

To find the total volume, V, we integrate this quantity between the points of intersection $x = 0$ and $x = 1.9$:

$$V = \int_0^{1.9} \left(\pi(5 - 0.5x)^2 - \pi(5 - \sin x)^2 \right) dx = \frac{\pi}{12}(6(\sin x - 20) \cos x + x(x^2 - 30x - 6)) \Bigg|_0^{1.9} = 11.550.$$

24. We divide the region into vertical strips of thickness Δx. As a slice is rotated about the x-axis, it creates a disk of radius r_{out} from which has been removed a disk of radius r_{in}. We see in Figure 8.144 that $r_{\text{out}} = 5 + 2x$ and $r_{\text{in}} = 5$. Thus,

$$\text{Volume of a slice} \approx \pi(r_{\text{out}})^2 \Delta x - \pi(r_{\text{in}})^2 \Delta x = \pi(5 + 2x)^2 \Delta x - \pi(5)^2 \Delta x.$$

To find the total volume, V, we integrate this quantity between $x = 0$ and $x = 4$:

$$V = \int_0^4 (\pi(5 + 2x)^2 - \pi(5)^2)dx = \pi \int_0^4 ((5 + 2x)^2 - 25) \, dx = \pi \left(\frac{4}{3}x^3 + 10x^2 \right) \Bigg|_0^4 = \frac{736\pi}{3} = 770.737.$$

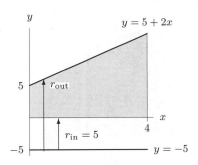

Figure 8.144

25. (a) We divide the region into vertical strips of thickness Δx. As a slice is rotated about the x-axis, it creates a disk of radius r_{out} from which has been removed a disk of radius r_{in}. We see in Figure 8.145 that $r_{\text{out}} = 2 + x^2$ and $r_{\text{in}} = 2$. Thus,

$$\text{Volume of a slice } \approx \pi(r_{\text{out}})^2 \Delta x - \pi(r_{\text{in}})^2 \Delta x = \pi(2 + x^2)^2 \Delta x - \pi(2)^2 \Delta x.$$

To find the total volume, V, we integrate this quantity between $x = 0$ and $x = 3$:

$$V = \int_0^3 (\pi(2 + x^2)^2 - \pi(2)^2) dx = \pi \int_0^3 ((2 + x^2)^2 - 4)\, dx = \frac{\pi}{15}(3x^5 + 20x^3)\Big|_0^3 = \frac{423\pi}{5} = 265.778.$$

(b) We see in Figure 8.146 that $r_{\text{out}} = 10$ and $r_{\text{in}} = 10 - x^2$. Thus,

$$\text{Volume of a slice } \approx \pi(r_{\text{out}})^2 \Delta x - \pi(r_{\text{in}})^2 \Delta x = \pi(10)^2 \Delta x - \pi(10 - x^2)^2 \Delta x.$$

To find the total volume, V, we integrate this quantity between $x = 0$ and $x = 3$:

$$V = \int_0^3 (\pi(10)^2 - \pi(10 - x^2)^2) dx = \pi \int_0^3 (100 - (10 - x^2)^2)\, dx = \frac{\pi}{15}(100x^3 - 3x^5)\Big|_0^3 = \frac{657\pi}{5} = 412.805.$$

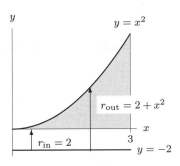

Figure 8.145

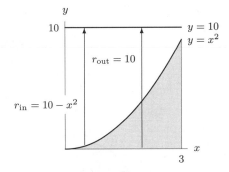

Figure 8.146

26. Slice the object into disks vertically, as in Figure 8.147. A typical disk has thickness Δx and radius $y = \sqrt{1 - x^2}$. Thus

$$\text{Volume of disk } \approx \pi y^2 \Delta x = \pi(1 - x^2)\, \Delta x.$$

$$\text{Volume of solid } = \lim_{\Delta x \to 0} \sum \pi(1 - x^2)\, \Delta x = \int_0^1 \pi(1 - x^2)\, dx = \pi\left(x - \frac{x^3}{3}\right)\Big|_0^1 = \frac{2\pi}{3}.$$

Note: As we expect, this is the volume of a half sphere.

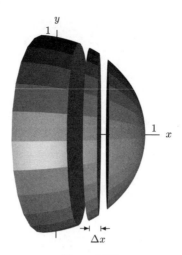

Figure 8.147

27. Slice the object into rings horizontally, as in Figure 8.148. A typical ring has thickness Δy, inner radius 2 and outer radius $2 + x = 2 + \sqrt{1 - y^2}$. Thus,

$$\text{Volume of ring } \approx \pi(2 + \sqrt{1 - y^2})^2 \Delta y - \pi 2^2 \Delta y = \pi(4\sqrt{1 - y^2} + 1 - y^2)\, \Delta y.$$

$$
\begin{aligned}
\text{Volume of solid } &= \int_0^1 \pi(4\sqrt{1 - y^2} + 1 - y^2)\, dy \\
&= 4\pi \int_0^1 \sqrt{1 - y^2}\, dy + \pi \int_0^1 1\, dy - \pi \int_0^1 y^2\, dy \\
&= 4\pi \left(\frac{1}{2} \left(y\sqrt{1 - y^2} \Big|_0^1 + \int_0^1 \frac{1}{\sqrt{1 - y^2}}\, dy \right) \right) + \pi y \Big|_0^1 - \frac{\pi y^3}{3} \Big|_0^1 \\
&= 2\pi y\sqrt{1 - y^2} + 2\pi \arcsin y + \pi y - \frac{\pi y^3}{3} \Big|_0^1 \\
&= 0 + 2\pi \arcsin 1 + \pi - \frac{\pi}{3} - 0 - 2\pi \arcsin 0 - 0 + 0 \\
&= \pi^2 + \frac{2\pi}{3} = 11.964.
\end{aligned}
$$

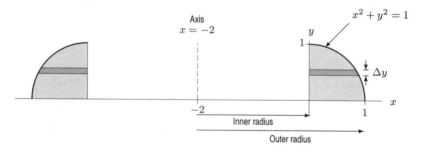

Figure 8.148: Cross-section of solid

28. Slice the object into rings horizontally, as in Figure 8.149. A typical ring has thickness Δy, outer radius 1, and inner radius $1 - x = 1 - \sqrt{1 - y^2}$. Thus,

$$\text{Volume of ring } \approx \pi 1^2 \Delta y - \pi(1 - \sqrt{1 - y^2})^2 \Delta y = \pi(2\sqrt{1 - y^2} - (1 - y^2))\, \Delta y.$$

$$\text{Volume of solid} = \int_0^1 \pi(2\sqrt{1-y^2} - 1 + y^2)\, dy$$

$$= 2\pi \int_0^1 \sqrt{1-y^2}\, dy - \pi \int_0^1 1\, dy + \pi \int_0^1 y^2\, dy$$

$$= 2\pi \cdot \frac{1}{2} \left(y\sqrt{1-y^2}\Big|_0^1 + 1^2 \int_0^1 \frac{1}{\sqrt{1-y^2}}\, dy \right) - \pi y \Big|_0^1 + \frac{\pi y^3}{3}\Big|_0^1$$

$$= \pi y\sqrt{1-y^2} + \pi \arcsin y - \pi y + \frac{\pi y^3}{3}\Big|_0^1$$

$$= 0 + \frac{\pi^2}{2} - \pi + \frac{\pi}{3} - 0 - 0 + 0 - 0$$

$$= \frac{\pi^2}{2} - \frac{2\pi}{3} = 2.840.$$

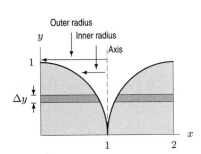

Figure 8.149: Cross-section of solid

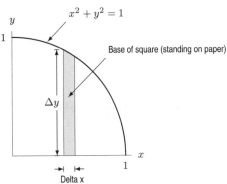

Figure 8.150: Base of solid

29. Slicing perpendicularly to the x-axis gives squares whose thickness is Δx and whose side is $y = \sqrt{1-x^2}$. See Figure 8.150. Thus,

$$\text{Volume of square slice} \approx (\sqrt{1-x^2})^2 \Delta x = (1-x^2)\,\Delta x.$$

$$\text{Volume of solid} = \int_0^1 (1-x^2)\, dx = x - \frac{x^3}{3}\Big|_0^1 = \frac{2}{3}.$$

30. Slicing perpendicularly to the y-axis gives semicircles whose thickness is Δy and whose diameter is $x = \sqrt{1-y^2}$. See Figure 8.151. Thus

$$\text{Volume of semicircular slice} \approx \pi \left(\frac{\sqrt{1-y^2}}{2} \right)^2 \Delta y = \frac{\pi}{4}(1-y^2)\,\Delta y.$$

$$\text{Volume of solid} = \int_0^1 \frac{\pi}{4}(1-y^2)\, dy = \frac{\pi}{4}\left(y - \frac{y^3}{3} \right)\Big|_0^1 = \frac{\pi}{4} \cdot \frac{2}{3} = \frac{\pi}{6}.$$

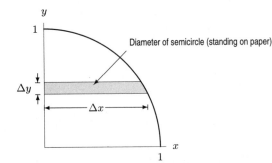

Figure 8.151: Base of Solid

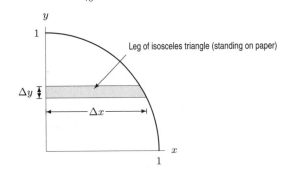

Figure 8.152: Base of solid

31. An isosceles triangle with legs of length s has

$$\text{Area} = \frac{1}{2}s^2.$$

Slicing perpendicularly to the y-axis gives isosceles triangles whose thickness is Δy and whose leg is $x = \sqrt{1 - y^2}$. See Figure 8.152. Thus

$$\text{Volume of triangular slice} \approx \frac{1}{2}(\sqrt{1 - y^2})\,\Delta y = \frac{1}{2}(1 - y^2)\,\Delta y.$$

$$\text{Volume of solid} = \int_0^1 \frac{1}{2}(1 - y^2)\,dy = \frac{1}{2}\left(y - \frac{y^3}{3}\right)\Bigg|_0^1 = \frac{1}{3}.$$

32. (a) Slice the headlight into N disks of height Δx by cutting perpendicular to the x-axis. The radius of each disk is y; the height is Δx. The volume of each disk is $\pi y^2 \Delta x$. Therefore, the Riemann sum approximating the volume of the headlight is

$$\sum_{i=1}^N \pi y_i^2 \Delta x = \sum_{i=1}^N \pi \frac{9x_i}{4} \Delta x.$$

(b)

$$\pi \int_0^4 \frac{9x}{4}\,dx = \pi \frac{9}{8}x^2 \Bigg|_0^4 = 18\pi.$$

33. (a) The line $y = ax$ must pass through (l, b). Hence $b = al$, so $a = b/l$.

(b) Cut the cone into N slices, slicing perpendicular to the x-axis. Each piece is almost a cylinder. The radius of the ith cylinder is $r(x_i) = \dfrac{bx_i}{l}$, so the volume

$$V \approx \sum_{i=1}^N \pi \left(\frac{bx_i}{l}\right)^2 \Delta x.$$

Therefore, as $N \to \infty$, we get

$$V = \int_0^l \pi b^2 l^{-2} x^2\,dx$$

$$= \pi \frac{b^2}{l^2}\left[\frac{x^3}{3}\right]_0^l = \left(\pi \frac{b^2}{l^2}\right)\left(\frac{l^3}{3}\right) = \frac{1}{3}\pi b^2 l.$$

34. (a) If you slice the apple perpendicular to the core, you expect that the cross section will be approximately a circle.

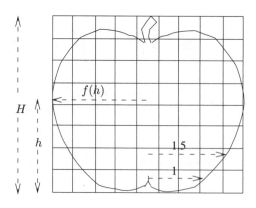

If $f(h)$ is the radius of the apple at height h above the bottom, and H is the height of the apple, then

$$\text{Volume} = \int_0^H \pi f(h)^2\,dh.$$

Ignoring the stem, $H \approx 3.5$. Although we do not have a formula for $f(h)$, we can estimate it at various points. (Remember, we measure here from the bottom of the *apple*, which is not quite the bottom of the graph.)

h	0	0.5	1	1.5	2	2.5	3	3.5
$f(h)$	1	1.5	2	2.1	2.3	2.2	1.8	1.2

Now let $g(h) = \pi f(h)^2$, the area of the cross-section at height h. From our approximations above, we get the following table.

h	0	0.5	1	1.5	2	2.5	3	3.5
$g(h)$	3.14	7.07	12.57	13.85	16.62	13.85	10.18	4.52

We can now take left- and right-hand sum approximations. Note that $\Delta h = 0.5$ inches. Thus

$$\text{LEFT}(9) = (3.14 + 7.07 + 12.57 + 13.85 + 16.62 + 13.85 + 10.18)(0.5) = 38.64.$$
$$\text{RIGHT}(9) = (7.07 + 12.57 + 13.85 + 16.62 + 13.85 + 10.18 + 4.52)(0.5) = 39.33.$$

Thus the volume of the apple is ≈ 39 cu.in.

(b) The apple weighs $0.03 \times 39 \approx 1.17$ pounds, so it costs about 94¢.

35.

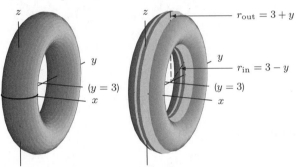

Figure 8.153: The Torus   **Figure 8.154**: Slice of Torus

As shown in Figure 8.154, we slice the torus perpendicular to the line $y = 3$. We obtain washers with width dx, inner radius $r_{\text{in}} = 3 - y$, and outer radius $r_{\text{out}} = 3 + y$. Therefore, the area of the washer is $\pi r_{\text{out}}^2 - \pi r_{\text{in}}^2 = \pi[(3 + y)^2 - (3 - y)^2] = 12\pi y$. Since $y = \sqrt{1 - x^2}$, the volume is gotten by summing up the volumes of the washers: we get

$$\int_{-1}^{1} 12\pi\sqrt{1 - x^2}\, dx = 12\pi \int_{-1}^{1} \sqrt{1 - x^2}\, dx.$$

But $\int_{-1}^{1} \sqrt{1 - x^2}\, dx$ is the area of a semicircle of radius 1, which is $\frac{\pi}{2}$. So we get $12\pi \cdot \frac{\pi}{2} = 6\pi^2 \approx 59.22$. (Or, you could use

$$\int \sqrt{1 - x^2}\, dx = \left[x\sqrt{1 - x^2} + \arcsin(x) \right],$$

by VI-30 and VI-28.)

36. Multiplying $r = 2a\cos\theta$ by r, converting to Cartesian coordinates, and completing the square gives

$$r^2 = 2ar\cos\theta$$
$$x^2 + y^2 = 2ax$$
$$x^2 - 2ax + a^2 + y^2 = a^2$$
$$(x - a)^2 + y^2 = a^2.$$

This is the standard form of the equation of a circle with radius a and center $(x, y) = (a, 0)$.

To check the limits on θ note that the circle is in the right half plane, where $-\pi/2 \le \theta \le \pi/2$. Rays from the origin at all these angles meet the circle because the circle is tangent to the y-axis at the origin.

37. The area is given by

$$\int_{-\pi/2}^{\pi/2} \frac{1}{2} r^2 \, d\theta = \int_{-\pi/2}^{\pi/2} \frac{1}{2} \left(2a \cos \theta \right)^2 \, d\theta = 2a^2 \int_{-\pi/2}^{\pi/2} \cos^2 \theta \, d\theta = 2a^2 \left(\frac{1}{2} \cos \theta \sin \theta + \frac{\theta}{2} \right) \Big|_{-\pi/2}^{\pi/2} = \pi a^2.$$

(We have used formula IV-18 from the integral table. The integral can also be done using a calculator or integration by parts.)

38. See Figure 8.155. The circles meet where

$$2a \cos \theta = a$$
$$\cos \theta = \frac{1}{2}$$
$$\theta = \pm \frac{\pi}{3}.$$

The area is obtained by subtraction:

$$\text{Area} = \int_{-\pi/3}^{\pi/3} \left(\frac{1}{2} \left(2a \cos \theta \right)^2 - \frac{1}{2} a^2 \right) \, d\theta$$

$$= \int_{-\pi/3}^{\pi/3} \left(2a^2 \cos^2 \theta - \frac{1}{2} a^2 \right) \, d\theta$$

$$= \left(2a^2 \left(\frac{1}{2} \cos \theta \sin \theta + \frac{\theta}{2} \right) - \frac{a^2}{2} \theta \right) \Big|_{-\pi/3}^{\pi/3}$$

$$= \left(\frac{\pi}{3} + \frac{\sqrt{3}}{2} \right) a^2.$$

Since

$$\frac{\left(\pi/3 + \sqrt{3}/2 \right) a^2}{\pi a^2} = 61\%$$

the shaded region covers 61% of circle C.

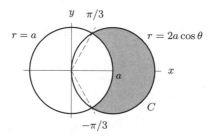

Figure 8.155

39. (a) Writing C in parametric form gives

$$x = 2a \cos^2 \theta \quad \text{and} \quad y = 2a \cos \theta \sin \theta,$$

so the slope is given by

$$\frac{dy}{dx} = \frac{dy/d\theta}{dx/d\theta} = \frac{-2a \sin^2 \theta + 2a \cos^2 \theta}{-4a \cos \theta \sin \theta} = \frac{\sin^2 \theta - \cos^2 \theta}{2 \cos \theta \sin \theta}.$$

(b) The maximum y-value occurs where $dy/dx = 0$, so

$$\sin^2 \theta - \cos^2 \theta = 0$$
$$\theta = \pm \frac{\pi}{4}.$$

The value $\theta = \pi/4$ gives the maximum y-value; $\theta = -\pi/4$ gives the minimum y-value.

40. Writing C in parametric form gives

$$x = 2a\cos^2\theta \quad \text{and} \quad y = 2a\cos\theta\sin\theta,$$

so

$$
\begin{aligned}
\text{Arc length} &= \int_{-\pi/2}^{\pi/2} \sqrt{(-4a\cos\theta\sin\theta)^2 + (-2a\sin^2\theta + 2a\cos^2\theta)^2}\, d\theta \\
&= 2a\int_{-\pi/2}^{\pi/2} \sqrt{4\cos^2\theta\sin^2\theta + \sin^4\theta - 2\sin^2\theta\cos^2\theta + \cos^4\theta}\, d\theta \\
&= 2a\int_{-\pi/2}^{\pi/2} \sqrt{\sin^4\theta + 2\sin^2\theta\cos^2\theta + \cos^4\theta}\, d\theta \\
&= 2a\int_{-\pi/2}^{\pi/2} \sqrt{(\sin^2\theta + \cos^2\theta)^2}\, d\theta \\
&= 2a\int_{-\pi/2}^{\pi/2} d\theta = 2\pi a.
\end{aligned}
$$

41. The total mass is 12 gm, so the center of mass is located at $\bar{x} = \frac{1}{12}(-5\cdot 3 - 3\cdot 3 + 2\cdot 3 + 7\cdot 3) = \frac{1}{4}$.

42. (a) Since the density is constant, the mass is the product of the area of the plate and its density.

$$\text{Area of the plate} = \int_0^1 (\sqrt{x} - x^2)\, dx = \left(\frac{2}{3}x^{3/2} - \frac{1}{3}x^3\right)\Big|_0^1 = \frac{1}{3}\,\text{cm}^2.$$

Thus the mass of the plate is $2\cdot 1/3 = 2/3\,\text{gm}$.

(b) See Figure 8.156. Since the region is "fatter" closer to the origin, $\bar{x}$ is less than $1/2$.

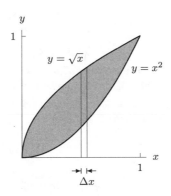

Figure 8.156

(c) To find $\bar{x}$, we slice the region into vertical strips of width Δx. See Figure 8.156.

$$\text{Area of strip} = A_x(x)\Delta x \approx (\sqrt{x} - x^2)\Delta x\,\text{cm}^2.$$

Then we have

$$\bar{x} = \frac{\int x\delta A_x(x)\, dx}{\text{Mass}} = \frac{\int_0^1 2x(\sqrt{x} - x^2)\, dx}{2/3} = \frac{3}{2}\int_0^1 2(x^{3/2} - x^3)\, dx = \frac{3}{2}\cdot 2\left(\frac{2}{5}x^{5/2} - \frac{1}{4}x^4\right)\Big|_0^1 = \frac{9}{20}\,\text{cm}.$$

This is less than $1/2$, as predicted in part (b). So $\bar{x} = \bar{y} = 9/20\,\text{cm}$.

43. Let x be the height from ground to the weight. It follows that $0 \le x \le 20$. At height x, to lift the weight Δx more, the work needed is $200\Delta x + 2(20 - x)\Delta x = (240 - 2x)\Delta x$. So the total work is

$$W = \int_0^{20} (240 - 2x)dx$$

$$= (240x - x^2)\Big|_0^{20}$$

$$= 240(20) - 20^2 = 4400 \text{ ft-lb.}$$

44. Let x be the distance from the bucket to the surface of the water. It follows that $0 \le x \le 40$. At x feet, the bucket weighs $\left(30 - \frac{1}{4}x\right)$, where the $\frac{1}{4}x$ term is due to the leak. When the bucket is x feet from the surface of the water, the work done by raising it Δx feet is $\left(30 - \frac{1}{4}x\right)\Delta x$. So the total work required to raise the bucket to the top is

$$W = \int_0^{40} (30 - \frac{1}{4}x)dx$$

$$= \left(30x - \frac{1}{8}x^2\right)\Big|_0^{40}$$

$$= 30(40) - \frac{1}{8}40^2 = 1000 \text{ ft-lb.}$$

45.

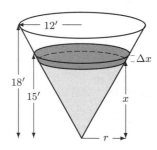

Figure 8.157

Let x be the depth of the water measured from the bottom of the tank. See Figure 8.157. It follows that $0 \le x \le 15$. Let r be the radius of the section of the cone with height x. By similar triangles, $\frac{r}{x} = \frac{12}{18}$, so $r = \frac{2}{3}x$. Then the work required to pump a layer of water with thickness of Δx at depth x over the top of the tank is $62.4\pi \left(\frac{2}{3}x\right)^2 \Delta x(18 - x)$. So the total work done by pumping the water over the top of the tank is

$$W = \int_0^{15} 62.4\pi \left(\frac{2}{3}x\right)^2 (18 - x)dx$$

$$= \frac{4}{9} 62.4\pi \int_0^{15} x^2(18 - x)dx$$

$$= \frac{4}{9} 62.4\pi \left(6x^3 - \frac{1}{4}x^4\right)\Big|_0^{15}$$

$$= \frac{4}{9} 62.4\pi(7593.75) \approx 661,619.41 \text{ ft-lb.}$$

46. We slice the gasoline horizontally. At a distance h feet below the surface, the horizontal slab is a cylinder with radius r and thickness Δh, so

$$\text{Volume of one slab} \approx \pi r^2 \Delta h.$$

To find the radius r at a depth h from the top as in Figure 8.158, we note that $h^2 + r^2 = 5^2$, so $r = \sqrt{25 - h^2}$. At depth h

$$\text{Volume of one slice} \approx \pi(\sqrt{25 - h^2})^2 \Delta h = \pi(25 - h^2)\Delta h \text{ ft}^3.$$

The gasoline at depth h must be lifted a distance of h ft, so

$$\text{Work to move one slice} = \rho \cdot \text{Volume} \cdot \text{Distance lifted}$$

$$\approx \rho(\pi(25 - h^2)\Delta h)(h) \text{ ft-lb.}$$

The work done, W, to lift all the gasoline is the sum of the work done on the pieces:

$$W \approx \sum \rho(\pi(25 - h^2)\Delta h)h \text{ ft-lb.}.$$

As $\Delta h \to 0$, we obtain a definite integral. Since h varies from $h = 0$ to $h = 5$ and $\rho = 42$, we have:

$$W = \int_0^5 \rho\pi(25h - h^3)dh = 42\pi \left(25\frac{h^2}{2} - \frac{h^4}{4}\right)\bigg|_0^5 = \frac{13125\pi}{2} = 20,617 \text{ ft-lb.}$$

The work to pump all the gasoline out is 20,617 ft-lbs.

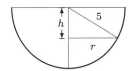

Figure 8.158

47. Let h be height above the bottom of the dam. Then

$$
\begin{aligned}
\text{Water force} &= \int_0^{25} (62.4)(25 - h)(60)\, dh \\
&= (62.4)(60)\left(25h - \frac{h^2}{2}\right)\bigg|_0^{25} \\
&= (62.4)(60)(625 - 312.5) \\
&= (62.4)(60)(312.5) \\
&= 1,170,000 \text{ lbs.}
\end{aligned}
$$

48. If the weight of the chain were negligible, the work required would be $1000 \cdot 20 = 20,000$ ft-lbs. Because of the chain, the total work is slightly more than 20,000 ft-lbs. When the object is h ft off the ground, the length of chain is $50 - h$ so the total weight being lifted is $1000 + 2(50 - h)$ lb. See Figure 8.159. Thus

$$
\begin{aligned}
\text{Work to lift the weight an addition } \Delta h \text{ higher} &= \text{Weight} \cdot \text{Distance lifted} \\
&\approx (1000 + 2(50 - h))\Delta h \text{ ft-lb.}
\end{aligned}
$$

To find the total work, we integrate this quantity from $h = 0$ to $h = 20$:

$$W = \int_0^{20} (1000 + 2(50 - h))dh = \int_0^{20} (1100 - 2h)dh = (1100h - h^2)\bigg|_0^{20} = 21,600 \text{ft-lbs.}$$

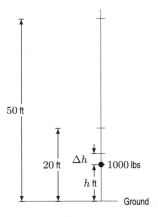

Figure 8.159

49. (a)

$$\text{Future Value} = \int_0^{20} 100e^{0.10(20-t)} \, dt$$

$$= 100 \int_0^{20} e^2 e^{-0.10t} \, dt$$

$$= \frac{100e^2}{-0.10} e^{-0.10t} \Big|_0^{20}$$

$$= \frac{100e^2}{0.10} (1 - e^{-0.10(20)}) \approx \$6389.06.$$

The present value of the income stream is

$$\int_0^{20} 100e^{-0.10t} \, dt = 100 \left(\frac{1}{-0.10} \right) e^{-0.10t} \Big|_0^{20}$$

$$= 1000 \left(1 - e^{-2} \right) = \$864.66.$$

Note that this is also the present value of the sum $6389.06.

(b) Let T be the number of years for the balance to reach $5000. Then

$$5000 = \int_0^T 100e^{0.10(T-t)} \, dt$$

$$50 = e^{0.10T} \int_0^T e^{-0.10t} \, dt$$

$$= \frac{e^{0.10T}}{-0.10} e^{-0.10t} \Big|_0^T$$

$$= 10e^{0.10T} \left(1 - e^{-0.10T} \right) = 10e^{0.10}T - 10.$$

So, $60 = 10e^{0.10T}$, and $T = 10 \ln 6 \approx 17.92$ years.

50. (a) Let's split the time interval into n parts, each of length Δt. During the interval from t_i to t_{i+1}, profit is earned at a rate of approximately $(2 - 0.1t_i)$ thousand dollars per year, or $(2000 - 100t_i)$ dollars per year. Thus during this period, a total profit of $(2000 - 100t_i)\Delta t$ dollars is earned. Since this profit is earned t_i years in the future, its present value is $(2000 - 100t_i)\Delta t e^{-0.1t_i}$ dollars. Thus

$$\text{Total present value} \approx \sum_{i=0}^{n-1} (2000 - 100t_i)e^{-0.1t_i} \Delta t.$$

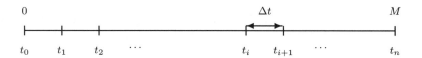

(b) The Riemann sum corresponds to the integral:

$$\text{Present value} = \int_0^M e^{-0.10t}(2000 - 100t) \, dt.$$

(c) To find where the present value is maximized, we take the derivative of

$$P(M) = \int_0^M e^{-0.10t}(2000 - 100t) \, dt,$$

with respect to M, and obtain

$$P'(M) = e^{-0.10M}(2000 - 100M).$$

This is 0 when $2000 - 100M = 0$, that is, when $M = 20$ years. The value $M = 20$ maximizes $P(M)$, since $P'(M) > 0$ for $M < 20$, and $P'(M) < 0$ for $M > 20$. To determine what the maximum is, we evaluate the integral representation for $P(20)$ by III-14 in the integral table:

$$P(20) = \int_0^{20} e^{-0.10t}(2000 - 100t)\, dt$$

$$= \left[\frac{(2000 - 100t)}{-0.10} e^{-0.10t} + 10000 e^{-0.10t} \right]\Bigg|_0^{20} \approx \$11353.35.$$

51. We divide up time between 1971 and 1992 into intervals of length Δt, and calculate how much of the strontium-90 produced during that time interval is still around.

Strontium-90 decays exponentially, so if a quantity S_0 was produced t years ago, and S is the quantity around today, $S = S_0 e^{-kt}$. Since the half-life is 28 years, $\frac{1}{2} = e^{-k(28)}$, giving $k = -\ln(1/2)/28 \approx 0.025$.

We measure t in years from 1971, so that 1992 is $t = 21$.

Since strontium-90 is produced at a rate of 3 kg/year, during the interval Δt, a quantity $3\Delta t$ kg was produced. Since this was $(21 - t)$ years ago, the quantity remaining now is $(3\Delta t)e^{-0.025(21-t)}$. Summing over all such intervals gives

$$\begin{array}{c} \text{Strontium remaining} \\ \text{in 1992} \end{array} \approx \int_0^{21} 3e^{-0.025(21-t)}\, dt = \frac{3e^{-0.025(21-t)}}{0.025}\Bigg|_0^{21} = 49 \text{ kg}.$$

[Note: This is like a future value problem from economics, but with a negative interest rate.]

52. (a) Slice the mountain horizontally into N cylinders of height Δh. The sum of the volumes of the cylinders will be

$$\sum_{i=1}^{N} \pi r^2 \Delta h = \sum_{i=1}^{N} \pi \left(\frac{3.5 \cdot 10^5}{\sqrt{h + 600}} \right)^2 \Delta h.$$

(b)

$$\text{Volume} = \int_{400}^{14400} \pi \left(\frac{3.5 \cdot 10^5}{\sqrt{h + 600}} \right)^2 dh$$

$$= 1.23 \cdot 10^{11} \pi \int_{400}^{14400} \frac{1}{(h + 600)}\, dh$$

$$= 1.23 \cdot 10^{11} \pi \ln(h + 600)\Bigg|_{400}^{14400}\, dh$$

$$= 1.23 \cdot 10^{11} \pi \left[\ln 15000 - \ln 1000 \right]$$

$$= 1.23 \cdot 10^{11} \pi \ln(15000/1000)$$

$$= 1.23 \cdot 10^{11} \pi \ln 15 \approx 1.05 \cdot 10^{12} \text{ cubic feet.}$$

53. Look at the disc-shaped slab of water at height y and of thickness Δy. The rate at which water is flowing out when it is at depth y is $k\sqrt{y}$ (Torricelli's Law, with k constant). Then, if $x = g(y)$, we have

$$\Delta t = \left(\begin{array}{c} \text{Time for water to} \\ \text{drop by this amount} \end{array} \right) = \frac{\text{Volume}}{\text{Rate}} = \frac{\pi (g(y))^2 \Delta y}{k\sqrt{y}}.$$

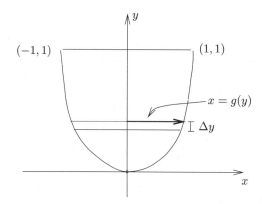

If the rate at which the depth of the water is dropping is constant, then dy/dt is constant, so we want

$$\frac{\pi(g(y))^2}{k\sqrt{y}} = \text{constant},$$

so $g(y) = c\sqrt[4]{y}$, for some constant c. Since $x = 1$ when $y = 1$, we have $c = 1$ and so $x = \sqrt[4]{y}$, or $y = x^4$.

54. For a given energy E, Figure 8.160 shows that the area under the graph to the right of E is larger for graph B than it is for graph A. Therefore graph B has more molecules at higher kinetic energies, so it is the hotter gas. So graph A corresponds to 300 kelvins and graph B corresponds to 500 kelvins.

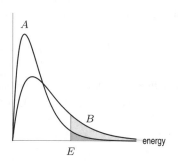

Figure 8.160

55. Graph B is more spread out to the right, and so it represents a gas in which more of the molecules are moving at faster velocities. Thus the average velocity in gas B is larger.

56. Every photon which falls a given distance from the center of the detector has the same probability of being detected. This suggests that we divide the plate up into concentric rings of thickness Δr. Consider one such ring having inner radius r and outer radius $r + \Delta r$. For this ring,

$$\text{Number of photons hitting ring per unit time} \approx N \cdot \text{Area of ring} \approx N \cdot 2\pi r \Delta r.$$

Then,

$$\text{Number of photons detected on ring per unit time} \approx \text{Number hitting} \cdot S(r) \approx N \cdot 2\pi r \Delta r \cdot S(r).$$

Summing over all rings gives us

$$\text{Total number of photons detected per unit time} \approx \sum 2\pi N r S(r) \Delta r.$$

Taking the limit as $\Delta r \to 0$ gives

$$\text{Total number of photons detected per unit time} = \int_0^R 2\pi N r S(r)\,dr.$$

57. First we find the volume of the body up to the horizontal line through Q.

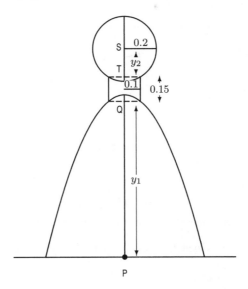

We put the origin at P, the x-axis horizontal and the y-axis pointing upward, and compute the volume obtained by rotating the curve $y = 1 - 4x^2$ around the y-axis up to Q. At Q, we have $x = 0.1$, so

$$y_1 = 1 - 4(0.1^2) = 0.96.$$

Slicing the body horizontally into disks of radius x, thickness Δy, we have

$$\text{Volume of disk in body} \approx \pi x^2 \Delta y = \frac{\pi}{4}(1 - y)\Delta y.$$

Thus,

$$\text{Volume of body up to Q} = \int_0^{0.96} \frac{\pi}{4}(1 - y)dy = \frac{\pi}{4}\left(y - \frac{y^2}{2}\right)\Bigg|_0^{0.96} = 0.3921.$$

To find the volume of the head, it is easiest to consider the origin at S, the x-axis horizontal, and the y-axis pointed upward. Then think of the head as the volume obtained by rotating the circle $x^2 + y^2 = (0.2)^2$ about the y-axis. We compute the volume of the head down to the horizontal line through T, at which point $x = 0.1$. Thus

$$(0.1)^2 + y_2{}^2 = (0.2)^2.$$

So

$$y_2 = -\sqrt{0.03} = -0.1732.$$

Slicing the head into circular disks, we have

$$\text{Volume of disk in head} \approx \pi x^2 \Delta y = \pi(0.2^2 - y^2)\Delta y.$$

Thus,

$$\text{Volume of head down to T} = \int_{-0.1732}^{0.2} \pi(0.2^2 - y^2)dy = \pi(0.2^2 y - \frac{y^3}{3})\Bigg|_{-0.1732}^{0.2}$$
$$= 0.0331.$$

The neck is exactly cylindrical, with

$$\text{Volume of neck} = \pi(0.1^2)0.15 = 0.0047.$$

Thus,

$$\text{Total volume} = \text{Vol body} + \text{Vol head} + \text{Vol neck}$$
$$= 0.3921 + 0.0331 + 0.0047$$
$$= 0.4299 \approx 0.43\text{m}^3.$$

58. (a) Divide the cross-section of the blood into rings of radius r, width Δr. See Figure 8.161.

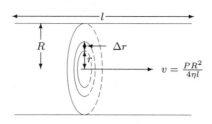

Figure 8.161

Then
$$\text{Area of ring} \approx 2\pi r \Delta r.$$

The velocity of the blood is approximately constant throughout the ring, so
$$\text{Rate blood flows through ring} \approx \text{Velocity} \cdot \text{Area}$$
$$= \frac{P}{4\eta l}(R^2 - r^2) \cdot 2\pi r \Delta r.$$

Thus, summing over all rings, we find the total blood flow:
$$\text{Rate blood flowing through blood vessel} \approx \sum \frac{P}{4\eta l}(R^2 - r^2)2\pi r \Delta r.$$

Taking the limit as $\Delta r \to 0$, we get
$$\text{Rate blood flowing through blood vessel} = \int_0^R \frac{\pi P}{2\eta l}(R^2 r - r^3)dr$$

$$= \frac{\pi P}{2\eta l}\left(\frac{R^2 r^2}{2} - \frac{r^4}{4}\right)\Big|_0^R = \frac{\pi P R^4}{8\eta l}.$$

(b) Since
$$\text{Rate of blood flow} = \frac{\pi P R^4}{8\eta l},$$

if we take $k = \pi P/(8\eta l)$, then we have
$$\text{Rate of blood flow} = kR^4,$$

that is, rate of blood flow is proportional to R^4, in accordance with Poiseuille's Law.

59. Pick a small interval of time Δt which takes place at time t. Fuel is consumed at a rate of $(25 + 0.1v)^{-1}$ gallons per mile. In the time Δt, the car moves $v\,\Delta t$ miles, so it consumes $v\,\Delta t/(25 + 0.1v)$ gallons during the instant Δt. Since $v = 50\frac{t}{t+1}$, the car consumes

$$\frac{v\,\Delta t}{25 + 0.1v} = \frac{50\frac{t}{t+1}\,\Delta t}{25 + 0.1\left(50\frac{t}{t+1}\right)} = \frac{50t\,\Delta t}{25(t+1) + 5t} = \frac{10t\,\Delta t}{6t + 5}$$

gallons of gas, in terms of the time t at which the instant occurs. To find the total gas consumed, sum up the instants in an integral:

$$\text{Gas consumed} = \int_2^3 \frac{10t}{6t + 5}dt \approx 1.25 \text{ gallons.}$$

60. (a) Slicing horizontally, as shown in Figure 8.162, we see that the volume of one disk-shaped slab is

$$\Delta V \approx \pi x^2 \Delta y = \frac{\pi y}{a} \Delta y.$$

Thus, the volume of the water is given by

$$V = \int_0^h \frac{\pi}{a} y \, dy = \frac{\pi}{a} \frac{y^2}{2} \Big|_0^h = \frac{\pi h^2}{2a}.$$

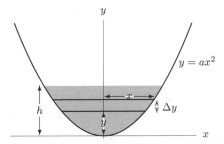

Figure 8.162

(b) The surface of the water is a circle of radius x. Since at the surface, $y = h$, we have $h = ax^2$. Thus, at the surface, $x = \sqrt{(h/a)}$. Therefore the area of the surface of water is given by

$$A = \pi x^2 = \frac{\pi h}{a}.$$

(c) If the rate at which water is evaporating is proportional to the surface area, we have

$$\frac{dV}{dt} = -kA.$$

(The negative sign is included because the volume is decreasing.) By the chain rule, $\frac{dV}{dt} = \frac{dV}{dh} \cdot \frac{dh}{dt}$. We know $\frac{dV}{dh} = \frac{\pi h}{a}$ and $A = \frac{\pi h}{a}$ so

$$\frac{\pi h}{a} \frac{dh}{dt} = -k \frac{\pi h}{a} \quad \text{giving} \quad \frac{dh}{dt} = -k.$$

(d) Integrating gives

$$h = -kt + h_0.$$

Solving for t when $h = 0$ gives

$$t = \frac{h_0}{k}.$$

61. (a) The volume of water in the centrifuge is $\pi(1^2) \cdot 1 = \pi$ cubic meters. The centrifuge has total volume 2π cubic meters, so the volume of the air in the centrifuge is π cubic meters. Now suppose the equation of the parabola is $y = h + bx^2$. We know that the volume of air in the centrifuge is the volume of the top part (a cylinder) plus the volume of the middle part (shaped like a bowl). See Figure 8.163.

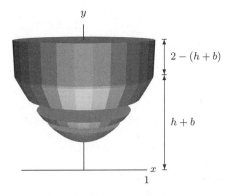

Figure 8.163: The Volume of Air

To find the volume of the cylinder of air, we find the maximum water depth. If $x = 1$, then $y = h + b$. Therefore the height of the water at the edge of the bowl, 1 meter away from the center, is $h + b$. The volume of the cylinder of air is therefore $[2 - (h + b)] \cdot \pi \cdot (1)^2 = [2 - h - b]\pi$.

To find the volume of the bowl of air, we note that the bowl is a volume of rotation with radius x at height y, where $y = h + bx^2$. Solving for x^2 gives $x^2 = (y - h)/b$. Hence, slicing horizontally as shown in the picture:

$$\text{Bowl Volume} = \int_h^{h+b} \pi x^2 \, dy = \int_h^{h+b} \pi \frac{y - h}{b} \, dy = \frac{\pi(y - h)^2}{2b} \bigg|_h^{h+b} = \frac{b\pi}{2}.$$

So the volume of both pieces together is $[2 - h - b]\pi + b\pi/2 = (2 - h - b/2)\pi$. But we know the volume of air should be π, so $(2 - h - b/2)\pi = \pi$, hence $h + b/2 = 1$ and $b = 2 - 2h$. Therefore, the equation of the parabolic cross-section is $y = h + (2 - 2h)x^2$.

(b) The water spills out the top when $h + b = h + (2 - 2h) = 2$, or when $h = 0$. The bottom is exposed when $h = 0$. Therefore, the two events happen simultaneously.

62. Any small piece of mass ΔM on either of the two spheres has kinetic energy $\frac{1}{2}v^2 \Delta M$. Since the angular velocity of the two spheres is the same, the actual velocity of the piece ΔM will depend on how far away it is from the axis of revolution. The further away a piece is from the axis, the faster it must be moving and the larger its velocity v. This is because if ΔM is at a distance r from the axis, in one revolution it must trace out a circular path of length $2\pi r$ about the axis. Since every piece in either sphere takes 1 minute to make 1 revolution, pieces farther from the axis must move faster, as they travel a greater distance.

Thus, since the thin spherical shell has more of its mass concentrated farther from the axis of rotation than does the solid sphere, the bulk of it is traveling faster than the bulk of the solid sphere. So, it has the higher kinetic energy.

63. Any small piece of mass ΔM on either of the two hoops has kinetic energy $\frac{1}{2}v^2 \Delta M$. Since the angular velocity of the two hoops is the same, the actual velocity of the piece ΔM will depend on how far away it is from the axis of revolution. The further away a piece is from the axis, the faster it must be moving and the larger its velocity v. This is because if ΔM is at a distance r from the axis, in one revolution it must trace out a circular path of length $2\pi r$ about the axis. Since every piece in either hoop takes 1 minute to make 1 revolution, pieces farther from the axis must move faster, as they travel a greater distance.

The hoop rotating about the cylindrical axis has all of its mass at a distance R from the axis, whereas the other hoop has a good bit of its mass close (or on) the axis of rotation. So, since the bulk of the hoop rotating about the cylindrical axis is traveling faster than the bulk of the other hoop, it must have the higher kinetic energy.

CAS Challenge Problems

64. (a) We need to check that the point with the given coordinates is on the curve, i.e., that

$$x = a \sin^2 t, \quad y = \frac{a \sin^3 t}{\cos t}$$

satisfies the equation

$$y = \sqrt{\frac{x^3}{a - x}}.$$

This can be done by substituting into the computer algebra system and asking it to simplify the difference between the two sides, or by hand calculation:

$$\text{Right-hand side} = \sqrt{\frac{(a \sin^2 t)^3}{a - a \sin^2 t}} = \sqrt{\frac{a^3 \sin^6 t}{a(1 - \sin^2 t)}}$$

$$= \sqrt{\frac{a^3 \sin^6 t}{a \cos^2 t}} = \sqrt{\frac{a^2 \sin^6 t}{\cos^2 t}}$$

$$= \frac{a \sin^3 t}{\cos t} = y = \text{Left-hand side}.$$

We chose the positive square root because both $\sin t$ and $\cos t$ are nonnegative for $0 \leq t \leq \pi/2$. Thus the point always lies on the curve. In addition, when $t = 0$, $x = 0$ and $y = 0$, so the point starts at $x = 0$. As t approaches $\pi/2$, the value of $x = a \sin^2 t$ approaches a and the value of $y = a \sin^3 t/\cos t$ increases without bound (or approaches ∞), so the point on the curve approaches the vertical asymptote at $x = a$.

(b) We calculate the volume using horizontal slices. See the graph of $y = \sqrt{x^3/(a-x)}$ in Figure 8.164.

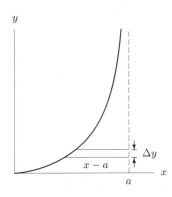

Figure 8.164

The slice at y is a disk of thickness Δy and radius $x - a$, hence it has volume $\pi(x-a)^2\Delta y$. So the volume is given by the improper integral

$$\text{Volume} = \int_0^\infty \pi(x-a)^2 \, dy.$$

(c) We substitute

$$x = a\sin^2 t, \quad y = \frac{a\sin^3 t}{\cos t}$$

and

$$dy = \frac{d}{dt}\left(\frac{a\sin^3 t}{\cos t}\right) dt = a\left(3\sin^2 t + \frac{\sin^4 t}{\cos^2 t}\right) dt.$$

Since $t = 0$ where $y = 0$ and $t = \pi/2$ at the asymptote where $y \to \infty$, we get

$$\text{Volume} = \int_0^{\pi/2} \pi(a\sin^2 t - a)^2 a\left(3\sin^2 t + \frac{\sin^4 t}{\cos^2 t}\right) dt$$

$$= \pi a^3 \int_0^{\pi/2}(3\sin^2 t\cos^4 t + \sin^4 t\cos^2 t)\, dt = \frac{\pi^2 a^3}{8}.$$

You can use a CAS to calculate this integral; it can also be done using trigonometric identities.

65. (a) The expression for arc length in terms of a definite integral gives

$$A(t) = \int_0^t \sqrt{1 + 4x^2}\, dx = \frac{2t\sqrt{1+4t^2} + \text{arcsinh}\,(2t)}{4}.$$

The integral was evaluated using a computer algebra system; different systems may give the answer in different forms. Here arcsinh is the inverse function of the hyperbolic sine function.

(b) Figure 8.165 shows that the graphs of $A(t)$ and t^2 look very similar. This suggests that $A(t) \approx t^2$.

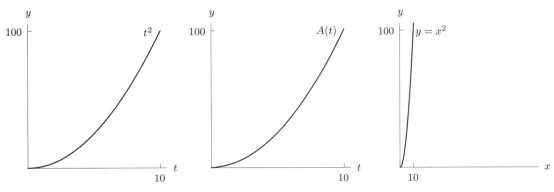

Figure 8.165   **Figure 8.166**

(c) The graph in Figure 8.166 is approximately vertical and close to the y axis. Thus, if we measure the arc length up to a certain y-value, the answer is approximately the same as if we had measured the length straight up the y-axis. Hence

$$A(t) \approx y = f(t) = t^2.$$

So

$$A(t) \approx t^2.$$

66. (a) The expression for arc length in terms of a definite integral gives

$$A(t) = \int_0^t \sqrt{1 + \left(\frac{1}{2\sqrt{x}}\right)^2}\, dx = \frac{2\sqrt{t}\sqrt{1+4t} + \text{arcsinh}\,(2\sqrt{t})}{4}.$$

The integral was evaluated using a computer algebra system; different systems may give the answer in different forms. Some may involve ln instead of arcsinh, which is the inverse function of the hyperbolic sine function.

(b) Figure 8.168 shows that the graphs of $A(t)$ and the graph of $y = t$ look very similar. This suggests that $A(t) \approx t$.

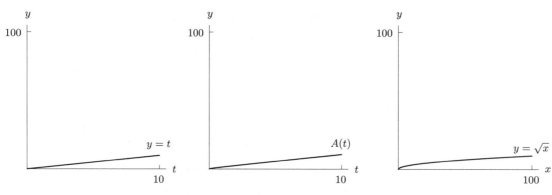

Figure 8.167   Figure 8.168

(c) The graph in Figure 8.168 is approximately horizontal and close to the x-axis. Thus, if we measure the arc length up to a certain x-value, the answer is approximately the same as if we had measured the length straight along the x-axis. Hence

$$A(t) \approx x = t.$$

So

$$A(t) \approx t.$$

67. (a) Slice the sphere at right angles to the axis of the cylinder. Consider a slice of thickness Δx at distance x from the center of the sphere. The cross-section is an annulus (ring) with internal radius $r_i = a$ and outer radius $r_o = \sqrt{r^2 - x^2}$. Thus

$$\text{Area of annulus} = \pi r_o{}^2 - \pi r_i{}^2 = \pi \left(\sqrt{r^2 - x^2}\right)^2 - \pi a^2 = \pi(r^2 - x^2 - a^2).$$

$$\text{Volume of slice} \approx \pi(r^2 - x^2 - a^2)\Delta x.$$

The lower and upper limits of the integral are where the cylinder meets the sphere, i.e., where $x^2 + a^2 = r^2$, or $x = \pm\sqrt{r^2 - a^2}$. Thus

$$\text{Volume of bead} = \int_{-\sqrt{r^2-a^2}}^{\sqrt{r^2-a^2}} \pi(r^2 - x^2 - a^2)\, dx.$$

(b) Using a computer algebra system to evaluate the integral, we have

$$\text{Volume of bead} = \frac{4\pi}{3}\left(r^2 - a^2\right)^{3/2}.$$

CHECK YOUR UNDERSTANDING

1. **True.** Since $y = \pm\sqrt{9 - x^2}$ represent the top and bottom halves of the sphere, slicing disks perpendicular to the x-axis gives

$$\text{Volume of slice } \approx \pi y^2 \Delta x = \pi(9 - x^2)\Delta x$$

$$\text{Volume} = \int_{-3}^{3} \pi(9 - x^2)\, dx.$$

2. **False.** Evaluating does not give the volume of a cone $\pi r^2 h/3$:

$$\int_0^h \pi(r - y)\, dy = \pi\left(ry - \frac{y^2}{2}\right)\Bigg|_0^h = \pi\left(rh - \frac{h^2}{2}\right).$$

Alternatively, you can show by slicing that the integral representing this volume is $\int_0^h \pi r^2(1 - y/h)^2\, dy$.

3. **False.** Using the table of integrals (VI-28 and VI-30) or a trigonometric substitution gives

$$\int_0^r \pi\sqrt{r^2 - y^2}\, dy = \frac{\pi}{2}\left(y\sqrt{r^2 - y^2} + r^2 \arcsin\left(\frac{y}{r}\right)\right)\Bigg|_0^r = \frac{\pi r^2}{2}(\arcsin 1 - \arcsin 0) = \frac{\pi^2 r^2}{4}.$$

The volume of a hemisphere is $2\pi r^3/3$.

Alternatively, you can show by slicing that the integral representing this volume is $\int_0^r \pi(r^2 - y^2)\, dy$.

4. **True.** Horizontal slicing gives rectangular slabs of length l, thickness Δy, and width $w = 2\sqrt{r^2 - y^2}$. So the volume of one slab is $2l\sqrt{r^2 - y^2}\Delta y$, and the integral is $\int_{-r}^{r} 2l\sqrt{r^2 - y^2}\, dy$.

5. **False.** Volume is always positive, like area.

6. **False.** The population density needs to be approximately constant on each ring. This is only true if the population density is a function of r, the distance from the center of the city.

7. **False.** Since the density varies with y, the region must be sliced perpendicular to the y-axis, along the lines of constant y.

8. **False.** Although the density is greater near the center, the area of the suburbs is much larger than the area of the inner city, and population is determined by both area and density. In fact, the population of the inner city:

$$\int_0^1 (10 - 3r)2\pi r\, dr = 2\pi(5r^2 - r^3)\Bigg|_0^1 = 8\pi$$

is less than the population of the suburbs:

$$\int_1^2 (10 - 3r)2\pi r\, dr = 2\pi(5r^2 - r^3)\Bigg|_1^2 = 16\pi.$$

9. **True.** One way to look at it is that the center of mass should not change if you change the units by which you measure the masses. If you double the masses, that is no different than using as a new unit of mass half the old unit. Alternatively, let the masses be m_1, m_2, and m_3 located at x_1, x_2, and x_3. Then the center of mass is given by:

$$\bar{x} = \frac{x_1 m_1 + x_2 m_2 + x_3 m_3}{m_1 + m_2 + m_3}.$$

Doubling the masses does not change the center of mass, since it doubles both the numerator and the denominator.

10. **False.** The center of mass of a circular ring (for example, a coin with a hole in it) is at the center.

11. **True.** The density of particles hitting the target is approximately constant on concentric rings.

12. **False.** If the density were constant this would be true, but suppose that all the mass on the left half is concentrated at $x = 0$ and all the mass on the right side is concentrated at $x = 3$. In order for the rod to balance at $x = 2$, the weight on the left side must be half the weight on the right side.

13. **False.** Work is the product of force and distance moved, so the work done in either case is 200 ft-lb.

14. **True.** Displacement in the same direction as the force gives positive work; displacement in the opposite direction as the force gives negative work.

15. False. Since the water pressure increases with depth, the force on the lower half of the new dam is greater than the force on the upper half of the new dam, which is the same as the force on the old dam. Thus the force on the new dam is more than double the force on the old dam.

16. True. Since pressure increases with depth and we want the pressure to be approximately constant on each strip, we use horizontal strips.

17. False. The pressure is positive and when integrated gives a positive force.

18. True. Although work is expressed in an integral, the average value is also expressed in an integral. We have:

$$\text{Average value of the force} = \frac{1}{4-1} \int_1^4 F(x)dx.$$

Thus if we multiply the average force by 3, we get $\int_1^4 F(x)dx$, which is the work done.

19. True. For an income stream $P(t)$ from $t = 0$ to $t = M$, we have:

$$\text{Present value} = \int_0^M P(t)e^{-rt}dt,$$

and

$$\text{Future value} = \int_0^M P(t)e^{r(M-t)}dt.$$

Since M and r are constant, we can factor out e^{rM} from the integral for the future value to get:

$$\text{Future value} = e^{rM}(\text{Present value}).$$

Since $r > 0$ and $M > 0$, this means $e^{rM} > 1$ so the future value is greater than the present value.

20. False. Since $p(x) < 0$ for $x < 0$, it cannot be a probability density function.

21. False. It is true that $p(x) \geq 0$ for all x, but we also need $\int_{-\infty}^{\infty} p(x)dx = 1$. Since $p(x) = 0$ for $x \leq 0$, we need only check the integral from 0 to ∞. We have

$$\int_0^{\infty} xe^{-x^2}dx = \lim_{b \to \infty} \left(-\frac{1}{2}e^{-x^2}\right)\bigg|_0^b = \frac{1}{2}.$$

22. False. The volume also depends on how far away the region is from the axis of revolution. For example, let R be the rectangle $0 \leq x \leq 8, 0 \leq y \leq 1$ and let S be the rectangle $0 \leq x \leq 3, 0 \leq y \leq 2$. Then rectangle R has area greater than rectangle S. However, when you revolve R about the x-axis you get a cylinder, lying on its side, of radius 1 and length 8, which has volume 8π. When you revolve S about the x-axis, you get a cylinder of radius 2 and length 3, which has volume 12π. Thus the second volume is larger, even though the region revolved has smaller area.

23. False. Suppose that the graph of f starts at the point $(0, 100)$ and then goes down to $(1, 0)$ and from there on goes along the x-axis. For example, if $f(x) = 100(x-1)^2$ on the interval $[0, 1]$ and $f(x) = 0$ on the interval $[1, 10]$, then f is differentiable on the interval $[0, 10]$. The arc length of the graph of f on the interval $[0, 1]$ is at least 100, while the arc length on the interval $[1, 10]$ is 9.

24. True. Since f is concave up, f' is an increasing function, so $f'(x) \geq f'(0) = 3/4$ on the interval $[0, 4]$. Thus $\sqrt{1 + (f'(x))^2} \geq \sqrt{1 + 9/16} = 5/4$. Then we have:

$$\text{Arc length} = \int_0^4 \sqrt{1 + (f'(x))^2}dx \geq \int_0^4 \frac{5}{4}dx = 5.$$

25. False. Since f is concave down, this means that $f'(x)$ is decreasing, so $f'(x) \leq f'(0) = 3/4$ on the interval $[0, 4]$. However, it could be that $f'(x)$ becomes negative so that $(f'(x))^2$ becomes large, making the integral for the arc length large also. For example, $f(x) = (3/4)x - x^2$ is concave down and $f'(0) = 3/4$, but $f(0) = 0$ and $f(4) = -13$, so the graph of f on the interval $[0, 4]$ has arc length at least 13.

26. False. Note that p is the density function for the population, not the cumulative density function. Thus $p(10) = 1/2$ means that the probability of x lying in a small interval of length Δx around $x = 10$ is about $(1/2)\Delta x$.

27. True. This follows directly from the definition of the cumulative density function.

28. True. The interval from $x = 9.98$ to $x = 10.04$ has length 0.06. Assuming that the value of $p(x)$ is near $1/2$ for $9.98 < x < 10.04$, the fraction of the population in that interval is $\int_{9.98}^{10.04} p(x)dx \approx (1/2)(0.06) = 0.03$.

29. False. Note that p is the density function for the population, not the cumulative density function. Thus $p(10) = p(20)$ means that x values near 10 are as likely as x values near 20.

30. True. By the definition of the cumulative distribution function, $P(20) - P(10) = 0$ is the fraction of the population having x values between 10 and 20.

PROJECTS FOR CHAPTER EIGHT

1. Let us make coordinate axes with the origin at the center of the box. The x and y axes will lie along the central axes of the cylinders, and the (height) axis will extend vertically to the top of the box. If one slices the cylinders horizontally, one gets a cross. The cross is what you get if you cut out four corner squares from a square of side length 2. If h is the height of the cross above (or below) the xy plane, the equation of a cylinder is $h^2 + y^2 = 1$ (or $h^2 + x^2 = 1$). Thus the "armpits" of the cross occur where $y^2 - 1 = -h^2 = x^2 - 1$ for some fixed height h—that is, out $\sqrt{1 - h^2}$ units from the center, or $1 - \sqrt{1 - h^2}$ units away from the edge. Each corner square has area $(1 - \sqrt{1 - h^2})^2 = 2 - h^2 - 2\sqrt{1 - h^2}$. The whole big square has area 4. Therefore, the area of the cross is

$$4 - 4(2 - h^2 - 2\sqrt{1 - h^2}) = -4 + 4h^2 + 8\sqrt{1 - h^2}.$$

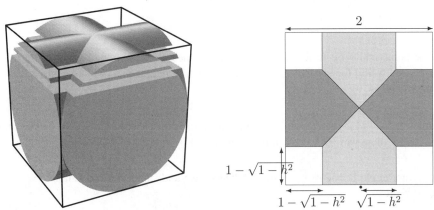

We integrate this from $h = -1$ to $h = 1$, and obtain the volume, V:

$$V = \int_{-1}^{1} -4 + 4h^2 + 8\sqrt{1 - h^2}\, dh$$

$$= \left[-4h + \frac{4h^3}{3} + 8 \cdot \frac{1}{2}\left(h\sqrt{1 - h^2} + \arcsin h \right) \right]\Big|_{-1}^{1}$$

$$= -8 + \frac{8}{3} + 4\pi = 4\pi - \frac{16}{3} \approx 7.23.$$

This is a reasonable answer, as the volume of the cube is 8, and the volume of one cylinder alone is $2\pi \approx 6.28$.

2. (a) Let y represent height, and let x represent horizontal distance from the lowest point of the cable. Then the stretched cable is a parabola of the form $y = kx^2$ passing through the point $(1280/2, 143) = (640, 143)$. Therefore, $143 = k(640)^2$ so $k \approx 3.491 \times 10^{-4}$. To find the arc length of the parabola, we take twice the arc length of the part to the right of the lowest point. Since $dy/dx = 2kx$,

$$\text{Arc Length} = 2\int_0^{640} \sqrt{1 + (2kx)^2}\, dx = 2\int_0^{640} \sqrt{1 + 4k^2x^2}\, dx.$$

The easiest way to find this integral is to substitute the value of k and find the integral's value numerically, giving

$$\text{Arc Length} \approx 1321.4 \text{ meters.}$$

Alternatively, we can make the substitution $w = 2kx$:

$$
\begin{aligned}
\text{Arc Length} &= \frac{2}{2k} \int_0^{1280k} \sqrt{1 + w^2}\, dw \\
&= \frac{1}{k} \int_0^{1280k} \sqrt{1 + w^2}\, dw \\
&= \frac{1}{2k} \left(w\sqrt{1+w^2} \Big|_0^{1280k} \right) + \frac{1}{2k} \left(\int_0^{1280k} \frac{1}{\sqrt{1+w^2}}\, dw \right)
\end{aligned}
$$

[Using the integral table, Formula VI-29, or substitute $w = \tan\theta$]

$$
\begin{aligned}
&= \frac{1}{2k} \left(1280k\sqrt{1 + (1280k)^2} \right) + \frac{1}{2k} \left(\ln\left| x + \sqrt{1+x^2} \right| \Big|_0^{1280k} \right) \\
&= \frac{1}{2k} \left(1280k\sqrt{1 + (1280k)^2} \right) + \frac{1}{2k} \left(\ln\left| 1280k + \sqrt{1 + (1280k)^2} \right| \right) \\
&\approx 1321.4 \text{ meters.}
\end{aligned}
$$

(b) Adding 0.05% to the length of the cable gives a cable length of $(1321.4)(1.0005) = 1322.1$. We now want to calculate the new shape of the parabola; that is, we want to find a new k so that the arc length is 1322.1. Since

$$
\text{Arc Length} = 2 \int_0^{640} \sqrt{1 + 4k^2 x^2}\, dx
$$

we can find k numerically by trial and error. Trying values close to our original value of k, we find $k \approx 3.52 \times 10^{-4}$. To find the sag for this new k, we find the height $y = kx^2$ for which the cable hangs from the towers. This is

$$
y = k(640)^2 \approx 144.2.
$$

Thus the cable sag is 144.2 meters, over a meter more than on a cold winter day. Notice, though, that although the length increases by 0.05%, the sag increases by more: $144.2/143 \approx 1.0084$, an increase of 0.84%.

3. (a) Revolving the semi-circle $y = \sqrt{r^2 - x^2}$ around the x-axis yields the sphere of radius r. See Figure 8.169. Differentiating yields:

$$
\frac{dy}{dx} = \frac{-1}{\sqrt{r^2 - x^2}} \cdot x = -\frac{x}{y}.
$$

Thus, substituting $-x/y$ for $f'(x)$, we get

$$
\text{Surface area} = 2\pi \int_{-r}^{r} y \sqrt{1 + \frac{x^2}{y^2}}\, dx = 2\pi \int_{-r}^{r} \sqrt{x^2 + y^2}\, dx
$$

$$
= 2\pi r \int_{-r}^{r} dx = 4\pi r^2.
$$

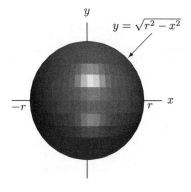

Figure 8.169

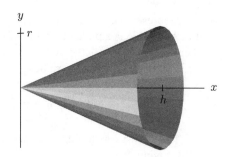

Figure 8.170

(b) Revolving the line $y = rx/h$ around the x-axis yields the cone. The base of the cone is a circle with area πr^2. See Figure 8.170. The area of the rest of the cone is

$$\text{Surface area} = 2\pi \int_0^h y\sqrt{1 + \frac{r^2}{h^2}}\, dx = 2\pi\sqrt{1 + \frac{r^2}{h^2}}\left(\frac{r}{h}\int_0^h x\, dx\right)$$

$$= 2\pi \frac{r}{h}\frac{h^2}{2}\sqrt{1 + \frac{r^2}{h^2}} = \pi r\sqrt{r^2 + h^2}$$

Adding the area of the base, we get

$$\text{Total surface area of cone} = \pi r^2 + \pi r\sqrt{r^2 + h^2}.$$

(c) We find the volume of $y = 1/x$ revolved about the x-axis as x runs from 1 to ∞. See Figure 8.171.

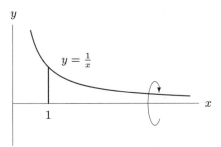

Figure 8.171

$$\text{Volume} = \int_1^\infty \pi y^2\, dx = \pi \int_1^\infty \frac{1}{x^2}\, dx = \pi \lim_{b\to\infty} \int_1^b \frac{dx}{x^2} = \pi \lim_{b\to\infty} \frac{-1}{x}\Big|_1^b = \pi$$

Thus, the volume of this solid is finite and equal to π.

(d) Now we show the surface area of this solid is unbounded. We have

$$\text{Surface area} = 2\pi \int_1^\infty y\sqrt{1 + \left(\frac{dy}{dx}\right)^2}\, dx = 2\pi \int_1^\infty \frac{1}{x}\sqrt{1 + \frac{1}{x^4}}\, dx$$

We cannot easily compute the antiderivative of $\frac{1}{x}\sqrt{1 + \frac{1}{x^4}}$, so we bound the integral from below by noticing that

$$\sqrt{1 + \frac{1}{x^4}} \geq 1.$$

Thus we see that

$$\text{Surface area} \geq 2\pi \int_1^\infty \frac{1}{x}\, dx = 2\pi \lim_{b\to\infty} \int_1^b \frac{dx}{x} = 2\pi \lim_{b\to\infty} \ln x\Big|_1^b.$$

Since $\ln x$ goes to infinity as x goes to infinity, the surface area is unbounded.

Alternatively, we can try calculating

$$2\pi \int_1^b \frac{1}{x}\sqrt{1 + \frac{1}{x^4}}\, dx$$

for larger and larger values of b. We would see that the integral seems to diverge.

(e) For a solid generated by the revolution of a curve $y = f(x)$ for $a \le x \le b$,

$$\text{Volume} = \int_a^b \pi y^2 \, dx$$

and

$$\text{Surface area} = \int_a^b 2\pi y \sqrt{1 + (f'(x))^2} \, dx.$$

The volume and the surface area will be equal if

$$f(x) = 2\sqrt{1 + (f'(x))^2}.$$

We find a function $y = f(x)$ which satisfies this relation:

$$y = 2\sqrt{1 + \left(\frac{dy}{dx}\right)^2}$$

$$\frac{y^2}{4} = 1 + \left(\frac{dy}{dx}\right)^2$$

$$\frac{dy}{dx} = \sqrt{\frac{y^2}{4} - 1}$$

$$\frac{dy}{\sqrt{y^2 - 4}} = \frac{1}{2} \, dx$$

$$\int \frac{dy}{\sqrt{y^2 - 4}} = \int \frac{1}{2} \, dx$$

$$\ln|y + \sqrt{y^2 - 4}| = \frac{x}{2} + C$$

$$y + \sqrt{y^2 - 4} = A e^{x/2}$$

Notice in the third line we have used the fact that $dy/dx \ge 0$. Any function, $y = f(x)$, which satisfies this relationship has the required property.

4. (a) We want to find a such that $\int_0^\infty p(v) \, dv = \lim_{r \to \infty} a \int_0^r v^2 e^{-mv^2/2kT} \, dv = 1$. Therefore,

$$\frac{1}{a} = \lim_{r \to \infty} \int_0^r v^2 e^{-mv^2/2kT} \, dv.$$

To evaluate the integral, use integration by parts with the substitutions $u = v$ and $w' = v e^{-mv^2/2kT}$:

$$\int_0^r \underbrace{v}_{u} \underbrace{v e^{-mv^2/2kT}}_{w'} \, dv = \underbrace{v}_{u} \underbrace{\frac{e^{-mv^2/2kT}}{-m/kT}}_{w} \Big|_0^r - \int_0^r \underbrace{1}_{u'} \underbrace{\frac{e^{-mv^2/2kT}}{-m/kT}}_{w} \, dv$$

$$= -\frac{kTr}{m} e^{-mr^2/2kT} + \frac{kT}{m} \int_0^r e^{-mv^2/2kT} \, dv.$$

From the normal distribution we know that $\int_0^\infty \frac{1}{\sqrt{2\pi}} e^{-x^2/2} \, dx = \frac{1}{2}$, so

$$\int_0^\infty e^{-x^2/2} \, dx = \frac{\sqrt{2\pi}}{2}.$$

Therefore in the above integral, make the substitution $x = \sqrt{\frac{m}{kT}} v$, so that $dx = \sqrt{\frac{m}{kT}} \, dv$, or $dv = \sqrt{\frac{kT}{m}} \, dx$. Then

$$\frac{kT}{m} \int_0^r e^{-mv^2/2kT} \, dv = \left(\frac{kT}{m}\right)^{3/2} \int_0^{\sqrt{\frac{m}{kT}} r} e^{-x^2/2} \, dx.$$

Substituting this into Equation 4a we get

$$\frac{1}{a} = \lim_{r \to \infty} \left(-\frac{kTr}{m} e^{-mr^2/2kT} + \left(\frac{kT}{m} \right)^{3/2} \int_0^{\sqrt{\frac{m}{kT}}r} e^{-x^2/2} \, dx \right) = 0 + \left(\frac{kT}{m} \right)^{3/2} \cdot \frac{\sqrt{2\pi}}{2}.$$

Therefore, $a = \frac{2}{\sqrt{2\pi}} \left(\frac{m}{kT} \right)^{3/2}$. Substituting the values for k, T, and m gives $a \approx 3.4 \times 10^{-8}$.

(b) To find the median, we wish to find the speed x such that

$$\int_0^x p(v) \, dv = \int_0^x av^2 e^{-\frac{mv^2}{2kT}} \, dv = \frac{1}{2},$$

where $a = \frac{2}{\sqrt{2\pi}} \left(\frac{m}{kT} \right)^{3/2}$. Using a calculator, by trial and error we get $x \approx 441$ m/sec.
To find the mean, we find

$$\int_0^\infty vp(v) \, dv = \int_0^\infty av^3 e^{-\frac{mv^2}{2kT}} \, dv.$$

This integral can be done by substitution. Let $u = v^2$, so $du = 2v\,dv$. Then

$$\int_0^\infty av^3 e^{-\frac{mv^2}{2kT}} \, dv = \frac{a}{2} \int_{v=0}^{v=\infty} v^2 e^{-\frac{mv^2}{2kT}} 2v \, dv$$

$$= \frac{a}{2} \int_{u=0}^{u=\infty} u e^{-\frac{mu}{2kT}} \, du$$

$$= \lim_{r \to \infty} \frac{a}{2} \int_0^r u e^{-\frac{mu}{2kT}} \, du.$$

Now, using the integral table, we have

$$\int_0^\infty av^3 e^{-\frac{mv^2}{2kT}} \, dv = \lim_{r \to \infty} \frac{a}{2} \left[-\frac{2kT}{m} u e^{-\frac{mu}{2kT}} - \left(-\frac{2kT}{m} \right)^2 e^{-\frac{mu}{2kT}} \right] \Big|_0^r$$

$$= \frac{a}{2} \left(-\frac{2kT}{m} \right)^2$$

$$\approx 457.7 \text{ m/sec.}$$

The maximum for $p(v)$ will be at a point where $p'(v) = 0$.

$$p'(v) = a(2v)e^{-\frac{mv^2}{2kT}} + av^2 \left(-\frac{2mv}{2kT} \right) e^{-\frac{mv^2}{2kT}}$$

$$= ae^{-\frac{mv^2}{2kT}} \left(2v - v^3 \frac{m}{kT} \right).$$

Thus $p'(v) = 0$ at $v = 0$ and at $v = \sqrt{\frac{2kT}{m}} \approx 405$. It's obvious that $p(0) = 0$, and that $p \to 0$ as $v \to \infty$.
So $v = 405$ gives us a maximum: $p(405) \approx 0.002$.

(c) The mean, as we found in part (b), is $\frac{a}{2} \frac{4k^2T^2}{m^2} = \frac{4}{\sqrt{2\pi}} \frac{k^{1/2}T^{1/2}}{m^{1/2}}$. It is clear, then, that as T increases so

does the mean. We found in part (b) that $p(v)$ reached its maximum at $v = \sqrt{\frac{2kT}{m}}$. Thus

$$\text{The maximum value of } p(v) = \frac{2}{\sqrt{2\pi}} \left(\frac{m}{kT} \right)^{3/2} \frac{2kT}{m} e^{-1}$$

$$= \frac{4}{e\sqrt{2\pi}} \frac{m^{1/2}}{kT^{1/2}}.$$

Thus as T increases, the maximum value decreases.

CHAPTER NINE

Solutions for Section 9.1

Exercises

1. The first term is $2^1 + 1 = 3$. The second term is $2^2 + 1 = 5$. The third term is $2^3 + 1 = 9$, the fourth is $2^4 + 1 = 17$, and the fifth is $2^5 + 1 = 33$. The first five terms are $3, 5, 9, 17, 33$.

2. The first term is $1 + (-1)^1 = 1 - 1 = 0$. The second term is $2 + (-1)^2 = 2 + 1 = 3$. The third term is $3 - 1 = 2$ and the fourth is $4 + 1 = 5$. The first five terms are $0, 3, 2, 5, 4$.

3. The first term is $2 \cdot 1/(2 \cdot 1 + 1) = 2/3$. The second term is $2 \cdot 2/(2 \cdot 2 + 1) = 4/5$. The first five terms are

$$2/3, 4/5, 6/7, 8/9, 10/11.$$

4. The first term is $(-1)^1(1/2)^1 = -1/2$. The second term is $(-1)^2(1/2)^2 = 1/4$. The first five terms are

$$-1/2, 1/4, -1/8, 1/16, -1/32.$$

5. The first term is $(-1)^2(1/2)^0 = 1$. The second term is $(-1)^3(1/2)^1 = -1/2$. The first five terms are

$$1, -1/2, 1/4, -1/8, 1/16.$$

6. The first term is $(1 - 1/(1+1))^{(1+1)} = (1/2)^2$. The second term is $(1 - 1/3)^3 = (2/3)^3$. The first five terms are

$$(1/2)^2, (2/3)^3, (3/4)^4, (4/5)^5, (5/6)^6.$$

7. The terms look like powers of 2 so we guess $s_n = 2^n$. This makes the first term $2^1 = 2$ rather than 4. We try instead $s_n = 2^{n+1}$. If we now check, we get the terms $4, 8, 16, 32, 64, \ldots$, which is right.

8. We compare with positive powers of 2, which are $2, 4, 8, 16, 32, \ldots$. Each term is one less, so we take $s_n = 2^n - 1$.

9. We observe that if we subtract 1 from each term of the sequence, we get $1, 4, 9, 16, 25, \ldots$, namely the squares $1^2, 2^2, 3^2, 4^2, 5^2, \ldots$. Thus $s_n = n^2 + 1$.

10. First notice that $s_n = 2n - 1$ is a formula for the general term of the sequence

$$1, 3, 5, 7, 9, \ldots.$$

To obtain the alternating signs in the original sequence, we try multiplying by $(-1)^n$. However, checking $(-1)^n(2n-1)$ for $n = 1, 2, 3, \ldots$ gives

$$-1, 3, -5, 7, -9, \ldots.$$

To get the correct signs, we multiply by $(-1)^{n+1}$ and take

$$s_n = (-1)^{n+1}(2n - 1).$$

11. The numerator is n. The denominator is then $2n + 1$, so $s_n = n/(2n + 1)$.

12. The denominators are the even numbers, so we try $s_n = 1/(2n)$. To get the signs to alternate, we try multiplying by $(-1)^n$. That gives

$$-1/2, 1/4, -1/6, 1/8, -1/10, \ldots,$$

so we multiply by $(-1)^{n+1}$ instead. Thus $s_n = (-1)^{n+1}/(2n)$.

13. We have $s_2 = s_1 + 2 = 3$ and $s_3 = s_2 + 3 = 6$. Continuing, we get

$$1, 3, 6, 10, 15, 21.$$

14. We have $s_2 = 2s_1 + 3 = 2 \cdot 1 + 3 = 5$ and $s_3 = 2s_2 + 3 = 2 \cdot 5 + 3 = 13$. Continuing, we get

$$1, 5, 13, 29, 61, 125.$$

15. We have $s_2 = s_1 + 1/2 = 0 + (1/2)^1 = 1/2$ and $s_3 = s_2 + (1/2)^2 = 1/2 + 1/4 = 3/4$. Continuing, we get

$$0, \frac{1}{2}, \frac{3}{4}, \frac{7}{8}, \frac{15}{16}, \frac{31}{32}.$$

16. We have $s_3 = s_2 + 2s_1 = 5 + 2 \cdot 1 = 7$ and $s_4 = s_3 + 2s_2 = 7 + 2 \cdot 5 = 17$. Continuing, we get

$$1, 5, 7, 17, 31, 65.$$

Problems

17. (a) matches (IV), since the sequence increases toward 1.
(b) matches (III), since the odd terms increase toward 1 and the even terms decrease toward 1.
(c) matches (II), since the sequence decreases toward 0.
(d) matches (I), since the sequence decreases toward 1.

18. (a) matches (II), since the sequence increases toward 2.
(b) matches (III), since the even terms decrease toward 2 and odd terms decrease toward -2.
(c) matches (IV), since the even terms decrease toward 2 and odd terms increase toward 2.
(d) matches (I), since the sequence decreases toward 2.
(e) matches (V), since the even terms decrease toward 2 and odd terms increase toward -2.

19. (a) matches (II), since $\lim_{n \to \infty}(n(n+1) - 1) = \infty$.
(b) matches (III), since $\lim_{n \to \infty}(1/(n+1)) = 0$ and $1/(n+1)$ is always positive.
(c) matches (I), since $\lim_{n \to \infty}(1 - n^2) = -\infty$.
(d) matches (IV), since $\lim_{n \to \infty} \cos(1/n) = \cos 0 = 1$.
(e) matches (V), since $\sin n$ is bounded above and below by ± 1, so $\lim_{n \to \infty}((\sin n)/n) = 0$ and the sign of $\sin n$ varies as $n \to \infty$.

20. Since $\lim\limits_{n \to \infty} x^n = 0$ if $|x| < 1$ and $|0.2| < 1$, we have $\lim\limits_{n \to \infty} (0.2)^n = 0$, so the sequence converges to 0

21. Since 2^n increases without bound as n increases, the sequence diverges.

22. Since $\lim\limits_{n \to \infty} x^n = 0$ if $|x| < 1$ and $|-0.3| < 1$, we have $\lim\limits_{n \to \infty} (-0.3)^n = 0$, so the sequence converges to 0.

23. Since $\lim\limits_{n \to \infty} x^n = 0$ if $|x| < 1$ and $|e^{-2}| < 1$, we have $\lim\limits_{n \to \infty} (e^{-2n}) = \lim\limits_{n \to \infty} (e^{-2})^n = 0$, so $\lim\limits_{n \to \infty} (3+e^{-2n}) = 3+0 = 3$, so the sequence converges to 3.

24. Since $\lim\limits_{n \to \infty} x^n = 0$ if $|x| < 1$ and $\left|\frac{2}{3}\right| < 1$, we have $\lim\limits_{n \to \infty} \left(\frac{2^n}{3^n}\right) = \lim\limits_{n \to \infty} \left(\frac{2}{3}\right)^n = 0$, so the sequence converges to 0.

25. We have:

$$\lim_{n \to \infty} \left(\frac{n}{10} + \frac{10}{n}\right) = \lim_{n \to \infty} \frac{n}{10} + \lim_{n \to \infty} 10n.$$

Since $n/10$ gets arbitrarily large and $10/n$ approaches 0 as $n \to \infty$, the sequence diverges.

26. We have:

$$\lim_{n \to \infty} \left(\frac{1}{n}\right) = 0.$$

The terms of the sequence alternate in sign, but they approach 0, so the sequence converges to 0.

27. We have

$$\lim_{n \to \infty} \frac{2n + 1}{n} = \lim_{n \to \infty} \left(2 + \frac{1}{n}\right) = 2,$$

so the sequence converges to 2.

28. Since $s_n = \cos(\pi n) = 1$ if n is even and $s_n = \cos(\pi n) = -1$ if n is odd, the values of s_n alternate between 1 and -1, so the limit does not exist. Thus, the sequence diverges.

29. Since $\lim_{n \to \infty} 1/n = 0$ and $-1 \leq \sin n \leq 1$, the terms approach zero and the sequence converges to 0.

30. As n increases, the term $2n$ is much larger in magnitude than $(-1)^n 5$ and the term $4n$ is much larger in magnitude than $(-1)^n 3$. Thus dividing the numerator and denominator by n and using the fact that $\lim\limits_{n \to \infty} 1/n = 0$, we have

$$\lim_{n \to \infty} \frac{2n + (-1)^n 5}{4n - (-1)^n 3} = \lim_{n \to \infty} \frac{2 + (-1)^n 5/n}{4 - (-1)^n 3/n} = \frac{1}{2}.$$

Thus, the sequence converges to $1/2$.

31. Since the exponential function 2^n dominates the power function n^3 as $n \to \infty$, the series diverges.

32. The first 6 terms of the sequence for the sampling is

$$\cos 0.5, \; \cos 1.0, \; \cos 1.5, \; \cos 2.0, \; \cos 2.5, \; \cos 3.0$$
$$= 0.878, \; 0.540, \; 0.071, \; -0.416, \; -0.801, \; -0.990.$$

33. The first 6 terms of the sequence for the sampling is

$$(-0.5)^2, \; (0.0)^2, \; (0.5)^2, \; (1.0)^2, \; (1.5)^2, \; (2.0)^2,$$
$$= 0.25, \; 0.00, \; 0.25, \; 1.00, \; 2.25, \; 4.00.$$

34. The first 6 terms of the sequence for the sampling are

$$\frac{\sin 1}{1}, \; \frac{\sin 2}{2}, \; \frac{\sin 3}{3}, \; \frac{\sin 4}{4}, \; \frac{\sin 5}{5}, \; \frac{\sin 6}{6}$$
$$= 0.841, \; 0.455, \; 0.047, \; -0.189, \; -0.192, \; -0.047.$$

35. The first smoothing gives

$$0, \; 6, \; -6, \; 6, \; -6, \; 6, \ldots$$

The second smoothing gives

$$3, \; 0, \; 2, \; -2, \; 2, \ldots$$

The smoothing process diminishes the peaks and valleys of this alternating sequence.

36. The first smoothing gives

$$0, \; 0, \; 6, \; 6, \; 6, \; 0, \; 0 \ldots$$

The second smoothing gives

$$0, \; 2, \; 4, \; 6, \; 4, \; 2 \ldots$$

The smoothing process spreads out the spike at the fourth term to the neighboring terms.

37. The first smoothing gives

$$1.5, \; 2, \; 3, \; 4, \; 5, \; 6, \; 7 \ldots$$

The second smoothing gives

$$1.75, \; 2.17, \; 3, \; 4, \; 5, \; 6 \ldots$$

Terms which are already the same as their average with their neighbors are not changed.

38. (a) Since month 10 is October, V_{10} is the number of SUVs sold in the US in October 2004.
   (b) The difference $V_n - V_{n-1}$ represents the increase in sales between month $(n-1)$ and month n.
   (c) The sum $\sum_{i=1}^{12} V_i$ represents the total sales of SUVs in the year 2004 (twelve months). The sum $\sum_{i=1}^{n} V_i$ represents the total sales in the n months starting from January 1, 2004.

39. (a) Since $c_1 = 75.747(1.003)$, $c_2 = 75.747(1.003)^2$, and so on, we have $c_n = 75.747(1.003)^n$.
   (b) Since c_n is consumption in year n and c_{n-1} is consumption in year $n-1$, we have

$$c_n - c_{n-1} = 75.747(1.003)^n - 75.747(1.003)^{n-1} = 75.747(1.003)^{n-1}(1.003 - 1) = 0.227(1.003)^{n-1},$$

   and $c_n - c_{n-1}$ represents the increase in consumption in million barrels per day between the year $(n-1)$ and the year n.
   (c) The sum represents the total oil consumed in years 1–18, that is, 2003–2020, inclusive.

40. (a) Since you have two parents and four grandparents, $s_1 = 2$ and $s_2 = 4$. In general, $s_n = 2^n$.
   (b) Solving $s_n = 6 \cdot 10^9$ gives

$$2^n = 6 \cdot 10^9$$
$$n = \frac{\ln(6 \cdot 10^9)}{\ln 2} = 32.482.$$

Thus, 33 or more generations ago, the number of ancestors is greater than the current population of the world. Since the population of the world 33 generations ago was much smaller than it is now, there must have been overlap among our ancestors.

41. In year 1, the payment is

$$p_1 = 10{,}000 + 0.05(100{,}000) = 15{,}000.$$

The balance in year 2 is $100{,}000 - 10{,}000 = 90{,}000$, so

$$p_2 = 10{,}000 + 0.05(90{,}000) = 14{,}500.$$

The balance in year 3 is $80{,}000$, so

$$p_3 = 10{,}000 + 0.05(80{,}000) = 14{,}000.$$

Thus,

$$p_n = 10{,}000 + 0.05(100{,}000 - (n-1) \cdot 10{,}000)$$
$$= 15{,}500 - 500n.$$

42. (a) (i) Since the number of bacteria doubles every half hour, the number quadruples every hour. Thus

$$R_1 = B_0 \cdot 4$$
$$R_2 = B_0 \cdot 4^2$$
$$\vdots$$
$$R_n = B_0 \cdot 4^n.$$

(ii) Each hour, the number of bacteria is multiplied by a factor a, so

$$F_n = B_0 a^n.$$

The bacteria doubles in number in 10 hours, so

$$F_{10} = 2B_0.$$

Thus,

$$B_0 a^{10} = 2B_0$$
$$a = 2^{1/10},$$

so

$$F_n = B_0(2^{1/10})^n = B_0 2^{n/10}.$$

(iii) The ratio is

$$Y_n = \frac{R_n}{F_n} = \frac{B_0 4^n}{B_0 2^{n/10}} = \left(\frac{4}{2^{1/10}}\right)^n = \left(2^{1.9}\right)^n.$$

(b) We want to solve for n making $Y_n = 1{,}000{,}000$:

$$\left(2^{1.9}\right)^n = 1{,}000{,}000$$
$$n = \frac{\ln(1{,}000{,}000)}{\ln(2^{1.9})} = 10.490.$$

Thus, in about ten and a half hours, there are a million times as many bacteria in the baby formula kept at room temperature.

43. (a) In the first year, $d_1 = 20{,}000(0.12)$, so the car's value at the end of the first year is $\$20{,}000(0.88)$. In the second year, $d_2 = 20{,}000(0.88)(0.12)$, so the car's value at the end of the second year is $\$20{,}000(0.88)^2$. Similarly, $d_3 = 20{,}000(0.88)^2(0.12)$. In general

$$d_n = 20{,}000(0.88)^{n-1}(0.12).$$

(b) The first year $r_1 = 400$; the second year $r_2 = 400(1.18)$, the third year $r_3 = 400(1.18)^2$. In general, $r_n = 400(1.18)^{n-1}$.

(c) We have

$$\text{Total cost} = d_1 + d_2 + d_3 + r_1 + r_2 + r_3$$
$$= 20{,}000(0.12)(1 + 0.88 + (0.88)^2) + 400(1 + 1.18 + (1.18)^2)$$
$$= 7799.52 \text{ dollars.}$$

(d) A two-year old car has the same pattern of expenses except that the initial price is $\$20{,}000(0.88)^2$ instead of $\$20{,}000$ and that the repair costs start at $\$400(1.18)^2$ instead of $\$400$. Then

$$\text{Total cost} = 20{,}000(0.88)^2(0.12)(1 + 0.88 + (0.88)^2) + 400(1.18)^2(1 + 1.18 + (1.18)^2)$$
$$= 6923.05 \text{ dollars.}$$

Thus, the two-year-old car costs you less and you should buy it.

44. We want to define $\lim\limits_{n \to \infty} s_n = L$ so that s_n is as close to L as we please for all sufficiently large n. Thus, the definition says that for any positive ϵ, there is a value N such that

$$|s_n - L| < \epsilon \quad \text{whenever} \quad n \geq N.$$

45. We use Theorem 9.1, so we must show that s_n is bounded. Since t_n converges, it is bounded so there is a number M, such that $t_n \leq M$ for all n. Therefore $s_n \leq t_n \leq M$ for all n. Since s_n is increasing, $s_1 \leq s_n$ for all n. Thus if we let $K = s_1$, we have $K \leq s_n \leq M$ for all n, so s_n is bounded. Therefore, s_n converges.

46. Each term is 2 more than the previous term, so a recursive definition is $s_n = s_{n-1} + 2$ for $n > 1$ and $s_1 = 1$.

47. Each term is 2 more than the previous term, so a recursive definition is $s_n = s_{n-1} + 2$ for $n > 1$ and $s_1 = 2$. Notice that the even positive integers and odd positive integers have the same recursive definition except for the starting term.

48. Each term is twice the previous term minus one, so a recursive definition is $s_n = 2s_{n-1} - 1$ for $n > 1$ and $s_1 = 3$. We also notice that the differences of consecutive terms are powers of 2, so $s_2 = s_1 + 2$, $s_3 = s_2 + 2^2$, and so on. Thus another recursive definition is $s_n = s_{n-1} + 2^{n-1}$ for $n > 1$ and $s_1 = 3$.

49. The differences between consecutive terms are $4, 9, 16, 25$, so, for example, $s_2 = s_1 + 4$ and $s_3 = s_2 + 9$. Thus, a possible recursive definition is $s_n = s_{n-1} + n^2$ for $n > 1$ and $s_1 = 1$.

50. The differences are $2, 3, 4, 5$, so, for example, $s_2 = s_1 + 2$, $s_3 = s_2 + 3$, and $s_4 = s_3 + 4$. Thus, a recursive definition is $s_n = s_{n-1} + n$ for $n > 1$ and $s_1 = 1$.

51. The numerator and denominator of each term are related to the numerator and denominator of the previous term. The denominator is the previous numerator and the numerator is the sum of the previous numerator and previous denominator. For example,

$$\frac{5}{3} = \frac{2+3}{3} \text{ and } \frac{8}{5} = \frac{3+5}{5}.$$

If we simplify, we get

$$\frac{5}{3} = \frac{2}{3} + 1, \text{ and } \frac{8}{5} = \frac{3}{5} + 1.$$

In words, we turn the previous term upside down and add 1. Thus, a recursive definition is $s_n = \dfrac{1}{s_{n-1}} + 1$ for $n > 1$ and $s_1 = 1$.

52. For $n > 1$, if $s_n = 3n - 2$, then $s_{n-1} = 3(n-1) - 2 = 3n - 5$, so

$$s_n - s_{n-1} = (3n - 2) - (3n - 5) = 3,$$

giving

$$s_n = s_{n-1} + 3.$$

In addition, $s_1 = 3 \cdot 1 - 2 = 1$.

53. For $n > 1$, if $s_n = n(n+1)/2$, then $s_{n-1} = (n-1)(n-1+1)/2 = n(n-1)/2$. Since

$$s_n = \frac{1}{2}(n^2 + n) = \frac{n^2}{2} + \frac{n}{2} \quad \text{and} \quad s_{n-1} = \frac{1}{2}(n^2 - n) = \frac{n^2}{2} - \frac{n}{2},$$

we have

$$s_n - s_{n-1} = \frac{n}{2} + \frac{n}{2} = n,$$

so

$$s_n = s_{n-1} + n.$$

In addition, $s_1 = 1(2)/2 = 1$.

54. For $n > 1$, if $s_n = 2n^2 - n$, then $s_{n-1} = 2(n-1)^2 - (n-1) = 2n^2 - 5n + 3$, so

$$s_n - s_{n-1} = (2n^2 - n) - (2n^2 - 5n + 3) = 4n - 3,$$

giving

$$s_n = s_{n-1} + 4n - 3.$$

In addition, $s_1 = 2 \cdot 1^2 - 1 = 1$.

55. (a) The bottom row contains k cans, the next one contains $(k-1)$ cans, then $(k-2)$ and so on. Thus, there are k rows. Since the top row contains 1 can, the second contains 2 cans, etc, we have $a_n = n$.

(b) Since the nth row contains n cans, $a_n = n$,

$$T_n = T_{n-1} + a_n$$

gives

$$T_n = T_{n-1} + n, \quad \text{for } n > 1.$$

In addition, $T_1 = 1$.

(c) If $T_n = \frac{1}{2}n(n+1)$, then $T_{n-1} = \frac{1}{2}(n-1)n$, so

$$T_n - T_{n-1} = \frac{1}{2}n(n+1) - \frac{1}{2}n(n-1) = \frac{n}{2}(n+1-(n-1)) = n.$$

In addition, $T_1 = \frac{1}{2} \cdot 1(2) = 1$.

56. (a) The first 12 terms are

$$1, 1, 2, 3, 5, 8, 13, 21, 34, 55, 89, 144.$$

(b) The sequence of ratios is

$$1, 2, \frac{3}{2}, \frac{5}{3}, \frac{8}{5}, \frac{13}{8}, \frac{21}{13}, \frac{34}{21}, \frac{55}{34}, \frac{89}{55} \cdots.$$

To three decimal places, the first ten ratios are

$$1, 2, 1.500, 1.667, 1.600, 1.625, 1.615, 1.619, 1.618, 1.618.$$

It appears that the sequence of ratios is converging to $r = 1.618$. We find $(1.618)^2 = 2.618 = 1.618 + 1$ so r seems to satisfy $r^2 = r + 1$. Alternatively, by the quadratic formula, the positive root of $x^2 - x - 1 = 0$ is $(1 + \sqrt{5})/2 = 1.618$.

(c) If we multiply both sides of the equation $r^2 = r + 1$ by Ar^{n-2}, we obtain

$$Ar^n = Ar^{n-1} + Ar^{n-2}.$$

Thus, if $s_n = Ar^n$, then $s_{n-1} = Ar^{n-1}$ and $s_{n-2} = Ar^{n-2}$, so the sequence satisfies $s_n = s_{n-1} + s_{n-2}$.

57. The sequence seems to converge. By the 25th term it stabilizes to four decimal places at $L = 0.7391$.

58. The sequence oscillates up and down, but by the 20th term it stabilizes to 4 decimal places at $L = 0.5671$.

Solutions for Section 9.2

Exercises

1. Yes, $a = 2$, ratio $= 1/2$.

2. Yes, $a = 1$, ratio $= -1/2$.

3. No. Ratio between successive terms is not constant: $\dfrac{1/3}{1/2} = 0.66\ldots$, while $\dfrac{1/4}{1/3} = 0.75$.

4. Yes, $a = 5$, ratio $= -2$.

5. No. Ratio between successive terms is not constant: $\dfrac{2x^2}{x} = 2x$, while $\dfrac{3x^3}{2x^2} = \dfrac{3}{2}x$.

6. No. Ratio between successive terms is not constant: $\dfrac{6z^2}{3z} = 2z$, while $\dfrac{9z^3}{6z^2} = \dfrac{3}{2}z$.

7. Yes, $a = 1$, ratio $= 2z$.

8. Yes, $a = y^2$, ratio $= y$.

9. Yes, $a = 1$, ratio $= -x$.

10. Yes, $a = 1$, ratio $= -y^2$.

11. Sum $= \dfrac{1}{1 - 2z}, |z| < 1/2$

12. Sum $= \dfrac{y^2}{1 - y}, |y| < 1$

13. Sum $= \dfrac{1}{1 - (-x)} = \dfrac{1}{1 + x}, |x| < 1$

14. Sum $= \dfrac{1}{1 - (-y^2)} = \dfrac{1}{1 + y^2}, |y| < 1.$

15. The series has 26 terms. The first term is $a = 2$ and the constant ratio is $x = 0.1$, so

$$\text{Sum} = \frac{a(1 - x^{26})}{(1 - x)} = \frac{2(1 - (0.1)^{26})}{0.9} = 2.222.$$

16. The series has 10 terms. The first term is $a = 0.2$ and the constant ratio is $x = 0.1$, so

$$\text{Sum} = \frac{0.2(1 - x^{10})}{(1 - x)} = \frac{0.2(1 - (0.1)^{10})}{0.9} = 0.222.$$

17. The series has 9 terms. The first term is $a = 0.00002$ and the constant ratio is $x = 0.1$, so

$$\text{Sum} = \frac{0.00002(1 - x^9)}{(1 - x)} = \frac{0.00002(1 - (0.1)^9)}{0.9} = 0.0000222.$$

18. $-2 + 1 - \dfrac{1}{2} + \dfrac{1}{4} - \dfrac{1}{8} + \dfrac{1}{16} - \cdots = \displaystyle\sum_{n=0}^{\infty} (-2) \left(-\dfrac{1}{2}\right)^n$, a geometric series.

Let $a = -2$ and $x = -\dfrac{1}{2}$. Then

$$\sum_{n=0}^{\infty} (-2) \left(-\frac{1}{2}\right)^n = \frac{a}{1 - x} = \frac{-2}{1 - (-\frac{1}{2})} = -\frac{4}{3}.$$

19. $3 + \dfrac{3}{2} + \dfrac{3}{4} + \dfrac{3}{8} \cdots + \dfrac{3}{2^{10}} = 3\left(1 + \dfrac{1}{2} + \cdots + \dfrac{1}{2^{10}}\right) = \dfrac{3\left(1 - \frac{1}{2^{11}}\right)}{1 - \frac{1}{2}} = \dfrac{3\left(2^{11} - 1\right)}{2^{10}}$

20. Using the formula for the sum of an infinite geometric series,

$$\sum_{n=4}^{\infty} \left(\frac{1}{3}\right)^n = \left(\frac{1}{3}\right)^4 + \left(\frac{1}{3}\right)^5 + \cdots = \left(\frac{1}{3}\right)^4 \left(1 + \frac{1}{3} + \left(\frac{1}{3}\right)^2 + \cdots\right) = \frac{\left(\frac{1}{3}\right)^4}{1 - \frac{1}{3}} = \frac{1}{54}$$

21. Using the formula for the sum of a finite geometric series,

$$\sum_{n=4}^{20} \left(\frac{1}{3}\right)^n = \left(\frac{1}{3}\right)^4 + \left(\frac{1}{3}\right)^5 + \cdots + \left(\frac{1}{3}\right)^{20} = \left(\frac{1}{3}\right)^4 \left(1 + \frac{1}{3} + \left(\frac{1}{3}\right)^2 + \cdots \left(\frac{1}{3}\right)^{16}\right) = \frac{(1/3)^4(1 - (1/3)^{17})}{1 - (1/3)} = \frac{3^{17} - 1}{2 \cdot 3^{20}}.$$

Problems

22. Yes. If the original series is finite, then

$$\text{Original series} = a + ax + ax^2 + \cdots + ax^{n-1},$$

then the new series obtained by multiplying termwise by c is

$$\text{New series} = ca + cax + cax^2 + \cdots + cax^{n-1},$$

which is also a geometric series: its first term is ca and the constant ratio of successive terms is still x. The argument works the same way for an infinite geometric series.

23. Yes. If the original finite geometric series is

$$\text{Original series} = a + ax + ax^2 + \cdots + ax^{n-1},$$

then the new series obtained by taking reciprocals termwise is

$$\text{New series} = \frac{1}{a} + \frac{1}{ax} + \frac{1}{ax^2} + \cdots + \frac{1}{ax^{n-1}},$$

which is also a geometric series: its first term is $1/a$ and the constant ratio of successive terms is $1/x$. The argument works the same way for an infinite geometric series.

24. Since the amount of ampicillin excreted during the time interval between tablets is 250 mg, we have

$$\text{Amount of ampicillin excreted} = \text{Original quantity} - \text{Final quantity}$$
$$250 = Q - (0.04)Q.$$

Solving for Q gives, as before,

$$Q = \frac{250}{1 - 0.04} \approx 260.42.$$

25. (a) The amount of atenolol in the blood is given by $Q(t) = Q_0 e^{-kt}$, where $Q_0 = Q(0)$ and k is a constant. Since the half-life is 6.3 hours,

$$\frac{1}{2} = e^{-6.3k}, \quad k = -\frac{1}{6.3} \ln \frac{1}{2} \approx 0.11.$$

After 24 hours

$$Q = Q_0 e^{-k(24)} \approx Q_0 e^{-0.11(24)} \approx Q_0(0.07).$$

Thus, the percentage of the atenolol that remains after 24 hours $\approx 7\%$.

(b)
$$Q_0 = 50$$
$$Q_1 = 50 + 50(0.07)$$
$$Q_2 = 50 + 50(0.07) + 50(0.07)^2$$
$$Q_3 = 50 + 50(0.07) + 50(0.07)^2 + 50(0.07)^3$$
$$\vdots$$
$$Q_n = 50 + 50(0.07) + 50(0.07)^2 + \cdots + 50(0.07)^n = \frac{50(1 - (0.07)^{n+1})}{1 - 0.07}$$

(c)
$$P_1 = 50(0.07)$$
$$P_2 = 50(0.07) + 50(0.07)^2$$
$$P_3 = 50(0.07) + 50(0.07)^2 + 50(0.07)^3$$
$$P_4 = 50(0.07) + 50(0.07)^2 + 50(0.07)^3 + 50(0.07)^4$$
$$\vdots$$
$$P_n = 50(0.07) + 50(0.07)^2 + 50(0.07)^3 + \cdots + 50(0.07)^n$$
$$= 50(0.07)\left(1 + (0.07) + (0.07)^2 + \cdots + (0.07)^{n-1}\right) = \frac{0.07(50)(1 - (0.07)^n)}{1 - 0.07}$$

26. (a)
$$P_1 = 0$$
$$P_2 = 250(0.04)$$
$$P_3 = 250(0.04) + 250(0.04)^2$$
$$P_4 = 250(0.04) + 250(0.04)^2 + 250(0.04)^3$$
$$\vdots$$
$$P_n = 250(0.04) + 250(0.04)^2 + 250(0.04)^3 + \cdots + 250(0.04)^{n-1}$$

(b) $P_n = 250(0.04)\left(1 + (0.04) + (0.04)^2 + (0.04)^3 + \cdots + (0.04)^{n-2}\right) = 250\dfrac{0.04(1 - (0.04)^{n-1})}{1 - 0.04}$

(c)

$$P = \lim_{n \to \infty} P_n$$

$$= \lim_{n \to \infty} 250\dfrac{0.04(1 - (0.04)^{n-1})}{1 - 0.04}$$

$$= \dfrac{(250)(0.04)}{0.96} = 0.04Q \approx 10.42$$

Thus, $\lim_{n \to \infty} P_n = 10.42$ and $\lim_{n \to \infty} Q_n = 260.42$. We would expect these limits to differ because one is right before taking a tablet, one is right after. We would expect the difference between them to be 250 mg, the amount of ampicillin in one tablet.

27.

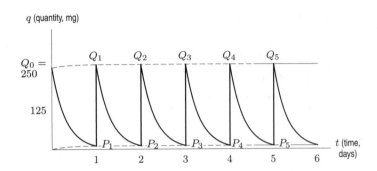

28. (a) Let h_n be the height of the nth bounce after the ball hits the floor for the nth time. Then from Figure 9.1,

$$h_0 = \text{height before first bounce} = 10 \text{ feet},$$

$$h_1 = \text{height after first bounce} = 10\left(\dfrac{3}{4}\right) \text{ feet},$$

$$h_2 = \text{height after second bounce} = 10\left(\dfrac{3}{4}\right)^2 \text{ feet}.$$

Generalizing gives

$$h_n = 10\left(\dfrac{3}{4}\right)^n.$$

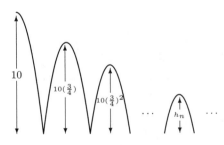

Figure 9.1

(b) When the ball hits the floor for the first time, the total distance it has traveled is just $D_1 = 10$ feet. (Notice that this is the same as $h_0 = 10$.) Then the ball bounces back to a height of $h_1 = 10\left(\dfrac{3}{4}\right)$, comes down and hits the floor for the second time. See Figure 9.1. The total distance it has traveled is

$$D_2 = h_0 + 2h_1 = 10 + 2 \cdot 10\left(\dfrac{3}{4}\right) = 25 \text{ feet}.$$

Then the ball bounces back to a height of $h_2 = 10 \left(\frac{3}{4}\right)^2$, comes down and hits the floor for the third time. It has traveled

$$D_3 = h_0 + 2h_1 + 2h_2 = 10 + 2 \cdot 10 \left(\frac{3}{4}\right) + 2 \cdot 10 \left(\frac{3}{4}\right)^2 = 25 + 2 \cdot 10 \left(\frac{3}{4}\right)^2 = 36.25 \text{ feet.}$$

Similarly,

$$\begin{aligned}
D_4 &= h_0 + 2h_1 + 2h_2 + 2h_3 \\
&= 10 + 2 \cdot 10 \left(\frac{3}{4}\right) + 2 \cdot 10 \left(\frac{3}{4}\right)^2 + 2 \cdot 10 \left(\frac{3}{4}\right)^3 \\
&= 36.25 + 2 \cdot 10 \left(\frac{3}{4}\right)^3 \\
&\approx 44.69 \text{ feet.}
\end{aligned}$$

(c) When the ball hits the floor for the nth time, its last bounce was of height h_{n-1}. Thus, by the method used in part (b), we get

$$\begin{aligned}
D_n &= h_0 + 2h_1 + 2h_2 + 2h_3 + \cdots + 2h_{n-1} \\
&= 10 + \underbrace{2 \cdot 10 \left(\frac{3}{4}\right) + 2 \cdot 10 \left(\frac{3}{4}\right)^2 + 2 \cdot 10 \left(\frac{3}{4}\right)^3 + \cdots + 2 \cdot 10 \left(\frac{3}{4}\right)^{n-1}}_{\text{finite geometric series}} \\
&= 10 + 2 \cdot 10 \cdot \left(\frac{3}{4}\right) \left(1 + \left(\frac{3}{4}\right) + \left(\frac{3}{4}\right)^2 + \cdots + \left(\frac{3}{4}\right)^{n-2}\right) \\
&= 10 + 15 \left(\frac{1 - \left(\frac{3}{4}\right)^{n-1}}{1 - \left(\frac{3}{4}\right)}\right) \\
&= 10 + 60 \left(1 - \left(\frac{3}{4}\right)^{n-1}\right).
\end{aligned}$$

29. (a) The acceleration of gravity is 32 ft/sec^2 so acceleration $= 32$ and velocity $v = 32t + C$. Since the ball is dropped, its initial velocity is 0 so $v = 32t$. Thus the position is $s = 16t^2 + C$. Calling the initial position $s = 0$, we have $s = 6t$. The distance traveled is h so $h = 16t$. Solving for t we get $t = \frac{1}{4}\sqrt{h}$.

(b) The first drop from 10 feet takes $\frac{1}{4}\sqrt{10}$ seconds. The first full bounce (to $10 \cdot \left(\frac{3}{4}\right)$ feet) takes $\frac{1}{4}\sqrt{10 \cdot \left(\frac{3}{4}\right)}$ seconds to rise, therefore the same time to come down. Thus, the full bounce, up and down, takes $2(\frac{1}{4})\sqrt{10 \cdot \left(\frac{3}{4}\right)}$ seconds. The next full bounce takes $2(\frac{1}{4})10 \cdot \left(\frac{3}{4}\right)^2 = 2(\frac{1}{4})\sqrt{10} \left(\sqrt{\frac{3}{4}}\right)^2$ seconds. The nth bounce takes $2(\frac{1}{4})\sqrt{10} \left(\sqrt{\frac{3}{4}}\right)^n$ seconds. Therefore the

$$\begin{aligned}
&\text{Total amount of time} \\
&= \frac{1}{4}\sqrt{10} + \underbrace{\frac{2}{4}\sqrt{10}\sqrt{\frac{3}{4}} + \frac{2}{4}\sqrt{10} \left(\sqrt{\frac{3}{4}}\right)^2 + \frac{2}{4}\sqrt{10} \left(\sqrt{\frac{3}{4}}\right)^3}_{\text{Geometric series with } a = \frac{2}{4}\sqrt{10}\sqrt{\frac{3}{4}} = \frac{1}{2}\sqrt{10}\sqrt{\frac{3}{4}} \text{ and } x = \sqrt{\frac{3}{4}}} + \cdots \\
&= \frac{1}{4}\sqrt{10} + \frac{1}{2}\sqrt{10}\sqrt{\frac{3}{4}} \left(\frac{1}{1 - \sqrt{3/4}}\right) \text{ seconds.}
\end{aligned}$$

30.

$$\begin{aligned}
\text{Total present value, in dollars} &= 1000 + 1000e^{-0.04} + 1000e^{-0.04(2)} + 1000e^{-0.04(3)} + \cdots \\
&= 1000 + 1000(e^{-0.04}) + 1000(e^{-0.04})^2 + 1000(e^{-0.04})^3 + \cdots
\end{aligned}$$

This is an infinite geometric series with $a = 1000$ and $x = e^{(-0.04)}$, and sum

$$\text{Total present value, in dollars} = \frac{1000}{1 - e^{-0.04}} = 25{,}503.$$

31. The amount of additional income generated directly by people spending their extra money is $100(0.8) = \$80$ million. This additional money in turn is spent, generating another $(\$100(0.8))(0.8) = \$100(0.8)^2$ million. This continues indefinitely, resulting in

$$\text{Total additional income} = 100(0.8) + 100(0.8)^2 + 100(0.8)^3 + \cdots = \frac{100(0.8)}{1 - 0.8} = \$400 \text{ million}$$

32. The total of the spending and respending of the additional income is given by the series: Total additional income $= 100(0.9) + 100(0.9)^2 + 100(0.9)^3 + \cdots = \frac{100(0.9)}{1-0.9} = \$900$ million.
Notice the large effect of changing the assumption about the fraction of money spent has: the additional spending more than doubles.

Solutions for Section 9.3

Exercises

1. We use the integral test with $f(x) = 1/x^3$ to determine whether this series converges or diverges. We determine whether the corresponding improper integral $\int_1^\infty \frac{1}{x^3}\,dx$ converges or diverges:

$$\int_1^\infty \frac{1}{x^3}\,dx = \lim_{b \to \infty} \int_1^b \frac{1}{x^3}\,dx = \lim_{b \to \infty} \left.\frac{-1}{2x^2}\right|_1^b = \lim_{b \to \infty} \left(\frac{-1}{2b^2} + \frac{1}{2}\right) = \frac{1}{2}.$$

Since the integral $\int_1^\infty \frac{1}{x^3}\,dx$ converges, we conclude from the integral test that the series $\sum_{n=1}^\infty \frac{1}{n^3}$ converges.

2. We use the integral test with $f(x) = x/(x^2 + 1)$ to determine whether this series converges or diverges. We determine whether the corresponding improper integral $\int_1^\infty \frac{x}{x^2 + 1}\,dx$ converges or diverges:

$$\int_1^\infty \frac{x}{x^2 + 1}\,dx = \lim_{b \to \infty} \int_1^b \frac{x}{x^2 + 1}\,dx = \lim_{b \to \infty} \left.\frac{1}{2}\ln(x^2 + 1)\right|_1^b = \lim_{b \to \infty} \left(\frac{1}{2}\ln(b^2 + 1) - \frac{1}{2}\ln 2\right) = \infty.$$

Since the integral $\int_1^\infty \frac{x}{x^2 + 1}\,dx$ diverges, we conclude from the integral test that the series $\sum_{n=1}^\infty \frac{n}{n^2 + 1}$ diverges.

3. We use the integral test with $f(x) = 1/e^x$ to determine whether this series converges or diverges. To do so we determine whether the corresponding improper integral $\int_1^\infty \frac{1}{e^x}\,dx$ converges or diverges:

$$\int_1^\infty \frac{1}{e^x}\,dx = \lim_{b \to \infty} \int_1^b e^{-x}\,dx = \lim_{b \to \infty} \left.-e^{-x}\right|_1^b = \lim_{b \to \infty} \left(-e^{-b} + e^{-1}\right) = e^{-1}.$$

Since the integral $\int_1^\infty \frac{1}{e^x}\,dx$ converges, we conclude from the integral test that the series $\sum_{n=1}^\infty \frac{1}{e^n}$ converges. We can also observe that this is a geometric series with ratio $x = 1/e < 1$, and hence it converges.

4. We use the integral test with $f(x) = 1/(x(\ln x)^2)$ to determine whether this series converges or diverges. We determine whether the corresponding improper integral $\int_2^\infty \frac{1}{x(\ln x)^2}\,dx$ converges or diverges:

$$\int_2^\infty \frac{1}{x(\ln x)^2}\,dx = \lim_{b \to \infty} \int_2^b \frac{1}{x(\ln x)^2}\,dx = \lim_{b \to \infty} \left.\frac{-1}{\ln x}\right|_2^b = \lim_{b \to \infty} \left(\frac{-1}{\ln b} + \frac{1}{\ln 2}\right) = \frac{1}{\ln 2}.$$

Since the integral $\int_2^\infty \frac{1}{x(\ln x)^2}\,dx$ converges, we conclude from the integral test that the series $\sum_{n=2}^\infty \frac{1}{n(\ln n)^2}$ converges.

5. The improper integral $\int_1^\infty x^{-3}\,dx$ converges to $\dfrac{1}{2}$, since

$$\int_1^b x^{-3}\,dx = \left.\frac{x^{-2}}{-2}\right|_1^b = \frac{b^{-2}}{-2} - \frac{1^{-2}}{-2} = \frac{1}{-2b^2} + \frac{1}{2}$$

and

$$\lim_{b\to\infty}\left(\frac{1}{-2b^2} + \frac{1}{2}\right) = \frac{1}{2}.$$

The terms of the series $\displaystyle\sum_{n=2}^\infty n^{-3}$ form a right hand sum for the improper integral; each term represents the area of a rectangle of width 1 fitting completely under the graph of the function x^{-3}. (See Figure 9.2.) Thus the sequence of partial sums is bounded above by $1/2$. Since the partial sums are increasing (every new term added is positive) the series is guaranteed to converge to some number less than or equal to $1/2$ by Theorem 9.1.

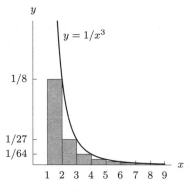

Figure 9.2

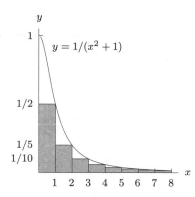

Figure 9.3

6. The improper integral $\int_0^\infty \dfrac{1}{x^2+1}\,dx$ converges to $\dfrac{\pi}{2}$, since

$$\int_0^b \frac{1}{x^2+1}\,dx = \arctan x\big|_0^b = \arctan b - \arctan 0 = \arctan b,$$

and $\displaystyle\lim_{b\to\infty}\arctan b = \frac{\pi}{2}$. The terms of the series $\displaystyle\sum_{n=1}^\infty \frac{1}{n^2+1}$ form a right hand sum for the improper integral; each term represents the area of a rectangle of width 1 fitting completely under the graph of the function $\dfrac{1}{x^2+1}$. (See Figure 9.3.) Thus the sequence of partial sums is bounded above by $\dfrac{\pi}{2}$. Since the partial sums are increasing (every new term added is positive), the series is guaranteed to converge to some number less than or equal to $\pi/2$ by Theorem 9.1.

7. The integral test requires that $f(x) = x^2$, which is not decreasing.

8. The integral test requires that $f(x) = (-1)^x/x$. However $(-1)^x$ is not defined for all x.

9. The integral test requires that $f(x) = e^{-x}\sin x$, which is not positive, nor is it decreasing.

Problems

10. Using the integral test, we compare the series with

$$\int_0^\infty \frac{3}{x+2}\,dx = \lim_{b\to\infty}\int_0^b \frac{3}{x+2}\,dx = 3\ln|x+2|\,\Big|_0^b.$$

Since $\ln(b+2)$ is unbounded as $b\to\infty$, the integral diverges and therefore so does the series.

11. We use the integral test and calculate the corresponding improper integral, $\int_1^\infty 3/(2x-1)^2\,dx$:

$$\int_1^\infty \frac{3\,dx}{(2x-1)^2} = \lim_{b\to\infty} \int_1^b \frac{3\,dx}{(2x-1)^2} = \lim_{b\to\infty} \frac{-3/2}{(2x-1)}\bigg|_1^b = \lim_{b\to\infty} \left(\frac{-3/2}{(2b-1)} + \frac{3}{2}\right) = \frac{3}{2}.$$

Since the integral converges, the series $\displaystyle\sum_{n=1}^\infty \frac{3}{(2n-1)^2}$ converges.

12. We use the integral test and calculate the corresponding improper integral, $\int_0^\infty 2/\sqrt{2+x}\,dx$:

$$\int_0^\infty \frac{2}{\sqrt{2+x}}\,dx = \lim_{b\to\infty} \int_0^b \frac{2\,dx}{\sqrt{2+x}} = \lim_{b\to\infty} 4(2+x)^{1/2}\bigg|_0^b = \lim_{b\to\infty} 4\left((2+b)^{1/2} - 2^{1/2}\right).$$

Since the limit does not exist, the integral diverges, so the series $\displaystyle\sum_{n=1}^\infty \frac{2}{\sqrt{2+n}}$ diverges.

13. Writing $a_n = n/(n+1)$, we have $\lim_{n\to\infty} a_n = 1$ so the series diverges by Property 3 of Theorem 9.2.

14. We use the integral test and calculate the corresponding improper integral, $\int_1^\infty 4/(2x+1)^3\,dx$. Using the substitution $w = 2x+1$, we have

$$\int_1^\infty \frac{4\,dx}{(2x+1)^3} = \lim_{b\to\infty} \int_1^b \frac{4\,dx}{(2x+1)^3} = \lim_{b\to\infty} -\frac{1}{(2x+1)^2}\bigg|_1^b = \lim_{b\to\infty} \left(-\frac{1}{(2b+1)^2} + \frac{1}{9}\right) = \frac{1}{9}.$$

Since the integral converges, the series $\displaystyle\sum_{n=1}^\infty \frac{4}{(2n+1)^3}$ converges.

15. Using the integral test, we compare the series with

$$\int_0^\infty \frac{3}{x^2+4}\,dx = \lim_{b\to\infty} \int_0^b \frac{3}{x^2+4}\,dx = \frac{3}{2}\lim_{b\to\infty} \arctan\left(\frac{x}{2}\right)\bigg|_0^b = \frac{3}{2}\lim_{b\to\infty} \arctan\left(\frac{b}{2}\right) = \frac{3\pi}{4},$$

by integral table V-24. Since the integral converges so does the series.

16. The series $\displaystyle\sum_{n=1}^\infty \left(\frac{3}{4}\right)^n$ is a convergent geometric series, but $\displaystyle\sum_{n=1}^\infty \frac{1}{n}$ is the divergent harmonic series.

If $\displaystyle\sum_{n=1}^\infty \left(\left(\frac{3}{4}\right)^n + \frac{1}{n}\right)$ converged, then $\displaystyle\sum_{n=1}^\infty \left(\left(\frac{3}{4}\right)^n + \frac{1}{n}\right) - \sum_{n=1}^\infty \left(\frac{3}{4}\right)^n = \sum_{n=1}^\infty \frac{1}{n}$ would converge by Theorem 9.2.

Therefore $\displaystyle\sum_{n=1}^\infty \left(\left(\frac{3}{4}\right)^n + \frac{1}{n}\right)$ diverges.

17. The series can be written as

$$\sum_{n=1}^\infty \frac{n+2^n}{n2^n} = \sum_{n=1}^\infty \left(\frac{1}{2^n} + \frac{1}{n}\right).$$

If this series converges, then $\displaystyle\sum_{n=1}^\infty \left(\frac{1}{2^n} + \frac{1}{n}\right) - \sum_{n=1}^\infty \frac{1}{2^n} = \sum_{n=1}^\infty \frac{1}{n}$ would converge by Theorem 9.2. Since this is the

harmonic series, which diverges, then the series $\displaystyle\sum_{n=1}^\infty \frac{n+2^n}{n}$ diverges.

18. Let $a_n = (\ln n)/n$ and $f(x) = (\ln x)/x$. We use the integral test and consider the improper integral

$$\int_c^\infty \frac{\ln x}{x}\,dx.$$

Since

$$\int_c^R \frac{\ln x}{x}\,dx = \frac{1}{2}(\ln x)^2\bigg|_c^R = \frac{1}{2}\left((\ln R)^2 - (\ln c)^2\right),$$

and $\ln R$ grows without bound as $R \to \infty$, the integral diverges. Therefore, the integral test tells us that the series, $\displaystyle\sum_{n=1}^\infty \frac{\ln n}{n}$, also diverges.

19. We use the integral test and calculate the corresponding improper integral, $\int_3^\infty (x+1)/(x^2+2x+2)\,dx$:

$$\int_3^\infty \frac{x+1}{x^2+2x+2}\,dx = \lim_{b\to\infty} \int_3^b \frac{x+1}{x^2+2x+2}\,dx = \lim_{b\to\infty} \frac{1}{2}\ln|x^2+2x+2|\Big|_3^b = \lim_{b\to\infty} \frac{1}{2}\left(\ln(b^2+2b+2) - \ln 17\right).$$

Since the limit does not exist (it is ∞), the integral diverges, so the series $\displaystyle\sum_{n=3}^\infty \frac{n+1}{n^2+2n+2}$ diverges.

20. Using $\ln(2^n) = n\ln 2$, we see that

$$\sum \frac{1}{\ln(2^n)} = \sum \frac{1}{(\ln 2)n}.$$

The series on the right is the harmonic series multiplied by $1/\ln 2$. Since the harmonic series diverges, $\sum_{n=1}^\infty 1/\ln(2^n)$ diverges.

21. Using $\ln(2^n) = n\ln 2$, we see that

$$\sum_{n=1}^\infty \frac{1}{(\ln(2^n))^2} = \sum_{n=1}^\infty \frac{1}{(\ln 2)^2 n^2}.$$

Since $\sum 1/n^2$ converges, $\sum 1/((\ln(2))^2 n^2)$ converges by property 1 of Theorem 9.2.

22. (a) With $a_n = \ln((n+1)/n)$ we have

$$\begin{aligned} S_n &= a_1 + a_2 + a_3 + \cdots + a_{n-1} + a_n \\ &= \ln(2/1) + \ln(3/2) + \ln(4/3) + \cdots + \ln(n/(n-1)) + \ln((n+1)/n) \\ &= \ln\left(\frac{2}{1}\cdot\frac{3}{2}\cdot\frac{4}{3}\cdots\frac{n}{n-1}\cdot\frac{n+1}{n}\right) = \ln(n+1). \end{aligned}$$

(b) Since the limit of the partial sums, $\lim_{n\to\infty} S_n = \lim_{n\to\infty} \ln(n+1)$, does not exist, the series diverges.

23. (a) Using $r = e^{\ln r}$ and $n = e^{\ln n}$ we have $r^{\ln n} = e^{(\ln r)(\ln n)} = n^{\ln r}$.

(b) By part (a) we have $r^{\ln n} = n^{\ln r} = 1/n^{-\ln r}$. Since the p-series $\sum 1/n^p$ converges if and only if $p > 1$, the series $\sum_{n=1}^\infty 1/n^{-\ln r}$ converges if and only if $-\ln r > 1$, which is equivalent to $\ln r < -1$ or $r < 1/e$. Thus $\sum_{n=1}^\infty r^{\ln n}$ converges if $0 < r < 1/e$ and diverges if $r \geq 1/e$.

24. (a) A common denominator is $k(k+1)$ so

$$\frac{1}{k} - \frac{1}{k+1} = \frac{k+1}{k(k+1)} - \frac{k}{k(k+1)} = \frac{k+1-k}{k(k+1)} = \frac{1}{k(k+1)}.$$

(b) Using the result of part (a), the partial sum can be written as

$$S_3 = \frac{1}{1\cdot 2} + \frac{1}{2\cdot 3} + \frac{1}{3\cdot 4} = \frac{1}{1} - \frac{1}{2} + \frac{1}{2} - \frac{1}{3} + \frac{1}{3} - \frac{1}{4} = 1 - \frac{1}{4}.$$

All of the intermediate terms cancel out, leaving only the first and last terms. Thus $S_{10} = 1 - \dfrac{1}{11}$ and $S_n = 1 - \dfrac{1}{n+1}$.

(c) The limit of S_n as $n \to \infty$ is $\displaystyle\lim_{n\to\infty}\left(1 - \frac{1}{n+1}\right) = 1 - 0 = 1$. Thus the series $\displaystyle\sum_{k=1}^\infty \frac{1}{k(k+1)}$ converges to 1.

25. (a) The partial sum

$$S_4 = \ln\left(\frac{1\cdot 3}{2\cdot 2}\right) + \ln\left(\frac{2\cdot 4}{3\cdot 3}\right) + \ln\left(\frac{3\cdot 5}{4\cdot 4}\right).$$

Using the property $\ln(A) + \ln(B) = \ln(AB)$, we get

$$S_4 = \ln\left(\frac{1\cdot 3\cdot 2\cdot 4\cdot 3\cdot 5}{2\cdot 2\cdot 3\cdot 3\cdot 4\cdot 4}\right).$$

The intermediate factors cancel out, leaving only $\ln\left(\dfrac{1\cdot 5}{2\cdot 4}\right)$, so $S_4 = \ln\left(\dfrac{5}{8}\right)$.

(b) For the partial sum S_n, similar steps yield

$$S_n = \ln\left(\frac{1\cdot 3\cdot 2\cdot 4\cdot 3\cdot 5\cdots(n-1)(n+1)}{2\cdot 2\cdot 3\cdot 3\cdot 4\cdot 4\cdots n\cdot n}\right).$$

As before, most of the factors cancel, leaving $S_n = \ln\left(\dfrac{n+1}{2n}\right)$.

(c) The limit of $S_n = \ln\left(\dfrac{n+1}{2n}\right)$ as $n \to \infty$ is $\lim\limits_{n\to\infty} \ln\left(\dfrac{n+1}{2n}\right) = \ln\left(\dfrac{1}{2}\right)$. Thus the series $\sum\limits_{k=2}^{\infty} \ln\left(\dfrac{(k-1)(k+1)}{k^2}\right)$

converges to $\ln\left(\dfrac{1}{2}\right)$.

26. Let S_n be the nth partial sum for $\sum a_n$ and let T_n be the nth partial sum for $\sum b_n$. Then the nth partial sums for $\sum(a_n + b_n)$, $\sum(a_n - b_n)$, and $\sum ka_n$ are $S_n + T_n$, $S_n - T_n$, and kS_n, respectively. To show that these series converge, we have to show that the limits of their partial sums exist. By the properties of limits,

$$\lim_{n\to\infty}(S_n + T_n) = \lim_{n\to\infty} S_n + \lim_{n\to\infty} T_n$$
$$\lim_{n\to\infty}(S_n - T_n) = \lim_{n\to\infty} S_n - \lim_{n\to\infty} T_n$$
$$\lim_{n\to\infty} kS_n = k \lim_{n\to\infty} S_n.$$

This proves that the limits of the partial sums exist, so the series converge.

27. Let S_n be the n-th partial sum for $\sum a_n$ and let T_n be the n-th partial sum for $\sum b_n$. Suppose that $S_N = T_N + k$. Since $a_n = b_n$ for $n \geq N$, we have $S_n = T_n + k$ for $n \geq N$. Hence if S_n converges to a limit, so does T_n, and vice versa. Thus, $\sum a_n$ and $\sum b_n$ either both converge or both diverge.

28. We have $a_n = S_n - S_{n-1}$. If $\sum a_n$ converges, then $S = \lim_{n\to\infty} S_n$ exists. Hence $\lim_{n\to\infty} S_{n-1}$ exists and is equal to S also. Thus

$$\lim_{n\to\infty} a_n = \lim_{n\to\infty}(S_n - S_{n-1}) = \lim_{n\to\infty} S_n - \lim_{n\to\infty} S_{n-1} = S - S = 0.$$

29. From Property 1 in Theorem 9.2, we know that if $\sum a_n$ converges, then so does $\sum ka_n$.

Now suppose that $\sum a_n$ diverges and $\sum ka_n$ converges for $k \neq 0$. Thus using Property 1 and replacing $\sum a_n$ by $\sum ka_n$, we know that the following series converges:

$$\sum \frac{1}{k}(ka_n) = \sum a_n.$$

Thus, we have arrived at a contradiction, which means our original assumption, that $\sum\limits_{n=1}^{\infty} ka_n$ converged, must be wrong.

30. A typical partial sum of the series $\sum\limits_{n=1}^{\infty}(a_{n+1} - a_n)$, say S_5, shows what happens in the general case:

$$S_5 = (a_2 - a_1) + (a_3 - a_2) + (a_4 - a_3) + (a_5 - a_4) + (a_6 - a_5) = a_6 - a_1$$

as all of the intermediate terms cancel out. The same thing will happen in the general partial sum: $S_n = a_{n+1} - a_1$.

Now the series $\sum\limits_{n=1}^{\infty}(a_{n+1} - a_n)$ converges if the sequence of partial sums S_n has a limit as $n \to \infty$. Since we're as-

suming that the original series $\sum\limits_{n=1}^{\infty} a_n$ converges, we know that $\lim\limits_{n\to\infty} a_n = \lim\limits_{n\to\infty} a_{n+1} = 0$ by property 3 of Theorem 9.2.
Thus

$$\lim_{n\to\infty} S_n = \lim_{n\to\infty}(a_{n+1} - a_1) = 0 - a_1 = -a_1.$$

Since the sequence of partial sums converges (to $-a_1$), the series $\sum\limits_{n=1}^{\infty}(a_{n+1} - a_n)$ converges (also to $-a_1$).

31. If $a_n = 1$ for all n, then $\sum a_n$ diverges but $\sum(a_{n+1} - a_n) = \sum 0$ converges. If $a_n = n$ for all n, then $\sum a_n$ diverges, and $\sum a_{n+1} - a_n = \sum 1$ diverges

32. (a) Let N an integer with $N \geq c$. Consider the series $\sum\limits_{i=N+1}^{\infty} a_i$. The partial sums of this series are increasing because all the terms in the series are positive. We show the partial sums are bounded using the right-hand sum in Figure 9.4. We see that for each positive integer k

$$f(N+1) + f(N+2) + \cdots + f(N+k) \leq \int_N^{N+k} f(x)\,dx.$$

Since $f(n) = a_n$ for all n, and $c \leq N$, we have

$$a_{N+1} + a_{N+2} + \cdots + a_{N+k} \leq \int_c^{N+k} f(x)\, dx.$$

Since $f(x)$ is a positive function, $\int_c^{N+k} f(x)\, dx \leq \int_c^b f(x)\, dx$ for all $b \geq N + k$. Since f is positive and $\int_c^\infty f(x)\, dx$ is convergent, $\int_c^{N+k} f(x)\, dx < \int_c^\infty f(x)\, dx$, so we have

$$a_{N+1} + a_{N+2} + \cdots + a_{N+k} \leq \int_c^\infty f(x)\, dx \quad \text{for all } k.$$

Thus, the partial sums of the series $\displaystyle\sum_{i=N+1}^\infty a_i$ are bounded and increasing, so this series converges by Theorem 9.1.

Now use Theorem 9.2, property 2, to conclude that $\displaystyle\sum_{i=1}^\infty a_i$ converges.

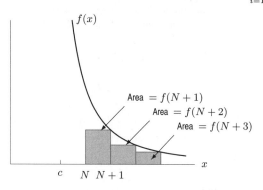

Figure 9.4   **Figure 9.5**

(b) We now suppose $\displaystyle\int_c^\infty f(x)\, dx$ diverges. In Figure 9.5 we see that for each positive integer k

$$\int_N^{N+k+1} f(x)\, dx \leq f(N) + f(N+1) + \cdots + f(N+k).$$

Since $f(n) = a_n$ for all n, we have

$$\int_N^{N+k+1} f(x)\, dx \leq a_N + a_{N+1} + \cdots + a_{N+k}.$$

Since $f(x)$ is defined for all $x \geq c$, if $\int_c^\infty f(x)\, dx$ is divergent, then $\int_N^\infty f(x)\, dx$ is divergent. So as $k \to \infty$, the the integral $\int_N^{N+k+1} f(x)\, dx$ diverges, so the partial sums of the series $\displaystyle\sum_{i=N}^\infty a_i$ diverge. Thus, the series $\displaystyle\sum_{i=1}^\infty a_i$ diverges.

More precisely, suppose the series converged. Then the partial sums would be bounded. (The partial sums would be less than the sum of the series, since all the terms in the series are positive.) But that would imply that the integral converged, by Theorem 9.1 on Convergence of Monotone Bounded Sequences. This contradicts the assumption that $\int_N^\infty f(x)\, dx$ is divergent.

33. (a) Show that the sum of each group of fractions is more than $1/2$.
    (b) Explain why this shows that the harmonic series does not converge.

(a) Notice that

$$\frac{1}{3} + \frac{1}{4} > \frac{1}{4} + \frac{1}{4} = \frac{2}{4} = \frac{1}{2}$$

$$\frac{1}{5} + \frac{1}{6} + \frac{1}{7} + \frac{1}{8} > \frac{1}{8} + \frac{1}{8} + \frac{1}{8} + \frac{1}{8} = \frac{4}{8} = \frac{1}{2}$$

$$\frac{1}{9} + \frac{1}{10} + \cdots + \frac{1}{16} > \frac{1}{16} + \frac{1}{16} + \cdots + \frac{1}{16} = \frac{8}{16} = \frac{1}{2}.$$

In the same way, we can see that the sum of the fractions in each grouping is greater than $1/2$.

(b) Since the sum of the first n groups is greater than $n/2$, it follows that the partial sums of the harmonic series are not bounded. Thus, the harmonic series diverges.

34. (a) Since for $x > 0$,

$$\int \frac{1}{x \ln x}\, dx = \ln(\ln x) + C$$

we have

$$\int_2^\infty \frac{1}{x \ln x}\, dx = \lim_{b \to \infty} \int_2^b \frac{1}{x \ln x}\, dx = \lim_{b \to \infty} \left(\ln(\ln b) - \ln(\ln 2)\right) = \infty.$$

The series diverges by the integral test.

(b) The terms in each group are decreasing so we can bound each group as follows:

$$\frac{1}{3 \ln 3} + \frac{1}{4 \ln 4} > \frac{1}{4 \ln 4} + \frac{1}{4 \ln 4} = \frac{1}{2 \ln 4}$$

and

$$\frac{1}{5 \ln 5} + \frac{1}{6 \ln 6} + \frac{1}{7 \ln 7} + \frac{1}{8 \ln 8} > 4 \frac{1}{8 \ln 8} = \frac{1}{2 \ln 8}.$$

Similarly, the group whose final term is $1/(2^n \ln(2^n))$ is greater than $1/(2 \ln(2^n)) = 1/(2(\ln 2)n)$. Thus

$$\sum_{n=2}^{2^N} \frac{1}{n \ln n} > \sum_{n=1}^{N} \frac{1}{2(\ln 2)n}.$$

The series on the right is the harmonic series multiplied by the constant $1/(2 \ln 2)$. Since the harmonic series diverges, $\sum 1/(n \ln n)$ diverges.

35. (a) The left-hand sum approximation to $\int_1^n \frac{1}{x}\, dx$ in Figure 9.6 shows that

$$\int_1^n \frac{dx}{x} < 1 + \frac{1}{2} + \frac{1}{3} + \cdots + \frac{1}{n}$$

$$\ln n - \ln 1 < 1 + \frac{1}{2} + \frac{1}{3} + \cdots + \frac{1}{n}$$

$$0 < 1 + \frac{1}{2} + \frac{1}{3} + \cdots + \frac{1}{n} - \ln n.$$

Thus, $0 < a_n$.

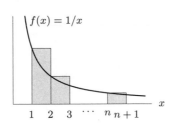

Figure 9.6

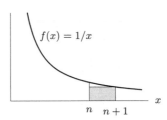

Figure 9.7

(b) We calculate

$$a_n - a_{n+1} = \left(1 + \frac{1}{2} + \frac{1}{3} + \cdots + \frac{1}{n}\right) - \ln n - \left(\left(1 + \frac{1}{2} + \frac{1}{3} + \cdots + \frac{1}{n+1}\right) - \ln(n+1)\right)$$

$$= \ln(n+1) - \ln n - \frac{1}{n+1}.$$

But using the right sum with one rectangle in Figure 9.7, we see that

$$\int_n^{n+1} \frac{dx}{x} > \frac{1}{n+1}$$

$$\ln(n+1) - \ln n > \frac{1}{n+1}.$$

Thus

$$a_n - a_{n+1} = \ln(n+1) - \ln n - \frac{1}{n+1} > 0.$$
$$a_n > a_{n+1}.$$

(c) Since a_n is a decreasing sequence bounded below by 0, Theorem 9.1 ensures that $\lim_{n\to\infty} a_n$ exists.

(d) The sequence converges slowly, but a calculator or computer gives $a_{200} = 0.5797$. For comparison, $a_{100} = 0.5822$, $a_{500} = 0.5782$. Thus, $\gamma = 0.58$. More extensive calculations show that $\gamma = 0.577216$.

36. (a) A calculator or computer gives

$$\sum_{1}^{20} \frac{1}{n^2} = \frac{1}{1^2} + \frac{1}{2^2} + \cdots + \frac{1}{20^2} = 1.596.$$

(b) Since $\displaystyle\sum_{1}^{\infty} \frac{1}{n^2} = \frac{\pi^2}{6}$, the answer to part (a) gives

$$\frac{\pi^2}{6} \approx 1.596$$
$$\pi \approx \sqrt{6 \cdot 1.596} = 3.09$$

(c) A calculator or computer gives

$$\sum_{1}^{100} \frac{1}{n^2} = \frac{1}{1^2} + \frac{1}{2^2} + \cdots + \frac{1}{100^2} = 1.635,$$

so

$$\frac{\pi^2}{6} \approx 1.635$$
$$\pi \approx \sqrt{6 \cdot 1.635} = 3.13.$$

(d) The error in approximating $\pi^2/6$ by $\sum_{1}^{20} 1/n^2$ is the tail of the series $\sum_{21}^{\infty} 1/n^2$. From Figure 9.8, we see that

$$\sum_{21}^{\infty} \frac{1}{n^2} < \int_{20}^{\infty} \frac{dx}{x^2} = -\frac{1}{x}\bigg|_{20}^{\infty} = \frac{1}{20} = 0.05.$$

A similar argument leads to a bound for the error in approximating $\pi^2/6$ by $\sum_{1}^{100} 1/n^2$ as

$$\sum_{101}^{\infty} \frac{1}{n^2} < \int_{100}^{\infty} \frac{dx}{x^2} = -\frac{1}{x}\bigg|_{100}^{\infty} = \frac{1}{100} = 0.01.$$

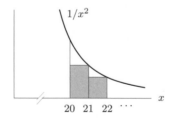

Figure 9.8

37. (a) We have $e > 1 + 1 + 1/2 + 1/6 + 1/24 = 65/24 = 2.708$.

(b) We have

$$\frac{1}{n!} = \frac{1}{1 \cdot 2 \cdot 3 \cdot 4 \cdots n} \leq \frac{1}{1 \cdot 2 \cdot 2 \cdot 2 \cdots 2} = \frac{1}{2^{n-1}}.$$

(c) The inequality in part (b) can be used to replace the given series with a geometric series that we can sum.

$$e = \sum_{n=0}^{\infty} \frac{1}{n!} = 1 + \sum_{n=1}^{\infty} \frac{1}{n!} < 1 + \sum_{n=1}^{\infty} \frac{1}{2^{n-1}} = 1 + \frac{1}{1 - 1/2} = 3.$$

38. (a) The right-hand sum for $\int_0^N x^N dx$ with $\Delta x = 1$ is the sum $1^5 \cdot 1 + 2^5 \cdot 1 + 3^5 \cdot 1 + \cdots + N^5 \cdot 1 = S_N$. This sum is greater than the integral because the integrand x^5 is increasing on the interval $0 < x < N$. Since $\int_0^N x^5 dx = N^6/6$, we have $S_N > N^6/6$.

(b) The left-hand sum for $\int_1^{N+1} x^N dx$ with $\Delta x = 1$ is the sum $1^5 \cdot 1 + 2^5 \cdot 1 + 3^5 \cdot 1 + \cdots + N^5 \cdot 1 = S_N$. This sum is less than the integral because the integrand x^5 is increasing on the interval $1 < x < N + 1$. Since $\int_1^{N+1} x^5 dx = ((N+1)^6 - 1)/6$, we have $S_N < ((N+1)^6 - 1)/6$.

(c) By parts (a) and (b) we have

$$\frac{N^6/6}{N^6/6} = 1 < \frac{S_N}{N^6/6} < \frac{((N+1)^6 - 1)/6}{N^6/6} = (1 + \frac{1}{N})^6 - \frac{1}{N^6}.$$

Since both $\lim_{N \to \infty} 1 = 1$ and $\lim_{N \to \infty}((1 + \frac{1}{N})^6 - \frac{1}{N^6}) = 1$, we conclude that the limit in the middle also equals 1, $\lim_{N \to \infty} S_N/(N^6/6) = 1$.

Solutions for Section 9.4

Exercises

1. Let $a_n = 1/(n - 3)$, for $n \geq 4$. Since $n - 3 < n$, we have $1/(n - 3) > 1/n$, so

$$a_n > \frac{1}{n}.$$

The harmonic series $\sum_{n=4}^{\infty} \frac{1}{n}$ diverges, so the comparison test tells us that the series $\sum_{n=4}^{\infty} \frac{1}{n - 3}$ also diverges.

2. Let $a_n = 1/(n^2 + 2)$. Since $n^2 + 2 > n^2$, we have $1/(n^2 + 2) < 1/n^2$, so

$$0 < a_n < \frac{1}{n^2}.$$

The series $\sum_{n=1}^{\infty} \frac{1}{n^2}$ converges, so the comparison test tells us that the series $\sum_{n=1}^{\infty} \frac{1}{n^2 + 2}$ also converges.

3. Let $a_n = e^{-n}/n^2$. Since $e^{-n} < 1$, for $n \geq 1$, we have $\frac{e^{-n}}{n^2} < \frac{1}{n^2}$, so

$$0 < a_n < \frac{1}{n^2}.$$

The series $\sum_{n=1}^{\infty} \frac{1}{n^2}$ converges, so the comparison test tells us that the series $\sum_{n=1}^{\infty} \frac{e^{-n}}{n^2}$ also converges.

4. Let $a_n = 1/(3^n + 1)$. Since $3^n + 1 > 3^n$, we have $1/(3^n + 1) < 1/3^n = \left(\frac{1}{3}\right)^n$, so

$$0 < a_n < \left(\frac{1}{3}\right)^n.$$

Thus we can compare the series $\sum_{n=1}^{\infty} \frac{1}{3^n + 1}$ with the geometric series $\sum_{n=1}^{\infty} \left(\frac{1}{3}\right)^n$. This geometric series converges since $|1/3| < 1$, so the comparison test tells us that $\sum_{n=1}^{\infty} \frac{1}{3^n + 1}$ also converges.

5. Let $a_n = 1/(n^4 + e^n)$. Since $n^4 + e^n > n^4$, we have

$$\frac{1}{n^4 + e^n} < \frac{1}{n^4},$$

so

$$0 < a_n < \frac{1}{n^4}.$$

Since the p-series $\sum_{n=1}^{\infty} \frac{1}{n^4}$ converges, the comparison test tells us that the series $\sum_{n=1}^{\infty} \frac{1}{n^4 + e^n}$ also converges.

6. Since $\ln n \leq n$ for $n \geq 2$, we have $1/\ln n \geq 1/n$, so the series diverges by comparison with the harmonic series, $\sum 1/n$.

7. Let $a_n = n^2/(n^4 + 1)$. Since $n^4 + 1 > n^4$, we have $\dfrac{1}{n^4 + 1} < \dfrac{1}{n^4}$, so

$$a_n = \frac{n^2}{n^4 + 1} < \frac{n^2}{n^4} = \frac{1}{n^2},$$

therefore

$$0 < a_n < \frac{1}{n^2}.$$

Since the p-series $\displaystyle\sum_{n=1}^{\infty} \frac{1}{n^2}$ converges, the comparison test tells us that the series $\displaystyle\sum_{n=1}^{\infty} \frac{n^2}{n^4 + 1}$ converges also.

8. We know that $|\sin n| < 1$, so

$$\left| \frac{n \sin n}{n^3 + 1} \right| \leq \frac{n}{n^3 + 1} < \frac{n}{n^3} = \frac{1}{n^2}.$$

Since the p-series $\displaystyle\sum_{n=1}^{\infty} \frac{1}{n^2}$ converges, comparison gives that $\displaystyle\sum_{n=1}^{\infty} \left| \frac{n \sin n}{n^3 + 1} \right|$ converges. Thus, by Theorem 9.6, $\displaystyle\sum_{n=1}^{\infty} \frac{n \sin n}{n^3 + 1}$ converges.

9. Let $a_n = (2^n + 1)/(n2^n - 1)$. Since $n2^n - 1 < n2^n + n = n(2^n + 1)$, we have

$$\frac{2^n + 1}{n2^n - 1} > \frac{2^n + 1}{n(2^n + 1)} = \frac{1}{n}.$$

Therefore, we can compare the series $\displaystyle\sum_{n=1}^{\infty} \frac{2^n + 1}{n2^n - 1}$ with the divergent harmonic series $\displaystyle\sum_{n=1}^{\infty} \frac{1}{n}$. The comparison test tells us that $\displaystyle\sum_{n=1}^{\infty} \frac{2^n + 1}{n2^n - 1}$ also diverges.

10. Since $a_n = 1/(2n)!$, replacing n by $n + 1$ gives $a_{n+1} = 1/(2n + 2)!$. Thus

$$\frac{|a_{n+1}|}{|a_n|} = \frac{\dfrac{1}{(2n + 2)!}}{\dfrac{1}{(2n)!}} = \frac{(2n)!}{(2n + 2)!} = \frac{(2n)!}{(2n + 2)(2n + 1)(2n)!} = \frac{1}{(2n + 2)(2n + 1)},$$

so

$$L = \lim_{n \to \infty} \frac{|a_{n+1}|}{|a_n|} = \lim_{n \to \infty} \frac{1}{(2n + 2)(2n + 1)} = 0.$$

Since $L = 0$, the ratio test tells us that $\displaystyle\sum_{n=1}^{\infty} \frac{1}{(2n)!}$ converges.

11. Since $a_n = (n!)^2/(2n)!$, replacing n by $n + 1$ gives $a_{n+1} = ((n + 1)!)^2/(2n + 2)!$. Thus,

$$\frac{|a_{n+1}|}{|a_n|} = \frac{\dfrac{((n + 1)!)^2}{(2n + 2)!}}{\dfrac{(n!)^2}{(2n)!}} = \frac{((n + 1)!)^2}{(2n + 2)!} \cdot \frac{(2n)!}{(n!)^2}.$$

However, since $(n + 1)! = (n + 1)n!$ and $(2n + 2)! = (2n + 2)(2n + 1)(2n)!$, we have

$$\frac{|a_{n+1}|}{|a_n|} = \frac{(n + 1)^2 (n!)^2 (2n)!}{(2n + 2)(2n + 1)(2n)!(n!)^2} = \frac{(n + 1)^2}{(2n + 2)(2n + 1)} = \frac{n + 1}{4n + 2},$$

so

$$L = \lim_{n \to \infty} \frac{|a_{n+1}|}{|a_n|} = \frac{1}{4}.$$

Since $L < 1$, the ratio test tells us that $\displaystyle\sum_{n=1}^{\infty} \frac{(n!)^2}{(2n)!}$ converges.

12. Since $a_n = (2n)!/(n!(n+1)!)$, replacing n by $n+1$ gives $a_{n+1} = (2n+2)!/((n+1)!(n+2)!)$. Thus,

$$\frac{|a_{n+1}|}{|a_n|} = \frac{\dfrac{(2n+2)!}{(n+1)!(n+2)!}}{\dfrac{(2n)!}{n!(n+1)!}} = \frac{(2n+2)!}{(n+1)!(n+2)!} \cdot \frac{n!(n+1)!}{(2n)!}.$$

However, since $(n+2)! = (n+2)(n+1)n!$ and $(2n+2)! = (2n+2)(2n+1)(2n)!$, we have

$$\frac{|a_{n+1}|}{|a_n|} = \frac{(2n+2)(2n+1)}{(n+2)(n+1)} = \frac{2(2n+1)}{n+2},$$

so

$$L = \lim_{n\to\infty} \frac{|a_{n+1}|}{|a_n|} = 4.$$

Since $L > 1$, the ratio test tells us that $\displaystyle\sum_{n=1}^{\infty} \frac{(2n)!}{n!(n+1)!}$ diverges.

13. Since $a_n = 1/(r^n n!)$, replacing n by $n+1$ gives $a_{n+1} = 1/(r^{n+1}(n+1)!)$. Thus

$$\frac{|a_{n+1}|}{|a_n|} = \frac{\dfrac{1}{r^{n+1}(n+1)!}}{\dfrac{1}{r^n n!}} = \frac{r^n n!}{r^{n+1}(n+1)!} = \frac{1}{r(n+1)},$$

so

$$L = \lim_{n\to\infty} \frac{|a_{n+1}|}{|a_n|} = \frac{1}{r} \lim_{n\to\infty} \frac{1}{n+1} = 0.$$

Since $L = 0$, the ratio test tells us that $\displaystyle\sum_{n=1}^{\infty} \frac{1}{r^n n!}$ converges for all $r > 0$.

14. Since $a_n = 1/(ne^n)$, replacing n by $n+1$ gives $a_{n+1} = 1/(n+1)e^{n+1}$. Thus

$$\frac{|a_{n+1}|}{|a_n|} = \frac{\dfrac{1}{(n+1)e^{n+1}}}{\dfrac{1}{ne^n}} = \frac{ne^n}{(n+1)e^{n+1}} = \left(\frac{n}{n+1}\right)\frac{1}{e}.$$

Therefore

$$L = \lim_{n\to\infty} \frac{|a_{n+1}|}{|a_n|} = \frac{1}{e} < 1.$$

Since $L < 1$, the ratio test tells us that $\displaystyle\sum_{n=1}^{\infty} \frac{1}{ne^n}$ converges.

15. Since $a_n = 2^n/(n^3 + 1)$, replacing n by $n+1$ gives $a_{n+1} = 2^{n+1}/((n+1)^3 + 1)$. Thus

$$\frac{|a_{n+1}|}{|a_n|} = \frac{\dfrac{2^{n+1}}{(n+1)^3 + 1}}{\dfrac{2^n}{n^3 + 1}} = \frac{2^{n+1}}{(n+1)^3 + 1} \cdot \frac{n^3 + 1}{2^n} = 2\frac{n^3 + 1}{(n+1)^3 + 1},$$

so

$$L = \lim_{n\to\infty} \frac{|a_{n+1}|}{|a_n|} = 2.$$

Since $L > 1$ the ratio test tells us that the series $\displaystyle\sum_{n=0}^{\infty} \frac{2^n}{n^3 + 1}$ diverges.

16. Even though the first term is negative, the terms alternate in sign, so it is an alternating series.

17. Since $\cos(n\pi) = (-1)^n$, this is an alternating series.

18. Since $(-1)^n \cos(n\pi) = (-1)^{2n} = 1$, this is not an alternating series.

19. Since $a_n = \cos n$ is not always positive, this is not an alternating series.

20. Let $a_n = 1/\sqrt{n}$. Then replacing n by $n+1$ we have $a_{n+1} = 1/\sqrt{n+1}$. Since $\sqrt{n+1} > \sqrt{n}$, we have $\dfrac{1}{\sqrt{n+1}} < \dfrac{1}{\sqrt{n}}$, hence $a_{n+1} < a_n$. In addition, $\lim_{n\to\infty} a_n = 0$ so $\displaystyle\sum_{n=0}^{\infty} \dfrac{(-1)^n}{\sqrt{n}}$ converges by the alternating series test.

21. Let $a_n = 1/(2n+1)$. Then replacing n by $n+1$ gives $a_{n+1} = 1/(2n+3)$. Since $2n+3 > 2n+1$, we have

$$0 < a_{n+1} = \frac{1}{2n+3} < \frac{1}{2n+1} = a_n.$$

We also have $\lim_{n\to\infty} a_n = 0$. Therefore, the alternating series test tells us that the series $\displaystyle\sum_{n=1}^{\infty} \dfrac{(-1)^{n-1}}{2n+1}$ converges.

22. Let $a_n = 1/(n^2 + 2n + 1) = 1/(n+1)^2$. Then replacing n by $n+1$ gives $a_{n+1} = 1/(n+2)^2$. Since $n+2 > n+1$, we have

$$\frac{1}{(n+2)^2} < \frac{1}{(n+1)^2}$$

so

$$0 < a_{n+1} < a_n.$$

We also have $\lim_{n\to\infty} a_n = 0$. Therefore, the alternating series test tells us that the series $\displaystyle\sum_{n=1}^{\infty} \dfrac{(-1)^{n-1}}{n^2 + 2n + 1}$ converges.

23. Let $a_n = 1/e^n$. Then replacing n by $n+1$ we have $a_{n+1} = 1/e^{n+1}$. Since $e^{n+1} > e^n$, we have $\dfrac{1}{e^{n+1}} < \dfrac{1}{e^n}$, hence $a_{n+1} < a_n$. In addition, $\lim_{n\to\infty} a_n = 0$ so $\displaystyle\sum_{n=1}^{\infty} \dfrac{(-1)^n}{e^n}$ converges by the alternating series test. We can also observe that the series is geometric with ratio $x = -1/e$ can hence converges since $|x| < 1$.

24. We have

$$\frac{a_n}{b_n} = \frac{(5n+1)/(3n^2)}{1/n} = \frac{5n+1}{3n},$$

so

$$\lim_{n\to\infty} \frac{a_n}{b_n} = \lim_{n\to\infty} \frac{5n+1}{3n} = \frac{5}{3} = c \neq 0.$$

Since $\displaystyle\sum_{n=1}^{\infty} \dfrac{1}{n}$ is a divergent harmonic series, the original series diverges.

25. We have

$$\frac{a_n}{b_n} = \frac{((1+n)/(3n))^n}{(1/3)^n} = \left(\frac{n+1}{n}\right)^n = \left(1 + \frac{1}{n}\right)^n,$$

so

$$\lim_{n\to\infty} \frac{a_n}{b_n} = \lim_{n\to\infty} \left(1 + \frac{1}{n}\right)^n = e = c \neq 0.$$

Since $\displaystyle\sum_{n=1}^{\infty} \left(\frac{1}{3}\right)^n$ is a convergent geometric series, the original series converges.

26. The nth term $a_n = 1/(n^4 - 7)$ behaves like $1/n^4$ for large n, so we take $b_n = 1/n^4$. We have

$$\lim_{n\to\infty} \frac{a_n}{b_n} = \lim_{n\to\infty} \frac{1/(n^4 - 7)}{1/n^4} = \lim_{n\to\infty} \frac{n^4}{n^4 - 7} = 1.$$

The limit comparison test applies with $c = 1$. The p-series $\sum 1/n^4$ converges because $p = 4 > 1$. Therefore $\sum 1/(n^4 - 7)$ also converges.

27. The nth term $a_n = (n+1)/(n^2 + 2)$ behaves like $n/n^2 = 1/n$ for large n, so we take $b_n = 1/n$. We have

$$\lim_{n\to\infty} \frac{a_n}{b_n} = \lim_{n\to\infty} \frac{(n+1)/(n^2 + 2)}{1/n} = \lim_{n\to\infty} \frac{n^2 + n}{n^2 + 2} = 1.$$

The limit comparison test applies with $c = 1$. Since the harmonic series $\sum 1/n$ diverges, the series $\sum (n+1)/(n^2 + 2)$ also diverges.

28. The nth term $a_n = (n^3 - 2n^2 + n + 1)/(n^4 - 2)$ behaves like $n^3/n^4 = 1/n$ for large n, so we take $b_n = 1/n$. We have

$$\lim_{n\to\infty} \frac{a_n}{b_n} = \lim_{n\to\infty} \frac{(n^3 - 2n^2 + n + 1)/(n^4 - 2)}{1/n} = \lim_{n\to\infty} \frac{n^4 - 2n^3 + n^2 + n}{n^4 - 2} = 1.$$

The limit comparison test applies with $c = 1$. The harmonic series $\sum 1/n$ diverges. Thus $\sum \left(n^3 - 2n^2 + n + 1\right) / \left(n^4 - 2\right)$ also diverges.

29. The nth term $a_n = 2^n/(3^n - 1)$ behaves like $2^n/3^n$ for large n, so we take $b_n = 2^n/3^n$. We have

$$\lim_{n\to\infty} \frac{a_n}{b_n} = \lim_{n\to\infty} \frac{2^n/(3^n - 1)}{2^n/3^n} = \lim_{n\to\infty} \frac{3^n}{3^n - 1} = \lim_{n\to\infty} \frac{1}{1 - 3^{-n}} = 1.$$

The limit comparison test applies with $c = 1$. The geometric series $\sum 2^n/3^n = \sum (2/3)^n$ converges. Therefore $\sum 2^n/(3^n - 1)$ also converges.

30. The nth term $a_n = 1/(2\sqrt{n} + \sqrt{n+2})$ behaves like $1/(3\sqrt{n})$ for large n, so we take $b_n = 1/(3\sqrt{n})$. We have

$$\lim_{n\to\infty} \frac{a_n}{b_n} = \lim_{n\to\infty} \frac{1/(2\sqrt{n} + \sqrt{n+2})}{1/(3\sqrt{n})} = \lim_{n\to\infty} \frac{3\sqrt{n}}{2\sqrt{n} + \sqrt{n+2}}$$

$$= \lim_{n\to\infty} \frac{3\sqrt{n}}{\sqrt{n}\left(2 + \sqrt{1 + 2/n}\right)}$$

$$= \lim_{n\to\infty} \frac{3}{2 + \sqrt{1 + 2/n}} = \frac{3}{2 + \sqrt{1 + 0}}$$

$$= 1.$$

The limit comparison test applies with $c = 1$. The series $\sum 1/(3\sqrt{n})$ diverges because it is a multiple of a p-series with $p = 1/2 < 1$. Therefore $\sum 1/(2\sqrt{n} + \sqrt{n+2})$ also diverges.

31. The nth term,

$$a_n = \frac{1}{2n - 1} - \frac{1}{2n} = \frac{1}{4n^2 - 2n},$$

behaves like $1/(4n^2)$ for large n, so we take $b_n = 1/(4n^2)$. We have

$$\lim_{n\to\infty} \frac{a_n}{b_n} = \lim_{n\to\infty} \frac{1/(4n^2 - 2n)}{1/(4n^2)} = \lim_{n\to\infty} \frac{4n^2}{4n^2 - 2n} = \lim_{n\to\infty} \frac{1}{1 - 1/(2n)} = 1.$$

The limit comparison test applies with $c = 1$. The series $\sum 1/(4n^2)$ converges because it is a multiple of a p-series with $p = 2 > 1$. Therefore $\sum \left(\frac{1}{2n-1} - \frac{1}{2n}\right)$ also converges.

Problems

32. The comparison test requires that $a_n = (-1)^n/n^2$ be positive. It is not.

33. The comparison test requires that $a_n = \sin n$ be positive for all n. It is not.

34. With $a_n = (-1)^n$, we have $|a_{n+1}/a_n| = 1$, and $\lim_{n\to\infty} |a_{n+1}/a_n| = 1$, so the test gives no information.

35. With $a_n = \sin n$, we have $|a_{n+1}/a_n| = |\sin(n+1)/\sin n|$, which does not have a limit as $n \to \infty$, so the test does not apply.

36. The sequence $a_n = n$ does not satisfy either $a_{n+1} < a_n$ or $\lim_{n\to\infty} a_n = 0$.

37. The alternating series test requires $a_n = \sin n$ be positive, which it is not. This is not an alternating series.

38. The alternating series test requires $a_n = 2 - 1/n$ which is positive and satisfies $a_{n+1} < a_n$ but $\lim_{n\to\infty} a_n = 2 \neq 0$.

39. The partial sums are $S_1 = 1$, $S_2 = -1$, $S_3 = 2$, $S_{10} = -5$, $S_{11} = 6$, $S_{100} = -50$, $S_{101} = 51$, $S_{1000} = -500$, $S_{1001} = 501$, which appear to be oscillating further and further from 0. This series does not converge.

40. The partial sums look like: $S_1 = 1$, $S_2 = 0.9$, $S_3 = 0.91$, $S_4 = 0.909$, $S_5 = 0.9091$, $S_6 = 0.90909$. The series appears to be converging to $0.909090\ldots$ or $10/11$.

   Since $a_n = 10^{-k}$ is positive and decreasing and $\lim_{n\to\infty} 10^{-n} = 0$, the alternating series test confirms the convergence of the series.

41. The partial sums look like: $S_1 = 1$, $S_2 = 0$, $S_3 = 0.5$, $S_4 = 0.3333$, $S_5 = 0.375$, $S_{10} = 0.3679$, $S_{20} = 0.3679$, and higher partial sums agree with these first 4 decimal places. The series appears to be converging to about 0.3679.

Since $a_n = 1/n!$ is positive and decreasing and $\lim_{n \to \infty} 1/n! = 0$, the alternating series test confirms the convergence of this series.

42. We use the ratio test and calculate

$$\lim_{n \to \infty} \frac{|a_{n+1}|}{|a_n|} = \lim_{n \to \infty} \frac{(0.1)^{n+1}/(n+1)!}{(0.1)^n/n!} = \lim_{n \to \infty} \frac{0.1}{n+1} = 0.$$

Since the limit is less than 1, the series converges.

43. We use the ratio test and calculate

$$\lim_{n \to \infty} \frac{|a_{n+1}|}{|a_n|} = \lim_{n \to \infty} \frac{n!/(n+1)^2}{(n-1)!/n^2} = \lim_{n \to \infty} \left(\frac{n!}{(n-1)!} \cdot \frac{n^2}{(n+1)^2} \right) = \lim_{n \to \infty} \left(n \cdot \frac{n^2}{(n+1)^2} \right).$$

Since the limit does not exist (it is ∞), the series diverges.

44. The first few terms of the series may be written

$$1 + e^{-1} + e^{-2} + e^{-3} + \cdots;$$

this is a geometric series with $a = 1$ and $x = e^{-1} = 1/e$. Since $|x| < 1$, the geometric series converges to
$S = \dfrac{1}{1-x} = \dfrac{1}{1-e^{-1}} = \dfrac{e}{e-1}$.

45. The first few terms of the series may be written

$$e + e^2 + e^3 + \cdots = e + e \cdot e + e \cdot e^2 + \cdots;$$

this is a geometric series with $a = e$ and $x = e$. Since $|x| > 1$, this geometric series diverges.

46. Let $a_n = 1/\sqrt{3n-1}$. Then replacing n by $n+1$ gives $a_{n+1} = 1/\sqrt{3(n+1)-1}$. Since

$$\sqrt{3(n+1)-1} > \sqrt{3n-1},$$

we have

$$a_{n+1} < a_n.$$

In addition, $\lim_{n \to \infty} a_n = 0$ so the alternating series test tells us that the series $\displaystyle\sum_{n=1}^{\infty} \frac{(-1)^{n-1}}{\sqrt{3n-1}}$ converges.

47. Since the exponential, 2^n, grows faster than the power, n^2, the terms are growing in size. Thus, $\lim_{n \to \infty} a_n \neq 0$. We conclude that this series diverges.

48. Since $0 \leq |\sin n| \leq 1$ for all n, we may be able to compare with $1/n^2$. We have $0 \leq |\sin n/n^2| \leq 1/n^2$ for all n. So $\sum |\sin n/n^2|$ converges by comparison with the convergent series $\sum(1/n^2)$. Therefore $\sum(\sin n/n^2)$ also converges, since absolute convergence implies convergence by Theorem 9.6.

49. Note that $\cos(n\pi)/n = (-1)^n/n$, so this is an alternating series. Therefore, since $1/(n+1) < 1/n$ and $\lim_{n \to \infty} 1/n = 0$, we see that $\sum(\cos(n\pi)/n)$ converges by the alternating series test.

50. As $n \to \infty$, we see that

$$\frac{n+2}{n^2-1} \to \frac{n}{n^2} = \frac{1}{n}.$$

Since $\sum(1/n)$ diverges, we expect our series to have the same behavior.

More precisely, for all $n \geq 2$, we have

$$0 \leq \frac{1}{n} = \frac{n}{n^2} \leq \frac{n+2}{n^2-1},$$

so $\displaystyle\sum_{n=2}^{\infty} \frac{n+2}{n^2-1}$ diverges by comparison with the divergent series $\displaystyle\sum \frac{1}{n}$.

51. Since
$$\frac{3}{\ln n^2} = \frac{3}{2 \ln n},$$
our series behaves like the series $\sum 1/\ln n$. More precisely, for all $n \geq 2$, we have
$$0 \leq \frac{1}{n} \leq \frac{1}{\ln n} \leq \frac{3}{2 \ln n} = \frac{3}{\ln n^2},$$
so $\sum_{n=2}^{\infty} \frac{3}{\ln n^2}$ diverges by comparison with the divergent series $\sum \frac{1}{n}$.

52. Let $a_n = 1/\sqrt{n^2(n+2)}$. Since $n^2(n+2) = n^3 + 2n^2 > n^3$, we have
$$0 < a_n < \frac{1}{n^{3/2}}.$$
Since the p-series $\sum_{n=1}^{\infty} \frac{1}{n^{3/2}}$ converges, the comparison test tells us that
$$\sum_{n=1}^{\infty} \frac{1}{\sqrt{n^2(n+2)}}$$
also converges.

53. Let $a_n = n(n+1)/\sqrt{n^3 + 2n^2}$. Since $n^3 + 2n^2 = n^2(n+2)$, we have
$$a_n = \frac{n(n+1)}{n\sqrt{n+2}} = \frac{n+1}{\sqrt{n+2}}$$
so a_n grows without bound as $n \to \infty$, therefore the series $\sum_{n=1}^{\infty} \frac{n(n+1)}{\sqrt{n^3 + 2n^2}}$ diverges.

54. The nth partial sum of the series is given by
$$S_n = 1 - \frac{1}{2} + \frac{1}{3} - \cdots + \frac{(-1)^{n-1}}{n},$$
so the absolute value of the first term omitted is $1/(n+1)$. By Theorem 9.9, we know that the value, S, of the sum differs from S_n by less than $1/(n+1)$. Thus, we want to choose n large enough so that $1/(n+1) \leq 0.01$. Solving this inequality for n yields $n \geq 99$, so we take 99 or more terms in our partial sum.

55. The nth partial sum of the series is given by
$$S_n = 1 - \frac{2}{3} + \frac{4}{9} - \cdots + (-1)^n \left(\frac{2}{3}\right)^n,$$
so the absolute value of the first term omitted is $(2/3)^{n+1}$. By Theorem 9.9, we know that the value, S, of the sum differs from S_n by less than $(2/3)^{n+1}$. Thus, we want to choose n large enough so that $(2/3)^{n+1} \leq 0.01$. Solving this inequality for n yields $n \geq 10.358$, so we take 11 or more terms in our partial sum.

56. The nth partial sum of the series is given by
$$S_n = \frac{1}{2} - \frac{1}{24} + \frac{1}{720} - \cdots + \frac{(-1)^{n-1}}{(2n)!},$$
so the absolute value of the first term omitted is $1/(2n+2)!$. By Theorem 9.9, we know that the value, S, of the sum differs from S_n by less than $1/(2n+2)!$. Thus, we want to choose n large enough so that $1/(2n+2)! \leq 0.01$. Substituting $n = 2$ into the expression $1/(2n+2)!$ yields $1/720$ which is less than 0.01. We therefore take 2 or more terms in our partial sum.

57. Both $\sum \frac{(-1)^n}{2^n} = \sum \left(\frac{-1}{2}\right)^n$ and $\sum \frac{1}{2^n} = \sum \left(\frac{1}{2}\right)^n$ are convergent geometric series. Thus $\sum \frac{(-1)^n}{2^n}$ is absolutely convergent.

58. The series $\sum \dfrac{(-1)^n}{2n}$ converges by the alternating series test. However $\sum \dfrac{1}{2n}$ diverges because it is a multiple of the harmonic series. Thus $\sum \dfrac{(-1)^n}{2n}$ is conditionally convergent.

59. Since
$$\lim_{n\to\infty} \left(1 + \frac{1}{n^2}\right) = 1,$$
the nth term $a_n = (-1)^n \left(1 + \frac{1}{n^2}\right)$ does not tend to zero as $n \to \infty$. Thus, the series $\sum (-1)^n \left(1 + \frac{1}{n^2}\right)$ is divergent.

60. The series $\sum \dfrac{(-1)^n}{n^4 + 7}$ converges by the alternating series test. Moreover, the series $\sum \dfrac{1}{n^4 + 7}$ converges by comparison with the convergent p-series $\sum \dfrac{1}{n^4}$. Thus $\sum \dfrac{(-1)^n}{n^4 + 7}$ is absolutely convergent.

61. Since $0 \le c_n \le 2^{-n}$ for all n, and since $\sum 2^{-n}$ is a convergent geometric series, $\sum c_n$ converges by the Comparison Test. Similarly, since $2^n \le a_n$, and since $\sum 2^n$ is a divergent geometric series, $\sum a_n$ diverges by the Comparison Test. We do not have enough information to determine whether or not $\sum b_n$ and $\sum d_n$ converge.

62. (a) The sum $\sum a_n \cdot b_n = \sum 1/n^5$, which converges, as a p-series with $p = 5$, or by the integral test:
$$\int_1^\infty \frac{1}{x^5}\, dx = \lim_{b\to\infty} \left.\frac{x^{-4}}{(-4)}\right|_1^b = \lim_{b\to\infty} \frac{b^{-4}}{(-4)} + \frac{1}{4} = \frac{1}{4}.$$
Since this improper integral converges, $\sum a_n \cdot b_n$ also converges.

(b) This is an alternating series that satisfies the conditions of the alternating series test: the terms are decreasing and have limit 0, so $\sum (-1)^n/\sqrt{n}$ converges.

(c) We have $a_n b_n = 1/n$, so $\sum a_n b_n$ is the harmonic series, which diverges.

63. Since $\lim\limits_{n\to\infty} a_n/b_n = 0$, for large enough n we have $|a_n/b_n| < 1/2$ and thus $0 \le |a_n| < b_n/2 < b_n$. By the comparison test applied to $\sum |a_n|$ and $\sum b_n$, the series $\sum |a_n|$ converges. The series $\sum a_n$ converges absolutely and thus it converges.

64. Since $\lim\limits_{n\to\infty} a_n/b_n = \infty$, for large enough n we have $a_n/b_n > 1$ and thus $a_n > b_n$. By the comparison test applied to $\sum a_n$ and $\sum b_n$, the series $\sum a_n$ diverges.

65. Each term in $\sum b_n$ is greater than or equal to a_1 times a term in the harmonic series:
$$b_1 = a_1 \cdot 1$$
$$b_2 = \frac{a_1 + a_2}{2} > a_1 \cdot \frac{1}{2}$$
$$b_3 = \frac{a_1 + a_2 + a_3}{3} > a_1 \cdot \frac{1}{3}$$
$$\vdots$$
$$b_n = \frac{a_1 + a_2 + \cdots + a_n}{n} > a_1 \cdot \frac{1}{n}$$

Adding these inequalities gives
$$\sum b_n > a_1 \sum \frac{1}{n}.$$
Since the harmonic series $\sum 1/n$ diverges, a_1 times the harmonic series also diverges. Then, by the comparison test, the series $\sum b_n$ diverges.

66. Suppose we let $c_n = (-1)^n a_n$. (We have just given the terms of the series $\sum (-1)^n a_n$ a new name.) Then
$$|c_n| = |(-1)^n a_n| = |a_n|.$$
Thus $\sum |c_n|$ converges, and by Theorem 9.6,
$$\sum c_n = \sum (-1)^n a_n \quad \text{converges.}$$

67. (a) Since

$$|a_n| = a_n \qquad \text{if } a_n \geq 0$$
$$|a_n| = -a_n \qquad \text{if } a_n < 0,$$

we have

$$a_n + |a_n| = 2|a_n| \qquad \text{if } a_n \geq 0$$
$$a_n + |a_n| = 0 \qquad \text{if } a_n < 0.$$

Thus, for all n,

$$0 \leq a_n + |a_n| \leq 2|a_n|.$$

(b) If $\sum |a_n|$ converges, then $\sum 2|a_n|$ is convergent, so, by comparison, $\sum (a_n + |a_n|)$ is convergent. Then

$$\sum ((a_n + |a_n|) - |a_n|) = \sum a_n$$

is convergent, as it is the difference of two convergent series.

68. The limit

$$\lim_{n \to \infty} \sqrt[n]{a_n} = \lim_{n \to \infty} \frac{2}{n} = 0 < 1,$$

so the series converges.

69. The limit

$$\lim_{n \to \infty} \sqrt[n]{a_n} = \lim_{n \to \infty} \frac{5n + 1}{3n^2} = 0 < 1,$$

so the series converges.

Solutions for Section 9.5

Exercises

1. Yes.

2. No, because it contains negative powers of x.

3. No, each term is a power of a different quantity.

4. Yes. It's a polynomial, or a series with all coefficients beyond the 7th being zero.

5. The general term can be written as $\dfrac{1 \cdot 3 \cdot 5 \cdots (2n - 1)}{2^n \cdot n!} x^n$ for $n \geq 1$. Other answers are possible.

6. The general term can be written as $\dfrac{p(p - 1)(p - 2) \cdots (p - n + 1)}{n!} x^n$ for $n \geq 1$. Other answers are possible.

7. The general term can be written as $\dfrac{(-1)^k (x - 1)^{2k}}{(2k)!}$ for $k \geq 0$. Other answers are possible.

8. The general term can be written as $\dfrac{(-1)^{k+1}(x - 1)^{2k+1}}{(2(k - 1))!}$ for $k \geq 1$ or as $\dfrac{(-1)^k (x - 1)^{2k+3}}{(2k)!}$ for $k \geq 0$. Other answers are possible.

9. The general term can be written as $\dfrac{(x - a)^n}{2^{n-1} \cdot n!}$ for $n \geq 1$. Other answers are possible.

10. The general term can be written as $\dfrac{(k + 1)(x + 5)^{2k+1}}{(k - 1)!}$ for $k \geq 1$ or as $\dfrac{(k + 2)(x + 5)^{2k+3}}{k!}$ for $k \geq 0$. Other answers are possible.

11. This series may be written as

$$1 + 5x + 25x^2 + \cdots$$

so $C_n = 5^n$. Using the ratio test, with $a_n = 5^n x^n$, we have

$$\lim_{n \to \infty} \frac{|a_{n+1}|}{|a_n|} = |x| \lim_{n \to \infty} \frac{|C_{n+1}|}{|C_n|} = |x| \lim_{n \to \infty} \frac{5^{n+1}}{5^n} = 5|x|.$$

Thus the radius of convergence is $R = 1/5$.

12. Since $C_n = n^3$, replacing n by $n+1$ gives $C_{n+1} = (n+1)^3$. Using the ratio test, with $a_n = n^3 x^n$, we have

$$\frac{|a_{n+1}|}{|a_n|} = |x|\frac{|C_{n+1}|}{|C_n|} = |x|\frac{(n+1)^3}{n^3} = |x|\left(\frac{n+1}{n}\right)^3.$$

We have

$$\lim_{n\to\infty}\frac{|a_{n+1}|}{|a_n|} = |x|.$$

Thus the radius of convergence is $R = 1$.

13. Since $C_n = (n+1)/(2^n + n)$, replacing n by $n+1$ gives $C_{n+1} = (n+2)/(2^{n+1} + n + 1)$. Using the ratio test, we have

$$\frac{|a_{n+1}|}{|a_n|} = |x|\frac{|C_{n+1}|}{|C_n|} = |x|\frac{(n+2)/(2^{n+1} + n + 1)}{(n+1)/(2^n + n)} = |x|\frac{n+2}{2^{n+1} + n + 1}\cdot\frac{2^n + n}{n+1} = |x|\frac{n+2}{n+1}\cdot\frac{2^n + n}{2^{n+1} + n + 1}.$$

Since

$$\lim_{n\to\infty}\frac{n+2}{n+1} = 1$$

and

$$\lim_{n\to\infty}\left(\frac{2^n + n}{2^{n+1} + n + 1}\right) = \frac{1}{2}\lim_{n\to\infty}\left(\frac{2^n + n}{2^n + (n+1)/2}\right) = \frac{1}{2},$$

because 2^n dominates n as $n \to \infty$, we have

$$\lim_{n\to\infty}\frac{|a_{n+1}|}{|a_n|} = \frac{1}{2}|x|.$$

Thus the radius of convergence is $R = 2$.

14. Since $C_n = 2^n/n$, replacing n by $n+1$ gives $C_{n+1} = 2^{n+1}/(n+1)$. Using the ratio test, we have

$$\frac{|a_{n+1}|}{|a_n|} = |x-1|\frac{|C_{n+1}|}{|C_n|} = |x-1|\frac{2^{n+1}/(n+1)}{2^n/n} = |x-1|\frac{2^{n+1}}{(n+1)}\cdot\frac{n}{2^n} = 2|x-1|\left(\frac{n}{n+1}\right),$$

so

$$\lim_{n\to\infty}\frac{|a_{n+1}|}{|a_n|} = 2|x-1|.$$

Thus the radius of convergence is $R = \frac{1}{2}$.

15. To find R, we consider the following limit, where the coefficient of the nth term is given by $C_n = n^2$.

$$\lim_{n\to\infty}\frac{|a_{n+1}|}{|a_n|} = \lim_{n\to\infty}\left|\frac{(n+1)^2 x^{n+1}}{n^2 x^n}\right| = \lim_{n\to\infty}|x|\frac{n^2 + 2n + 1}{n^2}$$

$$= |x|\lim_{n\to\infty}\left(\frac{1 + (2/n) + (1/n^2)}{1}\right) = |x|.$$

Thus, the radius of convergence is $R = 1$.

16. The coefficient of the nth term is $C_n = (-1)^{n+1}/n^2$. Now consider the ratio

$$\left|\frac{a_{n+1}}{a_n}\right| = \left|\frac{n^2 x^{n+1}}{(n+1)^2 x^n}\right| \to |x| \quad \text{as} \quad n \to \infty.$$

Thus, the radius of convergence is $R = 1$.

17. Here the coefficient of the nth term is $C_n = (2^n/n!)$. Now we have

$$\left|\frac{a_{n+1}}{a_n}\right| = \left|\frac{(2^{n+1}/(n+1)!)x^{n+1}}{(2^n/n!)x^n}\right| = \frac{2|x|}{n+1} \to 0 \text{ as } n \to \infty.$$

Thus, the radius of convergence is $R = \infty$, and the series converges for all x.

18. Here the coefficient of the nth term is $C_n = n/(2n+1)$. Now we have

$$\left|\frac{a_{n+1}}{a_n}\right| = \left|\frac{((n+1)/(2n+3))x^{n+1}}{(n/(2n+1))x^n}\right| = \frac{(n+1)(2n+1)}{n(2n+3)}|x| \to |x| \text{ as } n \to \infty.$$

Thus, by the ratio test, the radius of convergence is $R = 1$.

19. Here $C_n = (2n)!/(n!)^2$. We have:

$$\left| \frac{a_{n+1}}{a_n} \right| = \left| \frac{(2(n+1))!/((n+1)!)^2 x^{n+1}}{(2n)!/(n!)^2 x^n} \right| = \frac{(2(n+1))!}{(2n)!} \cdot \frac{(n!)^2}{((n+1)!)^2} |x|$$

$$= \frac{(2n+2)(2n+1)|x|}{(n+1)^2} \to 4|x| \text{ as } n \to \infty.$$

Thus, the radius of convergence is $R = 1/4$.

20. Here the coefficient of the nth term is $C_n = (2n+1)/n$. Applying the ratio test, we consider:

$$\left| \frac{a_{n+1}}{a_n} \right| = \left| \frac{((2n+3)/(n+1))x^{n+1}}{((2n+1)/n)x^n} \right| = |x| \frac{2n+3}{2n+1} \cdot \frac{n}{n+1} \to |x| \text{ as } n \to \infty.$$

Thus, the radius of convergence is $R = 1$.

21. We write the series as

$$x - \frac{x^3}{3} + \frac{x^5}{5} - \frac{x^7}{7} + \cdots + (-1)^{n-1} \frac{x^{2n-1}}{2n-1} + \cdots,$$

so

$$a_n = (-1)^{n-1} \frac{x^{2n-1}}{2n-1}.$$

Replacing n by $n+1$, we have

$$a_{n+1} = (-1)^{n+1-1} \frac{x^{2(n+1)-1}}{2(n+1)-1} = (-1)^n \frac{x^{2n+1}}{2n+1}.$$

Thus

$$\frac{|a_{n+1}|}{|a_n|} = \left| \frac{(-1)^n x^{2n+1}}{2n+1} \right| \cdot \left| \frac{2n-1}{(-1)^{n-1} x^{2n-1}} \right| = \frac{2n-1}{2n+1} x^2,$$

so

$$L = \lim_{n \to \infty} \frac{|a_{n+1}|}{|a_n|} = \lim_{n \to \infty} \frac{2n-1}{2n+1} x^2 = x^2.$$

By the ratio test, this series converges if $L < 1$, that is, if $x^2 < 1$, so $R = 1$.

22. (a) The general term of the series is x^n/n if n is odd and $-x^n/n$ if n is even, so $C_n = (-1)^{n-1}/n$, and we can use the ratio test. We have

$$\lim_{n \to \infty} \frac{|a_{n+1}|}{|a_n|} = |x| \lim_{n \to \infty} \frac{|(-1)^n/(n+1)|}{|(-1)^{n-1}/n|} = |x| \lim_{n \to \infty} \frac{n}{n+1} = |x|.$$

Therefore the radius of convergence is $R = 1$. This tells us that the power series converges for $|x| < 1$ and does not converge for $|x| > 1$. Notice that the radius of convergence does not tell us what happens at the endpoints, $x = \pm 1$.

(b) The endpoints of the interval of convergence are $x = \pm 1$. At $x = 1$, we have the series

$$1 - \frac{1}{2} + \frac{1}{3} - \frac{1}{4} + \cdots + \frac{(-1)^{n-1}}{n} + \cdots$$

This is an alternating series with $a_n = 1/n$, so by the alternating series test, it converges. At $x = -1$, we have the series

$$-1 - \frac{1}{2} - \frac{1}{3} - \frac{1}{4} - \cdots - \frac{1}{n} - \cdots$$

This is the negative of the harmonic series, so it does not converge. Therefore the right endpoint is included, and the left endpoint is not included in the interval of convergence, which is $-1 < x \leq 1$.

23. Let $C_n = 2^n/n$. Then replacing n by $n+1$ gives $C_{n+1} = 2^{n+1}/(n+1)$. Using the ratio test, we have

$$\frac{|a_{n+1}|}{|a_n|} = |x| \frac{|C_{n+1}|}{|C_n|} = |x| \frac{2^{n+1}/(n+1)}{2^n/n} = |x| \frac{2^{n+1}}{n+1} \cdot \frac{n}{2^n} = 2|x| \left(\frac{n}{n+1} \right).$$

Thus

$$\lim_{n \to \infty} \frac{|a_{n+1}|}{|a_n|} = 2|x|.$$

The radius of convergence is $R = 1/2$.

For $x = 1/2$ the series becomes the harmonic series $\displaystyle\sum_{n=1}^{\infty} \frac{1}{n}$ which diverges.

For $x = -1/2$ the series becomes the alternating series $\displaystyle\sum_{n=1}^{\infty} \frac{(-1)^n}{n}$ which converges. See Example 8 on page 460.

Problems

24. We use the ratio test:

$$\left|\frac{a_{n+1}}{a_n}\right| = \left|\frac{x^{n+1}}{3^{n+1}} \cdot \frac{3^n}{x^n}\right| = \frac{|x|}{3}.$$

Since $|x|/3 < 1$ when $|x| < 3$, the radius of convergence is 3 and the series converges for $-3 < x < 3$.
We check the endpoints:

$$x = 3: \quad \sum_{n=0}^{\infty} \frac{x^n}{3^n} = \sum_{n=0}^{\infty} \frac{3^n}{3^n} = \sum_{n=0}^{\infty} 1^n \quad \text{which diverges.}$$

$$x = -3: \quad \sum_{n=0}^{\infty} \frac{x^n}{3^n} = \sum_{n=0}^{\infty} \frac{(-3)^n}{3^n} = \sum_{n=0}^{\infty} (-1)^n \quad \text{which diverges.}$$

The series diverges at both the endpoints, so the interval of convergence is $-3 < x < 3$.

25. We use the ratio test:

$$\left|\frac{a_{n+1}}{a_n}\right| = \left|\frac{(x-3)^{n+1}}{n+1} \cdot \frac{n}{(x-3)^n}\right| = \frac{n}{n+1} \cdot |x-3|.$$

Since $n/(n+1) \to 1$ as $n \to \infty$, we have

$$\lim_{n\to\infty} \left|\frac{a_{n+1}}{a_n}\right| = |x-3|.$$

The series converges for $|x-3| < 1$. The radius of convergence is 1 and the series converges for $2 < x < 4$.
We check the endpoints. For $x = 2$, we have

$$\sum_{n=2}^{\infty} \frac{(x-3)^n}{n} = \sum_{n=2}^{\infty} \frac{(2-3)^n}{n} = \sum_{n=2}^{\infty} \frac{(-1)^n}{n}.$$

This is the alternating harmonic series and converges. For $x = 4$, we have

$$\sum_{n=2}^{\infty} \frac{(x-3)^n}{n} = \sum_{n=2}^{\infty} \frac{(4-3)^n}{n} = \sum_{n=2}^{\infty} \frac{1}{n}.$$

This is the harmonic series and diverges. The series converges at $x = 2$ and diverges at $x = 4$. Therefore, the interval of convergence is $2 \leq x < 4$.

26. We use the ratio test:

$$\left|\frac{a_{n+1}}{a_n}\right| = \left|\frac{(n+1)^2 x^{2(n+1)}}{2^{2(n+1)}} \cdot \frac{2^{2n}}{n^2 x^{2n}}\right| = \left(\frac{n+1}{n}\right)^2 \cdot \frac{x^2}{4}.$$

Since $(n+1)/n \to 1$ as $n \to \infty$, we have

$$\lim_{n\to\infty} \left|\frac{a_{n+1}}{a_n}\right| = \frac{x^2}{4}.$$

We have $x^2/4 < 1$ when $|x| < 2$. The radius of convergence is 2 and the series converges for $-2 < x < 2$.
We check the endpoints. For $x = -2$, we have

$$\sum_{n=1}^{\infty} \frac{n^2 x^{2n}}{2^{2n}} = \sum_{n=1}^{\infty} \frac{n^2 (-2)^{2n}}{2^{2n}} = \sum_{n=1}^{\infty} n^2,$$

which diverges. Similarly, for $x = 2$, we have

$$\sum_{n=1}^{\infty} \frac{n^2 x^{2n}}{2^{2n}} = \sum_{n=1}^{\infty} \frac{n^2 2^{2n}}{2^{2n}} = \sum_{n=1}^{\infty} n^2,$$

which diverges. The series diverges at both endpoints, so the interval of convergence is $-2 < x < 2$.

27. We use the ratio test:

$$\left|\frac{a_{n+1}}{a_n}\right| = \left|\frac{(-1)^{n+1}(x-5)^{n+1}}{2^{n+1}(n+1)^2} \cdot \frac{2^n n^2}{(-1)^n(x-5)^n}\right| = \left(\frac{n}{n+1}\right)^2 \cdot \frac{|x-5|}{2}.$$

Since $n/(n+1) \to 1$ as $n \to \infty$, we have

$$\lim_{n\to\infty}\left|\frac{a_{n+1}}{a_n}\right| = \frac{|x-5|}{2}.$$

We have $|x-5|/2 < 1$ when $|x-5| < 2$. The radius of convergence is 2 and the series converges for $3 < x < 7$.

We check the endpoints. For $x = 3$, we have

$$\sum_{n=1}^{\infty}\frac{(-1)^n(x-5)^n}{2^n n^2} = \sum_{n=1}^{\infty}\frac{(-1)^n(3-5)^n}{2^n n^2} = \sum_{n=1}^{\infty}\frac{(-1)^n(-2)^n}{2^n n^2} = \sum_{n=1}^{\infty}\frac{1}{n^2}.$$

This is a p-series with $p = 2$ and it converges. For $x = 7$, we have

$$\sum_{n=1}^{\infty}\frac{(-1)^n(x-5)^n}{2^n n^2} = \sum_{n=1}^{\infty}\frac{(-1)^n(7-5)^n}{2^n n^2} = \sum_{n=1}^{\infty}\frac{(-1)^n 2^n}{2^n n^2} = \sum_{n=1}^{\infty}\frac{(-1)^n}{n^2}.$$

Since $\sum \frac{1}{n^2}$ converges, the alternating series $\sum \frac{(-1)^n}{n^2}$ also converges. The series converges at both its endpoints, so the interval of convergence is $3 \le x \le 7$.

28. The coefficient of the nth term of the binomial power series is given by

$$C_n = \frac{p(p-1)(p-2)\cdots(p-(n-1))}{n!}.$$

To apply the ratio test, consider

$$\left|\frac{a_{n+1}}{a_n}\right| = |x|\left|\frac{p(p-1)(p-2)\cdots(p-(n-1))(p-n)/(n+1)!}{p(p-1)(p-2)\cdots(p-(n-1))/n!}\right|$$

$$= |x|\left|\frac{p-n}{n+1}\right| = |x|\left|\frac{p}{n+1} - \frac{n}{n+1}\right| \to |x| \text{ as } n \to \infty.$$

Thus, the radius of convergence is $R = 1$.

29. The kth coefficient in the series $\sum kC_k x^k$ is $D_k = k\cdot C_k$. We are given that the series $\sum C_k x^k$ has radius of convergence R by the ratio test, so

$$|x|\lim_{k\to\infty}\frac{|C_{k+1}|}{|C_k|} = \frac{|x|}{R}.$$

Thus, applying the ratio test to the new series, we have

$$\lim_{k\to\infty}\left|\frac{D_{k+1}x^{k+1}}{D_k x^k}\right| = \lim_{k\to\infty}\left|\frac{(k+1)C_{k+1}}{kC_k}\right||x| = \frac{|x|}{R}.$$

Hence the new series has radius of convergence R.

30. The radius of convergence, R, is between 5 and 7.

31. The series is centered at $x = -7$. Since the series converges at $x = 0$, which is a distance of 7 from $x = -7$, the radius of convergence, R, is at least 7. Since the series diverges at $x = -17$, which is a distance of 10 from $x = -7$, the radius of convergence is no more than 10. That is, $7 \le R \le 10$.

32. The radius of convergence of the series, R, is at least 4 but no larger than 7.

(a) False. Since $10 > R$ the series diverges.

(b) True. Since $3 < R$ the series converges.

(c) False. Since $1 < R$ the series converges.

(d) Not possible to determine since the radius of convergence may be more or less than 6.

33. The series is centered at $x = 3$. Since the series converges at $x = 7$, which is a distance of 4 from $x = 3$, we know $R \ge 4$. Since the series diverges at $x = 10$, which is a distance of 7 from $x = 3$, we know $R \le 7$. That is, $4 \le R \le 7$.

Since $x = 11$ is a distance of 8 from $x = 3$, the series diverges at $x = 11$.

Since $x = 5$ is a distance of 2 from $x = 3$, the series converges there.

Since $x = 0$ is a distance of 3 from $x = 3$, the series converges at $x = 3$.

34. (a) We use the ratio test:

$$\left| \frac{a_{n+1}}{a_n} \right| = \left| \frac{(-1)^{n+1}x^{2(n+1)}}{2^{2(n+1)}((n+1)!)^2} \cdot \frac{2^{2n}(n!)^2}{(-1)^n x^{2n}} \right|$$

$$= \frac{x^{2n+2}}{2^{2n+2}(n+1)^2(n!)^2} \cdot \frac{2^{2n}(n!)^2}{x^{2n}}$$

$$= \frac{x^2}{4(n+1)^2}.$$

For a fixed value of x, we have

$$\frac{x^2}{4(n+1)^2} \to 0 \quad \text{as} \quad n \to \infty.$$

The series converges for all x, so the domain of $J(x)$ is all real numbers.

(b) Since

$$J(x) = 1 - \frac{x^2}{4} + \cdots,$$

we have $J(0) = 1$.

(c) We have

$$S_0(x) = 1$$

$$S_1(x) = 1 - \frac{x^2}{4}$$

$$S_2(x) = 1 - \frac{x^2}{4} + \frac{x^4}{64}$$

$$S_3(x) = 1 - \frac{x^2}{4} + \frac{x^4}{64} - \frac{x^6}{2304}$$

$$S_4(x) = 1 - \frac{x^2}{4} + \frac{x^4}{64} - \frac{x^6}{2304} + \frac{x^8}{147,456}.$$

(d) The value of $J(1)$ can be approximated using partial sums. Substituting $x = 1$ into the partial sum polynomials, we have

$$S_0(1) = 1$$

$$S_1(1) = 0.75$$

$$S_2(1) = 0.765625$$

$$S_3(1) = 0.765191$$

$$S_4(1) = 0.765198.$$

We estimate that $J(1) \approx 0.765$. Theorem 9.9 can be used to bound the error.

(e) We see from the series that $J(x)$ is an even function, so $J(-1) = J(1)$. Thus, $J(-1) \approx 0.765$.

35. (a) We have

$$f(x) = 1 + x + \frac{x^2}{2} + \cdots,$$

so

$$f(0) = 1 + 0 + 0 + \cdots = 1.$$

(b) To find the domain of f, we find the interval of convergence.

$$\lim_{n \to \infty} \frac{|a_{n+1}|}{|a_n|} = \lim_{n \to \infty} \frac{|x^{n+1}/(n+1)!|}{|x^n/n!|} = \lim_{n \to \infty} \left(\frac{|x|^{n+1}n!}{|x|^n(n+1)!} \right) = |x| \lim_{n \to \infty} \frac{1}{n+1} = 0.$$

Thus the series converges for all x, so the domain of f is all real numbers.

(c) Differentiating term-by-term gives

$$f'(x) = \frac{d}{dx} \left(\sum_{n=0}^{\infty} \frac{x^n}{n!} \right) = \frac{d}{dx} \left(1 + x + \frac{x^2}{2!} + \frac{x^3}{3!} + \frac{x^4}{4!} + \cdots \right)$$

$$= 0 + 1 + 2\frac{x}{2!} + 3\frac{x^2}{3!} + 4\frac{x^3}{4!} + \cdots$$

$$= 1 + x + \frac{x^2}{2!} + \frac{x^3}{3!} + \cdots.$$

Thus, the series for f and f' are the same, so

$$f(x) = f'(x).$$

(d) We guess $f(x) = e^x$.

36. (a) Since only odd powers are involved in the series for $g(x)$,

$$g(x) = x - \frac{x^3}{3!} + \frac{x^5}{5!} - \frac{x^7}{7!} + \cdots,$$

we see that $g(x)$ is odd. Substituting $x = 0$ gives $g(0) = 0$.

(b) Differentiating term-by-term gives

$$g'(x) = 1 - 3\frac{x^2}{3!} + 5\frac{x^4}{5!} - 7\frac{x^6}{7!} + \cdots$$

$$= 1 - \frac{x^2}{2!} + \frac{x^4}{4!} - \frac{x^6}{6!} + \cdots.$$

$$g''(x) = 0 - 2\frac{x}{2!} + 4\frac{x^3}{4!} - 6\frac{x^5}{6!} + \cdots$$

$$= -x + \frac{x^3}{3!} - \frac{x^5}{5!} + \cdots.$$

So we see $g''(x) = -g(x)$.

(c) We guess $g(x) = \sin x$ since then $g'(x) = \cos x$ and $g''(x) = -\sin x = g(x)$. We check $g(0) = 0 = \sin 0$ and $g'(0) = 1 = \cos 0$.

37. (a) We have

$$(p(x))^2 = \left(1 - \frac{x^2}{2!} + \frac{x^4}{4!} - \frac{x^6}{6!} + \cdots\right)^2$$

$$= 1 - 2 \cdot \frac{x^2}{2} + \left(-\frac{x^2}{2!}\right)^2 + 2\frac{x^4}{4!} - 2\frac{x^6}{6!} - 2\frac{x^2}{2!} \cdot \frac{x^4}{4!} \cdots$$

$$= 1 - x^2 + \left(\frac{1}{4} + \frac{1}{12}\right)x^4 - x^6\left(\frac{1}{3 \cdot 5 \cdot 4!} + \frac{1}{4!}\right) \cdots$$

$$= 1 - x^2 + \frac{x^4}{3} - \frac{2}{45}x^6 \cdots.$$

$$(q(x))^2 = \left(x - \frac{x^3}{3!} + \frac{x^5}{5!} - \cdots\right)^2 = x^2\left(1 - \frac{x^2}{3!} + \frac{x^4}{5!} - \cdots\right)^2$$

$$= x^2\left(1 - 2\frac{x^2}{3!} + \left(-\frac{x^2}{3!}\right)^2 + 2\frac{x^4}{5!} \cdots\right)$$

$$= x^2\left(1 - \frac{x^2}{3} + x^4\left(\frac{1}{(3!)^2} + \frac{1}{5 \cdot 4 \cdot 3}\right) \cdots\right)$$

$$= x^2\left(1 - \frac{x^2}{3} + \frac{2}{45}x^4 \cdots\right)$$

$$= x^2 - \frac{x^4}{3} + \frac{2}{45}x^6 \cdots.$$

Thus, up to terms in x^6, we have

$$(p(x))^2 + (q(x))^2 = 1.$$

(b) The result of part (a) suggests that $p(x)$ and $q(x)$ could be the sine and cosine. Since $p(x)$ is even and $q(x)$ is odd, we guess that $p(x) = \cos x$ and $q(x) = \sin x$.

Solutions for Chapter 9 Review

Exercises

1. As n increases, the term $4n$ is much larger than 3 and $7n$ is much larger than 5. Thus dividing the numerator and denominator by n and using the fact that $\lim\limits_{n \to \infty} 1/n = 0$, we have

$$\lim_{n \to \infty} \frac{3 + 4n}{5 + 7n} = \lim_{n \to \infty} \frac{(3/n) + 4}{(5/n) + 7} = \frac{4}{7}.$$

Thus, the sequence converges to $4/7$.

2. We have:

$$\lim_{n \to \infty} \left(\frac{n+1}{n} \right) = 1.$$

The terms of the sequence do not approach 0, so the sequence diverges.

3. The first eight terms of the sequence are:

$$\frac{\sqrt{2}}{2}, 1, \frac{\sqrt{2}}{2}, 0, -\frac{\sqrt{2}}{2}, -1, -\frac{\sqrt{2}}{2}, 0.$$

The sequence then repeats this pattern, so it diverges.

4. Since $1/n$ approaches zero and $\ln n$ becomes arbitrarily large as $n \to \infty$, the sequence diverges.

5. If $b = 1$, then the sum is 6. If $b \neq 1$, we use the formula for the sum of a finite geometric series. This is a six-term geometric series ($n = 6$) with initial term $a = b^5$ and constant ratio $x = b$:

$$\text{Sum} = \frac{a(1 - x^n)}{1 - x} = \frac{b^5(1 - b^6)}{1 - b}.$$

6. This is a geometric series with $k - 2$ terms in it, so $n = k - 2$. The initial term is $a = (0.5)^3 = 0.125$ and the constant ratio is $x = 0.5$. Using the formula for the sum of a finite geometric series, we get

$$\text{Sum} = \frac{a(1 - x^n)}{1 - x} = \frac{0.125(1 - (0.5)^{k-2})}{1 - 0.5} = 0.25(1 - (0.5)^{k-2}).$$

7. $\displaystyle\sum_{n=0}^{\infty} \frac{3^n + 5}{4^n} = \sum_{n=0}^{\infty} \left(\frac{3}{4} \right)^n + \sum_{n=0}^{\infty} \frac{5}{4^n},$ a sum of two geometric series.

$$\sum_{n=0}^{\infty} \left(\frac{3}{4} \right)^n = \frac{1}{1 - \frac{3}{4}} = 4$$

$$\sum_{n=0}^{\infty} \frac{5}{4^n} = \frac{5}{1 - \frac{1}{4}} = \frac{20}{3}$$

so $\displaystyle\sum_{n=0}^{\infty} \frac{3^n + 5}{4^n} = 4 + \frac{20}{3} = \frac{32}{3}.$

8. We use the integral test to determine whether this series converges or diverges. To do so we determine whether the corresponding improper integral $\displaystyle\int_{1}^{\infty} \frac{1}{(x+2)^2} \, dx$ converges or diverges:

$$\int_{1}^{\infty} \frac{1}{(x+2)^2} \, dx = \lim_{b \to \infty} \int_{1}^{b} \frac{1}{(x+2)^2} \, dx$$

$$= \lim_{b \to \infty} \int_{3}^{b} \frac{1}{w^2} \, dw \qquad \text{(Substitute } w = x + 2)$$

$$= \lim_{b \to \infty} -\frac{1}{w} \Big|_{3}^{b}$$

$$= \lim_{b \to \infty} \left(-\frac{1}{b} + \frac{1}{3} \right) = \frac{1}{3}.$$

Since the integral $\displaystyle\int_{1}^{\infty} \frac{1}{(x+2)^2} \, dx$ converges, we conclude from the integral test that the series $\displaystyle\sum_{n=1}^{\infty} \frac{1}{(n+2)^2}$ converges.

9. We use the integral test to determine whether this series converges or diverges. To do so we determine whether the corresponding improper integral $\int_1^\infty \dfrac{3x^2 + 2x}{x^3 + x^2 + 1}\,dx$ converges or diverges. The integral can be calculated using the substitution $w = x^3 + x^2 + 1$, $dw = (3x^2 + 2x)\,dx$.

$$
\begin{aligned}
\int_1^\infty \frac{3x^2 + 2x}{x^3 + x^2 + 1}\,dx &= \lim_{b \to \infty} \int_1^b \frac{3x^2 + 2x}{x^3 + x^2 + 1}\,dx \\
&= \lim_{b \to \infty} \ln|x^3 + x^2 + 1|\Big|_1^b \\
&= \lim_{b \to \infty}\left(\ln|b^3 + b^2 + 1| - \ln 3\right) = \infty.
\end{aligned}
$$

Since the integral $\int_1^\infty \dfrac{3x^2 + 2x}{x^3 + x^2 + 1}\,dx$ diverges, we conclude from the integral test that the series $\displaystyle\sum_{n=1}^\infty \dfrac{3n^2 + 2n}{n^3 + n^2 + 1}$ diverges.

10. We use the integral test to determine whether this series converges or diverges. We determine whether the corresponding improper integral $\int_0^\infty x e^{-x^2}\,dx$ converges or diverges:

$$
\int_0^\infty x e^{-x^2}\,dx = \lim_{b \to \infty} \int_0^b x e^{-x^2}\,dx = \lim_{b \to \infty} -\frac{1}{2}e^{-x^2}\Big|_0^b = \lim_{b \to \infty}\left(-\frac{1}{2}e^{-b^2} + \frac{1}{2}\right) = \frac{1}{2}.
$$

Since the integral $\int_0^\infty x e^{-x^2}\,dx$ converges, we conclude from the integral test that the series $\displaystyle\sum_{n=0}^\infty n e^{-n^2}$ converges.

11. We use the integral test to determine whether this series converges or diverges. To do so we determine whether the corresponding improper integral $\int_2^\infty \dfrac{2}{x^2 - 1}\,dx$ converges or diverges:

$$
\begin{aligned}
\int_2^\infty \frac{2}{x^2 - 1}\,dx &= \lim_{b \to \infty} \int_2^b \frac{2}{x^2 - 1}\,dx \\
&= \lim_{b \to \infty}\left(\int_2^b \left(\frac{1}{x - 1} - \frac{1}{x + 1}\right)dx\right) \qquad \text{(Using partial fractions)} \\
&= \lim_{b \to \infty}\left(\ln|x - 1| - \ln|x + 1|\Big|_2^b\right) \\
&= \lim_{b \to \infty}\left(\ln\left|\frac{x - 1}{x + 1}\right|\,\Big|_2^b\right) \\
&= \lim_{b \to \infty}\left(\ln\left|\frac{b - 1}{b + 1}\right| - \ln\left(\frac{1}{3}\right)\right) = \ln 1 - \ln\frac{1}{3} = \ln 3.
\end{aligned}
$$

Since the integral $\int_2^\infty \dfrac{2}{x^2 - 1}\,dx$ converges, we conclude that the series $\displaystyle\sum_{n=2}^\infty \dfrac{2}{n^2 - 1}$ converges.

12. Let $a_n = n^2/(3n^2 + 4)$. Since $3n^2 + 4 > 3n^2$, we have $\dfrac{n^2}{3n^2 + 4} < \dfrac{1}{3}$, so

$$
0 < a_n < \left(\frac{1}{3}\right)^n.
$$

The geometric series $\displaystyle\sum_{n=1}^\infty \left(\frac{1}{3}\right)^n$ converges, so the comparison test tells us that the series $\displaystyle\sum_{n=1}^\infty \left(\frac{n^2}{3n^2 + 4}\right)^n$ also converges.

13. Let $a_n = 1/(n \sin^2 n)$. Since $0 < \sin^2 n < 1$, for any positive integer n, we have $n \sin^2 n < n$, so $\dfrac{1}{n \sin^2 n} > \dfrac{1}{n}$, thus

$$a_n > \frac{1}{n}.$$

The harmonic series $\displaystyle\sum_{n=1}^{\infty} \frac{1}{n}$ diverges, so the comparison test tells us that the series $\displaystyle\sum_{n=1}^{\infty} \frac{1}{n \sin^2 n}$ also diverges.

14. The nth term $a_n = \sqrt{n-1}/(n^2 + 3)$ behaves like $\sqrt{n}/n^2 = 1/n^{3/2}$ for large n, so we take $b_n = 1/n^{3/2}$. We have

$$\lim_{n \to \infty} \frac{a_n}{b_n} = \lim_{n \to \infty} \frac{\sqrt{n-1}/(n^2+3)}{1/n^{3/2}} = \lim_{n \to \infty} \frac{n^{3/2}\sqrt{n-1}}{n^2+3} = \lim_{n \to \infty} \frac{n^2\sqrt{1-1/n}}{n^2(1+3/n^2)} = 1.$$

The limit comparison test applies with $c = 1$. The p-series $\sum 1/n^{3/2}$ converges because $p = 3/2 > 1$. Therefore $\sum \sqrt{n-1}/(n^2+3)$ also converges.

15. The nth term $a_n = (n^3 - 2n^2 + n + 1)/(n^5 - 2)$ behaves like $n^3/n^5 = 1/n^2$ for large n, so we take $b_n = 1/n^2$. We have

$$\lim_{n \to \infty} \frac{a_n}{b_n} = \lim_{n \to \infty} \frac{(n^3 - 2n^2 + n + 1)/(n^5 - 2)}{1/n^2} = \lim_{n \to \infty} \frac{n^5 - 2n^4 + n^3 + n^2}{n^5 - 2} = 1.$$

The limit comparison test applies with $c = 1$. The p-series $\sum 1/n^2$ converges because $p = 2 > 1$. Therefore the series $\sum \left(n^3 - 2n^2 + n + 1\right) / \left(n^5 - 2\right)$ also converges.

16. The nth term is $a_n = \sin(1/n^2)$. When n is large, $1/n^2$ is near zero, so $\sin(1/n^2)$ is near $1/n^2$. We see that $\sin(1/n^2)$ behaves like $1/n^2$ for large n, so we take $b_n = 1/n^2$. We have

$$\lim_{n \to \infty} \frac{a_n}{b_n} = \lim_{n \to \infty} \frac{\sin(1/n^2)}{1/n^2}$$
$$= \lim_{x \to 0} \frac{\sin x}{x}$$
$$= 1.$$

The limit comparison test applies with $c = 1$. The p-series $\sum 1/n^2$ converges because $p = 2 > 1$. Therefore $\sum \sin(1/n^2)$ also converges.

17. The nth term $a_n = 1/(\sqrt{n^3 - 1})$ behaves like $1/\sqrt{n^3} = 1/n^{3/2}$ for large n, so we take $b_n = 1/n^{3/2}$. We have

$$\lim_{n \to \infty} \frac{a_n}{b_n} = \lim_{n \to \infty} \frac{1/\sqrt{n^3 - 1}}{1/n^{3/2}} = \lim_{n \to \infty} \frac{n^{3/2}}{\sqrt{n^3 - 1}} = \lim_{n \to \infty} \frac{n^{3/2}}{n^{3/2}\sqrt{1 - 1/n^3}} = \lim_{n \to \infty} \frac{1}{\sqrt{1 - 1/n^3}} = \frac{1}{\sqrt{1 - 0}} = 1.$$

The limit comparison test applies with $c = 1$. The p-series $\sum 1/n^{3/2}$ converges because $p = 3/2 > 1$. Therefore $\sum 1/\sqrt{n^3 - 1}$ also converges.

18. Since $a_n = 1/(2^n n!)$, replacing n by $n + 1$ gives $a_{n+1} = 1/(2^{n+1}(n+1)!)$. Thus

$$\frac{|a_{n+1}|}{|a_n|} = \frac{\dfrac{1}{2^{n+1}(n+1)!}}{\dfrac{1}{2^n n!}} = \frac{2^n n!}{2^{n+1}(n+1)!} = \frac{1}{2(n+1)},$$

so

$$L = \lim_{n \to \infty} \frac{|a_{n+1}|}{|a_n|} = \lim_{n \to \infty} \frac{1}{2n+2} = 0.$$

Since $L < 1$, the ratio test tells us that $\displaystyle\sum_{n=1}^{\infty} \frac{1}{2^n n!}$ converges.

19. Since $a_n = n!(n+1)!/(2n)!$, replacing n by $n+1$ gives $a_{n+1} = (n+1)!(n+2)!/(2n+2)!$. Thus,

$$\frac{|a_{n+1}|}{|a_n|} = \frac{\dfrac{(n+1)!(n+2)!}{(2n+2)!}}{\dfrac{n!(n+1)!}{(2n)!}} = \frac{(n+1)!(n+2)!}{(2n+2)!} \cdot \frac{(2n)!}{n!(n+1)!}.$$

However, since $(n+2)! = (n+2)(n+1)n!$ and $(2n+2)! = (2n+2)(2n+1)(2n)!$, we have

$$\frac{|a_{n+1}|}{|a_n|} = \frac{(n+2)(n+1)}{(2n+2)(2n+1)} = \frac{n+2}{2(2n+1)},$$

so

$$L = \lim_{n \to \infty} \frac{|a_{n+1}|}{|a_n|} = \frac{1}{4}.$$

Since $L < 1$, the ratio test tells us that $\sum_{n=1}^{\infty} \frac{n!(n+1)!}{(2n)!}$ converges.

20. Let $a_n = 1/(n^2+1)$. Then replacing n by $n+1$ gives $a_{n+1} = 1/((n+1)^2+1)$. Since $(n+1)^2+1 > n^2+1$, we have

$$0 < \frac{1}{(n+1)^2+1} < \frac{1}{n^2+1},$$

so

$$0 < a_{n+1} < a_n.$$

We also have $\lim_{n \to \infty} a_n = 0$, therefore, the alternating series test tells us that the series $\sum_{n=1}^{\infty} \frac{(-1)^n}{n^2+1}$ converges.

21. Let $a_n = 1/\sqrt{n^2+1}$. Then replacing n by $n+1$ we have $a_{n+1} = 1/\sqrt{(n+1)^2+1}$. Since $\sqrt{(n+1)^2+1} > \sqrt{n^2+1}$, we have

$$\frac{1}{\sqrt{(n+1)^2+1}} < \frac{1}{\sqrt{n^2+1}},$$

so

$$0 < a_{n+1} < a_n.$$

In addition, $\lim_{n \to \infty} a_n = 0$ so $\sum_{n=0}^{\infty} \frac{(-1)^n}{\sqrt{n^2+1}}$ converges by the alternating series test.

22. Since $f(x) = 1/(x+1)$ is continuous, positive and decreasing, we apply the integral test, and we obtain

$$\int_1^{\infty} \frac{1}{x+1}\,dx = \lim_{b \to \infty} \int_1^b \frac{1}{1+x}\,dx = \lim_{b \to \infty} (\ln(b+1) - \ln 2) = \infty.$$

Since this improper integral diverges, the series $\sum_{n=1}^{\infty} \frac{1}{n+1}$ also diverges. We can also observe the series is the harmonic series, with the first term missing, and hence diverges by Property 2 of Theorem 9.2.

23. This is a p-series with $p > 1$, so it converges.

24. We use the integral test to determine whether this series converges or diverges. To do so we determine whether the corresponding improper integral $\int_3^{\infty} \frac{2}{\sqrt{x-2}}\,dx$ converges or diverges:

$$\int_3^{\infty} \frac{2}{\sqrt{x-2}}\,dx = \lim_{b \to \infty} \int_3^b \frac{2}{\sqrt{x-2}}\,dx$$

$$= \lim_{b \to \infty} \int_1^b \frac{2}{\sqrt{w}}\,dw \qquad \text{(Substitute } w = x-2.\text{)}$$

$$= \lim_{b \to \infty} 4\sqrt{w}\,\Big|_1^b = \infty.$$

Since the limit does not exist, the integral $\int_3^{\infty} \frac{2}{\sqrt{x-2}}\,dx$ diverges, and we conclude from the integral test that the series $\sum_{n=3}^{\infty} \frac{2}{\sqrt{n-2}}$ diverges. The limit comparison test with $b_n = 1/\sqrt{n}$ can also be used.

25. This is an alternating series. Let $a_n = 1/(\sqrt{n} + 1)$. Then $\lim_{n \to \infty} a_n = 0$. Now replace n by $n + 1$ to give $a_{n+1} = 1/(\sqrt{n+1} + 1)$. Since $\sqrt{n+1} + 1 > \sqrt{n} + 1$, we have $\dfrac{1}{\sqrt{n+1}+1} < \dfrac{1}{\sqrt{n}+1}$, so

$$0 < a_{n+1} = \frac{1}{\sqrt{n+1}+1} < \frac{1}{\sqrt{n}+1} = a_n.$$

Therefore, the alternating series test tells us that the series $\displaystyle\sum_{n=1}^{\infty} \frac{(-1)^{n-1}}{\sqrt{n}+1}$ converges.

26. Writing $a_n = n^2/(n^2 + 1)$, we have $\lim_{n \to \infty} a_n = 1$ so the series diverges by Property 3 of Theorem 9.2.

27. We use the integral test to determine whether this series converges or diverges. To do so we determine whether the corresponding improper integral $\displaystyle\int_1^{\infty} \frac{x^2}{x^3 + 1}\, dx$ converges or diverges:

$$\int_1^{\infty} \frac{x^2}{x^3 + 1}\, dx = \lim_{b \to \infty} \int_1^b \frac{x^2}{x^3 + 1}\, dx = \lim_{b \to \infty} \frac{1}{3} \ln |x^3 + 1| \Big|_1^b = \lim_{b \to \infty} \left(\frac{1}{3} \ln(b^3 + 1) - \frac{1}{3} \ln 2 \right).$$

Since the limit does not exist, the integral $\displaystyle\int_1^{\infty} \frac{x^2}{x^3 + 1}\, dx$ diverges an so we conclude from the integral test that the series $\displaystyle\sum_{n=1}^{\infty} \frac{n^2}{n^3 + 1}$ diverges. The limit comparison test with $b_n = 1/n$ can also be used.

28. We use the ratio test. Since $a_n = 3^n/(2n)!$, replacing n by $n + 1$ gives $a_{n+1} = 3^{n+1}/(2n + 2)!$. Thus

$$\frac{a_{n+1}}{a_n} = \frac{3^{n+1}/(2n+2)!}{3^n/(2n)!} = \frac{3^{n+1}}{(2n+2)!} \cdot \frac{(2n)!}{3^n}.$$

Since $(2n + 2)! = (2n + 2)(2n + 1)(2n)!$, we have

$$\frac{a_{n+1}}{a_n} = \frac{3}{(2n+2)(2n+1)},$$

so

$$L = \lim_{n \to \infty} \frac{a_{n+1}}{a_n} = 0.$$

Since $L < 1$, the ratio test tells us that the series $\displaystyle\sum_{n=1}^{\infty} \frac{3^n}{(2n)!}$ converges.

29. We use the ratio test. Since $a_n = (2n)!/(n!)^2$, replacing n by $n + 1$ gives $a_{n+1} = (2n + 2)!/((n + 1)!)^2$. Thus

$$\frac{a_{n+1}}{a_n} = \frac{\dfrac{(2n+2)!}{((n+1)!)^2}}{\dfrac{(2n)!}{(n!)^2}} = \frac{(2n+2)!}{(n+1)!(n+1)!} \cdot \frac{n!n!}{(2n)!}.$$

Since $(2n + 2)! = (2n + 2)(2n + 1)(2n)!$ and $(n + 1)! = (n + 1)n!$, we have

$$\frac{a_{n+1}}{a_n} = \frac{(2n+2)(2n+1)}{(n+1)(n+1)},$$

therefore

$$L = \lim_{n \to \infty} \frac{a_{n+1}}{a_n} = 4.$$

As $L > 1$ the ratio test tells us that the series $\displaystyle\sum_{n=1}^{\infty} \frac{(2n)!}{(n!)^2}$ diverges.

30. The series can be written as

$$\sum_{n=1}^{\infty} \frac{n^2 + 2^n}{n^2 2^n} = \sum_{n=1}^{\infty} \frac{1}{2^n} + \sum_{n=1}^{\infty} \frac{1}{n^2}.$$

Since $\displaystyle\sum_{n=1}^{\infty} \frac{1}{2^n}$ is a convergent geometric series and $\displaystyle\sum_{n=1}^{\infty} \frac{1}{n^2}$ converges as a p-series with $p > 1$, we see $\displaystyle\sum_{n=1}^{\infty} \frac{n^2 + 2^n}{n^2 2^n}$ converges by Theorem 9.2.

31. Let $a_n = 2^{-n}\dfrac{(n+1)}{(n+2)} = \left(\dfrac{n+1}{n+2}\right)\left(\dfrac{1}{2^n}\right)$. Since $\dfrac{(n+1)}{(n+2)} < 1$ and $\dfrac{1}{2^n} = \left(\dfrac{1}{2}\right)^n$, we have

$$0 < a_n < \left(\frac{1}{2}\right)^n,$$

so that we can compare the series $\displaystyle\sum_{n=1}^{\infty} 2^{-n}\frac{(n+1)}{(n+2)}$ with the convergent geometric series $\displaystyle\sum_{n=1}^{\infty}\left(\frac{1}{2}\right)^n$. The comparison test tells us that

$$\sum_{n=1}^{\infty} 2^{-n}\frac{(n+1)}{(n+2)}$$

also converges.

32. We have
$$L = \lim_{n\to\infty}\left|\frac{a_{n+1}}{a_n}\right| = \lim_{n\to\infty}\frac{2^{n+1}}{(2n+3)!}\cdot\frac{(2n+1)!}{2^n} = \lim_{n\to\infty}\frac{2}{(2n+3)(2n+2)} = 0,$$
so the series converges by the ratio test, since $L < 1$.

33. Since there is an n in the numerator and a $\sqrt{n}$ in the denominator, the terms in this series are increasing in magnitude. We have
$$\lim_{n\to\infty}\left|\frac{n+1}{\sqrt{n}}(-1)^n\right| = \lim_{n\to\infty}\frac{n+1}{\sqrt{n}} = \infty,$$
so $\lim_{n\to\infty}(-1)^n(n+1)/\sqrt{n}$ does not approach zero. Therefore, the series diverges by Property 3 of Theorem 9.2.

34. The series can be written as
$$\sum_{n=0}^{\infty}\frac{2+3^n}{5^n} = \sum_{n=0}^{\infty}\left(\frac{2}{5^n} + \frac{3^n}{5^n}\right) = \sum_{n=0}^{\infty}\left(2\left(\frac{1}{5}\right)^n + \left(\frac{3}{5}\right)^n\right).$$

The series $\displaystyle\sum_{n=0}^{\infty}\left(\frac{1}{5}\right)^n$ is a geometric series which converges because $\left|\frac{1}{5}\right| < 1$. Likewise, the geometric series $\displaystyle\sum_{n=0}^{\infty}\left(\frac{3}{5}\right)^n$ converges because $\left|\frac{3}{5}\right| < 1$. Since both series converge, Property 1 of Theorem 9.2 tells us that the series $\displaystyle\sum_{n=0}^{\infty}\frac{2+3^n}{5^n}$ also converges.

35. Writing $a_n = 1/(2 + \sin n)$, we have $\lim_{n\to\infty} a_n$ does not exist, so the series diverges by Property 3 of Theorem 9.2.

36. We use the integral test to determine whether this series converges or diverges. To do so we determine whether the corresponding improper integral $\displaystyle\int_3^{\infty}\frac{1}{(2x-5)^3}\,dx$ converges or diverges:

$$\int_3^{\infty}\frac{1}{(2x-5)^3}\,dx = \frac{1}{2}\lim_{b\to\infty}\int_1^b\frac{1}{w^3}\,dw \qquad \text{(Substitute } w = 2x-5)$$

$$= -\frac{1}{2}\lim_{b\to\infty}\frac{1}{2w^2}\Big|_1^b$$

$$= -\frac{1}{2}\lim_{b\to\infty}\left(\frac{1}{2b^2} - \frac{1}{2}\right) = \frac{1}{4}.$$

Since the integral $\displaystyle\int_3^{\infty}\frac{1}{(2x-5)^3}\,dx$ converges, we conclude from the integral test that the series $\displaystyle\sum_{n=3}^{\infty}\frac{1}{(2n-5)^3}$ converges. The limit comparison test, with $b_n = 1/n^3$ can also be used.

37. The nth term $a_n = 1/(n^3 - 3)$ behaves like $1/n^3$ for large n, so we take $b_n = 1/n^3$. We have
$$\lim_{n\to\infty}\frac{a_n}{b_n} = \lim_{n\to\infty}\frac{1/(n^3-3)}{1/n^3} = \lim_{n\to\infty}\frac{n^3}{n^3-3} = 1.$$

The limit comparison test applies with $c = 1$. The p-series $\sum 1/n^3$ converges because $p = 3 > 1$. Therefore $\sum 1/(n^3 - 3$ also converges.

38. Note that

$$\sum_{n=1}^{\infty} \frac{\sin(n\pi/2)}{n^3} = 1 - \frac{1}{3^3} + \frac{1}{5^3} - \frac{1}{7^3} + \cdots$$

is an alternating series with the absolute values of the terms decreasing to 0. Thus, the series converges by the alternating series test.

39. Since $\ln(1 + 1/k) = \ln((k + 1)/k) = \ln(k + 1) - \ln k$, the nth partial sum of this series is

$$\begin{aligned}
S_n &= \sum_{k=1}^{n} \ln\left(1 + \frac{1}{k}\right) \\
&= \sum_{k=1}^{n} \ln(k + 1) - \sum_{k=1}^{n} \ln k \\
&= (\ln 2 + \ln 3 + \cdots + \ln(n + 1)) - (\ln 1 + \ln 2 + \cdots + \ln n) \\
&= \ln(n + 1) - \ln 1 \\
&= \ln(n + 1).
\end{aligned}$$

Thus, the partial sums, S_n, grow without bound as $n \to \infty$, so the series diverges by the definition.

40. The ratio test gives

$$L = \lim_{n\to\infty} \frac{a_{n+1}}{a_n} = \lim_{n\to\infty} \frac{(n+1)/2^{n+1}}{n/2^n} = \lim_{n\to\infty} \frac{n+1}{2n} = \frac{1}{2},$$

so the series converges since $L < 1$.

41. Since $\ln n$ grows much more slowly than n, we suspect that $(\ln n)^2 < n$ for large n. This can be confirmed with L'Hopital's rule.

$$\lim_{n\to\infty} \frac{(\ln n)^2}{n} = \lim_{n\to\infty} \frac{2(\ln n)/n}{1} = \lim_{n\to\infty} \frac{2(\ln n)}{n} = 0.$$

Therefore, for large n, we have $(\ln n)^2/n < 1$, and hence for large n,

$$\frac{1}{n} < \frac{1}{(\ln n)^2}.$$

Thus $\sum_{n=2}^{\infty} 1/(\ln n)^2$ diverges by comparison with the divergent harmonic series $\sum 1/n$.

42. Since $C_n = n$, replacing n by $n + 1$ gives $C_{n+1} = n + 1$. Using the ratio test with $a_n = nx^n$, we have

$$\lim_{n\to\infty} \frac{|a_{n+1}|}{|a_n|} = |x| \lim_{n\to\infty} \frac{|C_{n+1}|}{|C_n|} = |x| \lim_{n\to\infty} \frac{n+1}{n} = |x|.$$

Thus the radius of convergence is $R = 1$.

43. Let $C_n = \dfrac{(2n)!}{(n!)^2}$. Then replacing n by $n + 1$, we have $C_{n+1} = \dfrac{(2n + 2)!}{((n + 1)!)^2}$. Thus, with $a_n = (2n)!x^n/(n!)^2$, we have

$$\frac{|a_{n+1}|}{|a_n|} = |x| \frac{|C_{n+1}|}{|C_n|} = |x| \frac{(2n+2)!/((n+1)!)^2}{(2n)!/(n!)^2} = |x| \frac{(2n+2)!}{(2n)!} \cdot \frac{(n!)^2}{((n+1)!)^2}.$$

Since $(2n + 2)! = (2n + 2)(2n + 1)(2n)!$ and $(n + 1)! = (n + 1)n!$ we have

$$\frac{|C_{n+1}|}{|C_n|} = \frac{(2n+2)(2n+1)}{(n+1)(n+1)},$$

so

$$\lim_{n\to\infty} \frac{|a_{n+1}|}{|a_n|} = |x| \lim_{n\to\infty} \frac{|C_{n+1}|}{|C_n|} = |x| \lim_{n\to\infty} \frac{(2n+2)(2n+1)}{(n+1)(n+1)} = |x| \lim_{n\to\infty} \frac{4n+2}{n+1} = 4|x|,$$

so the radius of convergence of this series is $R = 1/4$.

44. Let $C_n = 2^n + n^2$. Then replacing n by $n+1$ gives $C_{n+1} = 2^{n+1} + (n+1)^2$. Using the ratio test, we have

$$\frac{|a_{n+1}|}{|a_n|} = |x|\frac{|C_{n+1}|}{|C_n|} = |x|\frac{2^{n+1} + (n+1)^2}{2^n + n^2} = 2|x|\left(\frac{2^n + \frac{1}{2}(n+1)^2}{2^n + n^2}\right).$$

Since 2^n dominates n^2 as $n \to \infty$, we have

$$\lim_{n \to \infty} \frac{|a_{n+1}|}{|a_n|} = 2|x|.$$

Thus the radius of convergence is $R = \frac{1}{2}$.

45. Let $C_n = 1/(n! + 1)$. Then replacing n by $n+1$ gives $C_{n+1} = 1/((n+1)! + 1)$. Using the ratio test, we have

$$\frac{|a_{n+1}|}{|a_n|} = |x|\frac{|C_{n+1}|}{|C_n|} = |x|\frac{1/((n+1)! + 1)}{1/(n! + 1)} = |x|\frac{n! + 1}{(n+1)! + 1}.$$

Since $n!$ and $(n+1)!$ dominate the constant term 1 as $n \to \infty$ and $(n+1)! = (n+1) \cdot n!$ we have

$$\lim_{n \to \infty} \frac{|a_{n+1}|}{|a_n|} = 0.$$

Thus the radius of convergence is $R = \infty$.

Problems

46. The series $\sum \frac{(-1)^n}{n^{1/2}}$ converges by the alternating series test. However $\sum \frac{1}{n^{1/2}}$ diverges because it is a p-series with $p = 1/2 \le 1$. Thus $\sum \frac{(-1)^n}{n^{1/2}}$ is conditionally convergent.

47. Since

$$\lim_{n \to \infty} \frac{n}{n+1} = 1 \ne 0$$

the series $\sum (-1)^n \frac{n}{n+1}$ does not converge. It is a divergent series.

48. The series can be written as

$$\sum_{n=1}^{\infty} \frac{n^r + r^n}{n^r r^n} = \sum_{n=1}^{\infty} \frac{1}{r^n} + \sum_{n=1}^{\infty} \frac{1}{n^r}.$$

If $0 < r < 1$, both series diverge, but if $r > 1$ both series converge.

If $r = 1$ the given series becomes $\sum_{n=1}^{\infty} \frac{n+1}{n}$ which diverges.

By Theorem 9.2 the given series converges if $r > 1$.

49. We use the ratio test:

$$\left|\frac{a_{n+1}}{a_n}\right| = \left|\frac{x^{n+1}}{3^{n+1}(n+1)^2} \cdot \frac{3^n n^2}{x^n}\right| = \left(\frac{n}{n+1}\right)^2 \cdot \frac{|x|}{3}.$$

Since $n/(n+1) \to 1$ as $n \to \infty$, we have

$$\lim_{n \to \infty} \left|\frac{a_{n+1}}{a_n}\right| = \frac{|x|}{3}.$$

We have $|x|/3 < 1$ when $|x| < 3$. The radius of convergence is 3 and the series converges for $-3 < x < 3$.

We check the endpoints. For $x = -3$, we have

$$\sum_{n=1}^{\infty} \frac{x^n}{3^n n^2} = \sum_{n=1}^{\infty} \frac{(-3)^n}{3^n n^2} = \sum_{n=1}^{\infty} \frac{(-1)^n}{n^2}.$$

We know $\sum \frac{1}{n^2}$ is a p-series with $p = 2$ so it converges. Therefore the alternating series $\sum \frac{(-1)^n}{n^2}$ also converges.
For $x = 3$, we have

$$\sum_{n=1}^{\infty} \frac{x^n}{3^n n^2} = \sum_{n=1}^{\infty} \frac{3^n}{3^n n^2} = \sum_{n=1}^{\infty} \frac{1}{n^2}.$$

This is a p-series with $p = 2$ and it converges. The series converges at both its endpoints and the interval of convergence is $-3 \le x \le 3$.

50. We use the ratio test:
$$\left|\frac{a_{n+1}}{a_n}\right| = \left|\frac{(-1)^{n+1}(x-2)^{n+1}}{5^{n+1}} \cdot \frac{5^n}{(-1)^n(x-2)^n}\right| = \frac{|x-2|}{5}.$$

Since $|x-2|/5 < 1$ when $|x-2| < 5$, the radius of convergence is 5 and the series converges for $-3 < x < 7$.
We check the endpoints:

$$x = -3 : \quad \sum_{n=0}^{\infty}\frac{(-1)^n(x-2)^n}{5^n} = \sum_{n=0}^{\infty}\frac{(-1)^n(-3-2)^n}{5^n} = \sum_{n=0}^{\infty}1 \quad \text{which diverges.}$$

$$x = 7 : \quad \sum_{n=0}^{\infty}\frac{(-1)^n(x-2)^n}{5^n} = \sum_{n=0}^{\infty}\frac{(-1)^n(7-2)^n}{5^n} = \sum_{n=0}^{\infty}(-1)^n \quad \text{which diverges.}$$

The series diverges at both the endpoints, so the interval of convergence is $-3 < x < 7$.

51. We use the ratio test:
$$\left|\frac{a_{n+1}}{a_n}\right| = \left|\frac{(-1)^{n+1}x^{n+1}}{n+1} \cdot \frac{n}{(-1)^n x^n}\right| = \frac{n}{n+1}\cdot|x|.$$

Since $n/(n+1) \to 1$ as $n \to \infty$, we have
$$\lim_{n\to\infty}\left|\frac{a_{n+1}}{a_n}\right| = |x|.$$

The series converges for $|x| < 1$. The radius of convergence is 1 and the series converges for $-1 < x < 1$.
We check the endpoints. For $x = -1$, we have

$$\sum_{n=1}^{\infty}\frac{(-1)^n x^n}{n} = \sum_{n=1}^{\infty}\frac{(-1)^n(-1)^n}{n} = \sum_{n=1}^{\infty}\frac{1}{n}.$$

This is the harmonic series and diverges. For $x = 1$, we have

$$\sum_{n=1}^{\infty}\frac{(-1)^n x^n}{n} = \sum_{n=1}^{\infty}\frac{(-1)^n(1)^n}{n} = \sum_{n=1}^{\infty}\frac{(-1)^n}{n}.$$

This is the alternating harmonic series and converges. The series diverges at $x = -1$ and converges at $x = 1$. Therefore, interval of convergence is $-1 < x \le 1$.

52. The series converges for $|x-2| = 2$ and diverges for $|x-2| = 4$, thus the radius of convergence of the series, R, is at least 2 but no larger than 4.

(a) False. If $x = 7$ then $|x-2| = 5$, so the series diverges.
(b) False. If $x = 1$ then $|x-2| = 1$, so the series converges.
(c) True. If $x = 0.5$ then $|x-2| = 1.5$, so the series converges.
(d) If $x = 5$ then $|x-2| = 3$ and it is not possible to determine whether or not the series converges at this point.
(e) False. If $x = -3$ then $|x-2| = 5$, so the series diverges.

53. (a) Using an argument similar to Example 5 in Section 9.5, we take

$$a_n = (-1)^n\frac{t^{2n}}{(2n)!},$$

so, replacing n by $n+1$,

$$a_{n+1} = (-1)^{n+1}\frac{t^{2(n+1)}}{(2(n+1))!} = (-1)^{n+1}\frac{t^{2n+2}}{(2n+2)!}.$$

Thus,

$$\frac{|a_{n+1}|}{|a_n|} = \frac{|(-1)^{n+1}t^{2n+2}/(2n+2)!|}{|(-1)^n t^{2n}/(2n)!|} = \frac{t^2}{(2n+2)(2n+1)},$$

so

$$\lim_{n\to\infty}\frac{|a_{n+1}|}{|a_n|} = \lim_{n\to\infty}\frac{t^2}{(2n+2)(2n+1)} = 0.$$

The radius of convergence is therefore ∞, so the series converges for all t. Therefore, the domain of h is all real numbers.

(b) Since h involves only even powers,

$$h(t) = 1 - \frac{t^2}{2!} + \frac{t^4}{4!} - \frac{t^6}{6!} + \cdots,$$

h is an even function.

(c) Differentiating term-by-term, we have

$$h'(t) = 0 - 2\frac{t}{2!} + 4\frac{t^3}{4!} - 6\frac{t^6}{6!} + \cdots$$
$$= -t + \frac{t^3}{3!} - \frac{t^5}{5!} + \cdots.$$

$$h''(t) = -1 + 3\frac{t^2}{3!} - 5\frac{t^4}{5!} + \cdots$$
$$= -1 + \frac{t^2}{2!} - \frac{t^4}{4!} + \cdots.$$

So we see $h''(t) = -h(t)$.

54. (a) It is easier to work with the value of the car first and then find the yearly losses. The value of the car goes down by 10% a year. Thus, the value at the end of the first years is $v_1 = 30{,}000(0.9)$. The value at the end of the second year is $v_2 = 30{,}000(0.9)^2$. The value at the end of n years is $v_n = 30{,}000(0.9)^n$. Thus, the losses in the first four years are

$$l_1 = 30{,}000(0.1)$$
$$l_2 = v_1 - v_2 = 30{,}000(0.9) - 30{,}000(0.9)^2 = 30{,}000(0.9)(0.1)$$
$$l_3 = v_2 - v_3 = 30{,}000(0.9)^2 - 30{,}000(0.9)^3 = 30{,}000(0.9)^2(0.1)$$
$$l_4 = v_3 - v_4 = 30{,}000(0.9)^3 - 30{,}000(0.9)^4 = 30{,}000(0.9)^3(0.1).$$

Thus,
$$l_n = v_{n-1} - v_n = 30{,}000(0.9)^{n-1}(0.1) = 3000(0.9)^{n-1}.$$

(b) In the first year, $m_1 = 500$; in the second year, $m_2 = 500(1.2)$; in the third year, $m_3 = 500(1.2)^2$. Thus
$$m_n = 500(1.2)^{n-1}.$$

(c) We want to find n such that $m_n \geq l_n$, so
$$500(1.2)^{n-1} \geq 3000(0.9)^{n-1}.$$

We solve
$$500(1.2)^{n-1} = 3000(0.9)^{n-1}$$
$$\frac{(1.2)^{n-1}}{(0.9)^{n-1}} = \frac{3000}{500}$$
$$\left(\frac{1.2}{0.9}\right)^{n-1} = 6$$
$$(n-1)\ln\left(\frac{1.2}{0.9}\right) = \ln 6$$
$$n - 1 = \frac{\ln 6}{\ln(1.2/0.9)}$$
$$n = 6.228 + 1 = 7.228.$$

So, maintenance first exceeds losses in year 8. In year 7,
$$l_7 = 3000(0.9)^6 = \$1594, \quad m_7 = 500(1.2)^6 = \$1493.$$

In year 8,
$$l_8 = 3000(0.9)^7 = \$1435, \quad m_8 = 500(1.2)^7 = \$1792.$$

55.

$$\text{Present value of first coupon} = \frac{50}{1.06}$$
$$\text{Present value of second coupon} = \frac{50}{(1.06)^2}, \text{ etc.}$$

$$\text{Total present value} = \underbrace{\frac{50}{1.06} + \frac{50}{(1.06)^2} + \cdots + \frac{50}{(1.06)^{10}}}_{\text{coupons}} + \underbrace{\frac{1000}{(1.06)^{10}}}_{\text{principal}}$$
$$= \frac{50}{1.06}\left(1 + \frac{1}{1.06} + \cdots + \frac{1}{(1.06)^9}\right) + \frac{1000}{(1.06)^{10}}$$
$$= \frac{50}{1.06}\left(\frac{1 - \left(\frac{1}{1.06}\right)^{10}}{1 - \frac{1}{1.06}}\right) + \frac{1000}{(1.06)^{10}}$$
$$= 368.004 + 558.395$$
$$= \$926.40$$

56.

$$\text{Present value of first coupon} = \frac{50}{1.04}$$
$$\text{Present value of second coupon} = \frac{50}{(1.04)^2}, \text{etc.}$$

$$\text{Total present value} = \underbrace{\frac{50}{1.04} + \frac{50}{(1.04)^2} + \cdots + \frac{50}{(1.04)^{10}}}_{\text{coupons}} + \underbrace{\frac{1000}{(1.04)^{10}}}_{\text{principal}}$$
$$= \frac{50}{1.04}\left(1 + \frac{1}{1.04} + \cdots + \frac{1}{(1.04)^9}\right) + \frac{1000}{(1.04)^{10}}$$
$$= \frac{50}{1.04}\left(\frac{1 - \left(\frac{1}{1.04}\right)^{10}}{1 - \frac{1}{1.04}}\right) + \frac{1000}{(1.04)^{10}}$$
$$= 405.545 + 675.564$$
$$= \$1081.11$$

57. (a)

$$\text{Present value of first coupon} = \frac{50}{1.05}$$
$$\text{Present value of second coupon} = \frac{50}{(1.05)^2}, \text{etc.}$$

$$\text{Total present value} = \underbrace{\frac{50}{1.05} + \frac{50}{(1.05)^2} + \cdots + \frac{50}{(1.05)^{10}}}_{\text{coupons}} + \underbrace{\frac{1000}{(1.05)^{10}}}_{\text{principal}}$$
$$= \frac{50}{1.05}\left(1 + \frac{1}{1.05} + \cdots + \frac{1}{(1.05)^9}\right) + \frac{1000}{(1.05)^{10}}$$
$$= \frac{50}{1.05}\left(\frac{1 - \left(\frac{1}{1.05}\right)^{10}}{1 - \frac{1}{1.05}}\right) + \frac{1000}{(1.05)^{10}}$$
$$= 386.087 + 613.913$$
$$= \$1000$$

(b) When the interest rate is 5%, the present value equals the principal.

(c) When the interest rate is more than 5%, the present value is smaller than it is when interest is 5% and must therefore be less than the principal. Since the bond will sell for around its present value, it will sell for less than the principal; hence the description *trading at discount*.

(d) When the interest rate is less than 5%, the present value is more than the principal. Hence the bond will be selling for more than the principal, and is described as *trading at a premium*.

58. The amount of cephalexin in the body is given by $Q(t) = Q_0 e^{-kt}$, where $Q_0 = Q(0)$ and k is a constant. Since the half-life is 0.9 hours,

$$\frac{1}{2} = e^{-0.9k}, \quad k = -\frac{1}{0.9} \ln \frac{1}{2} \approx 0.8.$$

(a) After 6 hours

$$Q = Q_0 e^{-k(6)} \approx Q_0 e^{-0.8(6)} = Q_0(0.01).$$

Thus, the percentage of the cephalexin that remains after 6 hours $\approx 1\%$.

(b)

$$Q_1 = 250$$
$$Q_2 = 250 + 250(0.01)$$
$$Q_3 = 250 + 250(0.01) + 250(0.01)^2$$
$$Q_4 = 250 + 250(0.01) + 250(0.01)^2 + 250(0.01)^3$$

(c)

$$Q_3 = \frac{250(1 - (0.01)^3)}{1 - 0.01}$$
$$\approx 252.5$$
$$Q_4 = \frac{250(1 - (0.01)^4)}{1 - 0.01}$$
$$\approx 252.5$$

Thus, by the time a patient has taken three cephalexin tablets, the quantity of drug in the body has leveled off to 252.5 mg.

(d) Looking at the answers to part (b) shows that

$$Q_n = 250 + 250(0.01) + 250(0.01)^2 + \cdots + 250(0.01)^{n-1}$$
$$= \frac{250(1 - (0.01)^n)}{1 - 0.01}.$$

(e) In the long run, $n \to \infty$. So,

$$Q = \lim_{n \to \infty} Q_n = \frac{250}{1 - 0.01} = 252.5.$$

59. (a) (i) On the night of December 31, 1999:

First deposit will have grown to $2(1.04)^7$ million dollars.
Second deposit will have grown to $2(1.04)^6$ million dollars.
$\cdots$

Most recent deposit (Jan.1, 1999) will have grown to $2(1.04)$ million dollars.

Thus

$$\text{Total amount} = 2(1.04)^7 + 2(1.04)^6 + \cdots + 2(1.04)$$
$$= 2(1.04)\underbrace{(1 + 1.04 + \cdots + (1.04)^6)}_{\text{finite geometric series}}$$
$$= 2(1.04)\left(\frac{1 - (1.04)^7}{1 - 1.04}\right)$$
$$= 16.43 \text{ million dollars.}$$

(ii) Notice that if 10 payments are made, there are 9 years between the first and the last. On the day of the last payment:

First deposit will have grown to $2(1.04)^9$ million dollars.

Second deposit will have grown to $2(1.04)^8$ million dollars.

$\cdots$

Last deposit will be 2 million dollars.

Therefore

$$\text{Total amount} = 2(1.04)^9 + 2(1.04)^8 + \cdots + 2$$
$$= 2\underbrace{(1 + 1.04 + (1.04)^2 + \cdots + (1.04)^9)}_{\text{finite geometric series}}$$
$$= 2\left(\frac{1 - (1.04)^{10}}{1 - 1.04}\right)$$
$$= 24.01 \text{ million dollars.}$$

(b) In part (a) (ii) we found the future value of the contract 9 years in the future. Thus

$$\text{Present Value} = \frac{24.01}{(1.04)^9} = 16.87 \text{ million dollars.}$$

Alternatively, we can calculate the present value of each of the payments separately:

$$\text{Present Value} = 2 + \frac{2}{1.04} + \frac{2}{(1.04)^2} + \cdots + \frac{2}{(1.04)^9}$$
$$= 2\left(\frac{1 - (1/1.04)^{10}}{1 - 1/1.04}\right) = 16.87 \text{ million dollars.}$$

Notice that the present value of the contract ($16.87 million) is considerably less than the face value of the contract, $20 million.

60. A person should expect to pay the present value of the bond on the day it is bought.

$$\text{Present value of first payment} = \frac{10}{1.04}$$
$$\text{Present value of second payment} = \frac{10}{(1.04)^2}, \text{ etc.}$$

Therefore,

$$\text{Total present value} = \frac{10}{1.04} + \frac{10}{(1.04)^2} + \frac{10}{(1.04)^3} + \cdots.$$

This is a geometric series with $a = \frac{10}{1.04}$ and $x = \frac{1}{1.04}$, so

$$\text{Total present value} = \frac{\frac{10}{1.04}}{1 - \frac{1}{1.04}} = \pounds 250.$$

61. (a)

$$\text{Total amount of money deposited} = 100 + 92 + 84.64 + \cdots$$
$$= 100 + 100(0.92) + 100(0.92)^2 + \cdots$$
$$= \frac{100}{1 - 0.92} = 1250 \quad \text{dollars}$$

(b) Credit multiplier $= 1250/100 = 12.50$

The 12.50 is the factor by which the bank has increased its deposits, from $100 to $1250.

62. If the half-life is T hours, then the exponential decay formula $Q = Q_0 e^{-kt}$ gives $k = \ln 2/T$. If we start with $Q_0 = 1$ tablet, then the amount of drug present in the body after $5T$ hours is

$$Q = e^{-5kT} = e^{-5 \ln 2} = 0.03125,$$

so 3.125% of a tablet remains. Thus, immediately after taking the first tablet, there is one tablet in the body. Five half-lives later, this has reduced to $1 \cdot 0.03125 = 0.03125$ tablets, and immediately after the second tablet there are $1 + 0.03125$ tablets in the body. Continuing this forever leads to

$$\text{Number of tablets in body } = 1 + 0.03125 + (0.03125)^2 + \cdots + (0.03125)^n + \cdots.$$

This is an infinite geometric series, with common ratio $x = 0.03125$, and sum $1/(1 - x)$. Thus

$$\text{Number of tablets in body } = \frac{1}{1 - 0.03125} = 1.0323.$$

63. This series converges by the alternating series test, so we can use Theorem 9.9. The nth partial sum of the series is given by

$$S_n = 1 - \frac{1}{6} + \frac{1}{120} - \cdots + \frac{(-1)^{n-1}}{(2n-1)!},$$

so the absolute value of the first term omitted is $1/(2n+1)!$. By Theorem 9.9, we know that the true value of the sum differs from S_n by less than $1/(2n+1)!$. Thus, we want to choose n large enough so that $1/(2n+1)! \leq 0.01$. Substituting $n = 2$ into the expression $1/(2n+1)!$ yields $1/720$ which is less than 0.01, so $S_2 = 1 - (1/6) = 5/6$ approximates the sum to within 0.01 of the actual sum.

64. No. If the series $\displaystyle\sum_{n=1}^{\infty}(-1)^{n-1}a_n$ converges then, using Theorem 9.2, part 3, we have $\displaystyle\lim_{n \to \infty}(-1)^{n-1}a_n = 0$, which cannot happen if $\displaystyle\lim_{n \to \infty} a_n \neq 0$.

65. If $\sum(a_n + b_n)$ converged, then $\sum(a_n + b_n) - \sum a_n = \sum b_n$ would converge by Theorem 9.2. Since we know that $\sum b_n$ does not converge, we conclude that $\sum(a_n + b_n)$ diverges.

66. We have $0 \leq a_n/n \leq a_n$ for all $n \geq 1$. Therefore, since $\sum a_n$ converges, $\sum a_n/n$ converges by the Comparison Test.

67. Since $\sum a_n$ converge, we know that $\lim_{n \to \infty} a_n = 0$. Thus $\lim_{n \to \infty}(1/a_n)$ does not exist, and it follows that $\sum(1/a_n)$ diverges by Property 3 of Theorem 9.2.

68. There is not enough information to determine whether or not na_n converges. To see that this is the case, note that if $a_n = 1/n^2$, then $\sum na_n = \sum(1/n)$, which diverges. However, if $a_n = 1/n^3$ then $\sum na_n = \sum(1/n^2)$, which converges.

69. We have $a_n + (a_n/2) = (3/2)a_n$, so the series $\sum(a_n + a_n/2)$ converges since it is a constant multiple of the convergent series $\sum a_n$.

70. Since $\sum a_n$ converges, we know that $\lim_{n \to \infty} a_n = 0$. Therefore, we can choose a positive integer N large enough so that $|a_n| \leq 1$ for all $n \geq N$, so we have $0 \leq a_n^2 \leq a_n$ for all $n \geq N$. Thus, by Property 2 of Theorem 9.2, $\sum a_n^2$ converges by comparison with the convergent series $\sum a_n$.

71. The series

$$\sum_{n=1}^{\infty} \left(\frac{1}{n} + \frac{1}{n} \right) = \sum_{n=1}^{\infty} \frac{2}{n}$$

diverges by Theorem 9.2 and the fact that $\displaystyle\sum_{n=1}^{\infty} \frac{1}{n}$ diverges.

The series

$$\sum_{n=1}^{\infty} \left(\frac{1}{n} - \frac{1}{n} \right) = \sum_{n=1}^{\infty} 0 = 0$$

converges. But $\displaystyle\sum_{n=1}^{\infty} -\frac{1}{n}$ diverges by Theorem 9.2 and the fact that $\displaystyle\sum_{n=1}^{\infty} \frac{1}{n}$ diverges.

Thus, if $a_n = 1/n$ and $b_n = 1/n$, so that $\sum a_n$ and $\sum b_n$ both diverge, we see that $\sum(a_n + b_n)$ may diverge.

If, on the other hand, $a_n = 1/n$ and $b_n = -1/n$, so that $\sum a_n$ and $\sum b_n$ both diverge, we see that $\sum(a_n + b_n)$ may converge.

Therefore, if $\sum a_n$ and $\sum b_n$ both diverge, we cannot tell whether $\sum(a_n + b_n)$ converges or diverges. Thus the statement is true.

72. We want to estimate $\displaystyle\sum_{k=1}^{100,000} \frac{1}{k}$ using left and right Riemann sum approximations to $f(x) = 1/x$ on the interval $1 \leq x \leq 100{,}000$. Figure 9.9 shows a left Riemann sum approximation with 99,999 terms. Since $f(x)$ is decreasing, the left Riemann sum overestimates the area under the curve. Figure 9.9 shows that the first term in the sum is $f(1) \cdot 1$ and the last is $f(99{,}999) \cdot 1$, so we have

$$\int_{1}^{100,000} \frac{1}{x}\, dx < \text{LHS} = f(1) \cdot 1 + f(2) \cdot 1 + \cdots + f(99{,}999) \cdot 1.$$

Since $f(x) = 1/x$, the left Riemann sum is

$$\text{LHS} = \frac{1}{1} \cdot 1 + \frac{1}{2} \cdot 1 + \cdots + \frac{1}{99{,}999} \cdot 1 = \sum_{k=1}^{99,999} \frac{1}{k},$$

so

$$\int_{1}^{100,000} \frac{1}{x}\, dx < \sum_{k=1}^{99,999} \frac{1}{k}.$$

Since we want the sum to go $k = 100{,}000$ rather than $k = 99{,}999$, we add $1/100{,}000$ to both sides:

$$\int_{1}^{100,000} \frac{1}{x}\, dx + \frac{1}{100{,}000} < \sum_{k=1}^{99,999} \frac{1}{k} + \frac{1}{100{,}000} = \sum_{k=1}^{100,000} \frac{1}{k}.$$

The left Riemann sum has therefore given us an underestimate for our sum. We now use the right Riemann sum in Figure 9.10 to get an overestimate for our sum.

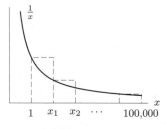

Figure 9.9

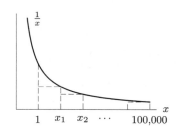

Figure 9.10

The right Riemann sum again has 99,999 terms, but this time the sum underestimates the area under the curve. Figure 9.10 shows that the first rectangle has area $f(2) \cdot 1$ and the last $f(100{,}000) \cdot 1$, so we have

$$\text{RHS} = f(2) \cdot 1 + f(3) \cdot 1 + \cdots + f(100{,}000) \cdot 1 < \int_{1}^{100,000} \frac{1}{x}\, dx.$$

Since $f(x) = 1/x$, the right Riemann sum is

$$\text{RHS} = \frac{1}{2} \cdot 1 + \frac{1}{3} \cdot 1 + \cdots + \frac{1}{100{,}000} \cdot 1 = \sum_{k=2}^{100,000} \frac{1}{k}.$$

So

$$\sum_{k=2}^{100,000} \frac{1}{k} < \int_{1}^{100,000} \frac{1}{x}\, dx.$$

Since we want the sum to start at $k = 1$, we add 1 to both sides:

$$\sum_{k=1}^{100,000} \frac{1}{k} = \frac{1}{1} + \sum_{k=2}^{100,000} \frac{1}{k} < 1 + \int_{1}^{100,000} \frac{1}{x}\, dx.$$

Putting these under- and overestimates together, we have

$$\int_1^{100,000} \frac{1}{x}\,dx + \frac{1}{100,000} < \sum_{k=1}^{100,000} \frac{1}{k} < 1 + \int_1^{100,000} \frac{1}{x}\,dx.$$

Since $\int_1^{100,000} \frac{1}{x}\,dx = \ln 100,000 - \ln 1 = 11.513$, we have

$$11.513 < \sum_{k=1}^{100,000} \frac{1}{k} < 12.513.$$

Therefore we have $\displaystyle\sum_{k=1}^{100,000} \frac{1}{k} \approx 12$.

73. Using a right-hand sum, we have

$$\frac{1}{2} + \frac{1}{3} + \frac{1}{4} + \cdots + \frac{1}{n} < \int_1^n \frac{dx}{x} = \ln n.$$

If a computer could add a million terms in one second, then it could add

$$60\,\frac{\text{sec}}{\text{min}} \cdot 60\,\frac{\text{min}}{\text{hour}} \cdot 24\,\frac{\text{hour}}{\text{day}} \cdot 365\,\frac{\text{days}}{\text{year}} \cdot 1\text{ million}\,\frac{\text{terms}}{\text{sec}}$$

terms per year. Thus,

$$1 + \frac{1}{2} + \frac{1}{3} \cdots + \frac{1}{n} < 1 + \ln n = 1 + \ln(60 \cdot 60 \cdot 24 \cdot 365 \cdot 10^6) \approx 32.082 < 33.$$

So the sum after one year is about 32.

74. The argument is false. Property 1 of Theorem 9.2 only applies to convergent series. In addition, by the limits comparison test with $b_n = 1/n^2$, the series converges.

CHECK YOUR UNDERSTANDING

1. False. The first 1000 terms could be the same for two different sequences and yet one sequence converges and the other diverges. For example, $s_n = 0$ for all n is a convergent sequence, but

$$t_n = \begin{cases} 0 & \text{if } n \leq 1000 \\ n & \text{if } n > 1000 \end{cases}$$

is a divergent sequence.

2. False. The limit could be zero. For example, $s_n = 1/n$ is a convergent sequence of positive terms and $\lim_{n \to \infty} s_n = 0$.

3. True. If there is no term greater than a million, then the sequence is bounded by $0 < s_n < 10^6$ for all n.

4. True. If there is only a finite number of terms greater than a million, then we can choose the largest of them to be an upper bound M for the sequence. Thus the sequence is bounded by $0 < s_n \leq M$ for all n.

5. False. The terms s_n tend to the limit of the sequence which may not be zero. For example, $s_n = 1 + 1/n$ is a convergent sequence and s_n tends to 1 as n increases.

6. True. The definition of convergence of a series is that its partial sums are a convergent sequence.

7. False. For example the sequence $-2, -1, 0, 1, 2, 3, \ldots$ with $s_n = n - 3$ is monotone increasing and has both positive and negative terms.

8. True. If a monotone sequence does not converge, then it is unbounded. If moreover the sequence contains only positive terms then it is bounded below by zero. Thus it is not bounded above, and in particular it is not bounded above by a million.

9. False. The sequence $-1, 1, -1, 1, \ldots$ given by $s_n = (-1)^n$ alternates in sign but does not converge.

10. False. The decreasing sequence $-1, -2, -3, \ldots$ has all terms less than a million, but it has no lower bound. Thus it is unbounded.

11. True. A geometric series, $a + ax + ax^2 + \cdots$, is a power series about $x = 0$ with all coefficients equal to a.

12. False. Writing out terms, we have

$$(x - 1) + (x - 2)^2 + (x - 3)^3 + \cdots.$$

A power series is a sum of powers of $(x - a)$ for constant a. In this case, the value of a changes from term to term, so it is not a power series.

13. True. This power series has an interval of convergence about $x = 0$. If the power series converges for $x = 2$, the radius of convergence is 2 or more. Thus, $x = 1$ is well within the interval of convergence, so the series converges at $x = 1$.

14. False. This power series has an interval of convergence about $x = 0$. Knowing the power series converges for $x = 1$ does not tell us whether the series converges for $x = 2$. Since the series converges at $x = 1$, we know the radius of convergence is at least 1. However, we do not know whether the interval of convergence extends as far as $x = 2$, so we cannot say whether the series converges at $x = 2$.

    For example, $\sum \dfrac{x^n}{2^n}$ converges for $x = 1$ (it is a geometric series with ratio of $1/2$), but does not converge for $x = 2$ (the terms do not go to 0).

    Since this statement is not true for all C_n, the statement is false.

15. True. This power series has an interval of convergence centered on $x = 0$. If the power series does not converge for $x = 1$, then the radius of convergence is less than or equal to 1. Thus, $x = 2$ lies outside the interval of convergence, so the series does not converge there.

16. False. It does not tell us anything to know that b_n is larger than a convergent series. For example, if $a_n = 1/n^2$ and $b_n = 1$, then $0 \le a_n \le b_n$ and $\sum a_n$ converges, but $\sum b_n$ diverges. Since this statement is not true for all a_n and b_n, the statement is false.

17. True. This is one of the statements of the comparison test.

18. True. Consider the series $\sum(-b_n)$ and $\sum(-a_n)$. The series $\sum(-b_n)$ converges, since $\sum b_n$ converges, and

$$0 \le -a_n \le -b_n.$$

By the comparison test, $\sum(-a_n)$ converges, so $\sum a_n$ converges.

19. False. It is true that if $\sum |a_n|$ converges, then we know that $\sum a_n$ converges. However, knowing that $\sum a_n$ converges does *not* tell us that $\sum |a_n|$ converges.

    For example, if $a_n = (-1)^{n-1}/n$, then $\sum a_n$ converges by the alternating series test. However, $\sum |a_n|$ is the harmonic series which diverges.

20. False. For example, if $a_n = 1/n$ and $b_n = -1/n$, then $|a_n + b_n| = 0$, so $\sum |a_n + b_n|$ converges. However $\sum |a_n|$ and $\sum |b_n|$ are the harmonic series, which diverge.

21. False. For example, if $a_n = 1/n^2$, then

$$\lim_{n \to \infty} \frac{|a_{n+1}|}{|a_n|} = \lim_{n \to \infty} \frac{1/(n+1)^2}{1/n^2} = \lim_{n \to \infty} \frac{n^2}{(n+1)^2} = 1.$$

However, $\sum 1/n^2$ converges.

22. False, since if we write out the terms of the series, using the fact that $\cos 0 = 1, \cos \pi = -1, \cos(2\pi) = 1, \cos(3\pi) = -1$, and so on, we have

$$(-1)^0 \cos 0 + (-1)^1 \cos \pi + (-1)^2 \cos 2\pi + (-1)^3 \cos 3\pi + \cdots$$
$$= (1)(1) + (-1)(-1) + (1)(1) + (-1)(-1) + \cdots$$
$$= 1 + 1 + 1 + 1 + \cdots.$$

This is not an alternating series.

23. True. Writing out the terms of this series, we have

$$(1 + (-1)^1) + (1 + (-1)^2) + (1 + (-1)^3) + (1 + (-1)^4) + \cdots$$
$$= (1 - 1) + (1 + 1) + (1 - 1) + (1 + 1) + \cdots$$
$$= 0 + 2 + 0 + 2 + \cdots.$$

24. False. This is an alternating series, but since the terms do not go to zero, it does not converge.

25. False. The terms in the series do not go to zero:

$$2^{(-1)^1} + 2^{(-1)^2} + 2^{(-1)^3} + 2^{(-1)^4} + 2^{(-1)^5} + \cdots = 2^{-1} + 2^1 + 2^{-1} + 2^1 + 2^{-1} + \cdots$$
$$= 1/2 + 2 + 1/2 + 2 + 1/2 + \cdots.$$

26. False. For example, if $a_n = (-1)^{n-1}/n$, then $\sum a_n$ converges by the alternating series test. But $(-1)^n a_n = (-1)^n (-1)^{n-1}/n = (-1)^{2n-1}/n = -1/n$. Thus, $\sum (-1)^n a_n$ is the negative of the harmonic series and does not converge.

27. This is true. It is a restatement of Theorem 9.9.

28. This statement is false. The statement is true if the series converges by the alternating series test, but not in general. Consider, for example, the alternating series

$$S = 10 - 0.01 + 0.8 - 0.7 - 0 + 0 - 0 + \cdots.$$

Since the later terms are all 0, we can find the sum exactly:

$$S = 10.69.$$

If we approximated the sum by the first term, $S_1 = 10$, the magnitude of the first term omitted would be 0.01. Thus, if the statement in this problem were true, we would say that the true value of the sum lay between $10 + 0.01 = 10.01$ and $10 - 0.01 = 9.99$ which it does not.

29. True. Let $c_n = (-1)^n |a_n|$. Then $|c_n| = |a_n|$ so $\sum |c_n|$ converges, and therefore $\sum c_n = \sum (-1)^n |a_n|$ converges.

30. True. Since the series is alternating, Theorem 9.9 gives the error bound. Summing the first 100 terms gives S_{100}, and if the true sum is S,

$$|S - S_{100}| < a_{101} = \frac{1}{101} < 0.01.$$

31. True. The radius of convergence, R, is given by $\lim_{n \to \infty} |C_{n+1}|/|C_n| = 1/R$, if this limit exists, and since these series have the same coefficients, C_n, the radii of convergence are the same.

32. False. Two series can have the same radius of convergence without having the same coefficients. For example, $\sum x^n$ and $\sum n x^n$ both have radius of convergence of 1:

$$\lim_{n \to \infty} \frac{C_{n+1}}{C_n} = \lim_{n \to \infty} \frac{1}{1} = 1 \quad \text{and} \quad \lim_{n \to \infty} \frac{B_{n+1}}{B_n} = \lim_{n \to \infty} \frac{n+1}{n} = 1.$$

33. True. If the terms do not tend to zero, the partial sums do not tend to a limit. For example, if the terms are all greater than 0.1, the partial sums will grow without bound.

34. False. Consider the series $\sum_{n=1}^{\infty} 1/n$. This series does not converge, but $1/n \to 0$ as $n \to \infty$.

35. False. If $a_n = b_n = 1/n$, then $\sum a_n$ and $\sum b_n$ do not converge. However, $a_n b_n = 1/n^2$, so $\sum a_n b_n$ does converge.

36. False. If $a_n b_n = 1/n^2$ and $a_n = b_n = 1/n$, then $\sum a_n b_n$ converges, but $\sum a_n$ and $\sum b_n$ do not converge.

37. True. If $\sum |a_n|$ is convergent, then so is $\sum a_n$.

38. False. The alternating harmonic series $\sum \frac{(-1)^n}{n}$ is conditionally convergent because it converges by the Alternating Series test, but the harmonic series $\sum \left| \frac{(-1)^n}{n} \right| = \sum \frac{1}{n}$ is divergent. The alternating harmonic series is not absolutely convergent.

39. False. There are power series, such as $\sum x^n/n$, which converge at one endpoint, -1, but not at the other, 1.

40. True. By the comparison test, if $\sum a_n$ is larger term-by-term than a divergent series, then $\sum a_n$ diverges. If $\sum b_n$ diverges, then so does $\sum 0.5 b_n$.

41. True. The power series $\sum C_n (x - a)^n$ converges at $x = a$.

42. True. Since the power series converges at $x = 10$, the radius of convergence is at least 10. Thus, $x = -9$ must be within the interval of convergence.

43. False. If $\sum C_n x^n$ converges at $x = 10$, the radius of convergence is at least 10. However, if the radius of convergence were exactly 10, then $x = 10$ is the endpoint of the interval of convergence and convergence there does not guarantee convergence at the other endpoint.

44. True. Intervals of convergence can be of any length and centered at any point and can include one endpoint and not the other.

45. False. The interval of convergence of $\sum C_n x^n$ is centered at the origin.

46. True. The interval of convergence is centered on $x = a$, so $a = (-11 + 1)/2 = -5$.

PROJECTS FOR CHAPTER NINE

1. (a) To show f is decreasing for $x > 1$, we look at $f'(x)$:

$$f'(x) = n(n + 1)x^{n-1} - n(n + 1)x^n = n(n + 1)x^{n-1}(1 - x).$$

Thus, for $x > 1$, we have $f'(x) < 0$, so f is decreasing. Since $f(1) = 1$, this means $f(x) < 1$ for $x > 1$. Factoring x^n out of $f(x)$, we get

$$f(x) = (n + 1)x^n - nx^{n+1} = x^n(n + 1 - nx) < 1.$$

(b) We simplify the value of x

$$x = \frac{1 + 1/n}{1 + 1/(n + 1)} = \frac{(n + 1)/n}{(n + 2)/(n + 1)} = \frac{(n + 1)^2}{n(n + 2)}.$$

Before substituting into $x^n(n + 1 - nx) < 1$, we calculate

$$
\begin{aligned}
n + 1 - nx &= n + 1 - n\frac{(n + 1)^2}{n(n + 2)} \\
&= \frac{(n + 1)(n + 2) - (n + 1)^2}{n + 2} \\
&= \frac{(n + 1)(n + 2 - (n + 1))}{n + 2} = \frac{n + 1}{n + 2}.
\end{aligned}
$$

Thus, substituting into the inequality from part (a), $x^n(n + 1 - nx) < 1$, gives

$$x^n\left(\frac{n + 1}{n + 2}\right) < 1.$$

(c) We want to show $s_n < s_{n+1}$. Since $s_n = (1 + 1/n)^n$ and $s_{n+1} = (1 + 1/(n + 1))^{n+1}$, using the definition of x, we have

$$
\begin{aligned}
\frac{s_n}{s_{n+1}} &= \frac{(1 + 1/n)^n}{(1 + 1/(n + 1))^n} \cdot \frac{1}{(1 + 1/(n + 1))} \\
&= x^n\left(\frac{n + 1}{n + 2}\right).
\end{aligned}
$$

Thus, by part (b), we have

$$\frac{s_n}{s_{n+1}} = x^n\left(\frac{n + 1}{n + 2}\right) < 1,$$

so

$$s_n < s_{n+1}.$$

Thus, the sequence is increasing.

(d) Substituting $x = 1 + 1/2n$ into the inequality from part (a) gives

$$\left(1 + \frac{1}{2n}\right)^n \left(n + 1 - n\left(1 + \frac{1}{2n}\right)\right) = \left(1 + \frac{1}{2n}\right)^n \left(1 - \frac{1}{2}\right) = \frac{1}{2}\left(1 + \frac{1}{2n}\right)^n < 1.$$

Thus

$$\left(1 + \frac{1}{2n}\right)^n < 2.$$

(e) When we square this inequality, we get

$$\left(1 + \frac{1}{2n}\right)^{2n} < 4,$$

that is, for all n

$$s_{2n} < 4.$$

Thus, the even terms are bounded above by 4. Because we have shown the sequence is increasing, for each odd term, we have

$$s_{2n-1} < s_{2n} < 4,$$

so the odd terms are also bounded above by 4. Since all terms are bounded below by 0, the sequence is bounded.

(f) From parts (c) and (e), we know that the sequence is increasing and bounded, and therefore, by Theorem 9.1, it has a limit.

2. (a) **(i)** p^2

(ii) There are two ways to do this. One way is to compute your opponent's probability of winning two in a row, which is $(1 - p)^2$. Then the probability that neither of you win the next points is:

$$1 - (\text{Probability you win next two} + \text{Probability opponent wins next two})$$
$$= 1 - (p^2 + (1 - p)^2)$$
$$= 1 - (p^2 + 1 - 2p + p^2)$$
$$= 2p^2 - 2p$$
$$= 2p(1 - p).$$

The other way to compute this is to observe either you win the first point and lose the second or vice versa. Both have probability $p(1 - p)$, so the probability you split the points is $2p(1 - p)$.

(iii)

$$\text{Probability} = (\text{Probability of splitting next two}) \cdot (\text{Probability of winning two after that})$$
$$= 2p(1 - p)p^2$$

(iv)

$$\text{Probability} = (\text{Probability of winning next two}) + (\text{Probability of splitting next two,}$$
$$\text{winning two after that})$$
$$= p^2 + 2p(1 - p)p^2$$

(v) The probability is:

$$w = (\text{Probability of winning first two})$$
$$+ (\text{Probability of splitting first two}) \cdot (\text{Probability of winning next two})$$
$$+ (\text{Prob. of split. first two}) \cdot (\text{Prob. of split. next two}) \cdot (\text{Prob. of winning next two})$$
$$+ \cdots$$
$$= p^2 + 2p(1 - p)p^2 + (2p(1 - p))^2 p^2 + \cdots.$$

This is an infinite geometric series with a first term of p^2 and a ratio of $2p(1 - p)$. Therefore the probability of winning is

$$w = \frac{p^2}{1 - 2p(1 - p)}.$$

(vi) For $p = 0.5$, $w = \frac{(0.5)^2}{1 - 2(0.5)(1 - (0.5))} = 0.5$. This is what we would expect. If you and your opponent are equally likely to score the next point, you and your opponent are equally likely to win the next game.

For $p = 0.6$, $w = \frac{(0.6)^2}{1 - 2(0.6)(0.4)} = 0.69$. Here your probability of winning the next point has been magnified to a probability 0.69 of winning the game. Thus it gives the better player an advantage to have to win by two points, rather than the "sudden death" of winning by just one point. This makes sense: when you have to win by two, the stronger player always gets a second chance to overcome the weaker player's winning the first point on a "fluke."

For $p = 0.7$, $w = \frac{(0.7)^2}{1 - 2(0.7)(0.3)} = 0.84$. Again, the stronger player's probability of winning is magnified.

For $p = 0.4$, $w = \frac{(0.4)^2}{1 - 2(0.4)(0.6)} = 0.31$. We already computed that for $p = 0.6$, $w = 0.69$. Thus the value for w when $p = 0.4$, should be the same as the probability of your opponent winning for $p = 0.6$, namely $1 - 0.69 = 0.31$.

(b) (i)

$S =$ (Prob. you score first point)

  $+$(Prob. you lose first point, your opponent loses the next,

  you win the next)

  $+$(Prob. you lose a point, opponent loses, you lose,

  opponent loses, you win)

  $+ \cdots$

$=$ (Prob. you score first point)

  $+$(Prob. you lose)·(Prob. opponent loses)·(Prob. you win)

  $+$(Prob. you lose)·(Prob. opponent loses)·(Prob. you lose)

  ·(Prob. opponent loses)·(Prob. you win)$+ \cdots$

$= p + (1 - p)(1 - q)p + ((1 - p)(1 - q))^2 p + \cdots$

$= \dfrac{p}{1 - (1 - p)(1 - q)}$

(ii) Since S is your probability of winning the next point, we can use the formula computed in part (v) of (a) for winning two points in a row, thereby winning the game:

$$w = \frac{S^2}{1 - 2S(1 - S)}.$$

- When $p = 0.5$ and $q = 0.5$,

$$S = \frac{0.5}{1 - (0.5)(0.5)} = 0.67.$$

Therefore

$$w = \frac{S^2}{1 - 2S(1 - S)} = \frac{(0.67)^2}{1 - 2(0.67)(1 - 0.67)} = 0.80.$$

- When $p = 0.6$ and $q = 0.5$,

$$S = \frac{0.6}{1 - (0.4)(0.5)} = 0.75 \quad \text{and} \quad w = \frac{(0.75)^2}{1 - 2(0.75)(1 - 0.75)} = 0.9.$$

3. (a) Let k by the relative rate of decay, per minute, of quinine. Since quinine's half-life is 11.5 hours, we have

$$\frac{1}{2} = e^{-k(11.5)(60)},$$

so

$$k = \frac{\ln 2}{(11.5)(60)} \approx 0.001.$$

Hence, $k = 0.1\%/\text{min}$.

(b) Just prior to 8 am of the first day the patient has no quinine in her body. Assuming the drug mixes rapidly in the patient's body, she has about $50/70 \approx 0.714$ mg/kg of the drug soon after 8 am. Suppose we represent the concentration of quinine in the patient (in mg/kg) by x and represent time since 8 am (in minutes) by t. Then

$$x = Ae^{-0.001t},$$

where A is the initial concentration and $k = -0.001$ is the rate at which quinine is metabolized per minute. There are $24 \cdot 60 = 1440$ minutes in a day. On the first day, the patient begins with 0.714 mg/kg in her system, so just before 8 am of the second day the patient's system holds

$$0.714e^{-0.001 \cdot 1440} \approx 0.169 \text{ mg/kg}.$$

After the patient's second dose of quinine, her system contains $0.714 + 0.169 = 0.883$ mg/kg of quinine.

(c) By continuing in a similar manner, we see that just prior to 8 am on the third day, she has $0.883e^{-0.001 \cdot 1440} \approx 0.209$ mg/kg; just after 8 am, she has $0.209 + 0.714 = 0.923$ mg/kg. Just prior to 8 am on the fourth day, she has $0.923e^{-0.001 \cdot 1440} \approx 0.218$ mg/kg; just after 8 am, she has $0.228 + 0.714 = 0.932$ mg/kg. We can keep going with these calculations: just prior to 8 am on the fifth day, the concentration is 0.221 mg/kg; on the sixth day, it is 0.222 mg/kg; on the seventh day, it is 0.222 mg/kg, and so on forever.

We find a formula for the concentration just after the nth dose as follows. The last dose contributes 0.714 mg/kg. The previous dose contributes $0.714e^{-0.001(1440)}$ mg/kg. The dose before that contributes $0.714e^{-0.001(2)(1440)}$ mg/kg, and so on, back to $0.714e^{-0.001(n-1)(1440)}$ mg/kg from the initial dose. So

$$\begin{array}{c}\text{Concentration just}\\\text{after } n \text{ doses}\end{array} = 0.714 + 0.714e^{-1.44} + 0.714\left(e^{-1.44}\right)^2 + \cdots + 0.714\left(e^{-1.44}\right)^{n-1}.$$

We notice that this is a geometric series, with sum given by

$$\begin{array}{c}\text{Concentration just}\\\text{after } n \text{ doses}\end{array} = 0.714\left(\frac{1 - e^{-1.44n}}{1 - e^{-1.44}}\right) = 0.936(1 - e^{-1.44n}).$$

Although the concentration of quinine does not reach an equilibrium it does fall into a steady-state pattern which repeats over and over again. This makes sense; at some point the patient must metabolize the daily dosage exactly. If we let $n \to \infty$ in our formula, we have $e^{-1.44n} \to 0$, which means that the concentration just after the nth dose gets very close to 0.936. So the concentration just before the nth dose is $0.936 - 0.714 = 0.222$, as we found in our calculations for the first few days.

(d)

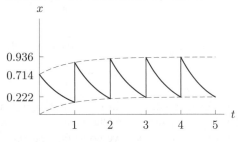

Figure 9.11

If we keep setting the clock back to 0 minutes each day at 8 am, then we have that at $t = 0$ each day, the concentration (starting on the fifth day or so) is 0.936 mg/kg. As the day progresses, we have

$$x = 0.936e^{-0.001 \cdot t}.$$

(e) The average concentration of quinine in the patient is given by the integral of the concentration over a day, divided by the time in a day:

$$\text{Average concentration} = \frac{1}{1440} \int_0^{1440} x\, dt = \frac{1}{1440} \int_0^{1440} 0.936 e^{-0.001t}\, dt$$

$$= \frac{0.936}{1440} \left(\frac{-e^{-0.001t}}{0.001} \right) \Big|_0^{1440} = \frac{0.936}{1.44}(1 - e^{-1.44})$$

$$\approx 0.496 \text{ mg/kg}.$$

(f) Since the average concentration is 0.496 mg/kg and the minimum effective average concentration is 0.4 mg/kg, this treatment is effective. It is also safe—the highest concentration (0.936 mg/kg, achieved shortly after 8 am) is less than the toxic concentration of 3.0 mg/kg.

(g) Each dose of 25 mg corresponds to $25/70 = 0.357$ mg/kg. Let x_s be the steady-state concentration just before each 0.357 mg/kg dose. Then $x_s + 0.357$ will be the concentration just after the dose. Since we are in a steady-state, this concentration decays to exactly x_s just before the next dose. So

$$x_s = (x_s + 0.357)e^{-0.001(12)(60)}.$$

This means

$$x_s = \frac{0.357 e^{-0.001(12)(60)}}{1 - e^{-0.001(12)(60)}} \approx 0.339 \text{ mg/kg},$$

so $x_s + 0.357 = 0.696$ mg/kg is the concentration just after each dose. At t minutes after a dose, for $0 \le t \le (12)(60)$, there is a steady-state concentration of

$$x = 0.696 e^{-0.001t} \text{ mg/kg}.$$

This means

$$\text{Average concentration} = \frac{1}{720} \int_0^{720} x\, dt \approx \frac{1}{720} \int_0^{720} 0.696 e^{-0.001t}\, dt$$

$$= \frac{0.696}{720} \left[\frac{-e^{-0.001t}}{0.001} \right] \Big|_0^{720} = \frac{0.696}{0.72}[1 - 0.487]$$

$$\approx 0.496 \text{ mg/kg}.$$

This treatment is also effective and safe. The average concentration of 0.496 mg/kg is greater than 0.4 mg/kg, and the highest concentration of 0.696 mg/kg is less than 3 mg/kg.

(h) For an exponentially decaying function, the average value between two points (x_0, y_0) and (x_1, y_1) is $\frac{(y_0 - y_1)}{(x_1 - x_0)r}$, where r is the relative rate of decay and A_0 is the initial concentration. The reason is as follows.

$$\text{Average} = \frac{1}{x_1 - x_0} \int_{x_0}^{x_1} A_0 e^{-rt}\, dt$$

$$= \frac{A_0}{x_1 - x_0} \left[\frac{e^{-rt}}{r} \right] \Big|_{x_0}^{x_1}$$

$$= \frac{y_0 - y_1}{(x_1 - x_0) \cdot r}$$

(i) Since a steady state has been reached, y_0 is the concentration right after a dose and y_1 is the concentration just prior to a dose. Thus, $y_0 - y_1$ represents the increase in concentration from each dose. Furthermore, $x_1 - x_0$ is the time between doses. When we go to the new protocol, we halve both the numerator and the denominator of the equation for the average concentration, and so the average remains unchanged. Similarly, if we were to double the dose to 100 mg and give it every 48 hours we would simply be doubling both the numerator and the denominator; again the average concentration would not change.

(j) We want the final concentration to be 10^{-10} kg/kg $= 10^{-4}$ mg/kg. We therefore need to solve for t in $10^{-4} = 0.883 \cdot e^{-0.001 \cdot t}$. Doing so yields $t \approx 9086$ min ≈ 6.3 days.

CHAPTER TEN

Solutions for Section 10.1

Exercises

1. Let $f(x) = \dfrac{1}{1-x} = (1-x)^{-1}$. Then $f(0) = 1$.

$$
\begin{aligned}
f'(x) &= 1!(1-x)^{-2} & f'(0) &= 1!, \\
f''(x) &= 2!(1-x)^{-3} & f''(0) &= 2!, \\
f'''(x) &= 3!(1-x)^{-4} & f'''(0) &= 3!, \\
f^{(4)}(x) &= 4!(1-x)^{-5} & f^{(4)}(0) &= 4!, \\
f^{(5)}(x) &= 5!(1-x)^{-6} & f^{(5)}(0) &= 5!, \\
f^{(6)}(x) &= 6!(1-x)^{-7} & f^{(6)}(0) &= 6!, \\
f^{(7)}(x) &= 7!(1-x)^{-8} & f^{(7)}(0) &= 7!.
\end{aligned}
$$

$$
\begin{aligned}
P_3(x) &= 1 + x + x^2 + x^3, \\
P_5(x) &= 1 + x + x^2 + x^3 + x^4 + x^5, \\
P_7(x) &= 1 + x + x^2 + x^3 + x^4 + x^5 + x^6 + x^7.
\end{aligned}
$$

2. Let $\dfrac{1}{1+x} = (1+x)^{-1}$. Then $f(0) = 1$.

$$
\begin{aligned}
f'(x) &= -1!(1+x)^{-2} & f'(0) &= -1, \\
f''(x) &= 2!(1+x)^{-3} & f''(0) &= 2!, \\
f'''(x) &= -3!(1+x)^{-4} & f'''(0) &= -3!, \\
f^{(4)}(x) &= 4!(1+x)^{-5} & f^{(4)}(0) &= 4!, \\
f^{(5)}(x) &= -5!(1+x)^{-6} & f^{(5)}(0) &= -5!, \\
f^{(6)}(x) &= 6!(1+x)^{-7} & f^{(6)}(0) &= 6!, \\
f^{(7)}(x) &= -7!(1+x)^{-8} & f^{(7)}(0) &= -7!, \\
f^{(8)}(x) &= 8!(1+x)^{-9} & f^{(8)}(0) &= 8!.
\end{aligned}
$$

$$
\begin{aligned}
P_4(x) &= 1 - x + x^2 - x^3 + x^4, \\
P_6(x) &= 1 - x + x^2 - x^3 + x^4 - x^5 + x^6, \\
P_8(x) &= 1 - x + x^2 - x^3 + x^4 - x^5 + x^6 - x^7 + x^8.
\end{aligned}
$$

3. Let $f(x) = \sqrt{1+x} = (1+x)^{1/2}$. Then $f(0) = 1$, and

$$
\begin{aligned}
f'(x) &= \tfrac{1}{2}(1+x)^{-1/2} & f'(0) &= \tfrac{1}{2}, \\
f''(x) &= -\tfrac{1}{4}(1+x)^{-3/2} & f''(0) &= -\tfrac{1}{4}, \\
f'''(x) &= \tfrac{3}{8}(1+x)^{-5/2} & f'''(0) &= \tfrac{3}{8}, \\
f^{(4)}(x) &= -\tfrac{15}{16}(1+x)^{-7/2} & f^{(4)}(0) &= -\tfrac{15}{16}.
\end{aligned}
$$

Thus,

$$
\begin{aligned}
P_2(x) &= 1 + \frac{1}{2}x - \frac{1}{8}x^2, \\
P_3(x) &= 1 + \frac{1}{2}x - \frac{1}{8}x^2 + \frac{1}{16}x^3, \\
P_4(x) &= 1 + \frac{1}{2}x - \frac{1}{8}x^2 + \frac{1}{16}x^3 - \frac{5}{128}x^4.
\end{aligned}
$$

4. Let $f(x) = \sqrt[3]{1-x} = (1-x)^{1/3}$. Then $f(0) = 1$, and

$$
\begin{aligned}
f'(x) &= -\tfrac{1}{3}(1-x)^{-2/3} & f'(0) &= -\tfrac{1}{3}, \\
f''(x) &= -\tfrac{2}{3^2}(1-x)^{-5/3} & f''(0) &= -\tfrac{2}{3^2}, \\
f'''(x) &= -\tfrac{10}{3^3}(1-x)^{-8/3} & f'''(0) &= -\tfrac{10}{3^3}, \\
f^{(4)}(x) &= -\tfrac{80}{3^4}(1-x)^{-11/3} & f^{(4)}(0) &= -\tfrac{80}{3^4}.
\end{aligned}
$$

Then,

$$
\begin{aligned}
P_2(x) &= 1 - \frac{1}{3}x - \frac{1}{2!}\frac{2}{3^2}x^2 = 1 - \frac{1}{3}x - \frac{1}{9}x^2, \\
P_3(x) &= P_2(x) - \frac{1}{3!}\left(\frac{10}{3^3}\right)x^3 = 1 - \frac{1}{3}x - \frac{1}{9}x^2 - \frac{5}{81}x^3, \\
P_4(x) &= P_3(x) - \frac{1}{4!}\frac{80}{3^4}x^4 = 1 - \frac{1}{3}x - \frac{1}{9}x^2 - \frac{5}{81}x^3 - \frac{10}{243}x^4.
\end{aligned}
$$

5. Let $f(x) = \cos x$. Then $f(0) = \cos(0) = 1$, and

$$
\begin{aligned}
f'(x) &= -\sin x & f'(0) &= 0, \\
f''(x) &= -\cos x & f''(0) &= -1, \\
f'''(x) &= \sin x & f'''(0) &= 0, \\
f^{(4)}(x) &= \cos x & f^{(4)}(0) &= 1, \\
f^{(5)}(x) &= -\sin x & f^{(5)}(0) &= 0, \\
f^{(6)}(x) &= -\cos x & f^{(6)}(0) &= -1.
\end{aligned}
$$

Thus,

$$
\begin{aligned}
P_2(x) &= 1 - \frac{x^2}{2!}, \\
P_4(x) &= 1 - \frac{x^2}{2!} + \frac{x^4}{4!}, \\
P_6(x) &= 1 - \frac{x^2}{2!} + \frac{x^4}{4!} - \frac{x^6}{6!}.
\end{aligned}
$$

6. Let $f(x) = \ln(1+x)$. Then $f(0) = \ln 1 = 0$, and

$$
\begin{aligned}
f'(x) &= (1+x)^{-1} & f'(0) &= 1, \\
f''(x) &= (-1)(1+x)^{-2} & f''(0) &= -1, \\
f'''(x) &= 2(1+x)^{-3} & f'''(0) &= 2, \\
f^{(4)}(x) &= -3!(1+x)^{-4} & f^{(4)}(0) &= -3!, \\
f^{(5)}(x) &= 4!(1+x)^{-5} & f^{(5)}(0) &= 4!, \\
f^{(6)}(x) &= -5!(1+x)^{-6} & f^{(6)}(0) &= -5!, \\
f^{(7)}(x) &= 6!(1+x)^{-7} & f^{(7)}(0) &= 6!, \\
f^{(8)}(x) &= -7!(1+x)^{-8} & f^{(8)}(0) &= -7!, \\
f^{(9)}(x) &= 8!(1+x)^{-9} & f^{(9)}(0) &= 8!.
\end{aligned}
$$

So,

$$
\begin{aligned}
P_5(x) &= x - \frac{x^2}{2} + \frac{x^3}{3} - \frac{x^4}{4} + \frac{x^5}{5}, \\
P_7(x) &= x - \frac{x^2}{2} + \frac{x^3}{3} - \frac{x^4}{4} + \frac{x^5}{5} - \frac{x^6}{6} + \frac{x^7}{7}, \\
P_9(x) &= x - \frac{x^2}{2} + \frac{x^3}{3} - \frac{x^4}{4} + \frac{x^5}{5} - \frac{x^6}{6} + \frac{x^7}{7} - \frac{x^8}{8} + \frac{x^9}{9}.
\end{aligned}
$$

7. Let $f(x) = \arctan x$. Then $f(0) = \arctan 0 = 0$, and

$$
\begin{aligned}
f'(x) &= 1/(1+x^2) = (1+x^2)^{-1} & f'(0) &= 1, \\
f''(x) &= (-1)(1+x^2)^{-2}2x & f''(0) &= 0, \\
f'''(x) &= 2!(1+x^2)^{-3}2^2x^2 + (-1)(1+x^2)^{-2}2 & f'''(0) &= -2, \\
f^{(4)}(x) &= -3!(1+x^2)^{-4}2^3x^3 + 2!(1+x^2)^{-3}2^3x & \\
&\quad + 2!(1+x^2)^{-3}2^2x & f^{(4)}(0) &= 0.
\end{aligned}
$$

Therefore,

$$
P_3(x) = P_4(x) = x - \frac{1}{3}x^3.
$$

8. Let $f(x) = \tan x$. So $f(0) = \tan 0 = 0$, and

$$
\begin{aligned}
f'(x) &= 1/\cos^2 x & f'(0) &= 1, \\
f''(x) &= 2\sin x/\cos^3 x & f''(0) &= 0, \\
f'''(x) &= (2/\cos^2 x) + (6\sin^2 x/\cos^4 x) & f'''(0) &= 2, \\
f^{(4)}(x) &= (16\sin x/\cos^3 x) + (24\sin^3 x/\cos^5 x) & f^{(4)}(0) &= 0.
\end{aligned}
$$

Thus,

$$
P_3(x) = P_4(x) = x + \frac{x^3}{3}.
$$

9. Let $f(x) = \dfrac{1}{\sqrt{1+x}} = (1+x)^{-1/2}$. Then $f(0) = 1$.

$$
\begin{aligned}
f'(x) &= -\tfrac{1}{2}(1+x)^{-3/2} & f'(0) &= -\tfrac{1}{2}, \\
f''(x) &= \tfrac{3}{2^2}(1+x)^{-5/2} & f''(0) &= \tfrac{3}{2^2}, \\
f'''(x) &= -\tfrac{3\cdot5}{2^3}(1+x)^{-7/2} & f'''(0) &= -\tfrac{3\cdot5}{2^3}, \\
f^{(4)}(x) &= \tfrac{3\cdot5\cdot7}{2^4}(1+x)^{-9/2} & f^{(4)}(0) &= \tfrac{3\cdot5\cdot7}{2^4}
\end{aligned}
$$

Then,

$$
\begin{aligned}
P_2(x) &= 1 - \frac{1}{2}x + \frac{1}{2!}\frac{3}{2^2}x^2 = 1 - \frac{1}{2}x + \frac{3}{8}x^2, \\
P_3(x) &= P_2(x) - \frac{1}{3!}\frac{3\cdot5}{2^3}x^3 = 1 - \frac{1}{2}x + \frac{3}{8}x^2 - \frac{5}{16}x^3, \\
P_4(x) &= P_3(x) + \frac{1}{4!}\frac{3\cdot5\cdot7}{2^4}x^4 = 1 - \frac{1}{2}x + \frac{3}{8}x^2 - \frac{5}{16}x^3 + \frac{35}{128}x^4.
\end{aligned}
$$

10. Let $f(x) = (1+x)^p$.

(a) Suppose that $p = 0$. Then $f(x) = 1$ and $f^{(k)}(x) = 0$ for any $k \geq 1$. Thus $P_2(x) = P_3(x) = P_4(x) = 1$.

(b) If $p = 1$ then $f(x) = 1 + x$, so

$$
\begin{aligned}
f(0) &= 1, \\
f'(x) &= 1, \\
f^{(k)}(x) &= 0 \qquad k \geq 2.
\end{aligned}
$$

Thus $P_2(x) = P_3(x) = P_4(x) = 1 + x$.

(c) In general:

$$
\begin{aligned}
f(x) &= (1+x)^p, \\
f'(x) &= p(1+x)^{p-1}, \\
f''(x) &= p(p-1)(1+x)^{p-2}, \\
f'''(x) &= p(p-1)(p-2)(1+x)^{p-3}, \\
f^{(4)}(x) &= p(p-1)(p-2)(p-3)(1+x)^{p-4}.
\end{aligned}
$$

$$f(0) = 1,$$
$$f'(0) = p,$$
$$f''(0) = p(p-1),$$
$$f'''(0) = p(p-1)(p-2),$$
$$f^{(4)}(0) = p(p-1)(p-2)(p-3).$$

$$P_2(x) = 1 + px + \frac{p(p-1)}{2}x^2,$$

$$P_3(x) = 1 + px + \frac{p(p-1)}{2}x^2 + \frac{p(p-1)(p-2)}{6}x^3,$$

$$P_4(x) = 1 + px + \frac{p(p-1)}{2}x^2 + \frac{p(p-1)(p-2)}{6}x^3$$
$$+ \frac{p(p-1)(p-2)(p-3)}{24}x^4.$$

11. Let $f(x) = e^x$. Since $f^{(k)}(x) = e^x = f(x)$ for all $k \geq 1$, the Taylor polynomial of degree 4 for $f(x) = e^x$ about $x = 1$ is

$$P_4(x) = e^1 + e^1(x-1) + \frac{e^1}{2!}(x-1)^2 + \frac{e^1}{3!}(x-1)^3 + \frac{e^1}{4!}(x-1)^4$$
$$= e\left[1 + (x-1) + \frac{1}{2}(x-1)^2 + \frac{1}{6}(x-1)^3 + \frac{1}{24}(x-1)^4\right].$$

12. Let $f(x) = \sqrt{1+x} = (1+x)^{1/2}$.

Then $f'(x) = \frac{1}{2}(1+x)^{-1/2}$, $f''(x) = -\frac{1}{4}(1+x)^{-3/2}$, and $f'''(x) = \frac{3}{8}(1+x)^{-5/2}$. The Taylor polynomial of degree three about $x = 1$ is thus

$$P_3(x) = (1+1)^{1/2} + \frac{1}{2}(1+1)^{-1/2}(x-1) + \frac{-\frac{1}{4}(1+1)^{-3/2}}{2!}(x-1)^2$$
$$+ \frac{\frac{3}{8}(1+1)^{-5/2}}{3!}(x-1)^3$$
$$= \sqrt{2}\left(1 + \frac{x-1}{4} - \frac{(x-1)^2}{32} + \frac{(x-1)^3}{128}\right).$$

13. Let $f(x) = \sin x$. $f(\frac{\pi}{2}) = 1$.

$$f'(x) = \cos x \qquad f'(\tfrac{\pi}{2}) = 0,$$
$$f''(x) = -\sin x \qquad f''(\tfrac{\pi}{2}) = -1,$$
$$f'''(x) = -\cos x \qquad f'''(\tfrac{\pi}{2}) = 0,$$
$$f^{(4)}(x) = \sin x \qquad f^{(4)}(\tfrac{\pi}{2}) = 1.$$

So,

$$P_4(x) = 1 + 0 - \frac{1}{2!}\left(x - \frac{\pi}{2}\right)^2 + 0 + \frac{1}{4!}\left(x - \frac{\pi}{2}\right)^4$$
$$= 1 - \frac{1}{2!}\left(x - \frac{\pi}{2}\right)^2 + \frac{1}{4!}\left(x - \frac{\pi}{2}\right)^4.$$

14. Let $f(x) = \cos x$. Then $\cos\frac{\pi}{4} = \sin\frac{\pi}{4} = \frac{\sqrt{2}}{2}$.

Then $f'(x) = -\sin x$, $f''(x) = -\cos x$, and $f'''(x) = \sin x$, so the Taylor polynomial for $\cos x$ of degree three about $x = \pi/4$ is

$$P_3(x) = \cos\frac{\pi}{4} + \left(-\sin\frac{\pi}{4}\right)\left(x - \frac{\pi}{4}\right) + \frac{-\cos\frac{\pi}{4}}{2!}\left(x - \frac{\pi}{4}\right)^2 + \frac{\sin\frac{\pi}{4}}{3!}\left(x - \frac{\pi}{4}\right)^3$$
$$= \frac{\sqrt{2}}{2}\left(1 - \left(x - \frac{\pi}{4}\right) - \frac{1}{2}\left(x - \frac{\pi}{4}\right)^2 + \frac{1}{6}\left(x - \frac{\pi}{4}\right)^3\right).$$

15. Let $f(x) = \ln(x^2)$. Then $\ln(1^2) = \ln 1 = 0$.

Then $f'(x) = 2x^{-1}$, $f''(x) = -2x^{-2}$, $f'''(x) = 4x^{-3}$, and $f^{(4)}(x) = -12x^{-4}$.

The Taylor polynomial of degree 4 for $f(x) = \ln(x^2)$ about $x = 1$ is

$$P_4(x) = \ln(1^2) + 2 \cdot 1^{-1}(x-1) + \frac{-2 \cdot 1^{-2}}{2!}(x-1)^2 + \frac{4 \cdot 1^{-3}}{3!}(x-1)^3 + \frac{-12 \cdot 1^{-4}}{4!}(x-1)^4$$

$$= 0 + 2(x-1) - (x-1)^2 + \frac{4}{6}(x-1)^3 - \frac{12}{24}(x-1)^4$$

$$= 2(x-1) - (x-1)^2 + \frac{2}{3}(x-1)^3 - \frac{1}{2}(x-1)^4.$$

16. Let $f(x) = \sin 2x$. Then $\sin\left(2\left(\frac{\pi}{4}\right)\right) = \sin\frac{\pi}{2} = 1$.

Then $f'(x) = 2\cos 2x$, $f''(x) = -4\sin 2x$, $f'''(x) = -8\cos 2x$, and $f^{(4)}(x) = 16\sin 2x$ so the Taylor polynomial for $\sin 2x$ of degree four about $x = \pi/4$ is

$$P_4(x) = \sin\left(\frac{2 \cdot \pi}{4}\right) + 2\cos\left(\frac{2 \cdot \pi}{4}\right)\left(x - \frac{\pi}{4}\right) - \frac{4\sin\left(\frac{2 \cdot \pi}{4}\right)}{2!}\left(x - \frac{\pi}{4}\right)^2 - \frac{8\cos\left(\frac{2 \cdot \pi}{4}\right)}{3!}\left(x - \frac{\pi}{4}\right)^3 + \frac{16\sin\left(\frac{2 \cdot \pi}{4}\right)}{4!}\left(x - \frac{\pi}{4}\right)^4$$

$$= 1 + 2 \cdot 0\left(x - \frac{\pi}{4}\right) - 2 \cdot 1\left(x - \frac{\pi}{4}\right)^2 - \frac{8 \cdot 0}{6}\left(x - \frac{\pi}{4}\right)^3 + \frac{16 \cdot 1}{24}\left(x - \frac{\pi}{4}\right)^4$$

$$= 1 - 2\left(x - \frac{\pi}{4}\right)^2 + \frac{2}{3}\left(x - \frac{\pi}{4}\right)^4.$$

Problems

17. Since $P_2(x)$ is the second degree Taylor polynomial for $f(x)$ about $x = 0$, $P_2(0) = f(0)$, which says $a = f(0)$. Since

$$\left.\frac{d}{dx}P_2(x)\right|_{x=0} = f'(0),$$

$b = f'(0)$; and since

$$\left.\frac{d^2}{dx^2}P_2(x)\right|_{x=0} = f''(0),$$

$2c = f''(0)$. In other words, a is the y-intercept of $f(x)$, b is the slope of the tangent line to $f(x)$ at $x = 0$ and c tells us the concavity of $f(x)$ near $x = 0$. So $c < 0$ since f is concave down; $b > 0$ since f is increasing; $a > 0$ since $f(0) > 0$.

18. As we can see from Problem 17, a is the y-intercept of $f(x)$, b is the slope of the tangent line to $f(x)$ at $x = 0$ and c tells us the concavity of $f(x)$ near $x = 0$.

So $a > 0, b < 0$ and $c < 0$.

19. As we can see from Problem 17, a is the y-intercept of $f(x)$, b is the slope of the tangent line to $f(x)$ at $x = 0$ and c tells us the concavity of $f(x)$ near $x = 0$.

So $a < 0, b > 0$ and $c > 0$.

20. As we can see from Problem 17, a is the y-intercept of $f(x)$, b is the slope of the tangent line to $f(x)$ at $x = 0$ and c tells us the concavity of $f(x)$ near $x = 0$.

So $a < 0, b < 0$ and $c > 0$.

21. Using the fact that

$$f(x) \approx P_2(x) = f(0) + f'(0)x + \frac{f''(0)}{2!}x^2$$

and identifying coefficients with those given for $P_2(x)$, we obtain the following:

(a) $f(0) = $ constant term which equals 5,   so $f(0) = 5$.

(b) $f'(0) = $ coefficient of x which equals -7,   so $f'(0) = -7$.

(c) $\frac{f''(0)}{2!} = $ coefficient of x^2 which equals 8,   so $f''(0) = 16$.

22. Using the fact that

$$f(x) \approx P_6(x) = f(0) + f'(0)x + \frac{f''(0)}{2!}x^2 + \frac{f'''(0)}{3!}x^3 + \frac{f^{(4)}(0)}{4!}x^4 + \frac{f^{(5)}(0)}{5!}x^5 + \frac{f^{(6)}(0)}{6!}x^6$$

and identifying coefficients with those given for $P_6(x)$, we obtain the following:

(a) $f(0) =$ constant term which equals 0, so $f(0) = 0.$
(b) $f'(0) =$ coefficient of x which equals 3, so $f'(0) = 3.$
(c) $\frac{f'''(0)}{3!} =$ coefficient of x^3 which equals -4, so $f'''(0) = -24.$
(d) $\frac{f^{(5)}(0)}{5!} =$ coefficient of x^5 which equals 0, so $f^{(5)}(0) = 0.$
(e) $\frac{f^{(6)}(0)}{6!} =$ coefficient of x^6 which equals 5, so $f^{(6)}(0) = 5(6!) = 3600.$

23. (a) We have

$$g(x) = g(5) + g'(5)(x - 5) + \frac{g''(5)}{2!}(x - 5)^2 + \frac{g'''(5)}{3!}(x - 5)^3 + \ldots$$

Substituting gives

$$g(x) = 3 - 2(x - 5) + \frac{1}{2!}(x - 5)^2 - \frac{3}{3!}(x - 5)^3 + \ldots$$

The degree 2 Taylor polynomial, $P_2(x)$, is obtained by truncating after the $(x - 5)^2$ term:

$$P_2(x) = 3 - 2(x - 5) + \frac{1}{2}(x - 5)^2.$$

The degree 3 Taylor polynomial, $P_3(x)$, is obtained by truncating after the $(x - 5)^3$ term:

$$P_3(x) = 3 - 2(x - 5) + \frac{1}{2}(x - 5)^2 - \frac{1}{2}(x - 5)^3.$$

(b) Substitute $x = 4.9$ into the Taylor polynomial of degree 2:

$$P_2(4.9) = 3 - 2(4.9 - 5) + \frac{1}{2}(4.9 - 5)^2 = 3.205.$$

From the Taylor polynomial of degree 3, we obtain

$$P_3(4.9) = 3 - 2(4.9 - 5) + \frac{1}{2}(4.9 - 5)^2 - \frac{1}{2}(4.9 - 5)^3 = 3.2055.$$

24. (a) The upper half of the circle is given by the function

$$y = f(x) = \sqrt{1 - x^2}.$$

We want to approximate the circle near the point where $x = 0$. Since $f(0) = 1$ and

$$f'(x) = \frac{1}{2}(1 - x^2)^{1/2}(-2x) = -\frac{x}{\sqrt{1 - x^2}},$$

$$f''(x) = -\frac{1}{\sqrt{1 - x^2}} - x\left(-\frac{1}{2}(1 - x^2)^{-3/2}\right)(-2x) = -\frac{1}{\sqrt{1 - x^2}} - \frac{x^2}{(1 - x^2)^{3/2}},$$

we have $f'(0) = 0$ and $f''(0) = -1$. The best fitting parabola is the second degree Taylor polynomial

$$P_2(x) = 1 - \frac{1}{2}x^2.$$

(b) Substituting $x = 0.1$ gives

$$f(0.1) \approx P_2(0.1) = 1 - \frac{1}{2}(0.1)^2 = 0.995,$$

so the point is $(0.1, 0.995)$.

25.

$$\begin{aligned}
f(x) &= 4x^2 - 7x + 2 & f(0) &= 2 \\
f'(x) &= 8x - 7 & f'(0) &= -7 \\
f''(x) &= 8 & f''(0) &= 8,
\end{aligned}$$

so $P_2(x) = 2 + (-7)x + \frac{8}{2}x^2 = 4x^2 - 7x + 2$. We notice that $f(x) = P_2(x)$ in this case.

26. $f'(x) = 3x^2 + 14x - 5$, $f''(x) = 6x + 14$, $f'''(x) = 6$. Thus, about $a = 0$,

$$P_3(x) = 1 + \frac{-5}{1!}x + \frac{14}{2!}x^2 + \frac{6}{3!}x^3$$
$$= 1 - 5x + 7x^2 + x^3$$
$$= f(x).$$

27. (a) We'll make the following conjecture:
"If $f(x)$ is a polynomial of degree n, i.e.

$$f(x) = a_0 + a_1x + a_2x^2 + \cdots + a_{n-1}x^{n-1} + a_nx^n,$$

then $P_n(x)$, the nth degree Taylor polynomial for $f(x)$ about $x = 0$, is $f(x)$ itself."

(b) All we need to do is to calculate $P_n(x)$, the nth degree Taylor polynomial for f about $x = 0$ and see if it is the same as $f(x)$.

$$f(0) = a_0;$$
$$f'(0) = (a_1 + 2a_2x + \cdots + na_nx^{n-1})\big|_{x=0}$$
$$= a_1;$$
$$f''(0) = (2a_2 + 3 \cdot 2a_3x + \cdots + n(n-1)a_nx^{n-2})\big|_{x=0}$$
$$= 2!a_2.$$

If we continue doing this, we'll see in general

$$f^{(k)}(0) = k!a_k, \qquad k = 1, 2, 3, \cdots, n.$$

Therefore,

$$P_n(x) = f(0) + \frac{f'(0)}{1!}x + \frac{f''(0)}{2!}x^2 + \cdots + \frac{f^{(n)}(0)}{n!}x^n$$
$$= a_0 + a_1x + a_2x^2 + \cdots + a_nx^n$$
$$= f(x).$$

28.

$$\lim_{x \to 0} \frac{\sin x}{x} = \lim_{x \to 0} \frac{x - \frac{x^3}{3!}}{x} = \lim_{x \to 0} \left(1 - \frac{x^2}{3!}\right) = 1.$$

29.

$$\lim_{x \to 0} \frac{1 - \cos x}{x^2} = \lim_{x \to 0} \frac{1 - (1 - \frac{x^2}{2!} + \frac{x^4}{4!})}{x^2} = \lim_{x \to 0} \left(\frac{1}{2} - \frac{x^2}{4!}\right) = \frac{1}{2}.$$

30. For $f(h) = e^h$, $P_4(h) = 1 + h + \frac{h^2}{2} + \frac{h^3}{3!} + \frac{h^4}{4!}$. So

(a)

$$\lim_{h \to 0} \frac{e^h - 1 - h}{h^2} = \lim_{h \to 0} \frac{P_4(h) - 1 - h}{h^2}$$
$$= \lim_{h \to 0} \frac{\frac{h^2}{2} + \frac{h^3}{3!} + \frac{h^4}{4!}}{h^2}$$
$$= \lim_{h \to 0} \left(\frac{1}{2} + \frac{h}{3!} + \frac{h^2}{4!}\right)$$
$$= \frac{1}{2}.$$

(b)

$$\lim_{h \to 0} \frac{e^h - 1 - h - \frac{h^2}{2}}{h^3} = \lim_{h \to 0} \frac{P_4(h) - 1 - h - \frac{h^2}{2}}{h^3}$$

$$= \lim_{h \to 0} \frac{\frac{h^3}{3!} + \frac{h^4}{4!}}{h^3} = \lim_{h \to 0} \left(\frac{1}{3!} + \frac{h}{4!} \right)$$

$$= \frac{1}{3!} = \frac{1}{6}.$$

Using Taylor polynomials of higher degree would not have changed the results since the terms with higher powers of h all go to zero as $h \to 0$.

31. (a) We use the Taylor polynomial of degree two for f and h about $x = 2$.

$$f(x) \approx f(2) + f'(2)(x - 2) + \frac{f''(2)}{2!}(x - 2)^2 = \frac{3}{2}(x - 2)^2$$

$$h(x) \approx h(2) + h'(2)(x - 2) + \frac{h''(2)}{2!}(x - 2)^2 = \frac{7}{2}(x - 2)^2$$

Thus, using the fact that near $x = 2$ we can approximate a function by Taylor polynomials

$$\lim_{x \to 2} \frac{f(x)}{g(x)} = \lim_{x \to 2} \frac{\frac{3}{2}(x - 2)^2}{\frac{7}{2}(x - 2)^2} = \frac{3}{7}.$$

(b) We use the Taylor polynomial of degree two for f and g about $x = 2$.

$$f(x) \approx f(2) + f'(2)(x - 2) + \frac{f''(2)}{2!}(x - 2)^2 = \frac{3}{2}(x - 2)^2$$

$$g(x) \approx g(2) + g'(2)(x - 2) + \frac{g''(2)}{2!}(x - 2)^2 = 22(x - 2) + \frac{5}{2}(x - 2)^2.$$

Thus,

$$\lim_{x \to 2} \frac{f(x)}{g(x)} = \lim_{x \to 2} \left(\frac{\frac{3}{2}(x - 2)^2}{22(x - 2) + 5(x - 2)^2} \right) = \lim_{x \to 2} \left(\frac{\frac{3}{2}(x - 2)}{22 + 5(x - 2)} \right) = \frac{0}{22} = 0.$$

32. Let $f(x)$ be a function that has derivatives up to order n at $x = a$. Let

$$P_n(x) = C_0 + C_1(x - a) + \cdots + C_n(x - a)^n$$

be the polynomial of degree n that approximates $f(x)$ about $x = a$. We require that $P_n(x)$ and all of its first n derivatives agree with those of the function $f(x)$ at $x = a$, i.e., we want

$$f(a) = P_n(a),$$
$$f'(a) = P_n'(a),$$
$$f''(a) = P_n''(a),$$
$$\vdots$$
$$f^{(n)}(a) = P_n^{(n)}(a).$$

When we substitute $x = a$ in $P_n(x)$, all the terms except the first drop out, so

$$f(a) = C_0.$$

Now differentiate $P_n(x)$:

$$P_n'(x) = C_1 + 2C_2(x - a) + 3C_3(x - a)^2 + \cdots + nC_n(x - a)^{n-1}.$$

Substitute $x = a$ again, which yields

$$f'(a) = P_n'(a) = C_1.$$

Differentiate $P_n'(x)$:

$$P_n''(x) = 2C_2 + 3 \cdot 2C_3(x - a) + \cdots + n(n - 1)C_n(x - a)^{n-2}$$

and substitute $x = a$ again:

$$f''(a) = P_n''(a) = 2C_2.$$

Differentiating and substituting again gives

$$f'''(a) = P_n'''(a) = 3 \cdot 2C_3.$$

Similarly,

$$f^{(k)}(a) = P_n^{(k)}(a) = k!C_k.$$

So, $C_0 = f(a)$, $C_1 = f'(a)$, $C_2 = \frac{f''(a)}{2!}$, $C_3 = \frac{f'''(a)}{3!}$, and so on.

If we adopt the convention that $f^{(0)}(a) = f(a)$ and $0! = 1$, then

$$C_k = \frac{f^{(k)}(a)}{k!}, \ k = 0, 1, 2, \cdots, n.$$

Therefore,

$$f(x) \approx P_n(x) = C_0 + C_1(x-a) + C_2(x-a)^2 \cdots + C_n(x-a)^n$$

$$= f(a) + f'(a)(x-a) + \frac{f''(a)}{2!}(x-a)^2 + \cdots + \frac{f^{(n)}(a)}{n!}(x-a)^n.$$

33. (a) $f(x) = e^{x^2}$.

$f'(x) = 2xe^{x^2}$, $f''(x) = 2(1 + 2x^2)e^{x^2}$, $f'''(x) = 4(3x + 2x^3)e^{x^2}$,

$f^{(4)}(x) = 4(3 + 6x^2)e^{x^2} + 4(3x + 2x^3)2xe^{x^2}$.

The Taylor polynomial about $x = 0$ is

$$P_4(x) = 1 + \frac{0}{1!}x + \frac{2}{2!}x^2 + \frac{0}{3!}x^3 + \frac{12}{4!}x^4$$

$$= 1 + x^2 + \frac{1}{2}x^4.$$

(b) $f(x) = e^x$. The Taylor polynomial of degree 2 is

$$Q_2(x) = 1 + \frac{x}{1!} + \frac{x^2}{2!} = 1 + x + \frac{1}{2}x^2.$$

If we substitute x^2 for x in the Taylor polynomial for e^x of degree 2, we will get $P_4(x)$, the Taylor polynomial for e^{x^2} of degree 4:

$$Q_2(x^2) = 1 + x^2 + \frac{1}{2}(x^2)^2$$

$$= 1 + x^2 + \frac{1}{2}x^4$$

$$= P_4(x).$$

(c) Let $Q_{10}(x) = 1 + \frac{x}{1!} + \frac{x^2}{2!} + \cdots + \frac{x^{10}}{10!}$ be the Taylor polynomial of degree 10 for e^x about $x = 0$. Then

$$P_{20}(x) = Q_{10}(x^2)$$

$$= 1 + \frac{x^2}{1!} + \frac{(x^2)^2}{2!} + \cdots + \frac{(x^2)^{10}}{10!}$$

$$= 1 + \frac{x^2}{1!} + \frac{x^4}{2!} + \cdots + \frac{x^{20}}{10!}.$$

(d) Let $e^x \approx Q_5(x) = 1 + \frac{x}{1!} + \cdots + \frac{x^5}{5!}$. Then

$$e^{-2x} \approx Q_5(-2x)$$

$$= 1 + \frac{-2x}{1!} + \frac{(-2x)^2}{2!} + \frac{(-2x)^3}{3!} + \frac{(-2x)^4}{4!} + \frac{(-2x)^5}{5!}$$

$$= 1 - 2x + 2x^2 - \frac{4}{3}x^3 + \frac{2}{3}x^4 - \frac{4}{15}x^5.$$

34. (a) The equation $\sin x = 0.2$ has one solution near $x = 0$ and infinitely many others, one near each multiple of π. See Figure 10.1. The equation $x - \dfrac{x^3}{3!} = 0.2$ has three solutions, one near $x = 0$ and two others. See Figure 10.2.

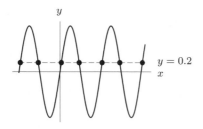

Figure 10.1: Graph of $y = \sin x$ and $y = 0.2$ **Figure 10.2**: Graph of $y = x - \frac{x^3}{3!}$ and $y = 0.2$

(b) Near $x = 0$, the cubic Taylor polynomial $x - x^3/3! \approx \sin x$. Thus, the solutions to the two equations near $x = 0$ are approximately equal. The other solutions are not close. The reason is that $x - x^3/3!$ only approximates $\sin x$ near $x = 0$ but not further away. See Figure 10.3.

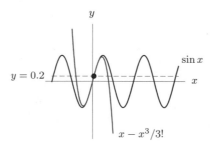

Figure 10.3

35. (a) $\dfrac{\sin t}{t} \approx \dfrac{t - \frac{t^3}{3!}}{t} = 1 - \dfrac{t^2}{6}$

$$\int_0^1 \frac{\sin t}{t}\, dt \approx \int_0^1 \left(1 - \frac{t^2}{6}\right) dt = t - \left.\frac{t^3}{18}\right|_0^1 = 0.94444\cdots$$

(b) $\dfrac{\sin t}{t} \approx \dfrac{t - \frac{t^3}{3!} + \frac{t^5}{5!}}{t} = 1 - \dfrac{t^2}{6} + \dfrac{t^4}{120}$

$$\int_0^1 \frac{\sin t}{t}\, dt \approx \int_0^1 \left(1 - \frac{t^2}{6} + \frac{t^4}{120}\right) dt = t - \frac{t^3}{18} + \left.\frac{t^5}{600}\right|_0^1 = 0.94611\cdots$$

36. (a) Since the coefficient of the x-term of each f is 1, we know $f_1'(0) = f_2'(0) = f_3'(0) = 1$. Thus, each of the fs slopes upward near 0, and are in the second figure.

The coefficient of the x-term in g_1 and in g_2 is 1, so $g_1'(0) = g_2'(0) = 1$. For g_3 however, $g_3'(0) = -1$. Thus, g_1 and g_2 slope up near 0, but g_3 slopes down. The gs are in the first figure.

(b) Since $g_1(0) = g_2(0) = g_3(0) = 1$, the point A is $(0, 1)$.
Since $f_1(0) = f_2(0) = f_3(0) = 2$, the point B is $(0, 2)$.

(c) Since g_3 slopes down, g_3 is I. Since the coefficient of x^2 for g_1 is 2, we know

$$\frac{g_1''(0)}{2!} = 2 \qquad \text{so} \qquad g_1''(0) = 4.$$

By similar reasoning $g_2''(0) = 2$. Since g_1 and g_2 are concave up, and g_1 has a larger second derivative, g_1 is III and g_2 is II.

Calculating the second derivatives of the fs from the coefficients x^2, we find

$$f_1''(0) = 4 \qquad f_2''(0) = -2 \qquad f_3''(0) = 2.$$

Thus, f_1 and f_3 are concave up, with f_1 having the larger second derivative, so f_1 is III and f_3 is II. Then f_2 is concave down and is I.

Solutions for Section 10.2

Exercises

1. Differentiating $(1+x)^{3/2}$:

$$
\begin{aligned}
f(x) &= (1+x)^{3/2} & f(0) &= 1, \\
f'(x) &= (3/2)(1+x)^{1/2} & f'(0) &= \tfrac{3}{2}, \\
f''(x) &= (1/2)(3/2)(1+x)^{-1/2} = (3/4)(1+x)^{-1/2} & f''(0) &= \tfrac{3}{4}, \\
f'''(x) &= (-1/2)(3/4)(1+x)^{-3/2} = (-3/8)(1+x)^{-3/2} & f'''(0) &= -\tfrac{3}{8}.
\end{aligned}
$$

$$
\begin{aligned}
f(x) = (1+x)^{3/2} &= 1 + \frac{3}{2} \cdot x + \frac{(3/4)x^2}{2!} + \frac{(-3/8)x^3}{3!} + \cdots \\
&= 1 + \frac{3x}{2} + \frac{3x^2}{8} - \frac{x^3}{16} + \cdots
\end{aligned}
$$

2. Differentiating $\sqrt[4]{x+1}$:

$$
\begin{aligned}
f(x) &= \sqrt[4]{x+1} = (x+1)^{1/4} & f(0) &= 1, \\
f'(x) &= (1/4)(x+1)^{-3/4} & f'(0) &= \tfrac{1}{4}, \\
f''(x) &= (-3/4)(1/4)(x+1)^{-7/4} = (-3/16)(x+1)^{-7/4} & f''(0) &= -\tfrac{3}{16}, \\
f'''(x) &= (-7/4)(-3/16)(x+1)^{-11/4} = (21/64)(x+1)^{-11/4} & f'''(0) &= \tfrac{21}{64}.
\end{aligned}
$$

$$
\begin{aligned}
f(x) = \sqrt[4]{x+1} &= 1 + \frac{1}{4} \cdot x + \frac{(-3/16)x^2}{2!} + \frac{(21/64)x^3}{3!} + \cdots \\
&= 1 + \frac{x}{4} - \frac{3x^2}{32} + \frac{7x^3}{128} - \cdots.
\end{aligned}
$$

3. Differentiating $\sin(-x)$:

$$
\begin{aligned}
f(x) &= \sin(-x) & f(0) &= 0, \\
f'(x) &= \cos(-x)(-1) = -\cos(-x) & f'(0) &= -1, \\
f''(x) &= -(-\sin(-x))(-1) = -\sin(-x) & f''(0) &= 0, \\
f'''(x) &= -\cos(-x)(-1) = \cos(-x) & f'''(0) &= 1 \\
f^{(4)}(x) &= -\sin(-x)(-1) = \sin(-x) & f^{(4)}(0) &= 0, \\
f^{(5)}(x) &= \cos(-x)(-1) = -\cos(-x) & f^{(5)}(0) &= -1, \\
f^{(6)}(x) &= -(-\sin(-x))(-1) = -\sin(-x) & f^{(6)}(0) &= 0, \\
f^{(7)}(x) &= -\cos(-x)(-1) = \cos(-x) & f^{(7)}(0) &= 1.
\end{aligned}
$$

$$
\begin{aligned}
f(x) = \sin(-x) &= 0 - 1 \cdot x + \frac{0x^2}{2!} + \frac{1x^3}{3!} + \frac{0x^4}{4!} + \frac{-1x^5}{5!} + \frac{0x^6}{6!} + \frac{1x^7}{7!} + \cdots \\
&= -x + \frac{x^3}{3!} - \frac{x^5}{5!} + \frac{x^7}{7!} + \cdots.
\end{aligned}
$$

Notice that the series for $\sin(-x)$ is obtained from the series for $\sin x$ by changing the signs. This is expected since $\sin(-x) = \sin x$.

4. Differentiating $\ln(1-x)$

$$
\begin{aligned}
f(x) &= \ln(1-x) & f(0) &= 0, \\
f'(x) &= \frac{1}{1-x}(-1) = -(1-x)^{-1} & f'(0) &= -1, \\
f''(x) &= -(-(1-x)^{-2})(-1) = -(1-x)^{-2} & f''(0) &= -1, \\
f'''(x) &= -2(-(1-x)^{-3})(-1) = -2(1-x)^{-3} & f'''(0) &= -2 \\
f^{(4)}(x) &= -3(-2(1-x)^{-4})(-1) = -6(1-x)^{-4} & f^{(4)}(0) &= -6.
\end{aligned}
$$

$$f(x) = \ln(1-x) = 0 - 1 \cdot x + \frac{(-1)x^2}{2!} + \frac{(-2)x^3}{3!} + \frac{(-6)x^4}{4!} + \cdots$$

$$= -x - \frac{x^2}{2} - \frac{x^3}{3} - \frac{x^4}{4} + \cdots.$$

5.

$$\begin{array}{ll} f(x) = \frac{1}{1-x} = (1-x)^{-1} & f(0) = 1, \\ f'(x) = -(1-x)^{-2}(-1) = (1-x)^{-2} & f'(0) = 1, \\ f''(x) = -2(1-x)^{-3}(-1) = 2(1-x)^{-3} & f''(0) = 2, \\ f'''(x) = -6(1-x)^{-4}(-1) = 6(1-x)^{-4} & f'''(0) = 6. \end{array}$$

$$f(x) = \frac{1}{1-x} = 1 + 1 \cdot x + \frac{2x^2}{2!} + \frac{6x^3}{3!} + \cdots$$

$$= 1 + x + x^2 + x^3 + \cdots$$

6.

$$\begin{array}{ll} f(x) = \frac{1}{\sqrt{1+x}} = (1+x)^{-\frac{1}{2}} & f(0) = 1 \\ f'(x) = -\frac{1}{2}(1+x)^{-\frac{3}{2}} & f'(0) = -\frac{1}{2} \\ f''(x) = \frac{3}{4}(1+x)^{-\frac{5}{2}} & f''(0) = \frac{3}{4} \\ f'''(x) = -\frac{15}{8}(1+x)^{-\frac{7}{2}} & f'''(0) = -\frac{15}{8} \end{array}$$

$$f(x) = \frac{1}{\sqrt{1+x}} = 1 + \left(-\frac{1}{2}\right)x + \frac{(\frac{3}{4})x^2}{2!} + \frac{(-\frac{15}{8})x^3}{3!} + \cdots$$

$$= 1 - \frac{x}{2} + \frac{3x^2}{8} - \frac{5x^3}{16} + \cdots$$

7.

$$\begin{array}{ll} f(x) = \sqrt{1+x} = (1+x)^{\frac{1}{2}} & f(0) = 1 \\ f'(x) = \frac{1}{2}(1+x)^{-\frac{1}{2}} & f'(0) = \frac{1}{2} \\ f''(x) = -\frac{1}{4}(1+x)^{-\frac{3}{2}} & f''(0) = -\frac{1}{4} \\ f'''(x) = \frac{3}{8}(1+x)^{-\frac{5}{2}} & f'''(0) = \frac{3}{8} \end{array}$$

$$f(x) = \sqrt{1+x} = 1 + \frac{1}{2}x + \frac{(-\frac{1}{4})x^2}{2!} + \frac{(\frac{3}{8})x^3}{3!} + \cdots$$

$$= 1 + \frac{x}{2} - \frac{x^2}{8} + \frac{x^3}{16} + \cdots$$

8.

$$\begin{array}{ll} f(y) = \sqrt[3]{1-y} = (1-y)^{\frac{1}{3}} & f(0) = 1 \\ f'(y) = \frac{1}{3}(1-y)^{-\frac{2}{3}}(-1) = -\frac{1}{3}(1-y)^{-\frac{2}{3}} & f'(0) = -\frac{1}{3} \\ f''(y) = \frac{2}{9}(1-y)^{-\frac{5}{3}}(-1) = -\frac{2}{9}(1-y)^{-\frac{5}{3}} & f''(0) = \frac{2}{9} \\ f'''(y) = \frac{10}{27}(1-y)^{-\frac{8}{3}}(-1) = -\frac{10}{27}(1-y)^{-\frac{8}{3}} & f'''(0) = -\frac{10}{27} \end{array}$$

$$f(y) = \sqrt[3]{1-y} = 1 + \left(-\frac{1}{3}\right)y + \frac{(-\frac{2}{9})y^2}{2!} + \frac{(-\frac{10}{27})y^3}{3!} + \cdots$$

$$= 1 - \frac{y}{3} - \frac{y^2}{9} - \frac{5y^3}{81} - \cdots$$

9.

$$\begin{array}{ll} f(x) = \sin x & f(\frac{\pi}{4}) = \frac{\sqrt{2}}{2}, \\ f'(x) = \cos x & f'(\frac{\pi}{4}) = \frac{\sqrt{2}}{2}, \\ f''(x) = -\sin x & f''(\frac{\pi}{4}) = -\frac{\sqrt{2}}{2}, \\ f'''(x) = -\cos x & f'''(\frac{\pi}{4}) = -\frac{\sqrt{2}}{2}. \end{array}$$

$$\sin x = \frac{\sqrt{2}}{2} + \frac{\sqrt{2}}{2}\left(x - \frac{\pi}{4}\right) - \frac{\sqrt{2}}{2}\frac{(x - \frac{\pi}{4})^2}{2!} - \frac{\sqrt{2}}{2}\frac{(x - \frac{\pi}{4})^3}{3!} - \cdots$$

$$= \frac{\sqrt{2}}{2} + \frac{\sqrt{2}}{2}\left(x - \frac{\pi}{4}\right) - \frac{\sqrt{2}}{4}\left(x - \frac{\pi}{4}\right)^2 - \frac{\sqrt{2}}{12}\left(x - \frac{\pi}{4}\right)^3 - \cdots$$

10.

$$\begin{aligned}
f(\theta) &= \cos\theta & f(\tfrac{\pi}{4}) &= \tfrac{\sqrt{2}}{2}, \\
f'(\theta) &= -\sin\theta & f'(\tfrac{\pi}{4}) &= -\tfrac{\sqrt{2}}{2}, \\
f''(\theta) &= -\cos\theta & f''(\tfrac{\pi}{4}) &= -\tfrac{\sqrt{2}}{2}, \\
f'''(\theta) &= \sin\theta & f'''(\tfrac{\pi}{4}) &= \tfrac{\sqrt{2}}{2}.
\end{aligned}$$

$$\cos\theta = \frac{\sqrt{2}}{2} - \frac{\sqrt{2}}{2}\left(\theta - \frac{\pi}{4}\right) - \frac{\sqrt{2}}{2}\frac{(\theta - \frac{\pi}{4})^2}{2!} + \frac{\sqrt{2}}{2}\frac{(\theta - \frac{\pi}{4})^3}{3!} - \cdots$$

$$= \frac{\sqrt{2}}{2} - \frac{\sqrt{2}}{2}\left(\theta - \frac{\pi}{4}\right) - \frac{\sqrt{2}}{4}\left(\theta - \frac{\pi}{4}\right)^2 + \frac{\sqrt{2}}{12}\left(\theta - \frac{\pi}{4}\right)^3 - \cdots$$

11.

$$\begin{aligned}
f(\theta) &= \sin\theta & f(-\tfrac{\pi}{4}) &= -\tfrac{\sqrt{2}}{2}, \\
f'(\theta) &= \cos\theta & f'(-\tfrac{\pi}{4}) &= \tfrac{\sqrt{2}}{2}, \\
f''(\theta) &= -\sin\theta & f''(-\tfrac{\pi}{4}) &= \tfrac{\sqrt{2}}{2}, \\
f'''(\theta) &= -\cos\theta & f'''(-\tfrac{\pi}{4}) &= -\tfrac{\sqrt{2}}{2}.
\end{aligned}$$

$$\sin\theta = -\frac{\sqrt{2}}{2} + \frac{\sqrt{2}}{2}\left(\theta + \frac{\pi}{4}\right) + \frac{\sqrt{2}}{2}\frac{(\theta + \frac{\pi}{4})^2}{2!} - \frac{\sqrt{2}}{2}\frac{(\theta + \frac{\pi}{4})^3}{3!} + \cdots$$

$$= -\frac{\sqrt{2}}{2} + \frac{\sqrt{2}}{2}\left(\theta + \frac{\pi}{4}\right) + \frac{\sqrt{2}}{4}\left(\theta + \frac{\pi}{4}\right)^2 - \frac{\sqrt{2}}{12}\left(\theta + \frac{\pi}{4}\right)^3 + \cdots.$$

12.

$$\begin{aligned}
f(x) &= \tan x & f(\tfrac{\pi}{4}) &= 1, \\
f'(x) &= \frac{1}{\cos^2 x} & f'(\tfrac{\pi}{4}) &= 2, \\
f''(x) &= \frac{-2(-\sin x)}{\cos^3 x} = \frac{2\sin x}{\cos^3 x} & f''(\tfrac{\pi}{4}) &= 4, \\
f'''(x) &= \frac{-6\sin x(-\sin x)}{\cos^4 x} + \frac{2}{\cos^2 x} & f'''(\tfrac{\pi}{4}) &= 16.
\end{aligned}$$

$$\tan x = 1 + 2\left(x - \frac{\pi}{4}\right) + 4\frac{(x - \frac{\pi}{4})^2}{2!} + 16\frac{(x - \frac{\pi}{4})^3}{3!} + \cdots$$

$$= 1 + 2\left(x - \frac{\pi}{4}\right) + 2\left(x - \frac{\pi}{4}\right)^2 + \frac{8}{3}\left(x - \frac{\pi}{4}\right)^3 + \cdots$$

13.

$$\begin{aligned}
f(x) &= \frac{1}{x} & f(1) &= 1 \\
f'(x) &= -\frac{1}{x^2} & f'(1) &= -1 \\
f''(x) &= \frac{2}{x^3} & f''(1) &= 2 \\
f'''(x) &= -\frac{6}{x^4} & f'''(1) &= -6
\end{aligned}$$

$$\frac{1}{x} = 1 - (x - 1) + \frac{2(x - 1)^2}{2!} - \frac{6(x - 1)^3}{3!} + \cdots$$

$$= 1 - (x - 1) + (x - 1)^2 - (x - 1)^3 + \cdots.$$

14. Again using the derivatives found in Problem 13, we have

$$f(2) = \frac{1}{2}, \qquad f'(2) = -\frac{1}{4}, \qquad f''(2) = \frac{1}{4}, \qquad f'''(2) = -\frac{3}{8}.$$

$$\frac{1}{x} = \frac{1}{2} - \frac{x-2}{4} + \frac{(x-2)^2}{4 \cdot 2!} - \frac{3(x-2)^3}{8 \cdot 3!} + \cdots$$
$$= \frac{1}{2} - \frac{(x-2)}{4} + \frac{(x-2)^2}{8} - \frac{(x-2)^3}{16} + \cdots$$

15. Using the derivatives from Problem 13, we have

$$f(-1) = -1, \quad f'(-1) = -1, \quad f''(-1) = -2, \quad f'''(-1) = -6.$$

Hence,

$$\frac{1}{x} = -1 - (x+1) - \frac{2(x+1)^2}{2!} - \frac{6(x+1)^3}{3!} - \cdots$$
$$= -1 - (x+1) - (x+1)^2 - (x+1)^3 - \cdots$$

16. The general term can be written as x^n for $n \geq 0$.

17. The general term can be written as $(-1)^n x^n$ for $n \geq 0$.

18. The general term can be written as $-x^n/n$ for $n \geq 1$.

19. The general term can be written as $(-1)^{n-1} x^n/n$ for $n \geq 1$.

20. The general term can be written as $(-1)^k x^{2k+1}/(2k+1)!$ for $k \geq 0$.

21. The general term can be written as $(-1)^k x^{2k+1}/(2k+1)$ for $k \geq 0$.

22. The general term can be written as $x^{2k}/k!$ for $k \geq 0$.

23. The general term can be written as $(-1)^k x^{4k+2}/(2k)!$ for $k \geq 0$.

Problems

24. (a)
$$f(x) = \sin x^2$$
$$f'(x) = (\cos x^2)2x$$
$$f''(x) = (-\sin x^2)4x^2 + (\cos x^2)2$$
$$f'''(x) = (-\cos x^2)8x^3 + (-\sin x^2)8x + (-\sin x^2)4x$$
$$= (-\cos x^2)8x^3 + (-\sin x^2)12x$$
$$f^{(4)}(x) = (\sin x^2)16x^4 + (-\cos x^2)24x^2 + (-\cos x^2)24x^2 + (-\sin x^2)12$$
$$= (\sin x^2)16x^4 + (-\cos x^2)48x^2 + (-\sin x^2)12$$
$$f^{(5)}(x) = (\cos x^2)32x^5 + (\sin x^2)64x^3 + (\sin x^2)96x^3$$
$$\qquad + (-\cos x^2)96x + (-\cos x^2)24x$$
$$= (\cos x^2)32x^5 + (\sin x^2)160x^3 + (-\cos x^2)120x$$
$$f^{(6)}(x) = (-\sin x^2)64x^6 + (\cos x^2)160x^4 + (\cos x^2)320x^4 + (\sin x^2)480x^2$$
$$\qquad + (\sin x^2)240x^2 + (-\cos x^2)120$$
$$= (-\sin x^2)64x^6 + (\cos x^2)480x^4 + (\sin x^2)720x^2 + (-\cos x^2)120$$

So,

$$\begin{aligned}
f(0) &= 0 & f^{(4)}(0) &= \quad 0, \\
f'(0) &= 0 & f^{(5)}(0) &= \quad 0, \\
f''(0) &= 2 & f^{(6)}(0) &= -120, \\
f'''(0) &= 0.
\end{aligned}$$

Thus

$$f(x) = \sin x^2 = \frac{2}{2!}x^2 - \frac{120}{6!}x^6 + \cdots$$

$$= x^2 - \frac{1}{3!}x^6 + \cdots.$$

As we can see, the amount of calculation in order to find the higher derivatives of $\sin x^2$ increases very rapidly. In fact, the next non-zero term in the Taylor expansion of $\sin x^2$ is the 10th derivative term, which really requires a lot of work to get.

(b)

$$\sin x = x - \frac{1}{3!}x^3 + \frac{1}{5!}x^5 - \cdots$$

The first couple of coefficients of the above expansion are the same as those in part (a). If we substitute x^2 for x in the Taylor expansion of $\sin x$, we should get the Taylor expansion of $\sin x^2$.

$$\sin x^2 = x^2 - \frac{1}{3!}(x^2)^3 + \frac{1}{5!}(x^2)^5 - \cdots$$

$$= x^2 - \frac{1}{3!}x^6 + \frac{1}{5!}x^{10} - \cdots.$$

25. (a) $f(x) = \ln(1 + 2x)$ $f(0) = 0$
   $f'(x) = \frac{2}{1+2x}$ $f'(0) = 2$
   $f''(x) = -\frac{4}{(1+2x)^2}$ $f''(0) = -4$
   $f'''(x) = \frac{16}{(1+2x)^3}$ $f'''(0) = 16$

$$\ln(1 + 2x) = 2x - 2x^2 + \frac{8}{3}x^3 + \cdots$$

(b) To get the expression for $\ln(1 + 2x)$ from the series for $\ln(1 + x)$, substitute $2x$ for x in the series

$$\ln(1 + x) = x - \frac{x^2}{2} + \frac{x^3}{3} - \frac{x^4}{4} + \cdots$$

to get

$$\ln(1 + 2x) = 2x - \frac{(2x)^2}{2} + \frac{(2x)^3}{3} - \frac{(2x)^4}{4} + \cdots$$

$$= 2x - 2x^2 + \frac{8x^3}{3} - 4x^4 + \cdots$$

(c) Since the interval of convergence for $\ln(1 + x)$ is $-1 < x < 1$, substituting $2x$ for x suggests the interval of convergence of $\ln(1 + 2x)$ is $-1 < 2x < 1$, or $-\frac{1}{2} < x < \frac{1}{2}$.

26. By looking at Figure 10.4, we see that the Taylor polynomials are reasonable approximations for the function $f(x) = \sqrt{1+x}$ between $x = -1$ and $x = 1$. Thus a good guess is that the interval of convergence is $-1 < x < 1$.

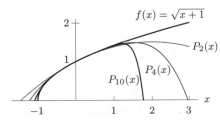

Figure 10.4

27. By looking at Figure 10.5 we can that the Taylor polynomials are reasonable approximations for the function $f(x) = \frac{1}{\sqrt{1+x}}$ between $x = -1$ and $x = 1$. Thus a good guess is that the interval of convergence is $-1 < x < 1$.

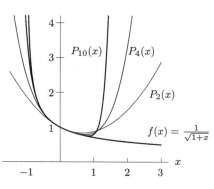

Figure 10.5

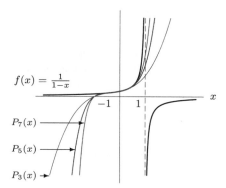

Figure 10.6

28. The graph suggests that the Taylor polynomials converge to $f(x) = \dfrac{1}{1-x}$ on the interval $-1 < x < 1$. See Figure 10.6. Since

$$\frac{1}{1-x} = 1 + x + x^2 + x^3 \cdots.$$

the ratio test gives

$$\lim_{n\to\infty} \frac{|a_{n+1}|}{|a_n|} = \lim_{n\to\infty} \frac{|x^{n+1}|}{|x^n|} = |x|.$$

Thus, the series converges if $|x| < 1|$; that is, $-1 < x < 1$.

29. The Taylor series for $\ln(1-x)$ is

$$\ln(1-x) = -x - \frac{x^2}{2} - \frac{x^3}{3} - \cdots - \frac{x^n}{n} - \cdots,$$

so

$$\lim_{n\to\infty} \frac{|a_{n+1}|}{|a_n|} = |x| \lim_{n\to\infty} \frac{1/(n+1)}{1/n} = |x| \lim_{n\to\infty} \left|\frac{n}{n+1}\right| = |x|.$$

Thus the series converges for $|x| < 1$, and the radius of convergence is 1. Note: This series can be obtained from the series for $\ln(1+x)$ by replacing x by $-x$ and has the same radius of convergence as the series for $\ln(1+x)$.

30. (a) We have shown that the series is

$$1 + px + \frac{p(p-1)}{2!}x^2 + \frac{p(p-1)(p-2)}{3!}x^3 + \cdots$$

so the general term is

$$\frac{p(p-1)\ldots(p-(n-1))}{n!}x^n.$$

(b) We use the ratio test

$$\lim_{n\to\infty} \frac{|a_{n+1}|}{|a_n|} = |x| \lim_{n\to\infty} \left|\frac{p(p-1)\ldots(p-(n-1))(p-n)\cdot n!}{(n+1)!p(p-1)\ldots(p-(n-1))}\right| = |x| \lim_{n\to\infty} \left|\frac{p-n}{n+1}\right|.$$

Since p is fixed, we have

$$\lim_{n\to\infty} \left|\frac{p-n}{n+1}\right| = 1, \quad \text{so} \quad R = 1.$$

31. This is the series for e^x with x replaced by 2, so the series converges to e^2.

32. This is the series for $\sin x$ with x replaced by 1, so the series converges to $\sin 1$.

33. This is the series for $1/(1-x)$ with x replaced by $1/4$, so the series converges to $1/(1-(1/4)) = 4/3$.

34. This is the series for $\cos x$ with x replaced by 10, so the series converges to $\cos 10$.

35. This is the series for $\ln(1+x)$ with x replaced by $1/2$, so the series converges to $\ln(3/2)$.

36. The Taylor series for $f(x) = 1/(1 + x)$ is

$$\frac{1}{1+x} = 1 - x + x^2 - x^3 + \cdots.$$

Substituting $x = 0.1$ gives

$$1 - 0.1 + (0.1)^2 - (0.1)^3 + \cdots = \frac{1}{1 + 0.1} = \frac{1}{1.1}.$$

Alternatively, this is a geometric series with $a = 1$, $x = -0.1$.

37. This is the series for e^x with $x = 3$ substituted. Thus

$$1 + 3 + \frac{9}{2!} + \frac{27}{3!} + \frac{81}{4!} + \cdots = 1 + 3 + \frac{3^2}{2!} + \frac{3^3}{3!} + \frac{3^4}{4!} + \cdots = e^3.$$

38. This is the series for $\cos x$ with $x = 1$ substituted. Thus

$$1 - \frac{1}{2!} + \frac{1}{4!} - \frac{1}{6!} + \cdots = \cos 1.$$

39. This is the series for e^x with -0.1 substituted for x, so

$$1 - 0.1 + \frac{0.01}{2!} - \frac{0.001}{3!} + \cdots = e^{-0.1}.$$

40. Since $1 + x + x^2 + x^3 + \cdots = \dfrac{1}{1-x}$, a geometric series, we solve $\dfrac{1}{1-x} = 5$ giving $\dfrac{1}{5} = 1 - x$, so $x = \dfrac{4}{5}$.

41. Since $x - \dfrac{1}{2}x^2 + \dfrac{1}{3}x^3 + \cdots = \ln(1 + x)$, we solve $\ln(1 + x) = 0.2$, giving $1 + x = e^{0.2}$, so $x = e^{0.2} - 1$.

42. (a) From the coefficients of the $(x - 1)$ terms of the fs, we see that

$$f_1'(1) = 1, \qquad f_2'(1) = -1 \qquad f_3'(1) = -2.$$

From the $(x - 1)^2$ terms of the fs, we see that

$$\frac{f_1''(1)}{2!} = -1, \qquad \frac{f_2''(1)}{2!} = 1, \qquad \frac{f_3''(1)}{2!} = 1,$$

so $f_1''(1) = -2$, $f_2''(1) = 2$, $f_3''(1) = 2$.

Thus, f_1 slopes up at $x = 1$ and f_2 and f_3 slope down; f_3 slopes down more steeply than f_2. This means that the fs are in the first figure, since graphs II and III in the second figure have the same negative slope at point B.

By a similar argument, we find

$$g_1'(4) = -1, \quad g_2'(4) = -1, \quad g_3'(4) = 1, \text{ and } g_1''(4) = -2, \quad g_2''(4) = 2, \quad g_3''(4) = 2.$$

Thus, two of the gs slope down, one of which is concave up and one is concave down; the third g slopes up and is concave up. This confirms that the gs are in the second figure.

(b) Since $f_1(1) = f_2(1) = f_3(1) = 3$, the point A is $(1, 3)$.

Since $g_1(4) = g_2(4) = g_3(4) = 5$, the point B is $(4, 5)$.

(c) In the first figure, graph I is f_1 since it slopes up. Graph II is f_2 since it slopes down, but less steeply than graph III, which is f_3.

In the second figure, graph I is g_3, since it slopes up. Graph II is g_2 since it slopes down and is concave up. Graph III is g_1 since it slopes down and is concave down.

43. Let C_n be the coefficient of the nth term in the series. Note that

$$0 = C_1 = \left.\frac{d}{dx}(x^2 e^{x^2})\right|_{x=0},$$

and since

$$\frac{1}{2} = C_6 = \frac{\left.\dfrac{d^6}{dx^6}(x^2 e^{x^2})\right|_{x=0}}{6!},$$

we have

$$\left.\frac{d^6}{dx^6}(x^2 e^{x^2})\right|_{x=0} = \frac{6!}{2} = 360.$$

44. Let C_n be the coefficient of the nth term in the series. $C_1 = f'(0)/1!$, so $f'(0) = 1!C_1 = 1 \cdot 1 = 1$.
Similarly, $f''(0) = 2!C_2 = 2! \cdot \frac{1}{2} = 1$;
$f'''(0) = 3!C_3 = 3! \cdot \frac{1}{3} = 2! = 2$;
$f^{(10)}(0) = 10!C_{10} = 10! \cdot \frac{1}{10} = \frac{10!}{10} = 9! = 362880$.

45. We define $e^{i\theta}$ to be

$$e^{i\theta} = 1 + i\theta + \frac{(i\theta)^2}{2!} + \frac{(i\theta)^3}{3!} + \frac{(i\theta)^4}{4!} + \frac{(i\theta)^5}{5!} + \frac{(i\theta)^6}{6!} + \cdots$$

Suppose we consider the expression $\cos\theta + i\sin\theta$, with $\cos\theta$ and $\sin\theta$ replaced by their Taylor series:

$$\cos\theta + i\sin\theta = \left(1 - \frac{\theta^2}{2!} + \frac{\theta^4}{4!} - \frac{\theta^6}{6!} + \cdots\right) + i\left(\theta - \frac{\theta^3}{3!} + \frac{\theta^5}{5!} - \cdots\right)$$

Reordering terms, we have

$$\cos\theta + i\sin\theta = 1 + i\theta - \frac{\theta^2}{2!} - \frac{i\theta^3}{3!} + \frac{\theta^4}{4!} + \frac{i\theta^5}{5!} - \frac{\theta^6}{6!} - \cdots$$

Using the fact that $i^2 = -1$, $i^3 = -i$, $i^4 = 1$, $i^5 = i, \cdots$, we can rewrite the series as

$$\cos\theta + i\sin\theta = 1 + i\theta + \frac{(i\theta)^2}{2!} + \frac{(i\theta)^3}{3!} + \frac{(i\theta)^4}{4!} + \frac{(i\theta)^5}{5!} + \frac{(i\theta)^6}{6!} + \cdots$$

Amazingly enough, this series is the Taylor series for e^x with $i\theta$ substituted for x. Therefore, we have shown that

$$\cos\theta + i\sin\theta = e^{i\theta}.$$

Solutions for Section 10.3

Exercises

1. Substitute $y = -x$ into $e^y = 1 + y + \frac{y^2}{2!} + \frac{y^3}{3!} + \cdots$. We get

$$e^{-x} = 1 + (-x) + \frac{(-x)^2}{2!} + \frac{(-x)^3}{3!} + \cdots$$
$$= 1 - x + \frac{x^2}{2!} - \frac{x^3}{3!} + \cdots.$$

2. Substitute $x = \theta^2$ into series for $\cos x$:

$$\cos(\theta^2) = 1 - \frac{(\theta^2)^2}{2!} + \frac{(\theta^2)^4}{4!} - \frac{(\theta^2)^6}{6!} + \cdots$$
$$= 1 - \frac{\theta^4}{2!} + \frac{\theta^8}{4!} - \frac{\theta^{12}}{6!} + \cdots.$$

3. We'll use

$$\sqrt{1+y} = (1+y)^{\frac{1}{2}} = 1 + \left(\frac{1}{2}\right)y + \left(\frac{1}{2}\right)\left(\frac{-1}{2}\right)\frac{y^2}{2!}$$
$$+ \left(\frac{1}{2}\right)\left(\frac{-1}{2}\right)\left(\frac{-3}{2}\right)\frac{y^3}{3!} + \cdots$$
$$= 1 + \frac{y}{2} - \frac{y^2}{8} + \frac{y^3}{16} - \cdots.$$

Substitute $y = -2x$.

$$\sqrt{1-2x} = 1 + \frac{(-2x)}{2} - \frac{(-2x)^2}{8} + \frac{(-2x)^3}{16} - \cdots$$
$$= 1 - x - \frac{x^2}{2} - \frac{x^3}{2} - \cdots.$$

4. Substituting $x = -2y$ into $\ln(1 + x) = x - \frac{x^2}{2} + \frac{x^3}{3} - \frac{x^4}{4} + \cdots$ gives

$$\ln(1 - 2y) = (-2y) - \frac{(-2y)^2}{2} + \frac{(-2y)^3}{3} - \frac{(-2y)^4}{4} + \cdots$$

$$= -2y - 2y^2 - \frac{8}{3}y^3 - 4y^4 - \cdots.$$

5. Since $\frac{d}{dx}(\arcsin x) = \frac{1}{\sqrt{1-x^2}} = 1 + \frac{1}{2}x^2 + \frac{3}{8}x^4 + \frac{5}{16}x^6 + \cdots$, integrating gives

$$\arcsin x = c + x + \frac{1}{6}x^3 + \frac{3}{40}x^5 + \frac{5}{112}x^7 + \cdots.$$

Since $\arcsin 0 = 0$, $c = 0$.

6.

$$\phi^3 \cos(\phi^2) = \phi^3 \left(1 - \frac{(\phi^2)^2}{2!} + \frac{(\phi^2)^4}{4!} - \frac{(\phi^2)^6}{6!} + \cdots \right)$$

$$= \phi^3 - \frac{\phi^7}{2!} + \frac{\phi^{11}}{4!} - \frac{\phi^{15}}{6!} + \cdots$$

7. Substituting $x = -z^2$ into $\frac{1}{\sqrt{1+x}} = (1 + x)^{-\frac{1}{2}} = 1 - \frac{1}{2}x + \frac{3}{8}x^2 - \frac{5}{16}x^3 + \cdots$ gives

$$\frac{1}{\sqrt{1 - z^2}} = 1 - \frac{(-z^2)}{2} + \frac{3(-z^2)^2}{8} - \frac{5(-z^2)^3}{16} + \cdots$$

$$= 1 + \frac{1}{2}z^2 + \frac{3}{8}z^4 + \frac{5}{16}z^6 + \cdots.$$

8.

$$\frac{z}{e^{z^2}} = ze^{-z^2} = z \left(1 + (-z^2) + \frac{(-z^2)^2}{2!} + \frac{(-z^2)^3}{3!} + \cdots \right)$$

$$= z - z^3 + \frac{z^5}{2!} - \frac{z^7}{3!} + \cdots$$

9. We substitute $3t$ into the series for $\sin x$ and multiply by t. Since

$$\sin x = x - \frac{x^3}{3!} + \frac{x^5}{5!} - \frac{x^7}{7!} + \cdots,$$

substituting $3t$ gives

$$\sin(3t) = (3t) - \frac{(3t)^3}{3!} + \frac{(3t)^5}{5!} - \frac{(3t)^7}{7!} + \cdots$$

$$= 3t + \frac{-9}{2}t^3 + \frac{81}{40}t^5 + \frac{-243}{560}t^7 + \cdots,$$

so

$$t \sin(3t) = 3t^2 - \frac{9}{2}t^4 + \frac{81}{40}t^6 - \frac{243}{560}t^8 + \cdots.$$

10. Substituting the series for $\sin \theta = \theta - \frac{\theta^3}{3!} + \frac{\theta^5}{5!} - \cdots$ into

$$\sqrt{1 + y} = 1 + \frac{1}{2}y - \frac{1}{8}y^2 + \frac{1}{16}y^3 - \cdots$$

gives

$$\sqrt{1 + \sin \theta} = 1 + \frac{1}{2} \left(\theta - \frac{\theta^3}{3!} + \frac{\theta^5}{5!} - \cdots \right) - \frac{1}{8} \left(\theta - \frac{\theta^3}{3!} + \frac{\theta^5}{5!} - \cdots \right)^2$$

$$+ \frac{1}{16} \left(\theta - \frac{\theta^3}{3!} + \frac{\theta^5}{5!} - \cdots \right)^3 - \cdots$$

$$= 1 + \frac{1}{2}\theta - \frac{\theta^2}{8} + \left(\frac{\theta^3}{16} - \frac{\theta^3}{2 \cdot 3!} \right) + \cdots$$

$$= 1 + \frac{1}{2}\theta - \frac{1}{8}\theta^2 - \frac{1}{48}\theta^3 + \cdots$$

11.

$$\sqrt{(1+t)}\sin t = \left(1 + \frac{t}{2} - \frac{t^2}{8} + \frac{t^3}{16} - \cdots\right)\left(t - \frac{t^3}{3!} + \frac{t^5}{5!} - \cdots\right)$$

Multiplying and collecting terms yields

$$\sqrt{(1+t)}\sin t = t + \frac{t^2}{2} - \left(\frac{t^3}{3!} + \frac{t^3}{8}\right) + \left(\frac{t^4}{16} - \frac{t^4}{12}\right) + \cdots$$

$$= t + \frac{1}{2}t^2 - \frac{7}{24}t^3 - \frac{1}{48}t^4 + \cdots.$$

12.

$$e^t \cos t = \left(1 + t + \frac{t^2}{2!} + \frac{t^3}{3!} + \frac{t^4}{4!} + \cdots\right)\left(1 - \frac{t^2}{2!} + \frac{t^4}{4!} - \frac{t^6}{6!} + \cdots\right)$$

Multiplying out and collecting terms gives

$$e^t \cos t = 1 + t + \left(\frac{t^2}{2!} - \frac{t^2}{2!}\right) + \left(\frac{t^3}{3!} - \frac{t^3}{2!}\right) + \left(\frac{t^4}{4!} + \frac{t^4}{4!} - \frac{t^4}{(2!)^2}\right) + \cdots$$

$$= 1 + t - \frac{t^3}{3} - \frac{t^4}{6} + \cdots.$$

13. Multiplying out gives $(1+x)^3 = 1 + 3x + 3x^2 + x^3$. Since this polynomial equals the original function for all x, it must be the Taylor series. The general term is $0 \cdot x^n$ for $n \geq 4$.

14. Substituting t^2 into the series for $\sin x$ gives

$$\sin(t^2) = t^2 - \frac{(t^2)^3}{3!} + \frac{(t^2)^5}{5!} + \cdots + \frac{(-1)^k(t^2)^{2k+1}}{(2k+1)!} + \cdots$$

$$= t^2 - \frac{t^6}{3!} + \frac{t^{10}}{5!} + \cdots + \frac{(-1)^k t^{4k+2}}{(2k+1)!} + \cdots$$

Therefore

$$t\sin(t^2) - t^3 = \left(t^3 - \frac{t^7}{3!} + \frac{t^{11}}{5!} + \cdots + \frac{(-1)^k t^{4k+3}}{(2k+1)!} + \cdots\right) - t^3$$

$$= -\frac{t^7}{3!} + \frac{t^{11}}{5!} + \cdots + \frac{(-1)^k t^{4k+3}}{(2k+1)!} + \cdots \quad \text{for } k \geq 1.$$

15. Using the Binomial theorem:

$$\frac{1}{\sqrt{1-x}}$$

$$= (1-x)^{-1/2}$$

$$= 1 + \left(-\frac{1}{2}\right)(-x) + \frac{(-1/2)(-3/2)(-x)^2}{2!} + \cdots + \frac{(-1/2)(-3/2)\cdots(-\frac{1}{2}-n+1)(-x)^n}{n!} + \cdots \text{ for } n \geq 1.$$

Substituting y^2 for x:

$$\frac{1}{\sqrt{1-y^2}} = (1-y^2)^{-1/2}$$

$$= 1 + \frac{1}{2}y^2 + \frac{3}{8}y^4 + \cdots + \frac{(1/2)(3/2)\cdots(\frac{1}{2}+n-1)y^{2n}}{n!} + \cdots \text{ for } n \geq 1.$$

16.

$$\frac{1}{2+x} = \frac{1}{2(1+\frac{x}{2})} = \frac{1}{2}\left(1+\frac{x}{2}\right)^{-1}$$

$$= \frac{1}{2}\left(1 - \frac{x}{2} + \left(\frac{x}{2}\right)^2 - \left(\frac{x}{2}\right)^3 + \cdots\right)$$

17. Using the binomial expansion for $(1+x)^{-1}$ with $x = -r/a$:

$$\frac{1}{a-r} = \frac{1}{a - a\left(\frac{r}{a}\right)} = \frac{1}{a\left(1 - \frac{r}{a}\right)} = \frac{1}{a}\left(1 + \left(-\frac{r}{a}\right)\right)^{-1}$$

$$= \frac{1}{a}\left(1 + (-1)\left(-\frac{r}{a}\right) + \frac{(-1)(-2)}{2!}\left(-\frac{r}{a}\right)^2 + \frac{(-1)(-2)(-3)}{3!}\left(-\frac{r}{a}\right)^3 + \cdots\right)$$

$$= \frac{1}{a}\left(1 - \left(-\frac{r}{a}\right) + \left(-\frac{r}{a}\right)^2 - \left(-\frac{r}{a}\right)^3 + \cdots\right)$$

$$= \frac{1}{a}\left(1 + \left(\frac{r}{a}\right) + \left(\frac{r}{a}\right)^2 + \left(\frac{r}{a}\right)^3 + \cdots\right).$$

18. Using the binomial expansion for $(1+x)^{1/2}$ with $x = h/T$:

$$\sqrt{T+h} = \left(T + \frac{T}{T}h\right)^{1/2} = \left(T\left(1 + \frac{h}{T}\right)\right)^{1/2} = \sqrt{T}\left(1 + \frac{h}{T}\right)^{1/2}$$

$$= \sqrt{T}\left(1 + (1/2)\left(\frac{h}{T}\right) + \frac{(1/2)(-1/2)}{2!}\left(\frac{h}{T}\right)^2 + \frac{(1/2)(-1/2)(-3/2)}{3!}\left(\frac{h}{T}\right)^3 \cdots\right)$$

$$= \sqrt{T}\left(1 + \frac{1}{2}\left(\frac{h}{T}\right) - \frac{1}{8}\left(\frac{h}{T}\right)^2 + \frac{1}{16}\left(\frac{h}{T}\right)^3 \cdots\right).$$

19.

$$\sqrt[3]{P+t} = \left(P + P\left(\frac{t}{P}\right)\right)^{1/3} = \left(P\left(1 + \frac{t}{P}\right)\right)^{1/3} = \sqrt[3]{P}\left(1 + \frac{t}{P}\right)^{1/3}$$

$$= \sqrt[3]{P}\left(1 + (1/3)\left(\frac{t}{P}\right) + \frac{(1/3)(-2/3)}{2!}\left(\frac{t}{P}\right)^2 + \frac{(1/3)(-2/3)(-5/3)}{3!}\left(\frac{t}{P}\right)^3 \cdots\right)$$

$$= \sqrt[3]{P}\left(1 + \frac{1}{3}\left(\frac{t}{P}\right) - \frac{1}{9}\left(\frac{t}{P}\right)^2 + \frac{5}{81}\left(\frac{t}{P}\right)^3 \cdots\right).$$

20. Using the binomial expansion for $(1+x)^{-2}$ with $x = r/a$:

$$\frac{1}{(a+r)^2} = \frac{1}{\left(a + a\left(\frac{r}{a}\right)\right)^2} = \frac{1}{\left(a\left(1 + \frac{r}{a}\right)\right)^2} = \frac{1}{a^2}\left(1 + \left(\frac{r}{a}\right)\right)^{-2}$$

$$= \frac{1}{a^2}\left(1 + (-2)\left(\frac{r}{a}\right) + \frac{(-2)(-3)}{2!}\left(\frac{r}{a}\right)^2 + \frac{(-2)(-3)(-4)}{3!}\left(\frac{r}{a}\right)^3 + \cdots\right)$$

$$= \frac{1}{a^2}\left(1 - 2\left(\frac{r}{a}\right) + 3\left(\frac{r}{a}\right)^2 - 4\left(\frac{r}{a}\right)^3 + \cdots\right).$$

21.

$$\frac{a}{\sqrt{a^2 + x^2}} = \frac{a}{a(1 + \frac{x^2}{a^2})^{\frac{1}{2}}} = \left(1 + \frac{x^2}{a^2}\right)^{-\frac{1}{2}}$$

$$= 1 + \left(-\frac{1}{2}\right)\frac{x^2}{a^2} + \frac{1}{2!}\left(-\frac{1}{2}\right)\left(-\frac{3}{2}\right)\left(\frac{x^2}{a^2}\right)^2$$

$$+ \frac{1}{3!}\left(-\frac{1}{2}\right)\left(-\frac{3}{2}\right)\left(-\frac{5}{2}\right)\left(\frac{x^2}{a^2}\right)^3 + \cdots$$

$$= 1 - \frac{1}{2}\left(\frac{x}{a}\right)^2 + \frac{3}{8}\left(\frac{x}{a}\right)^4 - \frac{5}{16}\left(\frac{x}{a}\right)^6 + \cdots$$

Problems

22. (a) Since the Taylor series for e^x and e^{-x} are given by

$$e^x = 1 + x + \frac{x^2}{2!} + \frac{x^3}{3!} + \frac{x^4}{4!} + \cdots$$

$$e^{-x} = 1 - x + \frac{x^2}{2!} - \frac{x^3}{3!} + \frac{x^4}{4!} + \cdots,$$

we have

$$e^x + e^{-x} = 2 + 0x + 2\frac{x^2}{2!} + 0\frac{x^3}{3!} + 2\frac{x^4}{4!} + \cdots = 2 + x^2 + \frac{x^4}{12} + \cdots.$$

(b) For x near 0, we can approximate $e^x + e^{-x}$ by its second degree Taylor polynomial, $P_2(x)$, whose graph is a parabola:

$$e^x + e^{-x} \approx P_2(x) = 2 + x^2.$$

23. (a) Since the Taylor series for e^x and e^{-x} are given by

$$e^x = 1 + x + \frac{x^2}{2!} + \frac{x^3}{3!} + \frac{x^4}{4!} + \frac{x^5}{5!} + \cdots$$

$$e^{-x} = 1 - x + \frac{x^2}{2!} - \frac{x^3}{3!} + \frac{x^4}{4!} - \frac{x^5}{5!} + \cdots,$$

we have

$$e^x - e^{-x} = 0 + 2x + 0\frac{x^2}{2!} + 2\frac{x^3}{3!} + 0\frac{x^4}{4!} + 2\frac{x^5}{5!} \cdots = 2x + \frac{x^3}{3} + \frac{x^5}{60} + \cdots.$$

(b) For x near 0, we can approximate $e^x - e^{-x}$ by its third degree Taylor polynomial, $P_3(x)$:

$$e^x - e^{-x} \approx P_3(x) = 2x + \frac{x^3}{3}.$$

The function $P_3(x)$ is a cubic polynomial whose graph is symmetric about the origin.

24. Since it does not depend on n, we can factor out e^{-k}, giving

$$\sum_{n=1}^{\infty} \frac{k^{n-1}}{(n-1)!} e^{-k} = e^{-k} \sum_{n=1}^{\infty} \frac{k^{n-1}}{(n-1)!}$$

$$= e^{-k} \underbrace{\left(\frac{1}{0!} + \frac{k}{1!} + \frac{k^2}{2!} + \frac{k^3}{3!} + \cdots \right)}_{\text{This is the series for } e^k}$$

$$= e^{-k} \cdot e^k$$

$$= 1.$$

25. Notice that $\sum px^{p-1}$, is the derivative, term-by-term, of a geometric series:

$$\sum_{p=1}^{\infty} px^{p-1} = 1 \cdot x^0 + 2 \cdot x^1 + 3 \cdot x^2 + \cdots = \frac{d}{dx} \underbrace{(x + x^2 + x^3 + \cdots)}_{\text{Geometric series}}.$$

For $|x| < 1$, the sum of the geometric series with first term x and common ratio x is

$$x + x^2 + x^3 + \cdots = \frac{x}{1-x}.$$

Differentiating gives

$$\sum_{p=1}^{\infty} px^{p-1} = \frac{d}{dx} \left(\frac{x}{1-x} \right) = \frac{1(1-x) - x(-1)}{(1-x)^2} = \frac{1}{(1-x)^2}.$$

26. The Taylor expansion about $\theta = 0$ for $\sin \theta$ is

$$\theta - \frac{\theta^3}{3!} + \frac{\theta^5}{5!} - \frac{\theta^7}{7!} + \cdots.$$

So

$$1 + \sin \theta = 1 + \theta - \frac{\theta^3}{3!} + \frac{\theta^5}{5!} - \frac{\theta^7}{7!} + \cdots.$$

The Taylor expansion about $\theta = 0$ for $\cos \theta$ is

$$\cos \theta = 1 - \frac{\theta^2}{2!} + \frac{\theta^4}{4!} - \frac{\theta^6}{6!} + \cdots.$$

The Taylor expansion for $\dfrac{1}{1+\theta}$ about $\theta = 0$ is

$$\frac{1}{1+\theta} = 1 - \theta + \theta^2 - \theta^3 + \theta^4 - \cdots.$$

So, substituting $-\theta^2$ for θ:

$$\frac{1}{1-\theta^2} = 1 - (-\theta^2) + (-\theta^2)^2 - (-\theta^2)^3 + (-\theta^2)^4 + \cdots$$
$$= 1 + \theta^2 + \theta^4 + \theta^6 + \theta^8 + \cdots.$$

For small θ, we can neglect the terms above quadratic in these expansions, giving:

$$1 + \sin \theta \approx 1 + \theta$$
$$\cos \theta \approx 1 - \frac{\theta^2}{2}$$
$$\frac{1}{1-\theta^2} \approx 1 + \theta^2.$$

For all $\theta \neq 0$, we have

$$1 - \frac{\theta^2}{2} < 1 + \theta^2.$$

Also, since $\theta^2 < \theta$ for $0 < \theta < 1$, we have

$$1 - \frac{\theta^2}{2} < 1 + \theta^2 < 1 + \theta.$$

So, for small positive θ, we have

$$\cos \theta < \frac{1}{1-\theta^2} < 1 + \sin \theta.$$

27. From the series for $\ln(1+y)$,

$$\ln(1+y) = y - \frac{y^2}{2} + \frac{y^3}{3} - \frac{y^4}{4} + \cdots,$$

we get

$$\ln(1+y^2) = y^2 - \frac{y^4}{2} + \frac{y^6}{3} - \frac{y^8}{4} + \cdots$$

The Taylor series for $\sin y$ is

$$\sin y = y - \frac{y^3}{3!} + \frac{y^5}{5!} - \frac{y^7}{7!} + \cdots$$

So

$$\sin y^2 = y^2 - \frac{y^6}{3!} + \frac{y^{10}}{5!} - \frac{y^{14}}{7!} + \cdots$$

The Taylor series for $\cos y$ is

$$\cos y = 1 - \frac{y^2}{2!} + \frac{y^4}{4!} - \frac{y^6}{6!} + \cdots$$

So

$$1 - \cos y = \frac{y^2}{2!} - \frac{y^4}{4!} + \frac{y^6}{6!} + \cdots$$

Near $y = 0$, we can drop terms beyond the fourth degree in each expression:

$$\ln(1 + y^2) \approx y^2 - \frac{y^4}{2}$$

$$\sin y^2 \approx y^2$$

$$1 - \cos y \approx \frac{y^2}{2!} - \frac{y^4}{4!}.$$

(Note: These functions are all even, so what holds for negative y will hold for positive y.)
Clearly $1 - \cos y$ is smallest, because the y^2 term has a factor of $\frac{1}{2}$. Thus, for small y,

$$\frac{y^2}{2!} - \frac{y^4}{4!} < y^2 - \frac{y^4}{2} < y^2$$

so

$$1 - \cos y < \ln(1 + y^2) < \sin(y^2).$$

28. The Taylor series about 0 for $y = \dfrac{1}{1 - x^2}$ is

$$y = 1 + x^2 + x^4 + x^6 + \cdots.$$

The series for $y = (1 + x)^{1/4}$ is, using the binomial expansion,

$$y = 1 + \frac{1}{4}x + \frac{1}{4}\left(-\frac{3}{4}\right)\frac{x^2}{2!} + \frac{1}{4}\left(-\frac{3}{4}\right)\left(-\frac{7}{4}\right)\frac{x^3}{3!} + \cdots.$$

The series for $y = \sqrt{1 + \dfrac{x}{2}} = (1 + \dfrac{x}{2})^{1/2}$ is, again using the binomial expansion,

$$y = 1 + \frac{1}{2} \cdot \frac{x}{2} + \frac{1}{2}\left(-\frac{1}{2}\right) \cdot \frac{x^2}{8} + \frac{1}{2}\left(-\frac{1}{2}\right)\left(-\frac{3}{2}\right) \cdot \frac{x^3}{48} + \cdots.$$

Similarly for $y = \dfrac{1}{\sqrt{1 - x}} = (1 - x)^{-(1/2)}$,

$$y = 1 + \left(-\frac{1}{2}\right)(-x) + \left(-\frac{1}{2}\right)\left(-\frac{3}{2}\right) \cdot \frac{x^2}{2!} + \left(-\frac{1}{2}\right)\left(-\frac{3}{2}\right)\left(-\frac{5}{2}\right) \cdot \frac{-x^3}{3!} + \cdots.$$

Near 0, let's truncate these series after their x^2 terms:

$$\frac{1}{1 - x^2} \approx 1 + x^2,$$

$$(1 + x)^{1/4} \approx 1 + \frac{1}{4}x - \frac{3}{32}x^2,$$

$$\sqrt{1 + \frac{x}{2}} \approx 1 + \frac{1}{4}x - \frac{1}{32}x^2,$$

$$\frac{1}{\sqrt{1 - x}} \approx 1 + \frac{1}{2}x + \frac{3}{8}x^2.$$

Thus $\frac{1}{1-x^2}$ looks like a parabola opening upward near the origin, with y-axis as the axis of symmetry, so (a) = I.

Now $\frac{1}{\sqrt{1-x}}$ has the largest positive slope ($\frac{1}{2}$), and is concave up (because the coefficient of x^2 is positive). So (d) = II.

The last two both have positive slope ($\frac{1}{4}$) and are concave down. Since $(1 + x)^{\frac{1}{4}}$ has the smallest second derivative (i.e., the most negative coefficient of x^2), (b) = IV and therefore (c) = III.

29.

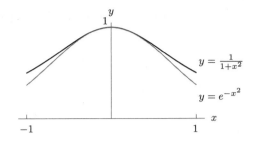

(a)

$$e^{-x^2} = 1 - x^2 + \frac{x^4}{2!} - \frac{x^6}{3!} + \cdots$$

$$\frac{1}{1 + x^2} = 1 - x^2 + x^4 - x^6 + \cdots$$

Notice that the first two terms are the same in both series.

(b) $\dfrac{1}{1 + x^2}$ is greater.

(c) Even, because the only terms involved are of even degree.

(d) The coefficients for e^{-x^2} become extremely small for higher powers of x, and we can "counteract" the effect of these powers for large values of x. The series for $\frac{1}{1+x^2}$ has no such coefficients.

30. (a) The Taylor approximation to $f(x) = \cosh x$ about $x = 0$ is of the form

$$\cosh x \approx \cosh(0) + f'(0)x + \frac{f''(0)x^2}{2!} + \ldots + \frac{f^{(n)}(0)x^n}{n!}.$$

We have the following results:

$$f(x) = \cosh x \quad \text{so } f(0) = 1,$$
$$f'(x) = \sinh x \quad \text{so } f'(0) = 0,$$
$$f''(x) = \frac{d}{dx}(\sinh x) = \cosh x \quad \text{so } f''(0) = 1,$$
$$f'''(x) = \sinh x \quad \text{so } f'''(0) = 0.$$

The derivatives continue to alternate between $\cosh x$ and $\sinh x$, so their values at 0 continue to alternate between 0 and 1. Therefore

$$\cosh x \approx 1 + 0 \cdot x + 1 \cdot \frac{x^2}{2!} + 0 \cdot \frac{x^3}{3!} + 1 \cdot \frac{x^4}{4!} + \cdots,$$

so the degree 8 Taylor approximation is given by

$$\cosh x \approx 1 + \frac{x^2}{2!} + \frac{x^4}{4!} + \frac{x^6}{6!} + \frac{x^8}{8!}.$$

(b) We use the polynomial obtained from part (a) to estimate $\cosh 1$,

$$\cosh 1 \approx 1 + \frac{1}{2!} + \frac{1}{4!} + \frac{1}{6!} + \frac{1}{8!} = 1.543080357.$$

Compared to the actual value of $\cosh 1 = 1.543080635\ldots$, the error is less than 10^{-6}.

(c) Since $\dfrac{d}{dx}(\cosh x) = \sinh x$, we have

$$\sinh x \approx \frac{d}{dx}\left(1 + \frac{x^2}{2!} + \frac{x^4}{4!} + \frac{x^6}{6!} + \frac{x^8}{8!}\right)$$
$$= \frac{2x}{2!} + \frac{4x^3}{4!} + \frac{6x^5}{6!} + \frac{8x^7}{8!}$$
$$= x + \frac{x^3}{3!} + \frac{x^5}{5!} + \frac{x^7}{7!}.$$

31. Since $e^x = \sum_{n=0}^{\infty} \dfrac{x^n}{n!}$ and $\sinh 2x = (e^{2x} - e^{-2x})/2$, the Taylor expansion for $\sinh 2x$ is

$$\sinh 2x = \frac{1}{2}\left(\sum_{n=0}^{\infty} \frac{(2x)^n}{n!} - \sum_{n=0}^{\infty} \frac{(-2x)^n}{n!}\right) = \frac{1}{2}\left(\sum_{n=0}^{\infty}(1 - (-1)^n)\frac{(2x)^n}{n!}\right)$$

$$= \sum_{m=0}^{\infty} \frac{(2x)^{2m+1}}{(2m+1)!}.$$

Since $\cosh 2x = (e^{2x} + e^{-2x})/2$, we have

$$\cosh 2x = \frac{1}{2}\left(\sum_{n=0}^{\infty} \frac{(2x)^n}{n!} + \sum_{n=0}^{\infty} \frac{(-2x)^n}{n!}\right) = \frac{1}{2}\left(\sum_{n=0}^{\infty}(1 + (-1)^n)\frac{(2x)^n}{n!}\right)$$

$$= \sum_{m=0}^{\infty} \frac{(2x)^{2m}}{(2m)!}.$$

32. (a) $\qquad f(x) = (1 + ax)(1 + bx)^{-1} = (1 + ax)\left(1 - bx + (bx)^2 - (bx)^3 + \cdots\right)$

$$= 1 + (a - b)x + (b^2 - ab)x^2 + \cdots$$

(b) $e^x = 1 + x + \frac{x^2}{2} + \cdots$
Equating coefficients:

$$a - b = 1,$$
$$b^2 - ab = \frac{1}{2}.$$

Solving gives $a = \frac{1}{2}$, $b = -\frac{1}{2}$.

33.

$$E = kQ\left(\frac{1}{(R-1)^2} - \frac{1}{(R+1)^2}\right)$$

$$= \frac{kQ}{R^2}\left(\frac{1}{(1 - \frac{1}{R})^2} - \frac{1}{(1 + \frac{1}{R})^2}\right)$$

Since $|\frac{1}{R}| < 1$, we can expand the two terms using the binomial expansion:

$$\frac{1}{(1 - \frac{1}{R})^2} = \left(1 - \frac{1}{R}\right)^{-2}$$

$$= 1 - 2\left(-\frac{1}{R}\right) + (-2)(-3)\frac{(-\frac{1}{R})^2}{2!} + (-2)(-3)(-4)\frac{(-\frac{1}{R})^3}{3!} + \cdots$$

$$\frac{1}{(1 + \frac{1}{R})^2} = \left(1 + \frac{1}{R}\right)^{-2}$$

$$= 1 - 2\left(\frac{1}{R}\right) + (-2)(-3)\frac{(\frac{1}{R})^2}{2!} + (-2)(-3)(-4)\frac{(\frac{1}{R})^3}{3!} + \cdots$$

Substituting, we get:

$$E = \frac{kQ}{R^2}\left[1 + \frac{2}{R} + \frac{3}{R^2} + \frac{4}{R^3} + \cdots - \left(1 - \frac{2}{R} + \frac{3}{R^2} - \frac{4}{R^3} + \cdots\right)\right] \approx \frac{kQ}{R^2}\left(\frac{4}{R} + \frac{8}{R^3}\right),$$

using only the first two non-zero terms.

34. Using the binomial expansion we have

$$\sqrt{a^2 + x^2} = a\left(1 + \frac{x^2}{a^2}\right)^{1/2}$$

$$= a\left(1 + \frac{1}{2}\frac{x^2}{a^2} + \frac{(1/2)(-1/2)}{2!}\frac{x^4}{a^4} + \frac{(1/2)(-1/2)(-3/2)}{3!}\frac{x^6}{a^6} + \cdots\right)$$

$$= a\left(1 + \frac{1}{2}\frac{x^2}{a^2} - \frac{1}{8}\frac{x^4}{a^4} + \frac{1}{16}\frac{x^6}{a^6} + \cdots\right).$$

Similarly, we have

$$\sqrt{a^2 - x^2} = a\left(1 - \frac{1}{2}\frac{x^2}{a^2} - \frac{1}{8}\frac{x^4}{a^4} - \frac{1}{16}\frac{x^6}{a^6} - \cdots\right).$$

Combining gives

$$z = \sqrt{a^2 + x^2} - \sqrt{a^2 - x^2} = a\left(2 \cdot \frac{1}{2}\frac{x^2}{a^2} + 2 \cdot \frac{1}{16}\frac{x^6}{a^6} + \cdots\right) = \frac{x^2}{a} + \frac{1}{8}\frac{x^6}{a^5} + \cdots.$$

35. This time we are interested in how a function behaves at large values in its domain. Therefore, we don't want to expand $V = 2\pi\sigma(\sqrt{R^2 + a^2} - R)$ about $R = 0$. We want to find a variable which becomes small as R gets large. Since $R > a$, it is helpful to write

$$V = R2\pi\sigma\left(\sqrt{1 + \frac{a^2}{R^2}} - 1\right).$$

We can now expand a series in terms of $\left(\frac{a}{R}\right)^2$. This may seem strange, but suspend your disbelief. The Taylor series for $\sqrt{1 + \frac{a^2}{R^2}}$ is

$$1 + \frac{1}{2}\frac{a^2}{R^2} + \frac{(1/2)(-1/2)}{2}\left(\frac{a^2}{R^2}\right)^2 + \cdots$$

So $V = R2\pi\sigma\left(1 + \frac{1}{2}\frac{a^2}{R^2} - \frac{1}{8}\left(\frac{a^2}{R^2}\right)^2 + \cdots - 1\right)$. For large R, we can drop the $-\frac{1}{8}\frac{a^4}{R^4}$ term and terms of higher order, so

$$V \approx \frac{\pi\sigma a^2}{R}.$$

Notice that what we really did by expanding around $\left(\frac{a}{R}\right)^2 = 0$ was expanding around $R = \infty$. We then get a series that converges for large R.

36. (a) If $\phi = 0$,

$$\text{left side} = b(1 + 1 + 1) = 3b \approx 0$$

so the equation is almost satisfied and there could be a solution near $\phi = 0$.

(b) We have

$$\sin\phi = \phi - \frac{\phi^3}{3!} + \frac{\phi^5}{5!} - \cdots$$

$$\cos\phi = 1 - \frac{\phi^2}{2!} + \frac{\phi^4}{4!} - \cdots$$

So

$$\cos^2\phi = \left(1 - \frac{\phi^2}{2!} + \frac{\phi^4}{4!} - \cdots\right)\left(1 - \frac{\phi^2}{2!} + \frac{\phi^4}{4!} - \cdots\right).$$

Neglecting terms of order ϕ^2 and higher, we get

$$\sin\phi \approx \phi$$
$$\cos\phi \approx 1$$
$$\cos^2\phi \approx 1.$$

So $\phi + b(1 + 1 + 1) \approx 0$, whence $\phi \approx -3b$.

37. (a) Factoring the expression for $t_1 - t_2$, we get

$$\Delta t = t_1 - t_2 = \frac{2l_2}{c(1 - v^2/c^2)} - \frac{2l_1}{c\sqrt{1 - v^2/c^2}} - \frac{2l_2}{c\sqrt{1 - v^2/c^2}} + \frac{2l_1}{c(1 - v^2/c^2)}$$

$$= \frac{2(l_1 + l_2)}{c(1 - v^2/c^2)} - \frac{2(l_1 + l_2)}{c\sqrt{1 - v^2/c^2}}$$

$$= \frac{2(l_1 + l_2)}{c} \left(\frac{1}{1 - v^2/c^2} - \frac{1}{\sqrt{1 - v^2/c^2}} \right).$$

Expanding the two terms within the parentheses in terms of v^2/c^2 gives

$$\left(1 - \frac{v^2}{c^2} \right)^{-1} = 1 + \frac{v^2}{c^2} + \frac{(-1)(-2)}{2!} \left(\frac{-v^2}{c^2} \right)^2 + \frac{(-1)(-2)(-3)}{3!} \left(\frac{-v^2}{c^2} \right)^3 + \cdots$$

$$= 1 + \frac{v^2}{c^2} + \frac{v^4}{c^4} + \frac{v^6}{c^6} + \cdots$$

$$\left(1 - \frac{v^2}{c^2} \right)^{-1/2} = 1 + \frac{1}{2} \frac{v^2}{c^2} + \frac{\left(\frac{-1}{2} \right) \left(\frac{-3}{2} \right)}{2!} \left(\frac{-v^2}{c^2} \right)^2 + \frac{\left(\frac{-1}{2} \right) \left(\frac{-3}{2} \right) \left(\frac{-5}{2} \right)}{3!} \left(\frac{-v^2}{c^2} \right)^3 + \cdots$$

$$= 1 + \frac{1}{2} \frac{v^2}{c^2} + \frac{3}{8} \frac{v^4}{c^4} + \frac{5}{16} \frac{v^6}{c^6} + \cdots$$

Thus, we have

$$\Delta t = \frac{2(l_1 + l_2)}{c} \left(1 + \frac{v^2}{c^2} + \frac{v^4}{c^4} + \frac{v^6}{c^6} + \cdots - 1 - \frac{1}{2} \frac{v^2}{c^2} - \frac{3}{8} \frac{v^4}{c^4} - \frac{5}{16} \frac{v^6}{c^6} - \cdots \right)$$

$$= \frac{2(l_1 + l_2)}{c} \left(\frac{1}{2} \frac{v^2}{c^2} + \frac{5}{8} \frac{v^4}{c^4} + \frac{11}{16} \frac{v^6}{c^6} + \cdots \right)$$

$$\Delta t \approx \frac{(l_1 + l_2)}{c} \left(\frac{v^2}{c^2} + \frac{5}{4} \frac{v^4}{c^4} \right).$$

(b) For small v. we can neglect all but the first nonzero term, so

$$\Delta t \approx \frac{(l_1 + l_2)}{c} \cdot \frac{v^2}{c^2} = \frac{(l_1 + l_2)}{c^3} v^2.$$

Thus, Δt is proportional to v^2 with constant of proportionality $(l_1 + l_2)/c^3$.

38. (a) $\mu = \dfrac{mM}{m + M}$.

If $M \gg m$, then the denominator $m + M \approx M$, so $\mu \approx \dfrac{mM}{M} = m$.

(b)

$$\mu = m \left(\frac{M}{m + M} \right) = m \left(\frac{\frac{1}{M} M}{\frac{m}{M} + \frac{M}{M}} \right) = m \left(\frac{1}{1 + \frac{m}{M}} \right)$$

We can use the binomial expansion since $\frac{m}{M} < 1$.

$$\mu = m \left[1 - \frac{m}{M} + \left(\frac{m}{M} \right)^2 - \left(\frac{m}{M} \right)^3 + \cdots \right]$$

(c) If $m \approx \dfrac{1}{1836} M$, then $\frac{m}{M} \approx \frac{1}{1836} \approx 0.000545$.

So a first order approximation to μ would give $\mu = m(1 - 0.000545)$. The percentage difference from $\mu = m$ is -0.0545%.

39. (a) For $a/h < 1$, we have

$$\frac{1}{(a^2 + h^2)^{1/2}} = \frac{1}{h(1 + a^2/h^2)^{1/2}} = \frac{1}{h} \left(1 - \frac{1}{2} \frac{a^2}{h^2} + \frac{3}{8} \frac{a^4}{h^4} - \cdots \right).$$

Thus

$$F = \frac{2GMmh}{a^2}\left(\frac{1}{h} - \frac{1}{h}\left(1 - \frac{1}{2}\frac{a^2}{h^2} + \frac{3}{8}\frac{a^4}{h^4} - \cdots\right)\right)$$

$$= \frac{2GMmh}{a^2h}\left(1 - 1 + \frac{1}{2}\frac{a^2}{h^2} - \frac{3}{8}\frac{a^4}{h^4} - \cdots\right)$$

$$= \frac{2GMm}{a^2}\frac{1}{2}\frac{a^2}{h^2}\left(1 - \frac{3}{4}\frac{a^2}{h^2}\cdots\right) = \frac{GMm}{h^2}\left(1 - \frac{3}{4}\frac{a^2}{h^2} - \cdots\right).$$

(b) Taking only the first nonzero term gives

$$F \approx \frac{GMm}{h^2}.$$

Notice that this approximation to F is independent of a.

(c) If $a/h = 0.02$, then $a^2/h^2 = 0.0004$, so

$$F \approx \frac{GMm}{h^2}(1 - \frac{3}{4}(0.0004)) = \frac{GMm}{h^2}(1 - 0.0003).$$

Thus, the approximations differ by $0.0003 = 0.03\%$.

40. (a) If h is much smaller than R, we can say that $(R + h) \approx R$, giving the approximation

$$F = \frac{mgR^2}{(R+h)^2} \approx \frac{mgR^2}{R^2} = mg.$$

(b)

$$F = \frac{mgR^2}{(R+h)^2} = \frac{mg}{(1 + h/R)^2} = mg(1 + h/R)^{-2}$$

$$= mg\left(1 + \frac{(-2)}{1!}\left(\frac{h}{R}\right) + \frac{(-2)(-3)}{2!}\left(\frac{h}{R}\right)^2 + \frac{(-2)(-3)(-4)}{3!}\left(\frac{h}{R}\right)^3 + \cdots\right)$$

$$= mg\left(1 - \frac{2h}{R} + \frac{3h^2}{R^2} - \frac{4h^3}{R^3} + \cdots\right)$$

(c) The first order correction comes from term $-2h/R$. The approximation for F is then given by

$$F \approx mg\left(1 - \frac{2h}{R}\right).$$

If the first order correction alters the estimate for F by 10%, we have

$$\frac{2h}{R} = 0.10 \quad \text{so} \quad h = 0.05R \approx 0.05(6400) = 320 \text{ km}.$$

The approximation $F \approx mg$ is good to within 10% — that is, up to about 300 km.

41. (a) We take the left-hand Riemann sum with the formula

$$\text{Left-hand sum} = (1 + 0.9608 + 0.8521 + 0.6977 + 0.5273)(0.2) = 0.8076.$$

Similarly,

$$\text{Right-hand sum} = (0.9608 + 0.8521 + 0.6977 + 0.5273 + 0.3679)(0.2) = 0.6812.$$

(b) Since

$$e^x = 1 + x + \frac{x^2}{2!} + \frac{x^3}{3!} + \cdots,$$

$$e^{-x^2} \approx 1 + (-x^2) + \frac{(-x^2)^2}{2!} + \frac{(-x^2)^3}{3!}$$

$$= 1 - x^2 + \frac{x^4}{2} - \frac{x^6}{6}.$$

(c)

$$\int_0^1 e^{-x^2}\, dx \approx \int_0^1 \left(1 - x^2 + \frac{x^4}{2} - \frac{x^6}{6}\right) dx$$

$$= \left(x - \frac{x^3}{3} + \frac{x^5}{10} - \frac{x^7}{42}\right)\Bigg|_0^1 = 0.74286.$$

(d) We can improve the left and right sum values by averaging them to get 0.74439 or by increasing the number of subdivisions. We can improve on the estimate using the Taylor approximation by taking more terms.

42. (a) The Taylor series for $1/(1-x) = 1 + x + x^2 + x^3 + \ldots$, so

$$\frac{1}{0.98} = \frac{1}{1 - 0.02} = 1 + (0.02) + (0.02)^2 + (0.02)^3 + \ldots$$

$$= 1.020408\ldots$$

(b) Since $d/dx(1/(1-x)) = (1/(1-x))^2$, the Taylor series for $1/(1-x)^2$ is

$$\frac{d}{dx}(1 + x + x^2 + x^3 + \ldots) = 1 + 2x + 3x^2 + 4x^3 + \cdots$$

Thus

$$\frac{1}{(0.99)^2} = \frac{1}{(1 - 0.01)^2} = 1 + 2(0.01) + 3(0.0001) + 4(0.000001) + \cdots$$

$$= 1.0203040506\ldots$$

Solutions for Section 10.4

Exercises

1. Let $f(x) = e^x$, so $f(0.1) = e^{0.1}$. The error bound in the Taylor approximation of degree 3 for $f(0.1) = 3^{0.1}$ about $x = 0$ is:

$$|E_3| = |f(0.1) - P_3(0.1)| \leq \frac{M \cdot |0.1 - 0|^4}{4!} = \frac{M(0.1)^4}{24},$$

where $|f^{(4)}(x)| \leq M$ for $0 \leq x \leq 0.1$. Now, $f^{(4)}(x) = e^x$. By looking at the graph of e^x, we see that $|f^{(4)}(x)|$ is maximized for x between 0 and 0.1 when $x = 0.1$. Thus,

$$|f^{(4)}| \leq e^{0.1},$$

so

$$|E_3| \leq \frac{e^{0.1} \cdot (0.1)^4}{24} \approx 0.00000460.$$

2. Let $f(x) = \sin x$, so $f(0.2) = \sin(0.2)$. The error bound in the Taylor approximation of degree 3 for $f(0.2) = \sin(0.2)$ about $x = 0$ is:

$$|E_3| = |f(0.2) - P_3(0.2)| \leq \frac{M \cdot |0.2 - 0|^4}{4!} = \frac{M(0.2)^4}{24},$$

where $|f^{(4)}(x)| \leq M$ for $0 \leq x \leq 0.2$. Now, $f^{(4)}(x) = \sin x$. By looking at the graph of $\sin x$, we see that $|f^{(4)}(x)|$ is maximized for x between 0 and 0.2 when $x = 0.2$. Thus,

$$|f^{(4)}| \leq \sin(0.2),$$

so

$$|E_3| \leq \frac{\sin(0.2) \cdot (0.2)^4}{24} \approx 0.0000132.$$

3. Let $f(x) = \cos x$, so $f(-0.3) = \cos(-0.3)$. The error bound in the Taylor approximation of degree 3 for $f(0.2) = \cos(-0.3)$ about $x = 0$ is:

$$|E_3| = |f(-0.3) - P_3(-0.3)| \leq \frac{M \cdot |-0.3 - 0|^4}{4!} = \frac{M(-0.3)^4}{24},$$

where $|f^{(4)}(x)| \leq M$ for $0 \geq x \geq -0.3$. Now, $f^{(4)}(x) = \cos x$. By looking at the graph of $\cos x$, we see that $|f^{(4)}(x)|$ is maximized for x between 0 and -0.3 when $x = 0$. Thus,

$$|f^{(4)}| \leq \cos 0 = 1,$$

so

$$|E_3| \leq \frac{1 \cdot (-0.3)^4}{24} \approx 0.000338.$$

4. Let $f(x) = \sqrt{1 + x}$. The error bound for the Taylor approximation of degree three for $f(2) = \sqrt{0.9}$ about $x = 0$ is:

$$|E_3| = |f(-0.1) - P_3(-0.1)| \leq \frac{M \cdot |-0.1 - 0|^4}{4!} = \frac{M \cdot (-0.1)^4}{24},$$

where $|f^{(4)}| \leq M$ for $0 \geq x \geq -0.1$. Since $f^{(4)}(x) = -\frac{15}{16}(1 + x)^{-(7/2)}$, we see that if x is between 0 and -0.1, the maximum is at -0.1. Thus $|f^{(4)}x)| \leq \frac{15}{16}(1 - 0.1)^{-7/2}$. Thus,

$$|E_3| \leq \frac{15}{16}(1 - 0.1)^{-7/2} \cdot \frac{(-0.1)^4}{24} \approx 0.00000565.$$

5. Let $f(x) = \ln(1 + x)$. The error bound in the Taylor approximation of degree 3 about $x = 0$ is:

$$|E_4| = |f(0.5) - P_3(0.5)| \leq \frac{M \cdot |0.5 - 0|^4}{4!} = \frac{M(0.5)^4}{24},$$

where $|f^{(4)}(x)| \leq M$ for $0 \leq x \leq 0.5$. Since

$$f^{(4)}(x) = \frac{3!}{(1 + x)^4}$$

and the denominator attains its minimum when $x = 0$, we have $|f^{(4)}(x)| \leq 3!$, so

$$|E_4| \leq \frac{3! (0.5)^4}{24} \approx 0.016.$$

6. Let $f(x) = (1 + x)^{-\frac{1}{2}} = \frac{1}{\sqrt{1 + x}}$. The error bound for the Taylor approximation of degree three for $f(2) = \frac{1}{\sqrt{3}}$ about $x = 0$ is:

$$|E_3| = |f(2) - P_3(2)| \leq \frac{M \cdot |2 - 0|^4}{4!} = \frac{M \cdot 2^4}{24},$$

where $|f^{(4)}| \leq M$ for $0 \leq x \leq 2$. Since

$$f^{(4)}(x) = \frac{105}{16}(1 + x)^{-(9/2)},$$

we see that if x is between 0 and 2, $|f^{(4)}x)| \leq \frac{105}{16}$. Thus,

$$|E_3| \leq \frac{105}{16} \cdot \frac{2^4}{24} = \frac{105}{24} = 4.375.$$

This is not a very helpful bound on the error, but that is to be expected as the Taylor series does not converge at $x = 2$. (At $x = 2$, we are outside the interval of convergence.)

7. Let $f(x) = \tan x$. The error bound for the Taylor approximation of degree three for $f(1) = \tan 1$ about $x = 0$ is:

$$|E_3| = |f(1) - P_3(x)| \leq \frac{M \cdot |1 - 0|^4}{4!} = \frac{M}{24}$$

where $|f^{(4)}(x)| \leq M$ for $0 \leq x \leq 1$. Now,

$$f^{(4)}(x) = \frac{16 \sin x}{\cos^3 x} + \frac{24 \sin^3 x}{\cos^5 x}.$$

From a graph of $f^{(4)}(x)$, we see that $f^{(4)}(x)$ is increasing for x between 0 and 1. Thus,

$$|f^{(4)}(x)| \leq |f^{(4)}(1)| \approx 396,$$

so

$$|E_3| \leq \frac{396}{24} = 16.5.$$

This is not a very helpful error bound! The reason the error bound is so huge is that $x = 1$ is getting near the vertical asymptote of the tangent graph, and the fourth derivative is enormous there.

8. Let $f(x) = (1-x)^{1/3}$, so $f(0.5) = (0.5)^{1/3}$. The error bound in the Taylor approximation of degree 3 for $f(0.5) = 0.5^{\frac{1}{3}}$ about $x = 0$ is:

$$|E_3| = |f(0.5) - P_3(0.5)| \leq \frac{M \cdot |0.5 - 0|^4}{4!} = \frac{M(0.5)^4}{24},$$

where $|f^{(4)}(x)| \leq M$ for $0 \leq x \leq 0.5$. Now,

$$f^{(4)}(x) = -\frac{80}{81}(1 - x)^{-(11/3)}.$$

By looking at the graph of $(1 - x)^{-(11/3)}$, we see that $|f^{(4)}(x)|$ is maximized for x between 0 and 0.5 when $x = 0.5$. Thus,

$$|f^{(4)}| \leq \frac{80}{81}\left(\frac{1}{2}\right)^{-(11/3)} = \frac{80}{81} \cdot 2^{11/3},$$

so

$$|E_3| \leq \frac{80 \cdot 2^{11/3} \cdot (0.5)^4}{81 \cdot 24} \approx 0.033.$$

Problems

9. (a) The Taylor polynomial of degree 0 about $t = 0$ for $f(t) = e^t$ is simply $P_0(x) = 1$. Since $e^t \geq 1$ on $[0, 0.5]$, the approximation is an underestimate.

   (b) Using the zero degree error bound, if $|f'(t)| \leq M$ for $0 \leq t \leq 0.5$, then

   $$|E_0| \leq M \cdot |t| \leq M(0.5).$$

   Since $|f'(t)| = |e^t| = e^t$ is increasing on $[0, 0.5]$,

   $$|f'(t)| \leq e^{0.5} < \sqrt{4} = 2.$$

   Therefore

   $$|E_0| \leq (2)(0.5) = 1.$$

   (Note: By looking at a graph of $f(t)$ and its 0th degree approximation, it is easy to see that the greatest error occurs when $t = 0.5$, and the error is $e^{0.5} - 1 \approx 0.65 < 1$. So our error bound works.)

10. (a) The second-degree Taylor polynomial for $f(t) = e^t$ is $P_2(t) = 1 + t + t^2/2$. Since the full expansion of $e^t = 1 + t + t^2/2 + t^3/6 + t^4/24 + \cdots$ is clearly larger than $P_2(t)$ for $t > 0$, $P_2(t)$ is an underestimate on $[0, 0.5]$.

    (b) Using the second-degree error bound, if $|f^{(3)}(t)| \leq M$ for $0 \leq t \leq 0.5$, then

    $$|E_2| \leq \frac{M}{3!} \cdot |t|^3 \leq \frac{M(0.5)^3}{6}.$$

    Since $|f^{(3)}(t)| = e^t$, and e^t is increasing on $[0, 0.5]$,

    $$f^{(3)}(t) \leq e^{0.5} < \sqrt{4} = 2.$$

    So

    $$|E_2| \leq \frac{(2)(0.5)^3}{6} < 0.047.$$

11. (a) θ is the first degree approximation of $f(\theta) = \sin\theta$; it is also the second degree approximation, since the next term in the Taylor expansion is 0.

$P_1(\theta) = \theta$ is an overestimate for $0 < \theta \leq 1$, and is an underestimate for $-1 \leq \theta < 0$. (This can be seen easily from a graph.)

(b) Using the second degree error bound, if $|f^{(3)}(\theta)| \leq M$ for $-1 \leq \theta \leq 1$, then

$$|E_2| \leq \frac{M \cdot |\theta|^3}{3!} \leq \frac{M}{6}.$$

For what value of M is $|f^{(3)}(\theta)| \leq M$ for $-1 \leq \theta \leq 1$? Well, $|f^{(3)}(\theta)| = |-\cos\theta| \leq 1$. So $|E_2| \leq \frac{1}{6} = 0.17$.

12. (a) $\theta - \dfrac{\theta^3}{3!}$ is the third degree Taylor approximation of $f(\theta) = \sin\theta$; it is also the fourth degree approximation, since the next term in the Taylor expansion is 0.

$P_3(\theta)$ is an underestimate for $0 < \theta \leq 1$, and is an overestimate for $-1 \leq \theta < 0$. (This can be checked with a calculator.)

(b) Using the fourth degree error bound, if $|f^{(5)}(\theta)| \leq M$ for $-1 \leq \theta \leq 1$, then

$$|E_4| \leq \frac{M \cdot |\theta|^5}{5!} \leq \frac{M}{120}.$$

For what value of M is $|f^{(5)}(\theta)| \leq M$ for $-1 \leq \theta \leq 1$? Since $f^{(5)}(\theta) = \cos\theta$ and $|\cos\theta| \leq 1$, we have

$$|E_4| \leq \frac{1}{120} \leq 0.0084.$$

13. (a) (i) The vertical distance between the graph of $y = \cos x$ and $y = P_{10}(x)$ at $x = 6$ is no more than 4, so

$$|\text{Error in } P_{10}(6)| \leq 4.$$

Since at $x = 6$ the $\cos x$ and $P_{20}(x)$ graphs are indistinguishable in this figure, the error must be less than the smallest division we can see, which is about 0.2 so,

$$|\text{Error in } P_{20}(6)| \leq 0.2.$$

(ii) The maximum error occurs at the ends of the interval, that is, at $x = -9, x = 9$. At $x = 9$, the graphs of $y = \cos x$ and $y = P_{20}(x)$ are no more than 1 apart, so

$$\left|\begin{matrix}\text{Maximum error in } P_{20}(x)\\ \text{for } -9 \leq x \leq 9\end{matrix}\right| \leq 1.$$

(b) We are looking for the largest x-interval on which the graphs of $y = \cos x$ and $y = P_{10}(x)$ are indistinguishable. This is hard to estimate accurately from the figure, though $-4 \leq x \leq 4$ certainly satisfies this condition.

14. The maximum possible error for the nth degree Taylor polynomial about $x = 0$ approximating $\cos x$ is $|E_n| \leq \frac{M \cdot |x-0|^{n+1}}{(n+1)!}$, where $|\cos^{(n+1)} x| \leq M$ for $0 \leq x \leq 1$. Now the derivatives of $\cos x$ are simply $\cos x, \sin x, -\cos x$, and $-\sin x$. The largest magnitude these ever take is 1, so $|\cos^{(n+1)}(x)| \leq 1$, and thus $|E_n| \leq \frac{|x|^{n+1}}{(n+1)!} \leq \frac{1}{(n+1)!}$. The same argument works for $\sin x$.

15. By the results of Problem 14, if we approximate $\cos 1$ using the nth degree polynomial, the error is at most $\frac{1}{(n+1)!}$. For the answer to be correct to four decimal places, the error must be less than 0.00005. Thus, the first n such that $\frac{1}{(n+1)!} < 0.00005$ will work. In particular, when $n = 7$, $\frac{1}{8!} = \frac{1}{40370} < 0.00005$, so the 7th degree Taylor polynomial will give the desired result. For six decimal places, we need $\frac{1}{(n+1)!} < 0.0000005$. Since $n = 9$ works, the 9th degree Taylor polynomial is sufficient.

16. (a)

Table 10.1

$E_1 = \sin x - x$

x	$\sin x$	E
-0.5	-0.4794	0.0206
-0.4	-0.3894	0.0106
-0.3	-0.2955	0.0045
-0.2	-0.1987	0.0013
-0.1	-0.0998	0.0002

Table 10.2

$E_1 = \sin x - x$

x	$\sin x$	E
0	0	0
0.1	0.0998	-0.0002
0.2	0.1987	-0.0013
0.3	0.2955	-0.0045
0.4	0.3894	-0.0106
0.5	0.4794	-0.0206

(b) See answer to part (a) above.

(c)

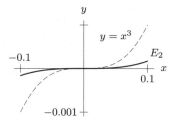

The fact that the graph of E_1 lies between the horizontal lines at ± 0.03 shows that $|E_1| < 0.03$ for $-0.5 \leq x \leq 0.5$.

17. (a) See Figure 10.7. The graph of E_1 looks like a parabola. Since the graph of E_1 is sandwiched between the graph of $y = x^2$ and the x axis, we have

$$|E_1| \leq x^2 \quad \text{for} \quad |x| \leq 0.1.$$

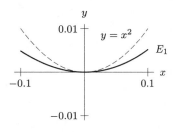

Figure 10.7

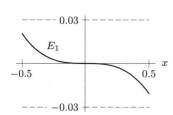

Figure 10.8

(b) See Figure 10.8. The graph of E_2 looks like a cubic, sandwiched between the graph of $y = x^3$ and the x axis, so

$$|E_2| \leq x^3 \quad \text{for} \quad |x| \leq 0.1.$$

(c) Using the Taylor expansion

$$e^x = 1 + x + \frac{x^2}{2!} + \frac{x^3}{3!} + \cdots$$

we see that

$$E_1 = e^x - (1 + x) = \frac{x^2}{2!} + \frac{x^3}{3!} + \frac{x^4}{4!} + \cdots.$$

Thus for small x, the $x^2/2!$ term dominates, so

$$E_1 \approx \frac{x^2}{2!},$$

and so E_1 is approximately a quadratic.

Similarly

$$E_2 = e^x - (1 + x + \frac{x^2}{2}) = \frac{x^3}{3!} + \frac{x^4}{4!} + \cdots.$$

Thus for small x, the $x^3/3!$ term dominates, so

$$E_2 \approx \frac{x^3}{3!}$$

and so E_2 is approximately a cubic.

18.

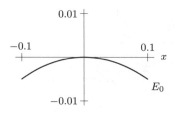

The graph of E_0 looks like a parabola, and the graph shows

$$|E_0| < 0.01 \quad \text{for} \quad |x| \leq 0.1.$$

(In fact $|E_0| < 0.005$ on this interval.) Since

$$\cos x = 1 - \frac{x^2}{2!} + \frac{x^4}{4!} - \frac{x^6}{6!} + \cdots,$$

$$E_0 = \cos x - 1 = -\frac{x^2}{2!} + \frac{x^4}{4!} - \frac{x^6}{6!} + \cdots.$$

So, for small x,

$$E_0 \approx -\frac{x^2}{2},$$

and therefore the graph of E_0 is parabolic.

19. Since $f(x) = e^x$, the $(n+1)^{\text{st}}$ derivative $f^{(n+1)}(x)$ is also e^x, no matter what n is. Now fix a number x and let $M = e^x$, then $|f^{(n+1)}(t)| \le e^t \le e^x$ on the interval $0 \le t \le x$. (This works for $x \ge 0$; if $x < 0$ then we can take $M = 1$.) The important observation is that for any x the *same* number M bounds all the higher derivatives $f^{(n+1)}(x)$.

By the error bound formula, we now have

$$|E_n(x)| = |e^x - P_n(x)| \le \frac{M|x|^{n+1}}{(n+1)!} \quad \text{for every } n.$$

To show that the errors go to zero, we must show that for a fixed x and a fixed number M,

$$\frac{M}{(n+1)!}|x|^{n+1} \to 0 \quad \text{as} \quad n \to \infty.$$

Since M is fixed, we need only show that

$$\frac{1}{(n+1)!}|x|^{n+1} \to 0 \quad \text{as} \quad n \to \infty.$$

This was shown in the text on page 500. Therefore, the Taylor series $1 + x + x^2/2! + \cdots$ does converge to e^x.

20.

$$\sin x = x - \frac{x^3}{3!} + \frac{x^5}{5!} - \cdots$$

Write the error in approximating $\sin x$ by the Taylor polynomial of degree $n = 2k + 1$ as E_n so that

$$\sin x = x - \frac{x^3}{3!} + \frac{x^5}{5!} - \cdots (-1)^k \frac{x^{2k+1}}{(2k+1)!} + E_n.$$

(Notice that $(-1)^k = 1$ if k is even and $(-1)^k = -1$ if k is odd.) We want to show that if x is fixed, $E_n \to 0$ as $k \to \infty$. Since $f(x) = \sin x$, all the derivatives of $f(x)$ are $\pm \sin x$ or $\pm \cos x$, so we have for all n and all x

$$|f^{(n+1)}(x)| \le 1.$$

Using the bound on the error given in the text on page 500, we see that

$$|E_n| \le \frac{1}{(2k+2)!}|x|^{2k+2}.$$

By the argument in the text on page 500, we know that for all x,

$$\frac{|x|^{2k+2}}{(2k+2)!} = \frac{|x|^{n+1}}{(n+1)!} \to 0 \quad \text{as} \quad n = 2k + 1 \to \infty.$$

Thus the Taylor series for $\sin x$ does converge to $\sin x$ for every x.

Solutions for Section 10.5

Exercises

1. No, a Fourier series has terms of the form $\cos nx$, not $\cos^n x$.

2. Not a Fourier series because terms are not of the form $\sin nx$.

3. Yes. Terms are of the form $\sin nx$ and $\cos nx$.

4. Yes. This is a Fourier series where the $\cos nx$ terms all have coefficients of zero.

5.

$$a_0 = \frac{1}{2\pi} \int_{-\pi}^{\pi} f(x)\,dx = \frac{1}{2\pi}\left[\int_{-\pi}^{0} -1\,dx + \int_{0}^{\pi} 1\,dx\right] = 0$$

$$a_1 = \frac{1}{\pi} \int_{-\pi}^{\pi} f(x)\cos x\,dx = \frac{1}{\pi}\left[\int_{-\pi}^{0} -\cos x\,dx + \int_{0}^{\pi} \cos x\,dx\right]$$

$$= \frac{1}{\pi}\left[-\sin x\Big|_{-\pi}^{0} + \sin x\Big|_{0}^{\pi}\right] = 0.$$

Similarly, a_2 and a_3 are both 0.

(In fact, notice $f(x)\cos nx$ is an odd function, so $\int_{-\pi}^{\pi} f(x)\cos nx = 0$.)

$$b_1 = \frac{1}{\pi} \int_{-\pi}^{\pi} f(x)\sin x\,dx = \frac{1}{\pi}\left[\int_{-\pi}^{0} -\sin x\,dx + \int_{0}^{\pi} \sin x\,dx\right]$$

$$= \frac{1}{\pi}\left[\cos x\Big|_{-\pi}^{0} + (-\cos x)\Big|_{0}^{\pi}\right] = \frac{4}{\pi}$$

$$b_2 = \frac{1}{\pi} \int_{-\pi}^{\pi} f(x)\sin 2x\,dx = \frac{1}{\pi}\left[\int_{-\pi}^{0} -\sin 2x\,dx + \int_{0}^{\pi} \sin 2x\,dx\right]$$

$$= \frac{1}{\pi}\left[\frac{1}{2}\cos 2x\Big|_{-\pi}^{0} + (-\frac{1}{2}\cos 2x)\Big|_{0}^{\pi}\right] = 0.$$

$$b_3 = \frac{1}{\pi} \int_{-\pi}^{\pi} f(x)\sin 3x\,dx = \frac{1}{\pi}\left[\int_{-\pi}^{0} -\sin 3x\,dx + \int_{0}^{\pi} \sin 3x\,dx\right]$$

$$= \frac{1}{\pi}\left[\frac{1}{3}\cos 3x\Big|_{-\pi}^{0} + (-\frac{1}{3}\cos 3x)\Big|_{0}^{\pi}\right] = \frac{4}{3\pi}.$$

Thus, $F_1(x) = F_2(x) = \frac{4}{\pi}\sin x$ and $F_3(x) = \frac{4}{\pi}\sin x + \frac{4}{3\pi}\sin 3x$.

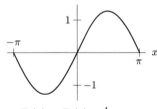

$F_1(x) = F_2(x) = \frac{4}{\pi}\sin x$

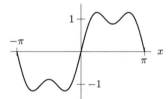

$F_3(x) = \frac{4}{\pi}\sin x + \frac{4}{3\pi}\sin 3x$

6. First,

$$a_0 = \frac{1}{2\pi} \int_{-\pi}^{\pi} f(x)\,dx = \frac{1}{2\pi}\left[\int_{-\pi}^{0} -x\,dx + \int_{0}^{\pi} x\,dx\right] = \frac{1}{2\pi}\left[-\frac{x^2}{2}\Big|_{-\pi}^{0} + \frac{x^2}{2}\Big|_{0}^{\pi}\right] = \frac{\pi}{2}.$$

To find the a_i's, we use the integral table. For $n \geq 1$,

$$a_n = \frac{1}{\pi} \int_{-\pi}^{\pi} f(x)\cos(nx)\,dx = \frac{1}{\pi}\left[\int_{-\pi}^{0} -x\cos(nx)\,dx + \int_{0}^{\pi} x\cos(nx)\,dx\right]$$

$$= \frac{1}{\pi}\left[\left(-\frac{x}{n}\sin(nx) - \frac{1}{n^2}\cos(nx)\right)\Big|_{-\pi}^{0}\right.$$

$$\left. + \left(\frac{x}{n}\sin(nx) + \frac{1}{n^2}\cos(nx)\right)\Big|_{0}^{\pi}\right]$$

$$= \frac{1}{\pi} \left(-\frac{1}{n^2} + \frac{1}{n^2} \cos(-n\pi) + \frac{1}{n^2} \cos(n\pi) - \frac{1}{n^2} \right)$$

$$= \frac{2}{\pi n^2} (\cos n\pi - 1)$$

Thus, $a_1 = -\frac{4}{\pi}, a_2 = 0$, and $a_3 = -\frac{4}{9\pi}$. To find the b_i's, note that $f(x)$ is even, so for $n \geq 1$, $f(x) \sin(nx)$ is odd.

Thus, $\int_{-\pi}^{\pi} f(x) \sin(nx) = 0$, so all the b_i's are 0. $F_1 = F_2 = \frac{\pi}{2} - \frac{4}{\pi} \cos x$, $F_3 = \frac{\pi}{2} - \frac{4}{\pi} \cos x - \frac{4}{9\pi} \cos 3x$.

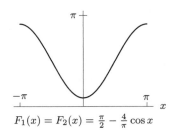

$F_1(x) = F_2(x) = \frac{\pi}{2} - \frac{4}{\pi} \cos x$

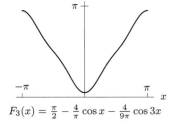

$F_3(x) = \frac{\pi}{2} - \frac{4}{\pi} \cos x - \frac{4}{9\pi} \cos 3x$

7. The energy of the function $f(x)$ is

$$E = \frac{1}{\pi} \int_{-\pi}^{\pi} (f(x))^2 \, dx = \frac{1}{\pi} \int_{-\pi}^{\pi} x^2 \, dx = \frac{1}{3\pi} x^3 \Big|_{-\pi}^{\pi}$$

$$= \frac{1}{3\pi} (\pi^3 - (-\pi^3)) = \frac{2\pi^3}{3\pi} = \frac{2}{3}\pi^2 = 6.57974.$$

From Problem 6, we know all the b_i's are 0 and $a_0 = \frac{\pi}{2}$, $a_1 = -\frac{4}{\pi}$, $a_2 = 0$, $a_3 = -\frac{4}{9\pi}$. Therefore the energy in the constant term and first three harmonics is

$$A_0^2 + A_1^2 + A_2^2 + A_3^2 = 2a_0^2 + a_1^2 + a_2^2 + a_3^2$$

$$= 2 \left(\frac{\pi^2}{4} \right) + \frac{16}{\pi^2} + 0 + \frac{16}{81\pi^2} = 6.57596$$

which means that they contain $\dfrac{6.57596}{6.57974} = 0.99942 \approx 99.942\%$ of the total energy.

8. First, we find a_0.

$$a_0 = \frac{1}{2\pi} \int_{-\pi}^{\pi} x^2 \, dx = \frac{1}{2\pi} \left(\frac{x^3}{3} \Big|_{-\pi}^{\pi} \right) = \frac{\pi^2}{3}$$

To find $a_n, n \geq 1$, we use the integral table (III-15 and III-16).

$$a_n = \frac{1}{\pi} \int_{-\pi}^{\pi} x^2 \cos nx \, dx = \frac{1}{\pi} \left[\frac{x^2}{n} \sin(nx) + \frac{2x}{n^2} \cos(nx) - \frac{2}{n^3} \sin(nx) \right] \Big|_{-\pi}^{\pi}$$

$$= \frac{1}{\pi} \left[\frac{2\pi}{n^2} \cos(n\pi) + \frac{2\pi}{n^2} \cos(-n\pi) \right]$$

$$= \frac{4}{n^2} \cos(n\pi)$$

Again, $\cos(n\pi) = (-1)^n$ for all integers n, so $a_n = (-1)^n \frac{4}{n^2}$. Note that

$$b_n = \frac{1}{\pi} \int_{-\pi}^{\pi} x^2 \sin nx \, dx.$$

x^2 is an even function, and $\sin nx$ is odd, so $x^2 \sin nx$ is odd. Thus $\int_{-\pi}^{\pi} x^2 \sin nx \, dx = 0$, and $b_n = 0$ for all n. We deduce that the nth Fourier polynomial for f (where $n \geq 1$) is

$$F_n(x) = \frac{\pi^2}{3} + \sum_{i=1}^{n} (-1)^i \frac{4}{i^2} \cos(ix).$$

In particular, we have the graphs in Figure 10.9.

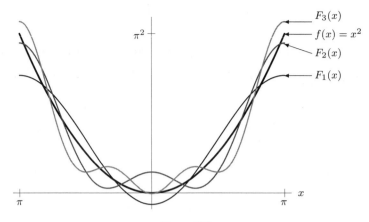

Figure 10.9

9.

$$a_0 = \frac{1}{2\pi} \int_{-\pi}^{\pi} h(x)\, dx = \frac{1}{2\pi} \int_0^{\pi} x\, dx = \frac{\pi}{4}$$

As in Problem 10, we use the integral table (III-15 and III-16) to find formulas for a_n and b_n.

$$a_n = \frac{1}{\pi} \int_{-\pi}^{\pi} h(x) \cos(nx)\, dx = \frac{1}{\pi} \int_0^{\pi} x \cos nx\, dx = \frac{1}{\pi} \left(\frac{x}{n} \sin(nx) + \frac{1}{n^2} \cos(nx) \right) \Bigg|_0^{\pi}$$

$$= \frac{1}{\pi} \left(\frac{1}{n^2} \cos(n\pi) - \frac{1}{n^2} \right)$$

$$= \frac{1}{n^2 \pi} \left(\cos(n\pi) - 1 \right).$$

Note that since $\cos(n\pi) = (-1)^n$, $a_n = 0$ if n is even and $a_n = -\frac{2}{n^2\pi}$ if n is odd.

$$b_n = \frac{1}{\pi} \int_{-\pi}^{\pi} h(x) \cos(nx)\, dx = \frac{1}{\pi} \int_0^{\pi} x \sin x\, dx$$

$$= \frac{1}{\pi} \left(-\frac{x}{n} \cos(nx) + \frac{1}{n^2} \sin(nx) \right) \Bigg|_0^{\pi}$$

$$= \frac{1}{\pi} \left(-\frac{\pi}{n} \cos(n\pi) \right)$$

$$= -\frac{1}{n} \cos(n\pi)$$

$$= \frac{1}{n} (-1)^{n+1} \quad \text{if } n \geq 1$$

We have that the nth Fourier polynomial for h (for $n \geq 1$) is

$$H_n(x) = \frac{\pi}{4} + \sum_{i=1}^{n} \left(\frac{1}{i^2 \pi} \left(\cos(i\pi) - 1 \right) \cdot \cos(ix) + \frac{(-1)^{i+1} \sin(ix)}{i} \right).$$

This can also be written as

$$H_n(x) = \frac{\pi}{4} + \sum_{i=1}^{n} \frac{(-1)^{i+1} \sin(ix)}{i} + \sum_{i=1}^{\left[\frac{n}{2}\right]} \frac{-2}{(2i-1)^2 \pi} \cos((2i-1)x)$$

where $\left[\frac{n}{2}\right]$ denotes the biggest integer smaller than or equal to $\frac{n}{2}$. In particular, we have the graphs in Figure 10.10.

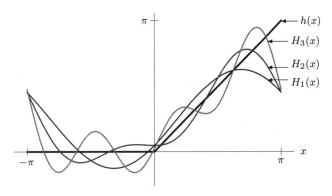

Figure 10.10

10. To find the nth Fourier polynomial, we must come up with a general formula for a_n and b_n. First, we find a_0.

$$a_0 = \frac{1}{2\pi} \int_{-\pi}^{\pi} g(x)\,dx = \frac{1}{2\pi} \int_{-\pi}^{\pi} x\,dx = \frac{1}{2\pi}\left[\frac{x^2}{2}\right]\Big|_{-\pi}^{\pi} = 0$$

Now we use the integral table (III-15 and III-16) to find a_n and b_n for $n \geq 1$.

$$a_n = \frac{1}{\pi} \int_{-\pi}^{\pi} x \cos nx\,dx = \frac{1}{\pi}\left(\frac{x}{n}\sin(nx) + \frac{1}{n^2}\cos(nx)\right)\Big|_{-\pi}^{\pi}$$

$$= \frac{1}{\pi}\left(\frac{1}{n^2}\cos(n\pi) - \frac{1}{n^2}\cos(-n\pi)\right) = 0$$

(Note that since $x \cos nx$ is odd, we could have deduced that $\int_{-\pi}^{\pi} x \cos nx = 0$.)

$$b_n = \frac{1}{\pi} \int_{-\pi}^{\pi} x \sin nx\,dx = \frac{1}{\pi}\left(-\frac{x}{n}\cos(nx) + \frac{1}{n^2}\sin(nx)\right)\Big|_{-\pi}^{\pi}$$

$$= \frac{1}{\pi}\left(-\frac{\pi}{n}\cos(n\pi) - \frac{\pi}{n}\cos(-n\pi)\right)$$

$$= -\frac{2}{n}\cos(n\pi)$$

Notice that $\cos(n\pi) = (-1)^n$ for all integers n, so $b_n = (-1)^{n+1}\left(\frac{2}{n}\right)$.
Thus the nth Fourier polynomial for g is

$$G_n(x) = \sum_{i=1}^{n} (-1)^{i+1}\frac{2}{i}\sin(ix).$$

In particular, we have the graphs in Figure 10.11.

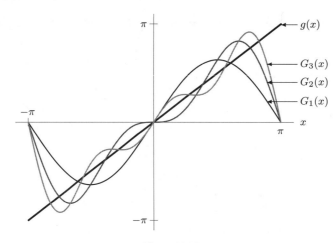

Figure 10.11

Problems

11. (a) The graph of $g(x)$ is

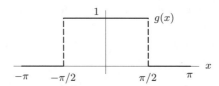

First find the Fourier coefficients: a_0 is the average value of g on $[-\pi, \pi]$ so from the graph, it is clear that

$$a_0 = \frac{1}{2\pi}(\pi \times 1) = \frac{1}{2},$$

or analytically,

$$a_0 = \frac{1}{2\pi}\int_{-\pi}^{\pi} g(x)\,dx = \frac{1}{2\pi}\int_{-\pi/2}^{\pi/2} 1\,dx = \frac{1}{2\pi}x\Big|_{-\pi/2}^{\pi/2} = \frac{1}{2\pi}\left(\frac{\pi}{2} - \left(-\frac{\pi}{2}\right)\right)$$

$$= \frac{1}{2\pi}(\pi) = \frac{1}{2},$$

$$a_k = \frac{1}{\pi}\int_{-\pi}^{\pi} g(x)\cos kx\,dx = \frac{1}{\pi}\int_{-\pi/2}^{\pi/2}\cos kx\,dx = \frac{1}{k\pi}\sin kx\Big|_{-\pi/2}^{\pi/2}$$

$$= \frac{1}{k\pi}\left(\sin\frac{k\pi}{2} - \sin\left(-\frac{k\pi}{2}\right)\right) = \frac{1}{k\pi}\left(2\sin\frac{k\pi}{2}\right),$$

$$b_k = \frac{1}{\pi}\int_{-\pi}^{\pi} g(x)\sin kx\,dx = \frac{1}{\pi}\int_{-\pi/2}^{\pi/2}\sin kx\,dx = -\frac{1}{k\pi}\cos kx\Big|_{-\pi/2}^{\pi/2}$$

$$= -\frac{1}{k\pi}\left(\cos\frac{k\pi}{2} - \cos\left(-\frac{k\pi}{2}\right)\right). = -\frac{1}{k\pi}(0) = 0$$

So,

$$a_1 = \frac{1}{\pi}\left(2\sin\frac{\pi}{2}\right) = \frac{2}{\pi},$$

$$a_2 = \frac{1}{2\pi}\left(2\sin\frac{2\pi}{2}\right) = 0,$$

$$a_3 = \frac{1}{3\pi}\left(2\sin\frac{3\pi}{2}\right) = -\frac{2}{3\pi},$$

which gives

$$F_3(x) = \frac{1}{2} + \frac{2}{\pi}\cos x - \frac{2}{3\pi}\cos 3x.$$

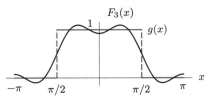

(b) There are cosines instead of sines (but the energy spectrum remains the same).

12. We have $f(x) = x$, $0 \le x < 1$. Let $t = 2\pi x - \pi$. Notice that as x varies from 0 to 1, t varies from $-\pi$ to π. Thus if we rewrite the function in terms of t, we can find the Fourier series in terms of t in the usual way. To do this, let $g(t) = f(x) = x = \frac{t+\pi}{2\pi}$ on $-\pi \le t < \pi$. We now find the fourth degree Fourier polynomial for g.

$$a_o = \frac{1}{2\pi}\int_{-\pi}^{\pi} g(t)\,dt = \frac{1}{2\pi}\int_{-\pi}^{\pi}\frac{t+\pi}{2\pi}\,dt = \frac{1}{(2\pi)^2}\left(\frac{t^2}{2} + \pi t\right)\bigg|_{-\pi}^{\pi} = \frac{1}{2}$$

Notice, a_0 is the average value of both f and g. For $n \ge 1$,

$$a_n = \frac{1}{\pi}\int_{-\pi}^{\pi}\frac{t+\pi}{2\pi}\cos(nt)\,dt = \frac{1}{2\pi^2}\int_{-\pi}^{\pi}(t\cos(nt) + \pi\cos(nt))\,dt$$

$$= \frac{1}{2\pi^2}\left[\frac{t}{n}\sin(nt) + \frac{1}{n^2}\cos(nt) + \frac{\pi}{n}\sin(nt)\right]\bigg|_{-\pi}^{\pi}$$

$$= 0.$$

$$b_n = \frac{1}{\pi}\int_{-\pi}^{\pi}\frac{t+\pi}{2\pi}\sin(nt)\,dt = \frac{1}{2\pi^2}\int_{-\pi}^{\pi}(t\sin(nt) + \pi\sin(nt))\,dt$$

$$= \frac{1}{2\pi^2}\left[-\frac{t}{n}\cos(nt) + \frac{1}{n^2}\sin(nt) - \frac{\pi}{n}\cos(nt)\right]\bigg|_{-\pi}^{\pi}$$

$$= \frac{1}{2\pi^2}(-\frac{4\pi}{n}\cos(\pi n)) = -\frac{2}{\pi n}\cos(\pi n) = \frac{2}{\pi n}(-1)^{n+1}.$$

We get the integrals for a_n and b_n using the integral table (formulas III-15 and III-16).

Thus, the Fourier polynomial of degree 4 for g is:

$$G_4(t) = \frac{1}{2} + \frac{2}{\pi}\sin t - \frac{1}{\pi}\sin 2t + \frac{2}{3\pi}\sin 3t - \frac{1}{2\pi}\sin 4t.$$

Now, since $g(t) = f(x)$, the Fourier polynomial of degree 4 for f can be found by replacing t in terms of x again. Thus,

$$F_4(x) = \frac{1}{2} + \frac{2}{\pi}\sin(2\pi x - \pi) - \frac{1}{\pi}\sin(4\pi x - 2\pi) + \frac{2}{3\pi}\sin(6\pi x - 3\pi) - \frac{1}{2\pi}\sin(8\pi x - 4\pi).$$

Now, using the fact that $\sin(x - \pi) = -\sin x$ and $\sin(x - 2\pi) = \sin x$, etc., we have:

$$F_4(x) = \frac{1}{2} - \frac{2}{\pi}\sin(2\pi x) - \frac{1}{\pi}\sin(4\pi x) - \frac{2}{3\pi}\sin(6\pi x) - \frac{1}{2\pi}\sin(8\pi x).$$

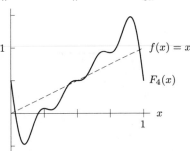

13. Since the period is 2, we make the substitution $t = \pi x - \pi$. Thus, $x = \frac{t+\pi}{\pi}$. We find the Fourier coefficients. Notice that all of the integrals are the same as in Problem 12 except for an extra factor of 2. Thus, $a_0 = 1$, $a_n = 0$, and $b_n = \frac{4}{\pi n}(-1)^{n+1}$, so:

$$G_4(t) = 1 + \frac{4}{\pi}\sin t - \frac{2}{\pi}\sin 2t + \frac{4}{3\pi}\sin 3t - \frac{1}{\pi}\sin 4t.$$

Again, we substitute back in to get a Fourier polynomial in terms of x:

$$F_4(x) = 1 + \frac{4}{\pi}\sin(\pi x - \pi) - \frac{2}{\pi}\sin(2\pi x - 2\pi)$$

$$+ \frac{4}{3\pi}\sin(3\pi x - 3\pi) - \frac{1}{\pi}\sin(4\pi x - 4\pi)$$

$$= 1 - \frac{4}{\pi}\sin(\pi x) - \frac{2}{\pi}\sin(2\pi x) - \frac{4}{3\pi}\sin(3\pi x) - \frac{1}{\pi}\sin(4\pi x).$$

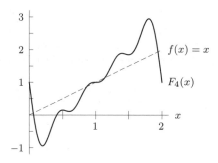

Notice in this case, the terms in our series are $\sin(n\pi x)$, not $\sin(2\pi nx)$, as in Problem 12. In general, the terms will be $\sin(n\frac{2\pi}{b}x)$, where b is the period.

14. The signal received on earth is in the form of a periodic function $h(t)$, which can be expanded in a Fourier series

$$h(t) = a_0 + a_1 \cos t + a_2 \cos 2t + a_3 \cos 3t + \cdots$$
$$+ b_1 \sin t + b_2 \sin 2t + b_3 \sin 3t + \cdots$$

If the periodic noise consists of *only* the second and higher harmonics of the Fourier series, then the original signal contributed the fundamental harmonic plus the constant term, i.e.,

$$\underbrace{a_0}_{\text{constant term}} + \underbrace{a_1 \cos t + b_1 \sin t}_{\text{fundamental harmonic}} = \underbrace{A \cos t}_{\text{original signal}} .$$

In order to find A, we need to find a_0, a_1, and b_1. Looking at the graph of $h(t)$, we see

$$a_0 = \text{average value of } h(t) = \frac{1}{2\pi}(\text{Area above the } x\text{-axis} - \text{Area below the } x\text{-axis})$$

$$= \frac{1}{2\pi}\left[80\left(\frac{\pi}{2}\right) - \left(50\left(\frac{\pi}{4}\right) + 30\left(\frac{\pi}{4}\right) + 30\left(\frac{\pi}{4}\right) + 50\left(\frac{\pi}{4}\right)\right)\right]$$

$$= \frac{1}{2\pi}\left[80\left(\frac{\pi}{2}\right) - 80\left(\frac{\pi}{2}\right)\right] = \frac{1}{2\pi}\cdot 0, = 0$$

$$a_1 = \frac{1}{\pi}\int_{-\pi}^{\pi} h(t)\cos t\, dt$$

$$= \frac{1}{\pi}\left[\int_{-\pi}^{-3\pi/4} -50\cos t\, dt + \int_{-3\pi/4}^{-\pi/2} 0\cos t\, dt + \int_{-\pi/2}^{-\pi/4} -30\cos t\, dt\right.$$

$$+ \int_{-\pi/4}^{\pi/4} 80\cos t\, dt + \int_{\pi/4}^{\pi/2} -30\cos t\, dt + \int_{\pi/2}^{3\pi/4} 0\cos t\, dt + \left.\int_{3\pi/4}^{\pi} -50\cos t\, dt\right]$$

$$= \frac{1}{\pi}\left[-50\sin t\Big|_{-\pi}^{-3\pi/4} - 30\sin t\Big|_{-\pi/2}^{-\pi/4}\right.$$

$$+80 \sin t \Big|_{-\pi/4}^{\pi/4} - 30 \sin t \Big|_{\pi/4}^{\pi/2} - 50 \sin t \Big|_{3\pi/4}^{\pi} \Bigg]$$

$$= \frac{1}{\pi} \left[-50 \left(-\frac{\sqrt{2}}{2} - 0 \right) - 30 \left(-\frac{\sqrt{2}}{2} - (-1) \right) + 80 \left(\frac{\sqrt{2}}{2} - \left(-\frac{\sqrt{2}}{2} \right) \right) \right.$$

$$\left. - 30 \left(1 - \frac{\sqrt{2}}{2} \right) - 50 \left(0 - \frac{\sqrt{2}}{2} \right) \right]$$

$$= \frac{1}{\pi} [25\sqrt{2} + 15\sqrt{2} - 30 + 40\sqrt{2} + 40\sqrt{2} - 30 + 15\sqrt{2} + 25\sqrt{2}]$$

$$= \frac{1}{\pi} [160\sqrt{2} - 60] = 52.93,$$

$$b_1 = \frac{1}{\pi} \int_{-\pi}^{\pi} h(t) \sin t \, dt$$

$$= \frac{1}{\pi} \left[\int_{-\pi}^{-3\pi/4} -50 \sin t \, dt + \int_{-3\pi/4}^{-\pi/2} 0 \sin t \, dt + \int_{-\pi/2}^{-\pi/4} -30 \sin t \, dt \right.$$

$$\left. + \int_{-\pi/4}^{\pi/4} 80 \sin t \, dt + \int_{\pi/4}^{\pi/2} -30 \sin t \, dt + \int_{\pi/2}^{3\pi/4} 0 \sin t \, dt + \int_{3\pi/4}^{\pi} -50 \sin t \, dt \right]$$

$$= \frac{1}{\pi} \left[50 \cos t \Big|_{-\pi}^{-3\pi/4} + 30 \cos t \Big|_{-\pi/2}^{-\pi/4} - 80 \cos t \Big|_{-\pi/4}^{\pi/4} + 30 \cos t \Big|_{\pi/4}^{\pi/2} + 50 \cos t \Big|_{3\pi/4}^{\pi} \right]$$

$$= \frac{1}{\pi} \left[50 \left(-\frac{\sqrt{2}}{2} - (-1) \right) + 30 \left(\frac{\sqrt{2}}{2} - 0 \right) - 80 \left(\frac{\sqrt{2}}{2} - \frac{\sqrt{2}}{2} \right) \right.$$

$$\left. + 30 \left(0 - \frac{\sqrt{2}}{2} \right) + 50 \left(-1 - (-\frac{\sqrt{2}}{2}) \right) \right]$$

$$= \frac{1}{\pi} \left[-25\sqrt{2} + 50 + 15\sqrt{2} - 0 - 15\sqrt{2} - 50 + 25\sqrt{2} \right] = \frac{1}{\pi} (0) = 0.$$

Also, we could have just noted that $b_1 = \frac{1}{\pi} \int_{-\pi}^{\pi} h(t) \sin t \, dt = 0$ because $h(t) \sin t$ is an odd function. Substituting in, we get

$$a_0 + a_1 \cos t + b_1 \sin t = 0 + 52.93 \cos t + 0 = A \cos t.$$

So $A = 52.93$.

15. The energy spectrum of the flute shows that the first two harmonics have equal energies and contribute the most energy by far. The higher harmonics contribute relatively little energy. In contrast, the energy spectrum of the bassoon shows the comparative weakness of the first two harmonics to the third harmonic which is the strongest component.

16. Let $f(x) = a_k \cos kx + b_k \sin kx$. Then the energy of f is given by

$$\frac{1}{\pi} \int_{-\pi}^{\pi} (f(x))^2 \, dx = \frac{1}{\pi} \int_{-\pi}^{\pi} (a_k \cos kx + b_k \sin kx)^2 \, dx$$

$$= \frac{1}{\pi} \int_{-\pi}^{\pi} (a_k^2 \cos^2 kx - 2a_k b_k \cos kx \sin kx + b_k^2 \sin^2 kx) \, dx$$

$$= \frac{1}{\pi} \left[a_k^2 \int_{-\pi}^{\pi} \cos^2 kx \, dx - 2a_k b_k \int_{-\pi}^{\pi} \cos kx \sin kx \, dx + b_k^2 \int_{-\pi}^{\pi} \sin^2 kx \, dx \right]$$

$$= \frac{1}{\pi} \left[a_k^2 \pi - 2a_k b_k \cdot 0 + b_k^2 \pi \right] = a_k^2 + b_k^2.$$

17. Since each square in the graph has area $\left(\frac{\pi}{4} \right) \cdot (0.2)$,

$$a_0 = \frac{1}{2\pi} \int_{-\pi}^{\pi} f(x) \, dx$$

$$= \frac{1}{2\pi} \cdot \left(\frac{\pi}{4}\right) \cdot (0.2) \text{ [Number of squares under graph above } x\text{-axis}$$

$$\qquad\qquad - \text{Number of squares above graph below } x \text{ axis]}$$

$$\approx \frac{1}{2\pi} \cdot \left(\frac{\pi}{4}\right) \cdot (0.2) \cdot [13 + 11 - 14] = 0.25.$$

Approximate the Fourier coefficients using Riemann sums.

$$a_1 = \frac{1}{\pi} \int_{-\pi}^{\pi} f(x) \cos x \, dx$$

$$\approx \frac{1}{\pi} \left[f(-\pi)\cos(-\pi) + f\left(-\frac{\pi}{2}\right)\cos\left(-\frac{\pi}{2}\right) + f(0)\cos(0) + f\left(\frac{\pi}{2}\right)\cos\left(\frac{\pi}{2}\right) \right] \cdot \frac{\pi}{2}$$

$$= \frac{1}{\pi} \left[(0.92)(-1) + (1)(0) + (-1.7)(1) + (0.7)(0) \right] \cdot \frac{\pi}{2}$$

$$= -1.31$$

Similarly for b_1:

$$b_1 = \frac{1}{\pi} \int_{-\pi}^{\pi} f(x) \sin x \, dx$$

$$\approx \frac{1}{\pi} \left[f(-\pi)\sin(-\pi) + f\left(-\frac{\pi}{2}\right)\sin\left(-\frac{\pi}{2}\right) + f(0)\sin(0) + f\left(\frac{\pi}{2}\right)\sin\left(\frac{\pi}{2}\right) \right] \cdot \frac{\pi}{2}$$

$$= \frac{1}{\pi} \left[(0.92)(0) + (1)(-1) + (-1.7)(0) + (0.7)(1) \right] \cdot \frac{\pi}{2}$$

$$= -0.15.$$

So our first Fourier approximation is

$$F_1(x) = 0.25 - 1.31 \cos x - 0.15 \sin x.$$

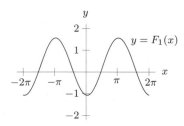

Similarly for a_2:

$$a_2 = \frac{1}{\pi} \int_{-\pi}^{\pi} f(x) \cos 2x \, dx$$

$$\approx \frac{1}{\pi} \left[f(-\pi)\cos(-2\pi) + f\left(-\frac{\pi}{2}\right)\cos(-\pi) + f(0)\cos(0) + f\left(\frac{\pi}{2}\right)\cos(-\pi) \right] \cdot \frac{\pi}{2}$$

$$= \frac{1}{\pi} \left[(0.92)(1) + (1)(-1) + (-1.7)(1) + (0.7)(-1) \right] \cdot \frac{\pi}{2}$$

$$= -1.24$$

Similarly for b_2:

$$b_2 = \frac{1}{\pi} \int_{-\pi}^{\pi} f(x) \sin 2x \, dx$$

$$\approx \frac{1}{\pi} \left[f(-\pi)\sin(-2\pi) + f\left(-\frac{\pi}{2}\right)\sin(-\pi) + f(0)\sin(0) + f\left(\frac{\pi}{2}\right)\sin(-\pi) \right] \cdot \frac{\pi}{2}$$

$$= \frac{1}{\pi} \left[(0.92)(0) + (1)(0) + (-1.7)(0) + (0.7)(0) \right] \cdot \frac{\pi}{2}$$

$$= 0.$$

So our second Fourier approximation is

$$F_2(x) = 0.25 - 1.31 \cos x - 0.15 \sin x - 1.24 \cos 2x.$$

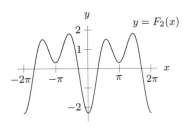

As you can see from comparing our graphs of F_1 and F_2 to the original, our estimates of the Fourier coefficients are not very accurate.

There are other methods of estimating the Fourier coefficients such as taking other Riemann sums, using Simpson's rule, and using the trapezoid rule. With each method, the greater the number of subdivisions, the more accurate the estimates of the Fourier coefficients.

The actual function graphed in the problem was

$$y = \frac{1}{4} - 1.3 \cos x - \frac{\sin(\frac{3}{5})}{\pi} \sin x - \frac{2}{\pi} \cos 2x - \frac{\cos 1}{3\pi} \sin 2x$$

$$= 0.25 - 1.3 \cos x - 0.18 \sin x - 0.63 \cos 2x - 0.057 \sin 2x.$$

18. The Fourier series for f is

$$f(x) = a_0 + \sum_{k=1}^{\infty} a_k \cos kx + \sum_{k=1}^{\infty} b_k \sin kx.$$

Pick any positive integer m. Then multiply through by $\sin mx$, to get

$$f(x) \sin mx = a_0 \sin mx + \sum_{k=1}^{\infty} a_k \cos kx \sin mx + \sum_{k=1}^{\infty} b_k \sin kx \sin mx.$$

Now, integrate term-by-term on the interval $[-\pi, \pi]$ to get

$$\int_{-\pi}^{\pi} f(x) \sin mx \, dx = \int_{-\pi}^{\pi} \left(a_0 \sin mx + \sum_{k=1}^{\infty} a_k \cos kx \sin mx + \sum_{k=1}^{\infty} b_k \sin kx \sin mx \right) dx$$

$$= a_0 \int_{-\pi}^{\pi} \sin mx \, dx + \sum_{k=1}^{\infty} \left(a_k \int_{-\pi}^{\pi} \cos kx \sin mx \, dx \right)$$

$$+ \sum_{k=1}^{\infty} \left(b_k \int_{-\pi}^{\pi} \sin kx \sin mx \, dx \right).$$

Since m is a positive integer, we know that the first term of the above expression is zero (because $\int_{-\pi}^{\pi} \sin mx \, dx = 0$). Since $\int_{-\pi}^{\pi} \cos kx \sin mx \, dx = 0$, we know that everything in the first infinite sum is zero. Since $\int_{-\pi}^{\pi} \sin kx \sin mx \, dx = 0$ where $k \neq m$, the second infinite sum reduces down to the case where $k = m$ so

$$\int_{-\pi}^{\pi} f(x) \sin mx \, dx = b_m \int_{-\pi}^{\pi} \sin mx \sin mx \, dx = b_m \pi.$$

Divide by π to get

$$b_m = \frac{1}{\pi} \int_{-\pi}^{\pi} f(x) \sin mx \, dx.$$

19. (a)

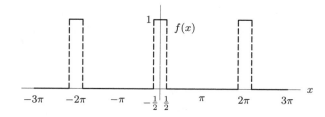

The energy of the pulse train f is

$$E = \frac{1}{\pi} \int_{-\pi}^{\pi} (f(x))^2 \, dx = \frac{1}{\pi} \int_{-1/2}^{1/2} 1^2 \, dx = \frac{1}{\pi} \left(\frac{1}{2} - \left(-\frac{1}{2} \right) \right) = \frac{1}{\pi}.$$

Next, find the Fourier coefficients:

$$a_0 = \text{average value of } f \text{ on } [-\pi, \pi] = \frac{1}{2\pi} (\text{ Area}) = \frac{1}{2\pi}(1) = \frac{1}{2\pi},$$

$$a_k = \frac{1}{\pi} \int_{-\pi}^{\pi} f(x) \cos kx \, dx = \frac{1}{\pi} \int_{-1/2}^{1/2} \cos kx \, dx = \frac{1}{k\pi} \sin kx \Big|_{-1/2}^{1/2}$$

$$= \frac{1}{k\pi} \left(\sin \left(\frac{k}{2} \right) - \sin \left(-\frac{k}{2} \right) \right) = \frac{1}{k\pi} \left(2 \sin \left(\frac{k}{2} \right) \right),$$

$$b_k = \frac{1}{\pi} \int_{-\pi}^{\pi} f(x) \sin kx \, dx = \frac{1}{\pi} \int_{-1/2}^{1/2} \sin kx \, dx = -\frac{1}{k\pi} \cos kx \Big|_{-1/2}^{1/2}$$

$$= -\frac{1}{k\pi} \left(\cos \left(\frac{k}{2} \right) - \cos \left(-\frac{k}{2} \right) \right) = \frac{1}{k\pi}(0) = 0.$$

The energy of f contained in the constant term is

$$A_0^2 = 2a_0^2 = 2 \left(\frac{1}{2\pi} \right)^2 = \frac{1}{2\pi^2}$$

which is

$$\frac{A_0^2}{E} = \frac{1/2\pi^2}{1/\pi} = \frac{1}{2\pi} \approx 0.159155 = 15.9155\% \quad \text{of the total.}$$

The fraction of energy contained in the first harmonic is

$$\frac{A_1^2}{E} = \frac{a_1^2}{E} = \frac{\left(\frac{2 \sin \frac{1}{2}}{\pi} \right)^2}{\frac{1}{\pi}} \approx 0.292653.$$

The fraction of energy contained in both the constant term and the first harmonic together is

$$\frac{A_0^2}{E} + \frac{A_1^2}{E} \approx 0.159155 + 0.292653 = 0.451808\%.$$

(b) The formula for the energy of the kth harmonic is

$$A_k^2 = a_k^2 + b_k^2 = \left(\frac{2 \sin \frac{k}{2}}{k\pi} \right)^2 + 0^2 = \frac{4 \sin^2 \frac{k}{2}}{k^2 \pi^2}.$$

By graphing it as a continuous function for $k \geq 1$, we see its overall behavior as k gets larger. See Figure 10.12. The energy spectrum for the first five terms is graphed below as well in Figure 10.13.

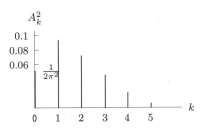

Figure 10.12   Figure 10.13

(c) The constant term and the first five harmonics are needed to capture 90% of the energy of f. This was determined by adding the fractions of energy of f contained in each harmonic until the sum reached at least 90% of the total energy of f:

$$\frac{A_0^2}{E} + \frac{A_1^2}{E} + \frac{A_2^2}{E} + \frac{A_3^2}{E} + \frac{A_4^2}{E} + \frac{A_5^2}{E} \approx 90.1995\%.$$

(d) $F_5(x) = \frac{1}{2\pi} + \frac{2\sin(\frac{1}{2})}{\pi}\cos x + \frac{\sin 1}{\pi}\cos 2x + \frac{2\sin(\frac{3}{2})}{3\pi}\cos 3x + \frac{\sin 2}{2\pi}\cos 4x + \frac{2\sin(\frac{5}{2})}{5\pi}\cos 5x$

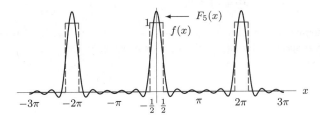

20. (a)

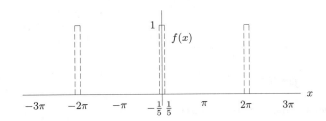

The energy of the pulse train f is

$$E = \frac{1}{\pi}\int_{-\pi}^{\pi}(f(x))^2\,dx = \frac{1}{\pi}\int_{-1/5}^{1/5}1^2\,dx = \frac{1}{\pi}\left(\frac{1}{5} - \left(-\frac{1}{5}\right)\right) = \frac{2}{5\pi}.$$

Next, find the Fourier coefficients:

$$a_0 = \text{average value of } f \text{ on } [-\pi, \pi] = \frac{1}{2\pi}(\text{ Area}) = \frac{1}{2\pi}\left(\frac{2}{5}\right) = \frac{1}{5\pi},$$

$$a_k = \frac{1}{\pi}\int_{-\pi}^{\pi}f(x)\cos kx\,dx = \frac{1}{\pi}\int_{-1/5}^{1/5}\cos kx\,dx = \frac{1}{k\pi}\sin kx\Big|_{-1/5}^{1/5}$$

$$= \frac{1}{k\pi}\left(\sin\left(\frac{k}{5}\right) - \sin\left(-\frac{k}{5}\right)\right) = \frac{1}{k\pi}\left(2\sin\left(\frac{k}{5}\right)\right),$$

$$b_k = \frac{1}{\pi}\int_{-\pi}^{\pi}f(x)\sin kx\,dx = \frac{1}{\pi}\int_{-1/5}^{1/5}\sin kx\,dx = -\frac{1}{k\pi}\cos kx\Big|_{-1/5}^{1/5}$$

$$= -\frac{1}{k\pi}\left(\cos\left(\frac{k}{5}\right) - \cos\left(-\frac{k}{5}\right)\right) = \frac{1}{k\pi}(0) = 0.$$

The energy of f contained in the constant term is

$$A_0^2 = 2a_0^2 = 2\left(\frac{1}{5\pi}\right)^2 = \frac{2}{25\pi^2}$$

which is

$$\frac{A_0^2}{E} = \frac{2/25\pi^2}{2/5\pi} = \frac{1}{5\pi} \approx 0.063662 = 6.3662\% \quad \text{of the total.}$$

The fraction of energy contained in the first harmonic is

$$\frac{A_1^2}{E} = \frac{a_1^2}{E} = \frac{\left(\frac{2\sin\frac{1}{5}}{\pi}\right)^2}{\frac{2}{5\pi}} \approx 0.12563.$$

The fraction of energy contained in both the constant term and the first harmonic together is

$$\frac{A_0^2}{E} + \frac{A_1^2}{E} \approx 0.06366 + 0.12563 = 0.18929 = 18.929\%.$$

(b) The formula for the energy of the kth harmonic is

$$A_k^2 = a_k^2 + b_k^2 = \left(\frac{2\sin\frac{k}{5}}{k\pi}\right)^2 + 0^2 = \frac{4\sin^2\frac{k}{5}}{k^2\pi^2}.$$

By graphing this formula as a continuous function for $k \geq 1$, we see its overall behavior as k gets larger in Figure 10.14. The energy spectrum for the first five terms is shown in Figure 10.15.

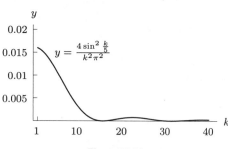

Figure 10.14

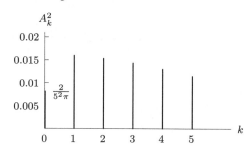

Figure 10.15

(c) The constant term and the first five harmonics contain

$$\frac{A_0^2}{E} + \frac{A_1^2}{E} + \frac{A_2^2}{E} + \frac{A_3^2}{E} + \frac{A_4^2}{E} + \frac{A_5^2}{E} \approx 61.5255\%$$

of the total energy of f.

(d) The fifth Fourier approximation to f is

$$F_5(x) = \frac{1}{5\pi} + \frac{2\sin(\frac{1}{5})}{\pi}\cos x + \frac{\sin(\frac{2}{5})}{\pi}\cos 2x + \frac{2\sin(\frac{3}{5})}{3\pi}\cos 3x + \frac{\sin(\frac{4}{5})}{2\pi}\cos 4x + \frac{2\sin 1}{5\pi}\cos 5x.$$

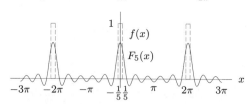

For comparison, below is the thirteenth Fourier approximation to f.

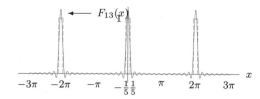

21. (a)

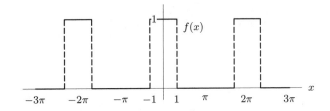

The energy of the pulse train f is

$$E = \frac{1}{\pi} \int_{-\pi}^{\pi} (f(x))^2\, dx = \frac{1}{\pi} \int_{-1}^{1} 1^2 = \frac{1}{\pi}(1 - (-1)) = \frac{2}{\pi}.$$

Next, find the Fourier coefficients:

$$a_0 = \text{average value of } f \text{ on } [-\pi, \pi] = \frac{1}{2\pi}(\text{ Area}) = \frac{1}{2\pi}(2) = \frac{1}{\pi},$$

$$a_k = \frac{1}{\pi} \int_{-\pi}^{\pi} f(x) \cos kx\, dx = \frac{1}{\pi} \int_{-1}^{1} \cos kx\, dx = \frac{1}{k\pi} \sin kx \Big|_{-1}^{1}$$

$$= \frac{1}{k\pi}(\sin k - \sin(-k)) = \frac{1}{k\pi}(2\sin k),$$

$$b_k = \frac{1}{\pi} \int_{-\pi}^{\pi} f(x) \sin kx\, dx = \frac{1}{\pi} \int_{-1}^{1} \sin kx\, dx = -\frac{1}{k\pi} \cos kx \Big|_{-1}^{1}$$

$$= -\frac{1}{k\pi}(\cos k - \cos(-k)) = \frac{1}{k\pi}(0) = 0.$$

The energy of f contained in the constant term is

$$A_0^2 = 2a_0^2 = 2\left(\frac{1}{\pi}\right)^2 = \frac{2}{\pi^2}$$

which is

$$\frac{A_0^2}{E} = \frac{2/\pi^2}{2/\pi} = \frac{1}{\pi} \approx 0.3183 = 31.83\% \quad \text{of the total.}$$

The fraction of energy contained in the first harmonic is

$$\frac{A_1^2}{E} = \frac{a_1^2}{E} = \frac{\left(\frac{2\sin 1}{\pi}\right)^2}{\frac{2}{\pi}} \approx 0.4508 = 45.08\%.$$

The fraction of energy contained in both the constant term and the first harmonic together is

$$\frac{A_0^2}{E} + \frac{A_1^2}{E} \approx 0.7691 = 76.91\%.$$

(b) The fraction of energy contained in the second harmonic is

$$\frac{A_2^2}{E} = \frac{a_2^2}{E} = \frac{\left(\frac{\sin 2}{\pi}\right)^2}{\frac{2}{\pi}} \approx 0.1316 = 13.16\%$$

so the fraction of energy contained in the constant term and first two harmonics is

$$\frac{A_0^2}{E} + \frac{A_1^2}{E} + \frac{A_2^2}{E} \approx 0.7691 + 0.1316 = 0.9007 = 90.07\%.$$

Therefore, the constant term and the first two harmonics are needed to capture 90% of the energy of f.

(c)

$$F_3(x) = \frac{1}{\pi} + \frac{2\sin 1}{\pi}\cos x + \frac{\sin 2}{\pi}\cos 2x + \frac{2\sin 3}{3\pi}\cos 3x$$

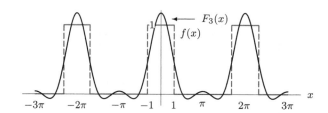

22. As c gets closer and closer to 0, the energy of the pulse train will also approach 0, since

$$E = \frac{1}{\pi}\int_{-\pi}^{\pi}(f(x))^2\,dx = \frac{1}{\pi}\int_{-c/2}^{c/2}1^2\,dx = \frac{1}{\pi}\left(\frac{c}{2} - \left(-\frac{c}{2}\right)\right) = \frac{c}{\pi}.$$

The energy spectrum shows the *relative* distribution of the energy of f among its harmonics. The fraction of energy carried by each harmonic gets smaller as c gets closer to 0, as shown by comparing the kth terms of the Fourier series for pulse trains with $c = 2, 1, 0.4$. For instance, notice that the *fraction* or *percentage* of energy carried by the constant term gets smaller as c gets smaller; the same is true for the energy carried by the first harmonic.

   If each harmonic contributes less energy, then more harmonics are needed to capture a fixed percentage of energy. For example, if $c = 2$, only the constant term and the first two harmonics are needed to capture 90% of the total energy of that pulse train. If $c = 1$, the constant term and the first five harmonics are needed to get 90% of the energy of that pulse train. If $c = 0.4$, the constant term and the first thirteen harmonics are needed to get 90% of the energy of that pulse train. This means that more harmonics, or more terms in the series, are needed to get an accurate approximation. Compare the graphs of the fifth and thirteenth Fourier approximations of f in Problem 20.

23. By formula II-11 of the integral table,

$$\int_{-\pi}^{\pi}\cos kx \cos mx\,dx = \frac{1}{m^2 - k^2}\left(m\cos(kx)\sin(mx) - k\sin(kx)\cos(mx)\right)\bigg|_{-\pi}^{\pi}.$$

Again, since $\sin(n\pi) = 0$ for any integer n, it is easy to see that this expression is simply 0.

24. We make the substitution $u = mx$, $dx = \frac{1}{m}du$. Then

$$\int_{-\pi}^{\pi}\cos^2 mx\,dx = \frac{1}{m}\int_{u=-m\pi}^{u=m\pi}\cos^2 u\,du.$$

By Formula IV-18 of the integral table, this equals

$$\frac{1}{m}\left[\frac{1}{2}\cos u \sin u\right]\bigg|_{-m\pi}^{m\pi} + \frac{1}{m}\frac{1}{2}\int_{-m\pi}^{m\pi}1\,du = 0 + \frac{1}{2m}u\bigg|_{-m\pi}^{m\pi} = \frac{1}{2m}u\bigg|_{-m\pi}^{m\pi}$$

$$= \frac{1}{2m}(2m\pi) = \pi.$$

25. The easiest way to do this is to use Problem 24.

$$\int_{-\pi}^{\pi}\sin^2 mx\,dx = \int_{-\pi}^{\pi}(1 - \cos^2 mx)\,dx = \int_{-\pi}^{\pi}dx - \int_{-\pi}^{\pi}\cos^2 mx\,dx$$

$$= 2\pi - \pi \quad \text{using Problem 24}$$

$$= \pi.$$

26. By formula II-12 of the integral table,

$$\int_{-\pi}^{\pi} \sin kx \cos mx \, dx$$

$$= \frac{1}{m^2 - k^2}\left(m\sin(kx)\sin(mx) + k\cos(kx)\cos(mx) \right)\Big|_{-\pi}^{\pi}$$

$$= \frac{1}{m^2 - k^2}\Big[m\sin(k\pi)\sin(m\pi) + k\cos(k\pi)\cos(m\pi)$$

$$- m\sin(-k\pi)\sin(-m\pi) - k\cos(-k\pi)\cos(-m\pi)\Big].$$

Since k and m are positive integers, $\sin(k\pi) = \sin(m\pi) = \sin(-k\pi) = \sin(-m\pi) = 0$. Also, $\cos(k\pi) = \cos(-k\pi)$ since $\cos x$ is even. Thus this expression reduces to 0. [Note: since $\sin kx \cos mx$ is odd, so $\int_{-\pi}^{\pi} \sin kx \cos mx \, dx$ must be 0.]

27. Using formula II-10 in the integral table,

$$\int_{-\pi}^{\pi} \sin kx \sin mx \, dx = \frac{1}{m^2 - k^2}\left[k\cos(kx)\sin(mx) - m\sin(kx)\cos(mx) \right]\Big|_{-\pi}^{\pi}.$$

Again, since $\sin(n\pi) = 0$ for all integers n, this expression reduces to 0.

28. (a) To show that $g(t)$ is periodic with period 2π, we calculate

$$g(t + 2\pi) = f\left(\frac{b(t + 2\pi)}{2\pi} \right) = f\left(\frac{bt}{2\pi} + b \right) = f\left(\frac{bt}{2\pi} \right) = g(t).$$

Since $g(t + 2\pi) = g(t)$ for all t, we know that $g(t)$ is periodic with period 2π. In addition

$$g\left(\frac{2\pi x}{b} \right) = f\left(\frac{b(2\pi x/b)}{2\pi} \right) = f(x).$$

(b) We make the change of variable $t = 2\pi x/b$, $dt = (2\pi/b)dx$ in the usual formulas for the Fourier coefficients of $g(t)$, as follows:

$$a_0 = \frac{1}{2\pi}\int_{t=-\pi}^{\pi} g(t)\,dt = \frac{1}{2\pi}\int_{x=-b/2}^{b/2} g\left(\frac{2\pi x}{b} \right)\frac{2\pi}{b}\,dx = \frac{1}{b}\int_{-\frac{b}{2}}^{\frac{b}{2}} f(x)\,dx$$

$$a_k = \frac{1}{\pi}\int_{t=-\pi}^{\pi} g(t)\cos(kt)\,dt = \frac{1}{\pi}\int_{x=-b/2}^{b/2} g\left(\frac{2\pi x}{b} \right)\cos\left(\frac{2\pi kx}{b} \right)\frac{2\pi}{b}\,dx$$

$$= \frac{2}{b}\int_{-b/2}^{b/2} f(x)\cos\left(\frac{2\pi kx}{b} \right)\,dx$$

$$b_k = \frac{1}{\pi}\int_{t=-\pi}^{\pi} g(t)\sin(kt)\,dt = \frac{1}{\pi}\int_{x=-b/2}^{b/2} g\left(\frac{2\pi x}{b} \right)\sin\left(\frac{2\pi kx}{b} \right)\frac{2\pi}{b}\,dx$$

$$= \frac{2}{b}\int_{-b/2}^{b/2} f(x)\sin\left(\frac{2\pi kx}{b} \right)\,dx$$

(c) By part (a), the Fourier series for $f(x)$ can be obtained by substituting $t = 2\pi x/b$ into the Fourier series for $g(t)$ which was found in part (b).

Solutions for Chapter 10 Review

Exercises

1. $e^x \approx 1 + e(x-1) + \dfrac{e}{2}(x-1)^2$

2. $\ln x \approx \ln 2 + \dfrac{1}{2}(x-2) - \dfrac{1}{8}(x-2)^2$

3. $\sin x \approx -\dfrac{1}{\sqrt{2}} + \dfrac{1}{\sqrt{2}}\left(x + \dfrac{\pi}{4}\right) + \dfrac{1}{2\sqrt{2}}\left(x + \dfrac{\pi}{4}\right)^2$

4. Differentiating $f(x) = \tan x$, we get $f'(x) = 1/\cos^2 x$, $f''(x) = 2\sin x/\cos^3 x$.

Since $\tan(\pi/4) = 1$, $\cos(\pi/4) = \sin(\pi/4) = 1/\sqrt{2}$, we have $f(\pi/4) = 1$, $f'(\pi/4) = 1/(1/\sqrt{2})^2 = 2$, $f''(\pi/4) = \frac{2(1/\sqrt{2})}{(1/\sqrt{2})^3} = 4$, so

$$\tan x \approx f\left(\frac{\pi}{4}\right) + f'\left(\frac{\pi}{4}\right)\left(x - \frac{\pi}{4}\right) + \frac{f''\left(\frac{\pi}{4}\right)}{2!}\left(x - \frac{\pi}{4}\right)^2$$

$$= 1 + 2\left(x - \frac{\pi}{4}\right) + \frac{4}{2!}\left(x - \frac{\pi}{4}\right)^2 = 1 + 2\left(x - \frac{\pi}{4}\right) + 2\left(x - \frac{\pi}{4}\right)^2.$$

5. $f'(x) = 3x^2 + 14x - 5$, $f''(x) = 6x + 14$, $f'''(x) = 6$. The Taylor polynomial about $x = 1$ is

$$P_3(x) = 4 + \frac{12}{1!}(x-1) + \frac{20}{2!}(x-1)^2 + \frac{6}{3!}(x-1)^3$$

$$= 4 + 12(x-1) + 10(x-1)^2 + (x-1)^3.$$

Notice that if you multiply out and collect terms in $P_3(x)$, you will get $f(x)$ back.

6. We multiply the series for e^t by t^2. Since

$$e^t = 1 + t + \frac{t^2}{2!} + \frac{t^3}{3!} + \cdots,$$

multiplying by t^2 gives

$$t^2 e^t = t^2 + t^3 + \frac{t^4}{2!} + \frac{t^5}{3!} + \cdots$$

$$= t^2 + t^3 + \frac{1}{2}t^4 + \frac{1}{6}t^5 + \cdots.$$

7. We substitute $3y$ into the series for $\cos x$. Since

$$\cos x = 1 - \frac{x^2}{2!} + \frac{x^4}{4!} - \frac{x^6}{6!} + \cdots,$$

substituting $x = 3y$ gives

$$\cos(3y) = 1 - \frac{(3y)^2}{2!} + \frac{(3y)^4}{4!} - \frac{(3y)^6}{6!} + \cdots$$

$$= 1 - \frac{9}{2}y^2 + \frac{27}{8}y^4 - \frac{81}{80}y^6 + \cdots.$$

8.

$$\theta^2 \cos \theta^2 = \theta^2\left(1 - \frac{(\theta^2)^2}{2!} + \frac{(\theta^2)^4}{4!} - \frac{(\theta^2)^6}{6!} + \cdots\right)$$

$$= \theta^2 - \frac{\theta^6}{2!} + \frac{\theta^{10}}{4!} - \frac{\theta^{14}}{6!} + \cdots$$

9. Substituting $y = t^2$ in $\sin y = y - \dfrac{y^3}{3!} + \dfrac{y^5}{5!} - \dfrac{y^7}{7!} + \cdots$ gives

$$\sin t^2 = t^2 - \frac{t^6}{3!} + \frac{t^{10}}{5!} - \frac{t^{14}}{7!} + \cdots$$

10.

$$\frac{1}{\sqrt{4-x}} = \frac{1}{2\sqrt{1 - \frac{x}{2}}} = \frac{1}{2}\left(1 - \frac{x}{2}\right)^{-\frac{1}{2}}$$

$$= \frac{1}{2}\left(1 - \left(-\frac{1}{2}\right)\left(\frac{x}{2}\right) + \frac{1}{2!}\left(-\frac{1}{2}\right)\left(-\frac{3}{2}\right)\left(\frac{x}{2}\right)^2\right.$$

$$\left. - \frac{1}{3!}\left(-\frac{1}{2}\right)\left(-\frac{3}{2}\right)\left(-\frac{5}{2}\right)\left(\frac{x}{2}\right)^3 + \cdots\right)$$

$$= \frac{1}{2} + \frac{1}{8}x + \frac{3}{64}x^2 + \frac{5}{256}x^3 + \cdots$$

11. Substituting $y = -4z^2$ into $\dfrac{1}{1+y} = 1 - y + y^2 - y^3 + \cdots$ gives

$$\frac{1}{1 - 4z^2} = 1 + 4z^2 + 16z^4 + 64z^6 + \cdots$$

12.

$$\frac{t}{1+t} = t(1+t)^{-1} = t\left(1 + (-1)t + \frac{(-1)(-2)}{2!}t^2 + \frac{(-1)(-2)(-3)}{3!}t^3 + \cdots\right)$$

$$= t - t^2 + t^3 - t^4 + \cdots$$

13. We use the binomial series to expand $1/\sqrt{1 - z^2}$ and multiply by z^2. Since

$$\frac{1}{\sqrt{1+x}} = (1+x)^{-1/2} = 1 - \frac{1}{2}x + \frac{(-1/2)(-3/2)}{2!}x^2 + \frac{(-1/2)(-3/2)(-5/2)}{3!}x^3 + \cdots$$

$$= 1 - \frac{1}{2}x + \frac{3}{8}x^2 - \frac{5}{16}x^3 + \cdots.$$

Substituting $x = -z^2$ gives

$$\frac{z^2}{\sqrt{1-z^2}} = 1 - \frac{1}{2}(-z^2) + \frac{3}{8}(-z^2)^2 - \frac{5}{16}(-z^2)^3 + \cdots$$

$$= 1 + \frac{1}{2}z^2 + \frac{3}{8}z^4 + \frac{15}{16}z^6 + \cdots.$$

Multiplying by z^2, we have

$$\frac{z^2}{\sqrt{1-z^2}} = z^2 + \frac{1}{2}z^4 + \frac{3}{8}z^6 + \frac{15}{16}z^8 + \cdots.$$

14.

$$\sqrt{R - r} = \sqrt{R}\left(1 - \frac{r}{R}\right)^{\frac{1}{2}}$$

$$= \sqrt{R}\left(1 + \frac{1}{2}\left(-\frac{r}{R}\right) + \frac{1}{2!}\left(\frac{1}{2}\right)\left(-\frac{1}{2}\right)\left(-\frac{r}{R}\right)^2\right.$$

$$\left. + \frac{1}{3!}\left(\frac{1}{2}\right)\left(-\frac{1}{2}\right)\left(-\frac{3}{2}\right)\left(-\frac{r}{R}\right)^3 + \cdots\right)$$

$$= \sqrt{R}\left(1 - \frac{1}{2}\frac{r}{R} - \frac{1}{8}\frac{r^2}{R^2} - \frac{1}{16}\frac{r^3}{R^3} - \cdots\right)$$

15.

$$\frac{a}{a+b} = \frac{a}{a(1+\frac{b}{a})} = \left(1+\frac{b}{a}\right)^{-1} = 1 - \frac{b}{a} + \left(\frac{b}{a}\right)^2 - \left(\frac{b}{a}\right)^3 + \cdots$$

16. Using the binomial expansion for $(1+x)^{3/2}$ with $x = y/B$.

$$(B^2 + y^2)^{3/2} = \left(B^2 + B^2\left(\frac{y^2}{B^2}\right)\right)^{3/2} = \left(B^2\left(1+\left(\frac{y}{B}\right)^2\right)\right)^{3/2} = B^3\left(1+\left(\frac{y}{B}\right)^2\right)^{3/2}$$

$$= B^3\left(1 + (3/2)\left(\left(\frac{y}{B}\right)^2\right)^1 + \frac{(3/2)(1/2)}{2!}\left(\left(\frac{y}{B}\right)^2\right)^2 + \frac{(3/2)(1/2)(-1/2)}{3!}\left(\left(\frac{y}{B}\right)^2\right)^3 \cdots\right)$$

$$= B^3\left(1 + \frac{3}{2}\left(\frac{y}{B}\right)^2 + \frac{3}{8}\left(\frac{y}{B}\right)^4 - \frac{1}{16}\left(\frac{y}{B}\right)^6 \cdots\right).$$

17. Using the binomial expansion for $(1+x)^{-3/2}$ with $x = r/a$:

$$\frac{1}{(a+r)^{3/2}} = \frac{1}{\left(a+a\left(\frac{r}{a}\right)\right)^{3/2}} = \frac{1}{\left(a\left(1+\frac{r}{a}\right)\right)^{3/2}} = \frac{1}{a^{3/2}}\left(1+\left(\frac{r}{a}\right)\right)^{-3/2}$$

$$= \frac{1}{a^{3/2}}\left(1 + (-3/2)\left(\frac{r}{a}\right) + \frac{(-3/2)(-5/2)}{2!}\left(\frac{r}{a}\right)^2 + \frac{(-3/2)(-5/2)(-7/2)}{3!}\left(\frac{r}{a}\right)^3 + \cdots\right)$$

$$= \frac{1}{a^{3/2}}\left(1 - \frac{3}{2}\left(\frac{r}{a}\right) + \frac{15}{8}\left(\frac{r}{a}\right)^2 - \frac{35}{16}\left(\frac{r}{a}\right)^3 + \cdots\right).$$

Problems

18. (a) Factoring out $7(1.02)^3$ and using the formula for the sum of a finite geometric series with $a = 7(1.02)^3$ and $r = 1/1.02$, we see

$$\text{Sum} = 7(1.02)^3 + 7(1.02)^2 + 7(1.02) + 7 + \frac{7}{(1.02)} + \frac{7}{(1.02)^3} + \cdots + \frac{7}{(1.02)^{100}}$$

$$= 7(1.02)^3\left(1 + \frac{1}{(1.02)} + \frac{1}{(1.02)^2} + \cdots + \frac{1}{(1.02)^{103}}\right)$$

$$= 7(1.02)^3\frac{\left(1 - \frac{1}{(1.02)^{104}}\right)}{1 - \frac{1}{1.02}}$$

$$= 7(1.02)^3\left(\frac{(1.02)^{104} - 1}{(1.02)^{104}}\frac{1.02}{0.02}\right)$$

$$= \frac{7(1.02^{104} - 1)}{0.02(1.02)^{100}}.$$

(b) Using the Taylor expansion for e^x with $x = (0.1)^2$, we see

$$\text{Sum} = 7 + 7(0.1)^2 + \frac{7(0.1)^4}{2!} + \frac{7(0.1)^6}{3!} + \cdots$$

$$= 7\left(1 + (0.1)^2 + \frac{(0.1)^4}{2!} + \frac{(0.1)^6}{3!} + \cdots\right)$$

$$= 7e^{(0.1)^2}$$

$$= 7e^{0.01}.$$

19. Infinite geometric series with $a = 1$, $x = -1/3$, so

$$\text{Sum} = \frac{1}{1 - (-1/3)} = \frac{3}{4}.$$

20. Finite geometric series which can be rewritten as

$$8\left(1 + \frac{1}{2} + \frac{1}{4} + \frac{1}{8} + \cdots + \frac{1}{2^{13}}\right) = 8\left(\frac{1 - 1/2^{14}}{1 - 1/2}\right) = 16\left(1 - \frac{1}{2^{14}}\right).$$

21. This is the series for e^x with $x = -2$ substituted. Thus

$$1 - 2 + \frac{4}{2!} - \frac{8}{3!} + \frac{16}{4!} + \cdots = 1 + (-2) + \frac{(-2)^2}{2!} + \frac{(-2)^3}{3!} + \frac{(-2)^4}{4!} + \cdots = e^{-2}.$$

22. This is the series for $\sin x$ with $x = 2$ substituted. Thus

$$2 - \frac{8}{3!} + \frac{32}{5!} - \frac{128}{7!} + \cdots = 2 - \frac{2^3}{3!} + \frac{2^5}{5!} - \frac{2^7}{7!} + \cdots = \sin 2.$$

23. Factoring out a 3, we see

$$3\left(1 + 1 + \frac{1}{2!} + \frac{1}{3!} + \frac{1}{4!} + \frac{1}{5!} + \cdots\right) = 3e^1 = 3e.$$

24. Factoring out a 0.1, we see

$$0.1\left(0.1 - \frac{(0.1)^3}{3!} + \frac{(0.1)^5}{5!} - \frac{(0.1)^7}{7!} + \cdots\right) = 0.1\sin(0.1).$$

25. Using the fact that

$$f(x) \approx P_3(x) = f(0) + f'(0)x + \frac{f''(0)}{2!}x^2 + \frac{f'''(0)}{3!}x^3$$

and identifying coefficients with those given for $P_3(x)$, we obtain the following:

(a) $f(0) = $ constant term which equals 2,   so $f(0) = 2$.
(b) $f'(0) = $ coefficient of x which equals -1,   so $f'(0) = -1$.
(c) $\frac{f''(0)}{2!} = $ coefficient of x^2 which equals $-1/3$,   so $f''(0) = -2/3$.
(d) $\frac{f'''(0)}{3!} = $ coefficient of x^3 which equals 2,   so $f'''(0) = 12$.

26. The second degree Taylor polynomial for $f(x)$ around $x = 3$ is

$$f(x) \approx f(3) + f'(3)(x - 3) + \frac{f''(3)}{2!}(x - 3)^2$$
$$= 1 + 5(x - 3) - \frac{10}{2!}(x - 3)^2 = 1 + 5(x - 3) - 5(x - 3)^2.$$

Substituting $x = 3.1$, we get

$$f(3.1) \approx 1 + 5(3.1 - 3) - 5(3.1 - 3)^2 = 1 + 5(0.1) - 5(0.01) = 1.45.$$

27. (a) Writing

$$f(x) = b\left(1 - \frac{x^2}{a^2}\right)^{1/2}$$

and using the Binomial expansion, we have

$$f(x) \approx P_2(x) = b\left(1 - \frac{1}{2}\frac{x^2}{a^2}\right) = b - \frac{bx^2}{2a^2}.$$

(b) A graph of the upper half the ellipse is shown in Figure 10.16. Since the graph has a horizontal tangent at $x = 0$, the coefficient of x is 0.

(c) The parabola is

$$y = b - \frac{bx^2}{2a^2}.$$

Its x-intercepts are $x = \pm\sqrt{2}a$.

(d) The graphs of

$$y = f(x) = 2\sqrt{1 - \frac{x^2}{9}} \quad \text{and} \quad y = 2 - \frac{x^2}{9}$$

are shown in Figure 10.17. The maximum difference occurs at $x = 0.1$ or $x = -0.1$, so

$$\text{Maximum error} = 2 - \frac{(0.1)^2}{9} - 2\sqrt{1 - \frac{(0.1)^2}{9}} \approx 3 \cdot 10^{-7}.$$

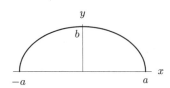

Figure 10.16: Graph of
$y = b\sqrt{1 - x^2/a^2}$

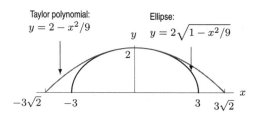

Figure 10.17

28. Write out series expansions about $x = 0$, and compare the first few terms:

$$\sin x = x - \frac{x^3}{3!} + \frac{x^5}{5!} + \cdots$$

$$\ln(1 + x) = x - \frac{x^2}{2} + \frac{x^3}{3} - \cdots$$

$$1 - \cos x = 1 - \left(1 - \frac{x^2}{2!} + \frac{x^4}{4!} - \cdots\right) = \frac{x^2}{2!} - \frac{x^4}{4!} + \cdots$$

$$e^x - 1 = x + \frac{x^2}{2!} + \frac{x^3}{3!} + \cdots$$

$$\arctan x = \int \frac{dx}{1 + x^2} = \int (1 - x^2 + x^4 - \cdots)\, dx$$

$$= x - \frac{x^3}{3} + \frac{x^5}{5} + \cdots \qquad \text{(note that the arbitrary constant is 0)}$$

$$x\sqrt{1 - x} = x(1 - x)^{1/2} = x\left(1 - \frac{1}{2}x + \frac{(1/2)(-1/2)}{2}x^2 + \cdots\right)$$

$$= x - \frac{x^2}{2} + \frac{x^3}{8} + \cdots$$

So, considering just the first term or two (since we are interested in small x)

$$1 - \cos x < x\sqrt{1 - x} < \ln(1 + x) < \arctan x < \sin x < x < e^x - 1.$$

29. The graph in Figure 10.18 suggests that the Taylor polynomials converge to $f(x) = \dfrac{1}{1 + x}$ on the interval $(-1, 1)$. The Taylor expansion is

$$f(x) = \frac{1}{1 + x} = 1 - x + x^2 - x^3 + x^4 - \cdots,$$

so the ratio test gives

$$\lim_{n \to \infty} \frac{|a_{n+1}|}{|a_n|} = \lim_{n \to \infty} \frac{|(-1)^{n+1}x^{n+1}|}{|(-1)^n x^n|} = |x|.$$

Thus, the series converges if $|x| < 1$; that is $-1 < x < 1$.

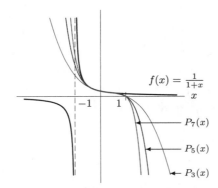

$$f(x) = \frac{1}{1+x}$$

-1 1

$P_7(x)$

$P_5(x)$

$P_3(x)$

Figure 10.18

30. First we use the Taylor series expansion for $\ln(1+t)$,

$$\ln(1+t) = t - \frac{1}{2}t^2 + \frac{1}{3}t^3 - \frac{1}{4}t^4 + \cdots$$

to find the Taylor series expansion of $\ln(1 + x + x^2)$ by putting $t = x + x^2$. We get

$$\ln(1 + x + x^2) = x + \frac{1}{2}x^2 - \frac{2}{3}x^3 + \frac{1}{4}x^4 + \cdots.$$

Next we use the Taylor series for $\sin x$ to get

$$\sin^2 x = (\sin x)^2 = \left(x - \frac{1}{6}x^3 + \frac{1}{120}x^5 - \cdots\right)^2 = x^2 - \frac{1}{3}x^4 + \cdots.$$

Finally,

$$\frac{\ln(1 + x + x^2) - x}{\sin^2 x} = \frac{\frac{1}{2}x^2 - \frac{2}{3}x^3 + \frac{1}{4}x^4 + \cdots}{x^2 - \frac{1}{3}x^4 + \cdots} \to \frac{1}{2}, \quad \text{as} \quad x \to 0.$$

31. (a) The series for $\frac{\sin 2\theta}{\theta}$ is

$$\frac{\sin 2\theta}{\theta} = \frac{1}{\theta}\left(2\theta - \frac{(2\theta)^3}{3!} + \frac{(2\theta)^5}{5!} - \cdots\right) = 2 - \frac{4\theta^2}{3} + \frac{4\theta^4}{15} - \cdots$$

so $\lim\limits_{\theta \to 0} \dfrac{\sin 2\theta}{\theta} = 2$.
(b) Near $\theta = 0$, we make the approximation

$$\frac{\sin 2\theta}{\theta} \approx 2 - \frac{4}{3}\theta^2$$

so the parabola is $y = 2 - \frac{4}{3}\theta^2$.

32. (a) $f(t) = te^t$.
Use the Taylor expansion for e^t :

$$f(t) = t\left(1 + t + \frac{t^2}{2!} + \frac{t^3}{3!} + \cdots\right)$$

$$= t + t^2 + \frac{t^3}{2!} + \frac{t^4}{3!} + \cdots$$

(b)

$$\int_0^x f(t)\,dt = \int_0^x te^t\,dt = \int_0^x \left(t + t^2 + \frac{t^3}{2!} + \frac{t^4}{3!} + \cdots\right) dt$$

$$= \frac{t^2}{2} + \frac{t^3}{3} + \frac{t^4}{4 \cdot 2!} + \frac{t^5}{5 \cdot 3!} + \cdots \Bigg|_0^x$$

$$= \frac{x^2}{2} + \frac{x^3}{3} + \frac{x^4}{4 \cdot 2!} + \frac{x^5}{5 \cdot 3!} + \cdots$$

(c) Substitute $x = 1$:

$$\int_0^1 te^t \, dt = \frac{1}{2} + \frac{1}{3} + \frac{1}{4 \cdot 2!} + \frac{1}{5 \cdot 3!} + \cdots$$

In the integral above, to integrate by parts, let $u = t$, $dv = e^t \, dt$, so $du = dt$, $v = e^t$.

$$\int_0^1 te^t \, dt = te^t \Big|_0^1 - \int_0^1 e^t \, dt = e - (e - 1) = 1$$

Hence

$$\frac{1}{2} + \frac{1}{3} + \frac{1}{4 \cdot 2!} + \frac{1}{5 \cdot 3!} + \cdots = 1.$$

33. (a) Since $\sqrt{4 - x^2} = 2\sqrt{1 - x^2/4}$, we use the Binomial expansion

$$\sqrt{4 - x^2} \approx 2\left(1 + \frac{1}{2}\left(-\frac{x^2}{4}\right) + \frac{1}{2!}\left(\frac{1}{2}\right)\left(-\frac{1}{2}\right)\left(-\frac{x^2}{4}\right)^2 \right)$$

$$= 2\left(1 - \frac{x^2}{8} - \frac{x^4}{128}\right) = 2 - \frac{x^2}{4} - \frac{x^4}{64}.$$

(b) Substituting the Taylor series in the integral gives

$$\int_0^1 \sqrt{4 - x^2} \, dx \approx \int_0^1 \left(2 - \frac{x^2}{4} - \frac{x^4}{64}\right) dx = 2x - \frac{x^3}{12} - \frac{x^5}{320}\Big|_0^1 = 1.9135.$$

(c) Since $x = 2\sin t$, we have $dx = 2\cos t \, dt$; in addition $t = 0$ when $x = 0$ and $t = \pi/6$ when $x = 1$. Thus

$$\int_0^1 \sqrt{4 - x^2} \, dx = \int_0^{\pi/6} \sqrt{4 - 4\sin^2 t} \cdot 2\cos t \, dt$$

$$= \int_0^{\pi/6} 2 \cdot 2\sqrt{1 - \sin^2 t} \cos t \, dt = 4\int_0^{\pi/6} \cos^2 t \, dt.$$

Using the table of integrals, we find

$$4\int_0^{\pi/6} \cos^2 t \, dt = 4 \cdot \frac{1}{2}(\cos t \sin t + t)\Big|_0^{\pi/6} = 2\left(\cos\frac{\pi}{6}\sin\frac{\pi}{6} + \frac{\pi}{6}\right) = \frac{\sqrt{3}}{2} + \frac{\pi}{3}.$$

(d) Using a calculator, $(\sqrt{3}/3) + (\pi/3) = 1.9132$, so the answers to parts (b) and (c) agree to three decimal places.

34. (a) Since $\int (1 - x^2)^{-1/2} dx = \arcsin x$, we use the Taylor series for $(1 - x^2)^{-1/2}$ to find the Taylor series for $\arcsin x$:

$$(1 - x^2)^{-1/2} = 1 + \frac{1}{2}x^2 + \frac{3}{8}x^4 + \frac{5}{16}x^6 + \frac{35}{128}x^8 + \cdots$$

so

$$\arcsin x = \int (1 - x^2)^{-1/2} dx = x + \frac{1}{6}x^3 + \frac{3}{40}x^5 + \frac{5}{112}x^7 + \frac{35}{1152}x^9 + \cdots$$

(b) From Example 4 in Section 10.3, we know

$$\arctan x = x - \frac{1}{3}x^3 + \frac{1}{5}x^5 - \frac{1}{7}x^7 + \cdots$$

so that

$$\frac{\arctan x}{\arcsin x} = \frac{x - \frac{1}{3}x^3 + \frac{1}{5}x^5 - \frac{1}{7}x^7 + \cdots}{x + \frac{1}{6}x^3 + \frac{3}{40}x^5 + \frac{5}{112}x^7 + \frac{35}{1152}x^9 + \cdots} \to 1, \quad \text{as} \quad x \to 0.$$

35. (a) The Taylor polynomial of degree 2 is

$$V(x) \approx V(0) + V'(0)x + \frac{V''(0)}{2}x^2.$$

Since $x = 0$ is a minimum, $V'(0) = 0$ and $V''(0) > 0$. We can not say anything about the sign or value of $V(0)$. Thus

$$V(x) \approx V(0) + \frac{V''(0)}{2}x^2.$$

(b) Differentiating gives an approximation to $V'(x)$ at points near the origin

$$V'(x) \approx V''(0)x.$$

Thus, the force on the particle is approximated by $-V''(0)x$.

$$\text{Force} = -V'(x) \approx -V''(0)x.$$

Since $V''(0) > 0$, the force is approximately proportional to x with negative proportionality constant, $-V''(0)$. This means that when x is positive, the force is negative, which means pointing toward the origin. When x is negative, the force is positive, which means pointing toward the origin. Thus, the force always points toward the origin.

Physical principles tell us that the particle is at equilibrium at the minimum potential. The direction of the force toward the origin supports this, as the force is tending to restore the particle to the origin.

36. (a) Since the expression under the square root sign, $1 - \frac{v^2}{c^2}$ must be positive in order to give a real value of m, we have

$$1 - \frac{v^2}{c^2} > 0$$
$$\frac{v^2}{c^2} < 1$$
$$v^2 < c^2,$$
$$\text{so} \quad -c < v < c.$$

In other words, the object can never travel faster that the speed of light.

(b)

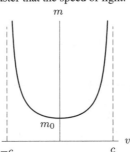

(c) Notice that $m = m_0 \left(1 - \frac{v^2}{c^2}\right)^{-1/2}$. If we substitute $u = -\frac{v^2}{c^2}$, we get $m = m_0(1 + u)^{-1/2}$ and we can use the binomial expansion to get:

$$m = m_0 \left(1 - \frac{1}{2}u + \frac{(-1/2)(-3/2)}{2!}u^2 + \cdots\right)$$
$$= m_0 \left(1 + \frac{1}{2}\frac{v^2}{c^2} + \frac{3}{8}\frac{v^4}{c^4} + \cdots\right).$$

(d) We would expect this series to converge only for values of the original function that exist, namely when $|v| < c$.

37. (a) To find when V takes on its minimum values, set $\frac{dV}{dr} = 0$. So

$$-V_0 \frac{d}{dr}\left(2\left(\frac{r_0}{r}\right)^6 - \left(\frac{r_0}{r}\right)^{12}\right) = 0$$

$$-V_0\left(-12r_0^6 r^{-7} + 12r_0^{12}r^{-13}\right) = 0$$

$$12r_0^6 r^{-7} = 12r_0^{12}r^{-13}$$

$$r_0^6 = r^6$$

$$r = r_0.$$

Rewriting $V'(r)$ as $\dfrac{12r_0^6 V_0}{r^7}\left(1 - \left(\dfrac{r_0}{r}\right)^6\right)$, we see that $V'(r) > 0$ for $r > r_0$ and $V'(r) < 0$ for $r < r_0$. Thus, $V = -V_0(2(1)^6 - (1)^{12}) = -V_0$ is a minimum.

(Note: We discard the negative root $-r_0$ since the distance r must be positive.)

(b)

$$V(r) = -V_0\left(2\left(\frac{r_0}{r}\right)^6 - \left(\frac{r_0}{r}\right)^{12}\right)$$

$$V'(r) = -V_0(-12r_0^6 r^{-7} + 12r_0^{12}r^{-13})$$

$$V''(r) = -V_0(84r_0^6 r^{-8} - 156r_0^{12}r^{-14})$$

$$V(r_0) = -V_0$$
$$V'(r_0) = 0$$
$$V''(r_0) = 72V_0 r_0^{-2}$$

The Taylor series is thus:

$$V(r) = -V_0 + 72V_0 r_0^{-2} \cdot (r - r_0)^2 \cdot \frac{1}{2} + \cdots$$

(c) The difference between V and its minimum value $-V_0$ is

$$V - (-V_0) = 36V_0 \frac{(r - r_0)^2}{r_0^2} + \cdots$$

which is approximately proportional to $(r - r_0)^2$ since terms containing higher powers of $(r - r_0)$ have relatively small values for r near r_0.

(d) From part (a) we know that $dV/dr = 0$ when $r = r_0$, hence $F = 0$ when $r = r_0$. Since, if we discard powers of $(r - r_0)$ higher than the second,

$$V(r) \approx -V_0\left(1 - 36\frac{(r - r_0)^2}{r_0^2}\right)$$

giving

$$F = -\frac{dV}{dr} \approx 72 \cdot \frac{r - r_0}{r_0^2}(-V_0) = -72V_0\frac{r - r_0}{r_o^2}.$$

So F is approximately proportional to $(r - r_0)$.

38. (a) $F = \frac{GM}{R^2} + \frac{Gm}{(R+r)^2}$

(b) $F = \frac{GM}{R^2} + \frac{Gm}{R^2}\frac{1}{(1+\frac{r}{R})^2}$

Since $\frac{r}{R} < 1$, use the binomial expansion:

$$\frac{1}{(1+\frac{r}{R})^2} = \left(1 + \frac{r}{R}\right)^{-2} = 1 - 2\left(\frac{r}{R}\right) + (-2)(-3)\frac{(\frac{r}{R})^2}{2!} + \cdots$$

$$F = \frac{GM}{R^2} + \frac{Gm}{R^2}\left[1 - 2\left(\frac{r}{R}\right) + 3\left(\frac{r}{R}\right)^2 - \cdots\right].$$

(c) Discarding higher power terms, we get

$$F \approx \frac{GM}{R^2} + \frac{Gm}{R^2} - \frac{2Gmr}{R^3}$$

$$= \frac{G(M+m)}{R^2} - \frac{2Gmr}{R^3}.$$

Looking at the expression, we see that the term $\frac{G(M+m)}{R^2}$ is the field strength at a distance R from a single particle of mass $M + m$. The correction term, $-\frac{2Gmr}{R^3}$, is negative because the field strength exerted by a particle of mass $(M + m)$ at a distance R would clearly be larger than the field strength at P in the question.

39. Since expanding $f(x + h)$ and $g(x + h)$ in Taylor series gives

$$f(x + h) = f(x) + f'(x)h + \frac{f''(x)}{2!}h^2 + \ldots,$$

$$g(x + h) = g(x) + g'(x)h + \frac{f''(x)}{2!}h^2 + \ldots,$$

we substitute to get

$$\frac{f(x + h)g(x + h) - f(x)g(x)}{h}$$

$$= \frac{(f(x) + f'(x)h + \frac{1}{2}f''(x)h^2 + \ldots)(g(x) + g'(x)h + \frac{1}{2}g''(x)h^2 + \ldots) - f(x)g(x)}{h}$$

$$= \frac{f(x)g(x) + (f'(x)g(x) + f(x)g'(x))h + \text{ Terms in } h^2 \text{ and higher powers } - f(x)g(x)}{h}$$

$$= \frac{h(f'(x)g(x) + f(x)g'(x) + \text{ Terms in } h \text{ and higher powers})}{h}$$

$$= f'(x)g(x) + f(x)g'(x) + \text{ Terms in } h \text{ and higher powers.}$$

Thus, taking the limit as $h \to 0$, we get

$$\frac{d}{dx}(f(x)g(x)) = \lim_{h \to 0} \frac{f(x + h)g(x + h) - f(x)g(x)}{h}$$

$$= f'(x)g(x) + f(x)g'(x).$$

40. Expanding $f(y + k)$ and $g(x + h)$ in Taylor series gives

$$f(y + k) = f(y) + f'(y)k + \frac{f''(y)}{2!}k^2 + \cdots,$$

$$g(x + h) = g(x) + g'(x)h + \frac{g''(x)}{2!}h^2 + \cdots.$$

Now let $y = g(x)$ and $y + k = g(x + h)$. Then $k = g(x + h) - g(x)$ so

$$k = g'(x)h + \frac{g''(x)}{2!}h^2 + \cdots.$$

Substituting $g(x + h) = y + k$ and $y = g(x)$ in the series for $f(y + k)$ gives

$$f(g(x + h)) = f(g(x)) + f'(g(x))k + \frac{f''(g(x))}{2!}k^2 + \cdots.$$

Now, substituting for k, we get

$$f(g(x + h)) = f(g(x)) + f'(g(x)) \cdot (g'(x)h + \frac{g''(x)}{2!}h^2 + \cdots) + \frac{f''(g(x))}{2!}(g'(x)h + \ldots)^2 + \cdots$$

$$= f(g(x)) + (f'(g(x))) \cdot g'(x)h + \text{Terms in } h^2 \text{ and higher powers.}$$

So, substituting for $f(g(x + h))$ and dividing by h, we get

$$\frac{f(g(x + h)) - f(g(x))}{h} = f'(g(x)) \cdot g'(x) + \text{Terms in } h \text{ and higher powers,}$$

and thus, taking the limit as $h \to 0$,

$$\frac{d}{dx}f(g(x)) = \lim_{h \to 0} \frac{f(g(x + h)) - f(g(x))}{h}$$

$$= f'(g(x)) \cdot g'(x).$$

41. (a) Notice $g'(0) = 0$ because g has a critical point at $x = 0$. So, for $n \geq 2$,

$$g(x) \approx P_n(x) = g(0) + \frac{g''(0)}{2!}x^2 + \frac{g'''(0)}{3!}x^3 + \cdots + \frac{g^{(n)}(0)}{n!}x^n.$$

(b) The Second Derivative test says that if $g''(0) > 0$, then 0 is a local minimum and if $g''(0) < 0$, 0 is a local maximum.

(c) Let $n = 2$. Then $P_2(x) = g(0) + \frac{g''(0)}{2!}x^2$. So, for x near 0,

$$g(x) - g(0) \approx \frac{g''(0)}{2!}x^2.$$

If $g''(0) > 0$, then $g(x) - g(0) \geq 0$, as long as x stays near 0. In other words, there exists a small interval around $x = 0$ such that for any x in this interval $g(x) \geq g(0)$. So $g(0)$ is a local minimum.
The case when $g''(0) < 0$ is treated similarly; then $g(0)$ is a local maximum.

42. The situation is more complicated. Let's first consider the case when $g'''(0) \neq 0$. To be specific let $g'''(0) > 0$. Then

$$g(x) \approx P_3(x) = g(0) + \frac{g'''(0)}{3!}x^3.$$

So, $g(x) - g(0) \approx \frac{g'''(0)}{3!}x^3$. (Notice that $\frac{g'''(0)}{3!} > 0$ is a constant.) Now, no matter how small an open interval I around $x = 0$ is, there are always some x_1 and x_2 in I such that $x_1 < 0$ and $x_2 > 0$, which means that $\frac{g'''(0)}{3!}x_1^3 < 0$ and $\frac{g'''(0)}{3!}x_2^3 > 0$, i.e. $g(x_1) - g(0) < 0$ and $g(x_2) - g(0) > 0$. Thus, $g(0)$ is neither a local minimum nor a local maximum. (If $g'''(0) < 0$, the same conclusion still holds. Try it! The reasoning is similar.)

Now let's consider the case when $g'''(0) = 0$. If $g^{(4)}(0) > 0$, then by the fourth degree Taylor polynomial approximation to g at $x = 0$, we have

$$g(x) - g(0) \approx \frac{g^{(4)}(0)}{4!}x^4 > 0$$

for x in a small open interval around $x = 0$. So $g(0)$ is a local minimum. (If $g^{(4)}(0) < 0$, then $g(0)$ is a local maximum.)

In general, suppose that $g^{(k)}(0) \neq 0$, $k \geq 2$, and all the derivatives of g with order less than k are 0. In this case g looks like cx^k near $x = 0$, which determines its behavior there. Then $g(0)$ is neither a local minimum nor a local maximum if k is odd. For k even, $g(0)$ is a local minimum if $g^{(k)}(0) > 0$, and $g(0)$ is a local maximum if $g^{(k)}(0) < 0$.

43. Let us begin by finding the Fourier coefficients for $f(x)$. Since f is odd, $\int_{-\pi}^{\pi} f(x)\,dx = 0$ and $\int_{-\pi}^{\pi} f(x)\cos nx\,dx = 0$. Thus $a_i = 0$ for all $i \geq 0$. On the other hand,

$$\begin{aligned}
b_i = \frac{1}{\pi}\int_{-\pi}^{\pi} f(x)\sin nx\,dx &= \frac{1}{\pi}\left[\int_{-\pi}^{0} -\sin(nx)\,dx + \int_{0}^{\pi}\sin(nx)\,dx\right]\\
&= \frac{1}{\pi}\left[\frac{1}{n}\cos(nx)\Big|_{-\pi}^{0} - \frac{1}{n}\cos(nx)\Big|_{0}^{\pi}\right]\\
&= \frac{1}{n\pi}\left[\cos 0 - \cos(-n\pi) - \cos(n\pi) + \cos 0\right]\\
&= \frac{2}{n\pi}\left(1 - \cos(n\pi)\right).
\end{aligned}$$

Since $\cos(n\pi) = (-1)^n$, this is 0 if n is even, and $\frac{4}{n\pi}$ if n is odd. Thus the nth Fourier polynomial (where n is odd) is

$$F_n(x) = \frac{4}{\pi}\sin x + \frac{4}{3\pi}\sin 3x + \cdots + \frac{4}{n\pi}\sin(nx).$$

As $n \to \infty$, the nth Fourier polynomial must approach $f(x)$ on the interval $(-\pi, \pi)$, except at the point $x = 0$ (where f is not continuous). In particular, if $x = \frac{\pi}{2}$,

$$\begin{aligned}
F_n(1) &= \frac{4}{\pi}\sin\frac{\pi}{2} + \frac{4}{3\pi}\sin\frac{3\pi}{2} + \frac{4}{5\pi}\sin\frac{5\pi}{2} + \frac{4}{7\pi}\sin\frac{7\pi}{2} + \cdots + \frac{4}{n\pi}\sin\frac{n\pi}{2}\\
&= \frac{4}{\pi}\left(1 - \frac{1}{3} + \frac{1}{5} - \frac{1}{7} + \cdots + (-1)^{2n+1}\frac{1}{2n+1}\right).
\end{aligned}$$

But $F_n(1)$ approaches $f(\frac{\pi}{2}) = 1$ as $n \to \infty$, so

$$\frac{\pi}{4} F_n(1) = 1 - \frac{1}{3} + \frac{1}{5} - \frac{1}{7} + \cdots + (-1)^{2n+1} \frac{1}{2n+1} \to \frac{\pi}{4} \cdot 1 = \frac{\pi}{4}.$$

44. Let $t = 2\pi x - \pi$. Then, $g(t) = f(x) = e^{2\pi x} = e^{t+\pi}$. Notice that as x varies from 0 to 1, t varies from $-\pi$ to π. Thus, we can find the Fourier coefficients for $g(t)$:

$$a_o = \frac{1}{2\pi} \int_{-\pi}^{\pi} g(t)dt = \frac{1}{2\pi} \int_{-\pi}^{\pi} e^{t+\pi} dt = \frac{1}{2\pi} e^{t+\pi} \Big|_{-\pi}^{\pi} = \frac{e^{2\pi} - 1}{2\pi},$$

$$a_n = \frac{1}{\pi} \int_{-\pi}^{\pi} e^{t+\pi} \cos(nt)dt = \frac{e^{\pi}}{\pi} \int_{-\pi}^{\pi} e^t \cos(nt)dt.$$

Using the integral table, Formula II-8, yields:

$$= \frac{e^{\pi}}{\pi} \frac{1}{n^2+1} e^t (\cos(nt) + n\sin(nt)) \Big|_{-\pi}^{\pi}$$

$$= \frac{e^{\pi}}{\pi} \frac{1}{n^2+1} (e^{\pi} - e^{-\pi})(\cos(n\pi))$$

$$= \frac{(e^{2\pi} - 1)}{\pi} \frac{(-1)^n}{n^2+1}$$

$$b_n = \frac{1}{\pi} \int_{-\pi}^{\pi} e^{t+\pi} \sin(nt)dt = \frac{e^{\pi}}{\pi} \int_{-\pi}^{\pi} e^t \sin(nt)dt.$$

Again, using the integral table, Formula II-9, yields:

$$= \frac{e^{\pi}}{\pi} \frac{1}{n^2+1} e^t (\sin(nt) - n\cos(nt)) \Big|_{-\pi}^{\pi}$$

$$= -\frac{e^{\pi}}{\pi} \frac{n}{n^2+1} (e^{\pi} - e^{-\pi}) \cos(n\pi)$$

$$= \frac{(e^{2\pi} - 1)}{\pi} \frac{(-1)^{n+1}n}{n^2+1}.$$

Thus, after factoring a bit, we get:

$$G_3(t) = \frac{e^{2\pi} - 1}{\pi} \left(\frac{1}{2} - \frac{1}{2}\cos t + \frac{1}{2}\sin t + \frac{1}{5}\cos 2t - \frac{2}{5}\sin 2t - \frac{1}{10}\cos 3t + \frac{3}{10}\sin 3t \right).$$

Now, we substitute x back in for t:

$$F_3(x) = \frac{e^{2\pi} - 1}{\pi} (\frac{1}{2} - \frac{1}{2}\cos(2\pi x - \pi) + \frac{1}{2}\sin(2\pi x - \pi) + \frac{1}{5}\cos(4\pi x - 2\pi)$$

$$- \frac{2}{5}\sin(4\pi x - 2\pi) - \frac{1}{10}\cos(6\pi x - 3\pi) + \frac{3}{10}\sin(6\pi x - 3\pi)).$$

Recalling that $\cos(x - \pi) = -\cos x$, $\sin(x - \pi) = -\sin x$, $\cos(x - 2\pi) = \cos x$, and $\sin(x - 2\pi) = \sin x$, we have:

$$F_3(x) = \frac{e^{2\pi} - 1}{\pi} \left(\frac{1}{2} + \frac{1}{2}\cos 2\pi x - \frac{1}{2}\sin 2\pi x + \frac{1}{5}\cos 4\pi x - \frac{2}{5}\sin 4\pi x \right.$$

$$\left. + \frac{1}{10}\cos 6\pi x - \frac{3}{10}\sin 6\pi x \right).$$

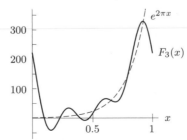

45. (a) Expand $f(x)$ into its Fourier series:

$$f(x) = a_0 + a_1 \cos x + a_2 \cos 2x + a_3 \cos 3x + \cdots + a_k \cos kx + \cdots$$
$$+ b_1 \sin x + b_2 \sin 2x + b_3 \sin 3x + \cdots + b_k \sin kx + \cdots$$

Then differentiate term-by-term:

$$f'(x) = -a_1 \sin x - 2a_2 \sin 2x - 3a_3 \sin 3x - \cdots - ka_k \sin kx - \cdots$$
$$+ b_1 \cos x + 2b_2 \cos 2x + 3b_3 \cos 3x + \cdots + kb_k \cos kx + \cdots$$

Regroup terms:

$$f'(x) = +b_1 \cos x + 2b_2 \cos 2x + 3b_3 \cos 3x + \cdots + kb_k \cos kx + \cdots$$
$$- a_1 \sin x - 2a_2 \sin 2x - 3a_3 \sin 3x - \cdots - ka_k \sin kx - \cdots$$

which forms a Fourier series for the derivative $f'(x)$. The Fourier coefficient of $\cos kx$ is kb_k and the Fourier coefficient of $\sin kx$ is $-ka_k$. Note that there is no constant term as you would expect from the formula ka_k with $k = 0$. Note also that if the kth harmonic f is absent, so is that of f'.

(b) If the amplitude of the kth harmonic of f is

$$A_k = \sqrt{a_k^2 + b_k^2}, \quad k \geq 1,$$

then the amplitude of the kth harmonic of f' is

$$\sqrt{(kb_k)^2 + (-ka_k)^2} = \sqrt{k^2(b_k^2 + a_k^2)} = k\sqrt{a_k^2 + b_k^2} = kA_k.$$

(c) The energy of the kth harmonic of f' is k^2 times the energy of the kth harmonic of f.

46. Let r_k and s_k be the Fourier coefficients of $Af + Bg$. Then

$$r_0 = \frac{1}{2\pi} \int_{-\pi}^{\pi} \left[Af(x) + Bg(x) \right] dx$$
$$= A\left[\frac{1}{2\pi} \int_{-\pi}^{\pi} f(x)\, dx \right] + B\left[\frac{1}{2\pi} \int_{-\pi}^{\pi} g(x)\, dx \right]$$
$$= Aa_0 + Bc_0.$$

Similarly,

$$r_k = \frac{1}{\pi} \int_{-\pi}^{\pi} \left[Af(x) + Bg(x) \right] \cos(kx)\, dx$$
$$= A\left[\frac{1}{\pi} \int_{-\pi}^{\pi} f(x) \cos(kx)\, dx \right] + B\left[\frac{1}{\pi} \int_{-\pi}^{\pi} g(x) \cos(kx)\, dx \right]$$
$$= Aa_k + Bc_k.$$

And finally,

$$s_k = \frac{1}{\pi} \int_{-\pi}^{\pi} \left[Af(x) + Bg(x) \right] \sin(kx)\, dx$$
$$= A\left[\frac{1}{\pi} \int_{-\pi}^{\pi} f(x) \sin(kx)\, dx \right] + B\left[\frac{1}{\pi} \int_{-\pi}^{\pi} g(x) \sin(kx)\, dx \right]$$
$$= Ac_k + Bd_k.$$

47. Since $g(x) = f(x + c)$, we have that $[g(x)]^2 = [f(x+c)]^2$, so g^2 is f^2 shifted horizontally by c. Since f has period 2π, so does f^2 and g^2. If you think of the definite integral as an area, then because of the periodicity, integrals of f^2 over any interval of length 2π have the same value. So

$$\text{Energy of } f = \int_{-\pi}^{\pi} (f(x))^2\, dx = \int_{-\pi+c}^{\pi+c} (f(x))^2\, dx.$$

Now we know that

$$\text{Energy of } g = \frac{1}{\pi} \int_{-\pi}^{\pi} (g(x))^2 \, dx$$

$$= \frac{1}{\pi} \int_{-\pi}^{\pi} (f(x + c))^2 \, dx.$$

Using the substitution $t = x + c$, we see that the two energies are equal.

CAS Challenge Problems

48. (a) The Taylor polynomials of degree 10 are

$$\text{For } \sin^2 x, \qquad P_{10}(x) = x^2 - \frac{x^4}{3} + \frac{2\,x^6}{45} - \frac{x^8}{315} + \frac{2\,x^{10}}{14175}$$

$$\text{For } \cos^2 x, \qquad Q_{10}(x) = 1 - x^2 + \frac{x^4}{3} - \frac{2\,x^6}{45} + \frac{x^8}{315} - \frac{2\,x^{10}}{14175}$$

(b) The coefficients in $P_{10}(x)$ are the negatives of the corresponding coefficients of $Q_{10}(x)$. The constant term of $P_{10}(x)$ is 0 and the constant term of $Q_{10}(x)$ is 1. Thus, $P_{10}(x)$ and $Q_{10}(x)$ satisfy

$$Q_{10}(x) = 1 - P_{10}(x).$$

This makes sense because $\cos^2 x$ and $\sin^2 x$ satisfy the identity

$$\cos^2 x = 1 - \sin^2 x.$$

49. (a) The Taylor polynomials of degree 7 are

$$\text{For } \sin x, \qquad P_7(x) = x - \frac{x^3}{6} + \frac{x^5}{120} - \frac{x^7}{5040}$$

$$\text{For } \sin x \cos x, \qquad Q_7(x) = x - \frac{2\,x^3}{3} + \frac{2\,x^5}{15} - \frac{4\,x^7}{315}$$

(b) The coefficient of x^3 in $Q_7(x)$ is $-2/3$, and the coefficient of x^3 in $P_7(x)$ is $-1/6$, so the ratio is

$$\frac{-2/3}{-1/6} = 4.$$

The corresponding ratios for x^5 and x^7 are

$$\frac{2/15}{1/120} = 16 \quad \text{and} \quad \frac{-4/315}{-1/5040} = 64.$$

(c) It appears that the ratio is always a power of 2. For x^3, it is $4 = 2^2$; for x^5, it is $16 = 2^4$; for x^7, it is $64 = 2^6$. This suggests that in general, for the coefficient of x^n, it is 2^{n-1}.

(d) From the identity $\sin(2x) = 2 \sin x \cos x$, we expect that $P_7(2x) = 2Q_7(x)$. So, if a_n is the coefficient of x^n in $P_7(x)$, and if b_n is the coefficient of x^n in $Q_7(x)$, then, since the x^n terms $P_7(2x)$ and $2Q_7(x)$ must be equal, we have

$$a_n(2x)^n = 2b_n x^n.$$

Dividing both sides by x^n and combining the powers of 2, this gives the pattern we observed. For $a_n \neq 0$,

$$\frac{b_n}{a_n} = 2^{n-1}.$$

50. (a) For $f(x) = x^2$ we have $f'(x) = 2x$ so the tangent line is

$$y = f(2) + f'(2)(x - 2) = 4 + 4(x - 2)$$
$$y = 4x - 4.$$

For $g(x) = x^3 - 4x^2 + 8x - 7$, we have $g'(x) = 3x^2 - 8x + 8$, so the tangent line is

$$y = g(1) + g'(1)(x - 1) = -2 + 3(x - 1)$$
$$y = 3x - 5.$$

For $h(x) = 2x^3 + 4x^2 - 3x + 7$, we have $h'(x) = 6x^2 + 8x - 3$. So the tangent line is

$$y = h(-1) + h'(-1)(x + 1) = 12 - 5(x + 1)$$
$$y = -5x + 7.$$

(b) Division by a CAS or by hand gives

$$\frac{f(x)}{(x-2)^2} = \frac{x^2}{(x-2)^2} = 1 + \frac{4x-4}{(x-2)^2} \quad \text{so} \quad r(x) = 4x - 4,$$

$$\frac{g(x)}{(x-1)^2} = \frac{x^3 - 4x^2 + 8x - 7}{(x-1)^2} = x - 2 + \frac{3x-5}{(x-1)^2} \quad \text{so} \quad r(x) = 3x - 5,$$

$$\frac{h(x)}{(x+1)^2} = \frac{2x^3 + 4x^2 - 3x + 7}{(x+1)^2} = 2x + \frac{-5x+7}{(x+1)^2} = \quad \text{so} \quad r(x) = -5x + 7.$$

(c) In each of these three cases, $y = r(x)$ is the equation of the tangent line. We conjecture that this is true in general.
(d) The Taylor expansion of a function $p(x)$ is

$$p(x) = p(a) + p'(a)(x - a) + \frac{p''(a)}{2!}(x - a)^2 + \frac{p'''(a)}{3!}(x - a)^3 + \cdots$$

Now divide $p(x)$ by $(x - a)^2$. On the right-hand side, all terms from $p''(a)(x - a)^2/2!$ onward contain a power of $(x-a)^2$ and divide exactly by $(x-a)^2$ to give a polynomial $q(x)$, say. So the remainder is $r(x) = p(a) + p'(a)(x-a)$, the tangent line.

51. (a) The Taylor polynomial is

$$P_{10}(x) = 1 + \frac{x^2}{12} - \frac{x^4}{720} + \frac{x^6}{30240} - \frac{x^8}{1209600} + \frac{x^{10}}{47900160}$$

(b) All the terms have even degree. A polynomial with only terms of even degree is an even function. This suggests that f might be an even function.
(c) To show that f is even, we must show that $f(-x) = f(x)$.

$$f(-x) = \frac{-x}{e^{-x} - 1} + \frac{-x}{2} = \frac{x}{1 - \frac{1}{e^x}} - \frac{x}{2} = \frac{xe^x}{e^x - 1} - \frac{x}{2}$$

$$= \frac{xe^x - \frac{1}{2}x(e^x - 1)}{e^x - 1}$$

$$= \frac{xe^x - \frac{1}{2}xe^x + \frac{1}{2}x}{e^x - 1} = \frac{\frac{1}{2}xe^x + \frac{1}{2}x}{e^x - 1} = \frac{\frac{1}{2}x(e^x - 1) + x}{e^x - 1}$$

$$= \frac{1}{2}x + \frac{x}{e^x - 1} = \frac{x}{e^x - 1} + \frac{x}{2} = f(x)$$

52. (a) The Taylor polynomial is

$$P_{11}(x) = \frac{x^3}{3} - \frac{x^7}{42} + \frac{x^{11}}{1320}.$$

(b) Evaluating, we get

$$P_{11}(1) = \frac{1^3}{3} - \frac{1^7}{42} + \frac{1^{11}}{1320} = 0.310281$$

$$S(1) = \int_0^1 \sin(t^2)\, dt = 0.310268.$$

We need to take about 6 decimal places in the answer as this allows us to see the error. (The values of $P_{11}(1)$ and $S(1)$ start to differ in the fifth decimal place.) Thus, the percentage error is $(0.310281 - 0.310268)/0.310268 = 0.000013/0.310268 = 0.000042 = 0.0042\%$. On the other hand,

$$P_{11}(2) = \frac{2^3}{3} - \frac{2^7}{42} + \frac{2^{11}}{1320} = 1.17056$$

$$S(2) = \int_0^2 \sin(t^2)\, dt = 0.804776.$$

The percentage error in this case is $(1.17056 - 0.804776)/0.804776 = 0.365784/0.804776 = 0.454517$, or about 45%.

CHECK YOUR UNDERSTANDING

1. False. For example, both $f(x) = x^2$ and $g(x) = x^2 + x^3$ have $P_2(x) = x^2$.

2. False. The approximation $\sin\theta \approx \theta - \theta^3/3!$ holds for θ in radians, not degrees.

3. False. $P_2(x) = f(5) + f'(5)(x-5) + (f''(5)/2)(x-5)^2 = e^5 + e^5(x-5) + (e^5/2)(x-5)^2$.

4. False. Since -1 is the coefficient of x^2 in $P_2(x)$, we know that $f''(0)/2! = -1$, so $f''(0) < 0$, which implies that f is concave down near $x = 0$.

5. False. The Taylor series for $\sin x$ about $x = \pi$ is calculated by taking derivatives and using the formula

$$f(a) + f'(a)(x-a) + \frac{f''(a)}{2!}(x-a)^2 + \cdots.$$

The series for $\sin x$ about $x = \pi$ turns out to be

$$-(x - \pi) + \frac{(x-\pi)^3}{3!} - \frac{(x-\pi)^5}{5!} + \cdots.$$

6. True. Since f is even, $f(-x) = f(x)$ for all x. Taking the derivative of both sides of this equation, we get $f'(-x)(-1) = f'(x)$, which at $x = 0$ gives $-f'(0) = f'(0)$, so $f'(0) = 0$. Taking the derivative again gives $f''(-x) = f''(x)$, i.e., f'' is even. Using the same reasoning again, we get that $f'''(0) = 0$, and, continuing in this way, we get $f^{(n)}(0) = 0$ for all odd n. Thus, for all odd n, the coefficient of x^n in the Taylor series is $f^{(n)}(0)/n! = 0$, so all the terms with odd exponent are zero.

7. True. Since the Taylor series for $\cos x$ has only even powers, multiplying by x^3 gives only odd powers.

8. True. The coefficient of x^7 is $-8/7!$, so

$$\frac{f^{(7)}(0)}{7!} = \frac{-8}{7!}$$

giving $f^{(7)}(0) = -8$.

9. False. The derivative of $f(x)g(x)$ is not $f'(x)g'(x)$. If this statement were true, the Taylor series for $(\cos x)(\sin x)$ would have all zero terms.

10. True. Since the derivative of a sum is the sum of the derivatives, Taylor series add.

11. False. For example the quadratic approximation to $\cos x$ for x near 0 is $1 - x^2/2$, whereas the linear approximation is the constant function 1. Although the quadratic approximation is better near 0, for large values of x it takes large negative values, whereas the linear approximation stays equal to 1. Since $\cos x$ oscillates between 1 and -1, the linear approximation is better than the quadratic for large x (although it is not very good).

12. False. The Taylor series converges on its interval of convergence, whereas f may be defined outside this interval.
    For example, the series

    $$1 + x + x^2 + x^3 + \cdots \quad \text{converges to} \quad \frac{1}{1-x} \text{ for } |x| < 1.$$

    But $1/(1-x)$ is defined for $|x| > 1$.

13. True. For large x, the graph of $P_{10}(x)$ looks like the graph of its highest powered term, $x^{10}/10!$. But e^x grows faster than any power, so e^x gets further and further away from $x^{10}/10! \approx P_{10}(x)$.

14. False. For example, if $a = 0$ and $f(x) = \cos x$, then $P_1(x) = 1$, and $P_1(x)$ touches $\cos x$ at $x = 0, 2\pi, 4\pi, \ldots$.

15. False. If f is itself a polynomial of degree n then it is equal to its nth Taylor polynomial.

16. True. By Theorem 10.1, $|E_n(x)| < 10|x|^{n+1}/(n+1)!$. Since $\lim_{n \to \infty} |x|^{n+1}/(n+1)! = 0$, $E_n(x) \to 0$ as $n \to \infty$, so the Taylor series converges to $f(x)$ for all x.
    True

17. True. Since f is even, $f(x)\sin(mx)$ is odd for any m, so

    $$b_m = \frac{1}{\pi} \int_{-\pi}^{\pi} f(x) \sin x(mx) \, dx = 0.$$

18. False. Since $f(-1) = g(-1)$ the graphs of f and g intersect at $x = -1$. Since $f'(-1) < g'(-1)$, the slope of f is less than the slope of g at $x = -1$. Thus $f(x) > g(x)$ for all x sufficiently close to -1 on the left, and $f(x) < g(x)$ for all x sufficiently close to -1 on the right.

19. True. If

    $$P_2(x) = \text{Quadratic approximation to } f = f(-1) + f'(-1)(x+1) + \frac{f''(-1)}{2}(x+1)^2$$

    $$Q_2(x) = \text{Quadratic approximation to } g = g(-1) + g'(-1)(x+1) + \frac{g''(-1)}{2}(x+1)^2$$

    then $P_2(x) - Q_2(x) = (f''(-1) - g''(-1))(x+1)^2/2 < 0$ for all $x \neq -1$. Thus $P_2(x) < Q_2(x)$ for all $x \neq -1$. This implies that for x sufficiently close to -1 (but not equal to -1), we have $f(x) < g(x)$.

20. True. We have

    $$L_1(x) + L_2(x) = (f_1(0) + f_1'(0)x) + (f_2(0) + f_2'(0)x) = (f_1(0) + f_2(0)) + (f_1'(0) + f_2'(0))x.$$

    The right hand side is the linear approximation to $f_1 + f_2$ near $x = 0$.

21. False. The quadratic approximation to $f_1(x)f_2(x)$ near $x = 0$ is

    $$f_1(0)f_2(0) + (f_1'(0)f_2(0) + f_1(0)f_2'(0))x + \frac{f_1''(0)f_2(0) + 2f_1'(0)f_2'(0) + f_1(0)f_2''(0)}{2}x^2.$$

    On the other hand, we have

    $$L_1(x) = f_1(0) + f_1'(0)x, \quad L_2(x) = f_2(0) + f_2'(0)x,$$

    so

    $$L_1(x)L_2(x) = (f_1(0) + f_1'(0)x)(f_2(0) + f_2'(0)x) = f_1(0)f_2(0) + (f_1'(0)f_2(0) + f_2'(0)f_1(0))x + f_1'(0)f_2'(0)x^2.$$

    The first two terms of the right side agree with the quadratic approximation to $f_1(x)f_2(x)$ near $x = 0$, but the term of degree 2 does not.
    For example, the linear approximation to e^x is $1+x$, but the quadratic approximation to $(e^x)^2 = e^{2x}$ is $1+2x+2x^2$, not $(1+x)^2 = 1 + 2x + x^2$.

22. False. The Taylor series for f near $x = 0$ always converges at $x = 0$, since $\sum_{n=0}^{\infty} C_n x^n$ at $x = 0$ is just the constant C_0.

23. True. When $x = 1$,

    $$\sum_{n=0}^{\infty} \frac{f^{(n)}(0)}{n!} x^n = \sum_{n=0}^{\infty} \frac{f^{(n)}(0)}{n!}.$$

    Since $f^{(n)}(0) \geq n!$, the terms of this series are all greater than 1. So the series cannot converge

24. False. For example, if $f^{(n)}(0) = n!$, then the Taylor series is

$$\sum_{n=0}^{\infty} \frac{f^{(n)}(0)}{n!} x^n = \sum_{n=0}^{\infty} x^n,$$

which converges at $x = 1/2$.

PROJECTS FOR CHAPTER TEN

1. (a) A calculator gives $4 \tan^{-1}(1/5) - \tan^{-1}(1/239) = 0.7853981634$, which agrees with $\pi/4$ to ten decimal places. Notice that you cannot verify that Machin's formula is *exactly* true numerically (because any calculator has only a finite number of digits.) Showing that the formula is exactly true requires a theoretical argument.

(b) The Taylor polynomial of degree 5 approximating $\arctan x$ is

$$\arctan x \approx x - \frac{x^3}{3} + \frac{x^5}{5}.$$

Thus,

$$\pi = 4 \left(4 \arctan \left(\frac{1}{5} \right) - \arctan \left(\frac{1}{239} \right) \right)$$

$$\approx 4 \left(4 \left(\frac{1}{5} - \frac{1}{3} \left(\frac{1}{5} \right)^3 + \frac{1}{5} \left(\frac{1}{5} \right)^5 \right) - \left(\frac{1}{239} - \frac{1}{3} \left(\frac{1}{239} \right)^3 + \frac{1}{5} \left(\frac{1}{239} \right)^5 \right) \right)$$

$$\approx 3.141621029.$$

The true value is $\pi = 3.141592653\ldots$.

(c) Because the values of x, namely $x = 1/5$ and $x = 1/239$, are much smaller than 1, the terms in the series get smaller much faster.

(d) (i) If $A = \arctan(120/119)$ and $B = -\arctan(1/239)$, then

$$\tan A = \frac{120}{119} \quad \text{and} \quad \tan B = -\frac{1}{239}.$$

Substituting

$$\tan(A + B) = \frac{(120/119) + (-1/239)}{1 - (120/119)(-1/239)} = 1.$$

Thus

$$A + B = \arctan 1,$$

so

$$\arctan \left(\frac{120}{119} \right) - \arctan \left(\frac{1}{239} \right) = \arctan 1.$$

(ii) If $A = B = \arctan(1/5)$, then

$$\tan(A + B) = \frac{(1/5) + (1/5)}{1 - (1/5)(1/5)} = \frac{5}{12}.$$

Thus

$$A + B = \arctan \left(\frac{5}{12} \right),$$

so

$$2 \arctan \left(\frac{1}{5} \right) = \arctan \left(\frac{5}{12} \right).$$

If $A = B = 2\arctan(1/5)$, then $\tan A = \tan B = 5/12$, so

$$\tan(A + B) = \frac{(5/12) + (5/12)}{1 - (5/12)(5/12)} = \frac{120}{119}.$$

Thus

$$A + B = \arctan\left(\frac{120}{119}\right),$$

so

$$4\arctan\left(\frac{1}{5}\right) = \arctan\left(\frac{120}{119}\right).$$

(iii) Using the result of part (a) and substituting the results of part (b), we obtain

$$4\arctan\left(\frac{1}{5}\right) - \arctan\left(\frac{1}{239}\right) = \arctan 1 = \frac{\pi}{4}.$$

2. (a) (i) Using a Taylor series expansion, we have

$$f(x_0 - h) = f(x_0) - f'(x_0)h + \frac{f''(x_0)}{2}h^2 - \frac{f'''(x_0)}{3!}h^3 + \cdots.$$

So we have

$$\frac{f(x_0) - f(x_0 - h)}{h} - f'(x_0) \approx \frac{f''(x_0)}{2}h + \cdots.$$

This suggests the following bound for small h:

$$\left|\frac{f(x_0) - f(x_0 - h)}{h} - f'(x_0)\right| \leq \frac{Mh}{2},$$

where $|f''(x)| \leq M$ for $|x - x_0| < |h|$.

(ii) We use Taylor series expansions:

$$f(x_0 + h) = f(x_0) + f'(x_0)h + \frac{f''(x_0)}{2}h^2 + \frac{f'''(x_0)}{3!}h^3 + \cdots$$

$$f(x_0 - h) = f(x_0) - f'(x_0)h + \frac{f''(x_0)}{2}h^2 - \frac{f'''(x_0)}{3!}h^3 + \cdots.$$

Subtracting gives

$$f(x_0 + h) - f(x_0 - h) = 2f'(x_0)h + \frac{2f'''(x_0)}{3!}h^3 + \cdots$$

$$= 2f'(x_0)h + \frac{1}{3}f'''(x_0)h^3 + \cdots.$$

So

$$\frac{f(x_0 + h) - f(x_0 - h)}{2h} = f'(x_0) + \frac{f'''(x_0)}{6}h^2 + \cdots.$$

This suggests the following bound for small h:

$$\left|\frac{f(x_0 + h) - f(x_0 - h)}{2h} - f'(x_0)\right| \leq \frac{Mh^2}{6},$$

where $|f'''(x)| \leq M$ for $|x - x_0| < |h|$.

(iii) Expanding each term in the numerator is a Taylor series, we have

$$f(x_0 + 2h) = f(x_0) + 2f'(x_0)h + 2f''(x_0)h^2 + \frac{4}{3}f'''(x_0)h^3$$
$$+ \frac{2}{3}f^{(4)}(x_0)h^4 + \frac{4}{15}f^{(5)}(x_0)h^5 + \cdots$$

$$f(x_0 + h) = f(x_0) + f'(x_0)h + \frac{f''(x_0)}{2}h^2 + \frac{f'''(x_0)}{3!}h^3$$
$$+ \frac{f^{(4)}(x_0)}{4!}h^4 + \frac{f^{(5)}(x_0)}{5!}h^5 + \cdots,$$

$$f(x_0 - h) = f(x_0) - f'(x_0)h + \frac{f''(x_0)}{2}h^2 - \frac{f'''(x_0)}{3!}h^3$$
$$+ \frac{f^{(4)}(x_0)}{4!}h^4 - \frac{f^{(5)}(x_0)}{5!}h^5 + \cdots,$$

$$f(x_0 - 2h) = f(x_0) - 2f'(x_0)h + 2f''(x_0)h^2 - \frac{4}{3}f'''(x_0)h^3$$
$$+ \frac{2}{3}f^{(4)}(x_0)h^4 - \frac{4}{15}f^{(5)}(x_0)h^5 + \cdots.$$

Combining the expansions in pairs, we have

$$8f(x_0 + h) - 8f(x_0 - h) = 16f'(x_0)h + \frac{8}{3}f'''(x_0)h^3 + \frac{2}{15}f^{(5)}(x_0)h^5 + \cdots$$

$$f(x_0 + 2h) - f(x_0 - 2h) = 4f'(x_0)h + \frac{8}{3}f'''(x_0)h^3 + \frac{8}{15}f^{(5)}(x_0)h^5 + \cdots.$$

Thus,

$$-f(x_0 + 2h) + 8f(x_0 + h) - 8f(x_0 - h) + f(x_0 - 2h) = 12f'(x_0)h - \frac{6}{15}f^{(5)}(x_0)h^5 + \cdots$$

so

$$\frac{-f(x_0 + 2h) + 8f(x_0 + h) - 8f(x_0 - h) + f(x_0 - 2h)}{12h} = f'(x_0) - \frac{f^{(5)}(x_0)}{30}h^4 + \cdots.$$

This suggests the following bound for small h,

$$\left| \frac{-f(x_0 + 2h) + 8f(x_0 + h) - 8f(x_0 - h) + f(x_0 - 2h)}{12h} - f'(x_0) \right| \leq \frac{Mh^4}{30},$$

where $|f^{(5)}(x)| \leq M$ for $|x - x_0| \leq |h|$.

(b) (i)

h	$(f(x_0) - f(x_0 - h))/h$	Error
10^{-1}	0.951626	4.837×10^{-2}
10^{-2}	0.995017	4.983×10^{-3}
10^{-3}	0.9995	4.998×10^{-4}
10^{-4}	0.99995	5×10^{-5}

The errors are roughly proportional to h, agreeing with part (a).

(ii)

h	$(f(x_0 + h) - f(x_0 - h))/(2h)$	Error
10^{-1}	1.00167	1.668×10^{-3}
10^{-2}	1.00001667	1.667×10^{-5}
10^{-3}	1.0000001667	1.667×10^{-7}
10^{-4}	1.000000001667	1.667×10^{-9}

The errors are roughly proportional to h^2, agreeing with part (a).

(iii)

h	$(-f(x_0 + 2h) + 8f(x_0 + h) - 8f(x_0 - h) + f(x_0 - 2h))/(12h)$	Error
10^{-1}	0.99999667	3.337×10^{-6}
10^{-2}	0.9999999999667	3.333×10^{-10}
10^{-3}	0.99999999999999667	3.333×10^{-14}
10^{-4}	0.999999999999999999667	3.333×10^{-18}

The errors are roughly proportional to h^4, agreeing with part (a). This is the most accurate formula.

(c) (i)

h	$(f(x_0) - f(x_0 - h))/h$	Error
10^{-1}	1.0001×10^6	1.00×10^{10}
10^{-2}	1.0001×10^7	1.00×10^{10}
10^{-3}	1.0101×10^8	1.01×10^{10}
10^{-4}	1.11111×10^9	1.11×10^{10}
10^{-5}	Undefined	Undefined
10^{-6}	-1.11111×10^{10}	-1.11×10^9
10^{-7}	-1.0101×10^{10}	-1.01×10^8
10^{-8}	-1.001×10^{10}	-1.00×10^7
10^{-9}	-1.0001×10^{10}	-1.00×10^6

(ii)

h	$(f(x_0 + h) - f(x_0 - h))/(2h)$	Error
10^{-1}	1×10^2	1×10^{10}
10^{-2}	1×10^4	1×10^{10}
10^{-3}	1.0001×10^6	1.0001×10^{10}
10^{-4}	1.0101×10^8	1.0101×10^{10}
10^{-5}	Undefined	Undefined
10^{-6}	-1.0101×10^{10}	-1.01×10^8
10^{-7}	-1.0001×10^{10}	-1.00×10^6
10^{-8}	-1.000001×10^{10}	-1.00×10^4
10^{-9}	$-1.00000001 \times 10^{10}$	-1.00×10^2

(iii)

h	$(-f(x_0 + 2h) + 8f(x_0 + h) - 8f(x_0 - h) + f(x_0 - 2h))/(12h)$	Error
10^{-1}	1.25×10^2	1.00×10^{10}
10^{-2}	1.25×10^4	1.00×10^{10}
10^{-3}	1.25013×10^6	1.00×10^{10}
10^{-4}	1.26326×10^8	1.01×10^{10}
10^{-5}	Undefined	Undefined
10^{-6}	-9.99579×10^9	4.21×10^6
10^{-7}	$-9.9999995998 \times 10^{10}$	4.00×10^2
10^{-8}	$-9.99999999996 \times 10^{10}$	4.00×10^{-2}
10^{-9}	$-9.999999999999996 \times 10^{10}$	4.00×10^{-6}

For relatively large values of h, these approximation formulas fail miserably. The main reason is that $f(x) = 1/x$ changes very quickly at $x_0 = 10^{-5}$. In fact, $f(x) \to \pm\infty$ as $x \to 0$. So we must use very small values for h when estimating a limit (involving f and $x_0 = 10^{-5}$) as $h \to 0$. Here, $h > 10^{-5}$ is too big, since the values of $x_0 - h$ cross over the discontinuity at $x = 0$. For smaller values of h, that make sure we stay on the good side of the abyss, these formulas work quite well. Already by $h = 10^{-6}$, formula (c) is the best approximation.

CHAPTER ELEVEN

Solutions for Section 11.1

Exercises

1. (a) (III) An island can only sustain the population up to a certain size. The population will grow until it reaches this limiting value.
    (b) (V) The ingot will get hot and then cool off, so the temperature will increase and then decrease.
    (c) (I) The speed of the car is constant, and then decreases linearly when the breaks are applied uniformly.
    (d) (II) Carbon-14 decays exponentially.
    (e) (IV) Tree pollen is seasonal, and therefore cyclical.

2. Since $y = x^3$, we know that $y' = 3x^2$. Substituting $y = x^3$ and $y' = 3x^2$ into the differential equation we get

$$
\begin{aligned}
0 = xy' - 3y \\
= x(3x^2) - 3(x^3) \\
= 3x^3 - 3x^3 \\
= 0.
\end{aligned}
$$

Since this equation is true for all x, we see that $y = x^3$ is in fact a solution.

3. In order to prove that $y = A + Ce^{kt}$ is a solution to the differential equation

$$
\frac{dy}{dt} = k(y - A),
$$

we must show that the derivative of y with respect to t is in fact equal to $k(y - A)$:

$$
\begin{aligned}
y &= A + Ce^{kt} \\
\frac{dy}{dt} &= 0 + (Ce^{kt})(k) \\
&= kCe^{kt} \\
&= k(Ce^{kt} + A - A) \\
&= k\left((Ce^{kt} + A) - A\right) \\
&= k(y - A).
\end{aligned}
$$

4. If $P = P_0 e^t$, then

$$
\frac{dP}{dt} = \frac{d}{dt}(P_0 e^t) = P_0 e^t = P.
$$

5. We know that at time $t = 0$ the value of y is 8. Since we are told that $dy/dt = 0.5y$, we know that at time $t = 0$ the derivative of y is $.5(8) = 4$. Thus as t goes from 0 to 1, y will increase by 4, so at $t = 1$, $y = 8 + 4 = 12$.
    Likewise, at $t = 1$, we get $dy/dt = 0.5(12) = 6$ so that at $t = 2$, we obtain $y = 12 + 6 = 18$.
    At $t = 2$, we have $dy/dt = 0.5(18) = 9$ so that at $t = 3$, we obtain $y = 18 + 9 = 27$.
    At $t = 3$, we have $dy/dt = 0.5(27) = 13.5$ so that at $t = 4$, we obtain $y = 27 + 13.5 = 40.5$.
    Thus we get the values in the following table

t	0	1	2	3	4
y	8	12	18	27	40.5

6. Since $y = x^2 + k$, we know that $y' = 2x$. Substituting $y = x^2 + k$ and $y' = 2x$ into the differential equation, we get

$$
\begin{aligned}
10 = 2y - xy' \\
= 2(x^2 + k) - x(2x) \\
= 2x^2 + 2k - 2x^2 \\
= 2k.
\end{aligned}
$$

Thus, $k = 5$ is the only solution.

7. If $Q = Ce^{kt}$, then

$$\frac{dQ}{dt} = Cke^{kt} = k(Ce^{kt}) = kQ.$$

We are given that $\frac{dQ}{dt} = -0.03Q$, so we know that $kQ = -0.03Q$. Thus we either have $Q = 0$ (in which case $C = 0$ and k is anything) or $k = -0.03$. Notice that if $k = -0.03$, then C can be any number.

8. If y satisfies the differential equation, then we must have

$$\frac{d\left(5 + 3e^{kx}\right)}{dx} = 10 - 2(5 + 3e^{kx})$$

$$3ke^{kx} = 10 - 10 - 6e^{kx}$$

$$3ke^{kx} = -6e^{kx}$$

$$k = -2.$$

So, if $k = -2$ the formula for y solves the differential equation.

9. If $y = \sin 2t$, then $\frac{dy}{dt} = 2\cos 2t$, and $\frac{d^2y}{dt^2} = -4\sin 2t$.
Thus $\frac{d^2y}{dt^2} + 4y = -4\sin 2t + 4\sin 2t = 0$.

10. If $y = \cos \omega t$, then

$$\frac{dy}{dt} = -\omega \sin \omega t, \qquad \frac{d^2y}{dt^2} = -\omega^2 \cos \omega t.$$

Thus, if $\frac{d^2y}{dt^2} + 9y = 0$, then

$$-\omega^2 \cos \omega t + 9\cos \omega t = 0$$

$$(9 - \omega^2) \cos \omega t = 0.$$

Thus $9 - \omega^2 = 0$, or $\omega^2 = 9$, so $\omega = \pm 3$.

11. Differentiating and using the fact that

$$\frac{d}{dt}(\cosh t) = \sinh t \quad \text{and} \quad \frac{d}{dt}(\sinh t) = \cosh t,$$

we see that

$$\frac{dx}{dt} = \omega C_1 \sinh \omega t + \omega C_2 \cosh \omega t$$

$$\frac{d^2x}{dt^2} = \omega^2 C_1 \cosh \omega t + \omega^2 C_2 \sinh \omega t$$

$$= \omega^2 \left(C_1 \cosh \omega t + C_2 \sinh \omega t\right).$$

Therefore, we see that

$$\frac{d^2x}{dt^2} = \omega^2 x.$$

12. Differentiating $x^2 + y^2 = r^2$ implicitly, with r a constant, gives

$$2x + 2y\frac{dy}{dx} = 0.$$

Solving for dy/dx, we get

$$\frac{dy}{dx} = -\frac{2x}{2y} = -\frac{x}{y}.$$

Problems

13. (a) If $y = Cx^n$ is a solution to the given differential equation, then we must have

$$x\frac{d\left(Cx^n\right)}{dx} - 3(Cx^n) = 0$$

$$x(Cnx^{n-1}) - 3(Cx^n) = 0$$

$$Cnx^n - 3Cx^n = 0$$

$$C(n - 3)x^n = 0.$$

Thus, if $C = 0$, we get $y = 0$ is a solution, for every n. If $C \neq 0$, then $n = 3$, and so $y = Cx^3$ is a solution.

(b) Because $y = 40$ for $x = 2$, we cannot have $C = 0$. Thus, by part (a), we get $n = 3$. The solution to the differential equation is

$$y = Cx^3.$$

To determine C if $y = 40$ when $x = 2$, we substitute these values into the equation.

$$40 = C \cdot 2^3$$
$$40 = C \cdot 8$$
$$C = 5.$$

So, now both C and n are fixed at specific values.

14. (a) $P = \frac{1}{1+e^{-t}} = (1 + e^{-t})^{-1}$

$\frac{dP}{dt} = -(1 + e^{-t})^{-2}(-e^{-t}) = \frac{e^{-t}}{(1+e^{-t})^2}$.

Then $P(1 - P) = \frac{1}{1+e^{-t}} \left(1 - \frac{1}{1+e^{-t}}\right) = \left(\frac{1}{1+e^{-t}}\right)\left(\frac{e^{-t}}{1+e^{-t}}\right) = \frac{e^{-t}}{(1+e^{-t})^2} = \frac{dP}{dt}$.

(b) As t tends to ∞, e^{-t} goes to 0. Thus $\lim\limits_{t \to \infty} \frac{1}{1+e^{-t}} = 1$.

15.

(I) $y = 2\sin x$, $dy/dx = 2\cos x$, $d^2y/dx^2 = -2\sin x$

(II) $y = \sin 2x$, $dy/dx = 2\cos 2x$, $d^2y/dx^2 = -4\sin 2x$

(III) $y = e^{2x}$, $dy/dx = 2e^{2x}$, $d^2y/dx^2 = 4e^{2x}$

(IV) $y = e^{-2x}$, $dy/dx = -2e^{-2x}$, $d^2y/dx^2 = 4e^{-2x}$

and so:

(a) (IV)

(b) (III)

(c) (III), (IV)

(d) (II)

16. It is easiest to begin by writing down the first and second derivatives for each possible solution:

(I) $y = \cos x$, so $y' = -\sin x$, and $y'' = -\cos x$.

(II) $y = \cos(-x)$, so $y' = \sin(-x)$, and $y'' = -\cos(-x)$.

(III) $y = x^2$, so $y' = 2x$, and $y'' = 2$.

(IV) $y = e^x + e^{-x}$, so $y' = e^x - e^{-x}$, and $y'' = e^x + e^{-x}$.

(V) $y = \sqrt{2x}$, so $y' = \frac{1}{2}(2x)^{-1/2} \cdot 2 = 1/\sqrt{2x}$, and $y'' = -\frac{1}{2}(2x)^{-3/2} \cdot 2 = -(2x)^{-3/2}$.

By substituting these into the given differential equations, we get following solutions:

(a) (IV)

(b) None

(c) (V)

(d) (I), (II)

(e) (III)

Solutions for Section 11.2

Exercises

1. There are many possible answers. One possibility is shown in Figures 11.1 and 11.2.

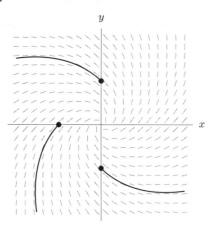

Figure 11.1

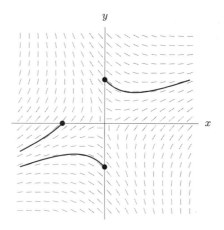

Figure 11.2

2. (a) See Figure 11.3.
   (b) The solution is $y(x) = 1$.
   (c) Since $y' = 0$ and $x(y - 1) = 0$, this is a solution.

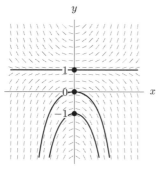

Figure 11.3

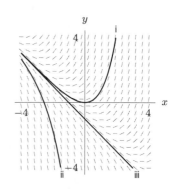

Figure 11.4

3. (a) See Figure 11.4.
   (b) The solution through $(-1, 0)$ appears to be linear, so its equation is $y = -x - 1$.
   (c) If $y = -x - 1$, then $y' = -1$ and $x + y = x + (-x - 1) = -1$, so this checks as a solution.

Problems

4. Notice that $y' = \dfrac{x + y}{x - y}$ is zero when $x = -y$ and is undefined when $x = y$. A solution curve will be horizontal (slope= 0) when passing through a point with $x = -y$, and will be vertical (slope undefined) when passing through a point with $x = y$. The only slope field for which this is true is slope field (b).

5. (a) See Figure 11.5.

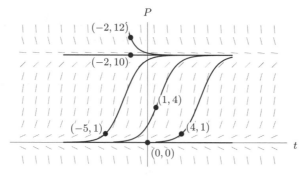

Figure 11.5

(b) If $0 < P < 10$, the solution is increasing; if $P > 10$, it is decreasing. So P tends to 10.

6. (a) and (b) See Figure 11.6

(c) Figure 11.6 shows that a solution will be increasing if its y-values fall in the range $-1 < y < 2$. This makes sense since if we examine the equation $y' = 0.5(1 + y)(2 - y)$, we will find that $y' > 0$ if $-1 < y < 2$. Notice that if the y-value ever gets to 2, then $y' = 0$ and the function becomes constant, following the line $y = 2$. (The same is true if ever $y = -1$.)

From the graph, the solution is decreasing if $y > 2$ or $y < -1$. Again, this also follows from the equation, since in either case $y' < 0$.

The curve has a horizontal tangent if $y' = 0$, which only happens if $y = 2$ or $y = -1$. This also can be seen on the graph in Figure 11.6.

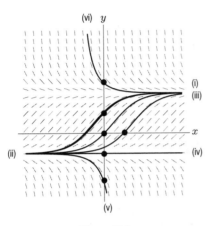

Figure 11.6

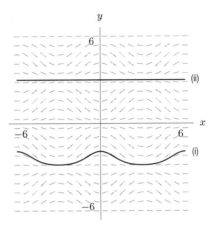

Figure 11.7

7. (a) See Figure 11.7.

(b) We can see that the slope lines are horizontal when y is an integer multiple of π. We conclude from Figure 11.7 that the solution is $y = n\pi$ in this case.

To check this, we note that if $y = n\pi$, then $(\sin x)(\sin y) = (\sin x)(\sin n\pi) = 0 = y'$. Thus $y = n\pi$ is a solution to $y' = (\sin x)(\sin y)$, and it passes through $(0, n\pi)$.

8. (a) Since $y' = -y$, the slope is negative above the x-axis (when y is positive) and positive below the x-axis (when y is negative). The only slope field for which this is true is II.

(b) Since $y' = y$, the slope is positive for positive y and negative for negative y. This is true of both I and III. As y get larger, the slope should get larger, so the correct slope field is I.

(c) Since $y' = x$, the slope is positive for positive x and negative for negative x. This corresponds to slope field V.

(d) Since $y' = \dfrac{1}{y}$, the slope is positive for positive y and negative for negative y. As y approaches 0, the slope becomes larger in magnitude, which correspond to solution curves close to vertical. The correct slope field is III.

(e) Since $y' = y^2$, the slope is always positive, so this must correspond to slope field IV.

9. (a) II   (b) VI   (c) IV   (d) I   (e) III   (f) V

10. The slope fields in (I) and (II) appear periodic. (I) has zero slope at $x = 0$, so (I) matches $y' = \sin x$, whereas (II) matches $y' = \cos x$. The slope in (V) tends to zero as $x \to \pm\infty$, so this must match $y' = e^{-x^2}$. Of the remaining slope fields, only (III) shows negative slopes, matching $y' = xe^{-x}$. The slope in (IV) is zero at $x = 0$, so it matches $y' = x^2e^{-x}$. This leaves field (VI) to match $y' = e^{-x}$.

Solutions for Section 11.3

Exercises

1. (a)

Table 11.1 *Euler's method for*
$y' = x + y$ *with* $y(0) = 1$

x	y	$\Delta y =$(slope)Δx
0	1	$0.1 = (1)(0.1)$
0.1	1.1	$0.12 = (1.2)(0.1)$
0.2	1.22	$0.142 = (1.42)(0.1)$
0.3	1.362	$0.1662 = (1.662)(0.1)$
0.4	1.5282	

So $y(0.4) \approx 1.5282$.

(b)

Table 11.2 *Euler's method for*
$y' = x + y$ *with* $y(-1) = 0$

x	y	$\Delta y =$(slope)Δx
-1	0	$-0.1 = (-1)(0.1)$
-0.9	-0.1	$-0.1 = (-1)(0.1)$
-0.8	-0.2	$-0.1 = (-1)(0.1)$
-0.7	-0.3	
$\vdots$	$\vdots$	Notice that y
0	-1	decreases by 0.1
$\vdots$	$\vdots$	for every step
0.4	-1.4	

So $y(0.4) = -1.4$. (This answer is exact.)

2. (a) The results from Euler's method with $\Delta x = 0.1$ are in Table 11.3.

(b) We have

$$y(x) = \frac{x^4}{4} + C,$$

so that $y(0) = 0$ gives $C = 0$, and the required solution is therefore

$$y(x) = \frac{x^4}{4}.$$

This is shown in the 3rd column of Table 11.3.

(c) The computed solution underestimates the real solution since the solution is concave up and is approximated in every interval by the tangent which is beneath the curve. See Figure 11.8.

Table 11.3

	Computed Solution	
x_n	Approx. $y(x_n)$	$y(x_n)$
0	0	0
0.1	0	0.000025
0.2	0.0001	0.0004
0.3	0.0009	0.002025
0.4	0.0036	0.0064
0.5	0.01	0.015625
0.6	0.0225	0.0324
0.7	0.0441	0.060025
0.8	0.0784	0.1024
0.9	0.1296	0.164025
1.0	0.2025	0.25

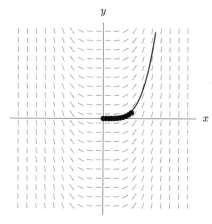

Figure 11.8

3. (a) See Figure 11.9.

 (b) $y(0) = 1$,

$$y(0.1) \approx y(0) + 0.1y(0) = 1 + 0.1(1) = 1.1$$
$$y(0.2) \approx y(0.1) + 0.1y(0.1) = 1.1 + 0.1(1.1) = 1.21$$
$$y(0.3) \approx y(0.2) + 0.1y(0.2) = 1.21 + 0.1(1.21) = 1.331$$
$$y(0.4) \approx 1.4641$$
$$y(0.5) \approx 1.61051$$
$$y(0.6) \approx 1.77156$$
$$y(0.7) \approx 1.94872$$
$$y(0.8) \approx 2.14359$$
$$y(0.9) \approx 2.35795$$
$$y(1.0) \approx 2.59374$$

 (c) See Figure 11.9. A smooth curve drawn through the solution points seems to match the slope field.

 (d) For $y = e^x$, we have $y' = e^x = y$ and $y(0) = e^0 = 1$. See Table 11.4.

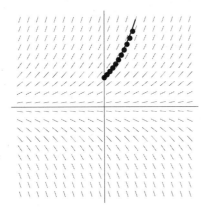

Figure 11.9

Table 11.4

	Computed Solution	
x_n	Approx. $y(x_n)$	$y(x_n)$
0	1	1
0.1	1.1	1.10517
0.2	1.21	1.22140
0.3	1.331	1.34986
0.4	1.4641	1.49182
0.5	1.61051	1.64872
0.6	1.77156	1.82212
0.7	1.94872	2.01375
0.8	2.14359	2.22554
0.9	2.35795	2.45960
1.0	2.59374	2.71828

4. (a) See Table 11.5. At $x = 1$, $y \approx 0.16$.

 (b) See Figure 11.10.

Table 11.5

x	y	$\Delta y = (\text{slope})\Delta x$
0	0	0
0.2	0	0.0016
0.4	0.0016	0.0128
0.6	0.0144	0.0432
0.8	0.0576	0.1024
1	0.1600	

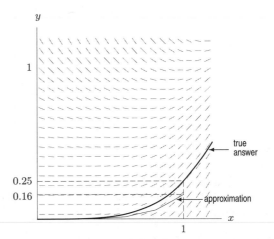

Figure 11.10

 (c) Our answer to (a) appears to be an underestimate. This is as we would expect, since the curve is concave up.

Problems

5. (a) $\Delta x = 0.5$

Table 11.6   *Euler's method for*
$y' = 2x$, *with* $y(0) = 1$

x	y	$\Delta y =$(slope)Δx
0	1	$0 = (2 \cdot 0)(0.5)$
0.5	1	$0.5 = (2 \cdot 0.5)(0.5)$
1	1.5	

$\Delta x = 0.25$

Table 11.7   *Euler's method for*
$y' = 2x$, *with* $y(0) = 1$

x	y	$\Delta y =$(slope)Δx
0	1	$0 = (2 \cdot 0)(0.25)$
0.25	1	$0.125 = (2 \cdot 0.25)(0.25)$
0.50	1.125	$0.25 = (2 \cdot 0.5)(0.25)$
0.75	1.375	$0.375 = (2 \cdot 0.75)(0.25)$
1	1.75	

(b) General solution is $y = x^2 + C$, and $y(0) = 1$ gives $C = 1$. Thus, the solution is $y = x^2 + 1$. So the true value of y when $x = 1$ is $y = 1^2 + 1 = 2$.

(c) When $\Delta x = 0.5$, error $= 0.5$.
When $\Delta x = 0.25$, error $= 0.25$.
Thus, decreasing Δx by a factor of 2 has decreased the error by a factor of 2, as expected.

6. (a)

Table 11.8

t	y	slope $= \frac{1}{t}$	$\Delta y = $ (slope)$\Delta t = \frac{1}{t}(0.1)$
1	0	1	0.1
1.1	0.1	0.909	0.091
1.2	0.191	0.833	0.083
1.3	0.274	0.769	0.077
1.4	0.351	0.714	0.071
1.5	0.422	0.667	0.067
1.6	0.489	0.625	0.063
1.7	0.552	0.588	0.059
1.8	0.610	0.556	0.056
1.9	0.666	0.526	0.053
2	0.719		

(b) If $\frac{dy}{dt} = \frac{1}{t}$, then $y = \ln|t| + C$.
Starting at $(1, 0)$ means $y = 0$ when $t = 1$, so $C = 0$ and $y = \ln|t|$.
After ten steps, $t = 2$, so $y = \ln 2 \approx 0.693$.

(c) Approximate $y = 0.719$, Exact $y = 0.693$.
Thus the approximate answer is too big. This is because the solution curve is concave down, and so the tangent lines are above the curve. Figure 11.11 shows the slope field of $y' = 1/t$ with the solution curve $y = \ln t$ plotted on top of it.

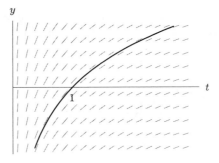

Figure 11.11

7. (a) (i)

Table 11.9 *Euler's method for*
$y' = (\sin x)(\sin y)$, *starting at* $(0, 2)$

x	y	$\Delta y =$(slope)Δx
0	2	$0 = (\sin 0)(\sin 2)(0.1)$
0.1	2	$0.009 = (\sin 0.1)(\sin 2)(0.1)$
0.2	2.009	$0.018 = (\sin 0.2)(\sin 2.009)(0.1)$
0.3	2.027	

(ii)

Table 11.10 *Euler's method for*
$y' = (\sin x)(\sin y)$, *starting at*
$(0, \pi)$

x	y	$\Delta y =$(slope)Δx
0	π	$0 = (\sin 0)(\sin \pi)(0.1)$
0.1	π	$0 = (\sin 0.1)(\sin \pi)(0.1)$
0.2	π	$0 = (\sin 0.2)(\sin \pi)(0.1)$
0.3	π	

(b) The slope field shows that the slope of the solution curve through $(0, \pi)$ is always 0. Thus the solution curve is the horizontal line with equation $y = \pi$.

8. For $\Delta x = 0.2$, we get the following results.

$$y(1.2) \approx y(1) + 0.2\sin(1 \cdot y(1)) = 1.168294$$
$$y(1.4) \approx y(1.2) + 0.2\sin(1.2 \cdot y(1.2)) = 1.365450$$
$$y(1.6) \approx y(1.4) + 0.2\sin(1.4 \cdot y(1.4)) = 1.553945$$
$$y(1.8) \approx y(1.6) + 0.2\sin(1.6 \cdot y(1.6)) = 1.675822$$
$$y(2.0) \approx y(1.8) + 0.2\sin(1.8 \cdot y(1.8)) = 1.700779$$

Repeating this with $\Delta x = 0.1$ and 0.05 gives the results in Table 11.11 below

Table 11.11

	Computed Solution		
x-value	$\Delta x = 0.2$	$\Delta x = 0.1$	$\Delta x = 0.05$
1.0	1	1	1
1.1		1.084147	1.086501
1.2	1.168294	1.177079	1.181232
1.3		1.275829	1.280619
1.4	1.365450	1.375444	1.379135
1.5		1.469214	1.469885
1.6	1.553945	1.549838	1.546065
1.7		1.611296	1.602716
1.8	1.675822	1.650458	1.637809
1.9		1.667451	1.652112
2.0	1.700779	1.664795	1.648231

The computed approximations for $y(2)$ using step sizes $\Delta x = 0.2, 0.1, 0.05$ are 1.700779, 1.664795, and 1.648231, respectively. Plotting these points we see that they lie approximately on a straight line.

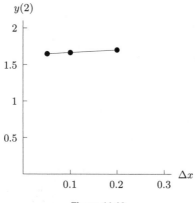

Figure 11.12

In the limit, as Δx tends to zero, the results produced by Euler's method should converge to the exact value of $y(2)$. This limiting value is the vertical intercept of the line drawn in Figure 11.12. This gives $y(2) \approx 1.632$.

9. (a) Using one step, $\frac{\Delta B}{\Delta t} = 0.05$, so $\Delta B = \left(\frac{\Delta B}{\Delta t}\right)\Delta t = 50$. Therefore we get an approximation of $B \approx 1050$ after one year.

(b) With two steps, $\Delta t = 0.5$ and we have

Table 11.12

t	B	$\Delta B = (0.05B)\Delta t$
0	1000	25
0.5	1025	25.63
1.0	1050.63	

(c) Keeping track to the nearest hundredth with $\Delta t = 0.25$, we have

Table 11.13

t	B	$\Delta B = (0.05B)\Delta t$
0	1000	12.5
0.25	1012.5	12.66
0.5	1025.16	12.81
0.75	1037.97	12.97
1	1050.94	

(d) In part (a), we get our approximation by making a single increment, ΔB, where ΔB is just $0.05B$. If we think in terms of interest, ΔB is just like getting one end of the year interest payment. Since ΔB is 0.05 times the balance B, it is like getting 5% interest at the end of the year.

(e) Part (b) is equivalent to computing the final amount in an account that begins with $1000 and earns 5% interest compounded twice annually. Each step is like computing the interest after 6 months. When $t = 0.5$, for example, the interest is $\Delta B = (0.05B) \cdot \frac{1}{2}$, and we add this to $1000 to get the new balance.

Similarly, part (c) is equivalent to the final amount in an account that has an initial balance of $1000 and earns 5% interest compounded quarterly.

10. Assume that $x > 0$ and that we use n steps in Euler's method. Label the x-coordinates we use in the process $x_0, x_1, \ldots, x_n$, where $x_0 = 0$ and $x_n = x$. Then using Euler's method to find $y(x)$, we get

Table 11.14

	x	y	$\Delta y = (\text{slope})\Delta x$
P_0	$0 = x_0$	0	$f(x_0)\Delta x$
P_1	x_1	$f(x_0)\Delta x$	$f(x_1)\Delta x$
P_2	x_2	$f(x_0)\Delta x + f(x_1)\Delta x$	$f(x_2)\Delta x$
$\vdots$	$\vdots$	$\vdots$	$\vdots$
P_n	$x = x_n$	$\displaystyle\sum_{i=0}^{n-1} f(x_i)\Delta x$	

Thus the result from Euler's method is $\displaystyle\sum_{i=0}^{n-1} f(x_i)\Delta x$. We recognize this as the left-hand Riemann sum that approximates $\int_0^x f(t)\,dt$.

Solutions for Section 11.4

Exercises

1. Separating variables gives

$$\int \frac{1}{P}\,dP = -\int 2\,dt,$$

so

$$\ln|P| = -2t + C.$$

Therefore

$$P = \pm e^{-2t+C} = Ae^{-2t}.$$

The initial value $P(0) = 1$ gives $1 = A$, so

$$P = e^{-2t}.$$

2. Separating variables gives

$$\int \frac{dP}{P} = \int 0.02\,dt,$$

so

$$\ln|P| = 0.02t + C.$$

Thus

$$|P| = e^{0.02t+C}$$

and

$$P = Ae^{0.02t}, \text{ where } A = \pm e^C.$$

We are given $P(0) = 20$. Therefore, $P(0) = Ae^{(0.02)\cdot 0} = A = 20$. So the solution is

$$P = 20e^{0.02t}.$$

3. Separating variables and integrating both sides gives

$$\int \frac{1}{L}\,dL = \frac{1}{2}\int dp$$

or

$$\ln|L| = \frac{1}{2}p + C.$$

This can be written

$$L = \pm e^{(1/2)p+C} = Ae^{p/2}.$$

The initial condition $L(0) = 100$ gives $100 = A$, so

$$L = 100e^{p/2}.$$

4. Separating variables gives

$$\int \frac{dQ}{Q} = \int \frac{dt}{5},$$

so

$$\ln|Q| = \frac{1}{5}t + C.$$

So

$$|Q| = e^{\frac{1}{5}t + C} = e^{\frac{1}{5}t}e^{C}$$

and

$$Q = Ae^{\frac{1}{5}t}, \text{ where } A = \pm e^{C}.$$

From the initial conditions we know that $Q(0) = 50$, so $Q(0) = Ae^{(\frac{1}{5})\cdot 0} = A = 50$. Thus

$$Q = 50e^{\frac{1}{5}t}.$$

5. Separating variables gives

$$\int \frac{dy}{y} = -\int \frac{1}{3}\,dx$$
$$\ln|y| = -\frac{1}{3}x + C.$$

Solving for y, we have

$$y = Ae^{-\frac{1}{3}x}, \text{ where } A = \pm e^{C}.$$

Since $y(0) = A = 10$, we have

$$y = 10e^{-\frac{1}{3}x}.$$

6. Separating variables gives

$$\int P\,dP = \int dt$$

so that

$$\frac{P^{2}}{2} = t + C$$

or

$$P = \pm\sqrt{2t + D}$$

(where $D = 2C$).

The initial condition $P(0) = 1$ implies we must take the positive root and that $1 = D$, so

$$P = \sqrt{2t + 1}.$$

7. Separating variables gives

$$\int \frac{dm}{m} = \int 3\,dt$$
$$\ln|m| = 3t + C$$
$$m = \pm e^{C}e^{3t} = Ae^{3t}.$$

Since $m = 5$ when $t = 1$, we have $5 = Ae^{3}$, so $A = 5/e^{3}$. Thus

$$m = \frac{5}{e^{3}}e^{3t} = 5e^{3t-3}.$$

8. Separating variables gives

$$\int \frac{dI}{I} = \int 0.2 \, dx,$$

so

$$\ln |I| = 0.2x + C.$$

Thus,

$$I = Ae^{0.2x}, \text{ where } A = \pm e^{C}.$$

According to the given boundary condition, $I(-1) = 6$. Therefore, $I(-1) = Ae^{0.2(-1)} = Ae^{-0.2} = 6$, so $A = 6e^{0.2}$. Thus

$$I = 6e^{0.2}e^{0.2x} = 6e^{0.2(x+1)}.$$

9. Separating variables gives

$$\int \frac{dz}{z} = \int 5 \, dt$$

$$\ln |z| = 5t + C.$$

Solving for z, we have

$$z = Ae^{5t}, \text{ where } A = \pm e^{C}.$$

Using the fact that $z(1) = 5$, we have $z(1) = Ae^{5} = 5$, so $A = 5/e^{5}$. Therefore,

$$z = \frac{5}{e^{5}} e^{5t} = 5e^{5t-5}.$$

10. Separating variables gives

$$\int \frac{1}{m} dm = \int ds.$$

Hence

$$\ln |m| = s + C$$

which gives

$$m = \pm e^{s+C} = Ae^{s}.$$

The initial condition $m(1) = 2$ gives $2 = Ae^{1}$ or $A = 2/e$, so

$$m = \frac{2}{e} e^{s} = 2e^{s-1}.$$

11. Separating variables gives

$$\int \frac{1}{u^2} du = \int \frac{1}{2} dt$$

or

$$-\frac{1}{u} = \frac{1}{2}t + C.$$

The initial condition gives $C = -1$ and so

$$u = \frac{1}{1 - (1/2)t}.$$

12. Separating variables and integrating gives

$$\int \frac{1}{z} dz = \int y \, dy$$

which gives

$$\ln |z| = \frac{1}{2}y^2 + C$$

or

$$z = \pm e^{(1/2)y^2 + C} = Ae^{y^2/2}.$$

The initial condition $y = 0$, $z = 1$ gives $A = 1$. Therefore

$$z = e^{y^2/2}.$$

13. Separating variables gives

$$\int \frac{dy}{y - 200} = \int 0.5 dt$$
$$\ln|y - 200| = 0.5t + C$$
$$y = 200 + Ae^{0.5t}, \quad \text{where } A = \pm e^C.$$

The initial condition, $y(0) = 50$, gives

$$50 = 200 + A, \quad \text{so} \quad A = -150.$$

Thus,

$$y = 200 - 150e^{0.5t}.$$

14. Separating variables gives

$$\int \frac{dP}{P + 4} = \int dt,$$

so

$$\ln|P + 4| = t + C$$
$$P + 4 = Ae^t$$
$$P = Ae^t - 4.$$

Since $P = 100$ when $t = 0$, we have $P(0) = Ae^0 - 4 = 100$, and $A = 104$. Therefore

$$P = 104e^t - 4.$$

15. Factoring out a 2 on the right makes the integration easier:

$$\frac{dy}{dx} = 2y - 4 = 2(y - 2)$$
$$\int \frac{dy}{y - 2} = \int 2 \, dx,$$

giving

$$\ln|y - 2| = 2x + C.$$

Thus,

$$|y - 2| = e^{2x+C},$$

so

$$y - 2 = Ae^{2x}, \text{ where } A = \pm e^C.$$

The curve passes through $(2, 5)$, which means $3 = Ae^4$, so $A = 3/e^4$. Thus,

$$y = 2 + \frac{3}{e^4}e^{2x} = 2 + 3e^{2x-4}.$$

16. Factoring and separating variables gives

$$\frac{dQ}{dt} = 0.3(Q - 400)$$
$$\int \frac{dQ}{Q - 400} = \int 0.3 \, dt$$
$$\ln|Q - 400| = 0.3t + C$$
$$Q = 400 + Ae^{0.3t}, \quad \text{where } A = \pm e^C.$$

The initial condition, $Q(0) = 50$, gives

$$50 = 400 + A \quad \text{so} \quad A = -350.$$

Thus

$$Q = 400 - 350e^{0.3t}.$$

17. Factoring out the 0.1 gives

$$\frac{dm}{dt} = 0.1m + 200 = 0.1(m + 2000)$$

$$\int \frac{dm}{m + 2000} = \int 0.1 \, dt,$$

so

$$\ln |m + 2000| = 0.1t + C,$$

and

$$m = Ae^{0.1t} - 2000, \text{ where } A = \pm e^C.$$

Using the initial condition, $m(0) = Ae^{(0.1) \cdot 0} - 2000 = 1000$, gives $A = 3000$. Thus

$$m = 3000e^{0.1t} - 2000.$$

18. Rearrange and write

$$\int \frac{1}{1 - R} dR = \int dy$$

or

$$-\ln |1 - R| = y + C$$

which can be written as

$$1 - R = \pm e^{-C-y} = Ae^{-y}$$

or

$$R = 1 - Ae^{-y}.$$

The initial condition $R(1) = 0.1$ gives $0.1 = 1 - Ae^{-1}$ and so

$$A = 0.9e.$$

Therefore

$$R = 1 - 0.9e^{1-y}.$$

19. Rewriting gives

$$\frac{dB}{dt} + 2B = 50$$

and

$$\frac{dB}{dt} = -2B + 50 = -2(B - 25),$$

so

$$\int \frac{dB}{B - 25} = -\int 2 \, dt$$

$$\ln |B - 25| = -2t + C.$$

Thus, we have

$$B - 25 = Ae^{-2t}, \text{ where } A = \pm e^C.$$

Using the initial condition, $B(1) = 100$, we have $75 = Ae^{-2}$, so $A = 75e^2$. Thus

$$B = 25 + 75e^2 e^{-2t} = 25 + 75e^{2-2t}.$$

20. Write

$$\int \frac{1}{y} dy = \int \frac{1}{3 + t} dt$$

and so

$$\ln |y| = \ln |3 + t| + C$$

or

$$\ln |y| = \ln D |3 + t|$$

where $\ln D = C$. Therefore

$$y = D(3 + t).$$

The initial condition $y(0) = 1$ gives $D = \frac{1}{3}$, so

$$y = \frac{1}{3}(3 + t).$$

21. Separating variables gives

$$\frac{dz}{dt} = te^z$$

$$e^{-z}\,dz = t\,dt$$

$$\int e^{-z}\,dz = \int t\,dt,$$

so

$$-e^{-z} = \frac{t^2}{2} + C.$$

Since the solution passes through the origin, $z = 0$ when $t = 0$, we must have

$$-e^{-0} = \frac{0}{2} + C, \text{ so } C = -1.$$

Thus

$$-e^{-z} = \frac{t^2}{2} - 1,$$

or

$$z = -\ln\left(1 - \frac{t^2}{2}\right).$$

22. Separating variables gives

$$\frac{dy}{dx} = \frac{5y}{x}$$

$$\int \frac{dy}{y} = \int \frac{5}{x}\,dx$$

$$\ln|y| = 5\ln|x| + C.$$

Thus

$$|y| = e^{5\ln|x|}e^C = e^C e^{\ln|x|^5} = e^C|x|^5,$$

giving

$$y = Ax^5, \quad \text{where} \quad A = \pm e^C.$$

Since $y = 3$ when $x = 1$, so $A = 3$. Thus

$$y = 3x^5.$$

23. Separating variables gives

$$\frac{dy}{dt} = y^2(1 + t)$$

$$\int \frac{dy}{y^2} = \int (1 + t)\,dt,$$

so

$$-\frac{1}{y} = t + \frac{t^2}{2} + C,$$

giving

$$y = -\frac{1}{t + t^2/2 + C}.$$

Since $y = 2$ when $t = 1$, we have

$$2 = -\frac{1}{1 + 1/2 + C}, \quad \text{so} \quad 2C + 3 = -1, \quad \text{and} \quad C = -2.$$

Thus

$$y = -\frac{1}{t^2/2 + t - 2} = -\frac{2}{t^2 + 2t - 4}.$$

24. Separating variables gives

$$\frac{dz}{dt} = z + zt^2 = z(1 + t^2)$$

$$\int \frac{dz}{z} = \int (1 + t^2)dt,$$

so

$$\ln|z| = t + \frac{t^3}{3} + C,$$

giving

$$z = Ae^{t+t^3/3}.$$

We have $z = 5$ when $t = 0$, so $A = 5$ and

$$z = 5e^{t+t^3/3}.$$

25. Separating variables gives

$$\frac{dw}{d\theta} = \theta w^2 \sin \theta^2$$

$$\int \frac{dw}{w^2} = \int \theta \sin \theta^2 \, d\theta,$$

so

$$-\frac{1}{w} = -\frac{1}{2} \cos \theta^2 + C.$$

According to the initial conditions, $w(0) = 1$, so $-1 = -\frac{1}{2} + C$ and $C = -\frac{1}{2}$. Thus,

$$-\frac{1}{w} = -\frac{1}{2} \cos \theta^2 - \frac{1}{2}$$

$$\frac{1}{w} = \frac{\cos \theta^2 + 1}{2}$$

$$w = \frac{2}{\cos \theta^2 + 1}.$$

26. Separating variables and integrating gives

$$\int \frac{1}{w^2} dw = -\int \tan \psi \, d\psi.$$

To integrate the right side, write $\tan \psi = \sin \psi / \cos \psi$ and use the substitution $w = \cos \psi$ giving

$$-\frac{1}{w} = \ln |\cos \psi| + C$$

so

$$w = \frac{-1}{\ln |\cos \psi| + C}.$$

Using the initial condition $w(0) = 2$ we have

$$2 = \frac{-1}{\ln |\cos 0| + C} = \frac{-1}{\ln 1 + C} = \frac{-1}{0 + C}$$

so

$$C = -\frac{1}{2}.$$

Thus the solution is

$$w = \frac{-1}{\ln |\cos \psi| - 1/2}.$$

27. Separating variables gives

$$x(x+1)\frac{du}{dx} = u^2$$

$$\int \frac{du}{u^2} = \int \frac{dx}{x(x+1)} = \int \left(\frac{1}{x} - \frac{1}{1+x}\right) dx,$$

so

$$-\frac{1}{u} = \ln|x| - \ln|x+1| + C.$$

We have $u(1) = 1$, so $-\frac{1}{1} = \ln|1| - \ln|1+1| + C$. So $C = \ln 2 - 1$. Solving for u yields

$$-\frac{1}{u} = \ln|x| - \ln|x+1| + \ln 2 - 1 = \ln \frac{2|x|}{|x+1|} - 1,$$

so

$$u = \frac{-1}{\ln\left|\frac{2x}{x+1}\right| - 1}.$$

28. (a) Yes   **(b)** No   **(c)** Yes
    (d) No   **(e)** Yes   **(f)** Yes
    (g) No   **(h)** Yes   **(i)** No
    (j) Yes   **(k)** Yes   **(l)** No

Problems

29. Separating variables gives

$$\int \frac{dR}{R} = \int k\,dt.$$

Integrating gives

$$\ln|R| = kt + C,$$

so

$$|R| = e^{kt+C} = e^{kt}e^C$$
$$R = Ae^{kt}, \quad \text{where } A = \pm e^C \quad \text{or} \quad A = 0.$$

30. Separating variables gives

$$\frac{dQ}{dt} = \frac{Q}{k}$$
$$\int \frac{dQ}{Q} = \int \frac{1}{k}\,dt$$

Integrating gives

$$\ln|Q| = \frac{t}{k} + C$$
$$Q = Ae^{t/k}, \quad \text{where } A = \pm e^C \quad \text{or} \quad A = 0.$$

31. Separating variables gives

$$\int \frac{dP}{P-a} = \int dt.$$

Integrating yields

$$\ln|P-a| = t + C,$$

so

$$|P-a| = e^{t+C} = e^t e^C$$
$$P = = a + Ae^t, \quad \text{where } A = \pm e^C \quad \text{or } A = 0.$$

32. Separating variables gives

$$\int \frac{dQ}{b - Q} = \int dt.$$

Integrating yields

$$-\ln|b - Q| = t + C,$$

so

$$|b - Q| = e^{-(t+C)} = e^{-t}e^{-C}$$
$$Q = b - Ae^{-t}, \quad \text{where } A = \pm e^{-C} \quad \text{or } A = 0.$$

33. Separating variables gives

$$\int \frac{dP}{P - a} = \int k\,dt.$$

Integrating yields

$$\ln|P - a| = kt + C,$$

so

$$P = a + Ae^{kt} \quad \text{where } A = \pm e^{C} \quad \text{or } A = 0.$$

34. Factoring and separating variables gives

$$\frac{dR}{dt} = a\left(R + \frac{b}{a}\right)$$
$$\int \frac{dR}{R + b/a} = \int a\,dt$$
$$\ln\left|R + \frac{b}{a}\right| = at + C$$
$$R = -\frac{b}{a} + Ae^{at}, \quad \text{where } A \text{ can be any constant.}$$

35. Separating variables and integrating gives

$$\int \frac{1}{aP + b}\,dP = \int dt.$$

This gives

$$\frac{1}{a}\ln|aP + b| = t + C$$
$$\ln|aP + b| = at + aC$$
$$aP + b = \pm e^{at+aC} = Ae^{at}, \quad \text{where } A = \pm e^{aC} \quad \text{or} \quad A = 0,$$

or

$$P = \frac{1}{a}(Ae^{at} - b).$$

36. Separating variables and integrating gives

$$\int \frac{1}{y^2}\,dy = \int k(1 + t^2)\,dt$$

or

$$-\frac{1}{y} = k\left(t + \frac{1}{3}t^3\right) + C.$$

Hence,

$$y = \frac{-1}{k(t + \frac{1}{3}t^3) + C}.$$

37. Separating variables and integrating gives

$$\int \frac{1}{R^2 + 1}\,dR = \int a\,dx$$

or

$$\arctan R = ax + C$$

so that

$$R = \tan(ax + C).$$

38. Separating variables and integrating gives

$$\int \frac{1}{L-b}dL = \int k(x+a)dx$$

or

$$\ln|L-b| = k\left(\frac{1}{2}x^2 + ax\right) + C.$$

Solving for L gives

$$L = b + Ae^{k(\frac{1}{2}x^2 + ax)}, \quad \text{where } A \text{ can be any constant.}$$

39. Separating variables gives

$$\frac{dy}{dt} = y(2-y),$$

so

$$\int \frac{dy}{y(y-2)} = -\int dt,$$

so

$$-\frac{1}{2}\int\left(\frac{1}{y} - \frac{1}{y-2}\right)dy = -\int dt.$$

Integrating yields

$$\frac{1}{2}(\ln|y-2| - \ln|y|) = -t + C,$$

so

$$\ln\frac{|y-2|}{|y|} = -2t + 2C.$$

Exponentiating both sides yields

$$\left|1 - \frac{2}{y}\right| = e^{-2t+2C}$$

$$\frac{2}{y} = 1 - Ae^{-2t}, \quad \text{where } A = \pm e^{2C}$$

$$y = \frac{2}{1 - Ae^{-2t}}.$$

But

$$y(0) = \frac{2}{1-A} = 1,$$

so $A = -1$, and

$$y = \frac{2}{1 + e^{-2t}}.$$

40. Separating variables gives

$$t\frac{dx}{dt} = (1 + 2\ln t)\tan x$$

$$\frac{dx}{\tan x} = \left(\frac{1 + 2\ln t}{t}\right)dt$$

$$\int \frac{\cos x}{\sin x}dx = \int\left(\frac{1}{t} + \frac{2\ln t}{t}\right)dt.$$

Integrating gives

$$\ln|\sin x| = \ln t + (\ln t)^2 + C$$

$$|\sin x| = e^{\ln t + (\ln t)^2 + C} = t(e^{\ln t})^{\ln t}e^C = t(t^{\ln t})e^C.$$

So

$$\sin x = At^{(\ln t)+1}, \quad \text{where } A = \pm e^C \quad \text{or} \quad A = 0.$$

Therefore

$$x = \arcsin(At^{(\ln t)+1}).$$

41. Separating variables gives

$$\frac{dx}{dt} = \frac{x \ln x}{t},$$

so

$$\int \frac{dx}{x \ln x} = \int \frac{dt}{t},$$

and thus

$$\ln |\ln x| = \ln t + C,$$

so

$$|\ln x| = e^C e^{\ln t} = e^C t.$$

Therefore

$$\ln x = At, \quad \text{where } A = \pm e^C \quad \text{or} \quad A = 0, \quad \text{so} \quad x = e^{At}.$$

42. Since

$$\frac{dy}{dt} = -y \ln \left(\frac{y}{2}\right),$$

we have

$$\frac{dy}{y \ln(y/2)} = -dt,$$

so that

$$\int \frac{dy}{y \ln(y/2)} = \int (-dt).$$

Substituting $w = \ln(y/2)$, $dw = \frac{1}{y} dy$ gives:

$$\int \frac{dw}{w} = -\int dt$$

so

$$\ln |w| = -t + C$$
$$\ln \left|\ln \left(\frac{y}{2}\right)\right| = -t + C.$$

Since $y(0) = 1$, we have $C = \ln |\ln \frac{1}{2}| = \ln(|-\ln 2|) = \ln(\ln 2)$. Thus

$$\ln \left|\ln \left(\frac{y}{2}\right)\right| = -t + \ln(\ln 2),$$

or

$$\left|\ln \left(\frac{y}{2}\right)\right| = e^{-t+\ln(\ln 2)}$$

Since $e^{\ln(\ln 2)} = \ln 2$, this simplifies to

$$\left|\ln \left(\frac{y}{2}\right)\right| = (\ln 2)e^{-t},$$

so

$$\ln \left(\frac{y}{2}\right) = \pm(\ln 2)e^{-t}.$$

Since $y(0) = 1$, and $\ln(1/2) = -\ln 2$, we take the $-$ sign, giving

$$\ln \left(\frac{y}{2}\right) = -(\ln 2)e^{-t}.$$

Thus,

$$y = 2e^{-(\ln 2)e^{-t}}$$
$$y = 2(e^{-\ln 2})^{e^{-t}} = 2(2^{-1})^{e^{-t}}$$
$$y = 2(2^{-e^{-t}}).$$

(Note that $\ln(y/2) = (\ln 2)e^{-t}$ does not satisfy $y(0) = 1$.)

43. (a) Separating variables and integrating gives

$$\int \frac{1}{100 - y} dy = \int dt$$

so that

$$-\ln|100 - y| = t + C$$

or

$$y(t) = 100 - Ae^{-t}.$$

(b) See Figure 11.13.

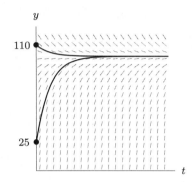

Figure 11.13

(c) The initial condition $y(0) = 25$ gives $A = 75$, so the solution is

$$y(t) = 100 - 75e^{-t}.$$

The initial condition $y(0) = 110$ gives $A = -10$ so the solution is

$$y(t) = 100 + 10e^{-t}.$$

(d) The increasing function, $y(t) = 100 - 75e^{-t}$.

44. (a) The slope field for $dy/dx = xy$ is in Figure 11.14.

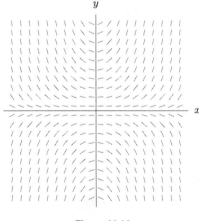

Figure 11.14

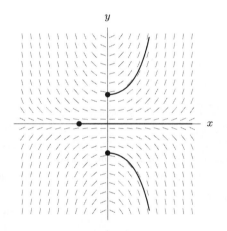

Figure 11.15

(b) Some solution curves are shown in Figure 11.15.

(c) Separating variables gives

$$\int \frac{1}{y} dy = \int x dx$$

or

$$\ln|y| = \frac{1}{2}x^2 + C.$$

Solving for y gives

$$y(x) = Ae^{x^2/2}$$

where $A = \pm e^C$. In addition, $y(x) = 0$ is a solution. So $y(x) = Ae^{x^2/2}$ is a solution for any A.

45. (a), (b)

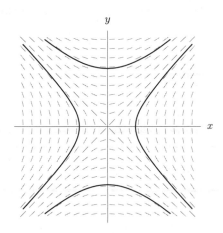

(c) Since $dy/dx = x/y$, we have

$$\int y\,dy = \int x\,dx,$$

and thus

$$\frac{y^2}{2} = \frac{x^2}{2} + C,$$

or

$$y^2 - x^2 = 2C.$$

This is the equation of the hyperbolas in part (b).

46. (a), (b)

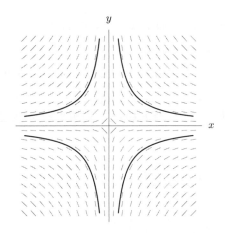

(c) Since

$$\frac{dy}{dx} = -\frac{y}{x},$$

we have

$$\int \frac{dy}{y} = -\int \frac{dx}{x},$$

so

$$\ln|y| = -\ln|x| + C,$$

giving

$$|y| = e^{-\ln|x|+C} = (|x|)^{-1}e^C.$$

Thus,

$$y = \frac{A}{x}, \quad \text{where } A = \pm e^C \quad \text{or} \quad A = 0.$$

47. By looking at the slope fields, we see that any solution curve of $y' = x/y$ intersects any solution curve to $y' = -y/x$. Now if the two curves intersect at (x, y), then the two slopes at (x, y) are negative reciprocals of each other, because

$$-\frac{1}{x/y} = -\frac{y}{x}.$$

Hence, the two curves intersect at right angles.

Solutions for Section 11.5

Exercises

1. (a) (I)
   (b) (IV)
   (c) (II) and (IV)
   (d) (II) and (III)

2. (a) = (I), (b) = (IV), (c) = (III). Graph (II) represents an egg originally at $0°$ C which is moved to the kitchen table ($20°$ C) two minutes after the egg in part (a) is moved.

3. (a) Separating variables, we have $\frac{dH}{H-200} = -k\,dt$, so $\int \frac{dH}{H-200} = \int -k\,dt$, whence $\ln|H - 200| = -kt + C$, and $H - 200 = Ae^{-kt}$, where $A = \pm e^C$. The initial condition is that the yam is $20°C$ at the time $t = 0$. Thus $20 - 200 = A$, so $A = -180$. Thus $H = 200 - 180e^{-kt}$.

   (b) Using part (a), we have $120 = 200 - 180e^{-k(30)}$. Solving for k, we have $e^{-30k} = \frac{-80}{-180}$, giving

$$k = \frac{\ln \frac{4}{9}}{-30} \approx 0.027.$$

   Note that this k is correct if t is given in *minutes*. (If t is given in hours, $k = \frac{\ln \frac{4}{9}}{-\frac{1}{2}} \approx 1.62$.)

4. (a) To find the equilibrium solutions, we must set

$$dy/dx = 0.5y(y - 4)(2 + y) = 0$$

   which gives three solutions: $y = 0$, $y = 4$, and $y = -2$.

   (b) From Figure 11.16, we see that $y = 0$ is stable and $y = 4$ and $y = -2$ are both unstable.

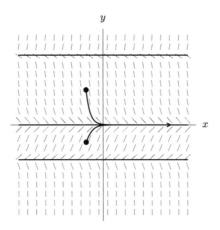

Figure 11.16

5. (a) The equilibrium solutions occur where the slope $y' = 0$, which occurs on the slope field where the lines are horizontal, or (looking at the equation) at $y = 2$ and $y = -1$. Looking at the slope field, we can see that $y = 2$ is stable, since the slopes at nearby values of y point toward it, whereas $y = -1$ is unstable.

(b) Draw solution curves passing through the given points by starting at these points and following the flow of the slopes, as shown in Figure 11.17.

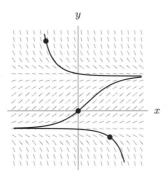

Figure 11.17

6. The equilibrium solutions of a differential equation are those functions satisfying the differential equation whose derivative is everywhere 0. Graphically, this means that a function is an equilibrium solution if it is a horizontal line that lies on the slope field. Looking at the figure in the problem, it appears that the equilibrium solutions for this problem are at $y = 1$ and $y = 3$. An equilibrium solution is stable if a small change in the initial value conditions gives a solution which tends toward equilibrium as $t \to \infty$. we see that $y = 3$ is a stable solution, while $y = 1$ is an unstable solution. See Figure 11.18.

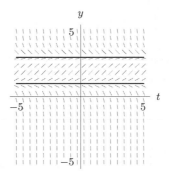

Figure 11.18

Problems

7. (a) Since the growth rate of the tumor is proportional to its size, we should have

$$\frac{dS}{dt} = kS.$$

(b) We can solve this differential equation by separating variables and then integrating:

$$\int \frac{dS}{S} = \int k \, dt$$
$$\ln|S| = kt + B$$
$$S = Ce^{kt}.$$

(c) This information is enough to allow us to solve for C:

$$5 = Ce^{0t}$$
$$C = 5.$$

(d) Knowing that $C = 5$, this second piece of information allows us to solve for k:

$$8 = 5e^{3k}$$
$$k = \frac{1}{3}\ln\left(\frac{8}{5}\right) \approx 0.1567.$$

So the tumor's size is given by

$$S = 5e^{0.1567t}.$$

8. (a) The rate of growth of the money in the account is proportional to the amount of money in the account. Thus

$$\frac{dM}{dt} = rM.$$

(b) Solving, we have $dM/M = r\,dt$.

$$\int \frac{dM}{M} = \int r\,dt$$
$$\ln|M| = rt + C$$
$$M = e^{rt+C} = Ae^{rt}, \qquad A = e^{C}.$$

When $t = 0$ (in 2000), $M = 1000$, so $A = 1000$ and $M = 1000e^{rt}$.

(c)

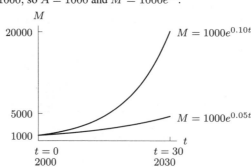

9. (a) Since we are told that the rate at which the quantity of the drug decreases is proportional to the amount of the drug left in the body, we know the differential equation modeling this situation is

$$\frac{dQ}{dt} = kQ.$$

Since we are told that the quantity of the drug is decreasing, we know that $k < 0$.

(b) We know that the general solution to the differential equation

$$\frac{dQ}{dt} = kQ$$

is

$$Q = Ce^{kt}.$$

(c) We are told that the half life of the drug is 3.8 hours. This means that at $t = 3.8$, the amount of the drug in the body is half the amount that was in the body at $t = 0$, or, in other words,

$$0.5Q(0) = Q(3.8).$$

Solving this equation gives

$$0.5Q(0) = Q(3.8)$$
$$0.5Ce^{k(0)} = Ce^{k(3.8)}$$
$$0.5C = Ce^{k(3.8)}$$
$$0.5 = e^{k(3.8)}$$
$$\ln(0.5) = k(3.8)$$
$$\frac{\ln(0.5)}{3.8} = k$$
$$k \approx -0.182.$$

(d) From part (c) we know that the formula for Q is

$$Q = Ce^{-0.182t}.$$

We are told that initially there are 10 mg of the drug in the body. Thus at $t = 0$, we get

$$10 = Ce^{-0.182(0)}$$

so

$$C = 10.$$

Thus our equation becomes

$$Q(t) = 10e^{-0.182t}.$$

Substituting $t = 12$, we get

$$Q(t) = 10e^{-0.182t}$$
$$Q(12) = 10e^{-0.182(12)}$$
$$= 10e^{-2.184}$$
$$Q(12) \approx 1.126 \text{ mg.}$$

10. (a) A very hot cup of coffee cools faster than one near room temperature. The differential equation given says that the rate at which the coffee cools is proportional to the difference between the temperature of the surrounding air and the temperature of the coffee. Since $\frac{dT}{dt} < 0$ (the coffee is cooling) and $T - 20 > 0$ (the coffee is warmer than room temperature), k must be positive.

(b) Separating variables gives

$$\int \frac{1}{T-20} dT = \int -k \, dt$$

and so

$$\ln|T - 20| = -kt + C$$

and

$$T(t) = 20 + Ae^{-kt}.$$

If the coffee is initially boiling (100° C), then $A = 80$ and so

$$T(t) = 20 + 80e^{-kt}.$$

When $t = 2$, the coffee is at $90°C$ and so $90 = 20 + 80e^{-2k}$ so that $k = \frac{1}{2} \ln \frac{8}{7}$.
Let the time when the coffee reaches $60°C$ be T_d, so that

$$60 = 20 + 80e^{-kT_d}$$

$$e^{-kT_d} = \frac{1}{2}.$$

Therefore, $T_d = \frac{1}{k} \ln 2 = \frac{2 \ln 2}{\ln \frac{8}{7}} \approx 10$ minutes.

11. (a) Letting k be the constant of proportionality, by Newton's Law of Cooling, we have

$$\frac{dH}{dt} = k(68 - H).$$

(b) We solve this equation by separating variables:

$$\int \frac{dH}{68 - H} = \int k \, dt$$
$$-\ln|68 - H| = kt + C$$
$$68 - H = \pm e^{C-kt}$$
$$H = 68 - Ae^{-kt}.$$

(c) We are told that $H = 40$ when $t = 0$; this tells us that

$$40 = 68 - Ae^{-k(0)}$$
$$40 = 68 - A$$
$$A = 28.$$

Knowing A, we can solve for k using the fact that $H = 48$ when $t = 1$:

$$48 = 68 - 28e^{-k(1)}$$
$$\frac{20}{28} = e^{-k}$$
$$k = -\ln\left(\frac{20}{28}\right) = 0.33647.$$

So the formula is $H(t) = 68 - 28e^{-0.33647t}$. We calculate H when $t = 3$, by

$$H(3) = 68 - 28e^{-0.33647(3)} = 57.8°\text{F}.$$

12. (a)

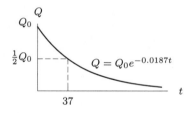

(b) $\dfrac{dQ}{dt} = -kQ$

(c) Since $25\% = 1/4$, it takes two half-lives = 74 hours for the drug level to be reduced to 25%. Alternatively, $Q = Q_0 e^{-kt}$ and $\frac{1}{2} = e^{-k(37)}$, we have

$$k = -\frac{\ln(1/2)}{37} \approx 0.0187.$$

Therefore $Q = Q_0 e^{-0.0187t}$. We know that when the drug level is 25% of the original level that $Q = 0.25Q_0$. Setting these equal, we get

$$0.25 = e^{-0.0187t}.$$

giving

$$t = -\frac{\ln(0.25)}{0.0187} \approx 74 \text{ hours} \approx 3 \text{ days}.$$

13. According to Newton's Law of Cooling, the temperature, T, of the roast as a function of time, t, satisfies

$$T'(t) = k(350 - T)$$
$$T(0) = 40.$$

Solving this differential equation, we get that $T = 350 - 310e^{-kt}$ for some $k > 0$. To find k, we note that at $t = 1$ we have $T = 90$, so

$$90 = 350 - 310e^{-k(1)}$$
$$\frac{260}{310} = e^{-k}$$
$$k = -\ln\left(\frac{260}{310}\right)$$
$$\approx 0.17589.$$

Thus, $T = 350 - 310e^{-0.17589t}$. Solving for t when $T = 140$, we have

$$140 = 350 - 310e^{-0.17589t}$$
$$\frac{210}{310} = e^{-0.17589t}$$
$$t = \frac{\ln(210/310)}{-0.17589}$$
$$t \approx 2.21 \text{ hours.}$$

14. (a) Since the amount leaving the blood is proportional to the quantity in the blood,

$$\frac{dQ}{dt} = -kQ \quad \text{for some positive constant } k.$$

Thus $Q = Q_0e^{-kt}$, where Q_0 is the initial quantity in the bloodstream. Only 20% is left in the blood after 3 hours. Thus $0.20 = e^{-3k}$, so $k = \frac{\ln 0.20}{-3} \approx 0.5365$. Therefore $Q = Q_0e^{-0.5365t}$.

   (b) Since 20% is left after 3 hours, after 6 hours only 20% of that 20% will be left. Thus after 6 hours only 4% will be left, so if the patient is given 100 mg, only 4 mg will be left 6 hours later.

15. (a) We know that the rate at which morphine leaves the body is proportional to the amount of morphine in the body at that particular instant. If we let Q be the amount of morphine in the body, we get that

$$\text{Rate of morphine leaving the body} = kQ,$$

where k is the rate of proportionality. The solution is $Q = Q_0e^{kt}$ (neglecting the continuously incoming morphine). Since the half-life is 2 hours, we have

$$\frac{1}{2}Q_0 = Q_0e^{k\cdot 2},$$

so

$$k = \frac{\ln(1/2)}{2} = -0.347.$$

   (b) Since

$$\text{Rate of change of quantity} = \text{Rate in} - \text{Rate out},$$

we have

$$\frac{dQ}{dt} = -0.347Q + 2.5.$$

   (c) Equilibrium occurs when $dQ/dt = 0$, that is, when $0.347Q = 2.5$ or $Q = 7.2$ mg.

16. Since it takes 6 years to reduce the pollution to 10%, another 6 years would reduce the pollution to 10% of 10%, which is equivalent to 1% of the original. Therefore it takes 12 years for 99% of the pollution to be removed. (Note that the value of Q_0 does not affect this.) Thus the second time is double the first because the fraction remaining, 0.01, in the second instance is the square of the fraction remaining, 0.1, in the first instance.

17. Michigan:

$$\frac{dQ}{dt} = -\frac{r}{V}Q = -\frac{158}{4.9 \times 10^3}Q \approx -0.032Q$$

so

$$Q = Q_0e^{-0.032t}.$$

We want to find t such that

$$0.1Q_0 = Q_0e^{-0.032t}$$

so

$$t = \frac{-\ln(0.1)}{0.032} \approx 72 \text{ years.}$$

Ontario:

$$\frac{dQ}{dt} = -\frac{r}{V}Q = \frac{-209}{1.6 \times 10^3}Q = -0.131Q$$

so

$$Q = Q_0 e^{-0.131t}.$$

We want to find t such that

$$0.1Q_0 = Q_0 e^{-0.131t}$$

so

$$t = \frac{-\ln(0.1)}{0.131} \approx 18 \text{ years.}$$

Lake Michigan will take longer because it is larger (4900 km^3 compared to 1600 km^3) and water is flowing through it at a slower rate (158 km^3/year compared to 209 km^3/year).

18. Lake Superior will take the longest, because the lake is largest (V is largest) and water is moving through it most slowly (r is smallest). Lake Erie looks as though it will take the least time because V is smallest and r is close to the largest. For Erie, $k = r/V = 175/460 \approx 0.38$. The lake with the largest value of r is Ontario, where $k = r/V = 209/1600 \approx 0.13$. Since e^{-kt} decreases faster for larger k, Lake Erie will take the shortest time for any fixed fraction of the pollution to be removed.

For Lake Superior,

$$\frac{dQ}{dt} = -\frac{r}{V}Q = -\frac{65.2}{12,200}Q \approx -0.0053Q$$

so

$$Q = Q_0 e^{-0.0053t}.$$

When 80% of the pollution has been removed, 20% remains so $Q = 0.2Q_0$. Substituting gives us

$$0.2Q_0 = Q_0 e^{-0.0053t}$$

so

$$t = -\frac{\ln(0.2)}{0.0053} \approx 301 \text{ years.}$$

(Note: The 301 is obtained by using the exact value of $\frac{r}{V} = \frac{65.2}{12,200}$, rather than 0.0053. Using 0.0053 gives 304 years.)

For Lake Erie, as in the text

$$\frac{dQ}{dt} = -\frac{r}{V}Q = -\frac{175}{460}Q \approx -0.38Q$$

so

$$Q = Q_0 e^{-0.38t}.$$

When 80% of the pollution has been removed

$$0.2Q_0 = Q_0 e^{-0.38t}$$
$$t = -\frac{\ln(0.2)}{0.38} \approx 4 \text{ years.}$$

So the ratio is

$$\frac{\text{Time for Lake Superior}}{\text{Time for Lake Erie}} \approx \frac{301}{4} \approx 75.$$

In other words it will take about 75 times as long to clean Lake Superior as Lake Erie.

19. (a) Suppose $Y(t)$ is the quantity of oil in the well at time t. We know that the oil in the well decreases at a rate proportional to $Y(t)$, so

$$\frac{dY}{dt} = -kY.$$

Integrating, and using the fact that initially $Y = Y_0 = 10^6$, we have

$$Y = Y_0 e^{-kt} = 10^6 e^{-kt}.$$

In six years, $Y = 500,000 = 5 \cdot 10^5$, so

$$5 \cdot 10^5 = 10^6 e^{-k \cdot 6}$$

so

$$0.5 = e^{-6k}$$
$$k = -\frac{\ln 0.5}{6} = 0.1155.$$

When $Y = 600{,}000 = 6 \cdot 10^5$,

$$\text{Rate at which oil decreasing} = \left|\frac{dY}{dt}\right| = kY = 0.1155(6 \cdot 10^5) = 69{,}300 \text{ barrels/year.}$$

(b) We solve the equation

$$5 \cdot 10^4 = 10^6 e^{-0.1155t}$$
$$0.05 = e^{-0.1155t}$$
$$t = \frac{\ln 0.05}{-0.1155} = 25.9 \text{ years.}$$

20. (a) Assuming that the world's population grows exponentially, satisfying $dP/dt = cP$, and that the land in use for crops is proportional to the population, we expect A to satisfy $dA/dt = kA$.

(b) We have $A(t) = A_0 e^{kt} = (1 \times 10^9)e^{kt}$, where t is the number of years after 1950. Since $2 \times 10^9 = (1 \times 10^9)e^{k(30)}$, we have $e^{30k} = 2$, so $k = \frac{\ln 2}{30} \approx 0.023$. Thus, $A \approx (1 \times 10^9)e^{0.023t}$. We want to find t such that $3.2 \times 10^9 = A(t) = (1 \times 10^9)e^{0.023t}$. Taking logarithms yields

$$t = \frac{\ln(3.2)}{0.023} \approx 50.6 \text{ years.}$$

Thus this model predicts land will have run out by the year 2001.

21. (a) $\dfrac{dT}{dt} = -k(T - A)$, where $A = 68°\text{F}$ is the temperature of the room, and t is time since 9 am.

(b)

$$\int \frac{dT}{T - A} = -\int k\,dt$$
$$\ln|T - A| = -kt + C$$
$$T = A + Be^{-kt}.$$

Using $A = 68$, and $T(0) = 90.3$, we get $B = 22.3$. Thus

$$T = 68 + 22.3e^{-kt}.$$

At $t = 1$, we have

$$89.0 = 68 + 22.3e^{-k}$$
$$21 = 22.3e^{-k}$$
$$k = -\ln\frac{21}{22.3} \approx 0.06.$$

Thus $T = 68 + 22.3e^{-0.06t}$.

We want to know when T was equal to $98.6°\text{F}$, the temperature of a live body, so

$$98.6 = 68 + 22.3e^{-0.06t}$$
$$\ln\frac{30.6}{22.3} = -0.06t$$
$$t = \left(-\frac{1}{0.06}\right)\ln\frac{30.6}{22.3}$$
$$t \approx -5.27.$$

The victim was killed approximately $5\frac{1}{4}$ hours prior to 9 am, at 3:45 am.

22. (a) The differential equation is

$$\frac{dT}{dt} = -k(T - A),$$

where $A = 10°F$ is the outside temperature.

(b) Integrating both sides yields

$$\int \frac{dT}{T - A} = -\int k \, dt.$$

Then $\ln|T - A| = -kt + C$, so $T = A + Be^{-kt}$. Thus

$$T = 10 + 58e^{-kt}.$$

Since 10:00 pm corresponds to $t = 9$,

$$57 = 10 + 58e^{-9k}$$
$$\frac{47}{58} = e^{-9k}$$
$$\ln \frac{47}{58} = -9k$$
$$k = -\frac{1}{9} \ln \frac{47}{58} \approx 0.0234.$$

At 7:00 the next morning ($t = 18$) we have

$$T \approx 10 + 58e^{18(-0.0234)}$$
$$= 10 + 58(0.66)$$
$$\approx 48°F,$$

so the pipes won't freeze.

(c) We assumed that the temperature outside the house stayed constant at $10°F$. This is probably incorrect because the temperature was most likely warmer during the day (between 1 pm and 10 pm) and colder after (between 10 pm and 7 am). Thus, when the temperature in the house dropped from $68°F$ to $57°F$ between 1 pm and 10 pm, the outside temperature was probably higher than $10°F$, which changes our calculation of the value of the constant k. The house temperature will most certainly be lower than $48°F$ at 7 am, but not by much—not enough to freeze.

23. (a) If $C' = -kC$, and then $C = C_0 e^{-kt}$. Since the half-life is 5730 years, $\frac{1}{2}C_0 = C_0 e^{-5730k}$. Solving for k, we have $-5730k = \ln(1/2)$ so $k = \frac{-\ln(1/2)}{5730} \approx 0.000121$.

(b) From the given information, we have $0.91 = e^{-kt}$, where t is the age of the shroud. Solving for t, we have $t = \frac{-\ln 0.91}{k} \approx 779.4$ years.

24. (a) Since speed is the derivative of distance, Galileo's mistaken conjecture was $\frac{dD}{dt} = kD$.

(b) We know that if Galileo's conjecture were true, then $D(t) = D_0 e^{kt}$, where D_0 would be the initial distance fallen. But if we drop an object, it starts out not having traveled any distance, so $D_0 = 0$. This would lead to $D(t) = 0$ for all t.

Solutions for Section 11.6

Exercises

1. (a) If $B = f(t)$, where t is in years,

$$\frac{dB}{dt} = \text{Rate of money earned from interest} + \text{Rate of money deposited}$$
$$\frac{dB}{dt} = 0.10B + 1000.$$

(b) We use separation of variables to solve the differential equation

$$\frac{dB}{dt} = 0.1B + 1000.$$

$$\int \frac{1}{0.1B + 1000} dB = \int dt$$

$$\frac{1}{0.1} \ln |0.1B + 1000| = t + C_1$$

$$0.1B + 1000 = C_2 e^{0.1t}$$

$$B = Ce^{0.1t} - 10{,}000$$

For $t = 0$, $B = 0$, hence $C = 10{,}000$. Therefore, $B = 10{,}000e^{0.1t} - 10{,}000$.

2. (a) There are two factors that are affecting B: the money leaving the account, which is at a constant rate of -2000 per year, and the interest accumulating in it, which accrues at a rate of $(0.08)B$. Since

$$\text{Rate of change of balance} = \text{Rate in} - \text{Rate out},$$

the differential equation for B is

$$\frac{dB}{dt} = 0.08B - 2000.$$

(b) We solve the differential equation by separating variables and then integrating:

$$\int \frac{dB}{0.08B - 2000} = \int dt$$

$$12.5 \ln |0.08B - 2000| = t + C$$

$$\ln |0.08B - 2000| = \frac{t}{12.5} + C$$

$$0.08B - 2000 = \pm e^{0.08t + C}$$

$$B = 25{,}000 + Ae^{0.08t}.$$

(c) (i) If the initial deposit is 20,000, then we have $B = 20{,}000$ when $t = 0$, which leads to $A = -5000$. Knowing A, we can find $B(5)$ as:

$$B(5) = 25{,}000 - 5000e^{0.08(5)} = \$17{,}540.88.$$

(ii) Now $B = 30{,}000$ when $t = 0$ leads to $A = 5000$, giving $B(5) = \$32{,}459.12$.

3. (a) By Newton's Law of Cooling, we have

$$\frac{dH}{dt} = k(H - 50)$$

for some k. Furthermore, we know the juice's original temperature $H(0) = 90$.

(b) Separating variables, we get

$$\int \frac{dH}{(H - 50)} = \int k\, dt.$$

We then integrate:

$$\ln |H - 50| = kt + C$$

$$H - 50 = e^{kt} \cdot A$$

$$H = 50 + Ae^{kt}.$$

Thus, $H(0) = 90$ gives $A = 40$, and $H(5) = 80$ gives

$$50 + 40e^{5k} = 80$$

$$e^{5k} = \frac{30}{40}$$

$$5k = \ln(0.75)$$

$$k = \frac{1}{5} \ln(0.75) \approx -0.05754.$$

Therefore

$$H(t) = 50 + 40e^{-0.05754t}.$$

(c) We now solve for t at which $H(t) = 60$:

$$60 = 50 + 40e^{-0.05754t}$$
$$\frac{1}{4} = e^{-0.05754t}$$
$$\ln(0.25) = -0.05754t$$
$$t = 24 \text{ minutes.}$$

4. Since mg is constant and $a = dv/dt$, differentiating $ma = mg - kv$ gives

$$m\frac{da}{dt} = -k\frac{dv}{dt} = -ma.$$

Thus, the differential equation is

$$\frac{da}{dt} = -\frac{k}{m}a.$$

Solving for a gives

$$a = a_0e^{-kt/m}.$$

At $t = 0$, we have $a = g$, the acceleration due to gravity. Thus, $a_0 = g$, so

$$a = ge^{-kt/m}.$$

Problems

5. (a) Since the rate of change is proportional to the amount present, $dy/dt = ky$ for some constant k.
   (b) Solving the differential equation, we have $y = Ae^{kt}$, where A is the initial amount. Since 100 grams become 54.9 grams in one hour, $54.9 = 100e^k$, so $k = \ln(54.9/100) \approx -0.5997$.
   Thus, after 10 hours, there remains $100e^{(-0.5997)10} \approx 0.2486$ grams.

6. Let $C(t)$ be the current flowing in the circuit at time t, then

$$\frac{dC}{dt} = -\alpha C$$

where $\alpha > 0$ is the constant of proportionality between the rate at which the current decays and the current itself.
   The general solution of this differential equation is $C(t) = Ae^{-\alpha t}$ but since $C(0) = 30$, we have that $A = 30$, and so we get the particular solution $C(t) = 30e^{-\alpha t}$.
   When $t = 0.01$, the current has decayed to 11 amps so that $11 = 30e^{-\alpha 0.01}$ which gives $\alpha = -100\ln(11/30) = 100.33$ so that,

$$C(t) = 30e^{-100.33t}.$$

7. Let $D(t)$ be the quantity of dead leaves, in grams per square centimeter. Then $\frac{dD}{dt} = 3 - 0.75D$, where t is in years. We factor out -0.75 and then separate variables.

$$\frac{dD}{dt} = -0.75(D - 4)$$
$$\int \frac{dD}{D - 4} = \int -0.75 \, dt$$
$$\ln|D - 4| = -0.75t + C$$
$$|D - 4| = e^{-0.75t+C} = e^{-0.75t}e^C$$
$$D = 4 + Ae^{-0.75t}, \text{ where } A = \pm e^C.$$

If initially the ground is clear, the solution looks like the following graph:

The equilibrium level is 4 grams per square centimeter, regardless of the initial condition.

8. (a) If I is intensity and l is the distance traveled through the water, then for some $k > 0$,

$$\frac{dI}{dl} = -kI.$$

(The proportionality constant is negative because intensity decreases with distance). Thus $I = Ae^{-kl}$. Since $I = A$ when $l = 0$, A represents the initial intensity of the light.

(b) If 50% of the light is absorbed in 10 feet, then $0.50A = Ae^{-10k}$, so $e^{-10k} = \frac{1}{2}$, giving

$$k = \frac{-\ln\frac{1}{2}}{10} = \frac{\ln 2}{10}.$$

In 20 feet, the percentage of light left is

$$e^{-\frac{\ln 2}{10}\cdot 20} = e^{-2\ln 2} = (e^{\ln 2})^{-2} = 2^{-2} = \frac{1}{4},$$

so $\frac{3}{4}$ or 75% of the light has been absorbed. Similarly, after 25 feet,

$$e^{-\frac{\ln 2}{10}\cdot 25} = e^{-2.5\ln 2} = (e^{\ln 2})^{-\frac{5}{2}} = 2^{-\frac{5}{2}} \approx 0.177.$$

Approximately 17.7% of the light is left, so 82.3% of the light has been absorbed.

9. Let the depth of the water at time t be y. Then $\frac{dy}{dt} = -k\sqrt{y}$, where k is a positive constant. Separating variables,

$$\int \frac{dy}{\sqrt{y}} = -\int k\,dt,$$

so

$$2\sqrt{y} = -kt + C.$$

When $t = 0$, $y = 36$; $2\sqrt{36} = -k \cdot 0 + C$, so $C = 12$.
When $t = 1$, $y = 35$; $2\sqrt{35} = -k + 12$, so $k \approx 0.17$.
Thus, $2\sqrt{y} \approx -0.17t + 12$. We are looking for t such that $y = 0$; this happens when $t \approx \frac{12}{0.17} \approx 71$ hours, or about 3 days.

10. We are given that the rate of change of pressure with respect to volume, dP/dV is proportional to P/V, so that

$$\frac{dP}{dV} = k\frac{P}{V}.$$

Using separation of variables and integrating gives

$$\int \frac{dP}{P} = k\int \frac{dV}{V}.$$

Evaluating these integral gives

$$\ln P = k\ln V + c$$

or equivalently,

$$P = AV^k.$$

11. (a) Since the rate of change of the weight is equal to

$$\frac{1}{3500}(\text{Intake} - \text{Amount to maintain weight})$$

we have

$$\frac{dW}{dt} = \frac{1}{3500}(I - 20W).$$

(b) Starting off with the equation

$$\frac{dW}{dt} = -\frac{2}{350}\left(W - \frac{I}{20}\right),$$

we separate variables and integrate:

$$\int \frac{dW}{W - \frac{I}{20}} = -\int \frac{2}{350}\, dt.$$

Thus we have

$$\ln\left|W - \frac{I}{20}\right| = -\frac{2}{350}t + C$$

so that

$$W - \frac{I}{20} = Ae^{-\frac{2}{350}t}$$

or in other words

$$W = \frac{I}{20} + Ae^{-\frac{2}{350}t}.$$

Let us call the person's initial weight W_0 at $t = 0$. Then $W_0 = \frac{I}{20} + Ce^0$, so $C = W_0 - \frac{I}{20}$. Thus

$$W = \frac{I}{20} + \left(W_0 - \frac{I}{20}\right)e^{-\frac{2}{350}t}.$$

(c) Using part (b), we have $W = 150 + 10e^{-\frac{2}{350}t}$. This means that $W \to 150$ as $t \to \infty$. See the following figure.

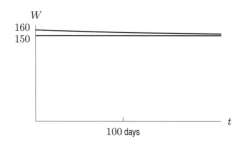

12. Since the rate at which the volume, V, is decreasing is proportional to the surface area, A, we have

$$\frac{dV}{dt} = -kA,$$

where the negative sign reflects the fact that V is decreasing. Suppose the radius of the sphere is r. Then $V = \frac{4}{3}\pi r^3$ and, using the chain rule, $\frac{dV}{dt} = 4\pi r^2 \frac{dr}{dt}$. The surface area of a sphere is given by $A = 4\pi r^2$. Thus

$$4\pi r^2 \frac{dr}{dt} = -k4\pi r^2$$

so

$$\frac{dr}{dt} = -k.$$

Since the radius decreases from 1 cm to 0.5 cm in 1 month, we have $k = 0.5$ cm/month. Thus

$$\frac{dr}{dt} = -0.5$$

so

$$r = -0.5t + r_0.$$

Since $r = 1$ when $t = 0$, we have $r_0 = 1$, so

$$r = -0.5t + 1.$$

We want to find t when $r = 0.2$, so

$$0.2 = -0.5t + 1$$

and

$$t = \frac{0.8}{0.5} = 1.6 \text{ months.}$$

13. Let $V(t)$ be the volume of water in the tank at time t, then

$$\frac{dV}{dt} = k\sqrt{V}$$

This is a separable equation which has the solution

$$V(t) = (\frac{kt}{2} + C)^2$$

Since $V(0) = 200$ this gives $200 = C^2$ so

$$V(t) = (\frac{kt}{2} + \sqrt{200})^2.$$

However, $V(1) = 180$ therefore

$$180 = (\frac{k}{2} + \sqrt{200})^2,$$

so that $k = 2\left(\sqrt{180} - \sqrt{200}\right) = -1.45146$. Therefore,

$$V(t) = (-0.726t + \sqrt{200})^2.$$

The tank will be half-empty when $V(t) = 100$, so we solve

$$100 = (-0.726t + \sqrt{200})^2$$

to obtain $t = 5.7$ days. The tank will be half empty in 5.7 days.
The volume after 4 days is $V(4)$ which is approximately 126.32 liters.

14. (a) If P = pressure and h = height, $\frac{dP}{dh} = -3.7 \times 10^{-5}P$, so $P = P_0 e^{-3.7 \times 10^{-5}h}$. Now $P_0 = 29.92$, since pressure at sea level (when $h = 0$) is 29.92, so $P = 29.92e^{-3.7 \times 10^{-5}h}$. At the top of Mt. Whitney, the pressure is

$$P = 29.92e^{-3.7 \times 10^{-5}(14500)} \approx 17.50 \text{ inches of mercury.}$$

At the top of Mt. Everest, the pressure is

$$P = 29.92e^{-3.7 \times 10^{-5}(29000)} \approx 10.23 \text{ inches of mercury.}$$

(b) The pressure is 15 inches of mercury when

$$15 = 29.92e^{-3.7 \times 10^{-5}h}$$

Solving for h gives $h = \frac{-1}{3.7 \times 10^{-5}} \ln(\frac{15}{29.92}) \approx 18{,}661.5$ feet.

15. We are given that

$$BC = 2OC.$$

If the point A has coordinates (x, y) then $OC = x$ and $AC = y$. The slope of the tangent line, y', is given by

$$y' = \frac{AC}{BC} = \frac{y}{BC},$$

so

$$BC = \frac{y}{y'}.$$

Substitution into $BC = 2OC$ gives

$$\frac{y}{y'} = 2x,$$

so

$$\frac{y'}{y} = \frac{1}{2x}.$$

Separating variables to integrate this differential equation gives

$$\int \frac{dy}{y} = \int \frac{dx}{2x}$$

$$\ln|y| = \frac{1}{2}\ln|x| + C = \ln\sqrt{|x|} + \ln A$$

$$|y| = A\sqrt{|x|}$$

$$y = \pm(A\sqrt{x}).$$

Thus, in the first quadrant, the curve has equation $y = A\sqrt{x}$.

16. (a) For this situation,

$$\left(\begin{array}{c} \text{Rate money added} \\ \text{to account} \end{array} \right) = \left(\begin{array}{c} \text{Rate money added} \\ \text{via interest} \end{array} \right) + \left(\begin{array}{c} \text{Rate money} \\ \text{deposited} \end{array} \right)$$

Translating this into an equation yields

$$\frac{dB}{dt} = 0.1B + 1200.$$

(b) Solving this equation via separation of variables gives

$$\frac{dB}{dt} = 0.1B + 1200$$

$$= (0.1)(B + 12000)$$

So

$$\int \frac{dB}{B + 12000} = \int 0.1 \, dt$$

and

$$\ln|B + 12000| = 0.1t + C$$

solving for B,

$$|B + 12000| = e^{(0.1)t + C} = e^C e^{(0.1)t}$$

or

$$B = Ae^{0.1t} - 12000, \text{ (where } A = e^c)$$

We may find A using the initial condition $B_0 = f(0) = 0$

$$A - 12000 = 0 \quad \text{or} \quad A = 12000$$

(c) After 5 years, the balance is

$$B = f(5) = 12{,}000(e^{(0.1)(5)} - 1)$$

$$\approx 7784.66 \text{ dollars.}$$

17. (a) The balance in the account at the beginning of the month is given by the following sum

$$\left(\begin{array}{c} \text{balance in} \\ \text{account} \end{array} \right) = \left(\begin{array}{c} \text{previous month's} \\ \text{balance} \end{array} \right) + \left(\begin{array}{c} \text{interest on} \\ \text{previous month's balance} \end{array} \right) + \left(\begin{array}{c} \text{monthly deposit} \\ \text{of \$100} \end{array} \right)$$

Denote month i's balance by B_i. Assuming the interest is compounded continuously, we have

$$\left(\begin{array}{c} \text{previous month's} \\ \text{balance} \end{array} \right) + \left(\begin{array}{c} \text{interest on previous} \\ \text{month's balance} \end{array} \right) = B_{i-1}e^{0.1/12}.$$

Since the interest rate is $10\% = 0.1$ per year, interest is $\frac{0.1}{12}$ per month. So at month i, the balance is

$$B_i = B_{i-1}e^{\frac{0.1}{12}} + 100$$

Explicitly, we have for the five years (60 months) the equations:

$$B_0 = 0$$
$$B_1 = B_0 e^{\frac{0.1}{12}} + 100$$
$$B_2 = B_1 e^{\frac{0.1}{12}} + 100$$
$$B_3 = B_2 e^{\frac{0.1}{12}} + 100$$
$$\vdots \quad \vdots$$
$$B_{60} = B_{59} e^{\frac{0.1}{12}} + 100$$

In other words,

$$B_1 = 100$$
$$B_2 = 100 e^{\frac{0.1}{12}} + 100$$
$$B_3 = (100 e^{\frac{0.1}{12}} + 100) e^{\frac{0.1}{12}} + 100$$
$$\quad = 100 e^{\frac{(0.1)2}{12}} + 100 e^{\frac{0.1}{12}} + 100$$
$$B_4 = 100 e^{\frac{(0.1)3}{12}} + 100 e^{\frac{(0.1)2}{12}} + 100 e^{\frac{(0.1)}{12}} + 100$$
$$\vdots \quad \vdots$$
$$B_{60} = 100 e^{\frac{(0.1)59}{12}} + 100 e^{\frac{(0.1)58}{12}} + \cdots + 100 e^{\frac{(0.1)1}{12}} + 100$$
$$B_{60} = \sum_{k=0}^{59} 100 e^{\frac{(0.1)k}{12}}$$

(b) The sum $B_{60} = \sum_{k=0}^{59} 100 e^{\frac{(0.1)k}{12}}$ can be written as $B_{60} = \sum_{k=0}^{59} 1200 e^{\frac{(0.1)k}{12}} \left(\frac{1}{12}\right)$ which is the left Riemann sum for

$\int_0^5 1200 e^{0.1t} dt$, with $\Delta t = \frac{1}{12}$ and $N = 60$. Evaluating the sum on a calculator gives $B_{60} = 7752.26$.

(c) The situation described by this problem is almost the same as that in Problem 16, except that here the money is being deposited once a month rather than continuously; however the nominal yearly rates are the same. Thus we would expect the balance after 5 years to be approximately the same in each case. This means that the answer to part (b) of this problem should be approximately the same as the answer to part (c) to Problem 16. Since the deposits in this problem start at the end of the first month, as opposed to right away, we would expect the balance after 5 years to be slightly smaller than in Problem 16, as is the case.

Alternatively, we can use the Fundamental Theorem of Calculus to show that the integral can be computed exactly

$$\int_0^5 1200 e^{0.1t} dt = 12000(e^{(0.1)5} - 1) = 7784.66$$

Thus $\int_0^5 1200 e^{0.1t} dt$ represents the exact solution to Problem 16. Since $1200 e^{0.1t}$ is an increasing function, the left hand sum we calculated in part (b) of this problem underestimates the integral. Thus the answer to part (b) of this problem should be less than the answer to part (c) of Problem 16.

18. (a) The quantity and the concentration both increase with time. As the concentration increases, the rate at which the drug is excreted also increases, and so the rate at which the drug builds up in the blood decreases; thus the graph of concentration against time is concave down. The concentration rises until the rate of excretion exactly balances the rate at which the drug is entering; at this concentration there is a horizontal asymptote. (See Figure 11.19.)

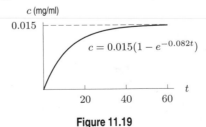

Figure 11.19

(b) Let's start by writing a differential equation for the quantity, $Q(t)$.

$$\text{Rate at which quantity of drug changes} = \text{Rate in} - \text{Rate out}$$

$$\frac{dQ}{dt} = 43.2 - 0.082Q$$

where Q is measured in mg. We want an equation for concentration $c(t) = Q(t)/v$, where $c(t)$ is measured in mg/ml and v is volume, so $v = 35,000$ ml.

$$\frac{1}{v}\frac{dQ}{dt} = \frac{43.2}{v} - 0.082\frac{Q}{v},$$

giving

$$\frac{dc}{dt} = \frac{43.2}{35,000} - 0.082c.$$

(c) Factor out -0.082 and separate variables to solve.

$$\frac{dc}{dt} = -0.082(c - 0.015)$$

$$\int \frac{dc}{c - 0.015} = -0.082 \int dt$$

$$\ln|c - 0.015| = -0.082t + B$$

$$c - 0.015 = Ae^{-0.082t} \quad \text{where} \quad A = \pm e^B$$

Since $c = 0$ when $t = 0$, we have $A = -0.015$, so

$$c = 0.015 - 0.015e^{-0.082t} = 0.015(1 - e^{-0.082t}).$$

Thus $c \to 0.015$ mg/ml as $t \to \infty$.

19. (a) $\dfrac{dy}{dt} = -k(y - a)$, where $k > 0$ and a are constants.

(b) $\displaystyle\int \frac{dy}{y - a} = \int -k\,dt$, so $\ln|y - a| = \ln(y - a) = -kt + C$. Thus, $y - a = Ae^{-kt}$ where $A = e^C$. Initially nothing has been forgotten, so $y(0) = 1$. Therefore, $1 - a = Ae^0 = A$, so $y - a = (1 - a)e^{-kt}$ or $y = (1 - a)e^{-kt} + a$.

(c) As $t \to \infty$, $e^{-kt} \to 0$, so $y \to a$.

Thus, a represents the fraction of material which is remembered in the long run. The constant k tells us about the rate at which material is forgotten.

20. (a) We have

$$\frac{dp}{dt} = -k(p - p^*),$$

where k is constant. Notice that $k > 0$, since if $p > p^*$ then dp/dt should be negative, and if $p < p^*$ then dp/dt should be positive.

(b) Separating variables, we have

$$\int \frac{dp}{p - p^*} = \int -k\,dt.$$

Solving, we find $p = p^* + (p_0 - p^*)e^{-kt}$, where p_0 is the initial price.

(c) See Figure 11.20.

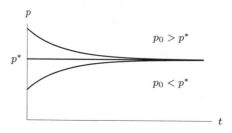

Figure 11.20

(d) As $t \to \infty$, $p \to p^*$. We see this in the solution in part (b), since as $t \to \infty$, $e^{-kt} \to 0$. In other words, as $t \to \infty$, p approaches the equilibrium price p^*.

21. (a)

$$\frac{dQ}{dt} = r - \alpha Q = -\alpha(Q - \frac{r}{\alpha})$$

$$\int \frac{dQ}{Q - r/\alpha} = = -\alpha \int dt$$

$$\ln \left| Q - \frac{r}{\alpha} \right| = -\alpha t + C$$

$$Q - \frac{r}{\alpha} = Ae^{-\alpha t}$$

When $t = 0$, $Q = 0$, so $A = -\frac{r}{\alpha}$ and

$$Q = \frac{r}{\alpha}(1 - e^{-\alpha t})$$

So,

$$Q_\infty = \lim_{t \to \infty} Q = \frac{r}{\alpha}.$$

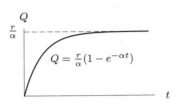

(b) Doubling r doubles Q_∞. Since $Q_\infty = r/\alpha$, the time to reach $\frac{1}{2}Q_\infty$ is obtained by solving

$$\frac{r}{2\alpha} = \frac{r}{\alpha}(1 - e^{-\alpha t})$$

$$\frac{1}{2} = 1 - e^{-\alpha t}$$

$$e^{-\alpha t} = \frac{1}{2}$$

$$t = -\frac{\ln(1/2)}{\alpha} = \frac{\ln 2}{\alpha}.$$

So altering r doesn't alter the time it takes to reach $\frac{1}{2}Q_\infty$. See Figure 11.21.

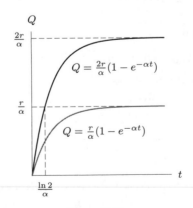

Figure 11.21

(c) Q_∞ is halved by doubling α, and so is the time, $t = \frac{\ln 2}{\alpha}$, to reach $\frac{1}{2}Q_\infty$.

22. (a) Concentration of carbon monoxide = $\dfrac{\text{Quantity in room}}{\text{Volume}}$.

If $Q(t)$ represents the quantity of carbon monoxide in the room at time t, $c(t) = Q(t)/60$.

$$\begin{array}{c}\text{Rate quantity of}\\ \text{carbon monoxide in room} \quad = \text{rate in} - \text{rate out}\\ \text{changes}\end{array}$$

Now

$$\text{Rate in} = 5\%(0.002\text{m}^3/\text{min}) = 0.05(0.002) = 0.0001\text{m}^3/\text{min}.$$

Since smoky air is leaving at $0.002\text{m}^3/\text{min}$, containing a concentration $c(t) = Q(t)/60$ of carbon monoxide

$$\text{Rate out} = 0.002\frac{Q(t)}{60}$$

Thus

$$\frac{dQ}{dt} = 0.0001 - \frac{0.002}{60}Q$$

Since $c = Q/60$, we can substitute $Q = 60c$, giving

$$\frac{d(60c)}{dt} = 0.0001 - \frac{0.002}{60}(60c)$$

$$\frac{dc}{dt} = \frac{0.0001}{60} - \frac{0.002}{60}c$$

(b) Factoring the right side of the differential equation and separating gives

$$\frac{dc}{dt} = -\frac{0.0001}{3}(c - 0.05) \approx 3 \times 10^{-5}(c - 0.05)$$

$$\int \frac{dc}{c - 0.05} = -\int 3 \times 10^{-5}dt$$

$$\ln|c - 0.05| = -3 \times 10^{-5}t + K$$

$$c - 0.05 = Ae^{-3\times10^{-5}t} \quad \text{where} A = \pm e^K.$$

Since $c = 0$ when $t = 0$, we have $A = -0.05$, so

$$c = 0.05 - 0.05e^{-3\times10^{-5}t}$$

(c) As $t \to \infty$, $e^{-3\times10^{-5}t} \to 0$ so $c \to 0.05$.

Thus in the long run, the concentration of carbon monoxide tends to 5%, the concentration of the incoming air.

23. $c = 0.05 - 0.05e^{-3\times10^{-5}t}$

We want to solve for t when $c = 0.001$

$$0.001 = 0.05 - 0.05e^{-3\times10^{-5}t}$$

$$-0.049 = -0.05e^{-3\times10^{-5}t}$$

$$e^{-3\times10^{-5}t} = 0.98$$

$$t = \frac{-\ln(0.98)}{3 \times 10^{-5}} = 673 \text{ min} \approx 11 \text{ hours } 13 \text{ min.}$$

24. (a) Now

$$\frac{dS}{dt} = (\text{Rate at which salt enters the pool}) - (\text{Rate at which salt leaves the pool}),$$

and, for example,

$$\left(\begin{array}{c}\text{Rate at which salt}\\ \text{enters the pool}\end{array}\right) = \left(\begin{array}{c}\text{Concentration of}\\ \text{salt solution}\end{array}\right) \times \left(\begin{array}{c}\text{Flow rate of}\\ \text{salt solution}\end{array}\right)$$

$$(\text{grams/minute}) = (\text{grams/liter}) \times (\text{liters/minute})$$

so

Rate at which salt enters the pool $=$

$(10 \text{ grams/liter}) \times (60 \text{ liters/minute}) = (600 \text{ grams/minute})$

The rate at which salt leaves the pool depends on the concentration of salt in the pool. At time t, the concentration is $\frac{S(t)}{2 \times 10^6 \text{ liters}}$, where $S(t)$ is measured in grams.
Thus

Rate at which salt leaves the pool $=$

$$\frac{S(t) \text{ grams}}{2 \times 10^6 \text{ liters}} \times \frac{60 \text{ liters}}{\text{minute}} = \frac{3S(t) \text{ grams}}{10^5 \text{ minutes}}.$$

Thus

$$\frac{dS}{dt} = 600 - \frac{3S}{100{,}000}.$$

(b) $\frac{dS}{dt} = -\frac{3}{100{,}000}(S - 20{,}000{,}000)$

$\int \frac{dS}{S - 20{,}000{,}000} = \int -\frac{3}{100{,}000} \, dt$

$\ln |S - 20{,}000{,}000| = -\frac{3}{100{,}000} t + C$

$S = 20{,}000{,}000 - Ae^{-\frac{3}{100{,}000}t}$

Since $S = 0$ at $t = 0$, $A = 20{,}000{,}000$. Thus $S(t) = 20{,}000{,}000 - 20{,}000{,}000e^{-\frac{3}{100{,}000}t}$.

(c) As $t \to \infty$, $e^{-\frac{3}{100{,}000}t} \to 0$, so $S(t) \to 20{,}000{,}000$ grams. The concentration approaches 10 grams/liter. Note that this makes sense; we'd expect the concentration of salt in the pool to become closer and closer to the concentration of salt being poured into the pool as $t \to \infty$.

25. (a) Newton's Law of Motion says that

Force $=$ (mass) $\times$ (acceleration).

Since acceleration, dv/dt, is measured upward and the force due to gravity acts downward,

$$-\frac{mgR^2}{(R+h)^2} = m\frac{dv}{dt}$$

so

$$\frac{dv}{dt} = -\frac{gR^2}{(R+h)^2}.$$

(b) Since $v = \frac{dh}{dt}$, the chain rule gives

$$\frac{dv}{dt} = \frac{dv}{dh} \cdot \frac{dh}{dt} = \frac{dv}{dh} \cdot v.$$

Substituting into the differential equation in part (a) gives

$$v\frac{dv}{dh} = -\frac{gR^2}{(R+h)^2}.$$

(c) Separating variables gives

$$\int v \, dv = -\int \frac{gR^2}{(R+h)^2} \, dh$$

$$\frac{v^2}{2} = \frac{gR^2}{(R+h)} + C$$

Since $v = v_0$ when $h = 0$,

$$\frac{v_0{}^2}{2} = \frac{gR^2}{(R+0)} + C \quad \text{gives} \quad C = \frac{v_0{}^2}{2} - gR,$$

so the solution is

$$\frac{v^2}{2} = \frac{gR^2}{(R+h)} + \frac{v_0{}^2}{2} - gR$$

$$v^2 = v_0{}^2 + \frac{2gR^2}{(R+h)} - 2gR$$

(d) The escape velocity v_0 ensures that $v^2 \geq 0$ for all $h \geq 0$. Since the positive quantity $\dfrac{2gR^2}{(R+h)} \to 0$ as $h \to \infty$, to ensure that $v^2 \geq 0$ for all h, we must have

$$v_0{}^2 \geq 2gR.$$

When $v_0{}^2 = 2gR$ so $v_0 = \sqrt{2gR}$, we say that v_0 is the escape velocity.

Solutions for Section 11.7

Exercises

1. A continuous growth rate of 0.2% means that

$$\frac{1}{P}\frac{dP}{dt} = 0.2\% = 0.002.$$

Separating variables and integrating gives

$$\int \frac{dP}{P} = \int 0.002\,dt$$
$$P = P_0 e^{0.002t} = (6.6 \times 10^6)e^{0.002t}.$$

2. (a) At $t = 0$, which corresponds to 1935, we have

$$P = \frac{1}{1 + 2.968e^{-0.0275(0)}} = 0.252$$

showing that about 25% of the land was in use in 1935.

(b) This model predicts that as t gets very large, P will approach 1. That is, the model predicts that in the long run, all the land will be used for farming.

(c) To solve this graphically, enter the function into a graphing calculator and trace the resulting curve until it reaches a height of 0.5, which occurs when $t \approx 39.6$. Since $t = 0$ corresponds to 1935, $t = 39.6$ corresponds to $1935 + 39.6 = 1974.6$. According to this model, the Tojolobal were using half their land in 1974. Alternatively, we solve for t:

$$\frac{1}{1 + 2.968e^{-0.0275t}} = 0.5$$
$$1 + 2.968e^{-0.0275t} = 2$$
$$2.968e^{-0.0275t} = 1$$
$$e^{-0.0275t} = \frac{1}{2.968}$$
$$t = \frac{\ln(1/2.968)}{-0.0275} = 39.6 \text{ years.}$$

(d) The inflection point occurs when $P = L/2$ or at one-half the carrying capacity. In this case, $P = \frac{1}{2}$ in 1974, as shown in part (c).

3. (a)

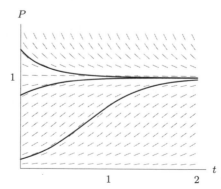

(b) The value $P = 1$ is a stable equilibrium. (See part (d) below for a more detailed discussion.)

(c) Looking at the solution curves, we see that P is increasing for $0 < P < 1$ and decreasing for $P > 1$. The values of $P = 0$, $P = 1$ are equilibria. In the long run, P tends to 1, unless you start with $P = 0$. The solution curves with initial populations of less than $P = \frac{1}{2}$ have inflection points at $P = \frac{1}{2}$. (This will be demonstrated algebraically in part (d) below.) At the inflection point, the population is growing fastest.

(d)

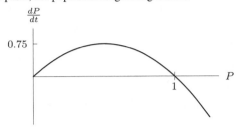

Since $\frac{dP}{dt} = 3P - 3P^2 = 3P(1 - P)$, the graph of $\frac{dP}{dt}$ against P is a parabola, opening downward with P intercepts at 0 and 1. The quantity $\frac{dP}{dt}$ is positive for $0 < P < 1$, negative for $P > 1$ (and $P < 0$). The quantity $\frac{dP}{dt}$ is 0 at $P = 0$ and $P = 1$, and maximum at $P = \frac{1}{2}$. The fact that $\frac{dP}{dt} = 0$ at $P = 0$ and $P = 1$ tells us that these are equilibria. Further, since $\frac{dP}{dt} > 0$ for $0 < P < 1$, we see that solution curves starting here will increase toward $P = 1$.

If the population starts at a value $P < \frac{1}{2}$, it increases at an increasing rate up to $P = \frac{1}{2}$. After this, P continues to increase, but at a decreasing rate. The fact that $\frac{dP}{dt}$ has a maximum at $P = \frac{1}{2}$ tells us that there is a point of inflection when $P = \frac{1}{2}$. Similarly, since $\frac{dP}{dt} < 0$ for $P > 1$, solution curves starting with $P > 1$ will decrease to $P = 1$. Thus, $P = 1$ is a stable equilibrium.

Problems

4. The US population in 1860 was 31.4 million. If between 1860 and 1870 the population had increased at the same rate as previous decades, 34.7%, the population in 1870 would have been $(31.4 \text{ million})(1.347) = 42.3$ million. In actuality the US population in 1870 was only 38.6 million. This is a shortfall of 3.7 million people.

History records that about 618,000 soldiers died (total, both sides) during the Civil War (according to Collier's Encyclopedia, 1968). This accounts for only $\frac{1}{6}$ (roughly) of the shortfall. The rest of the shortfall can be attributed to civilian deaths and a decrease in the birth rate caused by absent males and an unwillingness to have babies under harsh economic conditions and political uncertainty.

5. (a) The logistic model is a reasonable one because at first very few houses have a VCR. As movie rentals become popular and as VCRs get cheaper, more people will buy VCRs. However, we know that the rate of VCR buying will start slowing down at some point as it is impossible for more than 100% of houses to have VCRs.

(b) To find the point of inflection, we must find the year at which the rate of VCR buying changes from increasing to decreasing. The following table shows the rate of change in the years from 1978 to 1990.

Year	1978	1979	1980	1981	1982	1983	1984
% Change per year	0.2	0.6	0.7	1.3	2.4	5.1	10.2
Year	1985	1986	1987	1988	1989	1990	1991
% Change per year	15.2	12.7	9.3	6.6	7.3	0	

Looking at the table, we see that the rate of percent change per year changes from increasing to decreasing in the year 1986. At this time 36% of households own VCRs giving $P = (1986, 36)$. Since at the inflection point we expect the vertical coordinate to be $L/2$, we get

$$L/2 = 36$$
$$L = 72\%.$$

Thus we expect the limiting value to be 72%. This fits in well with the data that we have for 1990 and 1991.

(c) Since the general form of a logistic equation is

$$P = \frac{L}{1 + Ce^{-kt}}$$

where L is the limiting value, we have that in our case $L = 75$ and the limiting value is 75%.

6. Rewriting the equation as $\frac{1}{P}\frac{dP}{dt} = \frac{(100-P)}{1000}$, we see that this is a logistic equation. Before looking at its solution, we explain why there must always be at least 100 individuals. Since the population begins at 200, $\frac{dP}{dt}$ is initially negative, so the population decreases. It continues to do so while $P > 100$. If the population ever reached 100, however, then $\frac{dP}{dt}$ would be 0. This means the population would stop changing – so if the population ever decreased to 100, that's where it would stay. The fact that $\frac{dP}{dt}$ will always be negative also shows that the population will always be under 200, as shown below.

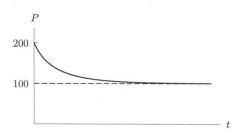

The solution, as given by the formula derived in the chapter, is

$$P = \frac{20000}{200 - 100e^{-t/10}}$$

7.

Table 11.15

Year	P	$\frac{dP}{dt} \approx \frac{P(t+10)-P(t-10)}{20}$
1790	3.9	
1800	5.3	$(7.2 - 3.9)/20 = 0.165$
1810	7.2	$(9.6 - 5.3)/20 = 0.215$
1820	9.6	$(12.9 - 7.2)/20 = 0.285$
1830	12.9	$(17.1 - 9.6)/20 = 0.375$
1840	17.1	$(23.2 - 12.9)/20 = 0.515$
1850	23.2	$(31.4 - 17.1)/20 = 0.715$
1860	31.4	$(38.6 - 23.2)/20 = 0.770$
1870	38.6	$(50.2 - 31.4)/20 = 0.940$
1880	50.2	$(62.9 - 38.6)/20 = 1.215$
1890	62.9	$(76.0 - 50.2)/20 = 1.290$
1900	76.0	$(92.0 - 62.9)/20 = 1.455$
1910	92.0	$(105.7 - 76.0)/20 = 1.485$
1920	105.7	$(122.8 - 92.0)/20 = 1.540$
1930	122.8	$(131.7 - 105.7)/20 = 1.300$
1940	131.7	$(150.7 - 122.8)/20 = 1.395$
1950	150.7	

According to these calculations, the largest value of dP/dt occurs in 1920 when the rate of change is $\frac{dP}{dt} = 1.540$ million people/year. The population in 1920 was 105.7 million. If we assume that the limiting value, L, is twice the population when it is changing most quickly, then $L = 2 \times 105.7 = 211.4$ million. This is greater than the estimate of 187 million computed in the text and closer to the actual 1990 population of 248.7 million.

8. (a) The equilibrium population will be reached when dP/dt approaches zero. Solving $1 - 0.0004P = 0$ gives $P = 2500$ fish as the equilibrium population.

(b) The solution of the differential equation is

$$P(t) = \frac{2500}{(1 + Ae^{-0.25t})}$$

subject to $P(-10) = 1000$ if $t = 0$ represents the present time. So we have

$$1000 = \frac{2500}{(1 + Ae^{2.5})}$$

from which $A = 0.123127$ and

$$P(0) = \frac{2500}{(1 + 0.123127)} \approx 2230.$$

Therefore, the current population is approximately 2230 fish.

(c) The effect of losing 10% of the fish each year gives the revised differential equation

$$\frac{dP}{dt} = (0.25 - 0.0001P)P - 0.1P$$

or

$$\frac{dP}{dt} = (0.15 - 0.0001P)P.$$

The revised equilibrium population is therefore about 1500 fish.

9. (a) We know that a logistic curve can be modeled by the function

$$P = \frac{L}{1 + Ce^{-kt}}$$

where $C = (L - P_0)/(P_0)$ and P is the number of people infected by the virus at a particular time t. We know that L is the limiting value, or the maximal number of people infected with the virus, so in our case

$$L = 5000.$$

We are also told that initially there are only ten people infected with the virus so that we get

$$P_0 = 10.$$

Thus we have

$$\begin{aligned}
C &= \frac{L - P_0}{P_0} \\
&= \frac{5000 - 10}{10} \\
&= 499.
\end{aligned}$$

We are also told that in the early stages of the virus, infection grows exponentially with $k = 1.78$. Thus we get that the logistic function for people infected is

$$P = \frac{5000}{1 + 499e^{-1.78t}}.$$

(b)

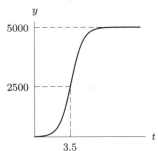

(c) Looking at the graph we see that the the point at which the rate changes from increasing to decreasing, the inflection point, occurs at roughly $t = 3.5$ giving a value of $P = 2500$. Thus after roughly 2500 people have been infected, the rate of infection starts dropping. See above.

10. (a) Let the population at time t be $P(t)$ and the relative growth rate be $G = \alpha - \beta P$. When $P = 600$, $G = 35 - 15 = 20\%$, and when $P = 800$, $G = 30 - 20 = 10\%$ so

$$\alpha - 600\beta = 0.20$$

$$\alpha - 800\beta = 0.10.$$

Therefore, $\alpha = \frac{1}{2}$ and $\beta = \frac{1}{2000}$, hence

$$\frac{1}{P}\frac{dP}{dt} = \frac{1}{2} - \frac{1}{2000}P.$$

(b) The differential equation is a logistic equation

$$\frac{dP}{dt} = \frac{1}{2000}P(1000 - P)$$

and so the equilibrium population is $P = 1000$. We expect the population of 900 to increase to the equilibrium value of 1000.

(c) If the additional elk are added, the population of 1350 elk is above the equilibrium value, and the population will decrease to about 1000.

(d)

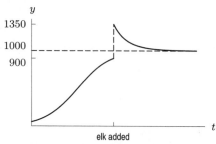

elk added

Importing more elk would be ecologically unsound, as the new population is in excess of the equilibrium population that Reading Island can support.

11. (a) Let I be the number of informed people at time t, and I_0 the number who know initially. Then this model predicts that $\frac{dI}{dt} = k(M - I)$ for some positive constant k. Solving this, we find the solution is

$$I = M - (M - I_0)e^{-kt}.$$

We sketch the solution with $I_0 = 0$. Notice that $\frac{dI}{dt}$ is largest when I is smallest, so the information spreads fastest in the beginning, at $t = 0$. In addition, the graph below shows that $I \to M$ as $t \to \infty$, meaning that everyone gets the information eventually.

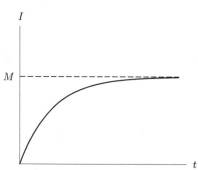

(b) In this case, the model suggests that $\frac{dI}{dt} = kI(M - I)$ for some positive constant k. This is a logistic model with carrying capacity M. We sketch the solutions for three different values of I_0 below.

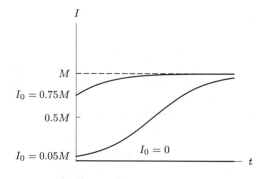

(i) If $I_0 = 0$ then $I = 0$ for all t. In other words, if nobody knows something, it does not spread by word of mouth!

(ii) If $I_0 = 0.05M$, then $\frac{dI}{dt}$ is increasing up to $I = \frac{M}{2}$. Thus, the information is spreading fastest at $I = \frac{M}{2}$.

(iii) If $I_0 = 0.75M$, then $\frac{dI}{dt}$ is always decreasing for $I > \frac{M}{2}$, so $\frac{dI}{dt}$ is largest when $t = 0$.

12. (a) By the chain rule

$$\frac{dP}{dt} = \frac{d}{dt}\left(\frac{1}{u}\right) = \frac{d}{du}\left(\frac{1}{u}\right) \cdot \frac{du}{dt} = -\frac{1}{u^2}\frac{du}{dt}$$

(b) Substituting for $P = 1/u$ in the equation

$$\frac{dP}{dt} = kP\left(1 - \frac{P}{L}\right)$$

gives

$$-\frac{1}{u^2}\frac{du}{dt} = k\frac{1}{u}\left(1 - \frac{1}{Lu}\right).$$

Simplifying leads to

$$\frac{du}{dt} = -k\left(u - \frac{1}{L}\right)$$

and separating variables gives

$$\int \frac{du}{u - 1/L} = -\int k\,dt$$

$$\ln\left|u - \frac{1}{L}\right| = -kt + C$$

$$u - \frac{1}{L} = Ae^{-kt} \quad \text{where } A = \pm e^C$$

$$u = \frac{1}{L} + Ae^{-kt}$$

(c) Since $u = 1/P$, we have

$$\frac{1}{P} = \frac{1}{L} + Ae^{-kt} = \frac{1 + LAe^{-kt}}{L}$$

so

$$P = \frac{L}{1 + LAe^{-kt}} \quad \text{where } A \text{ is an arbitrary constant.}$$

13.

(a)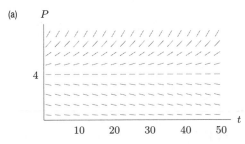

(b)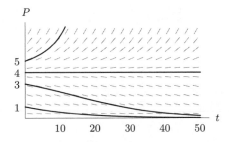

(c) There are two equilibrium values, $P = 0$, and $P = 4$. The first, representing extinction, is stable. The equilibrium value $P = 4$ is unstable because the populations increase if greater than 4, and decrease if less than 4. Notice that the equilibrium values can be obtained by setting $dP/dt = 0$:

$$\frac{dP}{dt} = 0.02P^2 - 0.08P = 0.02P(P - 4) = 0$$

so

$$P = 0 \text{ or } P = 4.$$

14. (a)

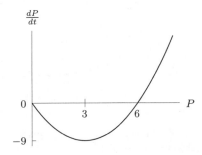

Figure 11.22

(b) Figure 11.22 shows that for $0 < P < 6$, the sign of dP/dt is negative. This means that P is decreasing over the interval $0 < P < 6$. As P decreases from $P(0) = 5$, the value of dP/dt gets more and more negative until $P = 3$. Thus the graph of P against t is concave down while P is decreasing from 5 to 3. As P decreases below 3, the slope of dP/dt increases toward 0, so the graph of P against t is concave up and asymptotic to the t-axis. At $P = 3$, there is an inflection point. See Figure 11.23.

(c) Figure 11.22 shows that for $P > 6$, the slope of dP/dt is positive and increases with P. Thus the graph of P against t is increasing and concave up. See Figure 11.23.

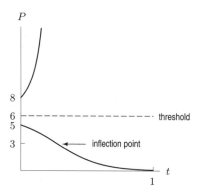

Figure 11.23

(d) For initial populations greater than the threshold value $P = 6$, the population increases without bound. Populations with initial value less than $P = 6$ decrease asymptotically toward 0, i.e. become extinct. Thus the initial population $P = 6$ is the dividing line, or threshold, between populations which grow without bound and those which die out.

15. (a)

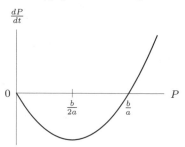

Figure 11.24

(b)

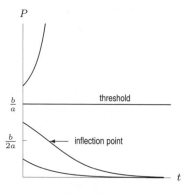

Figure 11.25

Figure 11.24 shows that dP/dt is negative for $P < \frac{b}{a}$, making P a decreasing function when $P(0) < \frac{b}{a}$. When $P > \frac{b}{a}$, the sign of dP/dt is positive, so P is an increasing function. Thus solution curves starting above $\frac{b}{a}$ are increasing, and those starting below $\frac{b}{a}$ are decreasing. See Figure 11.25.

For $P > \frac{b}{a}$, the slope, $\frac{dP}{dt}$, increases with P, so the graph of P against t is concave up. For $0 < P < \frac{b}{a}$, the value of P decreases with time. As P decreases, the slope $\frac{dP}{dt}$ decreases for $\frac{b}{2a} < P < \frac{b}{a}$, and increases toward 0 for $0 < P < \frac{b}{2a}$. Thus solution curves starting just below the threshold value of $\frac{b}{a}$ are concave down for $\frac{b}{2a} < P < \frac{b}{a}$ and concave up and asymptotic to the t-axis for $0 < P < \frac{b}{2a}$. See Figure 11.25.

(c) $P = \frac{b}{a}$ is called the threshold population because for populations greater than $\frac{b}{a}$, the population will increase without bound. For populations less than $\frac{b}{a}$, the population will go to zero, i.e. to extinction.

Solutions for Section 11.8

Exercises

1. Since

$$\frac{dS}{dt} = -aSI,$$

$$\frac{dI}{dt} = aSI - bI,$$

$$\frac{dR}{dt} = bI$$

we have

$$\frac{dS}{dt} + \frac{dI}{dt} + \frac{dR}{dt} = -aSI + aSI - bI + bI = 0.$$

Thus $\frac{d}{dt}(S + I + R) = 0$, so $S + I + R = $ constant.

2. This is an example of a predator-prey relationship. Normally, we would expect the worm population, in the absence of predators, to increase without bound. As the number of worms w increases, so would the rate of increase dw/dt; in other words, the relation $dw/dt = w$ might be a reasonable model for the worm population in the absence of predators.

However, since there are predators (robins), dw/dt won't be that big. We must lessen dw/dt. It makes sense that the more interaction there is between robins and worms, the more slowly the worms are able to increase their numbers. Hence we lessen dw/dt by the amount wr to get $dw/dt = w - wr$. The term $-wr$ reflects the fact that more interactions between the species means slower reproduction for the worms.

Similarly, we would expect the robin population to decrease in the absence of worms. We'd expect the population decrease at a rate related to the current population, making $dr/dt = -r$ a reasonable model for the robin population in absence of worms. The negative term reflects the fact that the greater the population of robins, the more quickly they are dying off. The wr term in $dr/dt = -r + wr$ reflects the fact that the more interactions between robins and worms, the greater the tendency for the robins to increase in population.

3. If there are no worms, then $w = 0$, and $\frac{dr}{dt} = -r$ giving $r = r_0 e^{-t}$, where r_0 is the initial robin population. If there are no robins, then $r = 0$, and $\frac{dw}{dt} = w$ giving $w = w_0 e^t$, where w_0 is the initial worm population.

4. There is symmetry across the line $r = w$. Indeed, since $\frac{dr}{dw} = \frac{r(w-1)}{w(1-r)}$, if we switch w and r we get $\frac{dw}{dr} = \frac{w(r-1)}{r(1-w)}$, so $\frac{dr}{dw} = \frac{r(1-w)}{w(r-1)}$. Since switching w and r changes nothing, the slope field must be symmetric across the line $r = w$. The slope field shows that the solution curves are either spirals or closed curves. Since there is symmetry about the line $r = w$, the solutions must in fact be closed curves.

5. If $w = 2$ and $r = 2$, then $\frac{dw}{dt} = -2$ and $\frac{dr}{dt} = 2$, so initially the number of worms decreases and the number of robins increases. In the long run, however, the populations will oscillate; they will even go back to $w = 2$ and $r = 2$.

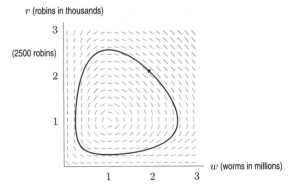

6. Sketching the trajectory through the point $(2, 2)$ on the slope field given shows that the maximum robin population is about 2500, and the minimum robin population is about 500. When the robin population is at its maximum, the worm population is about 1,000,000.

7.

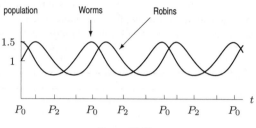

Figure 11.26

8. It will work somewhat; the maximum number the robins reach will increase. However, the minimum number the robins reach will decrease as well. (See graph of slope field.) In the long term, the robin-worm populations will again fall into a cycle. Notice, however, if the extra robins are added during the part of the cycle where there are the fewest robins, the new cycle will have smaller variation. See Figure 11.27.

Note that if too many robins are added, the minimum number may get so small the model may fail, since a small number of robins are more susceptible to disaster.

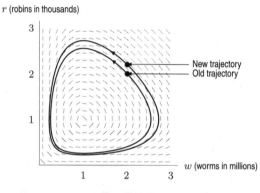

Figure 11.27

9. The numbers of robins begins to increase while the number of worms remains approximately constant. See Figure 11.28. The numbers of robins and worms oscillate periodically between 0.2 and 3, with the robin population lagging behind the worm population.

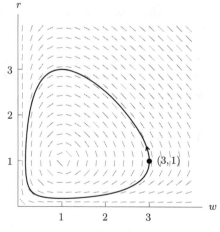

Figure 11.28

10. Estimating from the phase plane, we have

$$0.18 < r < 3$$

so the robin population lies between 180 and 3000. Similarly

$$0.2 < w < 3,$$

so the worm population lies between 200,000 and 3,000,000.

   When the robin population is at its minimum $r \approx 0.2$, then $w \approx 0.87$, so that there are approximately 870,000 worms.

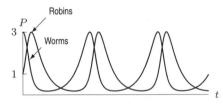

Figure 11.29

11. Here x and y both increase at about the same rate.

12. Initially $x = 0$, so we start with only y. Then y decreases while x increases. Then x continues to increase while y starts to increase as well. Finally y continues to increase while x decreases.

13. x decreases quickly while y increases more slowly.

14. The closed trajectory represents populations which oscillate repeatedly.

Problems

15. (a) Symbiosis, because both populations decrease while alone but are helped by the presence of the other.

   (b)

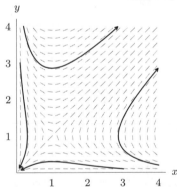

   Both populations tend to infinity or both tend to zero.

16. (a) Competition, because both populations grow logistically when alone, but are harmed by the presence of the other.

   (b)

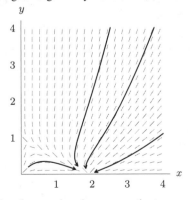

   In the long run, $x \to 2$, $y \to 0$. In other words, y becomes extinct.

17. (a) Predator-prey, because x decreases while alone, but is helped by y, whereas y increases logistically when alone, and is harmed by x. Thus x is predator, y is prey.

   (b)

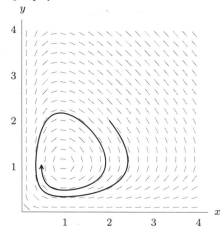

Provided neither initial population is zero, both populations tend to about 1. If x is initially zero, but y is not, then $y \to \infty$. If y is initially zero, but x is not, then $x \to 0$.

18. (a) Thinking of y as a function of x and x as a function of t, then by the chain rule: $\dfrac{dy}{dt} = \dfrac{dy}{dx}\dfrac{dx}{dt}$, so:

$$\frac{dy}{dx} = \frac{dy/dt}{dx/dt} = \frac{-0.01x}{-0.05y} = \frac{x}{5y}$$

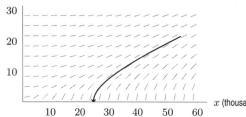

   (b) The figure above shows the slope field for this differential equation and the trajectory starting at $x_0 = 54$, $y_0 = 21.5$. The trajectory goes to the x-axis, where $y = 0$, meaning that the Japanese troops were all killed or wounded before the US troops were, and thus predicts the US victory (which did occur). Since the trajectory meets the x-axis at $x \approx 25$, the differential equation predicts that about 25,000 US troops would survive the battle.

   (c) The fact that the US got reinforcements, while the Japanese did not, does not alter the predicted outcome (a US victory). The US reinforcements have the effect of changing the trajectory, altering the number of troops surviving the battle. See the graph below.

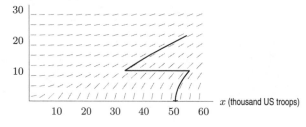

19. (a) Thinking of y as a function of x and x as a function of t, then by the chain rule: $\dfrac{dy}{dt} = \dfrac{dy}{dx}\dfrac{dx}{dt}$, so:

$$\frac{dy}{dx} = \frac{dy/dt}{dx/dt} = \frac{-bx}{-ay} = \frac{bx}{ay}$$

(b) Separating variables,

$$\int ay\, dy = \int bx\, dx$$

$$a\frac{y^2}{2} = b\frac{x^2}{2} + k$$

$$ay^2 - bx^2 = C \quad \text{where } C = 2k$$

20. (a) Lanchester's square law for the battle of Iwo Jima is

$$0.05y^2 - 0.01x^2 = C.$$

If we measure x and y in thousands, $x_0 = 54$ and $y_0 = 21.5$, so $0.05(21.5)^2 - 0.01(54)^2 = C$ giving $C = -6.0475$. Thus the equation of the trajectory is

$$0.05y^2 - 0.01x^2 = -6.0475$$

giving

$$x^2 - 5y^2 = 604.75.$$

(b) Assuming that the battle did not end until all the Japanese were dead or wounded, that is, $y = 0$, then the number of US soldiers remaining is given by $x^2 - 5(0)^2 = 604.75$. This gives $x = 24.59$, or about 25,000 troops. This is approximately what happened.

21. (a) Since the guerrillas are hard to find, the rate at which they are put out of action is proportional to the number of chance encounters between a guerrilla and a conventional soldier, which is in turn proportional to the number of guerrillas and to the number of conventional soldiers. Thus the rate at which guerrillas are put out of action is proportional to the product of the strengths of the two armies.

(b)

$$\frac{dx}{dt} = -xy$$

$$\frac{dy}{dt} = -x$$

(c) Thinking of y as a function of x and x a function of of t, then by the chain rule: $\dfrac{dy}{dt} = \dfrac{dy}{dx}\dfrac{dx}{dt}$ so:

$$\frac{dy}{dx} = \frac{dy/dt}{dx/dt} = \frac{-x}{-xy} = \frac{1}{y}$$

Separating variables:

$$\int y\, dy = \int dx$$

$$\frac{y^2}{2} = x + C$$

The value of C is determined by the initial strengths of the two armies.

(d) The sign of C determines which side wins the battle. Looking at the general solution $\dfrac{y^2}{2} = x + C$, we see that if $C > 0$ the y-intercept is at $\sqrt{2C}$, so y wins the battle by virtue of the fact that it still has troops when $x = 0$. If $C < 0$ then the curve intersects the axes at $x = -C$, so x wins the battle because it has troops when $y = 0$. If $C = 0$, then the solution goes to the point $(0, 0)$, which represents the case of mutual annihilation.

(e) We assume that an army wins if the opposing force goes to 0 first. Figure 11.30 shows that the conventional force wins if $C > 0$ and the guerrillas win if $C < 0$. Neither side wins if $C = 0$ (all soldiers on both sides are killed in this case).

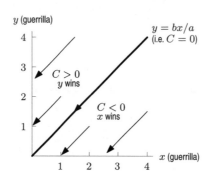

Figure 11.30

22. (a) Taking the constants of proportionality to be a and b, with $a > 0$ and $b > 0$, the equations are

$$\frac{dx}{dt} = -axy$$

$$\frac{dy}{dt} = -bxy$$

(b) $\dfrac{dy}{dx} = \dfrac{dy/dt}{dx/dt} = \dfrac{-bxy}{-axy} = \dfrac{b}{a}$. Solving the differential equation gives $y = \dfrac{b}{a}x + C$, where C depends on the initial sizes of the two armies.

(c) The sign of C determines which side wins the battle. Looking at the general solution $y = \dfrac{b}{a}x + C$, we see that if $C > 0$ the y-intercept is at C, so y wins the battle by virtue of the fact that it still has troops when $x = 0$. If $C < 0$ then the curve intersects the axes at $x = -\frac{a}{b}C$, so x wins the battle because it has troops when $y = 0$. If $C = 0$, then the solution goes to the point $(0, 0)$, which represents the case of mutual annihilation.

(d) We assume that an army wins if the opposing force goes to 0 first.

23. (a) We have

$$\frac{\frac{dy}{dt}}{\frac{dx}{dt}} = \frac{dy}{dx} = \frac{-3y - xy}{-2x - xy} = \frac{y(x+3)}{x(y+2)}.$$

Thus,

$$\left(\frac{y+2}{y}\right) dy = \left(\frac{x+3}{x}\right) dx$$

so

$$\int \left(1 + \frac{2}{y}\right) dy = \int \left(1 + \frac{3}{x}\right) dx.$$

So,

$$y + 2\ln|y| = x + 3\ln|x| + C.$$

Since x and y are non-negative,

$$y + 2\ln y = x + 3\ln x + C.$$

This is as far as we can go with this equation – we cannot solve for y in terms of x, for example. We can, however, put it in the form

$$e^{y+2\ln y} = e^{x+3\ln x+C}, \quad \text{or} \quad y^2 e^y = Ax^3 e^x.$$

(b) An equilibrium state satisfies

$$\frac{dx}{dt} = -2x - xy = 0 \quad \text{and} \quad \frac{dy}{dt} = -3y - xy = 0.$$

Solving the first equation, we have

$$-x(y+2) = 0, \quad \text{so} \quad x = 0 \quad \text{or} \quad y = -2.$$

The second equation has solutions

$$y = 0 \quad \text{or} \quad x = -3.$$

Since $x, y \geq 0$, the only equilibrium point is $(0, 0)$.

(c) We can use either of our forms for the solution. Looking at

$$y^2 e^y = Ax^3 e^x,$$

we see that if x and y are very small positive numbers, then

$$e^x \approx e^y \approx 1.$$

Thus,

$$y^2 \approx Ax^3, \quad \text{or} \quad \frac{y^2}{x^3} \approx A, \text{a constant.}$$

Looking at

$$y + 2\ln y = x + 3\ln x + C,$$

we note that if x and y are small, then they are negligible compared to $\ln y$ and $\ln x$. Thus,

$$2\ln y \approx 3\ln x + C,$$

giving

$$\ln y^2 - \ln x^3 \approx C,$$

so

$$\ln \frac{y^2}{x^3} \approx C$$

and therefore

$$\frac{y^2}{x^3} \approx e^C, \text{ a constant.}$$

(d) If

$$x(0) = 4 \quad \text{and} \quad y(0) = 8,$$

then

$$8 + 2\ln 8 = 4 + 3\ln 4 + C.$$

Note that

$$2\ln 8 = 3\ln 4 = \ln 64,$$

giving

$$4 = C.$$

So the phase trajectory is

$$y + 2\ln y = x + 3\ln x + 4.$$

(Or equivalently, $y^2 e^y = e^4 x^3 e^x = x^3 e^{x+4}$.)

(e) If the concentrations are equal, then

$$y + 2\ln y = y + 3\ln y + 4,$$

giving

$$-\ln y = 4 \quad \text{or} \quad y = e^{-4}.$$

Thus, they are equal when $y = x = e^{-4} \approx 0.0183$.

(f) Using part (c), we have that if x is small,

$$\frac{y^2}{x^3} \approx e^4.$$

Since $x = e^{-10}$ is certainly small,

$$\frac{y^2}{e^{-30}} \approx e^4, \quad \text{and} \quad y \approx e^{-13}.$$

Solutions for Section 11.9

Exercises

1. (a) To find the equilibrium points we set

$$20x - 10xy = 0$$
$$25y - 5xy = 0.$$

So, $x = 0$, $y = 0$ is an equilibrium point. Another one is given by

$$10y = 20$$
$$5x = 25.$$

Therefore, $x = 5$, $y = 2$ is the other equilibrium point.

(b) At $x = 2$, $y = 4$,

$$\frac{dx}{dt} = 20x - 10xy = 40 - 80 = -40$$

$$\frac{dy}{dt} = 25y - 5xy = 100 - 40 = 60.$$

Since these are not both zero, this point is not an equilibrium point.

2. (a) $dS/dt = 0$ where $S = 0$ or $I = 0$ (both axes).

$dI/dt = 0.0026I(S - 192)$, so $dI/dt = 0$ where $I = 0$ or $S = 192$.

Thus every point on the S axis is an equilibrium point (corresponding to no one being sick).

(b) In region I, where $S > 192$, $\dfrac{dS}{dt} < 0$ and $\dfrac{dI}{dt} > 0$.

In region II, where $S < 192$, $\dfrac{dS}{dt} < 0$ and $\dfrac{dI}{dt} < 0$. See Figure 11.31.

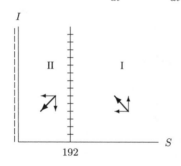

Figure 11.31

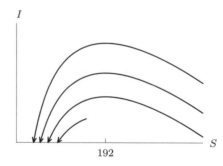

Figure 11.32

(c) If the trajectory starts with $S_0 > 192$, then I increases to a maximum when $S = 192$. If $S_0 < 192$, then I always decreases. See Figure 11.31. Regardless of the initial conditions, the trajectory always goes to a point on the S-axis (where $I = 0$). The S-intercept represents the number of students who never get the disease. See Figure 11.32.

3. The nullclines are where $\frac{dw}{dt} = 0$ or $\frac{dr}{dt} = 0$.

$\frac{dw}{dt} = 0$ when $w - wr = 0$, so $w(1 - r) = 0$ giving $w = 0$ or $r = 1$.

$\frac{dr}{dt} = 0$ when $-r + rw = 0$, so $r(w - 1) = 0$ giving $r = 0$ or $w = 1$.

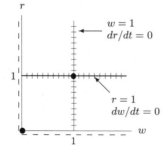

Figure 11.33: Nullclines and equilibrium points (dots)

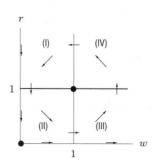

Figure 11.34

The equilibrium points are where the nullclines intersect: $(0, 0)$ and $(1, 1)$. The nullclines split the first quadrant into four sectors. See Figure 11.33. We can get a feel for how the populations interact by seeing the direction of the trajectories in each sector. See Figure 11.34. If the populations reach an equilibrium point, they will stay there. If the worm population dies out, the robin population will also die out, too. However, if the robin population dies out, the worm population will continue to grow.

Otherwise, it seems that the populations cycle around the equilibrium $(1, 1)$. The trajectory moves from sector to sector: trajectories in sector (I) move to sector (II); trajectories in sector (II) move to sector (III); trajectories in sector (III) move to sector (IV); trajectories in sector (IV) move back to sector (I). The robins keep the worm population down by feeding on them, but the robins need the worms (as food) to sustain the population. These conflicting needs keep the populations moving in a cycle around the equilibrium.

Problems

4. We first find the nullclines. Again, we assume x, $y \geq 0$.
Vertical nullclines occur where $dx/dt = 0$, which happens when $\frac{dx}{dt} = x(2 - x - y) = 0$,
i.e. when $x = 0$ or $x + y = 2$.
Horizontal nullclines occur where $dy/dt = 0$, which happens when $\frac{dy}{dt} = y(1 - x - y) = 0$, i.e. when $y = 0$ or $x + y = 1$. These nullclines are shown in Figure 11.35.

Equilibrium points (also shown in Figure 11.35) occur where both dy/dt and dx/dt are 0, i.e. at the intersections of vertical and horizontal nullclines. There are three such points for these equations: $(0, 0)$, $(0, 1)$, and $(2, 0)$.

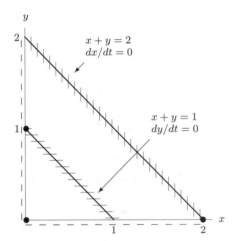

Figure 11.35: Nullclines and equilibrium points (dots)

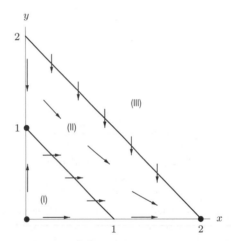

Figure 11.36: General directions of trajectories and equilibrium points (dots)

Looking at sectors in Figure 11.36, we see that no matter in what sector the initial point lies, the trajectory will head toward the equilibrium point $(2, 0)$.

5. We first find the nullclines. Vertical nullclines occur where $\frac{dx}{dt} = 0$, which happens when $x = 0$ or $y = \frac{1}{3}(2 - x)$. Horizontal nullclines occur where $\frac{dy}{dt} = y(1 - 2x) = 0$, which happens when $y = 0$ or $x = \frac{1}{2}$. These nullclines are shown in Figure 11.37.

Equilibrium points (also shown in Figure 11.37) occur at the intersections of vertical and horizontal nullclines. There are three such points for this system of equations; $(0, 0)$, $(\frac{1}{2}, \frac{1}{2})$ and $(2, 0)$.

The nullclines divide the positive quadrant into four regions as shown in Figure 11.37. Trajectory directions for these regions are shown in Figure 11.38.

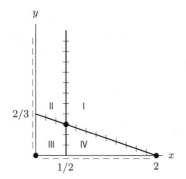

Figure 11.37: Nullclines and
equilibrium points (dots)

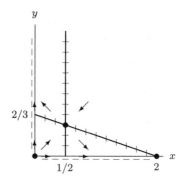

Figure 11.38: General directions of
trajectories and equilibrium points
(dots)

6. We first find nullclines. Vertical nullclines occur where $\frac{dx}{dt} = x(2 - x - 2y) = 0$, which happens when $x = 0$ or $y = \frac{1}{2}(2 - x)$. Horizontal nullclines occur where $\frac{dy}{dt} = y(1 - 2x - y) = 0$, which happens when $y = 0$ or $y = 1 - 2x$. These nullclines are shown in Figure 11.39.

Equilibrium points (also shown in the figure below) occur at the intersections of vertical and horizontal nullclines. There are three such points for this system; $(0, 0)$, $(0, 1)$, and $(2, 0)$.

The nullclines divide the positive quadrant into three regions as shown in the figure below. Trajectory directions for these regions are shown in Figure 11.40.

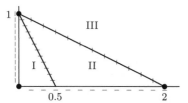

Figure 11.39: Nullclines and equilibrium
points (dots)

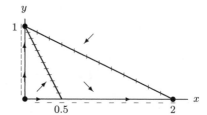

Figure 11.40: General directions of
trajectories and equilibrium points (dots)

7. We first find the nullclines. Vertical nullclines occur where $\frac{dx}{dt} = x(1 - y - \frac{x}{3}) = 0$, which happens when $x = 0$ or $y = 1 - \frac{x}{3}$. Horizontal nullclines occur where $\frac{dy}{dt} = y(1 - \frac{y}{2} - x) = 0$, which happens when $y = 0$ or $y = 2(1 - x)$. These nullclines are shown in Figure 11.41.

Equilibrium points (also shown in Figure 11.41) occur at the intersections of vertical and horizontal nullclines. There are four such points for this system: $(0, 0)$, $(0, 2)$, $(3, 0)$, and $\left(\frac{3}{5}, \frac{4}{5}\right)$.

The nullclines divide the positive quadrant into four regions as shown in Figure 11.41. Trajectory directions for these regions are shown in Figure 11.42.

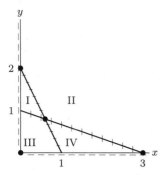

Figure 11.41: Nullclines and
equilibrium points (dots)

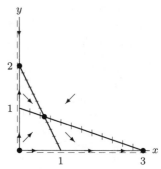

Figure 11.42: General directions
of trajectories and equilibrium
points (dots)

8. We first find the nullclines. Again, we assume x, $y \geq 0$.
$\frac{dx}{dt} = x(1 - x - \frac{y}{3}) = 0$ when $x = 0$ or $x + y/3 = 1$.
$\frac{dy}{dt} = y(1 - y - \frac{x}{2}) = 0$ when $y = 0$ or $y + x/2 = 1$.
These nullclines are shown in Figure 11.43. There are four equilibrium points for these equations. Three of them are the points, $(0,0)$, $(0,1)$, and $(1,0)$. The fourth is the intersection of the two lines $x + y/3 = 1$ and $y + x/2 = 1$. This point is $\left(\frac{4}{5}, \frac{3}{5}\right)$.

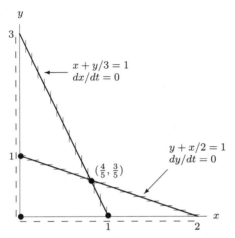

Figure 11.43: Nullclines and equilibrium points (dots)

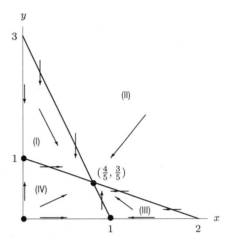

Figure 11.44: General directions of trajectories and equilibrium points (dots)

Looking at sectors in Figure 11.44, we see that no matter in what sector the initial point lies, the trajectory will head toward the equilibrium point $\left(\frac{4}{5}, \frac{3}{5}\right)$. Only if the initial point lies on the x- or y-axis, will the trajectory head toward the equilibrium points at $(1,0)$, $(0,1)$, or $(0,0)$. In fact, the trajectory will go to $(0,0)$ only if it starts there, in which case $x(t) = y(t) = 0$ for all t. From direction of the trajectories in Figure 11.44, it appears that if the initial point is in sectors (I) or (III), then it will remain in that sector as it heads toward the equilibrium.

9. We assume that x, $y \geq 0$ and then find the nullclines. $\frac{dx}{dt} = x(1 - \frac{x}{2} - y) = 0$ when $x = 0$ or $y + \frac{x}{2} = 1$.
$\frac{dy}{dt} = y(1 - \frac{y}{3} - x) = 0$ when $y = 0$ or $x + \frac{y}{3} = 1$.
We find the equilibrium points. They are $(2,0)$, $(0,3)$, $(0,0)$, and $\left(\frac{4}{5}, \frac{3}{5}\right)$. The nullclines and equilibrium points are shown in Figure 11.45.

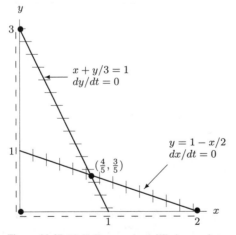

Figure 11.45: Nullclines and equilibrium points (dots)

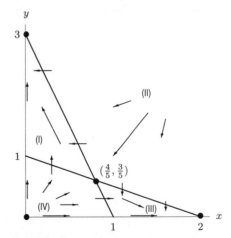

Figure 11.46: General directions of trajectories and equilibrium points (dots)

Figure 11.46 shows that if the initial point is in sector (I), the trajectory heads toward the equilibrium point $(0,3)$. Similarly, if the trajectory begins in sector (III), then it heads toward the equilibrium $(2,0)$ over time. If the trajectory begins in sector (II) or (IV), it can go to any of the three equilibrium points $(2,0)$, $(0,3)$, or $\left(\frac{4}{5}, \frac{3}{5}\right)$.

10. (a) If B were not present, then we'd have $A' = 2A$, so company A's net worth would grow exponentially. Similarly, if A were not present, B would grow exponentially. The two companies restrain each other's growth, probably by competing for the market.

(b) To find equilibrium points, find the solutions of the pair of equations

$$A' = 2A - AB = 0$$
$$B' = B - AB = 0$$

The first equation has solutions $A = 0$ or $B = 2$. The second has solutions $B = 0$ or $A = 1$. Thus the equilibrium points are (0,0) and (1,2).

(c) In the long run, one of the companies will go out of business. Two of the trajectories in the figure below go toward the A axis; they represent A surviving and B going out of business. The trajectories going toward the B axis represent A going out of business. Notice both the equilibrium points are unstable.

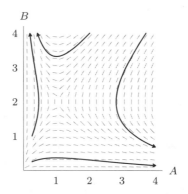

11. (a) The nullclines are $P = 0$ or $P_1 + 3P_2 = 13$ (where $dP_1/dt = 0$) and $P = 0$ or $P_2 + 0.4P_1 = 6$ (where $dP_2/dt = 0$).

(b) The phase plane in Figure 11.47 shows that P_2 will eventually exclude P_1 regardless of where the experiment starts so long as there were some P_2 originally. Consequently, the data points would have followed a trajectory that starts at the origin, crosses the first nullcline and goes left and upward between the two nullclines to the point $P_1 = 0$, $P_2 = 6$.

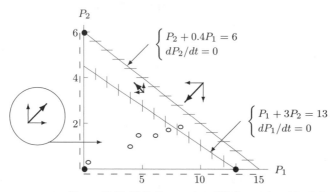

Figure 11.47: Nullclines and equilibrium points (dots) for Gause's yeast data (hollow dots)

12. (a) In the equation for dx/dt, the term involving x, namely $-0.2x$, is negative meaning that as x increases, dx/dt decreases. This corresponds to the statement that the more a country spends on armaments, the less it wants to increase spending.

On the other hand, since $+0.15y$ is positive, as y increases, dx/dt increases, corresponding to the fact that the more a country's opponent arms, the more the country will arm itself.

The constant term, 20, is positive means that if both countries are unarmed initially, (so $x = y = 0$), then dx/dt is positive and so the country will start to arm. In other words, disarmament is not an equilibrium situation in this model.

(b) The nullclines are shown in Figure 11.48. When $dx/dt = 0$, the trajectories are vertical (on the line $-0.2x + 0.15y + 20 = 0$); when $dy/dt = 0$ the trajectories are horizontal (on $0.1x - 0.2y + 40 = 0$). There is only one equilibrium point, $x = y = 400$.

(c) In region I, try $x = 400$, $y = 0$, giving

$$\frac{dx}{dt} = -0.2(400) + 0.15(0) + 20 < 0$$

$$\frac{dy}{dt} = 0.1(400) - 0.2(0) + 4 - 0 > 0$$

In region II, try $x = 500$, $y = 500$, giving

$$\frac{dx}{dt} = -0.2(500) + 0.15(500) + 20 < 0$$

$$\frac{dy}{dt} = 0.1(500) - 0.2(500) + 40 < 0$$

In region III, try $x = 0$, $y = 400$, giving

$$\frac{dx}{dt} = -0.2(0) + 0.15(400) + 20 > 0$$

$$\frac{dy}{dt} = 0.1(0) - 0.2(400) + 40 < 0$$

In region IV, try $x = 0$, $y = 0$, giving

$$\frac{dx}{dt} = -0.2(0) + 0.15(0) + 20 > 0$$

$$\frac{dy}{dt} = 0.1(0) - 0.2(0) + 40 > 0$$

See Figure 11.48.

(d) The one equilibrium point is stable.

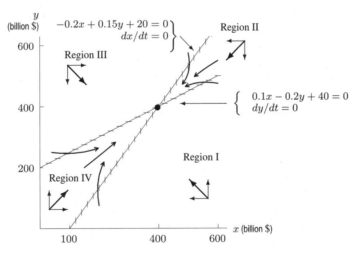

Figure 11.48: Nullclines and equilibrium point(dot) for arms race

(e) If both sides disarm, then both sides spend $0. Thus initially $x = y = 0$, and $dx/dt = 20$ and $dy/dt = 40$. Since both dx/dt and dy/dt are positive, both sides start arming. Figure 11.48 shows that they will both arm until each is spending about $400 billion.

(f) If the country spending y billion is unarmed, then $y = 0$ and the corresponding point on the phase plane is on the x-axis. Any trajectory starting on the x-axis tends toward the equilibrium point $x = y = 400$. Similarly, a trajectory starting on the y-axis represents the other country being unarmed; such a trajectory also tends to the same equilibrium point.

Thus, if either side disarms unilaterally, that is, if we start out with one of the countries spending nothing, then over time, they will still both end up spending roughly $400 billion.

(g) This model predicts that, in the long run, both countries will spend near to $400 billion, no matter where they start.

13. (a)

$$\frac{dx}{dt} = 0 \text{ when } x = \frac{10.5}{0.45} = 23.3$$

$$\frac{dy}{dt} = 0 \text{ when } 8.2x - 0.8y - 142 = 0$$

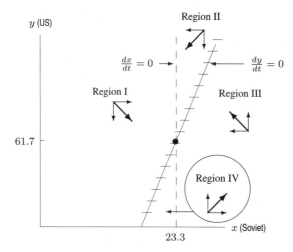

Figure 11.49: Nullclines and equilibrium point (dot) for US-Soviet arms race

There is an equilibrium point where the trajectories cross at $x = 23.3$, $y = 61.7$

In region I, $\frac{dx}{dt} > 0$, $\frac{dy}{dt} < 0$.

In region II, $\frac{dx}{dt} < 0$, $\frac{dy}{dt} < 0$.

In region III, $\frac{dx}{dt} < 0$, $\frac{dy}{dt} > 0$.

In region IV, $\frac{dx}{dt} > 0$, $\frac{dy}{dt} > 0$.

(b)

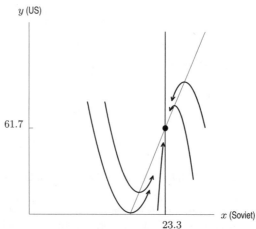

Figure 11.50: Trajectories for US-Soviet arms race.

(c) All the trajectories tend toward the equilibrium point $x = 23.3$, $y = 61.7$. Thus the model predicts that in the long run the arms race will level off with the Soviet Union spending 23.3 billion dollars a year on arms and the US 61.7 billion dollars.

(d) As the model predicts, yearly arms expenditure did tend toward 23 billion for the Soviet Union and 62 billion for the US.

Solutions for Section 11.10

Exercises

1. If $y = 2\cos t + 3\sin t$, then $y' = -2\sin t + 3\cos t$ and $y'' = -2\cos t - 3\sin t$. Thus, $y'' + y = 0$.

2. If $y(t) = 3\sin(2t) + 2\cos(2t)$ then
$$y' = 6\cos(2t) - 4\sin(2t)$$
$$y'' = -12\sin(2t) - 8\cos(2t) = -4(3\sin(2t) + 2\cos(2t)) = -4y$$
as required.

3. If $y = A\cos t + B\sin t$, then $y' = -A\sin t + B\cos t$ and $y'' = -A\cos t - B\sin t$. Thus, $y'' + y = 0$.

4. If $y(t) = A\sin(2t) + B\cos(2t)$ then
$$y' = 2A\cos(2t) - 2B\sin(2t)$$
$$y'' = -4A\sin(2t) - 4B\cos(2t)$$
therefore
$$y'' + 4y = -4A\sin(2t) - 4B\cos(2t) + 4(A\sin(2t) + B\cos(2t)) = 0$$
for all values of A and B, so the given function is a solution.

5. If $y(t) = A\sin(\omega t) + B\cos(\omega t)$ then
$$y' = \omega A\cos(\omega t) - \omega B\sin(\omega t)$$
$$y'' = -\omega^2 A\sin(\omega t) - \omega^2 B\cos(\omega t)$$
therefore
$$y'' + \omega^2 y = -\omega^2 A\sin(\omega t) - \omega^2 B\cos(2t) + \omega^2(A\sin(\omega t) + B\cos(\omega t)) = 0$$
for all values of A and B, so the given function is a solution.

6. $y = A\cos\alpha t$
$y' = -\alpha A\sin\alpha t$
$y'' = -\alpha^2 A\cos\alpha t$
If $y'' + 5y = 0$, then $-\alpha^2 A\cos\alpha t + 5A\cos\alpha t = 0$, so $A(5 - \alpha^2)\cos\alpha t = 0$. This is true for all t if $A = 0$, or if $\alpha = \pm\sqrt{5}$.
We also have the initial condition: $y'(1) = -\alpha A\sin\alpha = 3$. Notice that this equation will not work if $A = 0$. If $\alpha = \sqrt{5}$, then
$A = -\dfrac{3}{\sqrt{5}\sin\sqrt{5}} \approx -1.705$.
Similarly, if $\alpha = -\sqrt{5}$, we find that $A \approx -1.705$. Thus, the possible values are $A = -\dfrac{3}{\sqrt{5}\sin\sqrt{5}} \approx -1.705$ and $\alpha = \pm\sqrt{5}$.

7. (a)

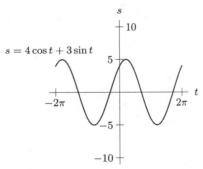

$s = 4\cos t + 3\sin t$

(b) Trace along the curve to the highest point; which has coordinates of about $(0.66, 5)$, so $A \approx 5$. If $s = 5\sin(t + \phi)$, then the maximum occurs where $t \approx 0.66$ and $t + \phi = \pi/2$, that is $0.66 + \phi \approx 1.57$, giving $\phi \approx 0.91$.

(c) Analytically
$$A = \sqrt{4^2 + 3^2} = 5$$
and
$$\tan\phi = \frac{4}{3} \quad \text{so} \quad \phi = \arctan\left(\frac{4}{3}\right) = 0.93.$$

8. We want to find A and ϕ such that

$$\cos t - \sin t = A \sin(t + \phi).$$

We know that $A = \sqrt{1^2 + (-1)^2} = \sqrt{2}$. Also, $\tan \phi = 1/(-1) = -1$, so $\phi = -\pi/4$ or $\phi = 3\pi/4$. Since $C_1 = 1 > 0$, we take $\phi = 3\pi/4$, giving

$$s(t) = \sqrt{2} \sin \left(t + \frac{3\pi}{4} \right)$$

as our solution. The graph of $s(t)$ is in Figure 11.51.

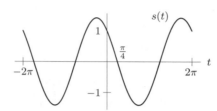

Figure 11.51: Graph of the function
$s(t) = \sqrt{2}\sin(t + \frac{3\pi}{4})$

9. The amplitude is $\sqrt{3^2 + 7^2} = \sqrt{58}$.

10. If we write $y = 3\sin 2t + 4\cos 2t$ in the form $y(t) = A\sin(2t + \phi)$, then $A = \sqrt{3^2 + 4^2} = 5$.

11. Take $\omega = 2$. The amplitude is $A = \sqrt{5^2 + 12^2} = \sqrt{169} = 13$. The phase shift is $\psi = \tan^{-1}\frac{12}{5}$.

12. The amplitude is $A = \sqrt{7^2 + 24^2} = \sqrt{625} = 25$.
The phase shift, ϕ, is given by $\tan \phi = \frac{24}{7}$, so $\phi = \arctan \frac{24}{7} \approx 1.287$ or $\phi \approx -1.855$.
Since $C_1 = 24 > 0$, we want $\phi = 1.287$, so the solution is $25\sin(\omega t + 1.287)$.

Problems

13. First, we note that the solutions of:
(a) $x'' + x = 0$ are $x = A\cos t + B\sin t$;
(b) $x'' + 4x = 0$ are $x = A\cos 2t + B\sin 2t$;
(c) $x'' + 16x = 0$ are $x = A\cos 4t + B\sin 4t$.
This follows from what we know about the general solution to $x'' + \omega^2 x = 0$.
The period of the solutions to (a) is 2π, the period of the solutions to (b) is π, and the period of the solutions of (c) is $\frac{\pi}{2}$.
Since the t-scales are the same on all of the graphs, we see that graphs (I) and (IV) have the same period, which is twice the period of graph (III). Graph (II) has twice the period of graphs (I) and (IV). Since each graph represents a solution, we have the following:

- equation (a) goes with graph (II)
  equation (b) goes with graphs (I) and (IV)
  equation (c) goes with graph (III)
- The graph of (I) passes through $(0, 0)$, so $0 = A\cos 0 + B\sin 0 = A$. Thus, the equation is $x = B\sin 2t$. Since the amplitude is 2, we see that $x = 2\sin 2t$ is the equation of the graph. Similarly, the equation for (IV) is $x = -3\sin 2t$. The graph of (II) also passes through $(0, 0)$, so, similarly, the equation must be $x = B\sin t$. In this case, we see that $B = -1$, so $x = -\sin t$.
  Finally, the graph of (III) passes through $(0, 1)$, and 1 is the maximum value. Thus, $1 = A\cos 0 + B\sin 0$, so $A = 1$. Since it reaches a local maximum at $(0, 1)$, $x'(0) = 0 = -4A\sin 0 + 4B\cos 0$, so $B = 0$. Thus, the solution is $x = \cos 4t$.

14. (a) Let $y = c_1 \sinh wt + c_2 \cosh wt$. Then

$$y' = w(c_1 \cosh wt + c_2 \sinh wt)$$

and

$$y'' = w^2(c_1 \sinh wt + c_2 \cosh wt) = w^2 y,$$

so $y'' - w^2 y = 0$.

(b) (i) Since $y(0) = 0$, we have $c_1 \sinh 0 + c_2 \cosh 0 = c_2 = 0$. Since $y(1) = 6$ and $c_2 = 0$, we have that

$$y(1) = c_1 \sinh w = 6,$$

so

$$c_1 = \frac{6}{\sinh w}$$

Therefore $y = \dfrac{6 \sinh wt}{\sinh w}$.

(ii) Since $y'(0) = 0$, we have $y'(0) = w(c_1 \cosh 0 + c_2 \sinh 0) = wc_1 = 0$, so $c_1 = 0$. Thus

$$y(1) = c_2 \cosh w = 6$$

implies that

$$c_2 = \frac{6}{\cosh w},$$

giving us that $y = \dfrac{6 \cosh wt}{\cosh w}$.

15. At $t = 0$, we find that $y = 2$, which is clearly the highest point since $-1 \le \cos 3t \le 1$. Thus, at $t = 0$ the mass is at its highest point. Since $y' = -6 \sin 3t$, we see $y' = 0$ when $t = 0$. Thus, at $t = 0$ the object is at rest, although it will move down after $t = 0$.

16. At $t = 0$, we find that $y = 0$. Since $-1 \le \sin 3t \le 1$, y ranges from -0.5 to 0.5, so at $t = 0$ it is starting in the middle. Since $y' = -1.5 \cos 3t$, we see $y' = -1.5$ when $t = 0$, so the mass is moving downward.

17. At $t = 0$, we find that $y = -1$, which is clearly the lowest point on the path. Since $y' = 3 \sin 3t$, we see that $y' = 0$ when $t = 0$. Thus, at $t = 0$ the object is at rest, although it will move up after $t = 0$.

18. All the differential equations have solutions of the form $s(t) = C_1 \sin \omega t + C_2 \cos \omega t$. Since for all of them, $s'(0) = 0$, we have $s'(0) = 0 = C_1 \omega \cos 0 - C_2 \omega \sin 0 = 0$, giving $C_1 \omega = 0$. Thus, either $C_1 = 0$ or $\omega = 0$. If $\omega = 0$, then $s(t)$ is a constant function, and since the equations represent oscillating springs, we don't want $s(t)$ to be a constant function. Thus, $C_1 = 0$, so all four equations have solutions of the form $s(t) = C \cos \omega t$.

i) $s'' + 4s = 0$, so $\omega = \sqrt{4} = 2$. $s(0) = C \cos 0 = C = 5$. Thus, $s(t) = 5 \cos 2t$.

ii) $s'' + \frac{1}{4}s = 0$, so $\omega = \sqrt{\frac{1}{4}} = \frac{1}{2}$. $s(0) = C \cos 0 = C = 10$. Thus, $s(t) = 10 \cos \frac{1}{2}t$.

iii) $s'' + 6s = 0$, so $\omega = \sqrt{6}$. $s(0) = C = 4$, Thus, $s(t) = 4 \cos \sqrt{6}t$.

iv) $s'' + \frac{1}{6}s = 0$, so $\omega = \sqrt{\frac{1}{6}}$. $s(0) = C = 20$. Thus, $s(t) = 20 \cos \sqrt{\frac{1}{6}}t$.

(a) Spring (iii) has the shortest period, $\frac{2\pi}{\sqrt{6}}$. (Other periods are $\pi, 4\pi, 2\pi\sqrt{6}$)

(b) Spring (iv) has the largest amplitude, 20.

(c) Spring (iv) has the longest period, $2\pi\sqrt{6}$.

(d) Spring (i) has the largest maximum velocity. We can see this by looking at $v(t) = s'(t) = -C\omega \sin \omega t$. The velocity is just a sine function, so we look for the derivative with the biggest amplitude, which will have the greatest value. The velocity function for Spring i) has amplitude 10, the largest of the four springs. (The other velocity amplitudes are $10 \cdot \frac{1}{2} = 5, 4\sqrt{6} \approx 9.8, \frac{20}{\sqrt{6}} \approx 8.2$)

19. (a) Since $\omega^2 = 9$, $\omega = 3$, and so the general solution is of the form

$$y(t) = A \sin(3t) + B \cos(3t).$$

(b) (i) $y(0) = 0$, gives $A \sin(0) + B \cos(0) = 0$ so that $B = 0$.

$$y'(t) = 3A \cos(3t)$$

$y'(0) = 1$ gives $3A = 1$ and so

$$y(t) = \frac{1}{3} \sin(3t).$$

(ii) $y(0) = 1$, gives $A \sin(0) + B \cos(0) = 1$ so that $B = 1$.

$$y'(t) = 3A \cos(3t) - 3 \sin(3t)$$

$y'(0) = 0$ gives $3A = 0$ and so

$$y(t) = \cos(3t).$$

(iii) $y(0) = 1$, gives $A\sin(0) + B\cos(0) = 1$ so that $B = 1$. $y(1) = 0$ gives $A\sin 3 + \cos 3 = 0$ and so $A = \dfrac{-\cos 3}{\sin 3}$, so

$$y(t) = \frac{-\cos 3}{\sin 3}\sin(3t) + \cos(3t).$$

Note that using the trigonometric identities, we can write this as:

$$
\begin{aligned}
y(t) &= \frac{-\cos 3}{\sin 3}\sin(3t) + \cos(3t) \\
&= \frac{1}{\sin 3}\left(\sin 3\cos(3t) - \cos 3\sin(3t)\right) \\
&= \frac{1}{\sin 3}\sin(3 - 3t).
\end{aligned}
$$

(iv) $y(0) = 0$, gives $A\sin(0) + B\cos(0) = 0$ so that $B = 0$. $y(1) = 1$ gives $A\sin(3) = 1$ and so $A = \dfrac{1}{\sin(3)}$ so

$$y(t) = \frac{1}{\sin(3)}\sin(3t).$$

(c)

(i)

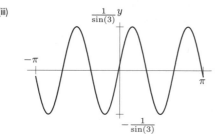

(ii)

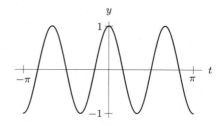

(iii)

(iv)

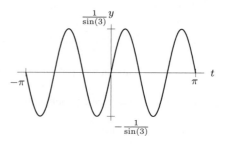

20. (a) General solution

$$x(t) = A\cos 4t + B\sin 4t.$$

Thus,

$$5 = A\cos 0 + B\sin 0 \quad \text{so } A = 5.$$

Since $x'(0) = 0$, we have

$$0 = -4A\sin 0 + 4B\cos 0 \quad \text{so } B = 0.$$

Thus,

$$x(t) = 5\cos 4t$$

so amplitude $= 5$, period $= \frac{2\pi}{4} = \frac{\pi}{2}$.

(b) General solution

$$x(t) = A\cos\left(\frac{t}{5}\right) + B\sin\left(\frac{t}{5}\right).$$

Since $x(0) = -1$, we have $A = -1$.

Since $x'(0) = 2$, we have

$$2 = -\frac{A}{5}\sin 0 + \frac{B}{5}\cos 0 \quad \text{so } B = 10.$$

Thus,

$$x(t) = -\cos\left(\frac{t}{5}\right) + 10\sin\left(\frac{t}{5}\right).$$

So, amplitude $= \sqrt{(-1)^2 + 10^2} = \sqrt{101}$, period $= \dfrac{2\pi}{1/5} = 10\pi$.

21. (a) Since a mass of 3 kg stretches the spring by 2 cm, the spring constant k is given by

$$3g = 2k \quad \text{so} \quad k = \frac{3g}{2}.$$

See Figure 11.52.

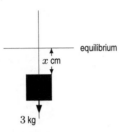

equilibrium

x cm

3 kg

Figure 11.52

Suppose we measure the displacement x from the equilibrium; then, using

$$\text{Mass} \cdot \text{Acceleration} = \text{Force}$$

gives

$$3x'' = -kx = -\frac{3gx}{2}$$

$$x'' + \frac{g}{2}x = 0$$

Since at time $t = 0$, the brick is 5 cm below the equilibrium and not moving, the initial conditions are $x(0) = 5$ and $x'(0) = 0$.

(b) The solution to the differential equation is

$$x = A\cos\left(\sqrt{\frac{g}{2}}t\right) + B\sin\left(\sqrt{\frac{g}{2}}t\right).$$

Since $x(0) = 5$, we have

$$x = A\cos(0) + B\sin(0) = 5 \quad \text{so} \quad A = 5.$$

In addition,

$$x'(t) = -5\sqrt{\frac{g}{2}}\sin\left(\sqrt{\frac{g}{2}}t\right) + B\sqrt{\frac{g}{2}}\cos\left(\sqrt{\frac{g}{2}}t\right)$$

so

$$x'(0) = -5\sqrt{\frac{g}{2}}\sin(0) + B\sqrt{\frac{g}{2}}\cos(0) = 0 \quad \text{so} \quad B = 0.$$

Thus,

$$x = 5\cos\sqrt{\frac{g}{2}}t.$$

22. (a) We are given $\frac{d^2x}{dt^2} = -\frac{g}{l}x$, so $x = C_1\cos\sqrt{\frac{g}{l}}t + C_2\sin\sqrt{\frac{g}{l}}t$. We use the initial conditions to find C_1 and C_2.

$$x(0) = C_1\cos 0 + C_2\sin 0 = C_1 = 0$$

$$x'(0) = -C_1\sqrt{\frac{g}{l}}\sin 0 + C_2\sqrt{\frac{g}{l}}\cos 0 = C_2\sqrt{\frac{g}{l}} = v_0$$

Thus, $C_1 = 0$ and $C_2 = v_0\sqrt{\frac{l}{g}}$, so $x = v_0\sqrt{\frac{l}{g}}\sin\sqrt{\frac{g}{l}}t$.

(b) Again, $x = C_1\cos\sqrt{\frac{g}{l}}t + C_2\sin\sqrt{\frac{g}{l}}t$, but this time, $x(0) = x_0$, and $x'(0) = 0$.

Thus, as before, $x(0) = C_1 = x_0$, and $x'(0) = C_2\sqrt{\frac{g}{l}} = 0$. In this case, $C_1 = x_0$ and $C_2 = 0$. Thus, $x = x_0\cos\sqrt{\frac{g}{l}}t$.

23. (a) If x_0 is increased, the amplitude of the function x is increased, but the period remains the same. In other words, the pendulum will start higher, but the time to swing back and forth will stay the same.

(b) If l is increased, the period of the function x is increased. (Remember, the period of $x_0 \cos \sqrt{\frac{g}{l}} t$ is $\frac{2\pi}{\sqrt{g/l}} = 2\pi \sqrt{l/g}$.)
In other words, it will take longer for the pendulum to swing back and forth.

24. (a) Let $x = \omega t$ and $y = \phi$. Then

$$A\sin(\omega t + \phi) = A(\sin \omega t \cos \phi + \cos \omega t \sin \phi)$$
$$= (A\sin \phi)\cos \omega t + (A\cos \phi)\sin \omega t.$$

(b) If we want $A\sin(\omega t + \phi) = C_1 \cos \omega t + C_2 \sin \omega t$ to be true for all t, then by looking at the answer to part (a), we must have $C_1 = A\sin \phi$ and $C_2 = A\cos \phi$. Thus,

$$\frac{C_1}{C_2} = \frac{A\sin \phi}{A\cos \phi} = \tan \phi,$$

and

$$\sqrt{C_1^2 + C_2^2} = \sqrt{A^2 \sin^2 \phi + A^2 \cos^2 \phi} = A\sqrt{\sin^2 \phi + \cos^2 \phi} = A,$$

so our formulas are justified.

25. (a) $36\dfrac{d^2Q}{dt^2} + \dfrac{Q}{9} = 0$ so $\dfrac{d^2Q}{dt^2} = -\dfrac{Q}{324}$.
Thus,

$$Q = C_1 \cos \frac{1}{18}t + C_2 \sin \frac{1}{18}t.$$
$$Q(0) = 0 = C_1 \cos 0 + C_2 \sin 0 = C_1,$$
$$\text{so} \quad C_1 = 0.$$

So, $Q = C_2 \sin \dfrac{1}{18}t$, and

$$Q' = I = \frac{1}{18}C_2 \cos \frac{1}{18}t.$$
$$Q'(0) = I(0) = 2 = \frac{1}{18}C_2 \cos \left(\frac{1}{18} \cdot 0\right) = \frac{1}{18}C_2,$$
$$\text{so} \quad C_2 = 36.$$

Therefore, $Q = 36 \sin \dfrac{1}{18}t$.

(b) As in part (a), $Q = C_1 \cos \dfrac{1}{18}t + C_2 \sin \dfrac{1}{18}t$.
According to the initial conditions:

$$Q(0) = 6 = C_1 \cos 0 + C_2 \sin 0 = C_1,$$
$$\text{so} \quad C_1 = 6.$$

So $Q = 6 \cos \dfrac{1}{18}t + C_2 \sin \dfrac{1}{18}t$.
Thus,

$$Q' = I = -\frac{1}{3} \sin \frac{1}{18}t + \frac{1}{18}C_2 \cos \frac{1}{18}t.$$
$$Q'(0) = I(0) = 0 = -\frac{1}{3} \sin \left(\frac{1}{18} \cdot 0\right) + \frac{1}{18}C_2 \cos \left(\frac{1}{18} \cdot 0\right) = \frac{1}{18}C_2,$$
$$\text{so} \quad C_2 = 0.$$

Therefore, $Q = 6 \cos \dfrac{1}{18}t$.

26. The equation we have for the charge tells us that:

$$\frac{d^2Q}{dt^2} = -\frac{Q}{LC},$$

where L and C are positive.

If we let $\omega = \sqrt{\frac{1}{LC}}$, we know the solution is of the form:

$$Q = C_1 \cos \omega t + C_2 \sin \omega t.$$

Since $Q(0) = 0$, we find that $C_1 = 0$, so $Q = C_2 \sin \omega t$.

Since $Q'(0) = 4$, and $Q' = \omega C_2 \cos \omega t$, we have $C_2 = \frac{4}{\omega}$, so $Q = \frac{4}{\omega} \sin \omega t$.

But we want the maximum charge, meaning the amplitude of Q, to be $2\sqrt{2}$ coulombs. Thus, we have $\frac{4}{\omega} = 2\sqrt{2}$, which gives us $\omega = \sqrt{2}$.

So we now have: $\sqrt{2} = \frac{1}{\sqrt{LC}} = \frac{1}{\sqrt{10C}}$. Thus, $C = \frac{1}{20}$ farads.

27. We know that the general formula for Q will be of the form:

$$Q = C_1 \cos \omega t + C_2 \sin \omega t.$$

and

$$I = Q' = -C_1 \sin \omega t + C_2 \cos \omega t$$

Thus, as $t \to \infty$, neither one approaches a limit. Instead, they vary sinusoidally, with the same frequency but out of phase. We can think of the charge on the capacitor as being analogous to the displacement of a mass on a spring, oscillating from positive to negative. The current is then like the velocity of the mass, also oscillating from positive to negative. When the charge is maximal or minimal, the current is zero (just like when the spring is at the top or bottom of its motion), and when the current is maximal, the charge is zero (just like when the spring is at the middle of its motion).

Solutions for Section 11.11

Exercises

1. The characteristic equation is $r^2 + 4r + 3 = 0$, so $r = -1$ or -3.
Therefore $y(t) = C_1 e^{-t} + C_2 e^{-3t}$.

2. The characteristic equation is $r^2 + 4r + 4 = 0$, so $r = -2$.
Therefore $y(t) = (C_1 t + C_2) e^{-2t}$.

3. The characteristic equation is $r^2 + 4r + 5 = 0$, so $r = -2 \pm i$.
Therefore $y(t) = C_1 e^{-2t} \cos t + C_2 e^{-2t} \sin t$.

4. The characteristic equation is $r^2 - 7 = 0$, so $r = \pm\sqrt{7}$.
Therefore $s(t) = C_1 e^{\sqrt{7}t} + C_2 e^{-\sqrt{7}t}$.

5. The characteristic equation is $r^2 + 7 = 0$, so $r = \pm\sqrt{7}i$.
Therefore $s(t) = C_1 \cos \sqrt{7}t + C_2 \sin \sqrt{7}t$.

6. If we try a solution $y(t) = Ae^{rt}$ then

$$r^2 - 3r + 2 = 0$$

which has the solutions $r = 2$ and $r = 1$ so that the general solution is of the form

$$y(t) = Ae^{2t} + Be^{t}$$

7. The characteristic equation is $4r^2 + 8r + 3 = 0$, so $r = -1/2$ or $-3/2$.
Therefore $z(t) = C_1 e^{-t/2} + C_2 e^{-3t/2}$.

8. The characteristic equation is $r^2 + 4r + 8 = 0$, so $r = -2 \pm 2i$.
Therefore $x(t) = C_1 e^{-2t} \cos 2t + C_2 e^{-2t} \sin 2t$.

9. The characteristic equation is $r^2 + r + 1 = 0$, so $r = -\frac{1}{2} \pm \frac{\sqrt{3}}{2}i$.
Therefore $p(t) = C_1 e^{-t/2} \cos \frac{\sqrt{3}}{2}t + C_2 e^{-t/2} \sin \frac{\sqrt{3}}{2}t$.

10. If we try a solution $z(t) = Ae^{rt}$ then

$$r^2 + 2 = 0$$

so that the general solution is of the form:

$$y(t) = A \sin \sqrt{2}t + B \cos \sqrt{2}t$$

11. If we try a solution $z(t) = Ae^{rt}$ then

$$r^2 + 2r = 0$$

which has solutions $r = 0$ and $r = -2$ so that the general solution is of the form

$$y(t) = A + Be^{-2t}$$

12. If we try a solution $P(t) = Ae^{rt}$ then

$$r^2 + 2r + 1 = 0$$

which has the repeated solution $r = -1$ so that the general solution is of the form

$$y(t) = (At + B)e^{-t}$$

13. The characteristic equation is

$$r^2 + 5r + 6 = 0$$

which has the solutions $r = -2$ and $r = -3$ so that

$$y(t) = Ae^{-3t} + Be^{-2t}$$

The initial condition $y(0) = 1$ gives

$$A + B = 1$$

and $y'(0) = 0$ gives

$$-3A - 2B = 0$$

so that $A = -2$ and $B = 3$ and

$$y(t) = -2e^{-3t} + 3e^{-2t}$$

14. The characteristic equation is

$$r^2 + 5r + 6 = 0$$

which has the solutions $r = -2$ and $r = -3$ so that

$$y(t) = Ae^{-3t} + Be^{-2t}$$

The initial condition $y(0) = 5$ gives

$$A + B = 5$$

and $y'(0) = 1$ gives

$$-3A - 2B = 1$$

so that $A = -11$ and $B = 16$ and

$$y(t) = -11e^{-3t} + 16e^{-2t}$$

15. The characteristic equation is

$$r^2 - 3r - 4 = 0$$

which has the solutions $r = 4$ and $r = -1$ so that

$$y(t) = Ae^{4t} + Be^{-t}$$

The initial condition $y(0) = 1$ gives

$$A + B = 1$$

and $y'(0) = 0$ gives

$$4A - B = 0$$

so that $A = \frac{1}{5}$ and $B = \frac{4}{5}$ and

$$y(t) = \frac{1}{5}e^{4t} + \frac{4}{5}e^{-t}$$

16. The characteristic equation is

$$r^2 - 3r - 4 = 0$$

which has the solutions $r = 4$ and $r = -1$ so that

$$y(t) = Ae^{4t} + Be^{-t}$$

The initial condition $y(0) = 0$ gives

$$A + B = 0$$

and $y'(0) = 0.5$ gives

$$4A - B = 0.5$$

so that $A = \frac{1}{10}$ and $B = -\frac{1}{10}$ and

$$y(t) = \frac{1}{10}e^{4t} - \frac{1}{10}e^{-t}$$

17. The characteristic equation is $r^2 + 6r + 5 = 0$, so $r = -1$ or -5.
Therefore $y(t) = C_1 e^{-t} + C_2 e^{-5t}$.
$y'(t) = -C_1 e^{-t} - 5C_2 e^{-5t}$
$y'(0) = 0 = -C_1 - 5C_2$
$y(0) = 1 = C_1 + C_2$
 Therefore $C_2 = -1/4$, $C_1 = 5/4$ and $y(t) = \frac{5}{4}e^{-t} - \frac{1}{4}e^{-5t}$.

18. The characteristic equation is $r^2 + 6r + 5 = 0$, so $r = -1$ or -5.
Therefore $y(t) = C_1 e^{-t} + C_2 e^{-5t}$.
$y'(t) = -C_1 e^{-t} - 5C_2 e^{-5t}$
$y'(0) = 5 = -C_1 - 5C_2$
$y(0) = 5 = C_1 + C_2$
 Therefore $C_2 = -5/2$, $C_1 = 15/2$ and $y(t) = \frac{15}{2}e^{-t} - \frac{5}{2}e^{-5t}$.

19. The characteristic equation is $r^2 + 6r + 10 = 0$, so $r = -3 \pm i$.
Therefore $y(t) = C_1 e^{-3t} \cos t + C_2 e^{-3t} \sin t$.
$y'(t) = C_1[e^{-3t}(-\sin t) + (-3e^{-3t})\cos t] + C_2[e^{-3t}\cos t + (-3e^{-3t})\sin t]$
$y'(0) = 2 = -3C_1 + C_2$
$y(0) = 0 = C_1$
 Therefore $C_1 = 0, C_2 = 2$ and $y(t) = 2e^{-3t}\sin t$.

20. The characteristic equation is $r^2 + 6r + 10 = 0$, so $r = -3 \pm i$.
Therefore $y(t) = C_1 e^{-3t} \cos t + C_2 e^{-3t} \sin t$.
$y'(t) = C_1[e^{-3t}(-\sin t) + (-3e^{-3t})\cos t] + C_2[e^{-3t}\cos t + (-3e^{-3t})\sin t]$
$y'(0) = 0 = -3C_1 + C_2$
$y(0) = 0 = C_1$
 Therefore $C_1 = C_2 = 0$ and $y(t) = 0$.

21. The characteristic equation is

$$r^2 + 5r + 6 = 0$$

which has the solutions $r = -2$ and $r = -3$ so that

$$y(t) = Ae^{-2t} + Be^{-3t}$$

The initial condition $y(0) = 1$ gives

$$A + B = 1$$

and $y(1) = 0$ gives

$$Ae^{-2} + Be^{-3} = 0$$

so that $A = \dfrac{1}{1 - e}$ and $B = -\dfrac{e}{1 - e}$ and

$$y(t) = \frac{1}{1-e}e^{-2t} + \frac{-e}{1-e}e^{-3t}$$

22. The characteristic equation is

$$r^2 + 5r + 6 = 0$$

which has the solutions $r = -2$ and $r = -3$ so that

$$y(t) = Ae^{-2t} + Be^{-3t}$$

The initial condition $y(-2) = 0$ gives

$$Ae^4 + Be^6 = 0$$

and $y(2) = 3$ gives

$$Ae^{-4} + Be^{-6} = 3$$

so that $A = \frac{3e^8}{e^4 - 1}$ and $B = -\frac{3e^6}{e^4 - 1}$ and

$$y(t) = \frac{3e^8}{e^4 - 1} e^{-2t} - \frac{3e^6}{e^4 - 1} e^{-3t}$$

23. The characteristic equation is $r^2 + 2r + 2 = 0$, so $r = -1 \pm i$.
Therefore $p(t) = C_1 e^{-t} \cos t + C_2 e^{-t} \sin t$.
$p(0) = 0 = C_1$ so $p(t) = C_2 e^{-t} \sin t$
$p(\pi/2) = 20 = C_2 e^{-\pi/2} \sin \frac{\pi}{2}$ so $C_2 = 20 e^{\pi/2}$
Therefore $p(t) = 20 e^{\frac{\pi}{2}} e^{-t} \sin t = 20 e^{\frac{\pi}{2} - t} \sin t$.

24. The characteristic equation is $r^2 + 4r + 5 = 0$, so $r = -2 \pm i$.
Therefore $p(t) = C_1 e^{-2t} \cos t + C_2 e^{-2t} \sin t$.
$p(0) = 1 = C_1$ so $p(t) = e^{-2t} \cos t + C_2 e^{-2t} \sin t$
$p(\pi/2) = 5 = C_2 e^{-\pi}$ so $C_2 = 5 e^{\pi}$.
Therefore $p(t) = e^{-2t} \cos t + 5 e^{\pi} e^{-2t} \sin t = e^{-2t} \cos t + 5 e^{\pi - 2t} \sin t$.

Problems

25. (a) $x'' + 4x = 0$ represents an undamped oscillator, and so goes with (IV).
(b) $x'' - 4x = 0$ has characteristic equation $r^2 - 4 = 0$ and so $r = \pm 2$. The solution is $C_1 e^{-2t} + C_2 e^{2t}$. This represents non-oscillating motion, so it goes with (II).
(c) $x'' - 0.2x' + 1.01x = 0$ has characteristic equation $r^2 - 0.2 + 1.01 = 0$ so $b^2 - 4ac = 0.04 - 4.04 = -4$, and $r = 0.1 \pm i$. So the solution is

$$C_1 e^{(0.1+i)t} + C_2 e^{(0.1-i)t} = e^{0.1t}(A \sin t + B \cos t).$$

The negative coefficient in the x' term represents an amplifying force. This is reflected in the solution by $e^{0.1t}$, which increases as t increases, so this goes with (I).
(d) $x'' + 0.2x' + 1.01x$ has characteristic equation $r^2 + 0.2r + 1.01 = 0$ so $b^2 - 4ac = -4$. This represents a damped oscillator. We have $r = -0.1 \pm i$ and so the solution is $x = e^{-0.1t}(A \sin t + B \cos t)$, which goes with (III).

26. We solve the characteristic equation in each case to obtain solutions to the differential equation.
(a) $r^2 + 5r + 6 = 0$, so $r = -2$ or -3. Then, $y = C_1 e^{-2t} + C_2 e^{-3t}$.
(b) $r^2 + r - 6 = 0$, so $r = 2$ or -3. Then, $y = C_1 e^{2t} + C_2 e^{-3t}$.
(c) $r^2 + 4r + 9 = 0$, so $r = -2 \pm \sqrt{5}i$. Then, $y = C_1 e^{-2t} \cos(\sqrt{5}t) + C_2 e^{-2t} \sin(\sqrt{5}t)$.
(d) $r^2 = -9$, so $r = \pm 3i$. Then, $y = C_1 \cos(3t) + C_2 \sin(3t)$.

Since (d) is undamped oscillations, it must be graph (I). Similarly, (c) is damped oscillations and so must be graph (II). Equation (a) is exponential decay, and so must be (IV). This leaves (III) to match with (b), which could be exponential growth or decay.

27. $0 = \frac{d^2}{dt^2}(e^{2t}) - 5\frac{d}{dt}(e^{2t}) + ke^{2t} = 4e^{2t} - 10e^{2t} + ke^{2t} = e^{2t}(k - 6)$. Since $e^{2t} \neq 0$, we must have $k - 6 = 0$. Therefore $k = 6$.

The characteristic equation is $r^2 - 5r + 6 = 0$, so $r = 2$ or 3. Therefore $y(t) = C_1 e^{2t} + C_2 e^{3t}$.

28. In the underdamped case, $b^2 - 4c < 0$ so $4c - b^2 > 0$. Since the roots of the characteristic equation are

$$\alpha \pm i\beta = \frac{-b \pm \sqrt{b^2 - 4c}}{2} = \frac{-b \pm i\sqrt{4c - b^2}}{2}$$

we have $\alpha = -b/2$ and $\beta = (\sqrt{4c - b^2})/2$ or $\beta = -(\sqrt{4c - b^2})/2$. Since the general solution is

$$y = C_1 e^{\alpha t} \cos \beta t + C_2 e^{\alpha t} \sin \beta t$$

and since α is negative, $y \to 0$ as $t \to \infty$.

29. Recall that $s'' + bs' + cs = 0$ is overdamped if the discriminant $b^2 - 4c > 0$, critically damped if $b^2 - 4c = 0$, and underdamped if $b^2 - 4c < 0$. Since $b^2 - 4c = b^2 - 20$, the solution is overdamped if $b > 2\sqrt{5}$ or $b < -2\sqrt{5}$, critically damped if $b = \pm 2\sqrt{5}$, and underdamped if $-2\sqrt{5} < b < 2\sqrt{5}$.

30. Recall that $s'' + bs' + cs = 0$ is overdamped if the discriminant $b^2 - 4c > 0$, critically damped if $b^2 - 4c = 0$, and underdamped if $b^2 - 4c < 0$. This has discriminant $b^2 - 4c = b^2 + 64$. Since $b^2 + 64$ is always positive, the solution is always overdamped.

31. Recall that $F_{\text{drag}} = -c\frac{ds}{dt}$, so to find the largest coefficient of damping we look at the coefficient of s'. Thus spring (iii) has the largest coefficient of damping.

32. The restoring force is given by $F_{\text{spring}} = -ks$, so we look for the smallest coefficient of s. Spring (iv) exerts the smallest restoring force.

33. The frictional force is $F_{\text{drag}} = -c\frac{ds}{dt}$. Thus spring (iv) has the smallest frictional force.

34. All of these differential equations have solutions of the form $C_1 e^{\alpha t} \cos \beta t + C_2 e^{\alpha t} \sin \beta t$. The spring with the longest period has the smallest β. Since $i\beta$ is the complex part of the roots of the characteristic equation, $\beta = \frac{1}{2}(\sqrt{4c - b^2})$. Thus spring (iii) has the longest period.

35. The stiffest spring exerts the greatest restoring force for a small displacement. Recall that by Hooke's Law $F_{\text{spring}} = -ks$, so we look for the differential equation with the greatest coefficient of s. This is spring (ii).

36. The characteristic equation is $r^2 + r - 2 = 0$, so $r = 1$ or -2. Therefore $z(t) = C_1 e^t + C_2 e^{-2t}$. Since $e^t \to \infty$ as $t \to \infty$, we must have $C_1 = 0$. Therefore $z(t) = C_2 e^{-2t}$. Furthermore, $z(0) = 3 = C_2$, so $z(t) = 3e^{-2t}$.

37. (a) If $r_1 = \frac{-b - \sqrt{b^2 - 4c}}{2}$ then $r_1 < 0$ since both b and $\sqrt{b^2 - 4c}$ are positive.

If $r_2 = \frac{-b + \sqrt{b^2 - 4c}}{2}$, then $r_2 < 0$ because

$$b = \sqrt{b^2} > \sqrt{b^2 - 4c}.$$

(b) The general solution to the differential equation is of the form

$$y = C_1 e^{r_1 t} + C_2 e^{r_2 t}$$

and since r_1 and r_2 are both negative, y must go to 0 as $t \to \infty$.

38. In the overdamped case, we have a solution of the form

$$s = C_1 e^{r_1 t} + C_2 e^{r_2 t}$$

where r_1 and r_2 are real. We find a t such that $s = 0$, hence $C_1 e^{r_1 t} = -C_2 e^{r_2 t}$.

If $C_2 = 0$, then $C_1 = 0$, hence $s = 0$ for all t. But this does not match with Figure 11.13, so $C_2 \neq 0$. We divide by $C_2 e^{r_1 t}$ and get:

$$-\frac{C_1}{C_2} = e^{(r_2 - r_1)t}, \quad \text{where} \quad -\frac{C_1}{C_2} > 0,$$

so the exponential is always positive. Therefore

$$(r_2 - r_1)t = \ln\left(-\frac{C_1}{C_2}\right)$$

and

$$t = \frac{\ln\left(-\frac{C_1}{C_2}\right)}{(r_2 - r_1)}.$$

So the mass passes through the equilibrium point only once, when $t = \frac{\ln\left(-\frac{C_1}{C_2}\right)}{(r_2 - r_1)}$.

39. (a) $\dfrac{d^2 y}{dt^2} = -\dfrac{dx}{dt} = y$ so $\dfrac{d^2 y}{dt^2} - y = 0.$

(b) Characteristic equation $r^2 - 1 = 0$, so $r = \pm 1$.

The general solution for y is $y = C_1 e^t + C_2 e^{-t}$, so $x = C_2 e^{-t} - C_1 e^t$.

40. The differential equation is $Q'' + 2Q' + \frac{1}{4}Q = 0$, so the characteristic equation is $r^2 + 2r + \frac{1}{4} = 0$. This has roots $\frac{-2 \pm \sqrt{3}}{2} = -1 \pm \frac{\sqrt{3}}{2}$. Thus, the general solution is

$$Q(t) = C_1 e^{(-1+\frac{\sqrt{3}}{2})t} + C_2 e^{(-1-\frac{\sqrt{3}}{2})t},$$

$$Q'(t) = C_1\left(-1 + \frac{\sqrt{3}}{2}\right)e^{(-1+\frac{\sqrt{3}}{2})t} + C_2\left(-1 - \frac{\sqrt{3}}{2}\right)e^{(-1-\frac{\sqrt{3}}{2})t}.$$

We have

(a)

$$Q(0) = C_1 + C_2 = 0$$

$$\text{and} \quad Q'(0) = \left(-1 + \frac{\sqrt{3}}{2}\right)C_1 + \left(-1 - \frac{\sqrt{3}}{2}\right)C_2 = 2.$$

Using the formula for $Q(t)$, we have $C_1 = -C_2$. Using the formula for $Q'(t)$, we have:

$$2 = \left(-1 + \frac{\sqrt{3}}{2}\right)(-C_2) + \left(-1 - \frac{\sqrt{3}}{2}\right)C_2 = -\sqrt{3}C_2$$

$$\text{so,} \quad C_2 = -\frac{2}{\sqrt{3}}.$$

Thus, $C_1 = \frac{2}{\sqrt{3}}$, and $Q(t) = \frac{2}{\sqrt{3}}\left(e^{(-1+\frac{\sqrt{3}}{2})t} - e^{(-1-\frac{\sqrt{3}}{2})t}\right).$

(b) We have

$$Q(0) = C_1 + C_2 = 2$$

$$\text{and} \quad Q'(0) = \left(-1 + \frac{\sqrt{3}}{2}\right)C_1 + \left(-1 - \frac{\sqrt{3}}{2}\right)C_2 = 0.$$

Using the first equation, we have $C_1 = 2 - C_2$. Thus,

$$\left(-1 + \frac{\sqrt{3}}{2}\right)(2 - C_2) + \left(-1 - \frac{\sqrt{3}}{2}\right)C_2 = 0$$

$$-\sqrt{3}C_2 = 2 - \sqrt{3}$$

$$C_2 = -\frac{2 - \sqrt{3}}{\sqrt{3}}$$

$$\text{and} \quad C_1 = 2 - C_2 = \frac{2 + \sqrt{3}}{\sqrt{3}}.$$

Thus, $Q(t) = \frac{1}{\sqrt{3}}\left((2 + \sqrt{3})e^{(-1+\frac{\sqrt{3}}{2})t} - (2 - \sqrt{3})e^{(-1-\frac{\sqrt{3}}{2})t}\right).$

41. In this case, the differential equation describing the charge is $Q'' + Q' + \frac{1}{4}Q = 0$, so the characteristic equation is $r^2 + r + \frac{1}{4} = 0$. This equation has one root, $r = -\frac{1}{2}$, so the equation for charge is

$$Q(t) = (C_1 + C_2 t)e^{-\frac{1}{2}t},$$

$$Q'(t) = -\frac{1}{2}(C_1 + C_2 t)e^{-\frac{1}{2}t} + C_2 e^{-\frac{1}{2}t}$$

$$= \left(C_2 - \frac{C_1}{2} - \frac{C_2 t}{2}\right)e^{-\frac{1}{2}t}.$$

(a) We have

$$Q(0) = C_1 = 0,$$

$$Q'(0) = C_2 - \frac{C_1}{2} = 2.$$

Thus, $C_1 = 0, C_2 = 2$, and

$$Q(t) = 2te^{-\frac{1}{2}t}.$$

(b) We have

$$Q(0) = C_1 = 2,$$
$$Q'(0) = C_2 - \frac{C_1}{2} = 0.$$

Thus, $C_1 = 2$, $C_2 = 1$, and

$$Q(t) = (2 + t)e^{-\frac{1}{2}t}.$$

(c) The resistance was decreased by exactly the amount to switch the circuit from the overdamped case to the critically damped case. Comparing the solutions of parts (a) and (b) in Problems 40, we find that in the critically damped case the net charge goes to 0 much faster as $t \to \infty$.

42. In this case, the differential equation describing charge is $8Q'' + 2Q' + \frac{1}{4}Q = 0$, so the characteristic equation is $8r^2 + 2r + \frac{1}{4} = 0$. This quadratic equation has solutions

$$r = \frac{-2 \pm \sqrt{4 - 4 \cdot 8 \cdot \frac{1}{4}}}{16} = -\frac{1}{8} \pm \frac{1}{8}i.$$

Thus, the equation for charge is

$$Q(t) = e^{-\frac{1}{8}t}\left(A\sin\frac{t}{8} + B\cos\frac{t}{8}\right).$$
$$Q'(t) = -\frac{1}{8}e^{-\frac{1}{8}t}\left(A\sin\frac{t}{8} + B\cos\frac{t}{8}\right) + e^{-\frac{1}{8}t}\left(\frac{1}{8}A\cos\frac{t}{8} - \frac{1}{8}B\sin\frac{t}{8}\right)$$
$$= \frac{1}{8}e^{-\frac{1}{8}t}\left((A - B)\cos\frac{t}{8} + (-A - B)\sin\frac{t}{8}\right).$$

(a) We have

$$Q(0) = B = 0,$$
$$Q'(0) = \frac{1}{8}(A - B) = 2.$$

Thus, $B = 0$, $A = 16$, and

$$Q(t) = 16e^{-\frac{1}{8}t}\sin\frac{t}{8}.$$

(b) We have

$$Q(0) = B = 2,$$
$$Q'(0) = \frac{1}{8}(A - B) = 0.$$

Thus, $B = 2$, $A = 2$, and

$$Q(t) = 2e^{-\frac{1}{8}t}\left(\sin\frac{t}{8} + \cos\frac{t}{8}\right).$$

(c) By increasing the inductance, we have gone from the overdamped case to the underdamped case. We find that while the charge still tends to 0 as $t \to \infty$, the charge in the underdamped case oscillates between positive and negative values. In the over-damped case of Problem 40, the charge starts nonnegative and remains positive.

43. The differential equation for the charge on the capacitor, given a resistance R, a capacitance C, and and inductance L, is

$$LQ'' + RQ' + \frac{Q}{C} = 0.$$

The corresponding characteristic equation is $Lr^2 + Rr + \frac{1}{C} = 0$. This equation has roots

$$r = -\frac{R}{2L} \pm \frac{\sqrt{R^2 - \frac{4L}{C}}}{2L}.$$

(a) If $R^2 - \frac{4L}{C} < 0$, the solution is

$$Q(t) = e^{-\frac{R}{2L}t}(A\sin\omega t + B\cos\omega t) \text{ for some } A \text{ and } B,$$

where $\omega = \frac{\sqrt{R^2 - \frac{4L}{C}}}{2L}$. As $t \to \infty$, $Q(t)$ clearly goes to 0.

(b) If $R^2 - \dfrac{4L}{C} = 0$, the solution is

$$Q(t) = e^{-\frac{R}{t}}(A + Bt) \text{ for some } A \text{ and } B.$$

Again, as $t \to \infty$, the charge goes to 0.

(c) If $R^2 - \dfrac{4L}{C} > 0$, the solution is

$$Q(t) = Ae^{r_1 t} + Be^{r_2 t} \text{ for some } A \text{ and } B,$$

where

$$r_1 = -\frac{R}{2L} + \frac{\sqrt{R^2 - \frac{4L}{C}}}{2L}, \quad \text{and} \quad r_2 = -\frac{R}{2L} - \frac{\sqrt{R^2 - \frac{4L}{C}}}{2L}.$$

Notice that r_2 is clearly negative. r_1 is also negative since

$$\frac{\sqrt{R^2 - \frac{4L}{C}}}{2L} < \frac{\sqrt{R^2}}{2L} \quad (L \text{ and } C \text{ are positive})$$

$$= \frac{R}{2L}.$$

Since r_1 and r_2 are negative, again $Q(t) \to 0$, as $t \to \infty$.

Thus, for any circuit with a resistor, a capacitor and an inductor, $Q(t) \to 0$ as $t \to \infty$. Compare this with Problem 27 in Section 11.10, where we showed that in a circuit with just a capacitor and inductor, the charge varied along a sine curve.

44. (a) Since $y = \dfrac{e^{r_1 t} - e^{r_2 t}}{r_1 - r_2}$, we have $y' = \dfrac{r_1 e^{r_1 t} - r_2 e^{r_2 t}}{r_1 - r_2}$ and $y'' = \dfrac{r_1^2 e^{r_1 t} - r_2^2 e^{r_2 t}}{r_1 - r_2}$. Thus

$$\begin{aligned}
y'' + by' + cy &= \frac{r_1^2 e^{r_1 t} - r_2^2 e^{r_2 t}}{r_1 - r_2} + b\frac{r_1 e^{r_1 t} - r_2 e^{r_2 t}}{r_1 - r_2} + c\frac{e^{r_1 t} - e^{r_2 t}}{r_1 - r_2} \\
&= \frac{(r_1^2 + br_1 + c)e^{r_1 t}}{r_1 - r_2} - \frac{(r_2^2 + br_2 + c)e^{r_2 t}}{r_1 - r_2} \\
&= 0,
\end{aligned}$$

since both r_1 and r_2 satisfy $r^2 + br + c = 0$.

(b) We have a solution $y = (e^{r_1 t} - e^{r_2 t})/(r_1 - r_2)$ and $r_1 = r_2 + h$. Thus

$$\begin{aligned}
y &= \frac{e^{(r_2 + h)t} - e^{r_2 t}}{h} \\
&= \frac{e^{r_2 t}e^{ht} - e^{r_2 t}}{h} \\
&= e^{r_2 t}\frac{e^{ht} - 1}{h}.
\end{aligned}$$

(c) The Taylor series for e^x is $1 + x + x^2/2! + x^3/3! + \cdots$, so

$$\begin{aligned}
\frac{e^{ht} - 1}{h} &= \frac{1 + ht + h^2 t^2/2! + \cdots - 1}{h} \\
&= t + \frac{ht^2}{2!} + \frac{h^2 t^3}{3!} + \cdots.
\end{aligned}$$

(d) $\displaystyle \lim_{h \to 0} e^{r_2 t}\frac{e^{ht} - 1}{h} = \lim_{h \to 0} e^{r_2 t}\left(t + \frac{ht^2}{2!} + \frac{h^2 t^3}{3!} + \cdots\right) = te^{r_2 t}.$

(e) The solutions to $r^2 + br + c = 0$ are $\dfrac{-b \pm \sqrt{b^2 - 4c}}{2} = -b/2$, since $b^2 - 4c = 0$ because we have a double root. Thus $r_1 = r_2 = -b/2$, so our solution is $y = te^{r_2 t} = te^{-bt/2}$. Thus

$$y' = \left(1 - \frac{bt}{2}\right)e^{-\frac{bt}{2}}$$

and

$$y'' = \left(-\frac{b}{2} + \frac{b^2 t}{4} - \frac{b}{2}\right) e^{-\frac{bt}{2}} = \left(-b + \frac{b^2 t}{4}\right) e^{-\frac{bt}{2}}.$$

So

$$y'' + by' + cy = \left(\left(-b + \frac{b^2 t}{4}\right) + b(1 - \frac{bt}{2}) + ct\right) e^{-\frac{bt}{2}} = \left(-\frac{b^2}{4} + c\right) t e^{-\frac{bt}{2}} = 0,$$

since $b^2 - 4c = 0$.

Solutions for Chapter 11 Review

Exercises

1. This equation is separable, so we integrate, giving

$$\int dP = \int t\, dt$$

so

$$P(t) = \frac{t^2}{2} + C.$$

2. This equation is separable, so we integrate, giving

$$\int \frac{1}{0.2y - 8}\, dy = \int dx$$

so

$$\frac{1}{0.2} \ln |0.2y - 8| = x + C.$$

Thus

$$y(x) = 40 + Ae^{0.2x}.$$

3. This equation is separable, so we integrate, giving

$$\int \frac{1}{10 - 2P}\, dP = \int dt$$

so

$$\frac{1}{-2} \ln |10 - 2P| = t + C.$$

Thus

$$P = 5 + Ae^{-2t}.$$

4. This equation is separable, so we integrate, giving

$$\int \frac{1}{10 + 0.5H}\, dH = \int dt$$

so

$$\frac{1}{0.5} \ln |10 + 0.5H| = t + C.$$

Thus

$$H = Ae^{0.5t} - 20.$$

5. This equation is separable, so we integrate, using the table of integrals or partial fractions, to get

$$\int \frac{1}{R - 3R^2} \, dR = 2 \int dt$$

$$\int \frac{1}{R} \, dR + \int \frac{3}{1 - 3R} \, dR = 2 \int dt$$

so

$$\ln |R| - \ln |1 - 3R| = 2t + C$$

$$\ln \left| \frac{R}{1 - 3R} \right| = 2t + C$$

$$\frac{R}{1 - 3R} = Ae^{2t}$$

$$R = \frac{Ae^{2t}}{1 + 3Ae^{2t}}.$$

6. This equation is separable, so we integrate, using the table of integrals or partial fractions, to get:

$$\int \frac{250}{100P - P^2} \, dP = \int dt$$

$$\frac{250}{100} \left(\int \frac{1}{P} \, dP + \int \frac{1}{100 - P} \, dP \right) = \int dt$$

so

$$2.5(\ln |P| - \ln |100 - P|) = t + C$$

$$2.5 \ln \left| \frac{P}{100 - P} \right| = t + C$$

$$\frac{P}{100 - P} = Ae^{0.4t}$$

$$P = \frac{100Ae^{0.4t}}{1 + Ae^{0.4t}}$$

7. $\frac{dy}{dx} + xy^2 = 0$ means $\frac{dy}{dx} = -xy^2$, so $\int \frac{dy}{y^2} = \int -x \, dx$ giving $-\frac{1}{y} = -\frac{x^2}{2} + C$. Since $y(1) = 1$ we have $-1 = -\frac{1}{2} + C$ so $C = -\frac{1}{2}$. Thus, $-\frac{1}{y} = -\frac{x^2}{2} - \frac{1}{2}$ giving $y = \frac{2}{x^2 + 1}$.

8. $\frac{dP}{dt} = 0.03P + 400$ so $\int \frac{dP}{P + \frac{40000}{3}} = \int 0.03 dt$.

$\ln \left| P + \frac{40000}{3} \right| = 0.03t + C$ giving $P = Ae^{0.03t} - \frac{40000}{3}$. Since $P(0) = 0$, $A = \frac{40000}{3}$, therefore $P = \frac{40000}{3}(e^{0.03t} - 1)$.

9. $1 + y^2 - \frac{dy}{dx} = 0$ gives $\frac{dy}{dx} = y^2 + 1$, so $\int \frac{dy}{1 + y^2} = \int dx$ and $\arctan y = x + C$. Since $y(0) = 0$ we have $C = 0$, giving $y = \tan x$.

10. $2 \sin x - y^2 \frac{dy}{dx} = 0$ giving $2 \sin x = y^2 \frac{dy}{dx}$. $\int 2 \sin x \, dx = \int y^2 \, dy$ so $-2 \cos x = \frac{y^3}{3} + C$. Since $y(0) = 3$ we have $-2 = 9 + C$, so $C = -11$. Thus, $-2 \cos x = \frac{y^3}{3} - 11$ giving $y = \sqrt[3]{33 - 6 \cos x}$.

11. $\frac{dk}{dt} = (1 + \ln t)k$ gives $\int \frac{dk}{k} = \int (1 + \ln t) dt$ so $\ln |k| = t \ln t + C$. $k(1) = 1$, so $0 = 0 + C$, or $C = 0$. Thus, $\ln |k| = t \ln t$ and $|k| = e^{t \ln t} = t^t$, giving $k = \pm t^t$.
But recall $k(1) = 1$, so $k = t^t$ is the solution.

12. $\frac{dy}{dx} = \frac{y(3 - x)}{x(\frac{1}{2}y - 4)}$ gives $\int \frac{(\frac{1}{2}y - 4)}{y} \, dy = \int \frac{(3 - x)}{x} \, dx$ so $\int (\frac{1}{2} - \frac{4}{y}) dy = \int (\frac{3}{x} - 1) dx$. Thus $\frac{1}{2}y - 4 \ln |y| = 3 \ln |x| - x + C$. Since $y(1) = 5$, we have $\frac{5}{2} - 4 \ln 5 = \ln |1| - 1 + C$ so $C = \frac{7}{2} - 4 \ln 5$. Thus,

$$\frac{1}{2}y - 4 \ln |y| = 3 \ln |x| - x + \frac{7}{2} - 4 \ln 5.$$

We cannot solve for y in terms of x, so we leave the equation in this form.

13. $\frac{dy}{dx} = \frac{0.2y(18+0.1x)}{x(100+0.5y)}$ giving $\int \frac{(100+0.5y)}{0.2y} \, dy = \int \frac{18+0.1x}{x} \, dx$, so

$$\int \left(\frac{500}{y} + \frac{5}{2} \right) dy = \int \left(\frac{18}{x} + \frac{1}{10} \right) dx.$$

Therefore, $500 \ln |y| + \frac{5}{2} y = 18 \ln |x| + \frac{1}{10} x + C$. Since the curve passes through (10,10), $500 \ln 10 + 25 = 18 \ln 10 + 1 + C$, so $C = 482 \ln 10 + 24$. Thus, the solution is

$$500 \ln |y| + \frac{5}{2} y = 18 \ln |x| + \frac{1}{10} x + 482 \ln 10 + 24.$$

We cannot solve for y in terms of x, so we leave the answer in this form.

14. This equation is separable and so we write it as

$$\frac{1}{z(z-1)} \frac{dz}{dt} = 1.$$

We integrate with respect to t, giving

$$\int \frac{1}{z(z-1)} dz = \int dt$$

$$\int \frac{1}{z-1} dz - \int \frac{1}{z} dz = \int dt$$

$$\ln |z-1| - \ln |z| = t + C$$

$$\ln \left| \frac{z-1}{z} \right| = t + C,$$

so that

$$\frac{z-1}{z} = e^{t+C} = ke^t.$$

Solving for z gives

$$z(t) = \frac{1}{1 - ke^t}.$$

The initial condition $z(0) = 10$ gives

$$\frac{1}{1-k} = 10$$

or $k = 0.9$. The solution is therefore

$$z(t) = \frac{1}{1 - 0.9e^t}.$$

15. Using the solution of the logistic equation given on page 563 in Section 11.7, and using $y(0) = 1$, we get $y = \frac{10}{1+9e^{-10t}}$.

16. $\frac{dy}{dx} = \frac{y(100-x)}{x(20-y)}$ gives $\int \left(\frac{20-y}{y} \right) dy = \int \left(\frac{100-x}{x} \right) dx$. Thus, $20 \ln |y| - y = 100 \ln |x| - x + C$. The curve passes through $(1, 20)$, so $20 \ln 20 - 20 = -1 + C$ giving $C = 20 \ln 20 - 19$. Therefore, $20 \ln |y| - y = 100 \ln |x| - x + 20 \ln 20 - 19$. We cannot solve for y in terms of x, so we leave the equation in this form.

17. $\frac{df}{dx} = \sqrt{xf(x)}$ gives $\int \frac{df}{\sqrt{f(x)}} = \int \sqrt{x} \, dx$, so $2\sqrt{f(x)} = \frac{2}{3} x^{\frac{3}{2}} + C$. Since $f(1) = 1$, we have $2 = \frac{2}{3} + C$ so $C = \frac{4}{3}$. Thus, $2\sqrt{f(x)} = \frac{2}{3} x^{\frac{3}{2}} + \frac{4}{3}$, so $f(x) = (\frac{1}{3} x^{\frac{3}{2}} + \frac{2}{3})^2$. (Note: this is only defined for $x \geq 0$.)

18. $\frac{dy}{dx} = e^{x-y}$ giving $\int e^y \, dy = \int e^x \, dx$ so $e^y = e^x + C$. Since $y(0) = 1$, we have $e^1 = e^0 + C$ so $C = e - 1$. Thus, $e^y = e^x + e - 1$, so $y = \ln(e^x + e - 1)$. [Note: $e^x + e - 1 > 0$ always.]

19. $\frac{dy}{dx} = e^{x+y} = e^x e^y$ implies $\int e^{-y} \, dy = \int e^x \, dx$ implies $-e^{-y} = e^x + C$. Since $y = 0$ when $x = 1$, we have $-1 = e + C$, giving $C = -1 - e$. Therefore $-e^{-y} = e^x - 1 - e$ and $y = -\ln(1 + e - e^x)$.

20. $e^{-\cos\theta} \frac{dz}{d\theta} = \sqrt{1 - z^2} \sin\theta$ implies $\int \frac{dz}{\sqrt{1-z^2}} = \int e^{\cos\theta} \sin\theta \, d\theta$ implies $\arcsin z = -e^{\cos\theta} + C$. According to the initial conditions: $z(0) = \frac{1}{2}$, so $\arcsin \frac{1}{2} = -e^{\cos 0} + C$, therefore $\frac{\pi}{6} = -e + C$, and $C = \frac{\pi}{6} + e$. Thus $z = \sin(-e^{\cos\theta} + \frac{\pi}{6} + e)$.

21. $(1+t^2)y\frac{dy}{dt} = 1-y$ implies that $\int \frac{y\,dy}{1-y} = \int \frac{dt}{1+t^2}$ implies that $\int \left(-1 + \frac{1}{1-y}\right) dy = \int \frac{dt}{1+t^2}$. Therefore $-y - \ln|1-y| = \arctan t + C$. $y(1) = 0$, so $0 = \arctan 1 + C$, and $C = -\frac{\pi}{4}$, so $-y - \ln|1-y| = \arctan t - \frac{\pi}{4}$. We cannot solve for y in terms of t.

22. We have
$$\frac{dy}{dt} = 2^y \sin^3 t,$$
so
$$\int 2^{-y}\,dy = \int \sin^3 t\,dt.$$

Using Integral Table Formula 17, gives
$$-\frac{1}{\ln 2}2^{-y} = -\frac{1}{3}\sin^2 t \cos t - \frac{2}{3}\cos t + C.$$

According to the initial conditions: $y(0) = 0$ so
$$-\frac{1}{\ln 2} = -\frac{2}{3} + C, \quad \text{and} \quad C = \frac{2}{3} - \frac{1}{\ln 2}.$$

Thus,
$$-\frac{1}{\ln 2}2^{-y} = -\frac{1}{3}\sin^2 t \cos t - \frac{2}{3}\cos t + \frac{2}{3} - \frac{1}{\ln 2}.$$

Solving for y gives:
$$2^{-y} = \frac{\ln 2}{3}\sin^2 t \cos t + \frac{2\ln 2}{3}\cos t - \frac{2\ln 2}{3} + 1.$$

It can be shown that the right side is always > 0, so we can take natural logs.
$$y\ln 2 = -\ln\left(\frac{\ln 2}{3}\sin^2 t \cos t + \frac{2\ln 2}{3}\cos t - \frac{2\ln 2}{3} + 1\right),$$
so
$$y = \frac{-\ln\left(\frac{\ln 2}{3}\sin^2 t \cos t + \frac{2\ln 2}{3}\cos t - \frac{2\ln 2}{3} + 1\right)}{\ln 2}.$$

23. The characteristic equation is
$$r^2 + \pi^2 = 0$$
so that $r = \pm i\pi$ and
$$z(t) = A\cos \pi t + B\sin \pi t$$

24. The characteristic equation of $9z'' - z = 0$ is
$$9r^2 - 1 = 0.$$
If this is written in the form $r^2 + br + c = 0$, we have that $r^2 - 1/9 = 0$ and
$$b^2 - 4c = 0 - (4)(-1/9) = 4/9 > 0$$

This indicates overdamped motion and since the roots of the characteristic equation are $r = \pm 1/3$, the general solution is
$$y(t) = C_1 e^{\frac{1}{3}t} + C_2 e^{-\frac{1}{3}t}.$$

25. The characteristic equation of $9z'' + z = 0$ is
$$9r^2 + 1 = 0$$
If we write this in the form $r^2 + br + c = 0$, we have that $r^2 + 1/9 = 0$ and
$$b^2 - 4c = 0 - (4)(1/9) = -4/9 < 0$$

This indicates underdamped motion and since the roots of the characteristic equation are $r = \pm\frac{1}{3}i$, the general equation is
$$y(t) = C_1 \cos\left(\frac{1}{3}t\right) + C_2 \sin\left(\frac{1}{3}t\right)$$

26. The characteristic equation of $y'' + 6y' + 8y = 0$ is

$$r^2 + 6r + 8 = 0.$$

We have that

$$b^2 - 4c = 6^2 - 4(8) = 4 > 0.$$

This indicates overdamped motion. Since the roots of the characteristic equation are $r_1 = -2$ and $r_2 = -4$, the general solution is

$$y(t) = C_1 e^{-2t} + C_2 e^{-4t}.$$

27. The characteristic equation is

$$r^2 + 2r + 3 = 0$$

which has the solution

$$r = \frac{-2 \pm \sqrt{4 - 4 \cdot 3}}{2} = -1 \pm \sqrt{-2}$$

so that the general solution is

$$y(t) = e^{-t}(A \sin \sqrt{2}t + B \cos \sqrt{2}t)$$

28. The characteristic equation of $x'' + 2x' + 10x = 0$ is

$$r^2 + 2r + 10 = 0$$

We have that

$$b^2 - 4c = 2^2 - 4(10) = -36 < 0$$

This indicates underdamped motion and since the roots of the characteristic equation are $r = -1 \pm 3i$, the general solution is

$$y(t) = C_1 e^{-t} \cos 3t + C_2 e^{-t} \sin 3t$$

Problems

29. Figure (I) shows a line segment at $(4, 0)$ with positive slope. The only possible differential equation is (b), where $y'(4, 0) = \cos 0 = 1$. Note that (a) is not possible as $y'(4, 0) = e^{-16} = 0.0000001$, a much smaller positive slope than that shown.

Figure (II) shows a line segment at $(0, 4)$ with zero slope. The possible differential equations are (d), where $y'(0, 4) = 4(4 - 4) = 0$, and (f), where $y'(0, 4) = 0(3 - 0) = 0$.

Figure (III) shows a line segment at $(4, 0)$ with negative slope of large magnitude. The only possible differential equation is (f), where $y'(4, 0) = 4(3 - 4) = -4$. Note that (c) is not possible as $y'(4, 0) = \cos(4 - 0) = -0.65$, a negative slope of smaller magnitude than that shown.

Figure (IV) shows a line segment at $(4, 0)$ with a negative slope of small magnitude. The only possible differential equation is (c), where $y'(4, 0) = \cos(4 - 0) = -0.65$. Note that (f) is not possible as $y'(4, 0) = 4(3 - 4) = -4$, a negative slope of larger magnitude than that shown.

Figure (V) shows a line segment at $(0, 4)$ with positive slope. Possible differential equations are (a), where $y'(0, 4) = e^{0^2} = 1$, and (c), where $y'(0, 4) = \cos(4 - 4) = 1$.

Figure (VI) shows a line segment at $(0, 4)$ with a negative slope of large magnitude. The only possible differential equation is (e), where $y'(0, 4) = 4(3 - 4) = -4$. Note that (b) is not possible as $y'(0, 4) = \cos 4 = -0.65$, a negative slope of smaller magnitude than that shown.

30. (a) The slope field for $dy/dx = y/x$ is in Figure 11.53.

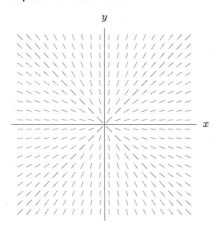

Figure 11.53

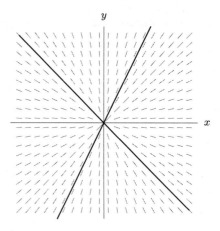

Figure 11.54

(b) See Figure 11.54.

(c) Separating variables gives

$$\int \frac{1}{y}dy = \int \frac{1}{x}dx$$

or

$$\ln|y| = \ln|x| + C$$

which can be written as

$$\ln|y| = \ln|x| + \ln|D|$$

so that

$$y = Dx.$$

Thus, the solutions are lines through the origin, as shown in part (b).

31. (a) We know that the equilibrium solutions are the functions satisfying the differential equation whose derivative everywhere is 0. Thus we have

$$\frac{dy}{dt} = 0$$
$$0.2(y-3)(y+2) = 0$$
$$(y-3)(y+2) = 0.$$

The solutions are $y = 3$ and $y = -2$.

(b)

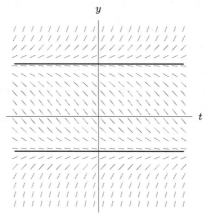

Figure 11.55

Looking at Figure 11.55, we see that the line $y = 3$ is an unstable solution, while the line $y = -2$ is a stable solution.

32. (a) $\Delta x = \frac{1}{5} = 0.2$.

At $x = 0$:

$y_0 = 1, y' = 4$; so $\Delta y = 4(0.2) = 0.8$. Thus, $y_1 = 1 + 0.8 = 1.8$.

At $x = 0.2$:

$y_1 = 1.8, y' = 3.2$; so $\Delta y = 3.2(0.2) = 0.64$. Thus, $y_2 = 1.8 + 0.64 = 2.44$.

At $x = 0.4$:

$y_2 = 2.44, y' = 2.56$; so $\Delta y = 2.56(0.2) = 0.512$. Thus, $y_3 = 2.44 + 0.512 = 2.952$.

At $x = 0.6$:

$y_3 = 2.952, y' = 2.048$; so $\Delta y = 2.048(0.2) = 0.4096$. Thus, $y_4 = 3.3616$.

At $x = 0.8$:

$y_4 = 3.3616, y' = 1.6384$; so $\Delta y = 1.6384(0.2) = 0.32768$. Thus, $y_5 = 3.68928$. So $y(1) \approx 3.689$.

(b)

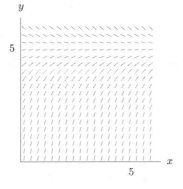

Since solution curves are concave down for $0 \le y \le 5$, and $y(0) = 1 < 5$, the estimate from Euler's method will be an overestimate.

(c) Solving by separation:

$$\int \frac{dy}{5 - y} = \int dx, \quad \text{so} \quad -\ln|5 - y| = x + C.$$

Then $5 - y = Ae^{-x}$ where $A = \pm e^{-C}$. Since $y(0) = 1$, we have $5 - 1 = Ae^0$, so $A = 4$.

Therefore, $y = 5 - 4e^{-x}$, and $y(1) = 5 - 4e^{-1} \approx 3.528$.

(Note: as predicted, the estimate in (a) is too large.)

(d) Doubling the value of n will probably halve the error and, therefore, give a value half way between 3.528 and 3.689, which is approximately 3.61.

33. (a) $\frac{dB}{dt} = \frac{r}{100} B$. The constant of proportionality is $\frac{r}{100}$.

(b) Solving, we have

$$\frac{dB}{B} = \frac{r\,dt}{100}$$

$$\int \frac{dB}{B} = \int \frac{r}{100}\,dt$$

$$\ln|B| = \frac{r}{100}t + C$$

$$B = e^{(r/100)t+C} = Ae^{(r/100)t}, \qquad A = e^C.$$

A is the initial amount in the account, since A is the amount at time $t = 0$.

(c)

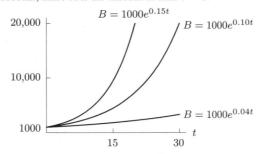

34. The rate of disintegration is proportional to the quantity of carbon-14 present. Let Q be the quantity of carbon-14 present at time t, with $t = 0$ in 1977. Then

$$Q = Q_0 e^{-kt},$$

where Q_0 is the quantity of carbon-14 present in 1977 when $t = 0$. Then we know that

$$\frac{Q_0}{2} = Q_0 e^{-k(5730)}$$

so that

$$k = -\frac{\ln(1/2)}{5730} = 0.000121.$$

Thus

$$Q = Q_0 e^{-0.000121t}.$$

The quantity present at any time is proportional to the rate of disintegration at that time so

$$Q_0 = c8.2 \quad \text{and} \quad Q = c13.5$$

where c is a constant of proportionality. Thus substituting for Q and Q_0 in

$$Q = Q_0 e^{-0.000121t}$$

gives

$$c13.5 = c8.2 e^{-0.000121t}$$

so

$$t = -\frac{\ln(13.5/8.2)}{0.000121} \approx -4120.$$

Thus Stonehenge was built about 4120 years before 1977, in about 2150 B.C.

35. (a) If A is surface area, we know that for some constant K

$$\frac{dV}{dt} = -KA.$$

If r is the radius of the sphere, $V = 4\pi r^3/3$ and $A = 4\pi r^2$. Solving for r in terms of V gives $r = (3V/4\pi)^{1/3}$, so

$$\frac{dV}{dt} = -K(4\pi r^2) = -K4\pi \left(\frac{3V}{4\pi}\right)^{2/3} \quad \text{so} \quad \frac{dV}{dt} = -kV^{2/3}$$

where k is another constant, $k = K(4\pi)^{1/3}3^{2/3}$.

(b) Separating variables gives

$$\int \frac{dV}{V^{2/3}} = -\int k\,dt$$

$$3V^{1/3} = -kt + C.$$

Since $V = V_0$ when $t = 0$, we have $3V_0^{1/3} = C$, so

$$3V^{1/3} = -kt + 3V_0^{1/3}.$$

Solving for V gives

$$V = \left(-\frac{k}{3}t + V_0^{1/3}\right)^3.$$

This function is graphed in Figure 11.56.

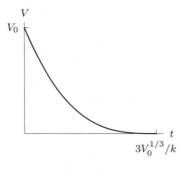

Figure 11.56

(c) The snowball disappears when $V = 0$, that is when

$$-\frac{k}{3}t + V_0^{1/3} = 0$$

giving

$$t = \frac{3V_0^{1/3}}{k}.$$

36. (a) Quantity of A present at time t equals $(a - x)$.
Quantity of B present at time t equals $(b - x)$.
So

$$\text{Rate of formation of } C = k(\text{Quantity of } A)(\text{Quantity of } B)$$

gives

$$\frac{dx}{dt} = k(a - x)(b - x)$$

(b) Separating gives

$$\int \frac{dx}{(a - x)(b - x)} = \int k\,dt.$$

Rewriting the denominator as $(a - x)(b - x) = (x - a)(x - b)$ enables us to use Formula 26 in the Table of Integrals provided $a \neq b$. For some constant K, this gives

$$\frac{1}{a - b}\left(\ln|x - a| - \ln|x - b|\right) = kt + K.$$

Thus

$$\ln\left|\frac{x - a}{x - b}\right| = (a - b)kt + K(a - b)$$

$$\left|\frac{x - a}{x - b}\right| = e^{K(a-b)}e^{(a-b)kt}$$

$$\frac{x - a}{x - b} = Me^{(a-b)kt} \quad \text{where } M = \pm e^{K(a-b)}.$$

Since $x = 0$ when $t = 0$, we have $M = \frac{a}{b}$. Thus

$$\frac{x - a}{x - b} = \frac{a}{b}e^{(a-b)kt}.$$

Solving for x, we have

$$bx - ba = ae^{(a-b)kt}(x - b)$$

$$x(b - ae^{(a-b)kt}) = ab - abe^{(a-b)kt}$$

$$x = \frac{ab(1 - e^{(a-b)kt})}{b - ae^{(a-b)kt}} = \frac{ab(e^{bkt} - e^{akt})}{be^{bkt} - ae^{akt}}.$$

37. Quantity of A left at time $t =$ Quantity of B left at time t equals $(a - x)$.
Thus

$$\text{Rate of formation of } C = k(\text{Quantity of } A)(\text{Quantity of } B)$$

gives

$$\frac{dx}{dt} = k(a - x)(a - x) = k(a - x)^2.$$

Separating gives

$$\int \frac{dx}{(x - a)^2} = \int k\,dt$$

Integrating gives, for some constant K,

$$-(x - a)^{-1} = kt + K.$$

When $t = 0$, $x = 0$ so $K = a^{-1}$. Solving for x:

$$-(x - a)^{-1} = kt + a^{-1}$$

$$x - a = -\frac{1}{kt + a^{-1}}$$

$$x = a - \frac{a}{akt + 1} = \frac{a^2 kt}{akt + 1}$$

38. Recall that $s'' + bs' + c = 0$ is overdamped if the discriminant $b^2 - 4c > 0$, critically damped if $b^2 - 4c = 0$, and underdamped if $b^2 - 4c < 0$. Since $b^2 - 4c = 16 - 4c$, the circuit is overdamped if $c < 4$, critically damped if $c = 4$, and underdamped if $c > 4$.

39. Recall that $s'' + bs' + cs = 0$ is overdamped if the discriminant $b^2 - 4c > 0$, critically damped if $b^2 - 4c = 0$, and underdamped if $b^2 - 4c < 0$. Since $b^2 - 4c = 8 - 4c$, the solution is overdamped if $c < 2$, critically damped if $c = 2$, and underdamped if $c > 2$.

40. Recall that $s'' + bs' + cs = 0$ is overdamped if the discriminant $b^2 - 4c > 0$, critically damped if $b^2 - 4c = 0$, and underdamped if $b^2 - 4c < 0$. Since $b^2 - 4c = 36 - 4c$, the solution is overdamped if $c < 9$, critically damped if $c = 9$, and underdamped if $c > 9$.

41. (a) $\frac{dp}{dt} = kp(B - p)$, where $k > 0$.

(b) To find when $\frac{dp}{dt}$ is largest, we notice that $\frac{dp}{dt} = kp(B - p)$, as a function of p, is a parabola opening downward with the maximum at $p = \frac{B}{2}$, i.e. when $\frac{1}{2}$ the tin has turned to powder. This is the time when the tin is crumbling fastest.

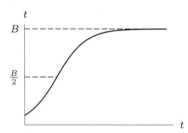

(c) If $p = 0$ initially, then $\frac{dp}{dt} = 0$, so we would expect p to remain 0 forever. However, since many organ pipes get tin pest, we must reconcile the model with reality. There are two possible ideas which solve this problem. First, we could assume that p is never 0. In other words, we assume that all tin pipes, no matter how new, must contain some small amount of tin pest. Assuming this means that all organ pipes must deteriorate due to tin pest eventually. Another explanation is that the powder forms at a slow rate even if there was none present to begin with. Since not all organ pipes suffer, it is possible that the conversion is catalyzed by some other impurities not present in all pipes.

42. Let I be the number of infected people. Then, the number of healthy people in the population is $M - I$. The rate of infection is

$$\text{Infection rate} = \frac{0.01}{M}(M - I)I.$$

and the rate of recovery is

$$\text{Recovery rate} = 0.009I.$$

Therefore,

$$\frac{dI}{dt} = \frac{0.01}{M}(M - I)I - 0.009I$$

or

$$\frac{dI}{dt} = 0.001I(1 - 10\frac{I}{M}).$$

This is a logistic differential equation, and so the solution will look like the following graph:

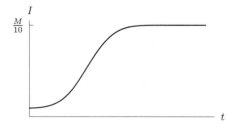

The limiting value for I is $\frac{1}{10}M$, so $1/10$ of the population is infected in the long run.

43. (a) When Juliet loves Romeo (i.e. $j > 0$), Romeo's love for her decreases (i.e. $\frac{dr}{dt} < 0$). When Juliet hates Romeo ($j < 0$), Romeo's love for her grows ($\frac{dr}{dt} > 0$). So j and $\frac{dr}{dt}$ have opposite signs, corresponding to the fact that $-B < 0$. When Romeo loves Juliet ($r > 0$), Juliet's love for him grows ($\frac{dj}{dt} > 0$). When Romeo hates Juliet ($r < 0$), Juliet's love for him decreases ($\frac{dj}{dt} < 0$). Thus r and $\frac{dj}{dt}$ have the same sign, corresponding to the fact that $A > 0$.

(b) Since $\frac{dr}{dt} = -Bj$, we have

$$\frac{d^2r}{dt^2} = \frac{d}{dt}(-Bj) = -B\frac{dj}{dt} = -ABr.$$

Rewriting the above equation as $r'' + ABr = 0$, we see that the characteristic equation is $R^2 + AB = 0$. Therefore $R = \pm\sqrt{AB}i$ and the general solution is

$$r(t) = C_1 \cos\sqrt{AB}t + C_2 \sin\sqrt{AB}t.$$

(c) Using $\frac{dr}{dt} = -Bj$, and differentiating r to find j, we obtain

$$j(t) = -\frac{1}{B}\frac{dr}{dt} = -\frac{\sqrt{AB}}{B}(-C_1 \sin\sqrt{AB}t + C_2 \cos\sqrt{AB}t).$$

Now, $j(0) = 0$ gives $C_2 = 0$ and $r(0) = 1$ gives $C_1 = 1$. Therefore, the particular solutions are

$$r(t) = \cos\sqrt{AB}t \quad \text{and} \quad j(t) = \sqrt{\frac{A}{B}} \sin\sqrt{AB}t$$

(d) Consider one period of the graph of $j(t)$ and $r(t)$:

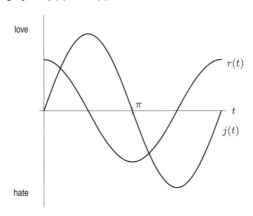

From the graph, we see that they both love each other only a quarter of the time.

44. (a) We have $\Psi = C_1 \cos(\omega x) + C_2 \sin(\omega x)$, and we want $\Psi(0) = \Psi(l) = 0$.

$$\Psi(0) = C_1 = 0 \quad \text{so } C_1 = 0.$$
$$\Psi(l) = C_2 \sin(\omega l) = 0 \quad \text{so } \omega l = n\pi \text{ for some positive integer } n.$$

Thus, $\omega = (n\pi)/l$, so

$$\Psi = C_2 \sin\left(\frac{n\pi x}{l}\right).$$

(b) Using this formula for Ψ, we have

$$\frac{d\Psi}{dx} = \frac{n\pi}{l}C_2 \cos\left(\frac{n\pi x}{l}\right)$$
$$\frac{d^2\Psi}{dx^2} = -\frac{n^2\pi^2}{l^2}C_2 \sin\left(\frac{n\pi x}{l}\right).$$

Thus, substituting for $d^2\Psi/dx^2$ and $\Psi = C_2 \sin(n\pi x/l)$, we have

$$\frac{-h^2}{8\pi^2 m}\frac{d^2\Psi}{dx^2} = \frac{h^2}{8\pi^2 m}\cdot\frac{n^2\pi^2}{l^2}C_2 \sin\left(\frac{n\pi x}{l}\right) = \frac{h^2 n^2}{8ml^2}\Psi,$$

so

$$E = \frac{h^2 n^2}{8ml^2}.$$

(c) Since n must be a positive integer, so $n = 1, 2, 3, 4, ...$, the possible values of E are

$$E_1 = \frac{h^2}{8ml^2}, \quad E_2 = \frac{4h^2}{8ml^2}, \quad E_3 = \frac{9h^2}{8ml^2}, \quad E_4 = \frac{16h^2}{8ml^2}, \quad ....$$

The lowest energy level is $E_1 = h^2/(8ml^2)$, and we see that other energy levels are multiples of E_1:

$$E_2 = 4E_1, \quad E_3 = 9E_1, \quad E_4 = 16E_1, \quad ....$$

CAS Challenge Problems

45. (a) We find the equilibrium solutions by setting $dP/dt = 0$, that is, $P(P - 1)(2 - P) = 0$, which gives three solutions, $P = 0$, $P = 1$, and $P = 2$.

(b) To get your computer algebra system to check that P_1 and P_2 are solutions, substitute one of them into the equation and form an expression consisting of the difference between the right and left hand sides, then ask the CAS to simplify that expression. Do the same for the other function. In order to avoid too much typing, define P_1 and P_2 as functions in your system.

(c) Substituting $t = 0$ gives

$$P_1(0) = 1 - \frac{1}{\sqrt{4}} = 1/2$$

$$P_2(0) = 1 + \frac{1}{\sqrt{4}} = 3/2.$$

We can find the limits using a computer algebra system. Alternatively, setting $u = e^t$, we can use the limit laws to calculate

$$\lim_{t \to \infty} \frac{e^t}{\sqrt{3 + e^{2t}}} = \lim_{u \to \infty} \frac{u}{\sqrt{3 + u^2}} = \lim_{u \to \infty} \sqrt{\frac{u^2}{3 + u^2}}$$

$$= \sqrt{\lim_{u \to \infty} \frac{u^2}{3 + u^2}} = \sqrt{\lim_{u \to \infty} \frac{1}{\frac{3}{u^2} + 1}}$$

$$= \sqrt{\frac{1}{\lim_{u \to \infty} \frac{3}{u^2} + 1}} = \sqrt{\frac{1}{0 + 1}} = 1.$$

Therefore, we have

$$\lim_{t \to \infty} P_1(t) = 1 - 1 = 0$$

$$\lim_{t \to \infty} P_2(t) = 1 + 1 = 2.$$

To predict these limits without having a formula for P, looking at the original differential equation. We see if $0 < P < 1$, then $P(P - 1)(2 - P) < 0$, so $P' < 0$. Thus, if $0 < P(0) < 1$, then $P'(0) < 0$, so P is initially decreasing, and tends toward the equilibrium solution $P = 0$. On the other hand, if $1 < P < 2$, then $P(P - 1)(2 - P) > 0$, so $P' > 0$. So, if $1 < P(0) < 2$, then $P'(0) > 0$, so P is initially increasing and tends toward the equilibrium solution $P = 2$.

46. (a) Using the integral equation with $n + 1$ replaced by n, we have

$$y_n(a) = b + \int_a^a \left(y_{n-1}(t)^2 + t^2\right) dt = b + 0 = b.$$

(b) We have $a = 1$ and $b = 0$, so the integral equation tells us that

$$y_{n+1}(s) = \int_1^s \left(y_n(t)^2 + t^2\right) dt.$$

With $n = 0$, since $y_0(s) = 0$, the CAS gives

$$y_1(s) = \int_1^s 0 + t^2 \, dt = -\frac{1}{3} + \frac{s^3}{3}.$$

Then

$$y_2(s) = \int_1^s \left(y_1(t)^2 + t^2\right) dt = -\frac{17}{42} + \frac{s}{9} + \frac{s^3}{3} - \frac{s^4}{18} + \frac{s^7}{63},$$

and

$$y_3(s) = \int_1^s \left(y_2(t)^2 + t^2\right) dt$$

$$= -\frac{157847}{374220} + \frac{289\,s}{1764} - \frac{17\,s^2}{378} + \frac{82\,s^3}{243} - \frac{17\,s^4}{252} + \frac{s^5}{42} - \frac{s^6}{486} + \frac{s^7}{63} - \frac{11\,s^8}{1764} +$$
$$\frac{5\,s^9}{6804} + \frac{2\,s^{11}}{2079} - \frac{s^{12}}{6804} + \frac{s^{15}}{59535}.$$

(c) The solution y, and the approximations y_1, y_2, y_3 are graphed in Figure 11.57. The approximations appear to be accurate on the range $0.5 \leq s \leq 1.5$.

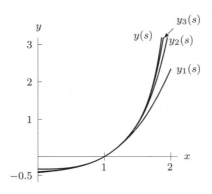

Figure 11.57

47. (a) See Figure 11.58.

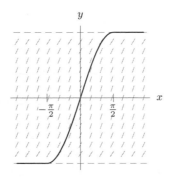

Figure 11.58

(b) Different CASs give different answers, for example they might say $y = \sin x$, or they might say

$$y = \sin x, \quad -\frac{\pi}{2} \leq x \leq \frac{\pi}{2}.$$

(c) Both the sample CAS answers in part (b) are wrong. The first one, $y = \sin x$, is wrong because $\sin x$ starts decreasing at $x = \pi/2$, where the slope field clearly shows that y should be increasing at all times. The second answer is better, but it does not give the solution outside the range $-\pi/2 \leq x \leq \pi/2$. The correct answer is the one sketched in Figure 11.58, which has formula

$$y = \begin{cases} -1 & x \leq -\frac{\pi}{2} \\ \sin x & -\frac{\pi}{2} \leq x \leq \frac{\pi}{2} \\ 1 & x \leq \frac{\pi}{2} \leq x. \end{cases}$$

CHECK YOUR UNDERSTANDING

1. True. The general solution to $y' = -ky$ is $y = Ce^{-kt}$.

2. False. Suppose $k = -1$. The equation $y'' - y = 0$ or $y'' = y$ has solutions $y = e^t$ and $y = e^{-t}$ and general solution $y = C_1 e^t + C_2 e^{-t}$.

3. False. The function $y = t^2$ is a solution to $y'' = 2$.

4. False. If $y(0) \le 0$, then $\lim_{x \to \infty} y = -\infty$.

5. True. No matter what initial value you pick, the solution curve has the x-axis as an asymptote.

6. False. There appear to be two equilibrium values dividing the plane into regions with different limiting behavior.

7. False. Euler's method approximates y-values of points on the solution curve.

8. False. In order to be solved using separation of variables, a differential equation must have the form $dy/dx = f(x)g(y)$, so we would need $x + y = f(x)g(y)$. This certainly does not appear to be true. If it were, setting $x = 0$ and $y = 0$, we would have $f(0)g(0) = 0$ so either $f(0) = 0$ or $g(0) = 0$. If $f(0) = 0$, then substituting in $x = 0$ and $y = 1$, we have $0 + 1 = f(0)g(1) = 0$, which is absurd. We get the same contradiction if we assume $g(0) = 0$.

9. True. Rewrite the equation as $dy/dx = xy + x = x(y + 1)$. Since the equation now has the form $dy/dx = f(x)g(y)$, it can be solved by separation of variables.

10. False. It is true that $y = x^3$ is a solution of the differential equation, since $dy/dx = 3x^2 = 3y^{2/3}$, but it is not the only solution passing through $(0, 0)$. Another solution is the constant function $y = 0$. Usually there is only one solution curve to a differential equation passing through a given point, but not always.

11. True. We have $dy/dx > 0$ at every point because $x^2 + y^2 + 1 > 0$, and a positive derivative indicates increasing function.

12. False. We have

$$\frac{d^2 y}{dx^2} = \frac{d(x^2 + y^2 + 1)}{dx}$$
$$= 2x + 2y \frac{dy}{dx}$$
$$= 2x + 2y(x^2 + y^2 + 1)$$
$$= 2x + 2y + 2x^2 y + 2y^3.$$

At the point $(x, y) = (-1, 0)$ we have $d^2 y/dx^2 = -2 < 0$. A negative second derivative indicates function concave down. The solution curve of the differential equation that passes through the point $(-1, 0)$ is concave down at $(-1, 0)$.

13. False. This is a logistic equation with equilibrium values $P = 0$ and $P = 2$. Solution curves do not cross the line $P = 2$ and do not go from $(0, 1)$ to $(1, 3)$.

14. True. This is a logistic differential equation. Any solution with $P(0) > 0$ tends toward the carrying capacity, L, as $t \to \infty$.

15. True. Specifying $x(0)$ and $y(0)$ corresponds to picking a starting point in the plane and thereby picking the unique solution curve through that point.

16. False. Competitive exclusion, in which one population drives out another, is modeled by a system of differential equations.

17. True. Since $f'(x) = g(x)$, we have $f''(x) = g'(x)$. Since $g(x)$ is increasing, $g'(x) > 0$ for all x, so $f''(x) > 0$ for all x. Thus the graph of f is concave up for all x.

18. False. We just need an example of a function $f(x)$ which is decreasing for $x > 0$, but whose derivative $f'(x) = g(x)$ is increasing for $x > 0$. An example is $f(x) = 1/x$. Clearly $f(x)$ is decreasing for $x > 0$ but its derivative $f'(x) = -1/x^2$ is clearly increasing for $x > 0$.

19. True. Since $g(x)$ is increasing, $g(x) \ge g(0) = 1$ for all $x \ge 0$. Since $f'(x) = g(x)$, this means that $f'(x) > 0$ for all $x \ge 0$. Therefore $f(x)$ is increasing for all $x \ge 0$.

20. False. If $g(x) > 0$ for all x, then $f(x)$ would have to be increasing for all x so $f(x + p) = f(x)$ would be impossible. For example, let $g(x) = 2 + \cos x$. Then a possibility for f is $f(x) = 2x + \sin x$. Then $g(x)$ is periodic, but $f(x)$ is not.

21. False. Let $g(x) = 0$ for all x and let $f(x) = 17$. Then $f'(x) = g(x)$ and $\lim_{x \to \infty} g(x) = 0$, but $\lim_{x \to \infty} f(x) = 17$.

22. True. Since $\lim_{x \to \infty} g(x) = \infty$, there must be some value $x = a$ such that $g(x) > 1$ for all $x > a$. Then $f'(x) > 1$ for all $x > a$. Thus, for some constant C, we have $f(x) > x + C$ for all $x > a$, which implies that $\lim_{x \to \infty} f(x) = \infty$. More precisely, let $C = f(a) - a$ and let $h(x) = f(x) - x - C$. Then $h(a) = 0$ and $h'(x) = f'(x) - 1 > 0$ for all $x > a$. Thus h is increasing so $h(x) > 0$ for all $x > a$, which means that $f(x) > x + C$ for all $x > a$.

23. False. Let $f(x) = x^3$ and $g(x) = 3x^2$. Then $y = f(x)$ satisfies $dy/dx = g(x)$ and $g(x)$ is even while $f(x)$ is odd.

24. False. The example $f(x) = x^3$ and $g(x) = 3x^2$ shows that you might expect $f(x)$ to be odd. However, the additive constant C can mess things up. For example, still let $g(x) = 3x^2$, but let $f(x) = x^3 + 1$ instead. Then $g(x)$ is still even, but $f(x)$ is not odd (for example, $f(-1) = 0$ but $-f(1) = -2$).

25. True. The slope of the graph of f is $dy/dx = 2x - y$. Thus when $x = a$ and $y = b$, the slope is $2a - b$.

26. True. Saying $y = f(x)$ is a solution for the differential equation $dy/dx = 2x - y$ means that if we substitute $f(x)$ for y, the equation is satisfied. That is, $f'(x) = 2x - f(x)$.

27. False. Since $f'(x) = 2x - f(x)$, we would have $1 = 2x - 5$ so $x = 3$ is the only possibility.

28. True. Differentiate $dy/dx = 2x - y$, to get:

$$\frac{d^2y}{dx^2} = \frac{d}{dx}(2x - y) = 2 - \frac{dy}{dx} = 2 - (2x - y).$$

29. False. Since $f'(1) = 2(1) - 5 = -3$, the point $(1, 5)$ could not be a critical point of f.

30. True. Since $dy/dx = 2x - y$, the slope of the graph of f is negative at any point satisfying $2x < y$, that is any point lying above the line $y = 2x$. The slope of the graph of f is positive at any point satisfying $2x > y$, that is any point lying below the line $y = 2x$.

31. True. When we differentiate $dy/dx = 2x - y$, we get:

$$\frac{d^2y}{dx^2} = 2 - \frac{dy}{dx} = 2 - (2x - y).$$

Thus at any inflection point of $y = f(x)$, we have $d^2y/dx^2 = 2 - (2x - y) = 0$. That is, any inflection point of f must satisfy $y = 2x - 2$.

32. False. Suppose that $g(x) = f(x) + C$, where $C \neq 0$. In order to be a solution of $dy/dx = 2x - y$ we would need $g'(x) = 2x - g(x)$. Instead we have:

$$g'(x) = f'(x) = 2x - f(x) = 2x - (g(x) - C) = 2x - g(x) + C.$$

Since $C \neq 0$, this means $g(x)$ is not a solution of $dy/dx = 2x - y$.

33. True. We will use the hint. Let $w = g(x) - f(x)$. Then:

$$\frac{dw}{dx} = g'(x) - f'(x) = (2x - g(x)) - (2x - f(x)) = f(x) - g(x) = -w.$$

Thus $dw/dx = -w$. This equation is the equation for exponential decay and has the general solution $w = Ce^{-x}$. Thus,

$$\lim_{x \to \infty} (g(x) - f(x)) = \lim_{x \to \infty} Ce^{-x} = 0.$$

34. An example is $dy/dx = e^x$. In fact, if $f(x)$ is any increasing positive function, then the solutions of $dy/dx = f(x)$ are increasing since $f(x) > 0$ and concave up since $d^2y/dx^2 = f'(x) > 0$.

35. We want to have $dy/dx = 0$ when $y - x^2 = 0$, so let $dy/dx = y - x^2$.

36. This family has $f'(x) = 2x$, so let $dy/dx = 2x$.

37. If we differentiate implicitly the equation for the family, we get $2x - 2ydy/dx = 0$. When we solve, we get the differential equation we want $dy/dx = x/y$.

PROJECTS FOR CHAPTER ELEVEN

1. (a) (i) Integrating we have

$$\frac{dP}{dt} = 30.2$$
$$P = 30.2t + C.$$

Since $P(0) = 95$, we have $C = 95$, so

$$P = 30.2t + 95.$$

Substituting $t = 87$ and rounding to the nearest person gives

$$P = 30.2 \cdot 87 + 95 = 2722.$$

The linear model predicts that 2722 people would have contracted SARS by June 12, 2003.

(ii) Separating variables, we have

$$\frac{1}{P} \frac{dP}{dt} = 0.12$$
$$\int \frac{dP}{P} = \int 0.12 \, dt$$
$$\ln|P| = 0.12t + C$$
$$P = Ae^{0.12t}.$$

Since $P(0) = 95$, we have $A = 95$, so

$$P = 95e^{0.12t}.$$

Substituting $t = 87$ and rounding to the nearest person gives

$$P = 95e^{0.12 \cdot 87} = 3,249,062.$$

The exponential model predicts that 3.249 million people would have contracted SARS by June 12, 2003.

(iii) Writing the differential equation in the form

$$\frac{dP}{dt} = 0.19P - 0.0002P^2$$
$$\frac{dP}{dt} = 0.19P \left(1 - \frac{0.0002}{0.19}P\right)$$
$$\frac{dP}{dt} = 0.19P \left(1 - \frac{P}{950}\right),$$

we use the analytic solution derived on page 563 of the text to obtain

$$P = \frac{950}{1 + Ae^{-0.19t}}, \quad \text{with } A = \frac{950 - 95}{95} = 9$$

so

$$P = \frac{950}{1 + 9e^{-0.19t}}.$$

Substituting $t = 87$ and rounding to the nearest person gives

$$P = \frac{950}{1 + 9e^{-0.19 \cdot 87}} = 950.$$

The logistic model predicts that 950 people will have contracted SARS by June 12, 2003.

(b) (i) The three methods give very different predictions. The linear and logistic are about 3000 and 1000, respectively, while the exponential model is 3 million, nearly half the population of Hong Kong.

(ii) The number of new cases per day is approximated by the derivative, dP/dt. The linear model predicts a constant number of new cases each day; the exponential model predicts an increasing number of new cases each day; the logistic model predicts that the number of new cases per day will first increase and then decrease.

(iii) The general trend in the figure shows that the number of new cases per day first climbed and then fell, suggesting that the logistic model fits best. The high values are largely Mondays, and represent two days of data recorded as one, since no new cases were reported on Sundays.

(c)   (i) The formula

$$P = \frac{950}{1 + 9e^{-0.19t}}$$

has limiting value $P = 950$ as $t \to \infty$. Thus, this formula predicts that the maximum number of cases expected is 950.

(ii) The graph allows us to estimate (very roughly) when the daily increase was largest, namely about April 10. Since the maximum rate of change of P (and the maximum daily increase in P) occurs at $L/2$, where L is the maximum value of P, we expect the maximum value of P to be about $2 \cdot 998 \approx 2000$.

(d) See Figures 11.59–11.61. The dots represent the actual data.

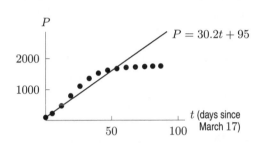

Figure 11.59: Linear predictions and actual data

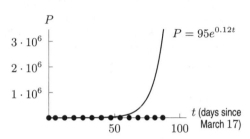

Figure 11.60: Exponential predictions and actual data

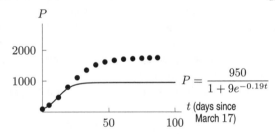

Figure 11.61: Logistic predictions and actual data

2. (a) Since I_0 is the number of infecteds on day $t = 0$, March 17, we have $I_0 = 95$. Since S_0 is the initial number of susceptibles, which is the whole population of Hong Kong, $S_0 \approx 6.8$ million.

(b) For $a = 1.25 \cdot 10^{-8}$ and $b = 0.06$, the system of equations is

$$\frac{dS}{dt} = -1.25 \cdot 10^{-8}SI$$

$$\frac{dI}{dt} = 1.25 \cdot 10^{-8}SI - 0.06I.$$

So, by the chain rule,

$$\frac{dI}{dS} = \frac{dI/dt}{dS/dt} = \frac{1.25 \cdot 10^{-8}SI - 0.06I}{-1.25 \cdot 10^{-8}SI} = -1 + \frac{4.8 \cdot 10^6}{S}.$$

The slope field and trajectory are in Figure 11.62.

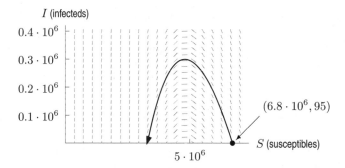

Figure 11.62

(c) The maximum value of I is about 300,000; this gives us the maximum number of infecteds at any one time—the total number of people infected during the course of the disease is much greater than this. The trajectory meets the S-axis at about 3.3 million; this tells us that when the disease dies out, there are still 3.3 million susceptibles who have never had the disease. Therefore $6.8 - 3.3 = 3.5$ million people are predicted to have had the disease.

The threshold value of S occurs where $dI/dt = 0$ and $I \neq 0$, so, for $a = 1.25 \cdot 10^{-8}$ and $b = 0.06$,

$$\frac{dI}{dt} = 1.25 \cdot 10^{-8}SI - 0.06I = 0,$$

giving

$$\text{Threshold value} = S = \frac{0.06}{1.25 \cdot 10^{-8}} = 4.8 \cdot 10^6 \text{ people.}$$

The threshold value tells us that if the initial susceptible population, S_0 is more than 4.8 million, there will be an epidemic. If S_0 is less than 4.8 million, there will not be an epidemic. Since the population of Hong Kong is over 4.8 million, an epidemic is predicted.

(d) The value of b represents the rate at which infecteds are removed from circulation. Quarantine increases the rate people are removed and thus increases b.

(e) For $a = 1.25 \cdot 10^{-8}$ and $b = 0.24$, the system of differential equations is

$$\frac{dS}{dt} = -1.25 \cdot 10^{-8}SI$$

$$\frac{dI}{dt} = 1.25 \cdot 10^{-8}SI - 0.24I.$$

So, by the chain rule,

$$\frac{dI}{dS} = \frac{dI/dt}{dS/dt} = \frac{1.25 \cdot 10^{-8}SI - 0.24I}{-1.25 \cdot 10^{-8}SI} = -1 + \frac{19.2 \cdot 10^6}{S}.$$

The slope field is in Figure 11.63. The solution trajectory does not show as the disease dies out right away.

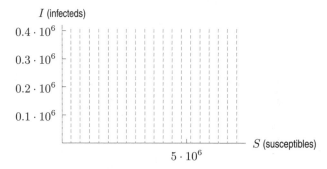

Figure 11.63

(f) The threshold value of S occurs where $dI/dt = 0$ and $I \neq 0$, so, for $b = 0.24$ and the same value of a,

$$\frac{dI}{dt} = 1.25 \cdot 10^{-8} SI - 0.24I = 0,$$

giving

$$\text{Threshold value } = S = \frac{0.24}{1.25 \cdot 10^{-8}} = 19.2 \cdot 10^6 \text{ people.}$$

The threshold value tells us that if S_0 is less than 19.2 million, there will be no epidemic. The population of Hong Kong is 6.8 million, so S_0 is below this value. Thus no epidemic is predicted.

Policies, such as quarantine, which raise the value of b can be effective in preventing an epidemic. In this case, the value of b increased sufficiently that the population of Hong Kong fell below the threshold value, and a potential epidemic was averted. However, we do not have evidence that the quarantine policy was responsible for the increase in b.

(g) Policy I: Closing off the city changes the initial values of S_0 and I_0 but not the values of a and b. If not one infected person enters the city, then $I_0 = 0$ and the solution trajectory is an equilibrium point on the S-axis. However, in practice it is almost impossible to cut off a city completely, so usually $I_0 > 0$. Also, by the time a policy to close off a city is put into effect, there may already be infected people inside the city, so again $I_0 > 0$. Thus, whether or not there is an epidemic depends on whether S_0 is greater than the threshold value, not on the value of I_0 (provided $I_0 > 0$).

For example, in the case of Hong Kong with the March values of a and b, changing the value of I_0 to 1 leaves the solution trajectory much as before; see Figure 11.64. The main difference is that the epidemic occus slightly later. So a policy of isolating a city only works if it keeps the disease out of the city of the city entirely. Thus, Policy I does not help the city except in the exceptional case that *every* infected person is kept out.

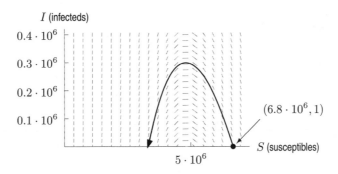

Figure 11.64

Policy II: From the analysis of the Hong Kong data, we see that a quarantine policy can help prevent an epidemic if the value of b is increased enough to bring S_0 below the threshold value. Thus, Policy II can be very effective.

3. (a)

$$p(x) = \text{the number of people with incomes} \geq x.$$

$$p(x + \Delta x) = \text{the number of people with incomes} \geq x + \Delta x.$$

So the number of people with incomes between x and $x + \Delta x$ is

$$p(x) - p(x + \Delta x) = -\Delta p.$$

Since all the people with incomes between x and $x + \Delta x$ have incomes of about x (if Δx is small), the total amount of money earned by people in this income bracket is approximately $x(-\Delta p) = -x\Delta p$.

(b) Pareto's law claims that the average income of all the people with incomes $\geq x$ is kx. Since there are $p(x)$ people with income $\geq x$, the total amount of money earned by people in this group is $kxp(x)$.

   The total amount of money earned by people with incomes $\geq (x + \Delta x)$ is therefore $k(x + \Delta x)p(x + \Delta x)$. Then the total amount of money earned by people with incomes between x and $x + \Delta x$ is

$$kxp(x) - k(x + \Delta x)p(x + \Delta x).$$

Since $\Delta p = p(x + \Delta x) - p(x)$, we can substitute $p(x + \Delta x) = p(x) + \Delta p$. Thus the total amount of money earned by people with incomes between x and $x + \Delta x$ is

$$kxp(x) - k(x + \Delta x)(p(x) + \Delta p).$$

Multiplying out, we have

$$kxp(x) - kxp(x) - k(\Delta x)p(x) - kx\Delta p - k\Delta x\Delta p$$

Simplifying and dropping the second order term $\Delta x\Delta p$ gives the total amount of money earned by people with incomes between x and $x + \Delta x$ as

$$-kp\Delta x - kx\Delta p.$$

(c) Setting the answers to parts (a) and (b) equal gives

$$-x\Delta p = -kp\Delta x - kx\Delta p.$$

Dividing by Δx, and letting $\Delta x \to 0$ so that $\frac{\Delta p}{\Delta x} \to p'$, we have

$$x\frac{\Delta p}{\Delta x} = kp + kx\frac{\Delta p}{\Delta x}$$
$$xp' = kp + kxp'$$

so

$$(1 - k)xp' = kp.$$

(d) We solve this equation by separating variables

$$\int \frac{dp}{p} = \int \frac{k}{(1 - k)}\frac{dx}{x}$$

$$\ln p = \frac{k}{(1 - k)}\ln x + C \quad \text{(no absolute values needed since } p, x > 0\text{)}$$

$$\ln p = \ln x^{k/(1-k)} + \ln A \quad \text{(writing } C = \ln A\text{)}$$

$$\ln p = \ln[Ax^{k/(1-k)}] \quad \text{(using } \ln(AB) = \ln A + \ln B\text{)}$$

$$p = Ax^{k/(1-k)}$$

(e) We take $A = 1$. For $k = 10$, $p = x^{-10/9} \approx x^{-1}$. For $k = 1.1$, $p = x^{-11}$. The functions are graphed in Figure 11.65. Notice that the larger the value of k, the less negative the value of $k/(1 - k)$ (remember $k > 1$), and the slower $p(x) \to 0$ as $x \to \infty$.

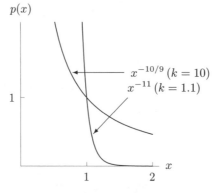

Figure 11.65

4. (a) Writing $F = b\left(\frac{a^2 - ar}{r^3}\right) = 0$ shows $F = 0$ when $r = a$, so $r = a$ gives the equilibrium position.

(b) Expanding $1/r^3$ about $r = a$ gives

$$\frac{1}{r^3} = \frac{1}{(a + r - a)^3} = \frac{1}{a^3}\left(1 + \frac{r - a}{a}\right)^{-3}$$

$$= \frac{1}{a^3}\left(1 - 3\left(\frac{r - a}{a}\right) + \frac{(-3)(-4)}{2!}\left(\frac{r - a}{a}\right)^2 - \cdots\right)$$

$$= \frac{1}{a^3}\left(1 - \frac{3(r - a)}{a} + \frac{6(r - a)^2}{a^2} - \cdots\right).$$

Similarly, expanding $1/r^2$ about $r = a$ gives

$$\frac{1}{r^2} = \frac{1}{(a + r - a)^2} = \frac{1}{a^2}\left(1 + \frac{r - a}{a}\right)^{-2}$$

$$= \frac{1}{a^2}\left(1 - 2\left(\frac{r - a}{a}\right) + \frac{(-2)(-3)}{2!}\left(\frac{r - a}{a}\right)^2 - \cdots\right)$$

$$= \frac{1}{a^2}\left(1 - 2\left(\frac{r - a}{a}\right) + 3\left(\frac{r - a}{a}\right)^2 - \cdots\right).$$

Thus, combining gives

$$F = b\left(\frac{1}{a}\left(1 - \frac{3(r - a)}{a} + \frac{6(r - a)^2}{a^2} - \cdots\right) - \frac{1}{a}\left(1 - \frac{2(r - a)}{a} + \frac{3(r - a)^2}{a^2} - \cdots\right)\right)$$

$$= \frac{b}{a}\left(-\frac{(r - a)}{a} + \frac{3(r - a)^2}{a^2} - \cdots\right)$$

$$= \frac{b}{a^2}\left(-(r - a) + \frac{3(r - a)^2}{a} - \cdots\right).$$

(c) Setting $x = r - a$ gives

$$F \approx \frac{b}{a^2}\left(-x + \frac{3x^2}{a}\right).$$

(d) For small x, we discard the quadratic term in part (c), giving

$$F \approx \frac{-b}{a^2}x.$$

The acceleration is d^2x/dt^2. Thus, using Newton's Second Law:

$$\text{Force} = \text{Mass} \cdot \text{Acceleration}$$

we get

$$\frac{-bx}{a^2} = m\frac{d^2x}{dt^2}.$$

So

$$\frac{d^2x}{dt^2} + \frac{b}{a^2m}x = 0.$$

This differential equation represents an oscillation of the form $x = C_1\cos\omega t + C_2\sin\omega t$, where $\omega^2 = b/(a^2 m)$ so $\omega = \sqrt{b/(a^2 m)}$. Thus, we have

$$\text{Period} = \frac{2\pi}{\omega} = 2\pi a\sqrt{\frac{m}{b}}.$$

APPENDIX

Solutions for Section A

1. The graph is

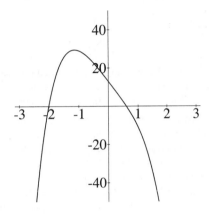

(a) The range appears to be $y \leq 30$.
(b) The function has two zeros.

2. (a) The root is between 0.3 and 0.4, at about 0.35.
(b) The root is between 1.5 and 1.6, at about 1.55.
(c) The root is between -1.8 and -1.9, at about -1.85.

3. The root occurs at about -1.05

4. The root is between -1.7 and -1.8, at about -1.75.

5. The largest root is at about 2.5.

6. There is one root at $x = -1$ and another at about $x = 1.35$.

7. There is one real root at about $x = -1.1$.

8. The root occurs at about 0.9, since the function changes sign between 0.8 and 1.

9. Using a graphing calculator, we see that when x is around 0.45, the graphs intersect.

10. The root occurs between 0.6 and 0.7, at about 0.65.

11. The root occurs between 1.2 and 1.4, at about 1.3.

12. Zoom in on graph: $t = \pm 0.824$. [Note: t must be in radians; one must zoom in two or three times.]

13. (a) Only one real zero, at about $x = -1.15$.
(b) Three real zeros: at $x = 1$, and at about $x = 1.41$ and $x = -1.41$.

14. First, notice that $f(3) \approx 0.5 > 0$ and that $f(4) \approx -0.25 < 0$.
1st iteration: $f(3.5) > 0$, so a zero is between 3.5 and 4.
2nd iteration: $f(3.75) < 0$, so a zero is between 3.5 and 3.75.
3rd iteration: $f(3.625) < 0$, so a zero is between 3.5 and 3.625.
4th iteration: $f(3.588) < 0$, so a zero is between 3.5 and 3.588.
5th iteration: $f(3.545) > 0$, so a zero is between 3.545 and 3.588.
6th iteration: $f(3.578) < 0$, so a zero is between 3.567 and 3.578.
7th iteration: $f(3.572) > 0$, so a zero is between 3.572 and 3.578.
8th iteration: $f(3.575) > 0$, so a zero is between 3.575 and 3.578.

Thus we know that, rounded to two places, the value of the zero must be 3.58. We know that this is the largest zero of $f(x)$ since $f(x)$ approaches -1 for larger values of x.

15. (a) Let $F(x) = \sin x - 2^{-x}$. Then $F(x) = 0$ will have a root where $f(x)$ and $g(x)$ cross. The first positive value of x for which the functions intersect is $x \approx 0.7$.

(b) The functions intersect for $x \approx 0.4$.

16. The graph is

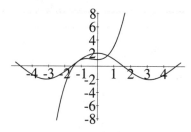

We find one zero at about 0.6. It looks like there might be another one at about -1.2, but zoom in close...closer...closer, and you'll see that though the graphs are very close together, they do not touch, and so there is no zero near -1.2. Thus the zero at about 0.6 is the only one. (How do you know there are no other zeros off the screen?)

17. (a) Since f is continuous, there must be one zero between $\theta = 1.4$ and $\theta = 1.6$, and another between $\theta = 1.6$ and $\theta = 1.8$. These are the only clear cases. We might also want to investigate the interval $0.6 \leq \theta \leq 0.8$ since $f(\theta)$ takes on values close to zero on at least part of this interval. Now, $\theta = 0.7$ is in this interval, and $f(0.7) = -0.01 < 0$, so f changes sign twice between $\theta = 0.6$ and $\theta = 0.8$ and hence has two zeros on this interval (assuming f is not *really* wiggly here, which it's not). There are a total of 4 zeros.

(b) As an example, we find the zero of f between $\theta = 0.6$ and $\theta = 0.7$. $f(0.65)$ is positive; $f(0.66)$ is negative. So this zero is contained in $[0.65, 0.66]$. The other zeros are contained in the intervals $[0.72, 0.73]$, $[1.43, 1.44]$, and $[1.7, 1.71]$.

(c) You've found all the zeros. A picture will confirm this; see Figure A.1.

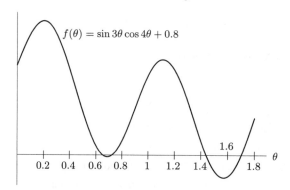

$$f(\theta) = \sin 3\theta \cos 4\theta + 0.8$$

Figure A.1

18. (a) There appear to be two solutions: one on the interval from 1.13 to 1.14 and one on the interval from 1.08 to 1.09. From 1.13 to 1.14, $\frac{x^3}{\pi^3}$ increases from 0.0465 to 0.0478 while $(\sin 3x)(\cos 4x)$ decreases from 0.0470 to 0.0417, so they must cross in between. Similarly, going from 1.08 to 1.09, $\frac{x^3}{\pi^3}$ increases from 0.0406 to 0.0418 while $(\sin 3x)(\cos 4x)$ increases from 0.0376 to 0.0442. Thus the difference between the two changes sign over that interval, so their difference must be zero somewhere in between.

(b) Reasonable estimates are $x = 1.085$ and $x = 1.131$.

19. (a) The first ten results are:

n	0	1	2	3	4	5	6	7	8
1	3.14159	5.05050	5.50129	5.56393	5.57186	5.57285	5.57297	5.57299	5.57299

(b) The solution is $x \approx 5.573$. We started with an initial guess of 1, and kept repeating the given procedure until our values converged to a limit at around 5.573. For each number on the table, the procedure was in essence asking the question "Does this number equal 4 times the arctangent of itself?" and then correcting the number by repeating the question for 4 times the arctangent of the number.

(c) P_0 represents our initial guess of $x = 1$ (on the line $y = x$). P_1 is 4 times the arctangent of 1. If we now use take this value for P_1 and slide it horizontally back to the line $y = x$, we can now use this as a new guess, and call it P_2. P_3, of course, represents 4 times the arctangent of P_2, and so on. Another way to make sense of this diagram is to consider the function $F(x) = 4 \arctan x - x$. On the diagram, this difference is represented by the vertical lines connecting P_0 and P_1, P_2 and P_3 and so on. Notice how these lines (and hence the difference between $\arctan x$ and x) get smaller as we approach the intersection point, where $F(x) = 0$.

(d) For an initial guess of $x = 10$, the procedure gives a decreasing sequence which converges (more quickly) to the same value of about 5.573. Graphically, our initial guess of P_0 will lie to the right of the intersection on the line $y = x$. The iteration procedure gives us a sequence of $P_1, P_2, \ldots$ that zigzags to the left, toward the intersection point. For an initial guess of $x = -10$, the procedure gives an increasing sequence converging to the other intersection point of these two curves at $x \approx -5.573$. Graphically, we get a sequence which is a reflection through the origin of the sequence we got for an initial guess of $x = 10$. This is so because both $y = x$ and $y = \arctan x$ are odd functions.

20. Starting with $x = 0$, and repeatedly taking the cosine, we get the numbers below. Continuing until the first three decimal places remain fixed under iteration, we have this list and diagram:

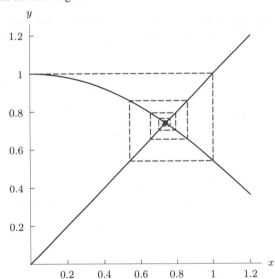

x	$\cos x$
0	0.735069
1	0.7401473
0.5403023	0.7356047
0.8575532	0.7414251
0.6542898	0.7375069
0.7934804	0.7401473
0.7013688	0.7383692
0.7639597	0.7395672
0.7221024	0.7387603
0.7504178	0.7393039
0.7314043	0.7389378
0.7442374	etc.

21.

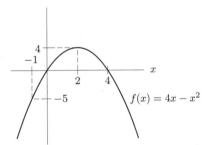

Bounded and $-5 \le f(x) \le 4$.

22.

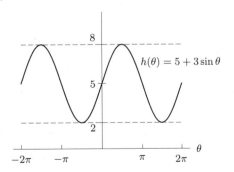

Bounded and $2 \le h(\theta) \le 8$.

23.

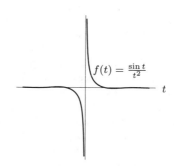

$$f(t) = \frac{\sin t}{t^2}$$

Not bounded because $f(t)$ goes to infinity as t goes to 0.

Solutions for Section B

1. $2e^{i\pi/2}$

2. $5e^{i\pi}$

3. $\sqrt{2}e^{i\pi/4}$

4. $5e^{i4.069}$

5. $0e^{i\theta}$, for any θ.

6. $e^{3\pi i/2}$

7. $\sqrt{10}e^{i\theta}$, where $\theta = \arctan(-3) \approx -1.249 + \pi = 1.893$ is an angle in the second quadrant.

8. $13e^{i\theta}$, where $\theta = \arctan(-\frac{12}{5}) \approx -1.176$ is an angle in the fourth quadrant.

9. $-3 - 4i$

10. $-11 + 29i$

11. $-5 + 12i$

12. $1 + 3i$

13. $\frac{1}{4} - \frac{9i}{8}$

14. $3 - 6i$

15. $\cos\frac{2\pi}{3} + i\sin\frac{2\pi}{3} = -\frac{1}{2} + i\frac{\sqrt{3}}{2}$

16. $\cos\frac{\pi}{6} + i\sin\frac{\pi}{6} = \frac{\sqrt{3}}{2} + \frac{i}{2}$ is one solution.

17. $5^3(\cos\frac{3\pi}{2} + i\sin\frac{3\pi}{2}) = -125i$

18. $\sqrt[4]{10}\cos\frac{\pi}{8} + i\sqrt[4]{10}\sin\frac{\pi}{8}$ is one solution.

19. One value of $\sqrt{i}$ is $\sqrt{e^{i\frac{\pi}{2}}} = (e^{i\frac{\pi}{2}})^{\frac{1}{2}} = e^{i\frac{\pi}{4}} = \cos\frac{\pi}{4} + i\sin\frac{\pi}{4} = \frac{\sqrt{2}}{2} + i\frac{\sqrt{2}}{2}$

20. One value of $\sqrt{-i}$ is $\sqrt{e^{i\frac{3\pi}{2}}} = (e^{i\frac{3\pi}{2}})^{\frac{1}{2}} = e^{i\frac{3\pi}{4}} = \cos\frac{3\pi}{4} + i\sin\frac{3\pi}{4} = -\frac{\sqrt{2}}{2} + i\frac{\sqrt{2}}{2}$

21. One value of $\sqrt[3]{i}$ is $\sqrt[3]{e^{i\frac{\pi}{2}}} = (e^{i\frac{\pi}{2}})^{\frac{1}{3}} = e^{i\frac{\pi}{6}} = \cos\frac{\pi}{6} + i\sin\frac{\pi}{6} = \frac{\sqrt{3}}{2} + \frac{i}{2}$

22. One value of $\sqrt{7i}$ is $\sqrt{7e^{i\frac{\pi}{2}}} = (7e^{i\frac{\pi}{2}})^{\frac{1}{2}} = \sqrt{7}e^{i\frac{\pi}{4}} = \sqrt{7}\cos\frac{\pi}{4} + i\sqrt{7}\sin\frac{\pi}{4} = \frac{\sqrt{14}}{2} + i\frac{\sqrt{14}}{2}$

23. $(1 + i)^{100} = (\sqrt{2}e^{i\frac{\pi}{4}})^{100} = (2^{\frac{1}{2}})^{100}(e^{i\frac{\pi}{4}})^{100} = 2^{50} \cdot e^{i\cdot 25\pi} = 2^{50}\cos 25\pi + i2^{50}\sin 25\pi = -2^{50}$

24. One value of $(1 + i)^{2/3}$ is $(\sqrt{2}e^{i\frac{\pi}{4}})^{2/3} = (2^{\frac{1}{2}}e^{i\frac{\pi}{4}})^{\frac{2}{3}} = \sqrt[3]{2}e^{i\frac{\pi}{6}} = \sqrt[3]{2}\cos\frac{\pi}{6} + i\sqrt[3]{2}\sin\frac{\pi}{6} = \sqrt[3]{2}\cdot\frac{\sqrt{3}}{2} + i\sqrt[3]{2}\cdot\frac{1}{2}$

25. One value of $(-4 + 4i)^{2/3}$ is $[\sqrt{32}e^{(i3\pi/4)}]^{(2/3)} = (\sqrt{32})^{2/3}e^{(i\pi/2)} = 2^{5/3}\cos\frac{\pi}{2} + i2^{5/3}\sin\frac{\pi}{2} = 2i\sqrt[3]{4}$

26. One value of $(\sqrt{3} + i)^{1/2}$ is $(2e^{i\frac{\pi}{6}})^{1/2} = \sqrt{2}e^{i\frac{\pi}{12}} = \sqrt{2}\cos\frac{\pi}{12} + i\sqrt{2}\sin\frac{\pi}{12} \approx 1.366 + 0.366i$

27. One value of $(\sqrt{3} + i)^{-1/2}$ is $(2e^{i\frac{\pi}{6}})^{-1/2} = \frac{1}{\sqrt{2}}e^{i(-\frac{\pi}{12})} = \frac{1}{\sqrt{2}}\cos(-\frac{\pi}{12}) + i\frac{1}{\sqrt{2}}\sin(-\frac{\pi}{12}) \approx 0.683 - 0.183i$

28. Since $\sqrt{5} + 2i = 3e^{i\theta}$, where $\theta = \arctan\frac{2}{\sqrt{5}} \approx 0.730$, one value of $(\sqrt{5} + 2i)^{\sqrt{2}}$ is $(3e^{i\theta})^{\sqrt{2}} = 3^{\sqrt{2}}e^{i\sqrt{2}\theta} = 3^{\sqrt{2}}\cos\sqrt{2}\theta + i3^{\sqrt{2}}\sin\sqrt{2}\theta \approx 3^{\sqrt{2}}(0.513) + i3^{\sqrt{2}}(0.859) \approx 2.426 + 4.062i$

29. We have

$$i^{-1} = \frac{1}{i} = \frac{1}{i} \cdot \frac{i}{i} = -i,$$

$$i^{-2} = \frac{1}{i^2} = -1,$$

$$i^{-3} = \frac{1}{i^3} = \frac{1}{-i} \cdot \frac{i}{i} = i,$$

$$i^{-4} = \frac{1}{i^4} = 1.$$

The pattern is

$$i^n = \begin{cases} -i & n = -1, -5, -9, \cdots \\ -1 & n = -2, -6, -10, \cdots \\ i & n = -3, -7, -11, \cdots \\ 1 & n = -4, -8, -12, \cdots. \end{cases}$$

Since 36 is a multiple of 4, we know $i^{-36} = 1$.
Since $41 = 4 \cdot 10 + 1$, we know $i^{-41} = -i$.

30. Substituting $A_1 = 2 - A_2$ into the second equation gives

$$(1 - i)(2 - A_2) + (1 + i)A_2 = 0$$

so

$$2iA_2 = -2(1 - i)$$

$$A_2 = \frac{-(1 - i)}{i} = \frac{-i(1 - i)}{i^2} = i(1 - i) = 1 + i$$

Therefore $A_1 = 2 - (1 + i) = 1 - i$.

31. Substituting $A_2 = 2 - A_1$ into the second equation gives

$$(i - 1)A_1 + (1 + i)(2 - A_1) = 0$$

$$iA_1 - A_1 - A_1 - iA_1 + 2 + 2i = 0$$

$$-2A_1 = -2 - 2i$$

$$A_1 = 1 + i$$

Substituting, we have

$$A_2 = 2 - A_1 = 2 - (1 + i) = 1 - i.$$

32. (a) To divide complex numbers, multiply top and bottom by the conjugate of $1 + 2i$, that is, $1 - 2i$:

$$\frac{3 - 4i}{1 + 2i} = \frac{3 - 4i}{1 + 2i} \cdot \frac{1 - 2i}{1 - 2i} = \frac{3 - 4i - 6i + 8i^2}{1^2 + 2^2} = \frac{-5 - 10i}{5} = -1 - 2i.$$

Thus, $a = -1$ and $b = -2$.

(b) Multiplying $(1 + 2i)(a + bi)$ should give $3 - 4i$, as the following calculation shows:

$$(1 + 2i)(a + bi) = (1 + 2i)(-1 - 2i) = -1 - 2i - 2i - 4i^2 = 3 - 4i.$$

33. To confirm that $z = \dfrac{a + bi}{c + di}$, we calculate the product

$$z(c + di) = \left(\frac{ac + bd}{c^2 + d^2} = \frac{bc - ad}{c^2 + d^2}i \right)(c + di)$$

$$= \frac{ac^2 + bcd - bcd + ad^2 + (bc^2 - acd + acd + bd^2)i}{c^2 + d^2}$$

$$= \frac{a(c^2 + d^2) + b(c^2 + d^2)i}{c^2 + d^2} = a + bi.$$

34. (a)
$$z_1 z_2 = (-3 - i\sqrt{3})(-1 + i\sqrt{3}) = 3 + (\sqrt{3})^2 + i(\sqrt{3} - 3\sqrt{3}) = 6 - i2\sqrt{3}.$$
$$\frac{z_1}{z_2} = \frac{-3 - i\sqrt{3}}{-1 + i\sqrt{3}} \cdot \frac{-1 - i\sqrt{3}}{-1 - i\sqrt{3}} = \frac{3 - (\sqrt{3})^2 + i(\sqrt{3} + 3\sqrt{3})}{(-1)^2 + (\sqrt{3})^2} = \frac{i \cdot 4\sqrt{3}}{4} = i\sqrt{3}.$$

(b) We find (r_1, θ_1) corresponding to $z_1 = -3 - i\sqrt{3}$:
$$r_1 = \sqrt{(-3)^2 + (\sqrt{3})^2} = \sqrt{12} = 2\sqrt{3};$$
$$\tan \theta_1 = \frac{-\sqrt{3}}{-3} = \frac{\sqrt{3}}{3}, \text{ so } \theta_1 = \frac{7\pi}{6}.$$
(See Figure B.2.) Thus,
$$-3 - i\sqrt{3} = r_1 e^{i\theta_1} = 2\sqrt{3}\, e^{i\frac{7\pi}{6}}.$$

We find (r_2, θ_2) corresponding to $z_2 = -1 + i\sqrt{3}$:
$$r_2 = \sqrt{(-1)^2 + (\sqrt{3})^2} = 2;$$
$$\tan \theta_2 = \frac{\sqrt{3}}{-1} = -\sqrt{3}, \text{ so } \theta_2 = \frac{2\pi}{3}.$$
(See Figure B.3.) Thus,
$$-1 + i\sqrt{3} = r_2 e^{i\theta_2} = 2e^{i\frac{2\pi}{3}}.$$

| **Figure B.2** | **Figure B.3** |

We now calculate $z_1 z_2$ and $\dfrac{z_1}{z_2}$.
$$z_1 z_2 = \left(2\sqrt{3}e^{i\frac{7\pi}{6}}\right)\left(2e^{i\frac{2\pi}{3}}\right) = 4\sqrt{3}e^{i\left(\frac{7\pi}{6} + \frac{2\pi}{3}\right)} = 4\sqrt{3}e^{i\frac{11\pi}{6}}$$
$$= 4\sqrt{3}\left[\cos\frac{11\pi}{6} + i\sin\frac{11\pi}{6}\right] = 4\sqrt{3}\left[\frac{\sqrt{3}}{2} - i\frac{1}{2}\right] = 6 - i2\sqrt{3}.$$
$$\frac{z_1}{z_2} = \frac{2\sqrt{3}e^{i\frac{7\pi}{6}}}{2e^{i\frac{2\pi}{3}}} = \sqrt{3}e^{i\left(\frac{7\pi}{6} - \frac{2\pi}{3}\right)} = \sqrt{3}e^{i\frac{\pi}{2}}$$
$$= \sqrt{3}\left(\cos\frac{\pi}{2} + i\sin\frac{\pi}{2}\right) = i\sqrt{3}.$$

These agrees with the values found in (a).

35. First we calculate
$$z_1 z_2 = (a_1 + b_1 i)(a_2 + b_2 i) = a_1 a_2 - b_1 b_2 + i(a_1 b_2 + a_2 b_1).$$
Thus, $\overline{z_1 z_2} = a_1 a_2 - b_1 b_2 - i(a_1 b_2 + a_2 b_1)$.

Since $\bar{z}_1 = a_1 - b_1 i$ and $\bar{z}_2 = a_2 - b_2 i$,
$$\bar{z}_1 \bar{z}_2 = (a_1 - b_1 i)(a_2 - b_2 i) = a_1 a_2 - b_1 b_2 - i(a_1 b_2 + a_2 b_1).$$
Thus, $\overline{z_1 z_2} = \bar{z}_1 \bar{z}_2$.

36. If the roots are complex numbers, we must have $(2b)^2 - 4c < 0$ so $b^2 - c < 0$. Then the roots are
$$x = \frac{-2b \pm \sqrt{(2b)^2 - 4c}}{2} = -b \pm \sqrt{b^2 - c}$$
$$= -b \pm \sqrt{-1(c - b^2)}$$
$$= -b \pm i\sqrt{c - b^2}.$$
Thus, $p = -b$ and $q = \sqrt{c - b^2}$.

37. True, since $\sqrt{a}$ is real for all $a \geq 0$.

38. True, since $(x - iy)(x + iy) = x^2 + y^2$ is real.

39. False, since $(1 + i)^2 = 2i$ is not real.

40. False. Let $f(x) = x$. Then $f(i) = i$ but $f(\bar{i}) = \bar{i} = -i$.

41. True. We can write any nonzero complex number z as $re^{i\beta}$, where r and β are real numbers with $r > 0$. Since $r > 0$, we can write $r = e^c$ for some real number c. Therefore, $z = re^{i\beta} = e^c e^{i\beta} = e^{c+i\beta} = e^w$ where $w = c + i\beta$ is a complex number.

42. False, since $(1 + 2i)^2 = -3 + 4i$.

43.

$$\begin{aligned}
1 = e^0 &= e^{i(\theta - \theta)} = e^{i\theta} e^{i(-\theta)} \\
&= (\cos\theta + i\sin\theta)(\cos(-\theta) + i\sin(-\theta)) \\
&= (\cos\theta + i\sin\theta)(\cos\theta - i\sin\theta) \\
&= \cos^2\theta + \sin^2\theta
\end{aligned}$$

44. Using Euler's formula, we have:

$$e^{i(2\theta)} = \cos 2\theta + i\sin 2\theta$$

On the other hand,

$$e^{i(2\theta)} = \left(e^{i\theta}\right)^2 = (\cos\theta + i\sin\theta)^2 = (\cos^2\theta - \sin^2\theta) + i(2\cos\theta\sin\theta)$$

Equating imaginary parts, we find

$$\sin 2\theta = 2\sin\theta\cos\theta.$$

45. Using Euler's formula, we have:

$$e^{i(2\theta)} = \cos 2\theta + i\sin 2\theta$$

On the other hand,

$$e^{i(2\theta)} = \left(e^{i\theta}\right)^2 = (\cos\theta + i\sin\theta)^2 = (\cos^2\theta - \sin^2\theta) + i(2\cos\theta\sin\theta)$$

Equating real parts, we find

$$\cos 2\theta = \cos^2\theta - \sin^2\theta.$$

46. Differentiating Euler's formula gives

$$\frac{d}{d\theta}\left(e^{i\theta}\right) = ie^{i\theta} = i(\cos\theta + i\sin\theta) = -\sin\theta + i\cos\theta$$

Since in addition $\dfrac{d}{d\theta}\left(e^{i\theta}\right) = \dfrac{d}{d\theta}(\cos\theta + i\sin\theta) = \dfrac{d}{d\theta}(\cos\theta) + i\dfrac{d}{d\theta}(\sin\theta)$, by equating imaginary parts, we conclude that $\dfrac{d}{d\theta}\sin\theta = \cos\theta$.

47. Differentiating Euler's formula twice gives

$$\frac{d^2}{d\theta^2}\left(e^{i\theta}\right) = \frac{d^2}{d\theta^2}(\cos\theta + i\sin\theta) = \frac{d^2}{d\theta^2}(\cos\theta) + i\frac{d^2}{d\theta^2}(\sin\theta).$$

But

$$\frac{d^2}{d\theta^2}\left(e^{i\theta}\right) = i^2 e^{i\theta} = -e^{i\theta} = -\cos\theta - i\sin\theta.$$

Equating real parts, we find

$$\frac{d^2}{d\theta^2}(\cos\theta) = -\cos\theta.$$

48. Replacing θ by $-x$ in the formula for $\sin\theta$:

$$\sin(-x) = \frac{1}{2i}\left(e^{-ix} - e^{ix}\right) = -\frac{1}{2i}\left(e^{ix} - e^{-ix}\right) = -\sin x.$$

49. Replacing θ by $(x+y)$ in the formula for $\sin\theta$:

$$\begin{aligned}
\sin(x+y) &= \frac{1}{2i}\left(e^{i(x+y)} - e^{-i(x+y)}\right) = \frac{1}{2i}\left(e^{ix}e^{iy} - e^{-ix}e^{-iy}\right) \\
&= \frac{1}{2i}\left((\cos x + i\sin x)(\cos y + i\sin y) - (\cos(-x) + i\sin(-x))(\cos(-y) + i\sin(-y))\right) \\
&= \frac{1}{2i}\left((\cos x + i\sin x)(\cos y + i\sin y) - (\cos x - i\sin x)(\cos y - i\sin y)\right) \\
&= \sin x \cos y + \cos x \sin y.
\end{aligned}$$

50. Since x_1, y_1, x_2, y_2 are each functions of the variable t, differentiating the sum gives

$$\begin{aligned}
(z_1 + z_2)' &= (x_1 + iy_1 + x_2 + iy_2)' = (x_1 + x_2 + i(y_1 + y_2))' \\
&= (x_1 + x_2)' + i(y_1 + y_2)' \\
&= (x_1' + x_2') + i(y_1' + y_2') \\
&= (x_1 + iy_1)' + (x_2 + iy_2)' \\
&= z_1' + z_2'.
\end{aligned}$$

Differentiating the product gives

$$\begin{aligned}
(z_1 z_2)' &= ((x_1 + iy_1)(x_2 + iy_2))' = (x_1 x_2 - y_1 y_2 + i(y_1 x_2 + x_1 y_2))' \\
&= (x_1 x_2 - y_1 y_2)' + i(y_1 x_2 + x_1 y_2)' \\
&= (x_1' x_2 + x_1 x_2' - y_1' y_2 - y_1 y_2') + i(y_1' x_2 + y_1 x_2' + x_1' y_2 + x_1 y_2') \\
&= [x_1' x_2 - y_1' y_2 + i(x_1' y_2 + y_1' x_2)] + [x_1 x_2' - y_1 y_2' + i(y_1 x_2' + x_1 y_2')] \\
&= (x_1' + iy_1')(x_2 + iy_2) + (x_1 + iy_1)(x_2' + iy_2') \\
&= z_1' z_2 + z_1 z_2'.
\end{aligned}$$

Solutions for Section C

1. (a) $f'(x) = 3x^2 + 6x + 3 = 3(x+1)^2$. Thus $f'(x) > 0$ everywhere except at $x = -1$, so it is increasing everywhere except perhaps at $x = -1$. The function is in fact increasing at $x = -1$ since $f(x) > f(-1)$ for $x > -1$, and $f(x) < f(-1)$ for $x < -1$.

(b) The original equation can have at most one root, since it can only pass through the x-axis once if it never decreases. It must have one root, since $f(0) = -6$ and $f(1) = 1$.

(c) The root is in the interval $[0, 1]$, since $f(0) < 0 < f(1)$.

(d) Let $x_0 = 1$.

$$x_0 = 1$$

$$x_1 = 1 - \frac{f(1)}{f'(1)} = 1 - \frac{1}{12} = \frac{11}{12} \approx 0.917$$

$$x_2 = \frac{11}{12} - \frac{f\left(\frac{11}{12}\right)}{f'\left(\frac{11}{12}\right)} \approx 0.913$$

$$x_3 = 0.913 - \frac{f(0.913)}{f'(0.913)} \approx 0.913.$$

Since the digits repeat, they should be accurate. Thus $x \approx 0.913$.

2. Let $f(x) = x^3 - 50$. Then $f(\sqrt[3]{50}) = 0$, so we can use Newton's method to solve $f(x) = 0$ to obtain $x = \sqrt[3]{50}$. Since $f'(x) = 3x^2$, f' is always positive, and f is therefore increasing. Consequently, f has only one zero. Since $3^3 = 27 < 50 < 64 = 4^3$, let $x_0 = 3.5$. Then

$$x_0 = 3.5$$
$$x_1 = 3.5 - \frac{f(3.5)}{f'(3.5)} \approx 3.694$$

Continuing, we find

$$x_2 \approx 3.684$$
$$x_3 \approx 3.684.$$

Since the digits repeat, x_3 should be correct, as can be confirmed by calculator.

3. Let $f(x) = x^4 - 100$. Then $f(\sqrt[4]{100}) = 0$, so we can use Newton's method to solve $f(x) = 0$ to obtain $x = \sqrt[4]{100}$. $f'(x) = 4x^3$. Since $3^4 = 81 < 100 < 256 = 4^4$, try 3.1 as an initial guess.

$$x_0 = 3.1$$
$$x_1 = 3.1 - \frac{f(3.1)}{f'(3.1)} \approx 3.164$$
$$x_2 = 3.164 - \frac{f(3.164)}{f'(3.164)} \approx 3.162$$
$$x_3 = 3.162 - \frac{f(3.162)}{f'(3.162)} \approx 3.162$$

Thus $\sqrt[4]{100} \approx 3.162$.

4. Let $f(x) = x^3 - \frac{1}{10}$. Then $f(10^{-1/3}) = 0$, so we can use Newton's method to solve $f(x) = 0$ to obtain $x = 10^{-1/3}$. $f'(x) = 3x^2$. Since $\sqrt[3]{\frac{1}{27}} < \sqrt[3]{\frac{1}{10}} < \sqrt[3]{\frac{1}{8}}$, try $x_0 = \frac{1}{2}$. Then $x_1 = 0.5 - \frac{f(0.5)}{f'(0.5)} \approx 0.467$. Continuing, we find $x_2 \approx 0.464$. $x_3 \approx 0.464$. Since $x_2 \approx x_3$, $10^{-1/3} \approx 0.464$.

5. Let $f(x) = \sin x - 1 + x$; we want to find all zeros of f, because $f(x) = 0$ implies $\sin x = 1 - x$.

Graphing $\sin x$ and $1 - x$ in Figure C.4, we see that $f(x)$ has one solution at $x \approx \frac{1}{2}$.

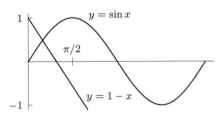

Figure C.4

Letting $x_0 = 0.5$, and using Newton's method, we have $f'(x) = \cos x + 1$, so that

$$x_1 = 0.5 - \frac{\sin(0.5) - 1 + 0.5}{\cos(0.5) + 1} \approx 0.511,$$

$$x_2 = 0.511 - \frac{\sin(0.511) - 1 + 0.511}{\cos(0.511) + 1} \approx 0.511.$$

Thus $\sin x = 1 - x$ has one solution at $x \approx 0.511$.

6. Let $f(x) = \cos x - x$. We want to find all zeros of f, because $f(x) = 0$ implies that $\cos x = x$. Since $f'(x) = -\sin x - 1$, f' is always negative (as $-\sin x$ never exceeds 1). This means f is always decreasing and consequently has at most 1 root. We now use Newton's method. Since $\cos 0 > 0$ and $\cos \frac{\pi}{2} < \frac{\pi}{2}$, $\cos x = x$ for $0 < x < \frac{\pi}{2}$. Thus, try $x_0 = \frac{\pi}{6}$.

$$x_1 = \frac{\pi}{6} - \frac{\cos \frac{\pi}{6} - \frac{\pi}{6}}{-\sin \frac{\pi}{6} - 1} \approx 0.7519,$$
$$x_2 \approx 0.7391,$$
$$x_3 \approx 0.7390.$$

$x_2 \approx x_3 \approx 0.739$. Thus $x \approx 0.739$ is the solution.

7. Let $f(x) = e^{-x} - \ln x$. Then $f'(x) = -e^{-x} - \frac{1}{x}$. We want to find all zeros of f, because $f(x) = 0$ implies that $e^{-x} = \ln x$. Since e^{-x} is always decreasing and $\ln x$ is always increasing, there must be only 1 solution. Since $e^{-1} > \ln 1 = 0$, and $e^{-e} < \ln e = 1$, then $e^{-x} = \ln x$ for some x, $1 < x < e$. Try $x_0 = 1$. We now use Newton's method.

$$x_1 = 1 - \frac{e^{-1} - 0}{-e^{-1} - 1} \approx 1.2689,$$
$$x_2 \approx 1.309,$$
$$x_3 \approx 1.310.$$

Thus $x \approx 1.310$ is the solution.

8. Let $f(x) = e^x \cos x - 1$. Then $f'(x) = -e^x \sin x + e^x \cos x$. Now we use Newton's method, guessing $x_0 = 1$ initially.

$$x_1 = 1 - \frac{f(1)}{f'(1)} \approx 1.5725$$

Continuing: $x_2 \approx 1.364$, $x_3 \approx 1.299$, $x_4 \approx 1.293$, $x_5 \approx 1.293$. Thus $x \approx 1.293$ is a solution. Looking at a graph of $f(x)$ suffices to convince us that there is only one solution.

9. Let $f(x) = \ln x - \frac{1}{x}$, so $f'(x) = \frac{1}{x} + \frac{1}{x^2}$.
Now use Newton's method with an initial guess of $x_0 = 2$.

$$x_1 = 2 - \frac{\ln 2 - \frac{1}{2}}{\frac{1}{2} + \frac{1}{4}} \approx 1.7425,$$
$$x_2 \approx 1.763,$$
$$x_3 \approx 1.763.$$

Thus $x \approx 1.763$ is a solution. Since $f'(x) > 0$ for positive x, f is increasing: it must be the only solution.

10. (a) One zero in the interval $0.6 < x < 0.7$.
   (b) Three zeros in the intervals $-1.55 < x < -1.45$, $x = 0$, $1.45 < x < 1.55$.
   (c) Two zeros in the intervals $0.1 < x < 0.2$, $3.5 < x < 3.6$.

11. $f'(x) = 3x^2 + 1$. Since f' is always positive, f is everywhere increasing. Thus f has only one zero. Since $f(0) < 0 < f(1)$, $0 < x_0 < 1$. Pick $x_0 = 0.68$.

$$x_0 = 0.68,$$
$$x_1 = 0.6823278,$$
$$x_2 \approx 0.6823278.$$

Thus $x \approx 0.682328$ (rounded up) is a root. Since $x_1 \approx x_2$, the digits should be correct.

12. Let $f(x) = x^2 - a$, so $f'(x) = 2x$.
Then by Newton's method, $x_{n+1} = x_n - \frac{x_n^2 - a}{2x_n}$
For $a = 2$:
$x_0 = 1$, $x_1 = 1.5$, $x_2 \approx 1.416$, $x_3 \approx 1.414215$, $x_4 \approx 1.414213$ so $\sqrt{2} \approx 1.4142$.
For $a = 10$:
$x_0 = 5$, $x_1 = 3.5$, $x_2 \approx 3.17857$, $x_3 \approx 3.162319$, $x_4 \approx 3.162277$ so $\sqrt{10} \approx 3.1623$.
For $a = 1000$:
$x_0 = 500$, $x_1 = 251$, $x_2 \approx 127.49203$, $x_3 \approx 67.6678$, $x_4 \approx 41.2229$, $x_5 \approx 32.7406$, $x_6 \approx 31.6418$, $x_7 \approx 31.62278$, $x_8 \approx 31.62277$ so $\sqrt{1000} \approx 31.6228$.
For $a = \pi$:
$x_0 = \frac{\pi}{2}$, $x_1 \approx 1.7853$, $x_2 \approx 1.7725$ $x_3 \approx 1.77245$, $x_4 \approx 1.77245$ so $\sqrt{\pi} \approx 1.77245$.

NOTES

NOTES

NOTES

NOTES

NOTES